CHRISTIAN DOCTRINE

CHRISTIAN DOCTRINE

by

J. S. WHALE
D.D.

President of Cheshunt College

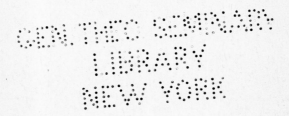
NEW YORK: THE MACMILLAN COMPANY
CAMBRIDGE, ENGLAND: AT THE UNIVERSITY PRESS
1941

Reprinted October, 1941

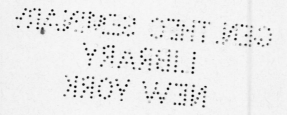
PRINTED IN THE UNITED STATES OF AMERICA

Dedicated
to

CHARLES HAROLD DODD
and to the memory of
JAMES VERNON BARTLET
the teachers to whom I owe most for my
understanding of Christian Truth

CONTENTS

7

PREFACE

This book reproduces and slightly expands eight lectures delivered in the University of Cambridge during the Michaelmas Term 1940 at the request of the Board of the Faculty of Theology. The lectures were intended for men and women of all Faculties, about six hundred of whom attended them throughout.

I have hesitated to publish these lectures in their original form because the spoken word runs an obvious risk by appearing in print. The kind importunity of many of my hearers has persuaded me, however, and I have gratefully accepted an offer of publication from the Syndics of the University Press.

If the title of the volume looks a little pretentious I must admit that these lectures offer neither a systematic nor a comprehensive survey of Christian doctrine; indeed, I am well aware of their many omissions, and of weaknesses which considerable expansion might have removed. On the other hand an outline of a great subject may have interest and value for many who have neither inclination nor leisure for the study of a fuller and more technical book.

I have to thank the Editor of the *Expository Times* for permission to incorporate material from articles recently contributed to that journal, and the Student Christian Movement Press for allowing me to make use of certain paragraphs from two previous books; details are given in the footnotes.

My other obligations are many and obvious, but I am particularly indebted to Mr B. L. Manning, M.A., Senior Tutor of Jesus College, and to the Rev. H. C. Carter, M.A., Minister of Emmanuel Church, Cambridge, for the pains they have taken in reading my manuscript and pointing out some of its infelicities of style and statement. I wish to thank Mr L. A. Pars, M.A., of Jesus College, for his valuable critical notes on one or two points. It would be almost impertinent to praise the readers and printers of the Cambridge University Press. I can only thank them for a meticulous accuracy which has been an education.

J. S. W.

CHESHUNT COLLEGE
January 1941

I

THE LIVING GOD

THE CHRISTIAN DOCTRINE OF CREATION

A YOUNG curate once called on William Stubbs, Bishop of Oxford, to ask him for advice about preaching. The great man was silent for a moment and then replied 'Preach about God; and preach about twenty minutes'. He meant, presumably, that the Christian preacher has many opportunities, but one theme. So, too, all lectures on Christian doctrine are concerned from first to last with the reality, nature and purpose of the living God.

But is there a God? Apparently not. God is not apparent to our senses. Nor is he indubitably apparent to human reason. The most eager theist knows that the classic arguments for the existence of God, even when restated, are arguments rather than proofs. Again, it is not compellingly apparent that God is the only possible explanation of human history; the problem of evil is a monument to facts which seem to deny it. Nevertheless, belief in the reality of God is the alpha and omega of the Christian religion. Christian doctrines presuppose and illustrate the fundamental doctrine that God is, and that man's chief end is to know him. Look, for example, at six of those doctrines.

The Christian answer to the ageless question, 'What is Man?' is not that man is a thinking animal or a tool-using animal, a cooking animal or a laughing animal.[1] These classic

---

[1] 'I told him, I had found out a perfect definition of human nature, as distinguished from the animal. An ancient philosopher said, Man

definitions have an obvious validity; but Christian anthropology rests on the conviction that man is an animal made in the image of God, which means that he is not an animal at all. His alleged evolution from mammalian stock, a theory which the biological evidence seems to require, does not affect the truth that he has his origin and essential being in a Word addressed to him by God, his Creator.

The Christian way of thinking about moral evil—all the horrifying and abiding depths of wrong in the human situation —is that moral evil can never have a purely manward reference. Moral evil is sin; more than a private thing like vice, and more than a social or public thing like crime, sin is moral evil seen in its relation to God.

The Christian way out of man's moral distress is not the Greek way of knowledge (ἐπιστήμη); that is, redemption from ignorance. Nor is it the ancient Egyptian way of redemption from mortality, with its elaborate ritual centred in the embalmed mummy and set forth in the *Book of the Dead*. Nor, again, is it the Buddhist way of self-elimination set out in the doctrine of Nirvana. The Christian religion understands redemption in terms of moral realities; sin and guilt, judgment and grace. Its primary and permanent emphasis is ethical. If salvation is to be real, therefore, God and God alone must

was "a two-legged animal without feathers", upon which his rival Sage had a Cock plucked bare, and set him down in the school before all the disciples, as a "Philosophick Man". Dr Franklin said, Man was "a tool-making animal", which is very well; for no animal but man makes a thing, by means of which he can make another thing. But this applies to very few of the species. My definition of *Man* is, "a Cooking animal". The beasts have memory, judgment, and all the faculties and passions of our mind in a certain degree; but no beast is a cook' (Boswell's *Journal of a Tour to the Hebrides with Samuel Johnson* (August 15)).

effect it; if it is to be anything more than a fiction, it must be the work of him who is of purer eyes than to behold iniquity. The agonizing quest of a Paul, a Luther, a Bunyan for re-conciliation with God, meant that nothing less and nothing else could meet their case. The Christian doctrine of redemption can mean one thing only, namely that the Holy One is gracious.

The Christian way of understanding Jesus Christ the Saviour is to worship him as divine. Christian doctrine does not speak of him as history speaks of Aristotle or Buddha, of Socrates or Confucius. He is more than teacher, reformer or prophet. That God was in Christ is the very basis and *raison d'être* of Christian doctrine. To the question, 'Is not this the carpenter?' its answer is 'Behold the Lamb of God'.

The Christian way of understanding the society which is the result and the extension in time of what Christ was and what he did, is not that it is just one among many forms of human association, something of man's contriving, an expression of human idealism whose *differentia* is mainly sociological. The Church is a wonderful and sacred mystery because God loved it, Christ purchased it and the Holy Spirit sanctifies it. The minister of the Word and the Sacraments is a steward of the mysteries of God.

The Christian way of understanding history is not the secular way, either of optimism or pessimism. For Christian doctrine, the pattern of history is not expressible in terms of evolutionary progress and human perfectibility here on earth, but in terms of creation and resurrection from the dead. In the beginning God created; in the end he will sum up all things, in heaven and on earth, in Christ. To conceive of a beginning in time is, admittedly, as impossible as to conceive of no beginning.

13

Again, an end to time is as inconceivable as an endless eternity. The Christian doctrine of creation is a symbolic assertion, not that the world was made by the Great Artificer as a carpenter makes a box, but that man in all his felt finitude comes from God and goes to God; he is not surrounded by a sheer abyss of nothingness. God, the God and Father of our Lord Jesus Christ, is the ground and goal of all that is. All is of God— our creation, preservation and all the blessings of this life; the redemption of the world, the means of grace and the hope of glory. He is the first and the last and the living One.

In short, all Christian doctrines are the same doctrine, the doctrine of God.

At once we meet a notorious difficulty which is illustrated and, as I hope to show, exaggerated by the unhappy divisions of Christendom. How is God known? What is the source of Christian knowledge and the authoritative foundation of Christian doctrine? What is the ultimate seat of authority to which Christian theology makes its appeal?

To these questions Christian history provides answers which are by no means uniform; they fall, in the main, into three great and distinctive types.

The first type emphasizes the authority of the Church, a visible, hierarchical institution, which is the divinely commissioned vehicle and guarantee of the truth and the grace of the Gospel. Such ecclesiasticism becomes nakedly explicit in the unyielding Latin dictum that there is no salvation outside the Church. The Roman Church, indeed, provides the classic form of this deification of the traditional institution, its ruler claiming to be God's Vicar upon earth. When he speaks *ex cathedra*, his pronouncements are infallible. The Vatican

Decrees of 1870 are no more than the logical climax of a long historical development.[1]

The second type emphasizes the sole authority of the Bible, and here historic Protestantism provides the classic example. *The Westminster Confession* (i. 6) is typical of all the credal confessions of the Reformation in saying that 'the whole counsel of God concerning all things necessary for His own glory, man's salvation, faith and life, is either expressly set down in Scripture or by good and necessary consequence may be deduced from Scripture: unto which nothing at any time is to be added, whether by new revelations of the Spirit or traditions

---

[1] The letters of St Cyprian, Bishop of Carthage (ob. A.D. 258), give classic and relatively early expression to this conception of authority. To Antonianus (*ep.* 55) he writes: 'In reference, however, to the character of Novatian and to your written request for information as to his heresy, you must know first of all that we ought not even to be inquisitive as to what he teaches, so long as he is an outsider (nos primo in loco nec curiosos esse debere quid ille doceat, cum foris doceat). Whoever and whatsoever he may be, he is not a Christian who is not in the church of Christ (christianus non est qui in Christi ecclesia non est).' Cyprian goes on to define the church as 'one church divided by Christ throughout the whole world into many members, and one episcopate diffused throughout a harmonious multitude of many bishops (episcopatus unus episcoporum multorum concordi numerositate diffusus)'. To Florentius (*ep.* 66) he writes: 'You ought to know, therefore, that the bishop is in the church and the church is in the bishop (et ecclesiam in episcopo).' The letter to Jubaianus (*ep.* 73) contains the famous sentence, 'salus extra ecclesiam non est'.

It is pertinent to add that St Augustine (ob. A.D. 430) did not use the famous words which certain Roman apologists have put into his mouth at the time of the Pelagian controversy, 'Roma locuta est, causa finita est'. All that he says (*Sermo* 131) is that two councils were sent to the apostolic see whence came the rescripts settling the matter. 'Causa finita est; utinam aliquando finiatur error (the issue is settled; would that error were now at last at an end).'

of men'. But within Protestantism, too, an excessive logic has sometimes played havoc with this its constitutive principle; and the Bible, instead of being a living Word sounding out from God's historic revelation in Hebrew nation and Christian Church, has sometimes become a literally inerrant law-book. Calvin's great principle, 'scriptura duce et magistra', could degenerate into a narrow biblicism in the hands of later Calvinism. Indeed, such biblicism almost became bibliolatry in a Swiss confession of the seventeenth century, which declared that the Hebrew manuscript of the Old Testament was accepted as inspired of God not only in regard to the consonants, but also in regard to the vowel points.[1]

The third type may be loosely described as mystical. Stressing the inwardness not only of religious but also of all true authority, its constitutive principle is the 'Inner Light'. To quote the Quaker classic, Barclay's *Apology*: 'These divine inward revelations...are not to be subjected to the test either of the outward testimony of the Scriptures or of the natural reason of man...for this divine revelation and inward illumination is that which is evident and clear of itself' (Prop. ii). Here the danger of an excessive subjectivism is obvious; when each man's private fancies claim absolute authority in the name of direct, divine inspiration, the step from the Inner Light to the Outer Darkness is a small one. The danger to which such mysticism is always exposed lies in its undisciplined attitude to history; it is virtually indifferent to those outward forms (Book, Institutions, Sacraments, Ministry) which have been

---

[1] *Formula Consensus Ecclesiarum Helvetiarum Reformatarum* (1675), canon ii: 'accepimus hodieque retinemus, tum quoad consonas, tum quoad vocalia, sive puncta ipsa, sive punctorum saltem potestatem, et tum quoad res, tum quoad verba....'

and are the historic channels for the mediation of Christian truth. Mysticism often pays a heavy price for its tendency to belittle the historical and the factual. You will remember Gibbon's annihilating comment on the whirling dervishes of the desert: 'they mistook the giddiness of the head for the illumination of the Spirit.' After all, not only in science and art, but also in religion, the wisdom of the expert, distilled from the deposit of the past, has a definite authority which is not inconsistent with the responsibility of the individual for his own judgments.

There, then, are the three great types; and the history of Christendom too often shows them confronting one another like the three duellists in Sheridan's play *The Critic*, each aware of its ultimate logical incompatibility with the other two, and each fighting on two fronts. In point of fact, however, they are not so much different answers to the question about authority as answers revealing differences of emphasis. All three occupy the same common ground; for all three the Bible, the Church and personal faith are authoritative. In theory they are mutually exclusive, but in fact they interlock. Each exercises an interpretative control over the other two.

For example, all Christians believe in the Inner Light, 'the inward testimony of the Holy Spirit', to use the language of the Reformed tradition. The truth that God was in Christ reconciling the world unto himself is not truth for any man, be he Roman or Calvinist, until he makes it his own. But the Quaker does not discover what God has done for him on the Cross *in vacuo*, as it were. Without the witness of the Bible and the corroborative testimony of ecclesiastical experience and thought in every age, how could the fact of Christ have been mediated to him at all? Christian faith is rooted in the soil of history;

17

though personally appropriated it is nevertheless historically mediated.

Again, all Christians believe in the Bible as the Word of God. Roman dogma no less than Quaker piety makes this sufficiently plain. The mediaeval sermon, as Canon Charles Smyth has reminded us, was firmly anchored to the Bible.[1] Indeed, the plenary inspiration of Scripture is a dogma of the Roman Church.[2] But without the hearing ear and the response of faith this speech of God in Holy Scripture would remain a dead letter. Nor could individual Christians—a St Francis, a Luther or an Elizabeth Fry—have this personal experience for ever or for long without the divine society which has been its vehicle and guarantee in history. To use the well-known words of St Augustine, 'Indeed, I should not believe in the Gospel unless the authority of the catholic church aroused the belief in me'.[3]

Again, all Christians believe in the authority of their Holy Mother, the Church, in whose womb they have been conceived, at whose bosom they have been fed and by whose discipline they have been nurtured. This, so far from being a piece of legalistic dogmatism, is a spiritual fact. It is not a narrow legal injunction but a reality of history. Here, Cyprian in the third century and Calvin in the sixteenth, speak almost

[1] *The Art of Preaching*, p. 45. On the other hand see pp. 46 n. and 53 for ignorance of the Bible in the Middle Ages.

[2] Council of Trent, Session iv, April 1546: *Decretum de canonicis scripturis*. Also Vatican Council, Session iii, April 1870: *Constitutio dogmatica de fide catholica*, c. 2, *De revelatione*. The books of the Old and New Testaments (Vulgate edition) are revered as sacred because, written by inspiration of the Holy Spirit, they have God for their author (propterea quod Spiritu Sancto inspirante conscripti Deum habent auctorem).

[3] 'Ego vero evangelio non crederem, nisi me catholicae ecclesiae commoveret auctoritas' (*Contra epistolam quam vocant fundamenti*, c. 4).

precisely the same language.[1] Christians everywhere confess that the Church is an extension of the Incarnation. True Christian experience is always ecclesiastical experience. But this truth may not be made a cloak for any authoritarian position claimed in the name of new presbyter or old priest; moreover, what is true of priest and presbyter is also true of the 'priesthood of all believers', a precious scriptural principle which degenerates all too easily into an unscriptural egalitarian cliché.

Christian doctrine is the historic monument to the fact that God speaks and the soul hears, within the orbit of tradition represented by Scripture and the Church. These two authorities are organically one, in that they mediate the Word of the Gospel to men. The believer receives the Word by these channels only. But, as Karl Barth has insisted, the channels are no more than channels; neither is infallible in the sense that it is identical with the Word. The treasure is given to us in earthen vessels; through these means of grace the life-giving waters are offered to every one that thirsteth. But thirsty souls must come to the waters; not until it is heard is the Word effectually

[1] Calvin, *Institutio*, IV. i. 1, 4: 'Incipiam autem ab Ecclesia: in cuius sinum aggregari vult Deus filios suos, non modo ut eius cura etiam materna regantur donec adolescant, ac tandem perveniant ad fidei metam.... Non alius est in vitam ingressus nisi nos ipsa concipiat in utero, nisi pariat, nisi nos alat suis uberibus, denique sub custodia et gubernatione sua nos tueatur.... Haec enim quae Deus coniunxit separari fas non est, ut quibus ipse est Pater, Ecclesia etiam mater sit.... Adde quod extra eius gremium nulla est speranda peccatorum remissio, nec ulla salus.'

Cf. Cyprian, *De catholicae ecclesiae unitate*, v, vi: 'Illius fetu nascimur, illius lacte nutrimur, spiritu eius animamur.... Habere iam non potest Deum patrem, qui Ecclesiam non habet matrem.' But see also *Inst*. IV. viii. 13.

uttered; without man's full response of faith to God's Word mediated through the Bible and the holy catholic Church, the means of grace would be ineffectual and meaningless.

This familiar doctrine of three interlocking authorities—the three-fold operation of the Holy Spirit in the Bible, in the Church and in the soul of the individual believer—is admirably stated by Professor Dodd in a recent article on Revelation.[1] 'God reveals himself to us in Christ his Son, the eternal Word incarnate, through the testimony of the Scriptures and the interior testimony of the Holy Spirit. We receive his revelation by faith, which is itself the gift of God. We receive it in the context of the life of the Church, the Body of Christ, the custodian of the Scriptures, the dwelling place of the Holy Spirit. When in the fellowship of the Church we read the Scriptures, hear the Gospel of Christ proclaimed and partake in the Sacraments (the Eucharist in particular) we believe that God deals with us, and makes himself known to us as our Father, our Saviour and our Lord.'

The word Revelation brings us to a problem which may be introduced with a sharp question. What of human reason and its rights? Has it no part to play in the tremendous assertion that God is, and that men may know him? It is all very well for Christian doctrine to assert that the believer lives by revelation, and to claim that for him God is not Aristotle's Unmoved First Mover, the virtually unknown God of metaphysical speculation, but the God of Isaiah and the Psalmist, the God and Father of our Lord Jesus Christ. Does this mean that philosophical theology is a contradiction in terms and that the traditional intellectual discipline of the *philosophia*

[1] *Expository Times*, July 1940.

perennis can give us no knowledge of ultimate reality? Surely human reason has been and is a valid instrument of religious enquiry. 'The flight from reason', says Dr Prestige, 'marks the first stage in the surrender of religion to intellectual nihilism and vulgar superstition.'[1]

This burning modern issue is by no means new to the history of Christian doctrine. The nature of revelation must always be a crucial problem for a religion which finds its living heart in an Incarnation.

On the one hand, giants like Origen in the third century, Thomas Aquinas in the thirteenth and Richard Hooker in the sixteenth, vindicated the place of reason in their great theological systems. They were debtors, supremely to Holy Scripture of course, but also to Plato and Aristotle.

On the other hand, Tertullian in the early third century mocked at Aristotle, and in one of his most mischievous books argued that the search for truth was a confession of apostasy.[2] Bernard of Clairvaux in the twelfth century condemned the whole philosophic method in theology as 'disgraceful curiosity'.[3] Luther used language of characteristic extravagance in rejecting the notion of an autonomous human reason which is able of itself to apprehend the divine; to him reason was 'the devil's bride'. Like Barth,[4] four centuries later, he denied the very possibility of 'natural' theology. Kant, too, was in line with modern continental Protestantism in denying that man

---

[1] *Fathers and Heretics*, p. 136. This is timely, but it must be read in the light of the fine passage in defence of Christianity as a revealed religion on pp. 20–21.

[2] *De praescriptionibus haereticorum*, cc. x–xiv.

[3] 'turpis curiositas'. See Prestige, *op. cit.* p. 134 n.

[4] 'Es gibt kein menschliches Vorher', i.e. here there are no philosophical presuppositions.

can ever prove God's existence by the speculation of the intellect. His *Critique of Pure Reason* is a barrier set up between all attempted demonstrations of God's existence and true knowledge of God. Even Goethe, in his *Conversations with Eckermann*, observed emphatically that the Christian religion has nothing to do with philosophy.[1] And Ritschl, one of the greatest theologians of the nineteenth century, despised metaphysics almost to the point of pragmatism; indeed, he once made the profound and dangerous statement, 'without Christ I should be an atheist'. Such a list may fittingly end with James Denney's dry remark that one of the most serious difficulties to be contended with in a theological college is the divinity student who has previously obtained second-class honours in philosophy.

But, granted that Denney rightly deplored in a minister of religion a proud reluctance to accept God's revelation of himself in history, did he mean that the Christian man may never serve God with the mind? What, for example, of the traditional arguments for the existence of God, as set forth in varying forms by some of the greatest thinkers? Must one say that a rational demonstration of the existence of the living God is impossible, and that such speculation is never more than an attempt, as pathetic as it is heroic, to attain the unattainable?

At the risk of absurd over-simplification let me try to state the essential content and meaning of six of those arguments.

One of the oldest is labelled Cosmological, because it looks at

---

[1] 'Hegel zieht die christliche Religion in die Philosophie herein, die doch nichts darin zu thun hat. Die christliche Religion ist ein mächtiges Wesen für sich, woran die gesunkene und leidende Menschheit von Zeit zu Zeit sich immer wieder emporgearbeitet hat; und indem man ihr dieser Wirkung zugesteht, ist sie über aller Philosophie erhaben und bedarf von ihr keiner Stütze' (*Gespräche*, ii. 39).

the cosmos, the visible universe, and denies that it is self-explanatory. The natural order does not contain its complete explanation within itself, but points beyond itself. 'This goodly frame, the earth,...this most excellent canopy, the air,... this brave o'erhanging firmament, this majestical roof fretted with golden fire' presupposes a transcendent source or ground, an Ultimate Reality on which everything else depends, an *ens necessarium* which is the *ens realissimum*. Our very sense of temporality, change and decay has meaning only if the eternal and the unchanging is its background; we cannot confess that all our knowledge is relative without thereby betraying our belief in an Absolute which alone gives meaning and measure to relativity. Our knowledge of any event in nature is complete only when the full reason for that event is found in an Ultimate which is its own *raison d'être*, and which, because it does not depend on anything else, is not of nature but above it.[1]

In the second place, there is the ever-recurring argument labelled Teleological, which is abandoned only to be revised and restated, because its appeal is irresistible. Here we are concerned not with the origin and ground of all 'becoming', but with its purpose and end. Thinking men cannot believe that the many signs of design in nature are a sheer accident, having no ultimate significance. The universe seems orderly rather than disorderly, in that it is always realizing 'ends' which only an excessive scepticism will dismiss as meaningless. Confronted with nature's indubitable purposiveness at all its levels, man cannot believe that it is all 'spots and jumps', an unmeaning chaos. Is the whole process of organic evolution explicable to our human minds save on the hypothesis that

[1] See A. E. Taylor's remarkable chapter in *Essays Catholic and Critical*, entitled 'The Vindication of Religion', especially pp. 46–55.

such purposiveness implies not only Mind, but creative Mind, beyond all that is, yet working out its purposes within all that is?

In the third place, there is the argument which may be labelled Rational, because it reckons seriously with the authority of human reason and our inexpugnable conviction that this world is rational. The most significant fact about the whole evolutionary process is the evolution of mind which is able to know that process, to think about it and to evaluate it. The very possibility of science depends on the fact that nature answers to our thought about it, and that our thought answers to nature. Science has to assume as axiomatic the authority of reason and the self-consistency of reality. Obviously reason cannot prove its own authority. We cannot help believing, therefore, that the system which thus responds to mind is itself the work of Mind, a Mind which is infinite and universal and which influences and directs the evolutionary process throughout, because 'It' is transcendent and creative. Such a Mind cannot be contained within the universe. To explain man's mind and the authority of reason over it by saying that 'Nature' has produced his mind as the oyster produces the pearl, is to explain 'six' by saying that it is 'half-a-dozen'— which is no explanation at all. Why and how does nature come to have this capacity? Is any answer possible save that nature produces mind because it never was without Mind? The alpha and omega of all things, their beginning and their end, is the creative Thought of God. In different ages there are different standards of rationality, admittedly. But what matters here is not so much the varying standard of rationality as the fact of it. Our very repudiation of this or that as 'irrational', implies faith in its opposite; the negation logically involves an affirmation.

24

In the fourth place, there is the argument labelled Moral, because it springs from that consciousness of moral obligation in man which makes him *man* and differentiates him from termites, elephants and the most intelligent sheep-dogs that ever were. Man's distinctive and imperious sense of 'oughtness' has a sanctity which refuses to be bargained with, or to be explained away in terms of any alien principle. The ancient Sophists who 'debunked' various institutions in the life of the Greek city-state, saying that these institutions were conventional (νόμῳ) rather than natural (φύσει), have perpetuated their memory in our word 'sophistry'. It is sophistry to argue that right and wrong have no foundation in the eternal order of things. The plain man's inescapable conviction that treachery, lies and lust are wrong, is not a socially begotten value-judgment, a useful human convention. His sense that mercy, truth and honour have eternal validity is no hedonistic calculus, subtly camouflaged, nor the unconscious rationalization of self-interest. Man cannot dismiss his sense of sacred obligation any more than he can escape from his shadow. The content of that felt obligation may vary from age to age, but the fact of it stands for ever, and its meaning is indubitable. As John Oman observes somewhere, 'whoever says "ought", really meaning "ought", is in that act bearing witness to the supernatural and supra-temporal as the destined home of man'. An obligation wholly independent of temporal consequences ('come rack, come rope') clearly cannot have its origin and justification in the temporal. Only to a being who has eternity in his heart,[1] because he is made in God's image, can the words 'Thou oughtest' have indestructible meaning. And if it be true that a moral ideal can exist only in a mind, an absolute moral ideal

[1] Eccles. iii. 11 (R.V. margin).

can exist only in a Mind which is the source and sustainer of all moral excellences, all reality.

In the fifth place, there is the argument labelled Ontological; it contends that the idea of God would not enter man's mind at all, unless man's being had its source and ground in him whose Being is wholly other than man's being and yet inclusive of it. The very idea of God is possible to us only because God already stands behind it. 'I believe', said Anselm, 'in order that I may understand.'[1] Human thought is always a signpost pointing to something beyond itself; deny this something, and all human thought is denied along with it. The mind of man is unintelligible unless Mind directs the whole creative process which has brought that mind to birth. On any other view it would be impossible to rely on the power of the mind to know truth. The ontological argument—always being shown out politely at the front door, but always quietly coming in again at the back, in a slightly different dress—is the affirmation of faith that belief in God is an absolute presupposition of all rational enquiry.

Lastly, there is the argument which might be labelled Human, because it springs out of the religious experiences and acts which, for all their bewildering variety, are integral to the history of humanity. Human history provides that basic religious experience to which the successive self-revelations of God make their appeal, and without which God's revelation in Jesus Christ would be impossible. The history of religion is not, in itself, revelation. Revelation is always more than religious experience. It is, to quote Paul Tillich,[2] the divine criticism and transformation of religious experience. Man's whole

[1] 'Credo ut intelligam' (*not* 'Intelligo ut credam').
[2] Dudleian Lecture (1935) on *Natural and Revealed Religion*.

religious history may not be explained as the mere outflow of his unique human nature. For man's nature is rooted in the mystery of his freedom to transcend his nature. It is this very freedom which is the basis of man's history. Our history is not determined by our nature; it is not the mere product of natural necessities; it is the creative context of God's living word to man.

The six arguments, stated here so baldly, have all played a vital role in the history of Christian doctrine. Their value lies in their cumulative testimony that God is. But *who* God is, God himself must tell us in revelation or we shall never know. Revelation means a dynamic self-disclosure on the part of the Other, to which man responds by faith. Man transcends his finiteness in the very act of being aware of his finiteness.

We ought to notice, in passing, that this response is not in principle peculiar to the religious man; it may not be dismissed as credulity which the natural sciences have outgrown. Faith is the presupposition of all discovery and of all progress in knowledge. Our most fundamental convictions—that we exist, or that the external world is no dream but really *there*—are not reached or proved by argument; they are given in experience. They may be defended by argument of course, but that is another matter. All men live by deep, inexorable intuitions, such as that of the plain man who trusts to common sense, that of the physicist who makes use of unprovable hypothesis,[1] and that of the religious man whose faith is response to revelation.

[1] 'The hypotheses of science are nothing more or less than explanations put forward to embrace a set of facts, or theories previously unrelated; and these hypotheses are not demonstrable in themselves. Such hypotheses as the force of gravity, space-time coincidences, the

This means, therefore, that revelation and response interpret one another. Divine self-disclosure is meaningless except in terms of human discovery, and *vice versa*. It means, further, that the great central tradition in Christian doctrine avoids two extreme views which are poles asunder in their mutual opposition.

The one view is represented by Spengler, whose dominant principle is a thorough-going relativism; he denies that there is any absolute truth for man. There is no revelation. Human convictions are always relative, one man's centre being another man's horizon. The search for absolute truth is like a fountain, striving to heaven and falling back in tears.

The other view is that of Karl Barth, who regards all natural theology as an attack on the absolute otherness and sole causality of God, and as no better than idolatry. Indeed, natural theology is a contradiction in terms. Revelation altogether transcends human philosophy; it occurs *in* the mind of regenerate man, but it comes from the Beyond, like a bolt from the blue. Its operation is exactly opposite to that of a fountain, in that it comes straight down from above (*senkrecht von oben*) in certain events, of which the Bible is the record. God's revelation is given; sinful man's passivity is complete; even the faith by which he responds to the sheer gift of God in Christ is altogether God's gift.

With the relativism and pessimism of Spengler's view, Christian doctrine can have nothing to do; the Bible is a

ether, the wave-theory of light, the general theory of relativity, are examples new and old of this kind of fruitful procedure which has not only connected seemingly random facts or theories, but lighted the way to the discovery of new and unsuspected facts' (Friend and Feibleman, *The Unlimited Community*, p. 183).

monument to the fact that the eternal God has never left himself without witness; its whole meaning is disclosed in the fact of the Incarnation; God has spoken to us in his Son.

What, on the other hand, must Christian doctrine say of the magnificent one-sidedness of Barth, whose theological transcendentalism has startled modern Christendom with its prophetic power and its indubitable desire to be loyal to the testimony of the Bible? Christian doctrine agrees that there is no experience of God without a revelation from God. Indeed, it insists with Barth that the God of natural theology is unable to give the religious certainty which is called forgiveness of sins, or grace; theism cannot give to sinful men a *saving* knowledge of God the Redeemer. But Christian doctrine asserts that divine revelation would be utterly impossible if there were no affinity or point of contact between man and God, no historical experience of the 'wholly Other', no capacity in unregenerate men to receive the sheer gift of grace. Man asks questions about God to which revelation is the answer; but the answer is intelligible only because the questions are intelligible. It is in this traffic between heaven and earth (Gen. xxviii. 11–19) that the divine revelation is given and received. Dreaming Jacob is not a mere cipher; his ladder is God's ladder; set up on earth, the top of it reached to heaven and the angels of God ascended and descended on it; and the Lord stood above it.

The problem of Revelation and Reason is to be understood, therefore, in terms of such a ladder rather than in terms of fountain or bolt from the blue. The Hebraic-Christian knowledge of the living God is always experience of the Object *in its relation to the subject*.[1] Since the Creator is altogether other than the creature, human experience of God's transcendent

[1] See further, ch. III.

otherness is plainly impossible. We do not know God as he is in himself; we know him only in his action and effect upon us; our very addressability is a fact of his appointing; our faith itself is his gift. To say that we love because he first loved us is to say that our love is the result which his initiative alone makes possible. Indeed, his effect upon us *is* our response. When St Paul insists that all is of God (Rom. xi. 36), he is drawing out the meaning of Christ's words to St Peter in Matt. xvi. 17. As often as Christ ends his teaching with the words 'he that hath ears to hear let him hear', he proclaims that the problem of Revelation and Reason is not a conundrum for man's intellect, but a demand made upon man's will by the infinite grace of God.

The fundamental question is this: How do we pass from abstract argument about God to living awareness of God? How have believing men found God, not as an inference from 'the starry world without and the moral law within', but as a living, saving God? Modern theology is returning to first principles in asking whether Christianity has its objective basis in moral idealism or in history. Is the Christian faith no more than a splendid illustration of the philosophy of moral values, or is it something given concretely in the events of time? Communism and Nazism are striking examples of the modern reaction against mere idealism, which is felt to be unrealistic and sentimental. Marx himself pointed men to facts, to the irresistible forces of history, not to the ineffectual aestheticism of value-judgments. Marx was a Jew, and although his debt to Hegel is obvious, his debt to the genius of Hebraism was more obvious than he realized.

For the Bible, which is Hebraic throughout, witnesses to

the holy will of God as purposive and continuously active in
history. The Scriptures are not a philosophical treatise but a
history book. The prophets did not believe in God because they
deduced his existence from the facts of nature and history; on
the contrary they brought a responsive belief in his revelation
to the interpretation of nature and history.

After all, there is so much in nature and in history which
is utterly inscrutable and mysterious to the boldest theistic
speculation. It constitutes what we know as the problem of evil,
a problem which is notoriously acute for all who believe in God.
The Hebrew prophets, whose ethical monotheism towers above
the common levels of history like a Himalaya range, were
always wrestling with a two-fold mystery springing out of their
faith that this is God's world and that man is the crown of
God's creation. In the first place they had to wrestle with man's
metaphysical distress at his own finitude and God's otherness.
So far from always finding God in nature and history, they
sometimes lost him there. 'Verily, thou art a God that hidest
thyself.' The prophets speak for Everyman in witnessing to an
irrational element in all religious experience. Like Rudolf
Otto to-day, they reminded their generation that the meaning
of human existence is not exhausted by the rational and the
ethical; it escapes man's net and passes out into the ocean of
ineffable mystery. In the second place, the prophets never
ceased to wrestle with man's moral distress, the fact of sin in
this world which God made and saw to be 'very good'—the
dark, abiding, universal mystery of iniquity.

Thus, Scripture is less concerned with the philosophy of
theism than with God's active and purposive revelation of
himself as a living God and a Saviour. God himself makes
answer to man's tragic estrangement from him. He, the

31

Creator and Sustainer of all that is, is the Holy One of Israel, working out the eternal purpose of his creation in judgment and mercy. He draws nigh to his world, mighty to save.

The Christian doctrine of creation does not arise from our interest in explaining the world or accounting for its 'origin' at some approximately dateable time in the cosmic past. The doctrine of creation 'out of nothing' is not a scientific description of the beginning of the time series. Here, no scientific statements are possible. 'Before Abraham was, I am' (John viii. 58). Belief in the creation means a way, *the* way, of understanding the present world. It is an act of faith (Hebr. xi. 3). Creation out of nothing is not to be understood as an historical event but as a description of existence. Here is truth which we receive by faith; we do not conceive it at all, since it transcends the utmost limit of all human conceiving. The doctrine of creation out of nothing is not a cosmological theory, but an expression of our adoring sense of the transcendent majesty of God and of our utter dependence upon him. The doctrine has a three-fold distinction.

In the first place it is distinguished from Deism, which isolates God from his universe and knows nothing about him except that he is the First Cause of all that is. The deist conceives of creation as a past act, the universe being like a wound-up clock working unaided by God, who exists in transcendent loneliness and inaccessibility. The Christian doctrine of creation, on the other hand, asserts that the transcendent God creates *in continuo actu*; i.e. he sustains the universe in every moment of its existence.

In the second place it is distinguished from Pantheism, which takes many forms and either resolves the whole universe into God or equates God with the universe. The whole of things is

God (the relation being one of identity, correlation or continuity); the world is the necessary self-unfolding of God, a divine emanation. The result is that God is depersonalized and lost. The World Soul of Pantheism is as abstract and unknowable as the First Cause of Deism. The Christian doctrine of creation through God's Word is a way of asserting that the Ultimate Reality is personal, creation being the free act of God's will and the continuous expression of his purpose.

In the third place it is distinguished from Dualism, which conceives of the universe as being formed out of a primal material, independent of God and in some sense hostile to him. According to Dualism God is the principle of Form battling against formless chaos; or he is Spirit warring against Matter in all its gross intractability. Christian doctrine repudiates all such forms of metaphysical dualism, by affirming that the universe is created by God alone 'out of nothing'; and that all things, though definitely distinct from him, are utterly dependent on him.

But the Christian doctrine of God the Creator cannot be adequately interpreted by the formal definitions of systematic theology; at any rate, a lecture on the living God should end, not with technical terminology but with the language of the heart. The living God is best interpreted by living men who have known him experimentally. One such man, George Fox, has told us in his journal what happened to him in Nottinghamshire in 1648: 'And one morning as I was sitting by the fire a great cloud came over me and a temptation beset me; but I sate still. And it was said: "All things come by nature"; and the elements and stars came over me, so that I was in a manner quite clouded with it.... And as I sate still under it, and let it alone, a living hope arose in me, and a true voice which said

"There is a living God who made all things". And immediately the cloud and temptation vanished away and life rose over it all; my heart was glad and I praised the living God. After some time I met with some people who had such a notion that there was no God, but that all things come by nature. I had a great dispute with them and overturned them and made some of them confess that there is a living God. Then I saw that it was good that I had gone through that exercise.'

II

MAN AND HIS SIN

THE CHRISTIAN DOCTRINE OF THE FALL

WHAT is the truth about the nature and end of man? This is the ultimate question behind the vast debate, the desperate struggles, of our time. Ideologies—to use the ugly modern jargon—are really anthropologies; they are answers to that question which man has not ceased to ask ever since he began asking questions at all; namely, What is Man? He asks this question about himself, because all his questions about the universe involve it. Who is the being who asks the questions?

We ought to notice at the outset that Christian doctrine decisively repudiates two classic attitudes towards this problem; two estimates of human nature and human history which have never lacked their defenders, and which are poles apart from one another. I mean, on the one hand, a naïve optimism; and, on the other hand, a cynical pessimism. Let us look at them in turn.

It is common form to-day to dismiss most forms of liberalism —in sociology, politics and theology, for example—as unrealistic and sentimental. To quote a mordant paragraph which T. E. Hulme wrote about moral idealism twenty-four years ago: 'it is as if you pointed out to an old lady at a garden party that there was an escaped lion twenty yards off, and she were to reply, "Oh, yes," and then quietly take another cucumber sandwich.'

In short, realism is in the ascendant, as a multitude of writers remind us; in the face of stubborn realities, the complacency of mere idealism is as nauseating as its moral inadequacy. Modern man is suffering from disillusionment, now that the evolutionary optimism of half a century ago is plainly discredited by facts. Even in America the romantic illusions of Utopianism are an ebbing tide, as the mystery of iniquity is seen to be a real and an abiding mystery: not something exceptional, a bad patch which a young civilization like that of the United States will soon mop up, but something typical of all civilizations: not the surface blemish which education, modern science, low-price technics and three-piece plumbing will rectify, but a deep-seated radical evil which is uncomfortably reminiscent of what Jonathan Edwards knew as original sin. The Americans are not as sure as they were that sin is only an 'evolutionary overhang'. They are no longer confident that what has been called the sin-obsession of Christianity is just so much 'crêpe-hanging'.

'We were getting richer, more numerous, busier, every year', says Professor Adams of the Capitalist era which arrived overnight in 1850. 'Back in the East, Hermann Melville had written an American classic, *Moby Dick*; but no one knew or cared what the White Whale signified or whether there was any evil in the Universe. We preferred Emerson, who asked us to be cultured and spiritual, and hopefully looked like the rest of us for spirit to evolve somehow out of matter; and blessed our railroads to a divine use. But the dark cloud in the American sky grew blacker and was spreading.'[1]

[1] *The Epic of America*, p. 234.

The fact is that our generation is rediscovering the abysmal depths of evil in the heart of man, and realizing that Public Enemy Number One is neither ignorance, nor stupidity, nor the defective social environment, but *sin*, which is the deep mysterious root of all these evils.

To be explicit, Christian doctrine brings a three-fold count against the confident optimism of modern civilization.

First, the root error of Utopian idealism is its failure to take a sufficiently tragic view of human nature. It blandly assumes the natural and fundamental goodness of man, shutting its eyes to the fact that under sufficient stress the modern man—not to mention the modern woman—will do deeds of evil as terrible as anything recorded in history.

Christianity's second count against the Utopian humanism of our time is that it clings to that peculiarly modern superstition, man's perfectibility and his inevitable progress. Granted, it says, that darkness covereth the earth and gross darkness the peoples, still, we shall ultimately achieve control over the demonic, irrational, and savage forces, which have, admittedly, tried men's faith and broken their hearts in every generation until now. Sin must not become an obsession, therefore. We need not take it too seriously. As some wag observed about the adolescence of the Quaker, George Fox, 'he had sown his wild oats, but they were only Quaker Oats'. That is, he grew out of his youthful difficulties and humanity will do the same.

The answer to this dogma of human perfectibility is that history does not disclose so neat and simple a pattern. There is a tragic antinomy in the whole world process, to which Christ himself bears witness in the parable of the Wheat and the Tares. They grow together until history reaches its climax of ultimate judgment; the New Testament knows nothing of history as the record of human progress wherein evil is steadily conquered by good. And we know nothing of it either. History is the record of 'an ever-increasing cosmos creating ever-increasing possibilities of chaos';[1] in other words, as our state of civilization makes progress, so the difficulties and dangers which keep it company make progress too. At every instant these difficulties and dangers bear a nearly constant ratio to the state of civilization which we have reached. Do the facts suggest that with our enormously extended mastery of nature, there goes a corresponding mastery of our evil wills, our lusts, our hypocrisies, our boundless egotisms—above all, our fears? They do not. The light of progress is real; granted. But the new dangers and degradations which are its accompanying shadow are also real. Along with the internal combustion engine there comes slaughter on the roads: along with aviation, bombs. Chemical research in the interests of medicine brings with it phosgene and vesicant dew, mustard gas and arsene. The education which was to have banished crime, only makes crime more efficient, increasing its range. Man's power to do more good is always power to do more evil. Chateaubriand, nourished like many a young Frenchman at the time of the French Revolution on legends of America, was surprised on landing there to be met at a farmyard gate by a negro girl, thirteen years old. 'We bought maize-cakes, chickens, eggs and milk and went abroad again with our baskets. I gave my silk handkerchief to the little African girl. It was a slave who welcomed me to the Land of Liberty.'[2]

But this is not all. Christian doctrine makes yet a third count against the optimistic estimate of human nature. Long

[1] Reinhold Niebuhr, *An Interpretation of Christian Ethics*, p. 108.
[2] André Maurois, *Chateaubriand*, p. 48.

before the advent of modern psycho-analysis, Christian doctrine
had unmasked much that passes for righteousness and high
moral principle. It had insisted that there is no sin so subtle as
the sin of 'goodness', as popularly or legalistically conceived.
'And he spake this parable unto certain which trusted in themselves that they were righteous.... Two men went up into the
temple to pray; the one a Pharisee, and the other a publican.
The Pharisee stood and prayed thus with himself, God, I thank
thee, that I am not as other men are, extortioners, unjust,
adulterers, or even as this publican.... And the publican,
standing afar off, would not lift up so much as his eyes unto
heaven, but smote upon his breast, saying, God be merciful
to me a sinner. I tell you, this man went down to his house
justified rather than the other' (Luke xviii. 9–14). Righteousness so easily cloaks the sin of self-righteousness. There is no
sin so subtly dangerous as the self-sufficiency of the morally
religious man. Indeed, all our righteousness is tainted. High-
sounding moral principles often include a rationalization of our
self-interest. Is it not fatally easy for a class or a nation to be
blind to the ways in which its interests condition its moral
pronouncements? The egotism of the will to power asserts itself
not as egotism of course, but as an idealism of some kind
or other. Modern Imperialism is the white man's burden.
Modern Communism is a crusade for social righteousness. The
militarist almost always regards modern war as a just war; the
pacifist almost always interprets his objection to its evil and
misery as a matter of conscience. Such high claims to disinterestedness are doubtless sincere, yet it may be doubted whether
they are always an exhaustive account of what they would
describe. We readily acknowledge that Satan appears as an
angel of light, but we are less ready to see that all culture,

including religious culture, is tainted with the same hypocrisy. Corruption touches even this. Even at its best, man's goodness is poisoned; there is this canker or flaw in it, so that it actually becomes a barrier to his reconciliation with God. The whole of the New Testament contrast between grace and works is bound up with this fact. It is fatally easy for a man to use his moral rectitude to veil the proud egocentricity which it supremely illustrates. This is the Christian version of the Greek ὕβρις. The self-sufficiency of the morally religious man is itself the full measure of sin. We come to understand the great word 'Grace' only when we perceive that this legalistic relation to God is itself sin. The parable of the Prodigal Son is an immortal illustration of this attempt to do business with God as though he were not the Holy Father but a banker keeping a debit and credit account with us. The attitude of both the sons was commercial. The younger son wanted an overdraft: the elder brother wanted to open a deposit account.[1] And the latter is sin at its deepest and deadliest.

To sum up: or, rather, to let Browning's well-known lines sum up the realism of the Christian faith:

> 'Tis the faith that launched point-blank its dart
> At the head of a lie; taught Original Sin,
> The corruption of man's heart.

Great thinkers of modern times, Montaigne and Pascal, Bunyan and Kierkegaard, Nietzsche and Sigmund Freud, have probed the human heart and told the truth about its strength. Their analysis only confirms the radical realism of the Biblical view of man. The congenital weakness of human nature is the submerged rock on which the complacent claims of an opti-

[1] Professor T. W. Manson's epigram.

40

mistic humanism are shipwrecked. Indeed, as Professor Hodges of Reading pointed out in a News-Letter some months back,[1] the gospel that good-will is the one thing needful is so clearly false, that people who see its falsehood have been driven away from Christianity because they have been led to think that this is Christian doctrine.

But, now, in the second place, Christian doctrine repudiates a cynical pessimism with equal decisiveness. Pessimism, if it be real and thorough, is as unchristian as an excessive optimism. Thorough-going despair is pagan. To despair of man is not unchristian—far from it. But to despair of man in such a way that you are really despairing of God is blasphemy. Indeed, it is atheism.

Thomas Hobbes, significantly enough, was charged with atheism. And atheism is implicit in his assertion of the utter self-centredness and lovelessness of man. According to Hobbes human life without the control of the totalitarian state at every point would be 'solitary, poor, nasty, brutish and short'. Hobbes had no real belief in the redeeming grace of God; he believed in Leviathan.

This view finds its exponents to-day. If the optimists (Social Democrats and others) have affirmed that the function of the state is to make a Utopia of human society, the sole function of the state according to the pessimists is to prevent human society from becoming Hell. Indeed, more than one continental theologian takes a very similar view, notably Gogarten.

All this inevitably raises an obvious question which may best be dealt with at this point. What are we to make of the grim and terrible doctrine of Total Corruption—found in Holy Scripture

[1] *Christian News-Letter*, Supp. No. 27.

certainly, but worked out with an unscriptural and pitiless logic by St Augustine and the Reformers? Man is 'utterly leprous and unclean'. If this is not blasphemous pessimism, what is? What did it mean?

Well, if it meant what a classic statement of it seems to mean when taken out of its historic context and interpreted literally, namely, that we 'are utterly indisposed, disabled and made opposite to all good, and wholly inclined to all evil' (*West. Conf.* vi. 4), it is plainly indefensible. If Total Corruption meant that every man is as bad as he can be, it would be totally absurd, simply because the conception is self-destroying, as Professor John Baillie has reminded us.[1] 'A totally corrupt being would be as incapable of sin as would a totally illogical being of fallacious argument.' But, in spite of the deplorable extravagance of the language of some Reformers here, notably Luther, this doctrine of Total Corruption was really insisting that the depravity which sin has produced in human nature *extends to the whole of it*, permeates human life and experience *in all its ranges*; that there is no part of man's nature, *not even his virtue*, which is unaffected by it. Total Corruption does not and never did mean that the stream of human history, instead of being crystal clear, is solid mud; but that it is impure, corrupted in every part of its course; that even the purest ideals and the most disinterested achievements of individuals and societies are, as we have already seen, tainted by sinful self-interest and pride. Human justice is itself proof of this, since anything short of love as revealed in Christ cannot be perfect justice. Perfect justice would be love. As Niebuhr has remarked, 'Love is the only final structure of freedom'. But our justice—our prisons and cash-registers, our private property, our elaborate

[1] *Our Knowledge of God*, p. 33.

devices for checking one another and our signatures on the dotted line—all this is a monument to the radical and abiding wrongness of humanity, as measured by the absolute norm of love.

The Reformers knew that if you look at human virtue and merit, not from the ethical but from the strictly theocentric standpoint, all righteousness is as filthy rags. There is none righteous, no not one. They said so. They meant that fallen and rebellious man is utterly impotent to come unaided to that saving knowledge of God for which he was created. He cannot bring his state into harmony with his true nature. He cannot fulfil the destiny for which he was created in the image of God. 'Thou must save, and thou alone.' The doctrine of Total Corruption was the intransigent answer which Reformation theology made to Renaissance Humanism. But to suppose, therefore, that the Reformers were antinomian, and that they had no interest in ethics, is nonsense. They recognized that, ethically considered, man is a mixture of good and evil, and that men's sins differ in degree as well as in direction. They were not blind to what the New Testament has to say about human conduct which is relatively good; about men's moral growth; about extenuating circumstances which make human guilt a matter of degree. Indeed, they had a Puritan horror of lawlessness and fully recognized man's positive achievements for good in the arts and sciences, and in politics. But they knew that such cultural values—admittedly excellent in themselves— are unable to answer the deepest longings of the soul of man; culture gives no answer to the question of the ages, 'What must I do to be saved?' In short, theirs was neither the easy optimism of the humanist, nor the dark pessimism of the cynic, but the radical realism of the Bible. Mere pessimism would

43

be a poor and pagan answer to a sentimental and irreligious optimism. It is an answer which Christian anthropology has never given, so long as it has remained true to its own first principles.

What are those principles? We are now in a position to state them, albeit summarily.

The first principle of Christian anthropology is that man, like the animals, is God's creature. Though he is God's last and highest earthly creature, his creatureliness is an inescapable and abiding fact. But, unlike the animals, man is more than a natural creature. He is lifted above all other earthly creatures in being made in the image of God, and in being aware of the fact. He is aware that the Creator is the Eternal Love who calls men into existence that their willing response to his love may fulfil his creative purpose. This responsible awareness which God created in man (*Ansprechbarkeit*, addressability, or answerability, as Brunner has called it) is man's greatness and his fatal temptation. As Brunner observes,[1] this responsibility or addressability was not a task, but a gift; not law, but grace. The Word, through which and in which man has his distinctive existence, was not an imperative of the divine law, but an indicative of the divine love. Man's 'Yes' was to be a response, not to 'Thou shalt', but to 'I have created and called thee; thou art mine'. Created in God's image, man was meant to be a son, not a bondservant under a law. There, then, is the first of the three fundamental principles of Christian anthropology. Man is a creature divinely endowed with gifts which set him above all other creatures; he is made in the image of God. It is impossible to understand man's fundamental disharmony and

[1] *Man in Revolt*, p. 98.

the immemorial misdirection of human life apart from this relationship of man to the Creator who made him in his own image.

The second principle witnesses to the universal fact of man's rebellious estrangement from God. Unlike the animals man is a sinner: he falls below all earthly creatures in his rebellious denial of a responsibility which they can never know.

The essence of sin is man's self-centred denial of his distinctive endowment. Its final ground is pride which rebels against God and repudiates his purpose. Its active manifestation is self-love which 'changes the glory of the incorruptible God into the image of the corruptible man'. The freedom of the filial spirit, man's freedom *for* God and *in* God, is perverted to mean freedom *from* God. *Imago Dei* is interpreted to mean 'Ye shall be as gods'. It is interesting and significant that in his last book the well-known psychologist, Jung, should describe man's proud trust in himself as 'his Godalmightiness'.[1]

The result is two-fold. First, alienation from God, as two immortal stories in Holy Scripture remind us: the story of the Garden of Eden, and the parable of the Prodigal Son. Man is not at home in his Father's house, but a needy outcast in a far country. Second, the wrath of God, which is the terrible way this alienation works out, both for the individual and in society. For man, though a sinner, remains God's creature. The prodigal among the husks is still a son: he does not become like one of Circe's swine. His initial endowment is indestructible. An animal, just because it is an animal, is unable to rebel against its endowment. And man, just because he is man, is unable to destroy his endowment. God's image is not destroyed.

[1] J. C. Jung, *The Integration of the Personality*, cited by Dr J. H. Oldham, *Christian News-Letter*, No. 36.

Sin always presupposes that which it defaces. 'Man could not be godless without God.'[1] And the form in which rebellious and fallen man experiences the eternal love of God is Wrath. His responsibility to God ceases to be a formula of his created being and becomes a formula of obligation. Liberty becomes bondage. This is 'the curse of the Law', that the will of God which it announces as the law of man's being is no longer a gift of life and the most natural thing in the world, but a death-bringing demand. It is all the difference between living at home, and being in prison. This is the second great principle of Christian anthropology.

The third principle witnesses to man's solidarity in evil. The word 'sin' has an individual reference, plainly enough: it is always a conscious and responsible act of will on the part of an individual. Yet this cannot be an exhaustive definition of it. Sin is also a state or condition of sinfulness mysteriously constitutive of our empirical make-up. It is never a man's private affair. Your failure matches mine and our lives interlock to form an organic system of evil. Indeed, St Augustine used the words 'sinful mass' (*massa peccatrix*) to describe this solidary aspect of human sin. Schleiermacher, too, described it as 'in each the work of all: in all the work of each'.[2] Dostoievsky reminds us that the solidarity of the race is a fact and, in view of the reality of sin, a terrible fact; 'we are each responsible to all for all'. The work which psychologists are now doing on the 'collective unconscious' goes to show that below not only the conscious, but also the unconscious life of the individual, there is a deep layer (as it were) of hidden, inborn forces: its content is not individual but universal and, as such, beyond the conscious control of the will. In speaking thus, psychology is only

[1] Brunner, *op. cit.* p. 187.   [2] *Glaubenslehre*, § 71. 2.

confirming the witness of the New Testament, that humanity is subject to a possession or infection by evil from which no individual can dissociate himself. This possession is so sinister, cunning and strong that the New Testament can only describe it in terms of demonic powers. The personification of evil as Satan, difficult though it is for our thought, stands for the fact of spiritual solidarity in evil which will not be evaded or ignored. An enemy hath done this—our common Enemy![1] Whatever images of thought we may employ, there is in the world of our experience a kingdom of evil by which the evil acts of each individual are inspired, sustained and reinforced.

So far, then, we have been considering the first principles of the Christian doctrine of man and his sin.

The question now confronting us is obvious: Can sin be accounted for? According to a widespread modern view, brilliantly expounded by Tennant,[2] sin is explicable as an evolutionary survival from man's animal origin. Sin is our conscious misuse of impulses and instinctive passions which are part of our animal inheritance. In themselves these primary incentives to sin are neutral and non-moral. Indeed, they are not only biologically but morally necessary to our growth as men: they are the raw material of our moral life, and as much the condition and occasion of virtue as of vice. Animals can neither sin nor achieve sainthood; man, as a responsible moral

[1] 'Ich bin der Geist, der stets verneint....
    So ist denn alles was ihr Sünde,
    Zerstörung, kurz das Böse nennt,
    Mein eigentliches Element.'
                    Mephistopheles (*Faust*, 1).

[2] In *The Origin and Propagation of Sin* (1903) and *The Concept of Sin* (1912).

agent, can and does. His inborn conative tendencies are morally neutral, but his will which shapes and uses them is not. The will may be good or evil and as such it alone calls for moral approval or disapproval. Thus propensities not in themselves sinful are the condition and the explanation of sin's emergence when responsible man is evolved from the irresponsible animal.

Three criticisms of this view suggest themselves at once. First, we meet the old and tragic question: Why is sin universal? Even if we admit that this evolutionary theory describes *how* sin happens, why does it happen always and everywhere? How are we to account for that bias or perversion of the human will which makes sin an empirically universal fact and therefore virtually inevitable? As the very condition of moral action man must be free to choose the evil: but why is it that all men without exception do so, unless a sinful tendency is somehow part of their very nature? All serious thought about the mystery of iniquity has had to grapple with this its constitutional, as well as its volitional, aspect.

Many of our modern difficulties with regard to this problem spring from theological terms which hinder rather than help us. It cannot be stated too emphatically that 'Original Sin' neither implies nor means 'Original Guilt'. The latter expression carries with it forensic and penal implications which outrage the moral sense. No man may be judged guilty because of the misdeeds of his ancestor. Such a judgment would destroy the very meaning of morality. Therefore, such terminology which is only a stumbling-block to-day is better abandoned. But the empirical fact of universal evil (what Kant called *das radikale Böse*) remains, and whether or not we describe it as 'Original Sin', it demands some adequate description.

48

We must abandon the classical doctrine of Original Sin
where it is bound up with the morally insupportable doctrine of
Original Guilt, but we are still left with the historical fact of
universal moral imperfection, whose reality that grim doctrine attested. As Edwyn Bevan has observed: 'When people
say that man is naturally good or that his good and bad
impulses are pretty evenly matched, how is it that all over
the world to follow the good impulses has seemed like going
uphill, and to follow the evil ones like going downhill?'[1] To
explain this by appealing to the chronological priority of
impulse to conscience, is only to carry the problem one stage
further back and to leave it unexplained. Why are men such
that conscience is always and everywhere outmatched? This
is the fundamental and universal mystery which cries out for
explanation.

In the second place, since sin necessarily implies guilt, how
are we to explain it, that is, determine its causes, without *eo
ipso* explaining its guilt away? Sin, like freedom, is by hypothesis inexplicable, since moral action presupposes freedom in
the sense of real choice. Personal responsibility and freedom are
the essence of what we mean by moral personality. But, if man
is free no scientific formula can possibly cover the universality
of sin, without taking away the element of responsibility which
makes it what it is. Any alleged explanation of the fact that all
men sin is only a new determinism.[2] If sin, universal as it is, is to
be treated as a moral fact and not as a natural fact (such as the
secretion of the bile) it must remain inexplicable. Determine

[1] *Symbolism and Belief*, p. 63.
[2] See H. W. Robinson, *The Christian Doctrine of Man* (second edition);
the Appendix entitled 'Recent Thought on the Doctrine of Sin',
pp. 353–4.

the causes of a universal moral fact and it ceases to be moral. It becomes natural, and is no more patient of moral evaluation than is gravitation or the beating of the heart or death. The attempt to trace sin back to an empirical fact which causes it, invalidates man's God-given sense that he is a will and a person. The will is *ex hypothesi* that which is non-derivable.[1] Man's sinful will cannot be explained: it must remain as the one completely irrational fact in a world which God created, and saw to be 'very good'.

The third difficulty here, on which von Hügel lays his sensitive finger, is that the permanent wound in man's nature which needs healing is deeper than anything biology can explain. The central, typical, fatal sin is self-sufficiency or pride. In the Christian view pride or self-love is the specific *differentia* of sin. The evolutionary hypothesis makes pride and self-sufficiency depend as truly upon our animal descent, as do gluttony or sloth. But, as von Hügel rightly observes, 'this single derivation will simply not work.... Impurity may be the viler sin, but even impurity is instinctively felt here to be less deadly than pride.... Whilst impurity is occasioned by the body, pride is not; the doctrine of the Fall of the Angels grandly illustrates this deep instinct.'[2]

After all, the fundamental instinct of the animal world is the will to survive. Man's sin cannot be so explained, because it cannot be so described. It is the will to power which differentiates man from the animals, and constitutes the tragic dissidences of human history. Selfishness measures the inexplicable tragedy of the world. Man's proud unwillingness to

[1] 'das was nicht abgeleitet werden kann' (Paul Althaus, *Grundriss der Dogmatik*, ii. 66).

[2] *Essays and Addresses on the Philosophy of Religion* (1921), pp. 8–9.

accept the absolute authority and claim of God in whose image
he has been made, is and remains the mystery of iniquity.

What, then, of the doctrine of the Fall? Serious thought
about sin involves an irresolvable antinomy. As a universal
fact of human experience it is virtually unavoidable. As a
moral fact it is a matter of personal decision and responsibility.
Or, to put it another way: sin is rooted in man's inmost disposition; yet it is indubitably that for which his will is responsible. We face this fundamental problem therefore: how
are we to express the idea of *un*-freedom without laying ourselves open to the danger of determinism?[1]

Christian doctrine has attempted to do so in terms of man's
original state and the Fall, but it has sometimes defeated its
own intention by treating as literal history what can only be
a mythological framework. Christian doctrine illustrates the
fatal difficulty of trying to construct a history of sin out of the
concept of its inevitability. Luther's extravagant description
of the perfections of man's primitive state is as fantastic as
South's sermon on 'Man created in God's Image', which
contained the famous sentence: 'An Aristotle was but the
rubbish of an Adam, and Athens but the rudiments of
Paradise.'

The difficulty is two-fold. First, the victory of the sciences,
palaeontology and biology, shatters this picture as history.
Second, the Adam story is the main source of that determinism which the classic anthropology of Christendom hardly
avoids.

The idea of a Fall from an original state of perfection is

[1] Cf. Calvin, *Institutio* (1536), c. ii, *De Fide*: 'difficilis et involuta
quaestio: an Deus autor sit peccati.'

really a limiting conception, a theological *Grenzbegriff*. It is not a scientific statement about the dawn of history. The Fall is symbolism, necessary to the intellect, but inconceivable by the imagination.[1] It involves no scientific description of absolute beginnings. Eden is on no map, and Adam's fall fits no historical calendar. Moses is not nearer to the Fall than we are, because he lived three thousand years before our time. The Fall refers not to some datable aboriginal calamity in the historic past of humanity, but to a dimension of human experience which is always present—namely, that we who have been created for fellowship with God repudiate it continually; and that the whole of mankind does this along with us. Everyman is his own 'Adam', and all men are solidarily 'Adam'. Thus, Paradise before the Fall, the *status perfectionis*, is not a period of history, but our 'memory' of a divinely intended quality of life, given to us along with our consciousness of guilt. It is, to quote Paul Althaus, 'nicht historischer sondern wesentlicher Art';[2] that is, it describes the quality rather than the history of 'man's first disobedience'.

Man's tragic apostasy from God is not something which happened once for all a long time ago. It is true in every moment of existence. If you believe in the Creation, you must go on to believe in the Fall. The symbolism of the one is a necessary complement to the symbolism of the other.

Christian anthropology affirms the notorious conflict between man's recalcitrant will, and that divine purpose in which

[1] Speaking of self-transcendence, Auguste Lecerf writes: 'cette image, irréalisable pour l'imagination, est en quelque sorte nécessaire pour l'intelligence' (*De la Nature de la Connaissance Religieuse*, p. 291). This is an apt comment on all theological symbolism.

[2] *Op. cit.* p. 67.

alone man and his world find their true meaning. It describes that age-long misdirection of human life which is the very presupposition of the Gospel. Any other presupposition would make the glorious gospel of the blessed God meaningless.

A second Adam to the fight,
And to the rescue came.

III

THE KINGDOM OF GOD

THE CHRISTIAN DOCTRINE OF HISTORY

W E are near enough to our schooldays to remember Macaulay's flattering but irritating references to what 'every schoolboy knows'. These blandishments deceived none of us, of course: we knew that by 'schoolboy' he really meant Thomas Babington Macaulay.

Had I the nerve to begin this lecture by saying that every schoolboy knows the difference between the Greek and Hebrew ways of thinking about God I should merely mean that there are few things more familiar to students of theology, or more fundamental to the understanding of Christian doctrine.

It is easy to make foolish generalizations here, and to exaggerate this well-known difference between Hellenism and Hebraism. But the difference is real. It turns on the meaning of history, and its relation to the eternal God, who is above history. Let me try to express the difference in four ways.

First of all, the Greek and the Hebrew thought differently about God's nature. To the Greek mind God is impersonal, rather like an all-pervasive ether; an Absolute transcending all differences; almost a complete Blank. The Ultimate Reality is the One, who is one and all alone and ever more shall be so. To the Hebrew, on the other hand, the Ultimate Reality is personal; a living God. God is certainly one and transcendent for the Hebrew mind, too; the Creator is eternally distinct

54

from his creation. But, as personal, righteous Will, he who is 'wholly other' is nevertheless very near to men.

In the second place, the Greek and the Hebrew thought differently about the way God is known. For the Greek, such knowledge is analogous to seeing; like looking at a distant landscape, for example. The knower is always at a distance from that which he would know. Contemplating the motionless, self-contained calm of Eternal Reality, he is not unlike a camera, photographing the most distant fixed star, millions of light-years away. His attitude is necessarily aesthetic. I mean that he is an observer and no more. There can be no relationship between knower and Known. Any communication across the separating abyss is unthinkable. Indeed it would be a disturbance, just as a photograph would be disturbed and spoiled by a movement of the Object, to say nothing of some clumsy movement on the part of the camera.

For the Hebrew, on the other hand, the knowledge of God comes to man by just such a movement, from the Beyond. For him, knowing God is analogous to hearing and answering. What is known is not the Object in itself, of course, but the Object in its action and effect on the knowing subject. God is known because his self-revealing Word is heard by an Isaiah or a Jeremiah, in and through the stuff of human history. Here is a living God whom to know is to obey. This is no mere aestheticism. Here, not only the intelligence but the will is involved. Deep calleth unto deep. It is no accident that after St Paul, the Hebrew, had seen a vision on the Damascus road, he could say, 'I was not disobedient unto the heavenly vision'. Only a Hebrew would talk of obeying a vision.

In the third place, the Greek and the Hebrew thought very differently about history. To the Greek, the time-process had no ultimate value. Nothing real ever moves. The glittering tumult of history in all its multiplicity, waywardness and concreteness is only a breaking wave on the ocean of Absolute Being. The wise man, said the Stoic, is not concerned with time.

But, to the Hebrew, time is God's creation and the workshop of his holy purpose. History is the arena wherein his will expresses itself as action. Revelation means that the acts and facts of history mediate and disclose the mighty acts of God. In short, to the Greek, history is not much more than a symbol: to the Hebrew, it is the instrument of the eternal God; the roaring loom on which the garment of his kingly rule is woven.

In the fourth place, Greek and Hebrew used what one might call different theological methods. Whereas intellectual speculation is the method of the Greek philosopher, the Hebrew prophet is not interested in it. His function is testimony. The prophets never ask whether God exists, nor do they infer his existence from the facts of nature. They witness, not even to the idea of God, but to God himself as morally and redeemingly active amid the movement of events. The Bible does not provide philosophical arguments for theism; it is a history book, witnessing to successive 'moments' in the creative and redemptive activity of God. Here, *Geschichte* is seen as *Heilsgeschichte*; that is, secular history is seen in terms of a framework of sacred history, which began in Paradise and will end in the New Jerusalem, where the Kingdom of God will find its victorious consummation, beyond time and death and corruption. Thus, the Christian doctrine of History is itself a history, a story rather than any abstract theory: it is, to quote the familiar hymn, 'the old, old story, of Jesus and his love'.

Since our immediate interest is theology, we have to join in this debate which is by no means peculiar to the ancient world of Athens and Jerusalem. This is no mere hobby-horse for antiquarians, but a living issue. The sons of Greece and the sons of Zion (Zech. ix. 13) confront one another through the generations: on the one side, men such as the Neo-Platonists, Spinoza and Hegel; on the other, men such as Origen, Calvin and Bishop Lightfoot.

Why is this? Well, there is a difficulty about each position, as its opponents have been quick to point out. If Greek thought creates a difficulty for religion, Hebrew religion creates a difficulty for thought.

How can the eternal God be revealed in and through the events of time? How can the relative disclose the Absolute? How can time be the vehicle of eternity? How can any human life, least of all a life ending on a gallows, make the Kingdom of God—the realm of the 'wholly other'—a matter of actual experience? The very expression 'historical revelation' is surely paradoxical to the verge of absurdity. Christ crucified—as the power of God and the wisdom of God! Is it surprising that this was, to the Greeks, foolishness? To quote those famous, almost hackneyed words of Lessing's Inaugural Lecture at Jena in the eighteenth century: 'Particular facts of history cannot establish eternal truths. There is the ugly wide ditch over which I cannot get, oft and earnestly though I spring.'

Christian doctrine makes a three-fold answer to this abiding problem, which is as much an ultimate problem for metaphysics as it is for theology.

In the first place, it fully admits the force of the difficulty, by taking the word 'God' seriously. No real believer can be what Dr Farmer has stigmatized as 'pally with the Deity'. God is infinite, eternal, transcendent, dwelling in light unapproachable, whom no man hath seen or can see. 'Thou art the Lord, and there is none else. From everlasting thou art he.'

> Thou art a sea without a shore,
> A sun without a sphere;
> Thy time is now and evermore,
> Thy place is everywhere.

God is, to use a technical phrase, *totum simul*. That is, in his ageless being there can be no past, present or future. As Professor Dodd has put it, 'in heaven, the eternal world, the Kingdom of God just *is*'. It is 'above the smoke and stir of this dim spot, that men call Earth'. God alone is self-sufficient; as Milton reminds us in another place:

> God doth not need
> Either man's work or his own gifts.

Professor Burkitt once told me a story about E. F. Benson's going to bed as a small child in summer and being unable to sleep. He climbed down out of his bed, crossed the room to the window, peeped through a chink in the Venetian blind, and saw his mother on the lawn playing croquet with some strange people. She was entirely unoccupied with him of course, and it came to his little mind as a shock. He had always assumed as a matter of course that she existed for him and was, as it were, adjectival to him rather than a being who enjoyed a substantive identity of her own. He now learned that she had a life of her own.

Well, God has a life of his own, so to speak, transcending time in his divine simultaneity. Christian thought has ever confessed the ineffable mystery of God's eternal being. Christian worship implies it. Man may only worship that than which nothing greater can be conceived. To worship anything less would be idolatry.

But, in the second place, it is just this which is finite man's difficulty. That alone which he *may* worship is precisely that which he cannot worship. It is high; he cannot attain unto it. Transcendence is really meaningless to him; this necessary category is an empty category.

> O, how can I, whose native sphere
>   Is dark, whose mind is dim,
> Before the Ineffable appear,
> And on my naked spirit bear
>   The uncreated beam?

God, as he is in himself—in the mysterious depths of his infinitude—is utterly inaccessible and unknowable. 'Verily thou art a God that hidest thyself.' Unless the eternal be somehow given to man in history, that is, in the only way which man can understand, God must remain for ever the unknown God. 'God is in heaven; thou art upon the earth'; and, as von Hügel once put it, unless there is some junction between 'simultaneity and successiveness'—that is, between God's eternal life and man's temporal life—man is really without God and without hope in this world.

But, in the third place, all Christian doctrines bear witness to the supreme paradox of the Christian religion, which is this: that God himself has bridged the ugly wide ditch, using human history as his instrument. In the 'here and now' of the time process, God the Omnipresent and the Eternal makes himself known. The Creator is himself Redeemer. Christian doctrine affirms the absolute significance of a particular historical process, and of a particular historic Person who is its climax, its last Word. The concern of religion is, necessarily and obviously, with the absolute, the supra-historical, the eternal. But the eternal God has given himself to man fully, freely and at a tremendous cost, in and through human history. 'The Word was made flesh, and dwelt among us.' It is the most wonderful statement in the Bible.

That the eternal God should give himself to man in terms of time is a great mystery, obviously enough; it is a mystery having no parallel since it is the only one of its class. Nevertheless, Christian faith lives on historical realities and refuses to disown them. Christian doctrine refuses to try to reduce the Gospel to a general philosophic truth. Great philosophical systems, notably those of Spinoza and Hegel (not to mention Hindu monism), have often disparaged history with its hard facts and its unique persons; there is something gross and carnal about its hurly-burly. Hegel can believe in the Logos, a great philosophical idea; but to believe in a Man who died for our sins and to whom we owe everything for our living relationship with God, is to ask too much of the philosopher of the Absolute.[1]

The Gospel is not superior to history in this way. Its secret lies with the divine Saviour who, being found in fashion as a Man, lived the human life 'under Pontius Pilate', and tasted death for every man. The Gospel, so far from being superior to history, *is* history.

What is history? A careful accumulation of all the facts? But that is a sheer impossibility. Facts are infinite in number; there are countless billions of events happening in every moment of historic time. History is always the selection and interpretation of facts. Amos and Jeremiah are interpreters, not of all events that ever were, but of contemporary events, in the light of faith in the God of Israel. They bring a God-given

[1] See H. R. Mackintosh, *Types of Modern Theology*, p. 136.

understanding of God's judging and redeeming activity to bear on a selected series of facts and political events—the life of a nomad sheikh named Abraham, for example; the emigration of Bedouin tribes from Egypt, led by one Moses; the careers of conquerors such as Sennacherib and Cyrus; the ruthless transplanting of a whole population across the desert to Babylon in the sixth century B.C. But in all this the prophets find evidence of the kingly rule of God, his moral judgments, his redeeming mercies, his promises, not only for the issue of Israel's history but also for the ultimate issue of all history.

The events themselves were capable of other explanations, of course, purely natural and secular explanations; but this was the explanation spoken by the prophets. Or, rather, they were confident that it was the explanation spoken by God. They do not say, Thus saith Isaiah, or Thus saith Hosea, but Thus saith the Lord.

Doubtless Sennacherib's private secretary interpreted Semitic history differently. Doubtless the court-chronicler of King Cyrus would have raised his eyebrows at the forty-fifth chapter of Isaiah. Cyrus was a military conqueror and, probably enough, a ruffian of the first order. Just here, however, came a Word from the Beyond, through Isaiah: 'Thus saith the Lord to his anointed, to Cyrus, whose right hand I have holden.... I, the Lord, which call thee by thy name, am the God of Israel. For Jacob my servant's sake, and Israel mine elect.... I have surnamed thee, though thou hast not known me.... I girded thee, though thou hast not known me.'

In short, the Christian faith asserts the significance for God of certain facts of history, which gives them their significance for man as revelation. The Kingdom, which is eternally in Heaven, comes to earth through facts which God accepts and transforms. God uses history to make his eternal and holy purposes of redemption actual. A Greek would say that time is only the moving image of eternity. But the Bible knows that it is more than this; it is an actual part of eternity because it has been taken up into eternity by God himself.

But here someone may raise a formidable difficulty. He may say: 'Surely this is arbitrary. Why just the history of Israel and its consummation in the events of the New Testament? Why not the history of, say, the Incas of Peru? Why not all history? Granted that historical facts, human activities, do give actuality in time to the eternal Thought of God, why limit this so narrowly to the "here-and-nowness", the "once-for-allness" of Palestinian history two thousand years ago? Surely the events of which Christian doctrine speaks are only examples, admittedly striking, but still only examples or illustrations of general religious truth.'

This difficulty has been called 'the stumbling-block of particularity',[1] and it is a real stumbling-block. The answer which Christian doctrine makes to it is, in the main, two-fold.

First: there is no such thing as general religious truth; this is an abstraction from historical reality. Living religion is always related to certain events in the past which are peculiarly its own. Real faith never exists *in vacuo*, but in a social context, an historical tradition. Even the most nebulous mysticism which contends that no events or facts are vital for religion, forgets that mystics themselves are not the individualists they think they are; they, too, belong to a continuous tradition of religious experience.

[1] 'Das Aergernis der Einmaligkeit.' Cf. the word ἐφάπαξ in Rom. vi. 10.

The fact is that the present is not merely present; in some sense it comes out of the past and is an extension of that past. That is why Bacon could write: We are the ancients. And, similarly, the only past which matters to us is no mere past; it is our past. That is why Croce can write: Real history is our contemporary.

Thus, those who contend that all events of history are equally significant for religious faith, and that Christianity is therefore as old as creation, forget that natural religion of this kind is a sheer abstraction. This notion of a ready-made natural reason, which the whole movement of history illustrates, is an illusion; it is not natural, in the sense of being independent of the continuous social experience of the community.

Now, Christian doctrine insists that Christian faith is what it is—that it only exists at all—because certain events in the time process have a present, abiding, growing meaning. In and by them a new relationship between God and Man was constituted; it really was. Our presence here to-day in this lecture room is only one of many proofs of it. The Events which constituted what Christianity knows as Incarnation and Atonement created something new, not so much for the historian perhaps (though it certainly did that), but for the believer. He believes that certain facts to which the New Testament bears witness have momentous meaning because they do in fact create a new relationship between God and Man. It is not merely that they exemplify certain perennial truths; they have a creative, revolutionary import for religion. 'No man cometh unto the Father, but by me.' That is what they mean. It is strange; extraordinary; uncompromising. Yes; it is. No satisfactory explanation of it can be given, save that it authenticates

63

itself to the heart of a believing Church, the Church of the Resurrection of Jesus Christ from the dead.

In the second place, the believer adds this: Jesus Christ is unique. No one is a revelation of God in the sense that He is. Perhaps there ought to be another history as enlightening about the will of God as Biblical history is. Perhaps there ought to be other revealers of his redeeming love as remarkable as the Man, Christ Jesus. But in fact there are none. Christian experience and Christian doctrine take their stand, not on what might be but on actuality, on something given. Not on a theory of natural reason (so called) but on *Sachlichkeit*, the factual; what has been and is.

Moral life is only possible for man as he is confronted by eternity. This temporal life of his is confronted by eternity in one unique event in time, of which the whole Bible is the record and the explanation. That event is Jesus Christ, crucified and risen from the dead. In it there is all the majesty of what has happened[1] and can never be turned back into the not-happened, by a reversal of time's wheel. The Cross towers over the wrecks of time; it is for evermore.

> Wisdom will repudiate thee if thou think to enquire
> *why* things are as they are, or whence they came; thy task
> is first to learn *what* is. . . .[2]

To learn what is means facing one fact to which the Bible witnesses throughout and which, if it be true, is amazing. I mean the forgiveness of sin. That is what the Kingdom of God

[1] What Karl Heim calls 'die Majestät der geschehenen Tat', and on which he comments: 'Geschehenes lässt sich nicht mehr ungeschehen machen' (*Jesus der Weltvollender*, pp. 77–8).

[2] Robert Bridges, *The Testament of Beauty*.

must mean if it really is the victorious clue to the history of this sinful world. The most astonishing thing announced by the Christian Gospel, the thing which makes the Gospel, the thing which is 'wholly other' than anything sinful humanity could have deserved or expected—is forgiveness, the redeeming activity of God in history. The prophets witness to this incalculable factor in history, which they can only describe as 'the mighty acts of God'. They testify to a dimension of the otherworldly and the supernatural, impinging upon history and transforming it into the sacred history of God's coming Kingdom. 'Behold, I will do a new thing' saith the Lord. Anything worthy to be called the Kingdom of God must be more than the product of a natural evolution. It must be something about which you can only say, 'This is the Lord's doing, and it is marvellous in our eyes'. This something is the sheer pardon of God. 'This spectacle of the beginning of good, there at the very heart of evil; this establishment of man's kingly freedom through the kingly freedom of God; man in his captive, limited, provisional life...disturbed by God yet borne up by God: is this anything which we can deduce psychologically, or prove or visualize? Is it not rather something outside all history, a sheerly new thing, an absolute datum?'[1] The most amazing fact in the world, if it is really true, is the redeeming pardon of God. The whole of the Christian doctrine of history is built on it. Is it true? If so, why and how?

Yes. It is true. But to see what it means, let us first dismiss what it does not mean. It cannot mean that God is a sentimentalist who makes light of the evil of the world, and that the dreary, desperate battle between good and evil in every genera-

[1] Karl Barth, quoted in H. R. Mackintosh's *Types of Modern Theology*, p. 307.

tion is of no consequence for his Kingdom. It does not mean that the Holy One condones the lies, brutalities and degradations of history. (That would be to make God into a devil.) The prophetic religion of the Old Testament and the New Testament religion of the Cross alike make it clear that God is a God of Judgment. Since he is King, his kingly rule must mean that the pain and woe of history are fundamentally the result of sin, and his judgment upon it. The wrath of God is revealed against all unrighteousness. Because this moral order is of his creation, sinful men collectively suffer as the result of their proud defiance of it. The denunciations of the prophets can mean nothing else. But the prophets never cease to proclaim that this tragic situation which man's selfishness, pride and rebellion bring upon himself is always the occasion of God's grace in redemption. God yearns after Israel. As is his majesty, so is his mercy. Though moral and political slavery be the result of Israel's sin, and is ultimately God's doing, nevertheless God is ever seeking to redeem Israel from slavery. This, too, is the Lord's doing, and it is marvellous in our eyes. God will restore the years that the locust hath eaten; he will remake the broken relationship between himself and his people, and write his law on their hearts for ever.[1] In the Old Testament, as crisis follows crisis, God's denunciations and God's promises are intermingled, simply because it is only in and through the evil situation that God can achieve his purpose of good. No different situation exists upon which God may work. The human tragedy is not only confronted with the divine judgments, as they work themselves out inexorably; it is transformed into an occasion of divine grace. Where sin did abound, grace did much more abound. This is what God's Kingship means; it is a

[1] Jer. xxxi. 31–33.

sovereignty of which he alone is capable, the sovereignty of grace.[1]

But the prophets of the Old Testament never said that this new day had dawned, or that the Kingdom had really come on earth. They pointed to it, ahead of them. Crisis, they said, would succeed crisis, until *the* crisis should come, the judgment of this rebellious and fallen world, which would also be the redemption of the world, and the presence of the Kingdom of God with power and great glory.

Now the New Testament asserts on every page that this which was spoken by the prophets had happened. The crisis, the climax to which the prophets had looked forward, was now a terrible and wonderful fact to which believing men looked back, with 'joy unspeakable' (their own words). The Kingdom had come with redeeming power through the dying of one who was completely powerless; the realm of the wholly other had become a matter of actual experience. Whereas the Old Testament is always expecting Christ, the New Testament is always remembering Christ. As the letters B.C. and A.D. indicate after nineteen centuries, he stands at the very centre of history.

At Colmar, there is a picture of the Crucifixion, painted by Matthias Grünewald. It depicts John the Baptist with an unnaturally elongated forefinger, pointing to the Crucified. Christian doctrine might well say that this is the very finger of history, since to the eye of faith all human history, both before and after Christ, points to him.

---

[1] 'Sovereign election means that we are *all* the subjects of double predestination. We are all rejected in that we are condemned; we are the elected in that we are received in Christ' (H. R. Mackintosh, *Types of Modern Theology*, p. 307, interpreting Barth).

The Christian religion means that Jesus Christ is the supreme and central miracle of history. He is the mightiest of God's mighty acts in time, and the earnest of the eternal Kingdom of Heaven. More than a prophet, more than a witness to God's redeeming activity, he is the full and final expression of that activity; he is God's presence and his very Self, under the veil of human life. The prophets had proclaimed the Word of God; he was and is the Word of God. The prophets promised the Kingdom; Jesus Christ was God's very agent and representative in bringing the Kingdom. Indeed, he was the lonely embodiment of its judgment and redemption, as he hung on the Cross and poured out his soul unto death.

Some words of Professor Dodd may be quoted here in exposition of this New Testament conviction that in the death and resurrection of Jesus Christ history reached its supreme crisis. 'The crucifixion of Jesus Christ was an immeasurable disaster, in which the rebellion of men against God came to a head, and sin wrote its own condemnation indelibly on the pages of history. His resurrection made out of the disaster itself a source of altogether new spiritual possibilities for men living in this world. By that two-fold event, the death and resurrection of Christ, the available range of communion between God and Men was enlarged to a point beyond which it is impossible to go. A new era was inaugurated. There was, in fact, a conclusive act of divine judgment and redemption in history. It was the coming of the Kingdom of God.'[1]

To say that God revealed himself in Jesus, or that God was in Christ reconciling the world unto himself, is to say nothing of

[1] *Christian News-Letter*, Supp. No. 31.

real meaning unless we take our stand with the New Testament at one decisive point. That point is where God manifests Jesus as the Son of God with power, by the Resurrection from the dead.

All the evidence of the New Testament goes to show that the burden of the good news or gospel was not 'Follow this Teacher and do your best', but 'Jesus and the Resurrection'. You cannot take that away from Christianity without radically altering its character and destroying its very identity. It is the presupposition, explicit and implicit, of every chapter in the New Testament. At the Cross, the Christian Church sees not merely a striking illustration of the Sublime, but the Sublime in omnipotent action. If the Passion had ended with the Cry of Dereliction in the darkness; if the immemorial problem of evil and pain is only intensified by the Cross; if he came, not to the rescue like a second Adam, but only to the old hopeless fight against sin and death, why should mortals worship this fellow-mortal as their victorious Saviour? If, after all is said, he is one more unfortunate gone to his death, the pathos of man's mortality is increased rather than lessened, and the dark riddle of human existence is darker, for ever. So far from unravelling the knot of human death, this death ties it tight once and for all; and the Christian faith, so far from lightening the burden and the mystery of all this unintelligible world, is its supreme and most pathetic illustration. That the God and Father of our Lord Jesus Christ should pronounce the doom, 'Out, out, brief candle' on him who is the Light which lighteth every man that cometh into the world, could only mean that there is no such God, and that Jesus Christ is his prophet(!). My meaning is that the very idea involves contradictions far less tolerable than the difficulty which it is supposed to meet. Indeed, no man can read the New Testament without realizing that the resurrection of Jesus Christ from the dead, though an inscrutable mystery, is not the contradiction which his annihilation in death would be. His resurrection contradicts all human experience, admittedly. But, as I hope to show in succeeding lectures, Christ himself contradicts all human experience. Unless the whole structure of Christian experience and belief is a gigantic illusion, Jesus Christ is 'eine wunderbare Erscheinung',[1] a unique phenomenon which we can explain only in terms of the miraculous; a particular which is its own universal.[2] Those who argue (with the best intentions, of course) that Jesus Christ is 'like us' are silenced as soon as they are asked 'like which of us?' The truth is that his likeness to us—'the likeness of sinful flesh'—only accentuates his qualitative and fundamental unlikeness to us, in that his relation to God is unlike anything that our race has seen.

All men, himself excepted, are wanderers in the far country. He alone among men has no need to return to the Father saying 'I have sinned...and am no more worthy to be called thy son', because for him alone the perfect filial relationship has never been broken. He is the eternal Son. He is our elder Brother who leaves the Father's home, coming into the far country to seek and to save that which was lost. He is in the far country, but not of it. Tempted in all points like as we are, he is nevertheless without sin (Hebr. iv. 15). Wordsworth's description of our mother earth as the homely nurse, doing all she can

---

[1] Schleiermacher, *Glaubenslehre*, § 93. 3.

[2] J. K. Mozley's phrase, *Essays Catholic and Critical*, p. 196. Cf. *Limborch*, III. xii. 4: 'The dogma of the union of God and man in one person is naturally inexplicable, being without analogy' (quoted by Franks, *Work of Christ*, ii. 36).

To make her foster-child, her inmate Man
    Forget the glories he hath known,
And that imperial palace whence he came,[1]

includes all men except the One who 'though he was divine by nature, did not clutch his equality with God, but emptied himself by taking the nature of a servant; born in human guise and appearing in human form, he humbly stooped in his obedience even to die, and to die upon the cross'.[2]

If this language corresponds to reality, any sequel to the Gospel story other than the Resurrection would be incredible and worse; it would shatter the very presuppositions of the Gospel story. The Resurrection of the Redeemer is logically inseparable from his uniqueness; his power in life and his power over death are necessarily correlative. The language of the Epistle to the Ephesians (i. 20) means that his cosmic

---

[1] Ode on the *Intimations of Immortality from Recollections of Early Childhood.*

[2] Phil. ii. 6–8: ὃς ἐν μορφῇ θεοῦ ὑπάρχων οὐχ ἁρπαγμὸν ἡγήσατο τὸ εἶναι ἴσα θεῷ, ἀλλ' ἑαυτὸν ἐκένωσε, μορφὴν δούλου λαβών, ἐν ὁμοιώματι ἀνθρώπων γενόμενος· καὶ σχήματι εὑρεθεὶς ὡς ἄνθρωπος ἐταπείνωσεν ἑαυτόν, γενόμενος ὑπήκοος μέχρι θανάτου, θανάτου δὲ σταυροῦ. The words μορφή, κενόω, ὁμοίωμα, σχῆμα, ταπεινόω, are notoriously difficult to translate here, because Incarnation transcends our reflective apprehension of it. Here we think in pictorial categories which St Paul seems to have inherited from the widespread religious speculations of the ancient world about a pre-existent heavenly Being, a primal Man-from-the-Beginning (Ur-Mensch). These are preserved in the Hermetic Corpus of writings, the first of which bears the name of Poimandres. There the heavenly Man is in the μορφή of God. Being immortal and having authority over all things, he becomes subject to Destiny and suffers mortality. For, though he was in tune with the harmony that is above, he became a slave (ἀθάνατος ὢν καὶ πάντων τὴν ἐξουσίαν ἔχων τὰ θνητοῦ πάσχει ὑποκείμενος τῇ εἱμαρμένῃ· ὑπεράνω γὰρ ὢν τῆς ἁρμονίας ἐναρμόνιος γέγονε δοῦλος, *Poimandres* xv, Reitzenstein's text). Cf. *The Ascension of Isaiah*, x. 29 f.

victory is the inevitable expression of his Sonship; with the result that to doubt his exaltation after death is to put everything else which the Gospel says about his redeeming power in jeopardy. 'If Christ be not raised, your faith is vain; ye are yet in your sins' (I Cor. xv. 17). St Paul's logic is unanswerable.

The conviction which possessed Christian men from the beginning and which is not only the historic basis of the Church but its animating principle, is that Jesus Christ overcame evil and death and is alive for ever 'at the right hand of God'. In speaking thus, the Church, the very Body of Christ, is not making a vague rhetorical flourish. It is affirming that Christ was really victorious in man's unending battle against Satan and the powers of darkness, and that he could not be held captive by the grave. The Church of Christ owes its very existence to the fact that in this open graveyard of the world there is one gaping tomb, one rent sepulchre. Indeed, for those who begin with the adoring recognition that in the life and death of the Lord Jesus Christ there is shown forth an unbroken communion with the Fountain of Life, in all its fulness, blessedness and glory, anything other than his glorious Resurrection and Exaltation would be the supreme problem demanding solution. From such premises any other conclusion would involve complete pessimism; it would wipe out everything in the Bible save the grim conclusion of Ecclesiastes: 'Vanity of vanities; all is vanity.'

In short, if we are to have a Christian philosophy of history at all, we have to choose between an unambiguously human martyr with whom 'the President of the Immortals had ended his sport',[1] and the Christ who is the Power of God, going down like a celestial Samson into Hades, carrying away the gates,

[1] T. Hardy, *Tess of the D'Urbervilles*, last paragraph.

leading captivity captive, and bringing life and immortality to light.[1] In the words of Karl Heim of Tübingen, 'Faith in Christ involves a question: Is he merely a great personality of the past, or is he the living Lord of history who can tell me with full authority what I have to do, amid all the complicated problems of the present? Jesus the Lord confronts us all with an Either-Or; we must either commit the whole of our life to him or repudiate him passionately and completely.'[2]

Belief in the Resurrection is not an appendage to the Christian faith; it is the Christian faith. The full diet of public worship on any Sunday, anywhere throughout Christendom, is the celebration of the Resurrection of the Redeemer. This is the only sufficient basis and guarantee of Christian faith and worship. It is not tacked on to the Gospel story to make a happy ending, or to hide what, without it, would be the supreme tragedy of history; it is implicit in the story from the beginning. It is from the foundation of the world.

We cannot begin to understand how it happened. The Gospels cannot explain the Resurrection; it is the Resurrection which alone explains the Gospels. Here is the mightiest of the mighty acts of God, foreign to the common experience of man, inscrutable to all his science, astounding to believer and un-believer alike. But here and only here is an activity of God, wrought out in this world of pain, sin and death, which is the key pattern for the world's true life. Here is the sure promise that life according to this pattern is eternal. This and this alone is the key to the Christian doctrine of history.

[1] J. S. Whale, *The Christian Answer to the Problem of Evil*, pp. 72–3. I am indebted to the Student Movement Press for permission to reproduce the substance of these pages here.
[2] *Jesus der Herr*, frontispiece.

IV

CHRIST CRUCIFIED

THE CHRISTIAN DOCTRINE OF THE
ATONEMENT

IN that lively and very human book, Mr G. K. Chesterton's autobiography, there is one sentence which sticks in the mind. Chesterton is explaining why he became a Papist, and he puts it with naked simplicity in six words: 'to get rid of my sins.'

If you know any history, and if you know your own heart, you will not dismiss these moving words as morbid eccentricity. A universal note beats through them. It was precisely the same urgent need which drove another man, Luther by name, away from the Papacy. 'Wie kriege ich einen gnädigen Gott?' That is, how can I get rid of my sin, and so get right with him who is of purer eyes than to behold iniquity?

The question is as wide as the world and as old as humanity. It belongs to the ages. That man needs to be reconciled to Something; that there is a tragic disharmony in the human situation which cries to Heaven itself for adjustment—this is a conviction to which the literature of the world bears witness. Oedipus and King Lear are haunted by the same shadow. If you could take this away from Aeschylus, Dante or Goethe, there would be little left but meaningless fragments. Take this away from the Bible, and there is nothing left.

All real religion presupposes the grim and inescapable fact of sin; the language it speaks, in judgment and mercy, is the language of atonement. Communion with God is the very end of man's being, but this is impossible without reconciliation to God. Atonement means, therefore, the creation of the conditions whereby God and man come together. And the heart of the problem or, to use a word which is peculiarly exact, the *crux* of the problem, is this: Who is to create those conditions?

Can Man do so? This is the first big question to be considered. Common sense, not to mention common ethical principles, would suggest that he ought. But can he? The answer of Christian doctrine is clear and unequivocal. He cannot. Christian doctrine takes its stand at the Cross, 'the jagged tree', and from that high vantage-ground looks out on man's unceasing and vain attempt to realize the conditions of reconciliation.

Speaking very generally, man's historic quest for reconciliation with God is always a pilgrimage to the Cross, marked by three stages; stages so related to one another that each is a criticism, explicit or implicit, of the one it leaves behind.

The first is the stage of crude bargaining. Man knows his unworthiness, but seeks to cancel it by bringing his gift and offering his sacrifice. He will thus appease the wrath and win the favour of God. (I hasten to say that here I am not speaking of Old Testament sacrifice.)

The second is the moralistic stage, where it has become clear that the mere routine of sacrifice, as such, is not only liable to abuse; it does not necessarily suffice to reconcile the sinful heart to God. 'Hath the Lord as great delight in burnt offerings and sacrifices, as in obeying the voice of the Lord?' What matters is the inward disposition, rather than the outward ritual act. The way to God is through ethical endeavour;

75

'to obey is better than sacrifice.' But the pilgrimage is not at an end, even here. The noblest moralism is never the goal of real religion.

A third stage is reached, that of utter self-abasement, when holy and humble men of heart see that even when man comes to God with his obedience and his righteousness, his highest and best, he is still guilty of presumption, still trying to keep an account with God. Mere moralism is a form of pride which befits a man least of all in the Holy Place. It is a further barrier rather than a further means to reconciliation. Only one attitude will do here: 'The sacrifices of God are a broken spirit: a broken and a contrite heart, O God, thou wilt not despise.'

But the pilgrimage is not quite at an end, even there. The progressive spiritualization of man's efforts to earn his salvation has not quite reached the limit of confident despair. The worshipper is not yet saying: 'Nothing in my hand I bring.' As Nietzsche put it with almost brutal insight: 'He who despises himself feels at the same time a certain respect for himself as being a despiser of himself.' The fact is that purely human attempts to create the conditions of Atonement involve an inner contradiction. In attempting to reconcile himself to God through his own activity, however spiritual, man is really putting himself on a transactional level with God, and so denying the very presuppositions of Atonement. Only when the pilgrim makes no sort of claim for himself, even on the basis of his humility, has he reached the threshold of the New Testament where he may fall down at the foot of the Cross.

The Cross is a place where one long road ends and a new road begins; it is a monument to two abiding facts.

The first is that man's age-long effort after reconciliation through sacrifice was no meaningless phantasy. It was a schoolmaster leading him to Christ. That there is no atonement without sacrifice, is a principle running through all great religion; it comes to its climax; it is fulfilled indeed, in the Cross.

But the second fact is that the Cross reveals an old truth in a new, victorious and final way; namely, that atonement must be and is the work of God alone.

'If any man be in Christ, he is a new creature: old things are passed away; behold, all things are become new. And all things are of God, who hath reconciled us to himself by Jesus Christ. ...God was in Christ, reconciling the world unto himself' (II Cor. v. 17–19).

All is of God. This divine initiative in redemption is the characteristic thought not only of Paul the great apostle of Grace, but also of the whole Bible. Grace means love in action; love which takes the initiative, invasively and creatively. 'While we were yet sinners, Christ died for us.'

It should be noticed that this is the dominant conception of the Old Testament, where all Israel's religious institutions, practices and ideas express the redeeming activity of God. For example, Israel's history began with a mighty act of deliverance which Israel owed, not to its own exertions or merits but to the mercy of God alone; the relation between God and his people was not a legal but a covenant relation. 'He hath not dealt with us after our sins; nor rewarded us according to our iniquities.' Indeed it is Israel which first teaches the world that redemption is God's way of being moral. The shocking and wonderful fact is that forgiveness is the divine way of doing right. We are so prone to think of justice and righteousness in

77

terms of law-courts and of the fulfilment of legal demands, that it comes almost as a shock to discover what the Book of Isaiah or the Epistle to the Romans really means by God's righteousness. So far from the righteousness of God standing in logical opposition to his redeeming mercy, it is because he is righteous that he loves and saves. The forensic antithesis with which we are familiar is 'a just God and yet a Saviour'. But the Old Testament says 'a just God and therefore a Saviour'. For the Old Testament as for the New, righteousness does not mean the rightness of moral perfection, the excellence of a man whose moral class is 'alpha plus'. It means being right with God, that is, being put right or acquitted at his throne of grace. Righteousness is God's demand because it is God's gift. All Israel's characteristic religious institutions operate within this context or covenant of grace. The sacrifices themselves were offered to a God already and always in a relation of grace with his people. As a great Old Testament scholar once put it: 'they were not offered to attain God's grace, but to retain it.'[1] Indeed, strange and even repulsive though Israel's sacrificial system is to us, its essential meaning and genius was that it was the vehicle of God's revelation to that Semitic people and through them to the world. It was the means of grace, the way provided and used by God himself, whereby he might say to Israel and to the world 'I have redeemed thee; thou art mine.'

It is not so surprising to us, of course, that this same strange, incredible, wonderful fact is the very foundation and rationale of the New Testament. There are many religions which know no divine welcome to the sinner until he has ceased to be

[1] A. B. Davidson, *The Theology of the Old Testament*, p. 317 (as quoted in H. W. Robinson's admirable book, *The Religious Ideas of the Old Testament*).

one. They would first make him righteous, and then bid him welcome to God. But God in Christ first welcomes him, and so makes him penitent and redeems him. The one demands newness of life; the other imparts it. The one demands human righteousness as the price of divine atonement; the other makes atonement in order to evoke righteousness. Christianity brings man to God by bringing God to man. The glory of the Gospel is the free pardon of God, offered to all who will receive it in humble faith.

It was this which amazed Saul of Tarsus. What Johannes Weiss called 'this coming of God to meet him', broke him down utterly. Paul discovered that God justifies the ungodly. No wonder that Luther once burst out, in that mixture of Latin and German of which his *Table Talk* is so full: *Remissio peccatorum sol dich fröhlich machen. Hoc est caput doctrinae Christianae, et tamen periculosissima praedicatio* (Forgiveness of sins ought to make thee rejoice; this is the very heart of Christianity, and yet it is a mighty dangerous thing to preach).

Paul discovered, through Jesus Christ and him crucified, that this incredible thing was true. He had 'tried out' the way of legally acquired righteousness to the end, and it had brought him to a dead end of failure and despair. He was a 'wretched man', to use his own words about himself in Rom. vii. And then the miracle happened. Paul discovered that the only really good man is the pardoned man, since he alone has been set free from the selfcentredness which underlies all sin.[1] His life has a new centre of gravity; he is 'in Christ' and no longer in bondage, the result being that he is living on a new level of moral competence. Seventeen centuries later, Kant wrote the

[1] Cf. C. H. Dodd, *The Epistle to the Romans*, a brilliant and lucid exposition of the fundamental theme of Christian doctrine.

famous sentence: 'Nothing in the whole world can possibly be regarded as good without limitation, except a good will.' Well, it is the evangelical experience of the saved soul that the pardoned man is the only man whose will is set free to *be* good and to do good. 'Being justified by faith, we have peace with God through our Lord Jesus Christ.' This does not mean any tampering with ethical realities. Justification means that through Christ's sacrifice on the Cross God calls sinful men into fellowship with himself. The only possibility open to men is the only condition imposed on them; namely, faith in God's redeeming activity. Moreover, such faith is the only soil out of which true goodness will grow.

And lest you should think this a theological extravagance on the part of the greatest of the Apostles, remember that when Jesus Christ speaks of the mystery of the Kingdom of God, the whole conception of merit and reward, so dear to the natural man, sinks into nothingness; I mean that book-keeping conception of religion to which a nation of shopkeepers is all too prone.

Jesus describes the Kingdom of God as a sheer gift of grace. In the parable of the labourers he says that God is like a householder hiring men to work in his vineyard at the beginning of the day and agreeing to pay each of them a daily wage of a Roman penny. 'And he went out about the third hour, and saw others standing idle in the marketplace. And said unto them; Go ye also into the vineyard, and whatsoever is right I will give you. And they went their way. Again he went out about the sixth and ninth hour, and did likewise. And about the eleventh hour he went out, and found others standing idle, and saith unto them, Why stand ye here all the day idle? They say unto him, Because no man hath hired us. He saith unto them, Go ye also into the vineyard; and whatsoever is right, that shall ye receive. So when even was come, the lord of the vineyard saith unto his steward, Call the labourers, and give them their hire, beginning from the last unto the first. And when they came that were hired about the eleventh hour, they received every man a penny. But when the first came, they supposed that they should have received more; and they like-wise received every man a penny. And when they had received it, they murmured against the goodman of the house, saying, These last have wrought but one hour, and thou hast made them equal unto us, which have borne the burden and heat of the day. But he answered one of them, and said, Friend, I do thee no wrong: didst not thou agree with me for a penny? Take that thine is, and go thy way: I will give unto this last, even as unto thee. Is it not lawful for me to do what I will with mine own? Is thine eye evil, because I am good?' (Matt. xx. 3–15).

If you would see clearly what this means, look at a parallel story in the Talmud, which is Judaism's answer to this picture of God and his Kingdom. It is this same parable, duly edited; there are the same details, but a different ending. Here, too, a labourer has worked for only two hours, and yet received a full day's pay. But to those who complain about unfairness, the householder answers: 'Ah, but this man has done more in two hours than you have done during the whole day.'[1]

By what authority does Jesus speak this language of sheer grace? The New Testament is perfectly clear that his authority is the authority of God. The mind and act of Jesus are the mind and act of him who was in Christ reconciling the world unto

[1] Strack-Billerbeck, iv. 492 f., cited by Lietzmann, *Geschichte der Alten Kirche*, i. 43.

himself. Indeed, as we shall see later in this lecture, un-satisfactory theories of Atonement might have been avoided by the popular mind through the centuries if the theologians of the Church had been more careful to preserve the emphatic witness of the New Testament that the Atonement is, through-out, the work of God. Any transactional theory which would separate Christ from God here, and so rob the Father of his divine initiative in redemption, not only misunderstands the Gospel, but betrays it at its crucial point.

This is not all, however. Man's response is the necessary complement to God's initiative, and any theory of Atonement which omitted it would betray the Gospel in another way. The whole history of sacrifice makes this plain.

What is sacrifice? What was the ancient religious significance of shed blood? And what did the Saviour and the writers of the New Testament mean when they used the ancient language of blood-sacrifice about the Cross? 'It is blood that maketh atonement by reason of the life.' Why does this idea from the Book of Leviticus come to mean something central and supremely precious to Christian faith and doctrine? The problem is vast and detailed, but if we look at Hebrew sacrifice in its broad aspect, as we may legitimately do, two main questions present themselves: What happened at the altar of sacrifice? What did it mean?

First, then, what happened? Something was done; what was it?[1] The sinner is seeking Atonement, reconciliation with God. (*a*) The whole sacrificial action begins, therefore, with his solemn approach to the altar. He does not come alone, but

[1] Here I am closely indebted to the scheme made familiar to us by Dr Hicks, Bishop of Lincoln, in his *Fulness of Sacrifice*.

with his victim. He 'draws near', a technical term for making an offering. (*b*) Next, he lays his hand on the head of the victim, meaning that he is thenceforward solemnly identified with it. What happens to it, in the rest of the action, happens inwardly and spiritually to himself, the sinner. Though it is to take his place in fact, it does not do so in theory; the victim is not substituted for the sinner; the sinner is symbolically one with the victim. (*c*) Next, he himself slays the victim, thus releasing its blood, which is its life. He thus surrenders its life to God, and in so doing he is surrendering his own life. That is the sacramental meaning of the shed blood. In shedding the blood of the victim with which he is now identified, the sinner is symbolically yielding up to God the most precious thing he has, his very life. (*d*) Next, the priest takes the blood, the surrendered life, symbolically into the nearer presence of God, the Altar or even the Holy of Holies. Thus God and the sinner are made one; there is Atonement. But this is not all. (*e*) Next, the body of the slain victim is offered on the altar of burnt offering. It represents the self offering of the restored and reconciled sinner himself, all that he is and has. This offering is accepted by God in the kindling upon it of the holy fire. It is burned. But the burning has a profound ritual meaning. It means the very opposite of mere destruction. The Hebrew word used for this burning is translated 'that which goes up'. As it rises in smoke to the ethereal heaven where God dwells, the offering is transformed. It is no longer gross and carnal and earthly, but spiritualized and heavenly, because God transforms it by thus accepting it. (*f*) Last of all, the flesh of the sacrifice is eaten in a ritual meal. Now that the rebel life has been surrendered and forgiven; now that the carnal man has been transformed into spirit through self

83

offering, not only God and man, but man and man—all who are worshipping there at that altar—become one, in the holy meal.

There, then, is a picture—composite and idealized, admittedly—but nevertheless a picture true in principle to what sacrifice was.

In the second place; what did it mean? Details apart, what was its fundamental import?

Sacrifice is gravely misinterpreted when its meaning is limited to the death of the victim. Thus to isolate one element in the ritual is to misconceive its purpose, which is not the destruction of life but the representative surrender of life. This is the God-given way whereby the sinner identifies himself with the life offered to God. The death of the victim is a ritual means; it is not the end of the rite, or its primary significance. Thus there is no vicarious punishment here, as though the victim were paying the penalty while the sinner goes free. To talk about penal substitution here is to mix up modern jurisprudence with Semitic psychology. Forensic ideas have no place here. The key-word is not the misleading word 'propitiation', nor even the difficult and ambiguous word 'expiation'. There is no thought of propitiating an angry God or of paying him compensation for wrong done to him. God is never the object of the Hebrew verb meaning 'to propitiate' or 'to expiate'. God himself 'expiates' sin by purging or covering it in this his appointed way.

The sacrificial system is a sacrament of forgiveness and deliverance. It is a ritual method ordained and provided by God, whereby sinners may be reconciled to him. God himself has prescribed this veritable means of grace. The Lamb for the burnt offering is his own provision.

If you would see this Hebrew theology in a form of imperishable sublimity, you may look at the fifty-third chapter of Isaiah. Indeed, the Christian must look at it, if only because its immortal words filled the vision of Christ, entered his Gospel, shaped his redeeming course and issued in his Cross. The Servant of God is the suffering Servant. He bears the sin of others. He was wounded for our transgressions. He was bruised for our iniquities. By his stripes we are healed.

Here, indeed, is the doctrine of representative suffering, vicarious suffering. Does this mean 'Substitution'? Yes; though not the simple transference of punishment from the guilty to the innocent. The nations are represented as standing around Israel, God's suffering Servant. They see him bearing the suffering which should have been theirs. And—this is the point—they see what it means: they recognize and acknowledge their sin, and repent. In this sense they share in the sacrificial offering of the Servant, and make it their own. 'It is the complete act,' says Dr. Vincent Taylor, 'including the Servant's suffering and the onlooker's response, which constitutes the sacrifice presented to God.'[1]

To sum up: sacrifice is two-fold in its meaning. It is the work of God throughout. But, at the same time, it is inevitably the complementary work of man. Sacrifice is both a category of divine revelation and a category of human response. Just as I cannot draw an arc of a circle, without drawing it both convex and concave, so sacrifice cannot be God's revelation without being man's response at the same time. We have seen how disastrous it is if theology ever presumes to separate the redeeming work of Christ from the mind and act of God. To separate Christ from man here, the divine Victim from the

[1] *Jesus and His Sacrifice*, p. 43.

believer who by faith shares in his sacrifice—this too is equally disastrous.

Amid all the multiplicity and rich variety of New Testament teaching, one testimony is presupposed or explicit on every page. Take this away from the New Testament and you have not only radically altered its character; you have destroyed it. The New Testament witnesses throughout to the astounding fact of a crucified yet triumphant Messiah. Its constant theme is the victorious passion of the Son of God.

Look at the earliest 'life' of Jesus, St Mark's Gospel, and you find that almost a third of it is concerned with his death. The earliest piece of continuous narrative in the Gospel tradition is the story of the Passion. The fact in which Christians gloried, and on which they took their stand as they faced and conquered the pagan world, was this scandalous fact of the Cross. 'I delivered unto you first of all that which I also received, how that Christ died for our sins according to the scriptures' (I Cor. xv. 3). It is the characteristic testimony of the first Christian man to whom we have direct access, namely St Paul. The New Testament is saying from beginning to end, 'Behold the Lamb of God, which taketh away the sin of the world.' What the New Testament means by this is an inexhaustible subject, but four things seem fundamental.

First, the New Testament affirms the necessity of the Cross; it regards the Crucifixion, not as a pathetic martyrdom, tragic and unexplained, but as the act of God. Jesus was consciously fulfilling the divine purpose as he poured out his soul unto death. The earliest preaching affirmed that he was 'delivered up by the determinate counsel and foreknowledge of God'. It is not enough to say that he was the victim of human sin, and that Calvary is its supreme unveiling and condemnation (true though that certainly is). Here is divine Action as well as human Passion. Christ steadfastly sets his face to go to the Cross as to the destined and necessary consummation of his mission. 'I have a baptism to be baptized with; and how am I straitened till it be accomplished!' (Luke xii. 50). The shocking paradox, the divine originality of the Gospel, is that God's Kingdom could come in no other way than by the suffering and death of his Representative. 'Jesus', says Rudolf Otto, 'did not believe that he was Messiah although he had to suffer, but because he had to suffer.'[1] It is the mystery of the Kingdom of God that only in this paradoxical and shocking form can Holiness manifest itself redemptively as Grace, in a sinful world.

Thus, Christ not only suffers; he acts. He is Priest as well as Victim. He is the Giver of the Feast and the Feast itself. He is the conscious Master of the situation throughout: 'No man taketh my life from me, but I lay it down of myself' (John x. 18). It is the strong Son of God, not the pain-racked figure of Guido Reni's sentimental pictures, who endures the contradiction of sinners against himself and despises the shame. He reigns from this Tree. His Passion is Action, strong and selfless to the last, when history itself is rent in twain, and he utters the words 'It is finished', and yields up the ghost.

In the second place, the New Testament points to the Cross as a representative sacrifice for the sins of the world.

What does the Cry of Dereliction mean? ('My God, my God, why hast thou forsaken me?' Matt. xxvii. 46.) The history of doctrine is full of attempted explanations of that terrible cry. None is successful. All lose themselves in the ultimate mysteries

[1] Quoted by Vincent Taylor, *Jesus and His Sacrifice*, p. 174.

of time and eternity. It will not have escaped you that the mystery of the Work of Christ is really the insoluble mystery of his Person; it raises tremendous and insoluble problems with which we grapple impotently as we speak of the Trinity.

What we do know is this. It was the love of God—that is, the grace of our Lord Jesus Christ—which identified him with sinners completely and to the uttermost. He who knew no sin was 'made sin' for us. We need this desperately bold New Testament metaphor to express the truth that the Saviour felt the fact and burden of human sin as though it were his own. He bore vicariously the burden of human guilt, and as he utters that Cry of Dereliction we see him stagger under the weight of it. The sinless Son of God was here saying Amen on behalf of humanity to the judgment of God upon sin. And the Church of his Body, participating in his self-offering, has been saying Amen to his Amen ever since. Only he could see and know sin for what it is, because only he could realize to the full the desolation which enmity against God always means.

Is this vicarious punishment? You may set this notion aside, perhaps, preferring to speak of vicarious penitence. Or you may rightly suspect any facile juggling with these well-worn terminological coins. God was in Christ doing whatever was done here. Yet the innocent One himself came so close to sinners here that his sense of *perdition* was real and terrible.[1] It is at this point alone in all human history that sinful men approach nearest to understanding what Sin means to Holy Love. The Man called Christ is the only Man in all history who has seen Sin for what it really is. This second Adam alone

---

[1] Cf. Calvin, *Inst.* II. xvi. 10: 'He endured in his soul the dreadful torments of a condemned and lost man (diros in anima cruciatus damnati ac perditi hominis pertulerit).'

has seen it with the eyes of God. Wherefore, let me humbly and adoringly confess with all saints and with the great multitude of the redeemed on earth and in heaven, 'he loved me and gave himself for me'; he died, the just for the unjust, that he might bring us to God.

In the third place, the New Testament testifies that here is atoning sacrifice. We 'draw near', and our Lord, our Victim, the Lamb of God, comes with us, for he makes himself one with us in the Incarnation. We crucify him. And he, our High Priest, takes his blood, his very life, through the veil of his broken flesh into the very presence of God. In so doing, he takes our life with him, by the power of the Incarnation and by our membership of his Body. Because we are identified with him, he bears on the heart of his divine humanity all the shame and hurt of our sin. His representative action is atoning action.

> Look, Father, look on his anointed face
> And only look on us as found in him.
> Look not on our misusings of thy grace,
> Our prayer so languid, and our faith so dim.
> For, lo, between our sins and their reward
> We set the Passion of thy Son, our Lord.

Bright's hymn finds a close parallel in one of the Forms of Prayer used by the Church in Geneva in Calvin's day: ... 'Us thou hast honoured with a more excellent covenant on which we may lean, that covenant which thou didst establish in the right hand of Jesus Christ our Saviour, and which thou wast pleased should be written in his blood and sealed with his death. Wherefore, O Lord, renouncing ourselves and abandoning all other hope, we flee to this precious covenant by which our Lord Jesus Christ, offering his own Body to thee in sacrifice, has reconciled us to thee. Look, therefore, O Lord, not on us but on the face of Christ, that by his intercession thy anger may be appeased, and thy face may shine forth upon us for our joy and salvation. . . .'[1]

Lastly, the New Testament witnesses to union with Christ, which comes about and is only made possible through his dying. There is no Atonement without this identification of believers with him. Just as no convex curve is ever without its complementary concave aspect, so all the objective truth about Christ's atoning work is incomplete and meaningless without this subjective appropriation of it. Unless the sinner is 'in Christ', to use St Paul's great phrase, Christ's atoning work has been done for him in vain. It is there, objectively and for ever, but it is ineffectual unless the redeemed man can confess, 'I am crucified with Christ; nevertheless I am alive; and yet not I, but Christ is alive in me. And the life which I now live under physical conditions, I live by the faith of the Son of God who loved me and gave himself for me.'

Our religion does not achieve or sustain this personal character unaided. In the long experience of the Church, this faith-union with the Redeemer is no formal possibility; it becomes a living reality through sacramental communion with him. At the Holy Table the remembered words and deeds of Jesus, as set forth in the pages of the Gospels, become the real presence of the Lord. Believers have fellowship with him, with one another, and with the great unseen company of the redeemed on earth and in heaven, through the communion of the Body and Blood of Christ. This is the end, use and effect of the Sacrament; it sets forth the means of grace and the hope of glory.

[1] Calvin, *Tracts*, ii. 109 (Calvin Translation Society, 1849).

> Behold, the Eternal King and Priest
>   Brings forth for me the Bread and Wine.

'Let us understand', says Calvin, 'that this sacrament is a medicine for the poor spiritual sick.... Let us believe in these promises which Jesus Christ, who is infallible truth, has pronounced with his own lips, namely that he is indeed willing to make us partakers of his own Body and Blood, in order that we may possess him entirely, in such a manner that he may live in us, and we in him. And although we see only bread and wine, yet let us not doubt that he accomplishes spiritually in our souls all that he shows us externally by these visible signs; in other words, he is heavenly Bread, to feed and nourish us unto life eternal.'[1]

One question, perplexing to the modern mind, remains to be considered here. As we have already seen, the New Testament undoubtedly uses the ancient language of blood-sacrifice to proclaim the saving work of Christ. This language is baptized into Christ, of course, but it is unintelligible apart from the sacrificial system of the Old Testament. The Church, in its dogmatic theology, its liturgies and hymns, uses the same language.

> The dying thief rejoiced to see
>   That fountain in his day;
> And there have I, as vile as he,
>   Washed all my sins away.
>
> Dear dying Lamb, thy precious Blood
>   Shall never lose its power,
> Till all the ransomed Church of God
>   Be saved to sin no more.

[1] *Form and Manner of administering the Sacraments. Tracts*, ii. 121.

Cowper and Doddridge here sing in unison with Bonaventura and Aquinas. The precious blood of Christ is the theme of the *Te Deum* and of the *Methodist Hymn Book*. Roman and Calvinist, Jesuit and Covenanter confess the mystery of the Cross in almost identical language; and Fortunatus sings with the whole Church militant and triumphant,

> Hic immolata est hostia.

But this language about the victim who is sacrificed perplexes and often alienates modern men, not so much because the language of blood-sacrifice is necessarily archaic, and inevitably repulsive to the modern imagination, but because all 'objective' theories of Atonement seem to use it in support of a doctrine of penal substitution which, on the face of it, is immoral and therefore insupportable. It outrages the moral sense. We are much moved when listening to the choir high on Magdalen Tower at dawn on May morning, but we are shocked to discover that the boys have been singing

> Actus in crucem, factus es
> Irato Deo victima.

We turn therefore to Abelard and to the modern theologians who have rediscovered him, content to confess that the Cross is no more and no less than history's supreme demonstration of the depth and splendour of the love of God. Because the 'objective' theories represent Christ's death as necessary, not only to man but to God; and because Western soteriology has used the legal word 'Satisfaction' to affirm the holiness of God's love and the eternal moral realities which are implicit in his forgiveness, modern men protest that such a word makes God out to be a capricious Oriental Sultan, a cruel tyrant who arbitrarily demands the suffering and death of an innocent Victim, that the guilty may be spared his avenging anger.

Plainly enough, this is a caricature of the Christian doctrine of Atonement if the substance of what has been said so far in this lecture is true. Yet the difficulty is real, and it is undoubtedly aggravated by the traditional language of formal and liturgical theology. Two comments ought to be made upon it.

Much popular criticism is irrelevant because it rests on a serious misconception; it is ignorant of those full implications of Christian doctrine which are never absent from the mind of the theologian. Christ's sacrifice is represented throughout the New Testament as a cosmic necessity; he is the Lamb slain from the foundation of the world. How is this to be expressed systematically? There are at least three classic types of answer. Suppose you hold with Duns Scotus, Occam, Luther and Zwingli that the necessity of Christ's sacrifice rests ultimately on an arbitrary divine decree. Or suppose that you hold with Irenaeus and Basil, Anselm and Beza, Piscator and Voetius that Christ died to satisfy the eternal exigencies of divine justice. Or, again, suppose that you follow Athanasius and Gregory, John of Damascus and Augustine, Peter Lombard and Aquinas, Calvin and Twiss, in recognizing that the exigencies of our moral sense suffice to explain why Christ had to die; that only thus could the divine veracity be asserted and the eternal moral foundations of the universe vindicated. The crucial point is that none of these theological standpoints allows you to think of God as a cruel tyrant exacting his due from an innocent Person on our behalf.

In all the classic soteriologies of the Church, he who is

93

sacrificed is not a human being chosen out from humanity to serve as a scapegoat.[1] That would be the Nestorian heresy. On the contrary it is the offended One himself, the Holy God who is of purer eyes than to behold iniquity, who as the second 'hypostasis' or 'person' of the Trinity assumes a human nature in order to be able to suffer for offending sinners, and in their stead. According to Christian theology, the Being who goes deliberately and freely to his death[2] is not a human personality but the second 'person' of the Trinity, God Incarnate in the clothing of human nature. As we shall see in the next lecture, the dogmatic formula of the Church is: two 'natures' in one 'person'. The link between those two natures is 'hypostatic' and the 'person' constituting the link is divine.

But this is technical Trinitarian theology. Yes, it is. Moreover, however you may criticize it (and in its traditional form it is certainly open to criticism), you cannot escape some such trinitarian formulation if you take the witness of the New Testament seriously. If Jesus is an unambiguously human martyr and no more, the gospels are a monument to a vast illusion, the Gospel is a mistake, and the extinction of the Church is only a question of time. But if Jesus really is the Word of God Incarnate, the problems of soteriology ultimately involve insoluble problems of the Trinity and the Incarnation which no theologian worth his salt has ever minimized or neglected. My point here is that even if you did hold with Duns Scotus that the sacrifice of the Cross was necessary to

[1] Incidentally, our popular metaphors based on the scapegoat of Lev. xvi are strikingly inept: the scapegoat was the goat which was *not* sacrificed, but driven into the wilderness.

[2] 'I have a baptism to be baptized with; and how am I straitened till it be accomplished!' (Luke xii. 50); 'The Son of man must suffer' (Mark ix. 12).

94

satisfy the divine caprice, you would have to recognize with Duns Scotus (who was not a fool) that it was the divine caprice of Love which sacrifices Itself, and that the Absolute Ruler of this universe (*dominium absolutum, potentia absoluta*) was here being 'cruel' towards himself alone.

Say, if you must, that here Christian doctrine is defective in its scriptural exegesis or its trinitarian metaphysics: in saying this you raise a legitimate and vital matter for discussion, notoriously enough.[1] But do not say that Christian soteriology makes God the Father an Oriental Tyrant, unless you wish to expose yourself to the charge of theological illiteracy. Such a contention is a pathetic caricature of the very truth which the doctrine of the Trinity is meant to conserve. One might as well tell a mathematician that the square root of minus one is mythological nonsense. He would only raise his eyebrows and ask for your mathematical credentials. The most elementary study of the history and meaning of Christian doctrine suffices to show that though no one 'understands' the vast mystery of the triune God, the doctrine of the Trinity is not unintelligible; it is fundamental to Christian soteriology and as such it demands my serious study if I am to evaluate it critically. If a mathematician found me waxing morally indignant over $A^0 = 1$ he would soon discover by cross-examination that I was not only criticizing something which I did not understand, but also caricaturing it. Similarly, the doctrine of the Trinity is easily caricatured; but the truths which it presupposes being inescapable, the doctrine itself is in some form inescapable, and anyone who dismisses it with impatience or contempt will be displaying intellectual sloth rather than intellectual acumen;

[1] See Friedrich Loofs, *What is the Truth about Jesus Christ?*

95

moreover, he will thereby be evading the very soteriological problems which his criticisms presuppose.

But another comment has to be made here which is equally important and more urgent. Theological formulations are never sacrosanct; the concept which obscures the essential idea, instead of illustrating or illuminating it, obviously does more harm than good. It is a stumbling-block. Plain men are not necessarily interested in theology. They know that religion is never the preserve of specialists, but the gift of God to wayfaring men. If, therefore, certain elements in the technical language of theology only succeed in veiling the light of the knowledge of God's glory on the face of Christ, their use should be abandoned. Unless those who preach the Gospel are prepared to expound the special Biblical meaning underlying words such as ἱλάσκεσθαι, ἱλαστήριον or ἱλασμός they do more harm than good by speaking of 'propitiation', or even of 'expiation'.[1] Or, to put the point positively, no man is preaching the Gospel who is not expounding its true, historic meaning and 'getting it across'.

The true meaning of the Christian doctrine of Atonement is that Christ died for our sins 'according to the Scriptures', not according to later forensic or philosophical ideas which use the language of Scripture only to misuse it. Christian theology, as

[1] These words all have a common root; they translate Hebrew words used in the Old Testament to describe God's gracious 'annulment' of sin. The English translation 'propitiation' is definitely misleading: even 'expiation' does not bring out for us the idea of God's grace in 'covering', that is to say 'wiping away', our sin. The vital point is that in the Old Testament God is always the subject, never the object, of the action denoted by these words. So far from needing to be propitiated, he it is who provides the means whereby sin is annulled and forgiven.

Luther insisted, is always *theologia crucis*, because the Cross is the supreme manifestation of the redeeming love of God.

> O Love of God! O sin of Man!
>   In this dread act your strength is tried;
> And victory remains with Love:
>   And He, our Love, is crucified.

V

MYSTERIUM CHRISTI

THE CHRISTIAN DOCTRINE OF THE TRINITY AND THE INCARNATION

You may remember the reference to the Crucifixion in Richard Jefferies' book, *Bevis; the Story of a Boy*. 'The Crucifixion hurt his feelings very much; the cruel nails; the unfeeling spear; he looked at the picture a long time and then turned the page saying, If God had been there, he would not have let them do it.'

If God had been there! That artless comment discloses the whole glory and mystery of the Incarnation. Shakespeare himself could not have made dramatic irony more complete. For the whole of the Christian religion rests on the fact that God *was* there. It is a matter of historic experience that out of this lowest depth to which the race of men could go down, God made his highest revelation. God's mind and act are shown forth out of the very stuff of events which supremely illustrate man's mind and act. This is the Lord's doing and it is marvellous in our eyes.

The testimony requiring interpretation is three-fold. For purposes of analysis we may conveniently consider it as historical, liturgical and dogmatic.

We begin, not with a philosophical dogma, but with the historic fact of Christ in the pages of the Gospels. Who is Jesus Christ, that he should be believed in as no other is believed in by us? Two great answers stand out in the Gospels; we must look at them in turn.

First of all, Jesus Christ was a Man, in the full psychological sense, sharing truly and fully in the conditions of our empirical humanity. The fact which confronts us in the New Testament in all the wonder of its perfection is an actual human life, which was at the same time true human life. He was no phantom, archangel or demi-god, playing a human role on the world's stage, like Apollo in the halls of Admetus, in order to edify and inspire us; 'for verily he took not on him the nature of angels; but...the seed of Abraham' (Hebr. ii. 16).

I think here of Carlyle's protest against the fog of romantic sentiment in which mediaeval history used to be enveloped. He was writing about Richard I and the Crusades, when he burst out, 'Cœur-de-Lion was not a theatrical popinjay with cap and steel greaves on it, but a man living upon victuals'.[1] It is vitally important that we do not in any way jeopardize the truth that Jesus was a Man living upon victuals. The spiteful and ridiculous calumny that he was gluttonous and a wine-bibber (Matt. xi. 19) is precious testimony to the fact that in all things he was like unto his brethren. He not only ate and drank; he knew hunger, thirst and weariness. Consider his bravery, his sense of humour, his severity, his tenderness. To use Pilate's words, 'Behold the Man'—poor, born in an outhouse, working, journeying, praying; tempted as we are tempted. We cannot conceive that Christ in the wilderness was truly pure unless we also conceive that he was able to sin, and that he even desired to sin, but did not. Behold him, healing and teaching the pathetic multitudes, touched with the feeling of men's infirmities, himself a Man of sorrows and acquainted

[1] *Past and Present*, Bk. ii, ch. i.

with grief. He was human enough to weep over the woes of those whom he was not ashamed to call his brethren. Bearing on his heart the burden and shame of their sin, he nevertheless stood in with them and loved them to the end. Utterly clear-sighted, he was the vigorous debater, ruthlessly exposing and fiercely denouncing the shams of much conventional religion. Without a trace of self-pity he went deliberately to Jerusalem to die. His was the highest, holiest Manhood which this world has seen or can see, and at the last—we men and women being what we are—he was nailed to a gallows to die with criminals, the innocent victim of fear, bigotry, jealous hatred, political opportunism and legalized murder. He was crucified, dead and buried.[1]

The essential truth here is that in all things it behoved him to be made like unto his brethren (Hebr. ii. 17, iv. 15). Jesus needed not that any should testify of man, for he knew what was in man (John ii. 25). As Sigrid Undset has put it in a biting sentence, 'to think of Jesus as a frail and kindly visionary with no knowledge of human nature as it really is, or as an amiable young preacher with a special talent for touching the hearts of women's unions'[2] is to be supremely sentimental where he, the great Lover of the race, was as hard as nails. The Incarnate Word is not, in Lord Morley's unhappy phrase, 'the far-off mystic of the Galilean hills'. The Word is nigh unto us (Deut. xxx. 14), as every awakened conscience can testify. The face on which uncounted generations have seen the light of the knowledge of the glory of God, was a face like all men's faces.[3]

[1] See the writer's *Facing the Facts*, ch. IV on 'The Fact of Christ'.

[2] *Men, Women and Places*, p. 28.

[3] 'I saw myself a youth, almost a boy, in a low-pitched wooden church.... There stood before me many people, all fair-haired peasant

This brings us to the second distinctive fact about Jesus Christ to which the New Testament witnesses from beginning to end. Here in this human life we meet the living God. It is God himself, personally present and redeemingly active, who comes to meet men in this Man of Nazareth. Jesus is more than a religious genius, such as George Fox, and more than a holy man, such as the lovable Lama in Kipling's *Kim*. He himself knows that he is more. The Jesus, who merely illustrates general religious truths (so called), is neither the Jesus of the Gospels nor the living Lord of the apostles and the martyrs. The Gospel story is a tree rooted in the familiar soil of time and sense; but its roots go down into the Abyss and its branches fill the Heavens; given to us in terms of a country in the Eastern Mediterranean no bigger than Wales, during the Roman Principate of Tiberius Caesar in the first century of our era, its range is universal; it is on the scale of eternity. God's presence and his very Self were made manifest in the words and works of this Man.

This is the second fact which has been indissolubly united

heads. From time to time they began swaying, falling, rising again, like the ripe ears of wheat, when the sun in summer passes over them. All at once a man came up from behind and stood beside me. I did not turn towards him, but I felt that the man was Christ. Emotion, curiosity, awe overmastered me. I made an effort and looked at my neighbour. A face like everyone's; a face like all men's faces. The eyes looked a little upward, quietly and intently; the lips closed, not compressed; the upper lip as it were resting on the other; a small beard parted in two; the hands folded and still; and the clothes on him like everyone's. "What sort of Christ is this?" I thought; "such an ordinary, ordinary man. It cannot be." I turned away; but I had hardly turned my eyes from this ordinary man when I felt again that it was none other than Christ standing beside me. Suddenly my heart sank; and I came to myself. Only then I realised that just such a face is the face of Christ—a face like all men's faces' (Turgenev).

with the first fact from the beginning. They belong together as two ways of experiencing the one historic series of events which believing men know as the Incarnation. The stupendous claim that the Son of Man is the Son of God goes back indubitably to Christ himself; his contemporaries and followers exhaust the available resources of religious terminology to make the same confession. The Christology of the New Testament, in all its developing variety, is no mere *Gemeindetheologie*—the wishful thinking of enthusiasts with little historic sense, a fantastic tune whistled by disillusioned fanatics to keep their courage up. The excessively sceptical rigour of modern 'Form Criticism' hardly commands the critical unanimity of New Testament scholars, but even if it did so it would only reinforce the historic fact that the literary forms known as Gospels are the title-deeds of the faith of Christendom. The Synoptic Gospels are not so much narrative chronicles of the life of Jesus of Nazareth (as such they reveal enormous gaps) as monuments to the selective and tenacious beliefs of the Church from its earliest beginnings. They are the fragmentary signs of a revolutionary spiritual fact—nothing less than the rule of God in power and great glory through Christ, and him crucified. The most cautiously scientific criticism of the Gospels confirms their historical testimony that Jesus' language about himself has at least a four-fold meaning: it implies unique oneness with God, a unique moral authority over men, a unique ministry of salvation towards them, and a unique mastery over the powers of evil. Indeed this Man speaks with the authority of God, consciously and deliberately; and we cannot avoid the questions which the Beatitudes forced upon R. W. Dale, namely: 'Who is this that places persecution for his sake side by side with persecution for righteousness-sake, and declares that whether men suffer for loyalty to him or for loyalty to righteousness they are to receive their reward in the divine Kingdom? Who is it that in that sermon places his own authority side by side with the authority of God, and gives to the Jewish people and to all mankind new laws which require a deeper and more inward righteousness than was required by the ten commandments? Who is it that in that sermon assumes the awful authority of pronouncing final judgment on men (Matt. vii. 21–23)?... These are not words that we ever heard before, or have ever heard since, from teacher or prophet. Who is he? That question cannot be silenced when words like these have once been spoken.'[1]

Moreover the question is answered by the unequivocal testimony, not only of the earliest Christian preaching, but of Christ's own teaching, embedded in the earliest Gospel. The Parable of the Vineyard speaks language which transcends history; it embraces eternity; an uncopyable note beats through the whole of it; if it does not mean that Jesus looked at death and past death, confident that he was therein charged by God with the redemptive recovery of our race, historical evidence is meaningless. 'A certain man planted a vineyard, and set an hedge about it, and digged a place for the winefat, and built a tower, and let it out to husbandmen, and went into a far country. And at the season he sent to the husbandmen a servant, that he might receive from the husbandmen of the fruit of the vineyard. And they caught him, and beat him, and sent him away empty. And again he sent unto them another servant; and at him they cast stones, and wounded him in the head, and sent him away shamefully handled. And again he sent another; and him they killed, and many others; beating

[1] R. W. Dale, *Ephesians*: Sermon on the Trinity (Eph. ii. 18).

some, and killing some. Having yet therefore one son, his well-beloved, he sent him also last unto them, saying, They will reverence my son. But those husbandmen said among themselves, This is the heir; come, let us kill him, and the inheritance shall be ours. And they took him, and killed him, and cast him out of the vineyard.... And have ye not read this scripture; The stone which the builders rejected is become the head of the corner: This was the Lord's doing, and it is marvellous in our eyes?' (Mark xii. 1–8, 10–11).

In short, the experience of Christian men confirms the classic experience of the first age of Christendom, that the Man Christ Jesus has the decisive place in man's ageless relationship with God. He is what God means by 'Man'. He is what man means by 'God'. His sinless perfection is a miracle, in the sense that history is ransacked in vain for another fact like it. Wherever men have been met by him, either in the pages of the New Testament or in the long story of his true followers, penitence, the vision of God and a new spiritual life have been one and the same experience. In the presence of this Man, men do not doubt that they are in the presence of something ultimate and eternal. We do not get away from the heart-breaking and life-giving certainty that his judgments and his forgiveness are the judgment and mercy of God. To rebel against this Prince of human life is the very meaning and measure of sin; the grace of our Lord Jesus Christ is the amazing grace of God; to doubt Christ's promises is to doubt God himself and to be without hope in the world. In him the promises of God are either Yea and Amen, or there is no Everlasting Yea, and the long story of human faith and worship is a tragic delusion. Jesus Christ is such that if he be not the destined climax of human faith, he is necessarily the very nadir of human despair.

Two, and only two, critical attitudes are possible towards the documents of the New Testament. (i) A man may refuse to have anything to do with them. He may repudiate them completely, such scepticism being irrefutable. (ii) He may sit down in front of these documents and reckon with their testimony, using all the resources of scholarship to discover what that testimony is. What he may not do, if his investigation is to have any scientific value, is to go behind the documents and rewrite them. That is unquestionably illegitimate. Evacuate the earliest Gospel of the faith which is its living content—namely that Jesus is the Son of God, giving his life as a ransom for many—and no historian with a reputation to lose will look at what is left. To eliminate the Prince of Denmark from *Hamlet* would be no more absurd. Either the Gospels are mythological fiction, or the One who moves through their pages to his appointed end did produce on his friends, contemporaries and later disciples, the unique impression to which men have never ceased to bear witness. The Christian Church knows what is at stake here; it stands or falls with the conviction which originated it, namely that Jesus Christ is nothing less than God's redeeming gift of himself to sinful men. God was in Christ reconciling the world unto himself; it is the unshakable testimony of the Gospels.

I come now to what I have called the liturgical testimony, which springs from the first like a tree from its deep roots. From the earliest days until now Christians have not been looking back to Palestine to revere the memory of a dead Jew. They have been looking up, as it were, to a living Lord, through whom alone they worship God. Not only to the earliest Christians of whom we have any knowledge, but to all

Christians, Christ has always been the object of faith rather than an example of faith. Here is One to believe in whom is to believe in God; to worship God is to worship Christ.[1] Thus the only language about Jesus Christ which has ever been really adequate to Christian experience is the language of amazement and thanksgiving which fills the New Testament, and the great Liturgies; which flows in a steady stream in the mediaeval Sequences and in the Genevan Psalter; which rings like a trumpet in Isaac Watts and in the 'Hymns for the use of the people called Methodists'. The truest dogma is the faith which authenticates itself experimentally in the adoring praise of the Church. 'Out of the abundance of the heart the mouth speaketh.' When Calvin said that to sing the Nicene Creed is preferable to using it as a confessional formula, this is what he meant.[2]

Anyone who has tried to reflect on the mystery of God will understand Hooker's words: 'Our safest eloquence concerning him is in our silence.' A deep instinct has always told the Church that our safest eloquence concerning the mystery of Christ is in our praise. A living Church is a worshipping, singing Church; not a school of people holding all the correct doctrines. Let me add at once that it is far from my intention

[1] Speaking of prayer to Christ, Origen distinguishes between κυριολεξία and κατάχρησις, that is to say, between its literal and its pragmatic sense. His own prayers to the Son, he says, are ejaculatory and brief. Origen knew the danger of Tritheism for those who, through Christ and by his Spirit, may worship One God only. Just because the worship of Christ creates no problem for the heart (II Cor. iv. 4–6), Christian doctrine cannot logically avoid the Binitarian or Trinitarian formulation of its own presuppositions. See Bigg, *Christian Platonists of Alexandria*, pp. 184–8.

[2] 'Vides ergo carmen esse magis cantillando aptum quam formulam confessionis' (*Adv. P. Caroli Calumnias*, Calvin, *Op.* VII. 316).

to seem to disparage correct doctrine here. Doctrine is not only important but inevitable, as I shall argue in a moment. Indeed, an undogmatic Christianity is a contradiction in terms; the Church is now paying dearly for its latter-day contempt for dogma. Nevertheless, believing men live, not by dogma but by the Word of God, whereof dogma is the systematic interpretation.

Open any Christian hymn-book and look with a discerning eye at phrase after phrase in the great hymns; their meaning is inescapable:

> O for a thousand tongues to sing
> My great Redeemer's praise,
> The glories of my God and King...

> At the Name of Jesus,
> Every knee shall bow...

> Jesus is worthy to receive
> Honour and Power divine...

> O Jesus, King most wonderful...

> Head of the Church triumphant,
> We joyfully adore Thee...

> Tu rex gloriae Christus,
> Tu Patris sempiternus es filius...

> Ecce panis Angelorum,
> Factus cibus viatorum...

> Kyrie eleison,
> Christe eleison,
> Kyrie eleison,...

This language means that the Christian Church maintains an attitude of mind and spirit towards its Lord which befits a man's relation to God, and to none else. The most precious hymns of the Church do indubitably treat Christ as an Object of Worship. Here is the beating heart of Christian experience in every age. Moreover, such experience does not necessarily need formal theological expression. For example, Hazlitt's famous essay, *Of persons one would like to have seen*, is in line with the great central tradition of Christendom. It describes a long and brilliant conversation between poets and critics about the great figures of the past, and ends thus: 'There is only one other Person', said Lamb; '...if Shakespeare were to come into the room we should all rise to meet him. But if that Person were to come into it, we should all fall down and try to kiss the hem of his garment.' Charles Lamb was not a theologian, of course: but he was there putting his finger on the religiously essential thing in the mystery of the Person of Christ.

But we cannot avoid theology, if all this be true. The witness of the Gospels to historic fact, and the witness of all living Christianity to the meaning of its worship, clearly imply a theology. Dogmatic formulations are implicit in this two-fold testimony. They are inevitable, if only because believing men are also thinking men.

Finally, then, there is the testimony of dogma which is given on every page of the New Testament and worked out painfully, explicitly and authoritatively by the Councils of the Church.

Let me insist at once that such dogmatic pronouncements are part of the data of our problem. Only a narrow and peddling historicism will omit them. The Christological debates of nineteen centuries are a monument to the uniqueness of him whom Christians know as the Incarnate Son of God. The very existence of a Christology is profoundly significant. There is no Mohammedology so far as I know. Nor have I ever heard of a Socratology. It is true that some highfalutin Humanists toyed with something of the sort in Northern Italy at the close of the fifteenth century; they invented fancy religions, and a Litany which contained the petition 'Sancte Socrates, ora pro nobis'. But that was mere Renaissance puerility, a very damp squib, and nothing more.

Dogma is inevitable here for two main reasons. The first is that the New Testament is full of it. It is explicit in the earliest Gospel, which connects Jesus' superhuman rank with his baptism from heaven. It is explicit in another form in the Gospels of St Matthew and St Luke, which describe his divine Sonship in terms of his miraculous Birth. The meaning of the Virgin Birth is ultimately dogmatic: it is one of the many ways in which the New Testament asserts that the Son of God came into history; he did not come out of it. In the Epistles of St Paul and in the fourth Gospel there is a further rich variety of images and profound doctrinal ideas, all endeavouring to describe the divine Redeemer adequately and worthily. He is the Heavenly Man; he is pre-existent ἐν μορφῇ θεοῦ; he is the Image of the invisible God; he is the eternal Word who was in the beginning with God; all things were made by him; before Abraham was, he *is*; he is before all things and by him all things consist. The Crucified is the Lamb slain from the foundation of the world.

But dogma is inevitable for a second main reason. Christian testimony which raises no questions for the heart, does raise them for thought. They may be insoluble, but not to tackle them would mean theological suicide: it would be to surrender the citadel of Christian truth to the enemy without and to the Fifth Columnist within. Carlyle hit the nail precisely on the head when he wrote, 'If Arianism had won, Christianity would have dwindled into a legend'. We are meant to serve God with the mind, even here where the mind is impotent to compass ultimate and ineffable mysteries. The obligation to be intelligent is always a moral obligation. Christian doctrine takes up the problem, therefore, where the New Testament leaves it.

The problem is plain enough. There is an unrelieved tension of opposites in Jesus Christ. The technical formula of the fifth century, 'two natures in one person', is a Greek way of saying that he transcends the power of our logic to make a synthesis of his qualities. The unending attempt to correlate the human and the divine in Jesus Christ is a monument to this mystery.

Of course, an explanation of Christ's person must always be beyond our reach if by 'explain' we mean 'put into a class'. Jesus is inexplicable just because he cannot be put into a class. His uniqueness constitutes the problem to be explained. It is impossible to describe him without becoming entangled in paradoxes. The great merit of the Creeds is that they left the paradox as such.

That is why Melanchthon, Lutheranism's first systematic theologian, wrote the oft-quoted words: 'To know Christ is not to speculate about the mode of his Incarnation, but to know his saving benefits.'[1] Yes; but this sentence was withdrawn from later editions of Melanchthon's work, not because it was deemed untrue (far from it!), but because an articulate and authoritative theology is necessary in every generation, if

[1] 'Hoc est Christum cognoscere, beneficia eius cognoscere, non... eius naturas, modos incarnationis intueri' (*Loci communes* of 1521, Introduction).

Christian faith is to be both continuous with its historic past, and alive in the present.

This does not mean, of course, that there is no danger in such theological speculation. We dare not forget that no part of Christian doctrine is more exposed to the menace of mere intellectualism than Christology. The sordid struggles and barren logomachies which make the history of the Church in the fourth and fifth centuries so shocking, are notorious enough. The more the Greek mind became preoccupied with abstract ideas covered by terms such as *nature, essence* and *hypostasis*, the further it drifted from the New Testament, with its Hebraic interest in concrete religious realities, and its witness to the human *experience* and holy *will* of the Redeemer. Religion largely gave place to speculation; or, rather, Christians of the post-Nicene era could be roughly divided into two groups—those who did not think at all and those who did nothing but think. No one saw the danger more clearly than Gregory of Nyssa, one of the three theologians in Cappadocia who did most to formulate the classic doctrine of the Trinity towards the end of the fourth century. His scathing caricature speaks for itself: 'Constantinople is full of mechanics and slaves, who are all of them profound theologians, preaching in the shops and the streets. If you want a man to change a piece of silver, he informs you wherein the Son differs from the Father; if you ask the price of a loaf, you are told by way of reply that the Son is inferior to the Father; and, if you enquire whether the bath is ready, the answer is that the Son was made out of nothing.'[1]

The grievous danger, both to theology and to religion, is obvious. But the use of anything may not be discontinued

---

[1] *Oratio de deitate Filii et Spiritus Sancti* (Migne, *Patr. Gr.* xlvi. 557).

because it is liable to abuse; human life itself would come to an end on such terms. Just because we may not disparage dogmatic theology without loss, we do well to heed the New Testament injunction, 'Be ready always to give an answer to every man that asketh you a reason of the hope that is in you with meekness and fear' (I Pet. iii. 15).

So much, then, for the three-fold testimony requiring interpretation. It brings us naturally and inevitably to the classic creeds and confessions of the Church.

Consider, first, the doctrine of the Trinity. How did it come to be formulated, and why? What did it mean?

As soon as the Church addressed itself to systematic doctrine it found itself wrestling with its fundamental axioms. I use the word 'wrestling' deliberately, because those axioms were, on the face of them, mutually incompatible. They were three in number.

The first was monotheism, the deep religious conviction that there is but one God, holy and transcendent, and that to worship anyone or anything else is idolatry. To Israel, and to the New Israel of the Christian Church, idolatry in all its forms was sin at its worst. 'Hear, O Israel: The Lord our God is one Lord' (Deut. vi. 4). 'I am the Lord, and there is none else, there is no God beside me' (Isa. xlv. 5). Monotheism was the living heart of the religion of the Old Testament; it was and is the very marrow of Christian divinity.

The second axiom for the Church's life and thought was the divinity of Christ; and, as we have seen, it carried with it, in some sense, the worship of Christ. The New Testament is not a formal text-book of systematic theology, but there is nothing in the classic creeds of the Church which is not explicit or implicit in its pages.[1] It represents the religious enthusiasm of the early Church rather than the reflective apprehensions of later centuries, and is Hebraic rather than Greek in its attitude to speculation. But even so, its Gospels are permeated with Christology, and it gives us in St Paul a first-rate and systematic thinker whose argument, though complicated, is strong, coherent and carefully articulated, every phrase of it serving to build up a philosophy of history with Jesus Christ as its centre. The soaring intellectual flights of the epistles to the Colossians (i. 12–20), to the Ephesians (i. 3–12, 18–23), and to the Hebrews (i. 2–3), like the great vision of the throne of God and of the Lamb in the Book of Revelation, are assertions of the unbroken witness of historical Christianity to the Incarnation. 'God was in Christ.' 'God hath spoken unto us in his Son.' 'The Word became flesh.' This is the corner-stone of all Christian faith and life, the very substance of the Gospel.

The third axiom was fundamental to Christian experience rather than to Christian thought; namely that God is Spirit, immanent in the whole creation as the Hebrews had known him to be, but now newly experienced and understood as the Holy Spirit of the God and Father of the Lord Jesus Christ. In the days of his flesh Christ had fully revealed the nature of the transcendent God of Israel and his purpose for the world; since the days of his flesh, and notably at Pentecost, this revelation had become a creative, continuous and life-giving experience for all believers.

The Hebraic-Christian knowledge of God is not knowledge of God in his transcendent 'otherness' (which is plainly im-

[1] 'Nihil enim continent quam puram et nativam scripturae interpretationem' (Calvin, *Inst.* IV. ix. 8; cf. I. xi. 13, xiii. 3 f; II. ii. 7, xvi. 5; III. iv. 12).

possible to man's finite spirit), but in his active nearness, as it is experienced in nature and history and in the inmost shrine of the individual soul. The most high God, though transcending his creation and abiding in his holy heaven, is nevertheless nigh unto men. He comes upon them 'from a distance', as it were, through his power or Spirit. Just as the wind from the desert Steppes in distant Siberia comes and breaks down the elm branches close to me here in a college court in East Anglia, so God, who is infinitely remote in the ontological sense, is nevertheless experienced as dynamically near, coming upon human life and controlling it, creatively and re-creatively.

For Christians this life-giving energy of God could be described only in terms of the living and exalted Christ, the same Christ who had redeemed men on the Cross in the days of his flesh and who, henceforward and for ever, was the ground and environment of the religious life of the race.

The transcendent God of Israel, who had revealed himself in Christ as the God of infinite grace, was now and always the life-giving Spirit of his Church. In Christ God had entered the limits of earthly sinful experience in order to become the adequate Judge and Redeemer of what One who is of purer eyes than to behold iniquity cannot (as such) experience. Through his Holy Spirit he perpetuates this redeeming and sanctifying activity. The Spirit takes of the things of Christ and shows them unto us.

To sum up: the Bible speaks of one God, and of one God only. It speaks of him in three distinct ways which are normative for Christian thinking. It bequeathes to the Church three axiomatic statements about the being, the purpose and the activity of the living God, leaving the Church to make of them what it can.

Now, fidelity to these axioms being unquestionable, the systematic thought of the Church inevitably involved a further definition of monotheism, an elaboration of the unitary conception of the Godhead, not in terms of Tritheism, but of tri-unity. At first the Church concerned itself mainly with the Christological aspect of Trinitarianism, discussing the problem of the relation of the Father to the Son and virtually leaving the problem of their relation to the Spirit on one side. Not until the middle of the fourth century (Council of Alexandria, A.D. 362) did the Church of the East come to see that what was true of the eternal divinity of the Son must also be true of the Spirit, and that the systematic formulation of Christian doctrine could not stop short of an explicit Trinitarianism. The data of Christian doctrine had been trinitarian from the beginning (Matt. xxviii. 19), but the early theologians virtually limited the field of discussion to the 'binitarian' problem of the divinity of Christ. This discussion tended to take one of two forms.

One form, reflecting Christian anxiety to preserve the unity of God and the divinity of Christ, tended to deny that there is any distinction between God and Christ. This position is known as Modalism, that is to say, Father, Son and Holy Spirit are merely modes or successive phases of the One Absolute God. Just as an actor on the Greek stage might wear three different masks in three different scenes, so there is one God manifesting himself under three passing names or functions. It was quickly pointed out that this meant that the Father was born and died. Hence the nickname of Patripassianism. The implicit tendency of such a doctrine of immanence was in the direction of Pantheism.

The other form, reflecting Christian anxiety not to undermine monotheism, endangered the divinity of Christ. Its emphasis was on the absolute transcendence of God the Father. The Son and the Spirit were subordinate to God; created by God, albeit before all worlds, but nevertheless created. Jesus Christ was a man adopted by God and raised to the rank of divinity rather than the co-eternal Son of God coming down from heaven and taking our nature upon him. This position is known as Subordinationism: its implicit logic was Polytheism. Christ is really a second God, and the Spirit is a third God. Such Subordinationism threatened a reversion to the 'gods many' of paganism, and in the Arian heresy of the fourth century such paganism within the Christian Church became nakedly explicit.

Clearly, the problem was to explain the Son's distinction from the Father, without destroying the unity of God. How are men to think of a divine unity which transcends distinctions without abolishing them? The Church knew what was at stake. It had to fight, as against Modalism, for a real Incarnation and not a piece of play-acting: it had to fight, as against Arianism, for an Incarnation which represents an eternal fact in the heart of God.

The result was the doctrine of the Trinity, slowly worked out and formulated during the fourth century. Christian thought, working with the data of the New Testament and using Greek philosophy as its instrument, constructed the doctrine of Trinity in Unity. It acknowledged in the Godhead, not one Individual nor three Individuals, but a personal unity existing eternally in three eternal modes or functions:

'Neither confounding the Persons, nor dividing the Substance.

'For there is one Person of the Father, another of the Son: and another of the Holy Ghost.

'But the Godhead of the Father, of the Son, and of the Holy Ghost, is all one: the Glory equal, the Majesty co-eternal.'[1]

The terminology of the Greek East and the Latin West differed here, of course, the Latins speaking of three persons in one substance and the Greeks of three subsistences in one essence. Such differences in terminology hardly concern us however, since they do not affect the fundamental meaning of the common formula. Our question is: What did ὑπόστασις (subsistence) mean to Greek, and *persona* (person) to Latin theologians?

Our previous discussion will suggest the answer. This formula, virtually common to East and West, steered between those two tendencies already considered, Modalism and Subordinationism, which became heretical as Sabellianism and

---

[1] *Quicunque Vult*, B.C.P. 4–6. The problem before the three Cappadocians, who gave final expression to this conception of triunity, was the reconciliation of substantial unity with hypostatic distinctions (μία οὐσία with τρεῖς ὑποστάσεις). The divine is indivisible in its divisions (ἀμέριστος ἐν μεμερισμένοις...ἡ θεότης, Greg. Naz. *Or.* xxxi. 14). The Oneness and its Distinctions are ineffable and inconceivable, the conjoinedness of the nature (τὸ τῆς φύσεως συνεχὲς) never being rent asunder by the distinction of the hypostases (τῆς τῶν ὑποστάσεων διαφορᾶς) nor the notes of proper distinction confounded in the community of essence; Basil Caes. *Ep.* xxxviii. 4. This is not Tritheism, as the Arians contended, though Basil (*Ep.* 214) had to admit that the hypostases were counted (εὐσεβῶς ἀριθμεῖν); for One (εἷς) is always presupposed—the unity of the Godhead always belonging to the hypostasis in question (Basil, *de Spir. Sanc.* xviii. 44). We confess one God, not in number but in nature (Basil, *Ep.* viii. 2).

Seeberg (*Dogmengeschichte*, ii. 134) describes this not unsympathetically as helpless swithering between the ideas of oneness and threeness: 'ein Rechnen mit Zahlen'. But how is this avoidable, given such a problem? The problem is not a monument to the Greek love of hair-splitting speculation, but to the inescapable testimony of history and the New Testament.

Arianism. The word ὑπόστασις or *persona*, which we translate as 'Person', meant more than 'phase' (thus avoiding the danger of Pantheism), and less than 'individual personality' (thus avoiding the danger of Tritheism).

But does it avoid this latter danger in fact? The question is no idle one since the popular view of the Trinity has often been a veiled Tritheism: as, for example, when the Emperor Constantine died in A.D. 337 and his army demanded three Augusti to succeed him, 'to represent on earth the Trinity in heaven'. Or, to quote Principal S. Cave, 'in the unthinking piety of the Church, the "persons" of the Godhead have been so distinguished that it is possible to read in a revivalist magazine of prayers for a sick child being offered in vain to God the Father and to God the Son, although, when offered to God the Holy Spirit the child immediately was healed'.[1]

That is not even heterodoxy, of course, but sheer paganism, and it has no more relation to the Christian doctrine of the Trinity than has that amusing and probably apocryphal story about Robinson Ellis of Trinity College, Oxford. It is said that some polite sightseers had asked him who were the figures on the roof of his College. 'Oh, the Trinity,' he answered vaguely. 'But', said a lady (with some diffidence), 'there are four of them.' 'Oh, yes,' was the reply, 'Three Persons and One God.'

Our recent question is the crucial one: What is the meaning of 'Person' in the doctrine of the Trinity? The answer is that it does not mean what we mean by 'Personality'. If you convert the Three which compose the Trinity into three subjects, Tritheism is inevitable. The Greek Fathers struggled to guard against this misinterpretation. According to Dr Prestige the

[1] *The Doctrines of the Christian Faith*, p. 268.

patristic doctrine of the Trinity means that God is 'One object in himself, and three objects to himself'. In the one God whom we worship, there are three divine organs of God-consciousness, but one centre of divine self-consciousness. That is, as seen and thought, God is three; as seeing and thinking, he is one.[1]

God is One. The doctrine of the Trinity excludes any activity on the part of the Son or the Spirit which is not equally the work of the Father; nevertheless, as we have seen, the words Father, Son and Spirit stand for distinctive and precious religious realities. With such a paradox, thought obviously approaches a limit where speculation is profitless, if not impossible. Yet it is important to remember that the doctrine of the Trinity is not a piece of speculative scholasticism remote from human experience and need. It proceeds from the facts of revelation and expresses their living meaning for religion. We do not begin with God and end, by some process of rarefied speculation, with the Trinity. We begin with revelation in the fulness of time which is implicitly if not explicitly Trinitarian. God is known to us as Father only in the Son, through the Spirit. Our awareness of God is given to us through worship in the most holy name of Christ; the Holy Spirit of God takes of the things of Christ and shows them unto us. Our life in God is possible only through eternal Spirit, proceeding from the Father and his Son our Saviour, 'which doctrine of the Trinity is the foundation of all our communion with God, and comfortable dependence upon him'.[2]

---

[1] *God in Patristic Thought,* p. 301.

[2] *A Declaration of the Faith and Order owned and practised in the Congregational Churches in England; agreed upon and consented unto by their Elders and Messengers in their meeting at The Savoy, October* 12, 1658, ch. II.

The doctrine of the Trinity, *qua* doctrine, is not the heart of the Gospel. Nor—to cite the almost blasphemous error with which the *Quicunque Vult* opens—is belief in its dogmatic formulation necessary to salvation. But its dogmatic formulation is the ultimate intellectual implicate of the Christian faith, and the historic monument to a mystery with which some of the greatest minds have wrestled. To ignore it as unessential to one's living piety is one thing; to criticize its metaphysical formulation and meaning is another; but to dismiss it with disgust or contempt is only to betray an inability to take theology seriously.

Consider, in the second place and finally, the classic Christian doctrine of the Incarnation. How did it come to be formulated, and why? What did it mean?

We have already noticed that the Church of the fourth century found itself obliged to elaborate and define the meaning of Christian monotheism, in terms of Father, Son and Holy Spirit. This was done at Nicaea in A.D. 325. The Nicene Creed is a short document of one hundred and one Greek words, eighty-four of which are concerned with the Son. That is, the dominant emphasis in this most famous of all Christian Confessions is on the Incarnation. Theology is mainly Christology.

The Son is first described as begotten of the essence of the Father and as being of the same essence as the Father (ὁμοούσιον τῷ Πατρί). Thereupon the Creed continues, 'Who for us men and for our salvation came down, and took flesh (σαρκωθέντα) and became man (ἐνανθρωπήσαντα)'.

The resultant problem is the old and abiding problem of Christology; namely, how to link together the two statements that he is truly God and truly Man.

Here again, given two axiomatic convictions which seemed on the face of them to be mutually exclusive, the Christological thought of the Church tended to take one or other of two forms. There were two main tendencies or schools, associated with the two great cities of the near East, Alexandria and Antioch. The school of Alexandria saw in Christ the second Person of the Trinity incarnate; its thought began in heaven with the eternal Son and then descended to earth. The emphasis of the school of Antioch was different. It tended to begin with the historic fact of Christ's humanity here on earth, and thence to soar up into heaven. These are not necessarily two different Christologies, but types of interpretation having a difference of emphasis. The one interprets Christ as the eternal Word of God incarnate, the other as the God-filled Man.

The defect of each interpretation soon became obvious. Alexandria, emphasizing the unity of Christ's person, really tended to obscure his true humanity. Antioch, by doing justice to Christ's historic life, sometimes came near to confessing a duality in him, as though he were two Sons (δυὰς υἱῶν); the concrete, living unity of his person was threatened.

Thus, the Alexandrians came very near to sacrificing the human Jesus of the Gospel story; in one notorious instance, Cyril of Alexandria explains the limitations of power and knowledge which are recorded in the Gospel about Jesus, by saying 'for the profit of his hearers he pretends not to know in so far as he is man' (σκήπτεται χρησίμως τὸ μὴ εἰδέναι καθ' ὃ ἄνθρωπος, Cyril Alex. *Adv. Anthrop.* xiv). This is Docetism, the heresy that the humanity of Jesus was not real but feigned; a semblance of human life and experience, a piece of pious play-acting.

But, on the other hand, the Antiochenes, ascribing all that the Gospels say about the Saviour's ignorance and weakness to the human Jesus, really jettison the unity of his person. To quote Dr Prestige: 'If we admit for a moment the separate existence of two Sons, the work of Jesus ceases to be the work of God; Nazareth and Calvary possess no deeper sanctity for us than Oxford University and Tower Hill; and God the Son has performed no essentially greater work in Jesus than he did in Moses or Isaiah. Some people think that this is indeed the case. But if they are right, the Christian Gospel is a fraud.'[1]

This vigorous argument is a sword which cuts both ways; in wounding Antioch it wounds Alexandria too; the one is no more prone to lose Christ's divinity than the other to lose his humanity. This is the notorious problem of Christ's Person which theologians in every generation have found to be insoluble. If the men of Ephesus and Chalcedon in the fifth century, like Brentz and Cheminitz in the sixteenth, sometimes look to us like walkers on Striding Edge, Helvellyn, where the slightest false step on either side means a headlong fall, this is not the true and permanent picture of their theological achievement. The official Christology of the Church is not an elaborate balancing feat, as though Cyril and Nestorius, Luther and Calvin, Thomasius and Dorner were tight-rope walkers in a circus. After all, there is a view from Helvellyn, which only those on Striding Edge may see. By confessing One Person in Two Natures, the official Christology of Christendom raises many unsolved problems and lays itself open to damaging criticism through the use of such categories; but it has one great and abiding merit: it leaves the paradox of Christ's Person as such, and in so doing it safeguards the truth as it is in

[1] *Fathers and Heretics*, p. 274.

Jesus, given to us for ever in the pages of the New Testament and in the ongoing life of the Church.

Some criticize this as the bankruptcy of patristic speculation. Is it? All speculation is bankrupt here. If what we know as the Incarnation be true, we cannot escape from a psychological puzzle which is intrinsically insoluble. The *how* of this fact is, as the Greeks put it, ἄφραστος, ἀπερινόητος, ἀπόρρητος.[1] What, then, is the value of formal Christology, and what is it trying to say?

Is it not trying to put into words the vast evangelical truth that in the coming of Jesus Christ into human life, God gave us nothing lower and nothing else than himself? As Professor H. R. Mackintosh has said, sacrifice that touches God's very Being is involved in Christ's being here at all. All the redemptive grace present in the Saviour existed in God, before all worlds; and 'it was out of immeasurable self-bestowal in personal mercy that he came forth whom we know in time as Jesus'.[2] This, in spite of the shortcomings of human language, is what the doctrines of the Trinity and the Incarnation enunciate. Take it away, and you have destroyed the very substance and meaning of the glorious Gospel of the Blessed God.

[1] I.e. inexpressible, inconceivable, ineffable. Cf. Cyril, *Ad Nest.* ii and Basil, *Ep.* xxxviii. 4.
[2] *Types of Modern Theology*, p. 167.

VI

LIFE IN THE SPIRIT

THE CHRISTIAN DOCTRINE OF
THE CHURCH

WE sometimes speak of a man's private life, and the phrase stands for a precious truth. If the citadel of his personal being is not respected as something sacred and inviolable; if he is not an end in himself but a mere thoroughfare for others to trample, his manhood is being exploited and denied. You will remember the Roman matron's contemptuous question: 'Is the slave a man?'

But, on the other hand, there is, strictly speaking, no such thing as a man's private life. There is nothing really private, that is, utterly isolated, in a universe where things exist only in relation to all other things; and where, according to the physicists, the most distant star is disturbed every time my son throws his teddy-bear out of his pram.

Indeed, the most private act that any man can perform is to die, to go out of life. As long as he is alive at all he cannot and does not live unto himself. Personality is mutual in its very being. For all its sovereign individuality, the self exists only in a community of selves. The lonely Robinson Crusoe is a possible fiction because he begins as a man before becoming a solitary; but the lonely Tarzan of the Apes is an impossible fiction because he begins as a solitary before becoming a man. Society is only the aggregate of individual selves, admittedly; yet individual selfhood is achieved only in society. In one sense, therefore, the part is prior to the whole: but in another sense the whole is prior to the part. In short, human life demands to be understood in terms of its two complementary aspects, the individual and the corporate, the part and the whole. Each has to be interpreted in terms of the other.

But here we meet a difficulty: let me try to state it on behalf of an objector. Someone may say: 'Surely religion is a man's private affair. Has not a great Cambridge mathematician defined religion as what a man does with his solitude? After all, what could be more private than the evangelical experience of the saved soul, experience which has found classic expression in words such as these:

> His dying crimson like a robe,
>   Spreads o'er his body on the tree:
> Then am I dead to all the globe,
>   And all the globe is dead to me.

Surely that personal note is the only authentic note of true religion. The burdened and needy sinner cannot come to God by proxy; no one may take his place in the secret place. The greatest hymn in the English language does not begin

> When *we* survey the wondrous Cross.

It is I who must come to the Mercy-Seat, I myself alone, if I am to appropriate the saving benefits of the Crucified. And though Edward Gibbon once described the word "I" as the most indecent of the personal pronouns, can you deny that its absence would be indecent here at the Cross? That great hymn ends, very properly, on the same personal note with which it begins:

> Love so amazing, so divine,
>   Demands my soul, my life, my all.'

Now, to all this, Christian doctrine certainly says Amen without any hesitation. It not only admits, it insists that religion is always inescapably personal. Religion without this would be like love without any lovers to illustrate it. But this truth does not stand alone; this is not the whole truth about even the most sacredly intimate religious experience.

Let us notice again what the issue is. It is contended that we meet God individually and we meet him alone, and this is certainly true. 'Except a man be born again, he cannot see the kingdom of God.' This, again, is no idle metaphor. The travail of rebirth differs from the travail of birth in that it takes place in one's own heart, and its pangs are all one's own. Not even your own mother can bear this for you. But here too the whole is conceptually and essentially prior to its parts; the Holy Catholic Church is both logically and chronologically prior to its individual members with their individual experiences. Christian doctrine knows nothing of an atomistic individualism. Though an intensely personal matter, faith is never a purely private matter. Man, as God has made him, is an individual ego, but not an isolated ego. A self-centred isolation is the corruption of human nature; it is the result and very illustration of sin. As I tried to show in my first two lectures, man is man only by virtue of his relation to God, a relation which carries with it and determines his relation to his fellow men. Just as we cannot really escape from God into rebellious isolation from him, so our isolation from one another, due to our sin, is an illusion. Human relationships do not cease to be because man is self-centred; they persist as a ghastly caricature of what they were meant to be. They go bad; they turn sour. This world becomes a jungle instead of being the Father's house and our home. Man's proud egocentricity punishes him not by destroying his relation to God and man (which is impossible), but by turning it inside out and so making what might have been a blessing into a curse.

This being so, redemption must mean the restoration of that community of sons which God wills eternally. Christ's work of reconciliation re-establishes not only our filial relation to God, but also our fraternal relation to one another. These are not two different facts requiring co-ordination: they are correlative: indeed they are one and the same fact. Christ is the head of a new humanity. To be saved by him is to be incorporated into the new community, his Church, of which he is not so much Founder as Foundation. The thought of the New Testament about redemption is as much corporate and communal, as it is individual and personal. This two-fold truth is the key to the Christian doctrine of the Church.

Tennyson was not wrong, of course, in saying that the main miracle of this universe is that 'Thou art Thou'; that 'I am I'. Man's personality is the wonder of God's creation. But the corruption of the best is the worst. The essential sin is pride, that is, where man's personality is rotten at its very core. And this sin is not less but more deadly when it takes the form of spiritual pride. Christ's denunciation of the Pharisees surely means that the wrong kind of religious individualism is the deadliest sin of all, just because Satan there disguises himself as an angel of light. It is not only the 'main miracle' but also the main tragedy of the universe, that 'I am I'. I need redemption from myself into the glorious liberty of the children of God. Only in that new and God-given context can I really find myself. You probably know Myers' poem *St Paul*, which tells you rather more about Frederick Myers than it does about St Paul. It mirrors its writer rather than his subject.

What is this lengthy introspection but self-centredness at its most subtle and most dangerous? It is hardly surprising that one comment on it has taken the form of parody:

> I, who am I, and no man may deny it;
> I, who am I, and none shall say me nay;
> Lo, from the housetops to the hills, I cry it—
> I have forgotten what I meant to say.

Certain it is that for St Paul, and for New Testament Christianity, to be a Christian is to be a member of a living organism whose life derives from Christ. There is no other way of being a Christian. In this sense, Christian experience is always ecclesiastical experience. The Gospel of pardon reaches you and me through the mediation of the Christian society, the living body of believers in whose midst the redeeming Gospel of Christ goes out across the centuries and the continents. To say that Christ founded the Church and to say that he mediates to needy men the assurance of forgiveness, is to say one and the same thing. The Work of Christ is perpetuated only in the Church of Christ. To adopt an emendation of the children's hymn:

> Jesus loves me, this I know,
> For my mother tells me so.

If the doctrine of Apostolic Succession means anything which excludes this, it is out of line with the only historic realities which matter. For the Apostolic conception of the Church is indubitably a brotherhood of those who are 'in Christ', loving spirits who set others on fire. It is the growing Society of the Kingdom of God. The Kingdom of God is present in Jesus Christ, through whom God gives the Kingdom by the agency of his Holy Spirit to those who will receive it.

The New Testament describes the life of this society as life in the Spirit. The Hebrew word for 'spirit' originally denoted 'wind', that mighty energy of the desert from which Israel sprang. The Church, as the community of the Redeemed, is the new Israel of God. It is a Body whose Head is Christ and whose members are individual believers. Looking back to Pentecost, its birthday, it uses this desert metaphor to describe the spiritual energy animating it. The Word and the Sacraments are the organs of its supernatural life, the means of grace. The Holy Spirit, proceeding from the Father and the Son, is ever the supreme agent of grace.

In short, the Christian life is not accidentally but necessarily corporate, always and everywhere. It is so by its very nature as the Body of Christ. The Holy Catholic Church, whether Greek, Roman or Reformed, has never thought of Churchmanship as an 'extra' to personal faith, an 'optional subject' so to speak, for those who happen to be gregariously inclined. A true and saving knowledge of the Redeemer is impossible without it. It is sometimes suggested that Christian doctrine speaks with this emphasis because mere individualism is now discredited in every field of thought and action; because of Coleridge with his philosophy of the corporate, or because Sir Walter Scott taught the nineteenth century the profound meaning of historical tradition. In fact, of course, vital Christianity has never existed apart from that Body of Christ, through which the Spirit takes of the things of Christ and shows them to every generation. The Oxford Movement was not an innovation but a recovery. The magnificent High Churchmanship of Calvin was nothing peculiar; it is in line with the Churchmanship of Innocent III and Gregory VII; Calvin is the Cyprian of the sixteenth century; his massive theological system and his momentous historical importance find their explanation in the four words which sum up the whole of Christian history, Ubi Christus ibi Ecclesia.

At once we meet a difficulty which needs no labouring. From the viewpoint of ecclesiastical polity the Church is divided. Christians do not face the world with any authoritative unanimity as to what the Church believes about itself. So far from being Christ's seamless robe, the visible Church is a coat of many colours.

Thus a public lecturer on the Christian doctrine of the Church is in an awkward position. He has to choose between two courses: either he will belittle the difficulties and run away from them, his lecture degenerating into a graceful but heartfelt appeal for ambiguity; or he will recognize and state the historic difficulties, the different presuppositions and interpretations which here divide sincere and devoted Christians from one another. If there are any positive principles, only in this way may he hope to get at them. Moreover, he will gain nothing by attempting to conceal his own point of view; you would not thank me if, out of a mistaken sense of courtesy, I watered down the historically conditioned ecclesiastical polity which I know and understand, into something vague enough to suit all tastes. It would suit none of course. To pretend that different doctrines of the Church are only aspects of one and the same doctrine would be frivolous, and palpably false to historical and theological fact. Mere syncretism will get us nowhere. Chesterton once defined syncretism in a grotesque but exact epigram as 'religion going to pot'; and I need not pause to win your assent to what is a matter of common experience, namely, that religion is solid meat and not the contents of the stock-pot boiled down into a smooth mush of vague religiosity. Every truly religious man, be he Hindu or Mohammedan, Jew or Christian, Jesuit or Puritan, is a man of precise notions; like the sons of Eli he prefers raw flesh to sodden.

Sidney Smith once witnessed a noisy slanging-match between two women who were standing at their doors and facing one another across a mean street. As he turned away he said to his friend: 'These women will never agree because they argue from different premis(s)es.' And yet, of course, that is all that anybody can do. I have to begin from where I live. I happen to be a minister of the Churches of the Congregational Order, one who stands gratefully and proudly in the Reformed tradition of Genevan High Churchmanship. It is from those premis(s)es that I have to look respectfully and sympathetically at great differences of emphasis in ecclesiology.

The study of Church History is not unlike a visit to Madame Tussaud's, where you find yourself in front of the distorting mirrors. There are two in particular which hold your attention. The one makes you look like a clothes-prop; the other makes you look like a barrel. You recognize yourself in both mirrors; it is *your* overcoat and muffler, your walking-stick and your face; but the exaggerations are deplorable, almost painful. It is a relief to turn to a plane mirror where, in spite of obvious and admitted imperfections, you see the normal thing. You wish it were better, but are glad it is no worse.

My meaning is that Church History is a series of mirrors in which Christianity sees itself, now with this and now with that element exaggerated and even distorted, in relation to the whole. The elements are the same in every case, remember. In each mirror you cannot fail to see the Bible; the Institutional

Church as a local fact—a gathered company of believers; a Ministry duly ordained; the observance, every Lord's Day, of the Feast of the Saviour's Resurrection from the dead; the preaching of the Word; the administration of the Sacraments; ecclesiastical discipline; Christian character and even sainthood; the most unchristian hypocrisies and sins. No Church has a monopoly in any of these facts; you cannot put a denominational ring-fence around them. Whether you look to Canterbury or Constantinople, to Dayton (Tennessee) or to Cornish Methodism, to Wittenberg or Upsala, to Rome or Geneva—you see the same marks of the Holy Catholic Church on earth, the same lineaments of him who is the Head of the whole Body. The differences are real, even enormous; but the essential and constitutive facts are the same. There are important differences of metre and accent, but all within the same sequence of musical notes.

Look first into this mirror on the right. Here the Church is visible as a great and impressive Institution. It is a fellowship of believers too, of course, who hold the true faith and participate in the Sacraments. But its specific *differentia* lies in centralized organization which is here at the maximum. This Church resembles a State and, what is more, an Autocracy. No system of ecclesiastical absolutism could be more thoroughgoing than one which reaches its logical climax in the divinely guaranteed infallibility of its head. This Church conceives of its nature and function in terms of a legalism which is defined with an almost brutal clarity. Its doctrine is as clear as it is uncompromising. Because it is the actual and only depository of salvation, outside it there is no salvation. Loyalty to Christ is defined as obedience to his Vicar on earth. Instead of thinking of the Church in terms of God, this system thinks of

God in terms of the Church. Through its divinely given system of mediation alone may the sinner find God. Its very *esse* lies in its ruling hierarchy rather than in the personal faith of its members. To quote the celebrated definition of Bellarmine (*De ecclesia militante*, c. 2): 'Our doctrine of the Church is distinguished from the others in this, that while all others require inward qualities (internas virtutes) in everyone who is to be admitted to the Church, we believe that all the virtues, faith, hope, charity and the others, are found in the Church. We do not think that any inward disposition (ullam internam virtutem) is requisite from anyone in order that he may be said to be part of the true Church whereof the Scriptures speak: all that is necessary is an outward confession of faith and participation in the sacraments (sed tantum externam professionem fidei et sacramentorum communionem). The Church, in fact, is a company of men (coetus hominum) as visible and palpable as the assembly of the Roman people, or the Kingdom of France, or the Republic of Venice.'

I cite this to illustrate a doctrine which explicitly excludes from the idea of the Church all subjective and personal elements. An Encyclical of Pope Pius X goes further and is more explicit: 'The Church is the mystical Body of Christ, a Body ruled by Pastors and Teachers, a society of men headed by rulers having full and perfect powers of governing, instructing and judging. It follows that this Church is essentially an unequal society, that is to say, a society comprising two categories of persons; pastors and the flock; those who hold rank in the different degrees of the hierarchy and the multitude of the faithful. And these categories are so distinct in themselves that in the pastoral body alone reside the necessary right and authority to guide and direct all the members towards the goal of the society. As for the multitude, it has no other right than that of allowing itself to be led and, as a docile flock, to follow its shepherds.'[1]

Here, plainly enough, there is no room for a purely pragmatic or utilitarian theory of episcopacy which would argue that the office of the bishop is of the *bene esse* of the Church, and an historic means whereby God has greatly blessed his people. The bishop is rather the very *esse* of the Church; his hands are the indispensable link between the blessed Trinity and the ordinary man; salvation is therefore impossible apart from the priestly hierarchy. My only comment is that this doctrine of an exclusively mediatorial priesthood is indubitably alien both to the letter and the spirit of the New Testament. Salvation through bishops, through presbyters, or through 'the priesthood of all believers' is a distortion of the faith once for all delivered to the saints. It is a return to that legalism after which we fallen men are always hankering, whether we call ourselves Catholics or Protestants, whether we say 'I am of Rome' or 'I am of Geneva'. Just because the Church's one sufficient treasure is the Gospel of God's sheer grace in all its sovereign sufficiency, we sinners are uneasy. We want to earn this treasure. We ask to be entangled again in the yoke of bondage. We manufacture legal guarantees. 'The essence of it is that an institution with official rule seems a better security than a fellowship with Divine gifts. . . . Against this veiling of the truth in flesh', says John Oman, 'it is in vain to be angry. Till man is wholly spiritual it will be God's necessary way with him.'[2]

But now, in the second place, will you look into this mirror on the left? Here, too, is distortion, but of an exactly opposite

[1] *Vehementer*, 11 February, 1906.
[2] Art. 'Church', *E.R.E.* iii. 622 a, 623 b.

kind. Here the aspect of the Church is individualist rather than totalitarian; it is not a great corporate Institution taking precedence of the individual, but the reverse. The believing individual being the important fact, the outward forms and corporate institutions of the visible Church tend to be of secondary importance. The Church is essentially a fellowship of individuals who have faith in Christ and seek to walk together in obedience to him. Right and impressive though this conception is, if it excludes certain other conceptions it is a distortion of the whole truth about the Church. Indeed it might be regarded as the antithesis of the Roman thesis.

I am reminded here of a profound remark which Pym made in the House of Commons when this very issue was being fought out in the sphere of politics: 'If the Prerogative overcome Liberty it will grow to Tyranny; if Liberty overcome the Prerogative it will grow to Anarchy.' *Mutatis mutandis* these wise words apply as much to ecclesiastical polity as to political science.

The weakness of mere association in the name of spiritual freedom is that it degenerates all too easily into something local and sectarian. After all, Church history is eloquent of the weakness as well as the strength of movements such as Montanism, Donatism and Anabaptism. The strength of all such reforming and enthusiastic movements lies in the truth that the Church does not make the believing individuals what they are: they are ceaselessly making it what it is. The part does come before the whole in the sense that without the parts there would be no whole. The weakness of such movements, however, lies in their blindness to the history which they cannot escape. For in a truly spiritual sense it is the Church which makes the individual what he is, because it is the Church alone which mediates Christ to him. In short, the peril of an excessive subjectivism is three-fold.

First, there is the peril of an Independence which loses sight of oecumenical realities. The Holy Catholic Church is absorbed into the local, gathered churches. About this one can only say that though the gathering together of a local congregation of believers for the breaking of bread and prayers is the oldest ecclesiastical fact in Christendom, it has never been the whole truth about the Church. The theory that each particular congregation is conceptually and constitutionally prior to the great body of the Church Catholic, is unknown not only to the Church of the New Testament, but also to classic Protestantism.[1]

Secondly, there is the peril of an Individualism which makes its appeal to the inwardness of the Word and finds the sanctuary within the individual heart. Hans Denck and Sebastian Franck, David Joris and George Fox illustrate its essential nobility, but its dangers are writ large in history. A healthy dread of formalism in religion has often worked out as an unhealthy indifference to all outward forms, and blindness to the truth that the life of the Church through its worship, ministry and sacraments is not a help to religion,—it is religion.

Thirdly, there is the peril of a Perfectionism which so easily becomes the sin of spiritual pride, and ends as the sin of schism. Just because 'Reformation without tarrying for any' is sometimes the call of God himself, the Devil's work has often been done in its name. And here no branch of the whole Church can escape condemnation, Greek, Roman, Lutheran, Reformed, Anglican, Puritan, Methodist. I think here of Calvin's striking words in defence of the ordinary people of

[1] See *Additional Note* at the end of this lecture, on the Reformation and Churchmanship.

a parish or city or nation, who make no high claim to be 'righteous overmuch'. Speaking of the Perfectionists or Rigorists, 'esprits phrenetiques' as he calls them, he says: 'Let them remember that the Word of God and his holy Sacraments have more virtue in conserving the Church than the vices of some of its members have in dissipating it.'[1] 'We have no right', he says in another place, 'lightly to abandon a Church because it is not perfect.'[2] The spectacle of a divided Christendom provoked these words: the history of a divided Protestantism confirms their wisdom.

To sum up: the Church cannot see the truth about its nature in either of these distorting mirrors, the one on the right hand, the other on the left. Neither thesis nor antithesis is free from distortion and error. Moreover, the true synthesis does not exist. There is no perfect mirror hanging between the other two, 'not having spot, or wrinkle, or any such thing'. All branches of the Church are subject to grievous mixture and error. None is pure. The pure Church, Christ's very Bride, is in heaven. The life we live is life on earth, historically conditioned. Its tensions and troubles belong to the mystery of sin in which all earthly existence is involved. Escape out of it we cannot. But freedom within it and sufficient light upon it we may have, in Christ, through faith. In him existence

[1] *Inst.* IV. i. 16.
[2] *Inst.* IV. i. 12; ii. 5. Calvin had a *magnus et intimus horror* of *aliquod in ecclesia schisma* (*Opera*, x b. 351). To Cranmer's letter to him (1552) suggesting a meeting of learned and godly men, in view of the urgent necessity of doctrinal agreement among Protestants, especially about the Sacrament, Calvin replies that he would willingly cross ten seas, if necessary, to achieve such an end ('ne decem quidem maria, si opus sit, ob eam rem traicere pigeat'). The letters are given in Cranmer, *Remains and Letters*, p. 432 (Parker Society).

becomes life. Yet it is life here and now in the body with all that this means; a progress in holiness, but not perfection. So it is with the Church. This brings us, therefore, to the concrete problem: What are the marks of a true Church?

The first mark of the Church is that it belongs to Christ, its one invisible Head. The Bride belongs to the Bridegroom alone. In theory, of course, all Christians recognize this, the Greeks and the Protestants explicitly; and even the Romans, implicitly, in spite of their claim that the Bishop of Rome was and is appointed by Christ to be his Vicar on earth, the visible head and absolute ruler of his Church. All Christians know that the Rights of the Redeemer are Crown Rights, however prone they may be to act as though either an Italian Bishop or an English King or a Puritan Parliament or an individual conscience were Head of the Church.

The Church is one in spite of its divisions; just as Humanity is one, in spite of its national and racial divisions. It is because there is no Congregational Church, no Latin or Greek, no Presbyterian or Methodist Church but one Church which is the very creation of the Incarnate Word, that Roman as well as Protestant, Puritan as well as Monk, Jesuit as well as Covenanter, are all Catholics, confessing one Lord, one Faith, one Baptism, one God and Father of all, who is above all and through all and in all. All Christians bless the same sacred Name by which they have been called; all partake of the same holy food (even those to whom the Cup is denied); all have been buried with Christ in Baptism and raised with him unto life eternal. All adore the mystery of the redeeming grace of God in its absolute sovereignty. The great New Testament doctrines of Election and Justification by Faith are thus the sheet-anchor of all true Churchmanship. They proclaim that our salvation is the sovereign act of the living God, untouchable by human activity or weakness, unshakable in its finality. Our citizenship is in heaven. The Church is, in one inescapable sense, the invisible church; the great company of the elect of God, stretching beyond the sight and the measurement of any man or any God-given institution. God is not bound even by institutions of his own appointing. He alone knows those who are his. In the words of St Augustine, 'there are many sheep without, and many wolves within'.[1] When Savonarola was about to be burnt at the stake in fifteenth-century Florence, the Bishop of Vasona, in his embarrassment, bungled the usual formula, saying: 'I separate thee from the Church militant and triumphant.' At once the martyr interjected: 'From the Church militant, not triumphant; for this is not thine' (hoc enim tuum non est). The Bishop accepted the correction, saying: 'Amen. May God number you therein.' Even Canon Law does not presume to legislate for God. It legislates on behalf of God, who alone knows whether its legislation is ratified in heaven. The same great truth of the absolute sovereignty of God gives point to the well-known words: 'Deus non alligatus sacramentis suis: nos autem alligamur.' And Calvin, whose doctrine of the Church and the Sacraments was no less rich and profound than that of mediaeval theology, made the same point when he wrote: 'The thief on the Cross became the brother of believers, though he never partook of the Lord's Supper.'

The first mark of the Church, then, is that it is more and other than an earthly society, a mere product of history. It is

[1] 'Secundum occultam Dei praedestinationem plurimae sunt foris oves, plurimi lupi intus' (Aug. *Homil. in Johan.* xlv).

invisible, that is, a spiritual fact, originating and depending wholly upon the sovereign grace of God, which no power on earth can either give, condition or take away. It is the whole company of the elect that have been, are or shall be, on earth and in heaven: one Body, whose sole Head is Christ.

But we cannot stop here. To do so would be to leave everything in the air, and to refuse to 'come down to brass tacks'. It would be an Irish result if the only discernible mark of the Church were its invisibility. How is the Church recognized and known in this world of time and sense? Who are its members? To say that God alone knows would be to make the Church irrelevant.

Thus, it is the second mark of the Church that, empirically considered, it is necessarily visible and institutional. This wonderful and sacred mystery is mediated to us through the visible and empirical; sacred Scriptures; sacred rites and sacraments, the outward, visible and efficacious signs of inward and spiritual realities; sacred offices of Christian ministry; sacred seasons, buildings, forms. Life in the spirit is never disembodied; it is incarnate in a Body whose organs are Word, Sacraments and Ministry. Indeed, the visible Church is the divinely given medium whereby God's sovereign grace is shed abroad. It is the 'means of grace', from which all others draw their life. It is the supreme agency of mediation following upon that of the Incarnate Son of God himself. That is why the Visible Church is rightly known by all Christians as 'an extension of the Incarnation'. For all Christians the Church is at once a fellowship and an institution, two correlative facts, each of which may only be defined in terms of the other. Christian life, as we have seen all along, is lived in terms of a tension between the individual and the ecclesiastical; between the local and the oecumenical; between the spontaneity of that Holy Spirit which is as lightning when it goeth from the East unto the West, and the settled tradition of Christian thought and praxis whereby all things are done decently and in order.

Thus, God's 'new creation by water and the Word' is seen and known wherever the Word is faithfully preached and heard, the Gospel Sacraments are purely administered and godly discipline is a reality. These are earthen vessels, but they hold treasure, nothing less than the unsearchable riches of Christ. To quote Luther: 'If thou wilt be saved thou must begin with the faith of the Sacraments (A fide sacramentorum tibi incipiendum est, si salvus fieri voles).'[1] And, as he says in another typical sentence, 'There would be no Bible and no Sacraments without the Church and the *ministerium ecclesiasticum.*'[2]

The third mark of the Church is that its corporate life is new life. To live in the Spirit means to be redeemed from the clutches of this present evil world and to walk in newness of life. This can only mean newness of social life, since there is no other kind of human life. If our faith is not indefeasibly social we are walking in craftiness and handling the Word of God deceitfully. The worst blasphemy is that of an unethical evangelicalism: it is what the sin against the Holy Ghost really means.

Christian people in every generation have never doubted this the implicit logic of the Gospel. God's holy will has to be done, even here in Babylon. Holy Scripture will never allow us to make any mistake about this; nor will Church History. There is no other way of knowing God than by responding to

[1] *W.A.* vi. p. 530.
[2] Quoted by O. Piper, *Gotteswahrheit und die Wahrheit der Kirche*, p. 17.

his claims upon us; and his claims are made here, just where we live. To attempt to evade this in quietist fashion, would be to throw the Bible into the dustbin. It would be to cut ourselves off from the witness of the Holy Spirit in the Church, as he spoke by the Prophets, and as he has spoken to the heart of an Aquinas, a Calvin, a Richard Baxter, a Thomas Chalmers, a Charles Gore. The Gospel can never be unethical without ceasing to be the Gospel. From beginning to end it is concerned with moral realities, and therefore with time, and with this strange world of necessity and freedom wherein God has set us, to live our life to his glory.

Here again, we feel the same tension between the individual and the corporate which we have been feeling all along. The Christian has two different problems to tackle here. There is, first and always, the problem of his own personal responsibility to God. 'Hier steh ich.' But, secondly, as a member of a corporate body, the community, he has to ask what is the right policy and decision for the common enterprise in which he is engaged with others. These two problems are distinct, though obviously related. If I may say so, it is one of the merits of Dr Oldham's *Christian News-Letter* that he makes Christians feel the complexity as well as the urgency of their common ethical problems, thanks to this dialectical tension. 'Many people either think almost exclusively in terms of the personal responsibility of the individual Christian and ignore the other quite different problem of corporate activities and the working of institutions. Or, alternatively, they resolve Christianity into a programme for the improvement of the collective life and forget the profound inner transformation which it demands from men and the heights of perfection to which it summons them.'[1]

[1] *Christian News-Letter*, No. 9.

142

The tension between these two truths, each of which demands active recognition from Christ's Church on earth, constitutes the peculiar problem of Christian social ethics. Modern realism in theology rightly repudiates the social idealism which would claim to be the sum and substance of the Gospel. A human society which has been forced by events to rediscover the exceeding sinfulness of sin, has also rediscovered that faith in man is the worship of an idol with feet of clay. Blue prints for Utopia are certainly discredited. No modern theologian has done more to recover this note of realism than Reinhold Niebuhr. We do well to heed his complementary warning, therefore, that Christians should beware of accepting the habits of a sinful world as the norm for their collective life. Frequently Christians are tempted by their recognition of the sinfulness of human existence to disavow their own responsibility for a tolerable social justice.

The tension remains and will remain. Only by living here and now in the eternal world are we able to live effectively in this fallen world to the glory of God. Only as we look for his Kingdom beyond time and death and the fashion of this world that passeth away, are we able to pray and work for this world, saying 'Thy Kingdom come'. Only as we worship are we able effectively to work. The Church in its worship praises God for the means of grace, and for the hope of glory. These two great themes form the climax, therefore, in any systematic account of Christian doctrine. We turn to them in the two concluding lectures.

Additional Note to Lecture VI

THE REFORMATION AND CHURCHMANSHIP

No misunderstanding of the Reformation is more pathetic and no misrepresentation of it more perverse, than the contention that it had no essential interest in Churchmanship, as traditional and authoritative. The ignorant, and this includes many whose ignorance is inexcusable, still persist in speaking of 'Protestant Individualism', as though Luther and Calvin were not great High Churchmen, but peevish little individualists shut up in the dungeons of their own subjectivism.

(i) *Luther.* It is deplorable that the learned Whitney, for example, who knew so much about Lutheranism in its politico-ecclesiastical aspect, was so little interested in Luther's religion and so ignorant of its theological expression in volume after volume of the *Weimar Ausgabe*. To be content with '*Wace and Buchheim*' in 1939 is to betray contempt for the *Lutherforschung* of the past fifty years. In Whitney's *Reformation Essays* the old clichés are repeated, unsupported by any evidence, that Luther made himself the symbol of the individual conscience and of individual liberty (pp. 36 and 112), and that he 'underestimated the value of good works' and 'really cared little for the Church' (p. 78). One wonders how a historian with any knowledge of what Luther actually wrote could be content with the repetition of errors so stale. Even the Romans are now more cautious, as a volume such as *Luther in ökumenischer Sicht* (ed. Martin, Stuttgart, 1929) testifies. The first-rate research of German, French and American scholars has long since registered a reaction against the too-triumphant onslaught of

Denifle and Grisar. No one may read Seeberg's volume on Luther in the second edition of his great *Dogmengeschichte* (IV), nor Karl Holl's *Gesammelte Aufsätze* (I) without realizing that the classic theology of continental Protestantism is largely unknown country to Anglican writers of a certain school, whose cheap attacks recall Newman at his worst, and represent neither malice nor ignorance, but both. Two points call for notice here.

(*a*) The first is made by Otto Piper in his *God in History* (p. 155): 'At the moment when the Occident seemed to be disintegrating completely and irreparably, the Reformers stepped into the breach and restored its unity. Roman Catholic and Anglican writers frequently blame the Reformation for destroying the unity of mediaeval Europe. They overlook, however, that that unity had actually broken down more than one hundred and fifty years before. In the fifteenth century the Roman Catholic Church not only was no longer capable of repressing the growing nationalism, but also was deeply involved itself in the rivalries of national groups. Moreover, the opponents of Protestantism underrate the harmful effects of the Renaissance... a movement aiming at delivering secular life from supra-natural bondages. This strife for independence, if left to itself, would have rushed Europe into chaos. As Nietzsche rightly observed, it was Luther who curbed its growth.'

(*b*) The second point demanding notice is that Luther, like St Paul, was never weary of enunciating the self-evident truth of the Gospel; namely that *glauben* and *lieben* are correlatives. Faith without ethical consequences is a lie. Good works must necessarily follow faith. God does not need our sacrifices but he has, nevertheless, appointed a representative to receive them, namely, our neighbour. The neighbour always represents the invisible Christ.

To insist on this familiar fact is not to deny that Lutheranism has sometimes been in danger of quietism; the Lutheran ethic was not unaffected by its strong eschatological interest. Nevertheless, it would be an absurd caricature of the Lutheran system to omit or belittle its emphasis on sanctification as an abiding process in the Church, complementary to the finished work of creation and redemption. The Holy Spirit governs the Church (Spiritus Rector) through the Word and the Sacraments; his work goes on until the Last Judgment, since our sanctification is ever imperfect in this world. Indeed, Luther includes sanctification in the process of justification; only a generation which has forgotten the scriptural meaning of eschatology will misunderstand him. Even Calvinism, with its more active piety and its stronger emphasis on the social ethic, has been interpreted as *meditatio futurae vitae* (Schulze).

(ii) *Calvin.* It is deplorable, too, that Dr Prestige's last book, to which I would again pay my grateful tribute, should be marred by a calumny on Calvin which is almost comic in its downright error. On pp. 404–5 of *Fathers and Heretics* we read that 'Calvin demanded of his followers a clean breach with historic Christendom', a breach which was complete in devotion as well as in doctrine. 'He treats of the tremendous themes of Christ's manhood and of man's redemption without a trace of unction; these subjects seem to stir his feelings no more profoundly than the compilation of a series of trade returns might excite the bosom of a government clerk.' When I first came upon these words I had just been spending some hours on the *Summa Theologica* of Thomas Aquinas, and I could not help reflecting that anyone who had not been trained to distinguish between formal theology and devotional homiletics might make the same querulous and foolish criticism of the great doctor and saint of the thirteenth century. There are fifty-eight volumes of Calvin's work in the great Strasburg edition; and even the two most famous and most often consulted of these, the *Institutio*, can hardly take the place of Commentaries, Theological Tractates, Catechisms, Confessions of Faith, Letters, Ecclesiastical Ordinances and Prayers, if Dr Prestige's statements are to be tested by evidence. But even so, the evidence of the *Institutio* (last and definitive edition) is enough to substantiate the findings of a score of modern scholars (Peter Barth, Bohatec, Mulhaupt, Wernle, Doumergue, Holl, A. Lang, N. Weiss, Niesel and Bauke, to name only these), namely that Calvin's massive theological and ecclesiological system is not a clean breach with historic Christendom, but a structure resting on Holy Scripture and ancient ecclesiastical usage. Calvin's championship of ancient catholic usage during the first five centuries, 'ante papatum', is well known (cf. I. 13. 3f.; II. 16. 5; IV. 9. 8). It is of the first five centuries that he says 'magis adhuc florebat religio et sincerior doctrina vigebat' (I. xi. 13). Calvin asserts, naturally enough, that when God does not prescribe any fixed rule for us in his Word, the conscience must not be burdened with traditional practices (III. 4. 12); yet he saw the significance of tradition and rated it highly (II. 2. 7). He begins his constructive work in Geneva (see the *Ordonnances Ecclésiastiques*) by asking 'quid ex antiquitate restituendum' and 'quis fuerit olim verus usus ecclesiasticae jurisdictionis?' He asks such questions because (as Book IV of the *Institutio* makes clear) Christ has willed to rule his Church, not directly and in person, but through institutions made known to us through the Scriptures and preserved in the constitution of the apostolic and old catholic church, itself a constitutive part of God's revelation to men. There is much, says Calvin, in the customary life of the Church 'quorum nec tempus nec modus nec forma praescribitur verbo Dei sed in ecclesiae judicio relinquitur'. The reply to Sadolet (*Op.* v. 394) is entirely in line with *Op.* xa. 15, 93. Calvin's churchmanship rests not only on the evidence of the Scriptures, but on the history of the Church. (See his letter to Farel on ancient Catholic usage, *Op.* xi. 281; cf. also *Op.* i. 561, 567 = ii. 776, 782.) He appeals constantly to Augustine and Chrysostom; to Cyprian, Jerome and Gregory. Indeed, next to Augustine, his most frequent appeal in the *Institutio* is to Bernard of Clairvaux; and even so, not to the *De Consideratione* (as might perhaps have been expected) where Bernard lashes the vices of the mediaeval church; but to that faith, evangelical and catholic, which is expounded in his *Sermons on the Canticles*. Dr Prestige says much about St Bernard in his valuable book, much that is severely critical. That Calvin should quote St Bernard so often and with approval is a strange comment on his 'clean breach with historic Christendom'.

Further, this very charge is refuted by Calvin himself in more than one place. 'Je ne suis pas tant aspre, ne tant extreme de vouloir interdire du tout et sans exception a l'homme chrestien, qu'il n'ait a se conformer avec les papistes en aucune ceremonie ou observation. Car je n'entens de condamner sinon ce qui est pleinement mauvais et appertement vitieux' (*Op.* vi. 522). He is careful to remind his readers that the elect are found within the Roman church (*Op.* vi. 583) and that it has preserved remnants of real Christianity (*Op.* xb. 149; xiii. 308, 487). He grants, too, that in theory everything in that church is referred to divine grace (*Op.* v. 411 and vi. 461). He recognizes that the veneration of saints is well-intentioned (*Op.* VI. 409). More-over, it gives him no pleasure to expose the vices of mediaeval Catholicism ('equidem nec traducendis eorum vitiis delector', *Op.* VI. 470).

Calvin's lifelong desire to restore the ancient practice of weekly communion for all the people explains his breach with the mediaeval custom of lay communion only once or twice a year, which he describes as a 'diabolic invention'. He wanted a celebration (with full participation of course), at least once a week ('singulis ad minimum hebdomadibus'; *Articles* of 1537). In this reform, as in much else, he is more in line with the Oxford Movement than is always realized.

VII

THE MEANS OF GRACE

THE CHRISTIAN DOCTRINE OF THE WORD AND THE SACRAMENTS

IF Cambridge were a continental University, we should all be regarded as a special social class, and labelled as such: 'Students'. The word suggests that intellectual activities are a specialized function. Some men are policemen or poets or even politicians, but we are students. We attend lectures, study prescribed books and pass examinations.

This idea is amusing and even annoying for one main reason. It isolates thought from life and fosters mere intellectualism. Every science is necessarily an abstraction from the whole content of reality. Merely to study, say, Political Science, Natural Science or Theology the Queen of Sciences would be like knowing all about the off-side rule, but never playing football. It would be as unreal as hanging a large-scale map of Cambridge and district in one's rooms, but never doing even the Grantchester Grind. What Alexander Pope said about the study of Biology is true of all the sciences, all purely academic study:

'Like following life through creatures you dissect,
    You lose it in the moment you detect.'

This selective character of the sciences is essential to their progress, admittedly, but it limits their scope. In short, as 'students' we are all inevitably concerned with analysis and measurement; we work out our formulae. But formulae have a smaller content than actual experience. There is a wholeness about Reality, which makes our reflective apprehension of it a partial thing. Unless we take care, the living subject-matter disintegrates as we handle it, and we are left with dry bones.[1]

This danger is nowhere more acute than in the study of theology. Indeed, one of the perils always threatening the religious life is that people get 'interested' in it, and begin to study it. They even go to lectures on Christian Doctrine. More dangerous still, they may go to special colleges and become students of theology, not fully realizing that reading books about God, so far from leading a man to the knowledge of God, may have the opposite effect. You may spend years on the sacred texts, the wearisome minutiae of linguistic and archaeological research, the arguments about the deepest things by which men have lived. But by studying these facts it is easy to lose the life which alone gives them unity and meaning. Nowhere is the need for synthesis as great as here. Here, as nowhere else, the 'student' longs for objectivity. The mind may labour with great concepts such as that of the Trinity in unity, but the whole man cries out for the living God. As Luther put it in a striking epigram: 'He who merely studies the commandments of God (*mandata Dei*) is not greatly moved. But he who listens to God commanding (*Deum mandantem*), how can he fail to be terrified by majesty so great?'[2]

[1] There is no more perfect expression of this in literature than the first hundred lines of Goethe's *Faust*, Part I:

> 'Statt der lebendigen Natur
> Da Gott die Menschen schuf hinein,
> Umgibt in Rauch und Moder nur
> Dich Tiergeripp und Totenbein.'

[2] *W.A.* IV. 305.

We have to get somehow from *mandata Dei* to *Deus mandans* if our study of Christian doctrine is to mean anything vital. We want a living synthesis where those very facts, which the intellect dissects and coldly examines, are given back to us with the wholeness which belongs to life. If this need for integration is not met, we are no better than children in the nursery playing 'Church'. We have, as Valentine said of Thurio, 'an exchequer of words, but no other treasure'. Instead of putting off our shoes from our feet because the place whereon we stand is holy ground, we are taking nice photographs of the burning Bush, from suitable angles: we are chatting about theories of Atonement with our feet on the mantelpiece, instead of kneeling down before the wounds of Christ.

The need is obvious. Is it met anywhere? The answer is that it is met in the worship of the Church, where the Christian religion is given to us in all its living meaning. Apart from this, Christianity is no more than archaeology, a museum piece for antiquarians. The Church lives, not on ideas about God, but on God's grace itself, mediated by his Spirit through the immemorial rites of corporate worship. There the Word of God, contained in the words of Holy Scripture, is proclaimed and heard as the Gospel. There in the Sacrament of the Eucharist, this Word reaches its climax, and action adds something to utterance.

'One of the clearest results of all religious history and religious psychology', said Troeltsch, 'is that the essence of all Religion is not the Dogma and Idea, but the Cultus and Communion; the living intercourse with God, an intercourse of the entire community, having its vital roots in religion and deriving its ultimate power of thus conjoining individuals, from its faith in God.' In short, saving faith comes to men not through any intellectual gymnastics of their own; it is wrought by the Holy Spirit of God in the heart through the preaching of the Gospel; the same Holy Spirit confirms or seals it through the Gospel Sacraments.

Thus, in the full diet of public worship in every Church throughout Christendom, two permanent elements together constitute 'the means of grace'; first, the preaching and hearing of the Word; second, the Sacrament of the Eucharist, where the highest is not spoken but acted; where the promises of the Gospel are visibly sealed by the Yea and Amen of a ritual act. Separable though they may be in our practice, these two elements are one service in our thought. They are the two foci of an ellipse, together forming a unity to which each is equally indispensable. Differing in their operation they are one in their essential function, which is the publication of the Gospel of Redemption in all its incomparable majesty and comfort. Whatever the rich variety of its historic forms Christian worship has always and everywhere received the blessing of the Gospel in this two-fold way of Christ's appointing.

The preaching of the Word: what, in brief, does it mean? Woe is me if I preach not the Gospel, says the greatest of the Apostles. The New Testament speaks with the same urgency and high confidence, because the greatest of human concerns is salvation. The Gospel is not a book but a living Word, which God himself cries aloud to all the world using as his mouth-piece those whom he calls to be his ministers. 'God's Word', says Calvin, 'is uttered by men like ourselves; common men who may even be much inferior to us in dignity and social importance. But when some insignificant little man (*homuncio quispiam*) is raised up out of the dust to speak God's Word, he is God's own minister,'[1] God's very lieutenant. The preaching of the Word of God is the Word of God.

[1] *Inst.* IV. iii. I.

Thus the preacher of the Word is more than a historian. He is a herald. He is no mere lecturer stimulating interest in the past, but an evangelist whose vocation and responsibility it is to cry 'This day is this scripture fulfilled in your ears...now is the accepted time'. The herald is not sent to deliver his own soul, but to preach the glorious gospel of the blessed God. He is a King's Messenger, no more and no less. The vitality of his message does not depend on him, or on his character; he may be a bad man. Nevertheless, says St Paul, Christ is preached. All Christian preaching finds its only sanction and power in the authority of a human life, death and resurrection through which God spoke in the fulness of time, and through which, by his Spirit in the Church, he speaks so long as time endures.

Let me repeat; the Word and the Sacraments make one indissoluble unity. The Pulpit and the Holy Table, Sermon and Eucharist, are means of grace provided for us from the very beginning of Christian history. The preached Word of the Gospel comes to its own climax in the visible Word of the Eucharist. Similarly, the Eucharist presupposes the preached Word of the Gospel; it is the sacred pledge and seal of the promises of God, just as the seal at the foot of parchment implies the precious covenant of which it is the guarantee, and without which it would be meaningless. The preaching of the Gospel and the administration of the Gospel Sacraments are of Christ's institution: to exalt one above the other would be to disobey him whose means of grace they are. I spoke just now of an ellipse with two foci: it would be more accurate to speak of two circles having a common centre. Here is the focal centre of the Church's undying life. Here, too, the life of God's people in every generation is integrated as One Body. The

Jesus whose words and works you may have studied in books, and whom you may have sought to understand through the classic formulae of Christian doctrine, here rises from the dead. Here the grave clothes of academic theology are neatly folded and put on one side. He is not entombed, either in history or in scholastic philosophy; he is risen. He is known of us in the breaking of Bread.

We come, then, to the Gospel Sacraments, their origin, nature and meaning.

First, as to their origin. Some will tell you that Sacraments originate in our need of them; which is true but misleading here. We do need symbols to compass the ineffable things of our experience. Goethe went to the root of this matter when he said that the highest cannot be spoken: it can only be acted. The inadequacy of words, the impotence of definitions is notorious. You may remember that Joe Vance always regarded Beethoven not only as a composer but as a revelation. 'His music always seemed to express everything that I can understand and to supply exhaustive conclusions in all the crucial questions of life and death.... How often I said to myself after some perfectly convincing phrase of Beethoven, "of course, if that is so, there is no occasion to worry". It could not be translated, naturally, into vulgar grammar and syntax, but it left no doubt on the point for all that.'

Joe Vance there speaks for many, and though his speech is extravagant, it does illustrate the fact that ideas, of which words are the clothing, cannot express all that we experience. That 'perfectly convincing phrase' was not made up of words, but of music. Great art needs no wordy explanations. It is in the music itself, in great pictures, great drama, great institutions embodying ethical ideas, that language is transcended. The symbolism is never the same for all, of course: for one it is a canvas by Raphael, for another it is 'the meanest flower that blows'. But for all, the Eternal may be seen in and through these temporal things, these outward signs of an inward and spiritual grace,

> When on some gilded cloud, or flower,
> My gazing soul would dwell an hour,
> And in those weaker glories spy
> Some shadows of eternity.

All this, let me repeat, is not untrue: moreover, it is a sound inference from the Christian doctrine of Creation, as St Augustine insisted. This is what people mean when they say that the Universe is 'sacramental'; that this world is the garment of the invisible God, the Soul of Reality who thus speaks to man, saying 'Hoc est corpus meum'.

But this is no true account of the Gospel Sacraments. In these symbols of bread and wine, the whole meaning of our religion comes to its focus and is made plain. But why *these* symbols? Why not anything arbitrarily chosen from the common stock, after the manner of Mysticism? Why not gilded cloud or flower? For Wordsworth the meanest flower that blows sufficed. Why, then, should not Christians choose—not just anything, but some great things—a *Mass in B minor*, a Sistine Madonna, a Passion Play at Oberammergau, a Parable like that of the Prodigal Son—to symbolize the ineffable deeps of religious experience?

The answer, as we have been reminding ourselves throughout these lectures, is that the Christian Revelation is rooted in history. The Gospel is a Gospel of Divine Action in time. We do not choose the symbols of water, bread and wine. They are chosen for us, given to us: these rites of Baptism and Eucharist go back to Christ himself. There is nothing older than this in Christendom. Before theology; before all our ecclesiasticism; before ever a word of the New Testament was written, this was. This is the earliest Gospel. Indeed, it is rooted in the immemorial covenant which God made with his people Israel. We take Bread and we take the Cup because the Redeemer himself is the fountain head of this living tradition. *Ipse Dominus fecit.* The Christian is born into an evangelical context, an historical heritage to which certain facts belong constitutively and for ever, namely the Commandments, the Beatitudes, the Lord's Prayer; a manger at Bethlehem; a Cross on Calvary; a broken body; an outpoured life; the Bread and the Wine. These things are not ours to accept or reject; they are there from the foundation of the world.

Go back to Goethe for a moment: 'The highest cannot be spoken; it can only be acted.' Well, the supreme Christian Sacrament is a drama. As often as we eat the Bread and drink the Cup we do show forth the dying of the Lord Jesus; we do re-enact the drama, which thus exhibits, truly and efficaciously, the mystery of our Redemption as no theology of Atonement has ever been able to do. This is our Symbol because he said: 'Do this in remembrance of me.'

Moreover, Christian men have done this ever since. Even if this rite meant little to us and made no living claim on our devotion, we should still have to account for its abiding energy in the life of the Church. It lasts because it speaks a universal, eternal word. Other symbols there certainly are, having their local, temporary significance. I have already mentioned three or four which move us deeply. But even so we cannot all go to

Dresden to see Raphael's Madonna. Bach's *Mass* may 'dissolve me into ecstasies, and bring all heaven before mine eyes', but it is not everybody's symbol. Oberammergau is a spectacle provided for the relatively few, once in ten years. Even the Parable of the Prodigal does not sum up all that is vital to the Christian faith. The very particularity of such symbolism separates it from the timeless simplicity and universality of water and bread and wine. Men have attempted to improve on the institution of Christ, often with the best motives. The evidence of the catacombs suggests that the Eucharist of the early Church was sometimes celebrated with fish, in memory of that eucharistic meal when Christ fed five thousand. The Kollyridians of the fourth century used something like cheese-cakes. Much later the Frisian Mennonites practised mutual feet-washing, taking the moving words of St John xiii to be a holy ordinance of Christ (*ritus praeceptus*). The Greek and Roman Churches reckon seven sacraments, that is, Baptism, Confirmation, Eucharist, Penance, Extreme Unction, Orders, Marriage. Yet, even so, the Roman Church does not attribute an equal dignity to all seven: three only have an indelible character and may on no account be repeated, namely Baptism, Confirmation and Orders (a sound practice at any rate, with which no Christian could disagree). But the sounder doctrine of the Thirty-nine Articles, and of Protestantism generally, limits the true Christian sacraments to the two visible signs or ceremonies, instituted by Christ himself.[1] As soon as we begin speaking of other sacraments beside the two given to us in the Gospels, a dangerous subjectivism threatens the historic faith. There is no limiting the number of such so-called sacraments. The Scholastics of the Middle Ages

[1] Cf. *Conf. Belg.* Art. 35.

enumerated thirty at different times,[1] and our modern interest in symbolism is ready to make the whole of nature symbolic, with the result that Sacraments in the Christian sense are destroyed. Baptism and the Lord's Supper are means of grace. They are, as Augustine put it, visible words[2] exhibiting with a moving actuality what has been received of the Lord, and continuously delivered to the whole company of the redeemed in every generation.

In the second place, what is the nature and meaning of these means of grace? The word 'symbol' may easily mislead us. The Swastika is the symbol of the Nazis. Or, to use a happier illustration, a primrose is symbolic of spring; but the Church means something different by the word 'Sacrament', because it means something more than a mere token or sign. In the ancient world a symbol was always, in some sense, the thing it symbolized. And there is no ecclesiastical confession in Christendom which does not insist that the Sacraments, as a Swiss Declaration puts it,[3] are never bare signs or mere illustrations, 'nuda, vacua, inania signa'. To use a classic expression, the Eucharist is a *signum efficax*; that is, it is a sign which verily effects something: it conveys what it signifies, namely the grace of Christ's finished work. The Sacraments do not add anything to the Word, any more than the kiss and the ring add anything to plighted troth. But they do movingly reiterate it; they give effect to it. 'They be certain sure witnesses and effectual signs of grace, and God's good will

---

[1] Cf. O. Fricke, *Die Sakramente in der Protestantischen Kirche*, p. 25.

[2] *Contra Faustum*, xix. 16. Cf. *de catechizandis rudibus* xxvi. 50: 'signacula quidem rerum divinarum esse visibilia, sed res ipsas invisibiles in eis honorari.'

[3] *Declar. Thor.* p. 61.

towards us, by the which he doth work invisibly in us, and doth not only quicken but also strengthen our Faith in him.' These familiar words from the Thirty-nine Articles, closely based on the Augsburg Confession, testify that the Sacraments do verily mediate God's grace. They are more than mere remembrances of heavenly things; the Church would be capable of such remembrance without Sacraments. They are signs whereby the Holy Spirit inwardly affects us. Like the printed score of the *Fifth Symphony*, through which the music in Beethoven's mind is mediated to successive generations, so the Sacraments are 'conveyances'; sign and effect coincide; the score is played and the music heard; so, God himself sacramentally unites the symbolic action and the grace which it conveys.

In short the emphasis here is always on God and his action. 'Prayer is a gift and a sacrifice that we make: Sacrament is a gift and a sacrifice that God makes. In prayer we go to God: in Sacrament God comes to us.'[1] The essential fact in the Eucharist is not man's remembrance and commemoration of Christ's death, but the fact that Christ here gives himself to man. If Sacraments are really important for our salvation, and the Church has never doubted that they are, their efficacy must have a basis independent of man. It is Christ himself, therefore, who administers the Sacraments. They are his, remember: not mine, or yours. He invites us to his Table. He is *hospes atque epulum*, that is, the Giver of the Feast as well as the Feast itself. Ordination does not mean that the priest or minister has now a higher rank than ordinary Christians and is able to minister instead of Christ. The Sacraments are efficacious only because

[1] P. T. Forsyth, quoted by N. Micklem, *Christian Worship, Studies in its history and meaning*, by members of Mansfield College (Oxford, 1936).

160

Christ himself uses the minister as his instrument. In short, vital to all Sacraments is God's action, not the priest's action.

This means something more. The efficacy of Sacraments cannot depend on the character and qualities of the man who administers them. The validity of the Sacrament is not destroyed because it has been celebrated by a man whose life is quite immoral or who has no faith at all. I am here postulating a situation scandalous and hurtful in the extreme, though by no means impossible. My point is that the character of the ministrant is strictly irrelevant. If it were not so, the Sacraments could never be celebrated at all, since all Christ's ministers are sinners. No man is ever good enough to 'be put in trust' with the Gospel, to be 'a steward of the Mysteries'. As the *Westminster Confession* has it: 'Neither does the efficacy of a Sacrament depend upon the piety or intention of him that doth administer it, but upon the Work of the Spirit and the Word of Institution' (xxvii. 3).

One vital question remains to be considered here; namely, on what does the operation of the Sacraments depend? Not on the ministrant, as we have already seen. Or, to use a technical expression which can hardly be bettered, not *ex opere operantis*. That is, it does not depend on what the celebrant, as such, does. The main thing is not the sacramental action in its manward aspect, but in its Godward aspect. In the Sacraments we have effectual signs of God acting.

Would it be sound doctrine, then, to teach, as Rome does, that the Sacraments exert their influence *ex opere operato*, that is, simply through the objective performance of the rite? (Just as inoculation exerts its influence on a man's body, irrespective of his feelings about it; he may be asleep or unconscious while it does its healing work: or just as a fire warms simply by the fact of our coming to stand in front of it; the burning coal is the *opus operatum*, and our bodily presence is alone necessary to make its warmth operative.) Do these analogies fairly describe the operation of the Sacraments in any sense? The answer is that they do: yet the answer may be made in so crude a way that it would be truer to say that they do not. Let me say two things in elucidation.

First, it is erroneous to suppose that Protestantism repudiates this great truth as to the objective operation and efficacy of the Gospel Sacraments. It is also misleading to say that Roman doctrine requires no faith at all from the recipient of the Sacraments. To quote Cardinal Bellarmine: 'Goodwill, faith and penitence are necessary in the adult communicant, not as the active cause of sacramental grace, nor as giving efficacy to the Sacrament. These dispositions merely remove the obstacles which might hinder its efficacy.'[1] Now, no Protestant would deny this, even though he means by 'faith' something notably different from what this great Jesuit meant. Indeed, the classic Protestant Confessions do not deny this, but they go much further.

Secondly, then, Protestantism has never even distantly denied that God's power dwells in the Sacraments in virtue of the Lord's institution. But it denies that grace is ever conferred *ex opere operato* without corresponding faith on the part of the recipient. The grace of the Gospel is not a 'thing', a sort of spiritual 'blood-plasm' for distribution to men through the channels of the sacramental system: a divine 'stuff', so to

[1] *De Sacram.* II. i: 'non ut causae activae, non enim fides et poenitentia efficiunt gratiam sacramentalem neque dant efficaciam sacramenti, sed solum tollunt obstacula, quae impedirent, ne sacramenta suam efficaciam exercere possent....'

speak, fused indissolubly with the sacramental elements, and working in magically objective fashion on the soul of the Communicant, without conscious response on his part, just as aspirin might work on his body. In a famous sentence of three words, St Augustine said: 'Believe and thou hast eaten of the Sacraments' (crede et manducasti).[1] He meant that faith in God's action is the ultimate requisite here. The grace of God is mediated not so much through faith as to faith. A grossly realistic objectivism here easily degenerates into superstition, as the history of the Church makes only too plain. This may be avoided only in one way. We have to remember that the Sacraments derive their whole meaning from the redeeming *Work* of Christ, if I may put it so, rather than from his *Essence*. The heart of the Sacrament is divine Action not divine Substance. God's grace is conveyed not through the elements but through the act. As my friend Nathaniel Micklem has put it: 'The efficacy of Baptism is not in water, but in washing: of the Communion, not in bread but in bread broken. The elements are as integral to the Sacrament as the words to the sentence; but as it is the whole sentence alone which is effectual as conveying meaning, so it is the Word (and not the elements) that conveys grace in the Sacrament.'[2]

Nothing illustrates the Christian doctrine of the Sacraments so unambiguously as the Sacrament of Baptism. For here the recipient of the Sacrament is, usually, not an adult but a tiny infant. Thus, some of the issues which we have been considering are here presented at their sharpest.

[1] *In Joh.* xxv. 12. Cf. *Ibid.* xxvi. 1, xxxv. 3. But see Seeberg, *DG*[2]. II. 460.
[2] *Christian Worship*, p. 245.

Let me remind you of the main issue. We met it when considering the doctrine of the Church, and we have met it again here. To use two clumsy and overworked yet useful words, it is the issue between the objective and the subjective in religion. Where is the accent, the main emphasis to be put in Christian doctrine? On the believer, or on God? Does it fall on our personal faith, our self-dedication, our fellowship, our moral idealism and moral achievements, or does it fall rather on the divine initiative; what God has done, the objective fact that God in Christ has redeemed men? Is the Church merely a number of local associations of believers, or is it something more; an undying Institution which is supra-personal and supra-temporal?

Obviously the answer is that both statements are true. We may not say 'Either...Or' here. God acts redemptively through his Church and his Sacraments: man responds by faith. Therefore Christian doctrine has always to be ready to fight on two fronts: against an excessive subjectivism on the one hand, which tends to belittle the Corporate, the Institutional, the Objective; and against an excessive subjectivism on the other hand, which would underestimate the personal, individual, intimate elements in all true religion.

Now the Sacrament of Baptism, administered almost exclusively to infants, and unrepeatable, obviously emphasizes the objective givenness of the Gospel of Redemption. Christ has redeemed all mankind, and the divinely given sign of this fact is baptism. It proclaims that Christ has done something for me, without ever consulting me or waiting for my approval; before ever I was born or thought of he died to redeem me. His Cross is not merely a moral appeal which may influence me; it is a fact in time where something was done for ever, to reconcile me and all other sinners to God. When Luther was most afflicted with temptations and doubts he would write two words on his table with a piece of chalk: *Baptizatus sum* (I have been baptized). He meant that baptism was the foundation of his Christian certainty. In the fact that he was baptized before he had any knowledge of salvation or any desire for it, God teaches him that the divine mercy sought him independently of his attitude towards God.

The significance of infant baptism is thus three-fold:

First, it guards against the menace of mere subjectivism. The great and world-wide denomination of Baptists is so named because its members rightly insist that to be a Christian a man or woman must be a believer. The faith must be his or her personal affair. Thus the Baptists recognize no other baptism than that which they administer to candidates who have reached years of discretion. They argue that to baptize a helpless infant only a few weeks old, who is obviously incapable of the responsive faith of the believer, is meaningless and worse. To this the universal tradition of Christendom replies, not of course by belittling personal faith in an adult who seeks baptism, but by insisting on our redemption as an objective fact just at that point in human life where no subjective response to it is possible on the part of the baptized individual.

In the second place, infant baptism guards against the irrelevant fancy known as 'dedicatory baptism', whereby parents who know no better suppose that in this rite they are dedicating the child to God. It is doubtless true that they are doing so, but compared with the main fact, the declaration of what Christ has done for this child on Calvary, such dedication is neither here nor there. The rite of baptism would, strictly speaking, be superfluous if it signified no more than an offering of the child by his parents to God. Such offering is doubtless good, but it is secondary here. Here, with the water of cleansing as the God-given sign, the Church proclaims the primary fact: namely, that God loves this child, and Christ died that it might be incorporate in the great company of his redeemed.

In the third place, the practice and the doctrine of infant baptism has been and is the great historical guarantee of the Church as something more than loose local associations of believers. This Sacrament is one of the foundation stones of the Church Institutional, Oecumenical and Corporate, a great supra-temporal fact in the heart of God. You perceive the difficulty, I think. No sacramental act achieves anything unless it corresponds to what happens in experience. Thus baptism has no efficacy apart from faith. Is infant baptism, then, the most blatant instance of *opus operatum*? The answer is that the faith is that of the Church, not of the child. Baptism is a real act of the Church and, therefore, of Christ. He it is who takes the child in his arms and declares what he has done and will do for it. Baptism is neither an act of dedication in which the main thing is what the celebrants do; nor is it a magic rite effecting regeneration. The child is baptized by Christ into his Church, the household of faith.

From this act of Christ in his Church we turn to the real presence of Christ in the Eucharist or the Lord's Supper, which is the other great Gospel Sacrament. What does this real presence mean?

The Eucharist has many aspects, and even if we could describe them all, the rite would still transcend our explanation. A sacrament which could be analysed into concepts

would cease to be a sacrament. But there are three aspects of
the Eucharist which may well concern us here:

The first is its historical or memorial aspect. The Holy Table
represents a direct and unbroken historical continuity with
Christian origins. It is a fact that not a single Sunday morning
has passed since the first Holy Week, without Christians meeting at this Table. What is said and done here formed the earliest
deposit of a Christian tradition which has never lapsed. Here
we do not read something out of the records of the historic
past, even though those records be the most precious books in
the world, the Gospels. We remember something earlier than
the written Gospels. The mysterious life of the Church is
continuously renewed through its unbroken remembrance and
dramatic repetition of certain mysterious words and acts of our
Saviour, on the night in which he was betrayed. This past is no
mere past. The supreme events of the life of Jesus, continuously
remembered, are a present fact.

Secondly, our remembrance is expressed in action, in the
manual acts of breaking the bread and taking the cup, of
eating and drinking together in the ritual meal of Holy
Communion. But, as you will remember from what I said in
my fourth lecture, on Christ Crucified, there is no meaning in
this meal except as the last stage of sacrifice. Just as our physical
life is sustained only because the wheat falls into the ground
and dies for us, and the grape yields up its life-blood for us,[1] so
the Bread and Wine are the effective signs of our spiritual
sustenance at the Table of him who is both our Victim, our
High Priest and our Food. He is the Bread of life sent down
from heaven, and broken for us. 'To us', says the earliest

---

[1] Fricke, *op. cit.* p. 38: 'Alle Nahrung ist geopfertes Leben.'

extant liturgy of the Church, the Didache, 'thou hast given spiritual food and drink through thy Servant.'[1]

The Servant is the Lamb of God who comes with us as we draw near to the Altar of God. He makes himself one with us in the Incarnation. We sinners kill our Victim; the Crucified takes his blood, his surrendered, outpoured life, now our life through our identification with him, through the veil of his broken flesh into God's very presence. He atones for us. In the offering of his Manhood, our separate manhoods conjoined with his, are also offered to God in eternal service. God accepts the offering by the fire of his Spirit, and so transforms it. Thus, does he receive us at his Board, the Table of the Lord which is the earthly image of the heavenly Altar. The very life of God, the Creator and the Redeemer, is here made available to us, through the Holy Spirit. We celebrate the mystery of life as corporate communion in and with the eternal God.

This is the second aspect of the Eucharist, its timeless or eternal aspect. The Feast mediates to us God's presence and his very Self.

In the third place, these two aspects here fuse into one. At this Table there is a unique synthesis of what is historical and what is beyond history. Through the remembered events of time the Church experiences the timeless presence of Christ. 'Past, present and future', says Professor Dodd, 'are indissolubly united in the Sacrament. It may be regarded as a dramatization of the advent of the Lord, which is at once his remembered coming in humiliation and his desired coming in glory, both realized in his true presence in the Sacrament.'[2] Thus, we know two things with certainty in this Sacrament.

---

[1] x. 3. Cf. also IX. 2–3.   [2] *The Apostolic Preaching*, p. 234.

First, Jesus Christ is not merely a figure of the historic past who is remembered because he is admired (like Isaiah, Epictetus or Boethius). He is the eternal Word, Bread from Heaven given to believers in every generation as the promise and foretaste of the Messianic feast in the Kingdom of God. The Eucharist lifts us, earth bound and time bound as we are, into 'the Heavenlies'. Here the temporal is known as eternal.

But secondly, the living God whom we worship is not adequately described as *ens realissimum* or as an impersonal Absolute transcending history. He is God revealed to us in Christ. Christian worship differs from Christian theism in that the Incarnation makes God real and present to us. Here the eternal is known as temporal.

In short, the Incarnation is the heart of our faith and the living nerve of our worship.

> Behold, the Eternal King and Priest
> Brings forth for me the Bread and Wine.

VIII

DEATH AND THE AGE TO COME

THE CHRISTIAN DOCTRINE OF THE LAST THINGS

THIS is the last of the lectures which I have been privileged to give here this term. As you know, they have been addressed to men and women of all faculties; people whose specialized interests are strikingly varied. Some of us are historians or economists; some read the classics or modern languages; some do highly technical work in laboratories.

But there is one intellectual interest common to us all. Indeed, the word 'intellectual' is not wide enough to describe it, since it is common to all human beings whether they think systematically about it or not. No living man avoids it, any more than he avoids food or sleep. Like the man in the great comedy who had been talking prose all his life without knowing it, we are all doing one thing willy-nilly, in virtue of facts which make man man, and differentiate him from stone or cabbage or the most intelligent chimpanzee that ever was. Trite though the remark is, we are all interpreting the Universe and trying to make sense of it. We are all looking at our world to discover what is the most significant thing about it. We look before and after. Men may not read books or enter laboratories, but in the very act of living the human life they seek wisdom, since wisdom means the capacity to understand things as a whole.

Indeed, man is the only part of creation known to us which is able to reflect about the ultimate meaning of creation.

Creation's 'ultimate' meaning; that is, its meaning as disclosed by its end, its final purpose and outcome. This is the real meaning of anything. Aristotle, in the *Physics* and the *Politics*, taught that the nature of a thing is determined not so much by its rudimentary stage as by its final stage, its τέλος or end. The word is used not only in the chronological, but in the metaphysical sense. The real meaning of the alphabet is given by the sentence. The true nature of this block of marble is the finished statue. A saw is made of steel: why not of putty or brown paper? Why not by the famous engineering firm of Heath Robinson? Because its end is to cut timber, or even iron. Its end alone explains its beginning. The completeness of a thing, says Aristotle, determines its nature.

What, then, is the ultimate meaning of man's life? What does the glittering tumult of human history, the glory and tragedy of the human centuries, all come to? The cynic has answered that life is a comedy to him who thinks, and a tragedy to him who feels. The religious man answers that it is a victory for him who believes. Believes what? What may we believe about the problem which has vexed thought and tried faith in every generation, namely, the problem of Death? It is no mere play upon words to say that man's life is only to be evaluated in terms of its end. Making sense of life means, ultimately and always, making sense of Death.

In the first place, Death is the one certain fact. Philip of Macedon had a slave to whom he gave a standing order. The man was to come in to the King every morning of his life, no matter what the King was doing, and to say to him in a loud voice: 'Philip, remember that thou must die.' The story is a parable because it speaks to Everyman, not only to sceptre and crown, but to tinker and tailor. Death is the only prediction which we can make about human history with absolute certainty. Prediction is one of the marks of a natural science, admittedly. If hydrochloric acid is poured on to zinc in the Cambridge laboratories a hundred years hence, we know that hydrogen will be given off and zinc chloride will remain. Indeed, other things being equal, we can predict by means of statistical averages a number of numerical facts about society, its births, marriages and deaths, for example, in some given period. But is there any certainty that other things will remain equal? They are very unequal at the present moment of world history. The great imponderables are as much a factor of world history as the facts which may be expressed in terms of statistical averages. Wars do not necessarily go according to formula. The laws of mathematical probability have no obvious relation to my neighbour's experience when a time-bomb drops in his backyard rather than in mine. The fact is that we cannot predict what will happen to us or to our world, even one day ahead. Much is highly probable, but nothing is certain, except ultimate death, soon or late. The literature of the race is one long testimony to the mystery and pathos of man's mortality. Like *Hamlet*, it is full of quotations, stock quotations, all but one of which I will spare you. Here is a man, a great Elizabethan, brought to the block. His last words were to the headsman who was hesitating: 'Why dost thou not strike? Strike, man!' But Sir Walter Raleigh's last word is really that last magnificent sentence of his unfinished *History of the World*, written there in the Tower: 'O eloquent, just and mighty Death! whom none could advise, thou hast persuaded; what none hath dared, thou hast done; and whom all the world hath flattered, thou only hast cast out of the world and despised. Thou hast drawne together all the farre stretched greatnesse, all the pride, crueltie and ambition of man, and covered it all over with these two narrow words: *Hic Jacet*!'

In the second place, Death is the supremely tragic fact. By 'tragic' I do not mean 'sad', a popular misuse of language. I mean that there is an irresolvable, inexplicable contradiction or tension in every human death. Man is not only conscious of the fact of death; that consciousness is his alone. The experience which equates him with animals and plants, at the same time sets him high above them. He thinks he was not made to die. Like Cleopatra, he has immortal longings in him. If he is meant to perish, as 'sheep or goats, that nourish a blind life within the brain', why is he tortured with dreams, and creative heroisms; with noble disinterestedness and, above all, with love, which makes bereavement his immemorial agony? If Death is the Everlasting No, striking him down to dust inexorably at the last, why is there an Everlasting Yea in his heart? What power has written this irrational and mocking gloss into his very constitution? If death means that all is over and there is nothing more, it is life which is pervaded with tragic irrationality. Every column in the great human tot-book adds up to precisely the same result, Zero. '...Alles was entsteht ist wert dass es zu Grunde geht.' Mephistopheles there tells Faust that the value of everything is ultimately nothing. He exploits the tragic enigma, that human values are not only gloriously affirmed by our empirical life in time; they are also basely denied. Their enemy is sin, but their last victorious enemy is Death.

Human death may not be explained and dismissed as a purely natural phenomenon, a biological fact which touches man as closely as it touches the bird or the beaver. Death cannot be a purely natural fact for one who is not a purely natural being, but a person made in God's image. May I presume to quote something I wrote in a recent volume, entitled *Facing the Facts*: 'There is a world of difference between "dying" (a purely zoological fact, admittedly), and "having to die" (which is uniquely and poignantly human).... Physical death as such is not a problem; granted. But having to die is: it is the supreme illustration of the incomprehensibility of our world'? Death is 'the burden and the mystery of all this unintelligible world', just because Wordsworth and Everyman know they have to die.

In the third place, Death is a universal fact, claiming the human race itself. It is arguable that what we call 'Nature', which was here before man, will be here when man has gone, and the insubstantial pageant of his history is no more. Even the Pyramids, his own monument, may conceivably outlast him, as Toynbee suggests. The Squinancy Wort was there on the high downs before man; you may know the lines which Edward Carpenter puts into the mouth of the little flower:

What have I done? Man came,
Evolutional upstart one!
With the gift of giving a name
To everything under the sun.
What have I done? Man came,
(They say nothing sticks like dirt)
Looked at me with eyes of blame
And called me Squinancy Wort...

Yet there is hope; I have seen
Many changes since I began.
The web-footed beasts have been
(Dear beasts!) and gone, being part of some wider plan.
Perhaps in His infinite mercy, God will remove this Man!

Well, perhaps man, who is not only a fool but a sinner, may remove himself. In any case, Christian doctrine will have nothing to do with an earthly eternity for the human race, as though the City of God were the goal of secular evolution here on this planet, where men will live happily ever afterwards. And this is the main answer which Christian doctrine makes to Positivists such as Auguste Comte and George Eliot, and to all whose evaluation of life's meaning is exclusively sociological. The Positivists argued that though death is a grim fact allowing no immortality to the individual, immortality is racial. We live on in those who come after us; when a man dies he bequeathes his record to the common stock of humanity; thus alone does he find what Comte calls 'subjective immortality'. There is no God: that 'stage', says Comte, is now over. Humanity is the only God, the only Object of religion. Humanity is the one Great Being. We mortals become 'his' objective servants in life and then 'his' subjective organs after death. We 'transmit, improved, to those who shall come after, the increasing heritage we received from those who went before'. One might call it 'Immortality by metaphysical fiction': 'Immortality which is always vicarious and never real.'

It is obvious that there is truth here. I mean that this worthless metaphysic is built on fact, the social solidarity of the successive generations. In George Eliot's poem, where the metaphysic is merely implicit, this truth receives a moving presentation; like Stoicism, it bears itself nobly. Life to come, she says, is to 'be the sweet presence of a good diffused'; 'to be to other souls the cup of strength in some great agony...'. The poem is really a prayer, not to God of course, but to George Eliot:

> O may I join the choir invisible
> Of those immortal dead who live again
> In minds made better by their presence: live
> In pulses stirred to generosity,
> In deeds of daring rectitude: in scorn
> For miserable aims that end with self...
>
> So shall I join the choir invisible
> Whose music is the gladness of the world.

The admission which this splendidly audacious rhetoric barely conceals, is that these immortal dead are alive only by a poetic fiction. Objectively considered they have perished for ever. The choir is invisible because it is non-existent, not because it is the multitude of the heavenly host, unseen but eternal, singing a new song about the throne of God and of the Lamb.

To anticipate the next main section of this lecture for a moment, the Christian doctrine of the Last Things is always affirming one great truth, through all its varied imagery, namely, that the only true evaluation of this world is one which recognizes the impermanence of this world. Here we have no abiding city; we seek one that is to come, beyond history and beyond death. We are always strangers and sojourners; our citizenship is in Heaven.

Theology is here nearer to facts than the Utopian Ideologies of the modern age. History knows little of the dogma of inevitable progress from primitive barbarism to the perfect

human society. It traces the rise and fall of successive civilizations. It has its own concrete way of illustrating what Christian
doctrine knows as Original Sin. Further, philosophy rightly
reminds evolutionary optimists, with their explicitly secularist,
this-worldly presuppositions, that such doctrinaire optimism is
only another name for a most ghastly pessimism. The worst
totalitarianism of all would be one which, beginning in 'the
dark backward and abysm of time' and going on and on into a
far distant future, cheerfully and ruthlessly sacrifices the toiling,
sorrowing, dying generations of men to eternal death, that the
last and luckiest generations may reach the Earthly Paradise—
the end to which all this is the means—before they too go down
in the darkness of death and annihilation. William Morris'
News from Nowhere come true, for three-score years and ten, or
perchance four- or even five-score years! Would Death be less
or more tragic in such a world of perfect justice and happiness?
Against such a background of felicity in a planet of garden
cities, William Watson's cry would surely be more, not less,
agonizing:

> But ah! to know not while with friends I sit,
> And while the purple joy is passed about,
> Whether 'tis ampler day divinelier lit
> Or homeless night without.

> And whether, stepping forth, my soul shall see
> New prospects, or fall sheer—a blinded thing:
> There is, O Grave, thy hourly victory,
> And there, O Death, thy sting.

In the fourth place, Death is the one inescapable fact which
compels men to choose between despair and faith.

Here the notorious problem of evil comes to a head; it reaches its climax, its breaking point. Here and here only we see the meaning of its stark inescapability. The problem is mainly two-fold. There is first, metaphysical evil; that is, man's sense of finitude and transitoriness, to which I have been drawing your attention all along. Well, it all comes to its maximum intensity here. It is seen for what it is against the vast, empty, senseless nothingness of Death. Death is, as a modern philosopher has put it, 'the supreme external manifestation of temporality'. One might say that it is the sacrament of time, time's most effectual sign. Secondly, there is moral evil; that is, man's sense of failure, sin and guilt. For all this, too, death is the supreme crisis. Crisis is a Greek word meaning Judgment. The Apostle wrote that the sting of death is sin. Why? Well the life-long drama of the soul here comes to a climax which is inevitable, inescapable, unrehearsable, unanalysable, final. Here, everything constituting life's record is seen to be unalterable, indelible, irremediable. Death has been called the sacrament of sin because it is the effective sign of opportunities gone for ever. Death is tremendous because life is, and because in it life says its last word. Little wonder that James Denney, in protesting against the modern tendency to make light of human death, should have added that 'it is the greatest thought of which we are capable, except the thought of God'. The fact which is here inescapable is a dilemma. Either we despair, or we believe. There is no middle course, no razor-edge of non-committal on which to balance precariously. Only he who believes in God wins the victory over despair. Only the infinite mercy of the Eternal Love, incarnate, suffering, dying, rising from the dead, is big enough for the tragedy of human existence. The dilemma is inescapable.

Either despair which is Hell, or faith in him who giveth us the victory.

Christian eschatology is the outcome of such a faith. The doctrine of the end of history and of the life of the age to come is the form taken by teleology in the Hebraic-Christian tradition. Because it seeks to make sense of things, every philosophy includes a teleology of some sort; that is, a doctrine of ultimate meanings or ends. It is true that the word 'teleology' is not derived from the Greek τέλος (meaning 'end'), but from τέλειος (meaning 'perfect' or 'complete'). But the difference is negligible. The real meaning of anything, as we have already noticed, is determined by what it is when completed or perfected; that is, when it has reached the end which was implicit in its very beginning.

What is the meaning of human history, the life of the whole human race? To the Hebrews, with their realism and their interest in history, teleology took the special form of eschatology, a doctrine of the End, when the evil of the world will be judged and righted by God himself. The prophets always expected this 'Day of the Lord' which should consummate and fully reveal the divine purpose being worked out in history. By fixing their vision on the End, the Prophets were able to hold on to their faith that the whole of history is divinely ordered. They interpreted the darkest hour of the battle in the light of the coming victory, God's victory. The Present Age, with all its woe and sin, will give place to the Age to Come, a supernatural, supra-historical order of existence which will be the Lord's doing. In one sense, this Day of the Lord, ushering in the new Age, is the last of the long series of historical events, the final link in the chain, the last note which makes a unity of the scale. But, in another sense, to quote Professor Dodd, 'it is not an event in history at all; for it is described in terms which remove it from the conditions of time and space.... It is such that no other event either could follow or need follow upon it, because in it the whole purpose of God is revealed and fulfilled.'[1] History thus reaches its goal, its absolute end, with the fulfilment of the divine purpose in creation.

But, how can there be an end to historic time? The idea is surely inconceivable; is it not therefore meaningless? We met precisely the same intellectual difficulty about the idea of a beginning of time, in creation. To conceive of such a beginning is just as impossible as to conceive of no beginning; similarly, to conceive of an end, when the eternal clock stops, so to speak, is as impossible as to conceive of no end, with the clock ticking away for ever and ever. As Dr Edwyn Bevan reminded us in his Gifford Lectures, the attempt to define or understand time is doomed to failure because time is wholly unique, something so wholly unlike anything else we know that when we try to explain it we find ourselves bringing terms of temporal significance into our explanation. Our definitions are necessarily circular, presupposing a knowledge of the very thing to be defined. This is what Augustine meant when he said: 'If nobody asks me what time is, I know: if I want to explain it to anyone who asks me, I am at a loss.'

The idea, then, of an absolute end to history, the End of the World, or the Last Judgment, is a *Grenzbegriff*, a symbol standing for the limit of all our conceiving; like the words *Ne plus ultra* on the maps of the old geographers. Eschatology is a symbolic way of expressing the reality of God's purpose within history. Like the Hebrew, and unlike the Greek, the Christian

[1] *The Apostolic Preaching*, p. 198.

knows that time matters; that history is God's roaring loom. That is why eschatology is the Christian teleology. Just as no living man knows or can know what death is, in all its mysterious nature and extent, so no man knows or can conceive what the end of history is. Everyman, whether he be an Old Testament prophet like Jeremiah or a New Testament apostle like St Paul; whether he be an H. G. Wells with his Time-Machine or an Eddington with his mathematical symbolism, Everyman is compelled to think here in terms of images. The vital point is that the symbolic imagery of the Bible always describes the End in terms of the supernatural, the eternal, the 'wholly-other'. The ultimate nature and meaning of history is only disclosed in its End, where God 'takes it up' as it were, into eternity, and it is seen to be part of eternity. To quote Professor Dodd again, the End 'is such that nothing more could happen in history because the eternal meaning which gives reality to history is now exhausted. To conceive any further event on the plane of history would be like drawing a cheque on a closed account.'[1] That is, the present Age ends with an Event which is itself the beginning of something new, the Age to Come, the Kingdom of God in all its perfection and glory.

The emphasis of Christian eschatology is thus two-fold; it makes an amazing statement which can be expressed only in the form of a dialectical tension or paradox.

On the one hand it proclaims that the End has already been realized. The Word became flesh, and dwelt among us, and we beheld his glory. The New Testament rings with this proclamation that the final outcome of history has already happened. The Age to Come is here, with power and great glory. That which was spoken by the prophet is come to pass. If any man is

[1] *The Apostolic Preaching*, p. 206.

in Christ there the new Creation, the Age to Come, is. He has tasted of its powers. Christ has rescued us out of the dominion of darkness and transferred us into the Kingdom of the Son of his love. The Kingdom of God has come upon us. Now is the crisis of this world: now is the Prince of this world cast out. This is the Judgment, that the Light has come into the world, and men love darkness rather than the light. The one far-off divine event to which the whole creation moves has burst into human history, in the coming, the miraculous ministry, the death and the resurrection of Jesus Christ. Christ is risen from the dead, the firstfruits of the Age to Come. We are raised with him in newness of life. He who believes on him has eternal life. This coming of the Incarnate Word is the decisive End; old things are passed away, all things henceforward are new; that is, different in quality. The whole human race stands in a new relation to the temporal, historic order; the old relation is broken and there can never be any going back to it. To attempt to do so is to be judged; it is to prefer the provisional to the absolute which has displaced it. Jesus Christ is the unique and final impact of the Kingdom of God on human experience; to go back behind it is as impossible as to go beyond it.

But, on the other hand (and this is what makes the dialectical tension), human history does not cease to be history, under the forms of time and sense, even though our life is now eternal life, and we sit in heavenly places with Christ. We still live in the body; we still sin; we still have to die. Ideally or potentially considered, our life is lived with Christ in God. But empirically considered, our life is still 'in the flesh'. The Kingdom of God has come; the Eternal Now has been given to our experience; the New Testament is a monument to this fact. Nevertheless, the New Testament also looks to a future consummation, a final judgment, an End which is 'not yet', an eternal order of blessedness in God of which our Christian life in time is the foretaste and the firstfruits. Thus, the Age to Come is a present experience; and yet it is a future consummation; that is the paradox of New Testament eschatology. How is it to be understood or resolved? Redemption, as we have seen, must mean redemption from Death, if it is to be a reality which matters. But this does not imply simply more life after death. That would have been nothing new to most Jews of the time when the Gospel was first preached. The life and immortality brought to light by the Gospel are not quantity but quality. All turns on quality, that eternal life of which the New Testament speaks and which is begun now, that it may reach its fruition hereafter under new conditions. We still have to die: but Death changes its meaning when a man knows that he has already tasted of the life beyond its portals (ζωὴ αἰώνιος).

There is the paradox. The New Testament speaks, therefore, not only of Christ's coming in Bethlehem, nineteen centuries ago, but also of his second coming. Christian doctrine teaches a *geminus adventus*, a two-fold advent, reminding men that the Christian life is lived in terms of this tension, between what has happened and what will happen; between this world where we have surely seen the light of the knowledge of God's glory on the face of Christ and the world to come where the whole meaning of Christian history as the accomplishment of God's purpose will be revealed in the Last Judgment. This tension, which the *geminus adventus* illustrates, can only be set forth in terms of a dialectic which holds together present experience and future hope. Indeed, the Christian hope cannot be precisely described; it can only be 'pictured' in symbolical language, suggested by the varied imagery of different New Testament writers. Such language wrestles with ineffable things lying beyond the utmost range of all human experience, things which 'eye hath not seen nor ear heard'. The drama of the Last Judgment takes place in the eternal world, to which Death is the inevitable and only gateway.

Christian eschatology means that the true evaluation of this world must rest against the background of its impermanence. 'Otherworldliness' is the differentia of Christian life in this world. Neville Figgis used to say that the core of the Gospel, the very essence of the Christian life, is 'otherworldliness'. He was in line, of course, with the New Testament and with Christian doctrine. Here we have no abiding city. We seek a better country, that is, a heavenly. Moreover, Figgis was in line with the New Testament and with Christian doctrine in insisting that here is the true motive for Christian social action. 'The heavenly life alone', he wrote, 'lends reality to all schemes of earthly amelioration; the life beyond which alone gives value to this; the eternal, the immortal, the invisible, which alone makes it worth while to lift mankind from the mire of selfishness and corruption.... Only as we live within the circle of the Ascended Glory shall we really be able for work here.'[1] Christian doctrine is unmistakably explicit about 'the life of the Age to Come', for which the Church of God on earth is preparation, forehint and foretaste. The Holy Spirit by which the Church lives is, here and now, the earnest of a heavenly inheritance. And I venture to add that we have too long halted in this matter in 'implicits' and should come out far more than we do into 'explicits'. For by now the development of the human situation is curing us, and seems like to

[1] From an article by F. J. E. Raby in *Theology*, May 1940.

cure us even more drastically, of trying to put the Catholic and Evangelical Churchmanship of the Christian ages into an exclusive context of social or world improvement, or other such alien ideology. It has to go back into the context which belongs to it and to which it belongs, namely the unworldly, if not the other-worldly, one. Bunyan's characteristic word, 'the milk and honey is beyond this wilderness', is what all great Christians have said, Christians whom no one may charge with being ineffectives while they were on this side of Jordan river. 'In Egypt, Rome and Carthage it was the custom to deliver to the candidates at their first communion, in addition to bread and wine, a cup of milk and honey, to give them a foretaste of the heavenly food of which the blessed partake in the Kingdom of God.'[1] The manna in the wilderness is never an end in itself. It points beyond itself; it is heavenly food; it is the foretaste as well as the promise, of the feast in the heavenly Kingdom.

Therefore I am neither afraid nor ashamed to remind you that Christian doctrine may never forget the sane but quite definite otherworldliness, which is one indisputable aspect of our religion in all its transcendent absoluteness. Our citizenship is in heaven. Its centre is in God. This is true of original Christianity; this is the unmistakable implication of our Churchmanship, and it has immense relevance to the predicament in which we now are.

The urgency of the issues raised by eschatology is obvious. Does the Christian faith matter? If so, how much does it matter? If it does not matter vitally and urgently, does it matter at all? Consider these moving words: 'But above all for

---

[1] *Cambridge Ancient History*, xii. 527.

thine inestimable love in the redemption of the world by our Lord Jesus Christ, for the means of grace, and for the hope of glory.' As a sinful man looking at death and beyond it, into the eternal world, I need salvation. Nothing else will meet my case. There is something genuinely at stake in every man's life, the climax whereof is death. Dying is inevitable, but arriving at the destination God offers to me is not inevitable. It is not impossible to go out of the way and fail to arrive. Christian doctrine has always urged that life eternal is something which may conceivably be missed. It is possible to neglect this great salvation and to lose it eternally, even though no man may say that anything is impossible with God or that his grace may ultimately be defeated.[1]

I know it is no longer fashionable to talk about Hell, one good reason for this being that to make religion into a prudential insurance policy is to degrade it. The Faith is not a fire-escape. But in rejecting the old mythology of eternity as grotesque and even immoral, many people make the mistake of rejecting the truth it illustrated (which is rather like rejecting a book as untrue because the pictures in it are bad). It is illogical to tell men that they must do the will of God and accept his gospel of grace, if you also tell them that the obligation has no eternal significance, and that nothing ultimately depends on it. The curious modern heresy that everything is bound to come right in the end is so frivolous that I will not insult you by refuting it. 'I remember', said Dr Johnson on one occasion, 'that my Maker has said that he will place the sheep on his right hand and the goats on his left.' That is a solemn truth

---

[1] The substance and phrasing of this and the succeeding paragraph are taken largely from one of my chapters in *The Way to God*, by permission of the S.C.M. Press.

which only the empty-headed and empty-hearted will neglect. It strikes at the very roots of life and destiny.

My lectures are at an end. I am acutely conscious of their many omissions and defects; but I am more conscious of the encouragement you have given me by honouring them so signally with your presence and attention.

BIBLIOGRAPHY

The general reader who is not a specialist in theology may find a guide for further reading in these lists of books:

GENERAL

BRUNNER, E. *Our Faith* (Harpers).
DENNEY, J. *Studies in Theology* (Hodder; out of print).
GARVIE, A.E. *The Christian Doctrine of the Godhead* (Hodder).
KIRK, K. (editor). *The Study of Theology* (Hodder), with special reference to the opening chapter contributed by N. P. Williams.
MATTHEWS, W.R. (editor). *The Christian Faith* (Eyre & Spottiswoode).
QUICK, O.C. *Doctrines of the Creed* (Nisbet).

I. BELIEF IN GOD

BAILLIE, J. *Our Knowledge of God* (Oxford).
FARMER, H.H. *The World and God* (Nisbet).
GORE, C. *The Philosophy of the Good Life* (Everyman).
MATTHEWS, W.R. *God in Christian Thought and Experience* (Nisbet).
ROBINSON, H.W. *The Religious Ideas of the Old Testament* (Duckworth).
TAYLOR, A.E. Essay in *Essays Catholic and Critical* (S.P.C.K.).

II. MAN AND SIN

BRUNNER, E. *Man in Revolt* (Lutterworth).
EDINBURGH CONFERENCE. *The Christian Understanding of Man* (Allen & Unwin).
HORTON, W.M. *Realistic Theology* (Hodder).
LEWIS, C.S. *The Problem of Pain* (Centenary).
NIEBUHR, R. *An Interpretation of Christian Ethics* (S.C.M.).
ROBINSON, H.W. *The Christian Doctrine of Man*, 2nd ed. (Clark).
TAYLOR, A.E. *The Faith of a Moralist*, vol. I, chap. v (Macmillan).
WHALE, J.S. *The Christian Answer to the Problem of Evil* (S.C.M.).
WILLIAMS, N.P. *The Ideas of the Fall and of Original Sin* (Longmans).

III. History and the Kingdom of God

BERDYAEV, N. *The Meaning of History* (Centenary).
BEVAN, E. *Christianity* (Thornton Butterworth).
DODD, C.H. *The Parables of the Kingdom* (Nisbet).
—— *The Apostolic Preaching* (Hodder).
EDINBURGH CONFERENCE. *The Kingdom of God and History* (Allen & Unwin).
WEBB, C.C.J. *The Historical Element in Religion* (Allen & Unwin).
WOOD, H.G. *Christianity and the Meaning of History* (Cambridge).

IV. The Work of Christ

AULÉN, G. *Christus Victor* (S.P.C.K.).
CAVE, S. *The Doctrine of the Work of Christ* (Hodder).
DENNEY, J. *The Death of Christ* (Hodder).
FRANKS, R.S. *The Atonement* (Oxford).
MACKINTOSH, H.R. *The Christian Experience of Forgiveness* (Nisbet).
TAYLOR, V. *Jesus and His Sacrifice* (Macmillan).

V. The Person of Christ

BARTLET, J.V. Three chapters in *The Lord of Life* (S.C.M.).
BRUNNER, E. *The Mediator* (Lutterworth).
CAVE, S. *The Doctrine of the Person of Christ* (Duckworth).
FORSYTH, P.T. *The Person and Place of Jesus Christ* (Independent).
GORE, C. *Belief in Christ* (Murray).
LOOFS, F. *What is the Truth about Jesus Christ?* (Clark).
RAWLINSON, A.E.J. *The New Testament Doctrine of the Christ* (Longmans).

VI. The Church

CALVIN. *Institutes*, Book IV, translated by H. Beveridge (Calvin Translation Society).
EHRENSTRÖM, N. *Christian Faith and the Modern State* (S.C.M.).
FLEW, R.N. *Jesus and His Church* (Epworth).
HORT, F.J.A. *The Christian Ecclesia* (Macmillan).
LUTHER. *Primary Works*, translated by Wace and Buchheim (Hodder).
OLDHAM, J.H. and HOOFT, V.'T. *The Church and its Function in Society* (Allen & Unwin).
OMAN, J. *The Church and the Divine Order* (Hodder).
STREETER, B.H. *The Primitive Church* (Macmillan).

VII. The Word and the Sacraments

BARCLAY, A. *The Protestant Doctrine of the Lord's Supper* (Glasgow).

DALE, R.W. *Manual of Congregational Principles* (Independent).

Encyclopaedia of Religion and Ethics. Articles on Eucharist, Sacraments and Worship.

HEADLAM, A.C. and DUNKERLEY, R. (editors). *The Ministry and the Sacraments* (S.C.M.).

MAXWELL, W.D. *An Outline of Christian Worship* (Oxford).

MICKLEM, N. (editor). *Christian Worship* (Oxford).

MOZLEY, J.K. *The Gospel Sacraments* (Hodder).

SCHENCK, L.B. *The Presbyterian Doctrine of Children in the Covenant* (Yale).

VIII. The Last Things

BAILLIE, J. *And the Life Everlasting* (Oxford).

CHARLES, R.H. *Eschatology: Hebrew, Jewish and Christian* (Black).

COMMISSION REPORT. *Doctrine in the Church of England* (S.P.C.K.).

DODD, C.H. *The Apostolic Preaching*, Appendix (Hodder).

MATTHEWS, W.R. *The Hope of Immortality* (S.C.M.).

VON HÜGEL, F. *Essays and Addresses*, No. 7 (Dent).

INDEX

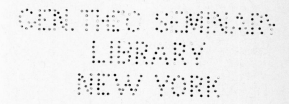

ANNUAL REVIEW OF PHYSIOLOGY

EDITORIAL COMMITTEE (1982)

Responsible of the organization of Volume 45
(Editorial Committee, 1981)

ANNUAL REVIEW OF PHYSIOLOGY

VOLUME 45, 1983

ROBERT M. BERNE, *Editor*
University of Virginia Medical School

JOSEPH F. HOFFMAN, *Associate Editor*
Yale University School of Medicine

ANNUAL REVIEWS INC.   4139 EL CAMINO WAY   PALO ALTO, CALIFORNIA 94306 USA

International Standard Serial Number: 0066-4278
International Standard Book Number: 0-8243-0345-8
Library of Congress Catalog Card Number: 39-15404

PREFACE

By rights this preface should have been written by Dr. I. S. Edelman, since the volume's conception occurred during his tenure as editor. However, fetal development (manuscript preparation, review, and redactory work) and the actual birth of the 45th *Annual Review of Physiology* have taken place since my appointment as editor. Furthermore, Dr. Edelman shrewdly wrote his farewell preface for volume 44, thereby assuring a rapid turnover of the reins.

I joined the Review's Editorial Committee in 1978, just prior to the planning of the first sectionalized volume. It was an exciting time, for we finally arranged, and later published, a format that had been suggested by previous editors and members of the Committee. Since then the sectionalized volumes have enhanced the value of the *Annual Review of Physiology* by highlighting the key areas of physiology while at the same time providing good coverage of the field as a whole. The selection of timely themes and appropriate authors has been carefully and expertly performed by the Section Editors, but most of the credit goes to Dr. Edelman, who skillfully orchestrated the whole operation. His breadth of knowledge was astonishing, and the meetings of the committee that he led were enlivened by incisiveness, perceptiveness, critical but kind advice, and a high level of delightful and appropriate humor. In brief, it was a pleasure to work with Dr. Edelman; and although I will do my best, I think his shoes will be hard to fill.

In addition, the series has in recent years been blessed with such outstanding Section Editors as S. G. Shultz, S. M. McCann, T. E. Andreoli, W. R. Dawson, A. P. Fishman, J. Gergely, D. T. Krieger, as well as Special Topics Editors W. J. Freeman, D. E. Koshland, Jr., P. H. Patterson, and G. Fischbach. We are equally fortunate in having top-flight scientists to replace the Section Editors who have completed their tours of duty. Dr. J. F. Hoffman has become Associate Editor as well as Section Editor for Cell and Membrane Physiology. In addition, Dr. J. G. Forte has become Section Editor for Gastrointestinal Physiology, Dr. C. W. Gottschalk for Renal Physiology, Dr. J. E. Heath for Comparative and Integrative Physiology, Dr. R. E. Forster for Respiratory Physiology, Dr. H. V. Sparks, Jr. for Cardiovascular Physiology, and Dr. J. L. Kostyo for Endocrinology and Metabolism.

Finally, I wish to express my appreciation to William Kaufmann, former Editor-In-Chief at Annual Reviews, for his excellent work, and to Dick Burke who, as Production Editor, carried out his job with expertise and cheerfully bore the brunt of the authors' and editors' comments and criticisms.

Dr. Alister Brass has recently assumed the position of Editor-In-Chief. It is with great pleasure that we all look forward to working with Dr. Brass in continuing the excellent tradition of the series and in striving to improve its quality and usefulness to the readership. In this regard, the Editorial Committee would welcome *all* comments, criticisms, and suggestions that may help us to maintain the highest standards for the *Annual Review of Physiology.*

Robert M. Berne
Editor

Annual Review of Physiology
Volume 45, 1983

CONTENTS

(*continued*)

(*continued*)

Special Announcement: New From Annual Reviews

Volume 1 of the *Annual Review of Immunology* (Editors: William E. Paul, C. Garrison Fathman, and Henry Metzger) will be published in April, 1983.

Some Historical and Modern Aspects of Amino Acids, Fermentations and Nucleic Acids, Proceedings of a Symposium held in St. Louis, Missouri, June 3, 1981, edited by Esmond E. Snell. Published October, 1982. 141 pp.; Softcover; $10.00 USA/$12 elsewhere, postpaid per copy

OTHER REVIEWS OF INTEREST TO PHYSIOLOGISTS

From the *Annual Review of Biochemistry,* Volume 51 (1982)

Enzymology of Oxygen, Bo G. Malmström

From the *Annual Review of Neuroscience,* Volume 6 (1983)

The Classification of Dopamine Receptors: Relationship to Radioligand Binding, Ian Creese, David R. Sibley, Mark W. Hamblin, and Stuart E. Leff

Mechanoelectrical Transduction by Hair Cells in the Acousticolateralis Sensory System, A. J. Hudspeth

Hypothalamic Integration: Organization of the Paraventricular and Supraoptic Nuclei, L. W. Swanson and P. E. Sawchenko

Experimental Approaches to Understanding the Role of Protein Phosphorylation in the Regulation of Neuronal Function, Mary B. Kennedy

From the *Annual Review of Medicine,* Volume 34 (1983)

Exercise and Coronary Heart Disease, Nancy A. Rigotti, Gregory S. Thomas, and Alexander Leaf

Pathogenesis of Hyperthyroidism, Inder J. Chopra and David H. Solomon

Mechanisms and Disorders of Gastric Emptying, J. N. Hunt

Sweating and Its Disorders, Paul M. Quinton

From the *Annual Review of Pharmacology and Toxicology,* Volume 22 (1982)

Cardiovascular Control by Cholinergic Mechanisms in the Central Nervous System, Henry E. Brezenoff and Rachel Giuliano

Pharmacological Salvage of Myocardium, Louis G. Lange and Burton E. Sobel

Sympathetic Control of Renin Release, J. Torretti

Pharmacology of Brain Epinephrine Neurons, Ray W. Fuller

Cholinergic System in Behavior: The Search for Mechanisms of Action, Roger W. Russell

Physiology and Pharmacology of LHRH and Somatostatin, S. M. McCann

From the *Annual Review of Fluid Mechanics,* Volume 15 (1983)

Flow in Curved Pipes, S. A. Berger, L. Talbot, and L.-S. Yao

Alan Hodgkin

Ann. Rev. Physiol. 1983. 45:1–16

BEGINNING: SOME REMINISCENCES OF MY EARLY LIFE (1914–1947)

A. L. Hodgkin [1]

Physiological Laboratory, Cambridge, England

INTRODUCTION

Some years ago the Physiological Society published a lecture, called "Chance and Design," in which I described the experiments on nerve that my colleagues and I carried out between 1934 and 1952 (1). The present article covers roughly the same period but from a different point of view. Instead of describing experiments in detail I have tried to convey an impression of the life of a young physiologist nearly fifty years ago. I have also given a brief account of my scientific education, which in retrospect seems fairly odd. If there is a moral it is that people are more important than organizations and that universities should not streamline their administrations to the point at which it is no longer possible for the green shoots to push up through the crazy pavement.

GROWING UP 1914–1932

My father died in 1918 leaving a 26 year old widow with three boys aged 4, 2, and 0, of whom I was the eldest. This disaster might have made my mother unduly protective of her young family, but it seemed to have the opposite effect, either because she was buoyed up by some inner faith or because she made a deliberate effort to avoid mollycoddling. At all events we were allowed to wander about the pleasant country near Banbury, where I was born, or after we had moved to Oxford to spend the whole day walking, bicycling, or canoeing, often going miles from home. Later on,

[1] For a bibliography of the author's early scientific papers, see (1).

1

when we had learned to use map and compass we were even permitted to walk long distances in the snow-covered hills of the Lake District where we occasionally spent the Christmas holidays.

From an early age I was interested in natural history and was greatly encouraged by a talented but somewhat eccentric aunt with whom we used to stay in a primitive holiday cottage in Northumberland. She taught me to record my observations in a bird-diary, and although her approach to natural history was thoroughly scientific she managed to endow the subject with an exciting quality that had a special appeal for a small boy. When I was about 15 I was recruited by a professional ornithologist, Wilfred Alexander, to help him with the surveys of rookeries and heronries that he had helped to initiate. And at my second school, Gresham's, near the Norfolk coast, I overlapped with the ornithologist David Lack and spent many hours with him or another friend looking at rare birds on the salt marshes, or hunting for nightjar's nests on which Lack was making a behavioral study of some importance. All this got me interested in biology and helped to blur the distinction between learning and research.

Perhaps because there was no very suitable school at Banbury I went to a preparatory school (the Downs) near Malvern when I was nine years old. I think the parting must have been more painful for my mother than it was for me, but she consoled herself with the picture of the charming wife of the headmaster reading Treasure Island to a group of small boys in front of a glowing fire. There was nothing wrong with the picture, and bedtime reading was certainly a consolation; but small boys can behave devilishly to one another, and going away to school at nine is something I would wish to avoid if I were offered my life again. Still there was much that was enjoyable about school. We were allowed plenty of time to follow our own pursuits, which in my case involved bringing up a pet owl or hunting for birds and flowers on the beautiful hillsides that look out across the wooded Herefordshire plain to the distant Welsh Mountains. Another more sociable activity consisted in helping the headmaster build a model railway with an engine and truck large enough to carry 6 or 7 boys for a distance of several hundred yards. I do not think we can have learned a great deal because I found myself in the bottom form of my next school, Gresham's, where I went at the age of 13½.

By then I had decided that I wanted to go to Cambridge and I had to work hard in order to reach the scholarship class. There were only about two hundred boys in the senior school but it can claim some distinguished alumni, including William Rushton, Wystan Auden, and Benjamin Britten. As one might expect in so small a school, teaching was somewhat patchy. Of the subjects that later became important to me, mathematics was well taught, but I have never been able to do sums against the clock and more or less gave up the subject during the two years that I worked for a scholarship. In the lower forms physics was taught atrociously by the headmaster, with extreme rigidity, not only as to the wording but also as to the pronunciation of the laws and definitions he made us learn by heart. Thus you had to distinguish between "that" (to rhyme with hat) as an adjective and "th't" as a conjunction. I could not bear this and gave up the subject before I reached the sixth form, where I might have learned something from a different master.

For a long time I could not decide between history and biology, but in the end natural history won the day and I managed to get a scholarship at Trinity, Cambridge, in botany, zoology, and chemistry. In all these subjects I was well taught by youngish masters. We were encouraged to read widely and to work on our own, and this I think is the most important thing I learned at school. During one summer holiday I spent an enjoyable week investigating the distribution of specialized plants that grow on the sand-dunes and saltmarshes of Scolt Head Island off the Norfolk coast. This must have helped me in my scholarship examination as I was lucky enough to be set a question covering the sort of ecological work that I had done. It also may have brought home to me the powerful physiological effects of a hostile ionic environment in which only the most thoroughly adapted plants can survive.

Getting a scholarship emboldened me to visit my future Director of Studies in Trinity, Dr. Carl Pantin, an experimental zoologist of great charm and distinction. I asked him what I should do in the nine months before I came to Cambridge and he gave me some excellent advice, which I had the sense to follow. The advice was that in my last term at school I should do no more biology but should concentrate on mathematics, physics, and German. He also said "You must continue to learn mathematics," and this I have endeavored to do during the rest of my life, or at any rate until a year or two ago. For a long time my bibles were Mellor's *Higher Mathematics for Students of Chemistry and Physics* and Piaggio's *Differential Equations.* But I cannot claim to have done all the examples in Piaggio, as another admirer of that work, Freeman Dyson, (2) has evidently done.

I told Pantin that I was going to a German family in June and July but that I would like to spend May of that year at a Biological Research Station. I suggested the marine laboratory at Plymouth, where I had once been on a schoolboys' course; but Pantin thought a shy eighteen year old would be lost in a relatively large laboratory like the one at Plymouth. He suggested that I go to the Freshwater Biological Station, which had just been set up at Wray Castle on Lake Windermere and was directed by two young men, Philip Ullyott and R. S. A. Beauchamp. I jumped at the idea, not least because it would provide an opportunity (as it happened probably the only one in my life) of spending May in the Lake District.

This was my first experience of research and a fairly odd one at that. Wray Castle was a large, ivy-covered, Gothic-revival castle built in the 19th century on the western shore of Lake Windermere. It was large enough to house many scientists but was otherwise utterly unsuitable as a laboratory. There was also something strange about the work being done there. Beauchamp was carrying out fairly standard freshwater ecology, but Ullyott was trying to find out how a light-shunning planarian (*Dendrocoelum lacteum*) moved down a nondirectional light gradient (3). This sounds straightforward enough, but Ullyott had managed to build up a reputation for black magic in the quite rural community outside the castle. He worked in a cellar wearing a black cloak and mask in order to make certain that no stray light reached his apparatus, in which all rays were supposed to be normal to the plate on which the planarians crawled. At the time I admired these precautions, but I have wondered since whether they were not partly done for their dramatic effect. Later on when Ullyott moved to Cambridge after being elected to a Trinity Fellowship his colleagues in Zoology tended to laugh at his methods and had no particular respect for the problem he was trying to solve. This is sad because Ullyott's experiments were interesting and his theory of movement in a light gradient was very like that advanced some forty years later by Berg and others to explain bacterial chemotaxis (4).

Ullyott suggested that I should study the effect of temperatures on another planarian, *Polycelis nigra* and in particular should see if the animals congregated at the cold end of a temperature gradient. I spent some time building an incredible haywire apparatus but reached no definite conclusions except that the animals did congregate in the cold and that this was only partly explained by the fact that they moved faster in the warm. Six months later I tried to continue the work in the spare bathroom at home but nothing concrete came from this, apart from the disturbance to our guests.

Just before I left Windermere, Ullyott told me teasingly that I had rescued his reputation in the local community, first by playing village cricket and second by going to church. As I am almost as bad about going to church as I am at playing cricket I can only attribute these astonishing facts (which I have verified in an old letter) to the persuasive powers of the local vicar, whom I dimly remember as a most engaging old boy.

CAMBRIDGE 1932–1937

After leaving Windermere I managed to learn some German in Frankfurt but did no more science until I came to Cambridge in the autumn of 1932. I felt very young and nervous but soon started to enjoy life. I had not been seriously unhappy at school but I much preferred the holidays and it came as a pleasant surprise to find that I looked forward to the beginning of term instead of dreading it.

Carl Pantin advised me to take Physiology with Chemistry and Zoology for the first two years. He suggested that I give up Botany, which I was reluctant to do as it had been my best subject in the scholarship examination. However, after going to one or two lectures, I concluded that Pantin was right and gave up the subject quite happily. Physiology, then combined with Biochemistry, was new and exciting, particularly in the experimental classroom. The regular lectures, except for some of Barcroft's and Winton's, were not brilliant, but I remember superb lectures by Krebs on the ornithine cycle and by Adrian on referred pain. I enjoyed Zoology supervisions (tutorials) with Pantin in the evening in Trinity, and it was a great disappointment when a serious attack of tuberculosis took him away from Cambridge for nearly two years. In Physiology Roughton was less conscientious as a teacher, but if you stuck to carbonic anhydrase and hemoglobin you could learn a great deal.

The scholarship exam I had taken a year before was a pretty stiff hurdle and I soon realized that I had already done a great deal of the Part I syllabus in Zoology and Chemistry. I was too diffident of my own abilities actually to cut lectures but found that I had a reasonable amount of time for library reading, either in math and physics or in general physiology and cytology. Some of the books that influenced me particularly were those by A. V. Hill, E. D. Adrian, James Gray, and J. B. S. Haldane. I also went on a vacation course to Plymouth and learned more invertebrate zoology there than in a whole year at Cambridge. This was partly because I have always disliked seeing the delicate beauty of marine creatures transformed into the formalin-pickled relics of the museum or zoological dissecting room.

After six months at Cambridge I became a member of the Natural Science Club, a small elitist organization which was founded in 1872 and in 1981 celebrated its 2500th meeting. The active members of this society were all junior members of the university (either undergraduates or research students). The club took itself pretty seriously, having elaborate rules, minutes, and weekly meetings at which someone read a paper for an hour or so. Some of the active members in my day were Edward Bullard, John Pringle, Dick Synge, Maurice Wilkins, and Andrew Huxley. I am afraid that I have never been a particularly clubbable person but I thoroughly enjoyed this club and it did much to counter the narrowness that is necessarily associated with studying one branch of science in depth at a university. The printed record of the club's proceedings makes interesting reading. You find that the subjects chosen for student papers are often those that scientists take up many years later, probably without remembering their early interest. Here are some examples: Synge, protein structures, techniques in biochemistry, cystine, distillation; Wilkins, mirrors, watches and clocks, seeing structures; Huxley, the ear and its functions, the conduction of nervous impulses, the use of the microscope, experiments on single cells; Hodgkin, nature of cell surface, membrane theory of nervous action, the behavior of sense organs, light-reception, and nerve-muscle function.

When the Physiological Society met in Cambridge, anyone keen enough was allowed to sneak into the audience and I remember a splendid debate on humoral transmission with Henry Dale, G. L. Brown, and Feldberg on one side and Jack Eccles on the other. My scientific sympathies were wholly on the side of acetylcholine but I thought Eccles put up a good fight. In May 1934 I was lucky enough to be present on the famous occasion when Adrian and Matthews demonstrated the effect of opening the eyes or of mental arithmetic on the Berger rhythm, using Adrian as a subject. (His rhythm was unusually responsive.)

I had difficulty deciding whether to read Physiology or Zoology in Part II. I preferred the former but was advised that there was little prospect of my getting a job unless I was medically qualified. There was a good deal of force in this argument, for Cambridge, one of the few universities that accepted nonmedical physiologists, already had more than its share of these, as Rushton found when Barcroft offered him a lectureship on condition that he spend three or four years getting a medical degree. Nevertheless Roughton strongly advised me to take up physiology, and this is what I did in the end. But I am not sure that I would have had the courage to make this decision if I had not been left a legacy that brought in about £300 a year. This does not seem much now, but it was enough to live on in those days.

After finishing the Part II Physiology course in 1935, I received a research scholarship from Trinity and settled down to study the blocked impulse effect, which I had come across a year before. I have written a brief history of this work in "Chance and Design," so here I shall use the space to give a picture of life in the Physiological Laboratory as it was in the 1930s.

The building we occupied was put up in 1912 with £20,000 given by the Draper's Company. Though not a thing of beauty, the old building has proved immensely serviceable and, with additions in every direction, is still the home of Cambridge physiology. A lecture theater and a new wing were added in the middle 1930s, but I have no clear memory of timing or of the disturbance the addition must have caused.

The head of the laboratory was Joseph Barcroft, who had succeeded Langley as Professor in 1925. I learned later that he was nicknamed Soapy Joe by some and that there were those who regarded him as a tricky character. But I saw nothing of this and he treated me with great kindness and friendliness, right up to the day he died when running to catch a bus after working late in the laboratory at the age of 75. Barcroft's enthusiasm was infectious and I admired *The Respiratory Function of the Blood* (5) as well as his splendid review on "La fixité du milieu intérieur" (6) which provided me with the kind of philosophical background to physiology that I then felt I needed.

When I finished writing my first paper in 1937 I took the manuscript to Barcroft and asked if it needed his approval before I sent it to a journal. He was quite taken aback and explained first that we did not do that sort of thing in Cambridge and, second, that anything I wrote was entirely my own affair. The only time I remember his getting cross was when I rather tactlessly asked him if he wanted me to light the way to the door late one evening. He said, indignantly, that after 30 years he could find his way around the lab with his eyes shut. My concern was understandable, because the basement where we were was pitch-black and unless you were careful you were liable to fall into a large bath containing bloody saline and a dead sheep on which a caesarian operation had been performed earlier in the day. But they were Barcroft's sheep and I suppose he knew where they were. This was after the war, perhaps in 1946–47.

I do not think there were any laboratory secretaries or typists in prewar days, though I have a mental picture of the chief assistant operating with one finger on a very old-fashioned typewriter in the office next door to Barcroft's lab. His name was Secker and both his son and grandson, now head of our machineshop, have worked in the same laboratory. Old Secker was an ex-sergeant major and had a fine military moustache. He looked irascible but wasn't, except when struggling with the lab accounts. If you were sensible you did not ask him for anything at the end of the financial year when the auditors were around. ("They have me sweating," he used to say.)

There were no centralized laboratory stores and if you wanted a valve or an electrical component you went to a local wireless shop that provided components for several laboratories. You might be able to scrounge nuts and bolts or sheet metal from the workshop but it was generally better to go to one of the local ironmongers, as we call hardware stores in England. Mr. Hall, the machinist in the workshop, was often busy with class equipment; but if you could persuade him to make something for you it worked pretty well, and his ideas about design were generally better than yours. I think we were allowed to spend about £30 per annum, which was quite a lot in those days. If you wanted anything more, or needed your manuscript typed in the town, you paid for it yourself. It was some time before I realized that one might be able to get a grant from a research council or from the Royal Society.

I think that I first met Adrian in 1933 at Seatoller in the Lake District where a long-standing tradition takes a party of Trinity students and dons for a few days at the end of the summer term. I have a clear memory of him as a figure in a mackintosh cape running swiftly downhill, emerging briefly from the mist and then disappearing again as another cloud swirled up the Ennerdale valley. Three years later I had the alarming experience of being driven by him from Cambridge to the Lake District at what then seemed a terrifying speed. I am afraid that by modern standards Adrian would be considered a dangerous driver because he relied to a great extent on the quickness of his reflexes to avoid accidents. Indeed this did not always work, as I found on another occasion when he ran into a taxi in Trafalgar Square. As a young man driven by his Professor I kept my mouth shut but was surprised to find that Adrian's command of language was quite equal to that of the taxi driver.

Adrian regarded the Physiological Laboratory as a place to work and we rarely talked there for more than a few minutes. After I had given a lab seminar about my nerve-block experiments in 1936 I remember him saying "Why not work on crab nerve?" which was advice I took. On another occasion he did not actually say anything but managed to show his disapproval of the way I had soldered a joint by rushing out of the workshop with a muttered curse.

Although Adrian was not given to obvious enthusiasms you could see that he was really pleased if you told him about some technical advance such as isolating a single crab fiber or getting a microelectrode into a cell. This was very encouraging. In addition, of course, I owe Adrian a great debt for all he did to promote my scientific career. I am sure that he was largely responsible for my becoming a University Demonstrator and Teaching Fellow at Trinity in 1938, as well as for a great deal of help after the war. But it was not possible to thank him for such things and I know that if I had tried he would have choked me off at once.

As a research student I did not have a formal supervisor, but there were plenty of people one could talk to about technical matters, including Bryan Matthews and Grey Walter in Physiology and Rawdon-Smith in Psychology. On the theoretical side I learned a lot from William Rushton, with whom I did a joint piece of work in 1939. Victor Rothschild, who was then working in Zoology on fertilization, lent me apparatus from time to time and had a considerable influence on my life by softening the strongly puritanical streak I had acquired from my Quaker upbringing. The Rothschilds were infinitely hospitable and gave splendid parties, sometimes illuminated with fireworks, at their beautiful house on the Backs in Cambridge. This provided a welcome change from political discussion or gloomy contemplation of the international scene, these being two of the principal occupations of most of young Cambridge in the late 1930s.

Another person who helped me in many ways was A. V. Hill. Polly and

David, his two elder children, were close friends of mine, and I sometimes stayed with the Hills at their country cottage near Plymouth when working there in the summer. On the first of these occasions in 1935, Charles Fletcher and I camped in the garden but on the second (July 1939) I stayed in the house, as can be seen from the following extract from a letter to my mother, which I now find entertaining: "There was a rather holy atmosphere over the weekend as A. V. Hill came down bringing with him Sir William Bragg. A. V. is Secretary and Sir Wm. President of the Royal Society. They are both quite friendly and easy but all the same I felt that to have the President and Secretary of the Royal Society in one house was a bit too much of a good thing."

And while we are on the subject, perhaps I can quote from another letter from the same period in which the Royal Society gets a slightly better write-up.

Langmuir's lecture at the Royal Society was excellent. He is one of the few scientists who have been able to think out immediate practical applications of their discoveries. And his experiments are always so beautifully simple that you wonder why on earth no one ever thought of doing the same thing before. The Royal Society is always amusing. The rather pompous rooms, the royal mace and the charters going back to Charles II all give it a very dignified air. Langmuir is an American and his address was an amusing contrast to the R. S. politeness and Bragg's dignified and rather wordy presidential address. After 5 minutes of flowing sentences and sentiments about the traditions of English and American science it was nice to hear Langmuir begin "Ladies and Gentlemen, if you put a piece of camphor on water...." (11 December 1938)

One of the advantages Plymouth shares with Woods Hole is that you meet people from other laboratories and disciplines. I got to know J. Z. Young at Plymouth and also Bernard Katz, with both of whom I have kept in close touch all my life. In prewar days scientific meetings meant little to me. I went to the Physiological Society from time to time but never attended a large international meeting until the Oxford congress in 1947. For this reason informal contacts such as those I made at Plymouth or later at Woods Hole were particularly important.

As Trinity College was responsible for founding the Cambridge school of physiology by bringing Michael Foster there in 1870, I may perhaps be forgiven for extending these reminiscences to include some anecdotes about the scientists who belonged there. When I came up in 1932 the Master was the legendary Sir Joseph Thomson (J. J.), who is best known for his measurements of the mass and charge of the electron. He was then aged 76 and full of life, though becoming increasingly eccentric. Mr. Prior, who until a year ago was Head Porter at Trinity, remembers that one of his first duties as a junior porter was to rescue the Master, who had been misled by the newfangled open display of goods in a well-known chainstore, from an accusation of shoplifting. The shop in question couldn't believe that anyone so shabbily dressed could be Master of Trinity, and Mr. Prior looked so young that he had difficulty convincing them of J. J.'s position. However, all ended well and the shop realized that J. J. thought 'Help yourself counter' meant what it said. Soon after I arrived at Trinity a group of new scholars were invited to dine at the Lodge. In my letter home I reported that this awe-inspiring occasion was relieved by a comic episode. After dinner the Master turned on the wireless to some "rather vulgar" dance music. Apparently he was very pleased with this and went around chuckling to himself, but Lady Thomson who was extremely conventional, was shocked. She transported as many scholars as possible to another part of the room.

The only other time that I can remember dining with J. J. was just after I had become a research fellow in 1936. One of the guests was Enoch Powell, also a research fellow but two years my senior. At that time he had no interest in politics but worked at classics with a single-minded ferocity that I have never seen equalled. One of his heroes was Bentley, the famous classical scholar and friend of Newton, who had managed to remain Master of Trinity from 1700 to 1742 in spite of the strenuous efforts of the Fellows to have him impeached and ejected. At dinner Powell insisted that Bentley was the best Master that Trinity had ever had. Lady Thomson did not like this at all, partly because she disapproved of Bentley's scandalous conduct and partly because she had no doubt that J. J. was better than any former Master. As we left she said severely to me, "Really, Mr. Powell, I do think Mr. Hodgkin's views on Bentley are too distressing for words." I was never asked to dine again, but one dinner as a research fellow was the ration so I must not complain.

I gradually got to know Trinity's great men, of whom Rutherford was the most dominating. He divided science into physics and stamp-collecting but made an honorary exception of physiology and was extremely nice to me. He had a tremendously loud voice, which could be heard all over the College dining hall, and hated anything that interfered with his weekend golf. I remember the indignation with which he spoke at a college meeting called for a Saturday afternoon to decide whether or not to give £1000 for a squash court at a women's college. "Of course we must give it," he said, "and not waste a beautiful summer afternoon debating this futile topic like a bunch of schoolgirls"—or something of the kind. This did not go down well with some of the elderly bachelor dons, but Rutherford won the day as he usually did.

When I got back to Cambridge in the autumn of 1938 after a year in America I found myself living in a beautiful set of rooms above F. W. Aston, the inventor of the mass-spectrograph and the discoverer of many isotopes. He was a complete contrast to Rutherford—a quiet bachelor with extremely regular habits but, like Rutherford, pleasant and friendly to his junior colleagues. He hated noise and, alarmed at the prospect of a young man living above him, went to the trouble of soundproofing his ceiling before my return. I thought this unnecessary but I fear he may have been justified. I remember him appearing in a dressing gown to complain gently about noise on the occasion when a friend and I entertained some of the Sadlers Wells Ballet at the end of their fortnight in Cambridge. There used to be many anecdotes about the Thomson-Rutherford-Aston trio. Someone should write them down before they are forgotten, but the *Annual Review of Physiology* is clearly not the place to do so.

NEW YORK AND WOODS HOLE 1937–1938

Fairly soon after being elected to a Trinity Research Fellowship, in the autumn of 1936, I received a letter from Herbert Gasser, then Director of the Rockefeller Institute in New York, inviting me to work in his laboratory during 1937–38. I also learned that I had been awarded a travelling fellowship by the Rockefeller Foundation. This enabled me to spend a most productive year in America, working mainly in Gasser's Laboratory, where I joined a small group consisting of Grundfest, Lorente de Nó, Toennies, and Hursch. I was able to travel and in the early summer worked with Cole and Curtis at Woods Hole, where they introduced me to the squid giant axon.

During my last few months in Cambridge I had found that it wasn't too difficult to isolate single nerve fibers from the shore crab *Carcinus maenas,* and had shown that there were transitional stages in the initiation of the nerve impulse: subthreshold responses with properties similar to those Katz and Rushton had deduced from their studies of excitation. For some time Gasser was skeptical about subthreshold activity, but he provided me with a room and equipment and didn't mind my continuing on my own. No one at the Rockefeller had heard of *Carcinus,* and I assumed the genus did not occur in America. I tried several kinds of edible crab, but in none were the fibers as robust or easy to dissect as in *Carcinus.* After some frustrating weeks I visited the Natural History Museum where I learned that *Carcinus maenas* was common on the Eastern Seaboard and that I could obtain a supply from Woods Hole. This failed in mid-winter, but by then I had arranged to have a consignment sent from Plymouth on the *Queen Mary.*

The Rockefeller Institute, which was full of distinguished people, was a somewhat formal place and I missed the free and easy life of the Cambridge laboratories. At lunchtime the great men led their teams to separate tables. You could see little processions led by Landsteiner, Carrel, Avery, or P. A. Levene. In addition to Gasser's own group the people who influenced me most were Osterhout (large plant cells), Michaelis (membranes), MacInnes and Shedlovsky (electrochemistry), as well as Peyton Rous and his family on the personal side. I met Cole and Curtis at Columbia University and they invited me to Woods Hole in the summer. In "Chance and Design" I have given an account of this visit, which had a strong influence on my scientific life. I shall not say more about it here, except to quote, again, from a letter to my mother:

> Woods Hole . . . consists of a very large laboratory and a small fishing village. It is a nice place. The village is on a little bay and you look across a smooth sea to islands, promontories and distant sand dunes. It reminds me vaguely of Blakeney or Scolt Head —mainly because of the continued screaming of terns in the harbour. I came because some scientists here (Dr. Cole and collaborators) have been getting most exciting results on the giant nerve fibres of the squid (7). As you know I spend my time working with single nerve fibres from crabs which are only 1/1000 of an inch thick. Well the squid has one fiber which is about 50 times larger than mine and Cole has been using this and getting results which made everyone else's look silly. Their results are almost too exciting because it is a little disturbing to see the answers to experiments that you have planned to do coming out so beautifully in someone else's hands. No, I dont really mind this at all [sic], what I do dislike is the fact that at present English laboratories can't catch squids so that I dont see any prospect of being able to do this myself.

In fact Young, Pumphrey & Schmitt (8) got the squid supply going at Plymouth that summer (1938), and Huxley and I worked on squid there the following year.

Someone, probably Herbert Gasser, had suggested that the Rockefeller Foundation might provide me with a grant to buy or build a modern set of electronic equipment. Toennies helped me to prepare a list of things I might need. Before I left New York I was electrified to find that I might receive an equipment grant of £300, a very large sum in those days.

CAMBRIDGE-PLYMOUTH 1938–1939

When I got back to Cambridge I joined forces with A. F. Rawdon-Smith, K. J. W. Craik, and R. S. Sturdy in Psychology. Between us we built three or four sets of equipment, some of which were still in use 25 years later. Rawdon-Smith designed the d.c. amplifier. I had help from Toennies on cathode followers, from Otto Schmitt on multivibration, and from Matthews on the camera and many other details. I also had a certain amount of teaching to do. At Trinity I gave tutorials in Physiology and had the good fortune to teach some brilliant people, including Andrew Huxley in his fourth year and Richard Keynes in his first. In the Physiological Laboratory I gave a course of lectures on the cell surface and helped with two practical classes, one on electrophysiology and one mammalian class for which I had to get up early to prepare six or seven decerebrate cats for the Undergraduates to use later. This wasn't something I enjoyed.

I got my equipment going by mid-January 1939 and started to measure the relative size of resting and action potentials using external electrodes. This led to the internal electrode experiments, carried out with Huxley at Plymouth, which showed that the action potential might exceed the resting potential by some 40 mV. There was obviously much to be done with the new technique, and it was a bitter disappointment when Hitler marched into Poland and war was declared on September 3, 1939. We left the equipment at Plymouth in the faint hope that the war might soon be over and that we could continue the experiments. In the event the war lasted six years and it was eight years before it was possible to return to Plymouth.

AVIATION MEDICINE, RADAR 1939–1945

Although I had been brought up as a Quaker, Hitler removed all my pacifist beliefs. I was anxious to do some kind of military service as soon as possible. I was pleased when Bryan Matthews offered me a temporary post at the Royal Aircraft Establishment Farnborough, where he had been working for several months on Aviation Medicine. There were two major problems to worry about. At that time aircraft were not pressurized and at high altitudes aircrew were kept going by breathing a mixture of air and oxygen. The oxygen was stored at about 100 atmospheres in small cylinders. Many cylinders had to be carried on a long flight, and their weight became a serious problem. What made matters worse was that an oxygen cylinder takes off like a rocket when hit by a bullet. After a few weeks we learned that the Germans had solved the problem by means of a very beautifully designed lung-controlled device, of which we obtained a sample early in the war. Matthews rightly felt that it would be extremely difficult to get such a device mass-produced quickly in Britain. We also thought that the RAF with its brave but individualistic traditions would not take kindly to the strict discipline required in wearing a tightly fitting mask. One of the difficulties at that time was to persuade aircrew to take oxygen at all. They felt that if mountaineers could get to 27,000 feet on Everest without oxygen, they should not have to bother with it at 20,000 feet. These considerations led us to design and build an oxygen economizer that blew oxygen into the pilot's mask when he inspired but not during the rest of the respiratory cycle. This got into service about a year later and was widely used by the RAF. A modified form was used by Hilary and Tensing in their first ascent of Everest in 1951.

The other question that concerned us was whether bubbles of nitrogen came out of the blood and produced bends at high altitudes. Matthews and I proved this the hard way by sitting in a decompression chamber evacuated to the equivalent of 40,000 feet (about one fifth of an atmosphere) breathing pure oxygen to keep us going and waiting till something happened. High altitude bends seem to come on more slowly than the decompression bends that divers used to experience, but you get them all right in the end—and very unpleasant they are, too.

I met Patrick Blackett at Farnborough. Partly through him and partly through A. V. Hill I eventually got a job with one of the teams developing centimeter radar for the RAF. This research, which occupied me for the next five years, was interesting and important; but we worked too hard, and there were too many accidents and tragedies for it to be enjoyable. The best thing that happened to me was that in 1944 I was sent for two months as a liaison officer to the MIT Radiation Laboratory. My work took me to New York, and there I married Peyton Rous's daughter Marion, whom I had first met in 1937. The authorities in Britain complained that I hadn't been sent to America to get married, but by then they'd been presented with a *fait accompli.*

GETTING BACK; CAMBRIDGE-PLYMOUTH 1945–1947

Towards the end of 1944 my work on radar slackened off and I started working on physiology again in the evenings and at weekends. I was released from military service soon after the end of the German war and my wife, small daughter, and I returned to Cambridge at the end of July 1945. Cambridge looked as beautiful as ever, but although I was mad keen to start research it was as difficult to get going in the Laboratory as it was to set up house. In six months' time universities were to be flooded with a great mass of war-surplus equipment, but to begin with there was nothing in the Laboratory and very little in the shops. I remember hunting for a piece of insulated sleeving. Eventually I found what I thought was a suitable piece in a drawer of miscellaneous electrical components. I was surprised to find that the object I held in my hand was tapered and seemed stiffer than I expected. I looked at it with a binocular microscope and was amazed at the intricate design I saw. Why on earth, I thought, should anyone go to so much trouble to make a flexible tube out of those beautifully articulated joints, and how difficult it must be to mass-produce such an object. Then I realized that what I was looking at was a lobster feeler that had fallen into the drawer and lain there since the days when I'd worked on lobsters before the war.

Some of the equipment that I had left at Plymouth was damaged in an air raid, but I managed to salvage a good deal. Fortunately I had lent the racks of electronic equipment to Rawdon-Smith and R. S. Sturdy, and they had removed them before the bad air raids began. Somehow or other I managed to collect everything and get the equipment going well enough to start experiments on *Carcinus* axons.

E. D. Adrian had obtained my release from military service on the grounds that he needed help with teaching. This was true, for the laboratory still had its full quota of medical students and many members of staff were away. One of my first jobs was to lecture on Human Physiology to student nurses. This was good practice, but not enjoyable. The nurses were in the charge of a fearsome-looking matron, and I couldn't get a flicker out of them. I felt better when Adrian, who had been giving the lectures before, told me he'd had the same experience.

Adrian let me off with a light teaching load, but I found it much harder to give tutorials than before the war. This was partly because I had forgotten a good deal and partly because I had ceased to believe in many of the principles that had once seemed to hold physiology together. The constancy of the internal environment remained as important as it had ever been, but the ways in which constancy was achieved had become much more complicated. It was also clear that much that I had read and taught before the war had been wildly oversimplified, if not downright wrong. An example is the hierarchical arrangement of respiratory centers postulated by Lumsden in the 1920s. I suppose that after five years working as a physicist I had little use for biological generalizations and always wanted to concentrate on the physicochemical approach to physiology. This doesn't go down well with most medical students.

After a rocky start my experiments on *Carcinus* began to go well. They went even better after Andrew Huxley returned to Cambridge from the Admiralty in 1945. Professor Adrian, who was head of the Department, obtained a grant of £3,000 per annum from the Rockefeller Foundation which helped to support a group working on the biophysics of nerve and muscle. The original members of the "unit" were D. K. Hill, A. F. Huxley, and myself. We were soon joined by distinguished visitors from overseas, of whom R. Stampfli and S. Weidmann were among the earliest.

I returned to Plymouth in the summer of 1947, soon after the Laboratory acquired a trawler to replace the one taken away at the beginning of the war. To begin with I was on my own as Andrew Huxley was getting married and Bernard Katz wasn't free till September. Life was not easy. Much of the Laboratory had been destroyed in the great air raids of 1941 and was being rebuilt, squid were in short supply, my hotel was squalid, and it was difficult to get enough to eat. But I was terribly pleased to be back where we had left off in 1939 and very excited when the sodium experiments started to come out so well. I don't think one ever stops trying to learn new things in science, and embarking on a new piece of work feels like starting research all over again. But in a general way Plymouth 1947 marks the end of the beginning and this was the time when I forgave fate for robbing me of what I once thought might have been the best years of my scientific life.

Literature Cited

1. Hodgkin, A. L. 1976. Chance and design in electrophysiology, an informal account of experiments carried out between 1934 and 1952. *J. Physiol. London* 263:1–21
2. Dyson, F. J. 1980. *Disturbing the Universe.* NY: Harper & Row
3. Ullyott, P. 1936. The behaviour of *Dendrocoelum lacteum.* II. Responses in non-directional gradients. *J. Exp. Biol.* 13:265–78
4. Berg, H. C. 1975. Chemotaxis in bacteria. *Ann. Rev. Biophys. Bioeng.* 4:119–36

5. Barcroft, J. 1914. *The Respiratory Function of the Blood.* London: Cambridge Univ. Press
6. Barcroft, J. 1932. 'La fixité du milieu intérieur est la condition de la vie libre' (Claude Bernard). *Biol. Rev.* 7:24–87
7. Cole, K. S., Curtis H. J. 1939. Electric impedance of the squid giant axon during activity. *J. Gen. Physiol.* 22:649–70
8. Pumphrey, R. J., Schmitt, O. H., Young, J. Z. 1940. Correlation of local excitability with local physiological response in the giant axon of the squid (*Loligo*). *J. Physiol. London* 98:47–72

ENDOCRINOLOGY AND METABOLISM

Introduction, Dorothy T. Krieger, *Section Editor*

The themes of this year's section are those of (*a*) enzymes as modifiers of steroid and thyroid hormone action, and (*b*) peptide hormones: their synthesis, processing, regulation, and function.

Over the past decade, this section of the Annual Review of Physiology has dealt with the elucidation of hormone action in the domains of hormone receptor binding, nuclear translocation of the hormone receptor complex, its DNA binding and subsequent genomic activation. However, a number of other factors influence hormone action and have been the subject of active recent investigation. Some of these are considered in the first four chapters of this section. Dr. Fevold reviews mechanisms for regulating microsomal enzyme activity (induction, indirect and direct modulation by steroids, and phosphorylation). Such regulation alters the rate of reactions important in determining both the quantity of production of a given steroid and the identity of the steroid produced in a given glandular compartment. Hormone action can also be altered by enzymatic biotransformation (i.e. as discussed in Volume 43, 1981, for Vitamin D) and is here critically considered by Dr. Fishman for the instance of estrogen hydroxylation, in which such products may act via pathways not mediated by estrogen receptors. Another factor influencing hormone action, considered in the chapter by Gustafsson, Mode, Norstedt & Skett, is that of sexual dimorphism of steroid-metabolizing enzymes. This appears to be a pituitary-dependent phenomenon, involving sexual differences in the level and pattern of growth-hormone secretion. Roy & Chatterjee also consider the roles of such sexual dimorphism in the maintenance of reproductive competence, and both of the latter two chapters consider the role of sexual dimorphism in the neonatal imprinting that leads to altered hormone responses in adulthood. Such sexual dimorphism, in addition to influencing the effects of hormones, may be important in human pharmacology, affecting the dimorphic metabolism of drugs.

A description of peptide hormones in brain, some of which have previously been isolated in nonneural tissues, has raised questions about their source and physiological function. Dr. Pardridge critically reviews the factors governing modes of entry of peptides from the periphery into the central nervous system (i.e. questions of lipid insolubility, degradative enzymes, first-pass extraction efficiency, presence of receptors), as well as evidence for anteluminal peptidases that may degrade material released from brain. Conversely, peptides originally described in brain have been demonstrated in extra-CNS tissues. Hsueh & Jones discuss the evidence for the synthesis and local action of extrahypothalamic gonadotropin-releasing hormone. The question of whether integrated physiological actions of the CNS and peripheral forms of a given hormone exist, as in the case of somatostatin and glucoregulation, is considered by Dr. Frohman, together with the multiplicity of CNS and gastrointestinal interactions of neurotransmitters and other CNS and extra-CNS peptides involved in such glucoregulation. Although neural regulation of prolactin secretion has been extensively studied (mostly with regard to inhibition), there is also evidence for neural peptidergic stimulatory factors whose nature has not been clarified. These are reviewed by Leong, Frawley & Neill, who also consider other factors that may mediate prolactin responsiveness at a pituitary level. Last, a major advance in peptide chemistry and physiology has been the demonstration that virtually all known secretory proteins are synthesized as parts of larger precursor molecules. After elucidation of their cDNA or genomic DNA structure, these may be revealed to contain thus far uncharacterized additional peptides. Dr. Brownstein's chapter summarizes current studies of such a precursor molecule for bovine vasopressin and neurophysin, pointing out the remaining questions common to a variety of secretory proteins derived from precursors, namely, how precursors move from the rough ER to the Golgi, and where the described processing reactions occur.

Ann. Rev. Physiol. 1983. 45:19–36

REGULATION OF THE ADRENAL AND GONADAL MICROSOMAL MIXED FUNCTION OXYGENASES OF STEROID HORMONE BIOSYNTHESIS

H. Richard Fevold

Chemistry Department, University of Montana, Missoula, Montana 59812

INTRODUCTION

The microsomal steroidogenic enzymes catalyze reactions important in determining both the quantity and the identity of glandular secretory products. By determining cell function, changes in the rates of these reactions can effect differentiation. The recognition of these control points in steroid hormone biosynthesis lagged because major research effort was directed at the rate-limiting reaction, mitochondrial cholesterol side-chain cleavage (140). The mechanism of the control of this site of tropic hormone action has been recently reviewed (132).

A cell can alter the rates of the individual steps in steroidogenesis in several ways. The two most thoroughly documented are at the extremes—modulation of gene expression and direct modulation of enzyme activity by inhibition. More nebulous and tantalizing are the possibilities for regulation of the amount of specific enzyme protein at a post-transcriptional or translation site and the regulation of enzyme activity or specificity by post-translational modification—either covalent or protein–protein interaction. The ubiquitous protein phosphorylation and the possible requirement for substrate binding specificity proteins to allow interaction with different substrates are the most obvious examples of the latter.

Here I review the control of the adrenal and gonadal microsomal mixed-function oxygenase enzymes that catalyze the reactions leading to the major

19

0066-4278/83/0315-0019$02.00

steroid secretory products. Although 3β-hydroxysteroid dehydrogenase (3β-HSD) is also an important steroidogenic regulatory enzyme (reviewed in 38), it has been omitted because of space limitations. I focus on the enzymes and their control, emphasizing the similarities and differences among the ovary, testis, and adrenal. Many excellent reviews emphasize steroidogenesis and its control in specific loci (15, 30, 48, 65, 82, 104, 109, 113, 118, 119, 133, 134, 143, 144).

21-HYDROXYLASE

21-Hydroxylase activity occurs both in adrenals and in gonads. No direct evidence exists for enzymes with differing substrate specificities in any single tissue. The existence of two types of congenital adrenal hyperplasia resulting from 21-hydroxylase deficiencies (9) can be explained as well by separate mutations on the same enzyme (108) as by different enzymes (75, 152). A reconstituted enzyme using a homogeneous P-450 preparation from bovine microsomes catalyzes hydroxylation of both 17α-hydroxyprogesterone and progesterone (57), and the reaction rates are approximately three times greater with 17α-hydroxprogesterone in assays with either crude microsomes or the reconstituted enzyme. Cortisol-producing species 21-hydroxylate 17α-hydroxyprogesterone more efficiently than progesterone (11, 93, 103). The substrate preference in corticosterone-producing species is variable (64, 78, 93, 108). Δ^5-3β-Hydroxysteroids are generally poor substrates (120), and we have not observed 21-hydroxylation of pregnenolone in enzyme assays with rabbit adrenal microsomes even when the competing 3β-HSD reaction is blocked with cyanoketone (44). Others, however, have reported significant 21-hydroxylation of pregnenolone by adrenal tissue from several other species (26, 86, 110, 150). Details of the characteristics and properties of 21-hydroxylase have been reviewed (21, 38).

Total 21-hydroxylase activity in rat adrenal microsomes decreases with a half-life of 4.5 days after hypophysectomy, while cytochrome P-450 in the same subcellular location has a 2.9 day half-life (115). The authors suggested either a pool of microsomal cytochrome P-450 not associated with 21-hydroxylase activity, or a rate-limiting step independent of the cytochrome as possible explanations for the discrepancy between the half-lives of enzyme activity and cytochrome. Rat adrenal microsomes have since been shown to contain a significant amount of aryl hydrocarbon hydroxylase and a corresponding cytochrome P-450 (51). Injection of 10 IU ACTH per day for 10 days commencing 14 days after hypophysectomy results in nearly a three-fold increase in 21-hydroxylase activity per two adrenal glands, and the specific activity increases from a value of 60% of normal in the hypophysectomized rats to values equivalent to the controls (115).

It is relevant to emphasize that this chronic stimulation with high doses of ACTH does not increase the specific activity above the control level. Others have reported no increase in rat (25) or rabbit (39, 137) 21-hydroxylase specific activities when intact animals are chronically stimulated with ACTH and enzyme activity is assayed in the presence of excess NADPH. The evidence for the maintenance of 21-hydroxylase and other adrenal microsomal enzyme levels by ACTH is firm; however, it is difficult to stimulate an increase in the specific activity of the enzyme above that found in the intact animal.

17α-HYDROXYLASE

17α-Hydroxylase activity occurs in significant amounts in all adrenal and gonadal steroidogenic cell types with the exception of Sertoli (19, 29, 63, 94) and glomerulosa (reviewed in 143). The adrenal and gonadal enzyme from cortisol-producing species appears to utilize pregnenolone in preference to progesterone (100, 154), thus reducing corticosterone formation via progesterone. Corticosterone-producing species, on the other hand, may have gonadal 17α-hydroxylase activities with relative specificity for either pregnenolone (5, 43) or progesterone (45). Nakajin & Hall (99) have reported the most highly purified enzyme preparation to date and suggest a single cytochrome responsible for both 17-hydroxylase and C-17,20 activities (101). However, the instances of independent expression and regulation of hydroxylase and lyase caution against concluding that a single protein with both enzyme activities exists in tissues other than neonatal pig testis. The general properties of the enzyme have recently been reviewed (38, 52).

Adrenal

On the basis of the ability of ACTH to elicit cortisol secretion by rabbits, Kass and co-workers (71) proposed an effect of tropic hormone stimulation on 17α-hydroxylase activity, and Krum & Glenn (74) suggested that the substrate for the stimulated 17-hydroxylase might be pregnenolone rather than progesterone. The pregnenolone subtrate preference and intermediate role of 17α-hydroxpregnenolone have since been verified experimentally (37, 43, 136). From rate measurements with microsome preparations we have shown that the K_m of the 17α-hydroxylase for pregnenolone is lower than that of 3β-HSD competing for the same substrate, explaining the preferential formation of cortisol after chronic ACTH stimulation (44.) This stimulatory action of ACTH on rabbit adrenal tissue is specific for 17α-hydroxylase activity with little if any effect on total adrenal microsomal 3β-HSD or 21-hydroxylase activities (39, 137, 153) and no consistent effect on microsomal cytochrome P-450 specific activity (44, 137; J. E. Peterson,

H. R. Fevold, unpublished); however, the enzyme is inhibited by carbon monoxide (44). The stimulation may be partially dependent on protein synthesis (40), but we have been unable to correlate changes in microsomal protein SDS-PAGE patterns with increases in 17α-hydroxylase activity when rabbits were stimulated for varying lengths of time with ACTH (J. E. Peterson, H. R. Fevold, unpublished).

ACTH preparations from pig, steer, and rabbit pituitaries as well as synthetic $ACTH_{1-24}$ stimulate rabbit 17α-hydroxylase (33, 42). Coslovsky & Yalow (22) suggested that stimulation of cortisol formation might be a property of the $ACTH_{1-39}$ molecule, as corticosterone-secreting species seemed to have a higher percentage of immunoreactive intermediate-sized pituitary ACTH. Later work (46, 47) has not supported this suggestion.

In at least two species in which adrenal 17α-hydroxylase is essentially inactive in adult animals, the activity is present in fetal or neonatal adrenals. The enzyme is active in fetal rabbit adrenals (17, 18, 56, 76, 89, 90, 98, 146), and Idler and co-workers (62) identified cortisol in plasma of embryonic chickens. The activity decreases in chick adrenal glands 7–14 days after hatching (102), but can be maintained by ACTH treatment (70).

Control of human adrenal 17α-hydroxylase activity during the adrenarche has been demonstrated by direct assay of microsomal enzyme activities in tissue from subjects of different ages (124). Adult 17α-hydroxylase specific activity slightly more than doubles and 3β-HSD-isomerase specific activity remains unchanged. The ratio of C-17,20 lyase to 17α-hydroxylase remains relatively constant in humans from post-natal to adult periods (124), while a 17α-hydroxylase increases in dog adrenals upon sexual maturation without significant changes in C-17,20 lyase activity (123).

Testis

The action of hCG to increase 17α-hydroxylase activity was originally observed subsequent to in vivo stimulation of both mammalian (1, 28, 125, 128) and avian (41) testes. It is unclear whether the increased activity was a result of specific stimulation of the enzyme or of preferential stimulation of Leydig cell proliferation as noted by Fevold & Eik-Nes (41) and Schoen & Samuels (125). LH injections have since been shown to increase testicular microsomal cytochrome P-450 levels in one-day-old chicks in parallel with increases in 17α-hydroxylase activity, although the increases in the cytochrome concentration is 2–3 times that of the enzyme activity (95). Dibutyryl-3',5'-adenosine monophosphate (Bt_2cAMP) administration also increases the cytochrome concentration, but neither progesterone nor pregnenolone has any effect (96). The latter finding suggests that the tropic hormone does not affect microsomal cytochrome levels by substrate induction or enzyme stabilization. Hypophysectomy of male rats results in decays of testicular microsomal 17α-hydroxylase and C-17,20 lyase activity and of cytochrome P-450 levels with half-lives for the major fraction of each being 2.3, 3.4, and 3.3 days, respectively (114). Daily hCG administration increases all three to above normal levels after four or more days (114). Neither the ratio of enzyme activity to microsomal cytochrome P-450 concentration nor the ratio of lyase to hydroxylase remains constant (114). Injections of hCG also increase cytochrome P-450, C-17,20 lyase, and 17α-hydroxylase activities in intact rat testis microsomes after 4–16 days of treatment; however, the initial response after two days of treatment is a decrease in all three parameters (91, 114). In this case activity of each enzyme per nanomole of cytochrome remains relatively constant after various periods of hCG stimulation. 17α-Hydroxylase varies from 1.9 to 3.2 and C-17,20 lyase varies from 0.92 to 1.27 nmol min^{-1} nmol^{-1}.

In addition to the long-term stimulatory effects of hCG on microsomal enzymes, intravenous injections reduce the capacity of rat Leydig cells to respond to subsequent tropic hormone stimulation of testosterone synthesis (reviewed in 15). This effect is due, in part, to a measured decrease in the activities of 17α-hydroxylase and C-17,20 lyase (106) and corresponds to the initial decrease in cytochrome P-450 concentration observed by Mason and co-workers (91). Because the effects on 17α-hydroxylase and C-17,20 lyase have not been clearly separated, they will be discussed together. The effect of hCG on rats is dose-dependent, accompanied by decreases in microsomal cytochrome P-450, demonstrable in both intact and hypophysectomized animals, and specific for the cytochrome-dependent enzymes (106); it lasts 60–96 hr after a single injection of 500 IU (16). The effect can also be correlated with an hCG-induced increase in testicular estradiol levels (92) and decreases in estrogen receptors (10), although this later decrease is not observed in immature rat testes (97). Estradiol administration mimics all of these hCG effects (10, 69, 92) and similarly reduces the response to subsequent gonadotropin stimulation in vivo and in vitro (105, 106). The lowering of enzyme activities after the addition of 17β-estradiol, LH, or hCG to rat Leydig cell cultures was assumed from observed increases in progesterone and 17α-hydroxyprogesterone accumulation and a reduction in testosterone accumulation (105). These inhibitory actions of gonadotropins are either unrelated or subsequent to their action on cAMP levels, as estradiol does not affect the cAMP response of Leydig cells to hCG (105).

The action of an estrogen antagonist, tamoxifen, in this system is controversial. It has been reported to be both effective (20) and ineffective (10) in blocking the hCG-induced inhibition of subsequent stimulation of steroidogenesis. Tamoxifen alone does not inhibit testosterone production (10). Nevertheless, prior addition to rat Leydig cell cultures blocks the inhibitory action of both gonadotropins and estradiol and prevents the induction of the synthesis of a 27,000 dalton protein that occurs concomitantly with the inhibition of the lyase activity (106). Studies in which testicular, spermatic, and peripheral venous concentrations of steroids were measured in humans also were consistent with inhibition of C-17,20 lyase and 17α-hydroxylase by prior 17β-estradiol or diethylstilbestrol administration (79); tamoxifen administration blocks this apparent inhibition (138).

Current data thus support a negative regulation of testosterone biosynthesis in Leydig cells by LH gonadotropins as a result of a stimulation of testicular estrogen synthesis. The negative regulation occurs subsequent to the acute stimulation but preceding the chronic stimulatory effect on microsomal enzyme levels. Estrogen acts directly to inhibit C-17,20 lyase activity and decrease testosterone synthesis, and the weight of evidence favors an additional action mediated by estrogen receptor interaction. The latter action is correlated with the induction of a 27,000 dalton protein (106). These data elucidate the findings of Samuels and co-workers (121) with regard to the inhibitory effects of estradiol on testicular androgen production.

Ovary

Pregnant mare serum gonadotropin (PMSG) injections increase rat ovarian 17α-hydroxylase specific activity (67), but the activity in isolated granulosa cells is not increased by LH, FSH, or prolactin addition to the incubation medium. Low concentrations of phospholipase A_2, arachidonic acid, or prostaglandin E_2 (PGE_2) stimulate, while indomethacin inhibits, the in vitro activity assayed by measuring the appearance of tritium from 17α-^{3}H-progesterone in ^3H_2O. The degree of stimulation is relatively small and ranges from approximately 10% by arachidonate to 50% by phospholipase. Histamine also increases the activity ($\sim$ 40%), while higher concentrations of phospholipase or arachidonate inhibit the enzyme (68). The LH surge in female rats has been suggested to be responsible for a decrease in 17α-hydroxylase/17,20-lyase activities in preovulatory follicles; follicular atresia presumably results from the loss of estrogen production required for follicular maintenance (2).

C-17,20 LYASE

The cleavage of a two-carbon acetic acid unit from 17α-hydroxylated C_{21}-Δ^4- or -Δ^5-compounds occurs in the microsomal fraction of gonads (130) and adrenals (123, 124). The cytochrome P-450 component from both neonatal pig [(99); see discussion in the 17α-Hydroxylase section, above] and rat testes (6) has been purified and used to reconstitute active enzymes.

The cellular locations and properties of the enzyme have been reviewed (38, 52).

Testis

Unlabeled progesterone inhibits C_{19}-steroid formation from labeled 17α-hydroxyprogesterone (87,100), although prior 17α-hydroxylation of the purported inhibitor and resulting isotope dilution of the substrate are suspected. Both 20α-and 20β-dihydroprogesterone inhibit utilization of Δ^4-and Δ^5-substrates with K_i values near 10^{-6} M (7, 58, 100). The 20α-reduction product of 17α-hydroxyprogesterone, $17\alpha,20\alpha$-dihydroxy-4-pregnen-3-one, competitively inhibits the neonatal pig enzyme but is 20 times less effective than the reduced progesterones. No significant levels of $17\alpha,20\alpha$- dihydroxy-4-pregnen-3-one could be found in rat testes, however (24). Pig (107) and human (58) testicular lyase preparations are inhibited by 17β-estradiol with K_i values between 3×10^{-5} and 5×10^{-6}M. Estradiol also produces a type I binding difference spectrum and competes with lyase substrates in this regard (107). The concentration of 17β-estradiol in neonatal pig testis is of the same order of magnitude as the K_i value for C-17,20 lyase (107), suggesting a possible physiological role.

Early experiments demonstrated that hCG stimulation could increase C-17,20 lyase activity in testicular interstitial tissue (14, 27, 125). Shikita & Hall refined the enzyme assays and demonstrated that hCG stimulation is effective only in immature animals (128, 129); however, it was not clear whether stimulation was increasing the enzyme in the Leydig cells or increasing the percentage of Leydig cells in the testis. A single injection of 500 IU hCG produces marked increases in lyase activity measured in the microsomal fraction of adult rat Leydig cells (16). The increase correlates with rises in plasma and testicular testosterone levels and with the appearance of a cytoplasmic enzyme activator. The control of testicular microsomal cytochrome P-450 and C-17,20 lyase levels in one-day-old chicks, hypophysectomized rats, and intact rats as well as the gonadotropin effect to decrease testicular Leydig cell lyase activity by estrogen mediation were discussed in the 17α-Hydroxylase section, above.

Ovary

Treatment of immature female rats with a single injection of 10 IU PMSG results in an apparent doubling in total ovarian C-17,20 lyase activity. Subsequent inducement of ovulation with hCG returns the value to preinjection levels and decreases serum testosterone levels (141). Later work has shown that postovulatory ovarian content of 17β-estradiol can be increased by supplying aromatase substrate, testosterone (142). The authors suggest that the postovulatory decline in estrogen production is due to decreases in the C-17,20 lyase and 17α-hydroxylase activities. Furthermore, results of similar assays indicate that both 17-hydroxylase and lyase activities are maximal in the late follicular phase but decrease dramatically on luteniza-tion (122). Chinese hamster ovary cells in culture respond to hCG plus FSH with increases in ^{14}C-pregnenolone metabolism that suggest stimulation of several enzymes including C-17,20 lyase (34); however, it is difficult to interpret the locus of stimulation in whole-cell systems.

Estrogen administration to intact immature female rats decreases the concentrations of ovarian androgens and inhibits the response of both intact and hypophysectomized animals to stimulation with LH (80, 83). Increases in ovarian progesterone concentration in response to LH by intact rats in vivo is not affected by prior estrogen treatment nor is the in vitro progester-one respones to either LH or cAMP. Thecal cells isolated from ovaries of estrogen treated animals show the same in vitro responses to LH as the whole ovarian tissue (81). Ovarian estrogen production thus may be self-regulating through an inhibition of C-17,20 lyase and/or 17α-hydroxylase activities.

Adrenal

Human adrenal microsomal lyase specific activity decreases by 50% after the first year of life and subsequently increases to become four times as high in adults as in prepubertal children (124). The results demonstrate a definite regulation of this activity in adrenal tissue, and ACTH is the apparent effector (117; reviewed in 109). ACTH also increases microsomal cyto-chrome P-450 levels in adrenals of hypophysectomized rats, but no concom-itant measurement was made of adrenal C-17,20 lyase activity (115).

AROMATASE

Aromatase catalyzes three mixed-function oxidations (116) and is normally expressed in all steroidogenic tissues. The enzyme and reaction mechanism have been characterized in detail only in placental tissue (reviewed in 133).

It is clear from early studies (36) that FSH stimulation is necessary for ovarian estrogen production, and FSH stimulation of aromatase activity has been inferred. The two-cell hypothesis of ovarian estrogen production (35, 85, 88) is generally accepted, and the extensive studies of Dorrington, Armstrong, and their co-workers (reviewed in 30) show that FSH and Bt$_2$-cAMP increase aromatase activity in cultures of both granulosa and Sertoli cells.

Ovary

FSH or PMSG administration to immature (142) or immature hypophysec-tomized female rats (3) or FSH addition to cultures of rat granulosa cells (32, 59, 84) stimulates estrogen production only when given with exogenous androgen as aromatase substrate. These results show that FSH increases estrogen biosynthesis by acting on the aromatase step but do not differentiate between a direct or indirect stimulation of enzyme activity. More recently Gore-Langton & Dorrington (49) reported that 48-hr exposure to FSH of rat granulosa cells in culture results in increased aromatase activity assayed with cell-free sonicates in the presence of an NADPH generating system, thus demonstrating a true increase in the activity of the enzyme. The stimulation of ovarian aromatase activity by PMSG is blocked by actinomycin D and cycloheximide (139), findings taken as evidence of enzyme induction. hCG administration following the initial in vivo stimulation with FSH or PMSG (141, 142) elicits a much greater increase in labeled estrogen formation, but this increase is still dependent on an exogenous androgen source.

The stimulation of aromatase activity by either FSH or LH in cultures of granulosa cells from FSH-primed rats is inhibited by concomitant treatment with prolactin (Prl) (151). Epidermal growth factor (EGF) added with FSH to cultures of rat ovarian granulosa cells also inhibits the stimulation by FSH of estrogen production from 10^{-7} M exogenous androstenedione, while fibroblast growth factor is ineffective (61). Gonadotropin releasing hormone (GnRH) stimulates estrogen concentration in rat testis (77); in contrast, it inhibits the FSH stimulation of estrogen production by rat granulosa cells in vivo and in vitro but has no consistent effect on the stimulation of cAMP production by FSH (54, 55, 60). Both EGF and GnRH or an agonist also block the stimulation of estrogen production by cholera toxin (CT) and Bt_2cAMP, demonstrating a post-cAMP locus of action (55, 60, 61). Consistent with this conclusion are the observations that a phosphodiesterase inhibitor enhances the FSH stimulation and that the enhancement is inhibited by GnRH in a dose-dependent manner (55). The inhibition by GnRH is competitive with FSH since it shifts the dose-response curve to the right (55) but does not change the maximal response.

Another factor of physiological import that influences FSH stimulation of aromatase activity, or at least estrogen production from C_{19}-precursors, is progesterone concentration. The inhibitory effect of various progestins added to rat granulosa cell cultures is in the same relative order as their affinity for ovarian progesterone receptors (126). In a manner similar to that of GnRH and EGF in their inhibition of FSH action, progesterone acts subsequent to cAMP formation. It does not block FSH stimulation of cAMP production but does block the stimulation of estrogen formation by CT, PGE_2, and Bt_2cAMP (127). Kinetic analyses show that the progestins do *not* act as competitive inhibitors of granulosa cell aromatase (127). Cortisol and dexamethasone also inhibit FSH-induced increases in aromatase activity of granulosa cell cultures while not affecting the stimulation of progesterone production or the basal level of aromatase activity (59). An interesting suggestion was made by Siiteri & Thompson (131) for the physiological role of 5α-reduced androstenedione in depressing the level of ovarian estrogen formation. This compound is a potent competitive inhibitor of ovarian aromatase, and ovarian 5α-reductase activity is influenced by gonadotropin treatment (114, 131). Unexplained to date is the demonstration that, in addition to serving as aromatase substrate (23), androgens in the culture medium augment the in vitro stimulation by FSH of granulosa cell aromatase activity, although the actions seem to be mediated by androgen receptors (53). This augmentation may be of physiological import during the stimulation of thecal cell androgen production.

Testis

Aromatase activity in testes is also regulated by gonadotropins (reviewed in 118). In vivo hCG or LH (but not FSH) administration stimulates the activity measured in microsome preparations from both immature and adult rat testes assayed in the presence of an NADPH generating system (12, 147). Human chorionic gonadotropin added to cultures of Leydig cells from mature rats stimulates ^{3}H-estradiol formation from ^{3}H-testosterone at concentrations of the latter sufficient to saturate the aromatase (148). The stimulation is measurable after 1 hr of exposure to hCG and is linear from 1–4 hr. A 1.0 mM concentration of Bt$_2$cAMP mimics the hCG effect.

In spite of the reported lack of in vivo stimulation of testicular aromatase (147), FSH does stimulate estrogen production from androgens by Sertoli cells in culture. The stimulation is dependent on the experimental conditions (29, 50, 145). FSH apparently acts on Sertoli cells in rats 20 days of age or less, while LH acts on Leydig cells of older animals (118). The period in culture prior to stimulation is also significant. Stimulation of estradiol formation from androstenedione, testosterone, 19-hydroxyandrostenedione or 19-hydroxytestosterone substrates is equal, leading to the conclusion that the stimulus locus is the reaction between 19-hydroxylated intermediates and estrone or estradiol (31). This conclusion assumes different enzymes for the first and second hydroxylation steps. If the first and second hydroxylations at C-19 are catalyzed by the same enzyme, both could be stimulated and be compatible with the results of Dorrington and co-workers (31). The data also do not distinguish between stimulation of the second 19-hydroxylation and 2β-hydroxylation.

Other factors may affect testicular aromatase activity and its stimulation by FSH. Treatment with a GnRH agonist results in increased testicular concentrations of estrogens and decreased androstenedione concentrations, suggesting increased aromatase activity (77). Boitani (8) has reported that spermatogenic stages VII and VIII of rat seminiferous tubule cultures produce a heat stable reversible inhibitor of FSH stimulation of cAMP and estrogen production. The identity of this inhibitor is unknown. There remain conflicting reports of gonadotropin effects on testicular testosterone and estrogen concentrations and presumed production that may, as with Sertoli cell cultures, reflect age differences in the responses of the different cell-types, as well as various degrees of androgen utilization due to aromatase stimulation (92, 97, 111, 112, 147).

General

Regulation of aromatase activity may occur in other vertebrates as well. Addition of a trout maturational gonadotropin preparation to perfusions of trout ovaries decreases the percent conversion of ^{3}H-testosterone to estrone and 17β-estradiol (135). Although the interpretation of percent conversion data is generally tenuous because of the possibility of changes in the specific activity of the substrate, the authors showed similar decreases in the percent conversion at several exogenous substrate concentrations, supporting an effect of the gonadotropin on either enzyme activity or cofactor availability. Plasma estrogen levels in trout varied directly with the percent conversion of ^{3}H-Androstenedione to labeled estrone and estradiol as well (149). The inference is a control of aromatase during the course of the annual cycle of ovarian activity.

In summary, LH and FSH gonadotropins control aromatase activity in both ovaries and testes. In adult Leydig cells and ovarian follicles sensitized by FSH stimulation, LH (hCG) control is more important; whereas FSH stimulation is important in granulosa cells of preovulatory follicles and in Sertoli cells of immature animals. The enzyme activities from these latter two sources require a source of androgen substrate. The mechanism by which aromatase increases in response to gonadotropin stimulation seems to be an induction, and cAMP mimics the action.

CONCLUDING REMARKS

Future progress in elucidating the mechanism of regulation of the microsomal steroidogenic enzymes depends on an understanding of their components and structures. Considerable progress has been made in their purification in recent years (57, 99). Several questions need to be answered in subsequent investigations. Lyase and 17α-hydroxylase may be properties of the same protein (101); however, seemingly independent expressions of the activities caution against such a conclusion. The question of how many proteins are involved in the complex aromatase reaction also needs to be answered. Are the two 19-hydroxylation steps separate enzymes or one? Is the 2β-hydroxylase separate or part of the same protein?

The activities of the microsomal enzymes catalyzing steroidogenic reactions are actively regulated. It is likely that they are regulated by at least four different mechanisms of varying importance: induction; indirect modulation by steroids; direct inhibition by steroids; and phosphorylation. This last mechanism is surmised from suggestive evidence and by inference from other systems (4, 13, 66, 72, 73). A change in the rate of enzyme degradation could also be important (115). Future investigations no doubt will elucidate the details of these mechanisms and how they are integrated.

ACKNOWLEDGEMENT

Partial support for writing this review was provided by a University of Montana Research Grant.

Literature Cited

1. Acevedo, H. F., Dominguez, O. V. 1960. The effects of aging and in vivo stimulation with human chorionic gonadotropin of the 17α-hydroxylating activity of rat testicular tissue. *Acta Endocrinol. (Copenhagen)* (*Suppl.*) 51:711 (Abstr.)
2. Ahrén, K., Hamberger, L., Hillensjö, T., Nilsson, L., Nordenström, K. 1979. Control of steroidogenesis in the preovulatory rat follicle. *J. Steroid Biochem.* 11:791–98
3. Armstrong, D. T., Papkoff, H. 1976. Stimulation of aromatization of exogenous and endogenous androgens in ovaries of hypophysectomized rats in vivo by follicle stimulating hormone. *Endocrinology* 99:1144–51
4. Bakker, G. H., Hoogerbrugge, J. W., Rommerts, F. G., van der Molen, H. J. 1981. Lutropin-dependent protein phosphorylation and steroidogenesis in rat tumor Leydig cells. *Biochem. J.* 198:339–46
5. Becker, S., Chubb, C., Ewing, L. 1980. Mathematical model of steroidogenesis in rat and rabbit testes. *Am. J. Physiol.* 239:R184–95
6. Betz, G., Tsai, P., Hales, D. 1980. Reconstitution of steroid 17,20-lyase activity after separation and purification of cytochrome P-450 and its reductase from rat testis microsomes. *Endocrinology* 107:1055–60
7. Betz, G., Tsai, P., Weakley, R. 1976. Heterogeneity of cytochrome P-450 in rat testis microsomes. *J. Biol. Chem.* 251:2839–41
8. Boitani, C., Ritzén, E. M. 1981. Inhibition of rat Sertoli cell aromatase by factor(s) secreted specifically at spermato-genic stages VII and VIII. *Mol. Cell. Endocrinol.* 23:11–12
9. Bongiovanni, A. M., Eberlein, W. R. 1958. Adrenogenital syndrome: uncomplicated and hypertensive forms. *Pediatrics* 21:661–67
10. Brinkman, A. O., Leemborg, F. G., van der Molen, H. J. 1981. hCG-induced inhibition of steroidogenesis: an estradiol mediated process. *Mol. Cell. Endocrinol.* 24:64–72
11. Bryan, G. T., Lewis, A. M., Harkins, J. B., Micheletti, S. F. 1974. Cytochrome P-450 and steroid 21-hydroxylation in microsomes from beef adrenal cortex. *Steroids* 23:185–201
12. Canick, J. A., Markis, A., Gunsalus, G. L., Ryan, K. J. 1979. Testicular aromatization in immature rats: localization and stimulation after gonadotropin stimulation *in vivo. Endocrinology* 104:285–88
13. Caron, M. G., Goldstein, S., Savard, K., Marsh, J. M. 1975. Protein kinase stimulation of a reconstituted cholesterol side chain cleavage enzyme system in the bovine corpus luteum. *J. Biol. Chem.* 250:5137–43
14. Carstensen, H. C. 1961. The effect of human interstitial cell-stimulating hormone on the biosynthesis *in vitro* of testosterone from 17α-hydroxy-Δ⁵-pregnen-3β-ol,20-One by human and rat testes. *Acta Soc. Med. Upsal.* 66:129–38
15. Catt, K. J., Harwood, J. P., Clayton, R. N., Davies, T. F., Chan, V., Katikineni, M., Nozu, K., Dufau, M. L. 1980. Regulation of peptide hormone receptors and gonadal steroidogenesis. *Rec. Prog. Horm. Res.* 36:557–622

16. Chasalow, F., Marr, H., Haour, F., Saez, J. M. 1979. Testicular steroidogenesis after human chorionic gonadotropin desensitization in rats. *J. Biol. Chem.* 254:5613–17

17. Chouraqui, J., Weniger, J. P. 1970. Identification des corticosteroides secretes par les surrenales embryonnaires de veau, lapin, et souris cultivees in vitro. *Acta Endocrinol. (Copenhagen)* 65: 650–62

18. Chouraqui, J., Weniger, J. P. 1973. Aspect quantitatif de la synthese de corticosteroides par la surrenale embryonnaire de Lapin cultivee in vitro. *J. Steroid Biochem.* 4:519–23

19. Christensen, A. K., Mason, N. R. 1965. Comparative ability of seminiferous tubules and interstitial tissue of rat testes to synthesize androgens from progesterone in vitro. *Endocrinology* 76: 646–56

20. Cigorraga, S. B., Sorrell, S., Bator, J., Catt, K. J., Dufau, M. L. 1980. Estrogen dependence of a gonadotropin-induced steroidogenic lesion in rat testicular Leydig cells. *J. Clin. Invest.* 65:699–705

21. Cooper, D. J., Narasimhulu, S., Rosenthal, O., Estabrook, R. W. 1968. Studies on the mechanism of C-21-hydroxylation of steroids by the adrenal cortex. In *Functions of the Adrenal Cortex,* ed. K. W. McKerns, 2:897–942. NY: Appleton-Century Crofts

22. Coslovsky, R., Yalow, R. S. 1974. Influence of the hormonal forms of ACTH on the pattern of corticosteroid secretion. *Biochem. Biophys. Res. Commun.* 60:1351–56

23. Daniel, S. A. J., Armstrong, D. T. 1980. Enhancement of follicle-stimulating hormone-induced aromatase activity by androgens in cultured rat granulosa cells. *Endocrinology* 107:1027–33

24. DeBruijn, H. W. A., van der Molen, H. J. 1974. An assessment of the possible role of 17α,20α-dihydroxy-4-pregnen-3-one in the regulation of testosterone synthesis by rat and rabbit testis. *J. Endocrinol.* 61:401–10

25. DeNicola, A. F. 1975. Effects of ACTH on steroid C-21 hydroxylation in rat adrenal glands. *J. Steroid Biochem.* 6: 1219–22

26. Diedrichsen, G., Sinterhauf, K., Wolff, H. P., Lommer, D. 1977. Indication for the existence of alternative pathways of steroid synthesis via 21-hydroxypregnenolone in the rat adrenal cortex. *J. Steroid Biochem.* 8:631–41

27. Dominguez, O. V., Huseby, R. A., Samuels, L. T. 1960. Biosynthetic enzyme systems in induced interstitial cell testicular tumors and their alterations during repeated transplantation. *Acta Endocrinol. (Copenhagen) (Suppl.)* 51: 709(Abstr.)

28. Dominguez, O. V., Samuels, L. T., Huseby, R. A. 1958. Steroid biosynthesis in induced testicular interstitial cell tumors of mice. *Ciba Fnd. Endocrinol.* 12:231–38

29. Dorrington, J. H., Armstrong, D. T. 1975. Follicle-stimulating hormone stimulates estradiol-17β synthesis in cultured Sertoli cells. *Proc. Natl. Acad. Sci. USA* 72:2677–81

30. Dorrington, J. H., Armstrong, D. T. 1979. Effects of FSH on gonadal functions. *Rec. Prog. Horm. Res.* 35:301–31

31. Dorrington, J. H., Fritz, I. B., Armstrong, D. T. 1976. Site at which FSH regulates estradiol-17β biosynthesis in Sertoli cell preparations in culture. *Mol. Cell. Endocrinol.* 6:117–22

32. Dorrington, J. H., Moon, Y. S., Armstrong, D. T. 1975. Estradiol-17β biosynthesis in cultured granulosa cells from hypophysectomized immature rats; stimulation by follicle stimulating hormone. *Endocrinology* 97:1328–31

33. Drummond, H. B., Fevold, H. R. 1972. The effect of a rabbit ACTH preparation on adrenal steroid biosynthesis. *Steroids* 19:605–19

34. Evain, D., Anderson, W. B., Saez, J. M. 1981. Gonadotropin stimulation of pregnenolone metabolism in Chinese hamster ovary cells in culture. *J. Cell. Physiol.* 108:9–14

35. Falk, B. 1959. Site of production of oestrogen in rat ovaries as studied in microtransplants. *Acta Physiol. Scand.* 47(Suppl. 163):1–101

36. Fevold, H. L. 1941. Synergism of the follicle stimulating and luteinizing hormones in producing estrogen secretion. *Endocrinology* 28:33–36

37. Fevold, H. R. 1967. Regulation of the adrenal cortex secretory pattern by adrenocorticotropin. *Science* 156: 1753–55

38. Fevold, H. R. 1982. The microsomal enzymes of steroid hormone biosynthesis and their control. *Prog. Horm. Biochem. Pharmacol.* In press

39. Fevold, H. R., Brown, R. L. 1978. The apparent lack of stimulation of rabbit adrenal 21-hydroxylase activity by ACTH. *J. Steroid Biochem.* 9:583–84

40. Fevold, H. R., Drummond, H. B. 1973. Factors affecting the adrenocortico-

tropic hormone stimulation of rabbit adrenal 17α-hydroxylase activity. *Biochim. Biophys. Acta* 313:211–20

41. Fevold, H. R., Eik-Nes, K. B. 1962. Progesterone metabolism by testicular tissue of the English sparrow (*Passer domesticus*) during the annual reproductive cycle. *Gen. Comp. Endocrinol.* 2:506–15

42. Fevold, H. R., Hubert, T. D. 1968. Synthetic β^{1-24}-corticotropin stimulation of cortisol biosynthesis by rabbit adrenal tissue. *Steroids* 12:697–704

43. Fevold, H. R., Hubert, T. D. 1969. The pathways of corticosteroid biosynthesis by homogenates of adrenal tissue from rabbits stimulated with adrenocorticotropin. *Biochemistry* 8:3433–39

44. Fevold, H. R., Wilson, P. L., Slanina, S. M. 1978. ACTH-stimulated rabbit adrenal 17α-hydroxylase. Kinetic properties and a comparison with those of 3 β-hydroxysteroid dehydrogenase. *J. Steroid Biochem.* 9:1033–41

45. Ford, H. C., O'Donnell, V. J. 1971. Studies on an extract of rat testicular microsomal fraction that catalyses the transformation of progesterone into 17-hydroxyprogesterone and androgens. *Biochem. J.* 123:105–16

46. Gasson, J. 1979. Steroidogenic activity of high molecular weight forms of corticotropin. *Biochemistry* 18:4215–24

47. Gasson, J. 1980. High molecular weight forms of adrenocorticotropin: presence in guinea pig pituitary and steroidogenic activity on guinea pig adrenal cells. *Peptides* 1:223–29

48. Gill, G. N., Hornsby, P. T., Simonian, M. H. 1980. Hormonal regulation of the adrenocortical cell. *J. Supramol. Struct.* 14:353–69

49. Gore-Langton, R., Dorrington, J. H. 1981. FSH induction of aromatase in cultured rat granulosa cells measured by a radiometric assay. *Mol. Cell. Endocrinol.* 22:135–51

50. Gore-Langton, R., McKeracher, H., Dorrington, J. H. 1980. An alternative method for the study of follicle-stimulating hormone effects on aromatase activity in Sertoli cell cultures. *Endocrinology* 107:464–71

51. Guenthner, T., Nebert, D., Menard, R. 1978. Microsomal aryl hydrocarbon hydroxylase in rat adrenal: regulation by ACTH, but not polycyclic hydrocarbons. *Mol. Pharmacol.* 15:719–28

52. Hall, P. F. 1980. The roles of cytochrome P-450 in the synthesis and metabolism of steroids. *Dev. Biochem.* 13:461–75

53. Hillier, S. G., DeZwart, F. A. 1981. Evidence that granulosa cell aromatase induction/activation by follicle-stimulating hormone is an androgen receptor-regulated process in-vitro. *Endocrinology* 109:1303–5

54. Hillier, S. G., Reichert, L. E. Jr., van Hall, E. V. 1981. Control of preovulatory follicular estrogen biosynthesis in the human ovary. *J. Clin. Endocrinol. Metab.* 52:847–56

55. Hillier, S. G., Reichert, L. E. Jr., van Hall, E. V. 1981. Modulation of FSH-controlled steroidogenesis in rat granulosa cells: direct in-vitro effects of LHRH and ICI-118630. *Mol. Cell Endocrinol.* 23:193–205

56. Hirose, T. 1977. Cortisol and corticosterone production of isolated adrenal cells in neonatal rabbits. *Acta Endocrinol. (Copenhagen)* 84:349–56

57. Hiwatashi, A., Ichikawa, Y. 1981. Purification and reconstitution of the steroid 21-hydroxylase system (cytochrome P-450-linked mixed function oxidase system) of bovine adrenocortical microsomes. *Biochim. Biophys. Acta* 664:33–48

58. Hosaka, M., Oshima, H., Troen, P. 1980. Studies on the human testis. XIV. Properties of C17-C20 lyase. *Acta Endocrinol. (Copenhagen)* 94:389–96

59. Hsueh, A. J., Erickson, G. F. 1978. Glucocorticoid inhibition of FSH-induced estrogen production in cultured rat granulosa cells. *Steroids* 32:639–48

60. Hsueh, A. J. W., Wang, C., Erickson, G. 1980. Direct inhibitory effect of gonadotropin-releasing hormone upon follicle stimulating hormone induction of lutenizing hormone receptor and aromatase activity in rat granulosa cells. *Endocrinology* 106:1697–1705

61. Hsueh, A. J. W., Welsh, T. H., Jones, P. B. C. 1981. Inhibition of ovarian and testicular steroidogenesis by epidermal growth factor. *Endocrinology* 108:2002–4

62. Idler, D. R., Walsh, J. M., Kalliecharan, R., Hall, B. K. 1976. Identification of authentic cortisol in plasma of the embryonic chick. *Gen. Comp. Endocrinol.* 30:539–40

63. Inano, H. 1974. Studies on enzyme reactions related to steroid biosynthesis. III. Distribution of the testicular enzymes related to androgen production between siminiferous tubules and interstitial tissue. *J. Steroid. Biochem.* 5:145–49

64. Inano, H., Inano, A., Tamaoki, B. 1969. Submicrosomal distribution of adrenal enzymes and cytochrome P-450 related to corticoidogenesis. *Biochem. Biophys. Acta* 191:257–71

65. Jaffe, R. B., Serön-Ferré, M., Crickard, K., Koritnik, D., Mitchell, B. F., Huhtaniemi, I. T. 1981. Regulation and function of the primate fetal adrenal gland and gonad. *Rec. Prog. Horm. Res.* 37:41–103

66. Joh, T. H., Park, D. H., Reis, D. J. 1978. Direct phosphorylation of brain tyrosine hydroxylase by cyclic AMP-dependent protein kinase: mechanism of enzyme activation. *Proc. Natl. Acad. Sci. USA* 75:4744–48

67. Johnson, D. C. 1978. Temporal changes in ovarian steroid-17α-hydroxylase in immature rats treated with immature mare's serum gonadotropin. *Proc. Soc. Exp. Biol. Med.* 159:484–87

68. Johnson, D. C., Tsai-Morris, C., Hoversland, R. C. 1981. Steroid 17α-hydroxylase activity of ovarian granulosa cells from hypophysectomized immature rats treated with pregnant mare serum gonadotropin (PMS). *Steroids* 38:581–92

69. Kalla, N. R., Nisula, B. C., Menard, R., Loriaux, D. L. 1980. The effect of estradiol on testicular testosterone biosynthesis. *Endocrinology* 106:35–39

70. Kalliecharan, R. 1981. The influence of exogenous ACTH on the levels of corticosterone and cortisol in plasma of young chicks (*Gallus domesticus*) *Gen. Comp. Endocrinol.* 44:249–51

71. Kass, E. H., Hechter, O., Macchi, I. A., Mou, T. W. 1954. Changes in patterns of secretion of corticosteroids in rabbits after prolonged treatment with ACTH. *Proc. Soc. Exp. Biol. Med.* 85:583–87

72. Koroscil, T. M., Gallant, S. 1980. On the mechanism of action of adrenocorticotropic hormone. The role of ACTH-stimulated phosphorylation and dephosphorylation of adrenal proteins. *J. Biol. Chem.* 255:6276–83

73. Koroscil, T. M., Gallant, S. 1981. The phosphorylation of adrenal proteins in response to adrenocorticotropic hormone. *J. Biol. Chem.* 256:6700–7

74. Krum, A. A., Glenn, R. E. 1965. Adrenal steroid secretion in rabbits following prolonged ACTH administration. *Proc. Soc. Exp. Biol. Med.* 118:255–58

75. Kuhnle, U., Chow, D., Rapaport, R., Pangs, S., Levine, L. S., New, M. I. 1981. The 21-hydroxylase activity in the glomerulosa and fasciculata of the adrenal cortex in congenital adrenal hyper-

plasia. *J. Clin. Endocrinol. Metab.* 52: 534–44

76. Kurachi, K., Miyazaki, M., Mori, H., Matsumoto, K. 1971. In vitro steroid synthesis by foetal rabbit adrenals. *Acta Endocrinol. (Copenhagen)* 68:209–18

77. Labrie, F., Cusan, L., Séguin, C., Bélanger, A., Pelletier, G., Reeves, J., Kelley, P. A., Lemay, A., Raynaud, J. P. 1980. Antifertility effects of LHRH agonists in the male rat and inhibition of testicular steroidogenesis in man. *Int. J. Fertil.* 25:157–70

78. Leblanc, H., Lehoux, J. G., Sandor, T. 1972. Etude de la 21-hydroxylase des glandes surrenales du canard domestique (*Anas platyrhynchos*). *J. Steroid Biochem.* 3:683–92

79. Leinonen, P., Ruokonen, A., Kontturi, M., Vihko, R. 1981. Effects of estrogen treatment on human testicular unconjugated steroid and steroid sulfate production in vivo. *J. Clin. Endocrinol. Metab.* 53:569–73

80. Leung, P. C. K., Armstrong, D. T. 1979. Estrogen treatment of immature rats inhibits ovarian androgen production in vitro. *Endocrinology* 104: 1411–17

81. Leung, P. C. K., Armstrong, D. T. 1980. Further evidence in support of a short-loop feedback action of estrogen on ovarian androgen production. *Life Sci.* 27:415–20

82. Leung, P. C. K., Armstrong, D. T. 1980. Interactions of steroids and gonadotropins in the control of steroidogenesis in the ovarian follicle. *Ann. Rev. Physiol.* 42:71–82

83. Leung, P. C. K., Goff, A. K., Kennedy, T. G., Armstrong, D. T. 1978. An intraovarian inhibitory action of estrogen on angrogen (sic) production in vivo. *Biol. Reprod.* 19:641–47

84. Liu, W.-K., Burleigh, B. D., Ward, D. N. 1981. Steroid and plasminogen activator production by cultured rat granulosa cells in response to hormone treatment. *Mol. Cell Endocrinol.* 21: 63–73

85. McNatty, K. P., Makris, A., DeGrazia, C., Osathanondh, R., Ryan, K. J. 1980. Steroidogenesis by recombined follicular cells from the human ovary in vitro. *J. Clin. Endocrinol. Metab.* 51:1286–92

86. Mackler, B., Haynes, B., Tattoni, D. S., Tippit, D. F., Kelley, V. S. 1971. Studies of adrenal steroid hydroxylation. I. Purification of the microsomal 21-hydroxylase system. *Arch. Biochem. Biophys.* 145:194–98

34   FEVOLD

87. Mahajan, D. K., Samuels, L. T. 1975. Inhibition of 17,20 (17-hydroxyprogesterone)-lyase by progesterone. *Steroids* 25:217-28

88. Makris, A., Ryan, K. J. 1975. Progesterone, androstenedione, testosterone, estrone, and estradiol synthesis in hamster ovarian follicle cells. *Endocrinology* 96:694-701

89. Malinowska, K. W., Hardy, R. N., Nathanielsz, P. W. 1972. Plasma adrenocorticosteroid concentrations immediately after birth in the rat, rabbit, and guinea pig. *Experientia* 28: 1366-67

90. Malinowska, K. W., Hardy, R. N., Nathanielsz, P. W. 1972. Neonatal adrenocortical function and its possible relation to the uptake of macromolecules by the small intestine of the guinea pig and rabbit. *J. Endocrinol.* 55:397-404

91. Mason, J. I., Estabrook, R. W., Purvis, J. L. 1973. Testicular cytochrome P-450 and iron-sulfur protein as related to steroid metabolism. *Ann. N.Y. Acad. Sci.* 212:406-19

92. Melner, M. H., Abney, T. O. 1980. Depletion of cytoplasmic estrogen receptor in gonadotropin-desensitized testes. *Endocrinology* 107:1620-26

93. Menard, R. H., Baxter, F. C., Gillette, J. R. 1976. Spironolactone and cytochrome P-450: impairment of steroid 21-hydroxylation in the adrenal cortex. *Arch. Biochem. Biophys.* 173:395-402

94. Menard, R. H., Latif, S. A., Purvis, J. L. 1975. The intratesticular localization of cytochrome P-450 and cytochrome P-450 dependent enzymes in rat testis. *Endocrinology* 97:1587-92

95. Menard, R. H., Purvis, J. L. 1972. Stimulation of the levels of cytochrome P-450 and 17α-hydroxylase in chick testes microsomes by pituitary hormones. *Endocrinology* 91:1506-12

96. Menard, R. H., Purvis, J. L. 1973. Studies of cytochrome P-450 in testis microsomes. *Arch. Biochem. Biophys.* 154: 8-18

97. Moger, W. H. 1980. Temporal changes in testicular estradiol and testosterone concentrations, cytoplasmic estradiol binding, and desensitization after human chorionic gonadotropin administration to the immature rat. *Endocrinology* 106:495-503

98. Mulay, S., Giannopoulos, G., Solomon, S. 1973. Corticosteroid levels in the mother and fetus of the rabbit during gestation. *Endocrinology* 93:1342-48

99. Nakajin, J., Hall, P. F. 1981. Microsomal cytochrome P-450 from neonatal pig testis. Purification and properties of a C_{21} steroid side-chain cleavage system (17α-hydroxylase-$C_{17,20}$-lyase). *J. Biol. Chem.* 256:3871-76

100. Nakajin, S., Hall, P. F., Onoda, M. 1981. Testicular microsomal cytochrome P-450 for C_{21} steroid side-chain cleavage. Spectral and binding studies. *J. Biol. Chem.* 256:6134-39

101. Nakajin, S., Shively, J. E., Yuan, P.-M., Hall, P. F. 1981. Microsomal cytochrome P-450 from neonatal pig testis: two enzymatic activities (17α-hydroxylase and $C_{17,20}$-lyase) associated with one protein. *Biochemistry* 20: 4037-42

102. Nakamura, T., Tanabi, Y., Hirano, H. 1978. Evidence of the *in vitro* formation of cortisol by the adrenal gland of embryonic and young chickens (*Gallus domesticus*). *Gen. Comp. Endocrinol.* 35:302-8

103. Nelson, E. B., Bryan, G. T. 1975. Steroid hydroxylations by human adrenal cortex microsomes. *J. Clin. Endocrinol. Metab.* 41:7-12

104. Niswender, G. D., Sawyer, H. R., Chen, T. T., Endres, D. B. 1980. Action of luteinizing hormone at the luteal cell level. *Adv. Sex Horm. Res.* 4:153-85

105. Nozu, K., Dehejia, A., Zawistowich, L., Catt, K. J., Dufau, M. L. 1981. Gonadotropin-induced receptor regulation and steroidogenic lesions in cultured Leydig cells. Induction of specific protein synthesis by chorionic gonadotropin and estradiol. *J. Biol. Chem.* 256:12875-82

106. Nozu, K., Matsuura, S., Catt, K. J., Dufau, M. L. 1981. Modulation of Leydig cell androgen biosynthesis and cytochrome P-450 levels during estrogen treatment and human chorionic gonadotropin-induced desensitization. *J. Biol. Chem.* 256:10012-17

107. Onoda, M., Hall, P. F. 1981. Inhibition of testicular microsomal cytochrome P-450 (17α-hydroxylase/C-17,20-lyase) by estrogens. *Endocrinology* 109: 763-67

108. Orta-Flores, Z., Cantú, J. M., Domingues, O. V. 1976. Reciprocal interactions of progesterone and 17α-hydroxyprogesterone as exogenous substrates of rat adrenal 21-hydroxylase. *J. Steroid Biochem.* 7:761-67

109. Parker, L. N., Odell, W. D. 1980. Control of adrenal androgen secretion. *Endocr. Rev.* 1:392-410

110. Pasqualini, J. R., Lafoscade, G., Jayle, M. F. 1964. Role of 17α,21-dihydroxypregnenolone in the biogenesis of C_{21} and C_{19} steroids by adrenal gland slices. *Steroids* 4:739–57

111. Pomerantz, D. K. 1980. Developmental changes in the ability of follicle stimulating hormone to stimulate estrogen synthesis *in vivo* by the testis of the rat. *Biol. Reprod.* 23:948–54

112. Pomerantz, D. K. 1981. Human chorionic gonadotropin enhances the ability of gonadotropic hormones to stimulate aromatization in the testis of the rat. *Endocrinology* 109:2004–8

113. Preslock, J. P. 1980. Steroidogenesis in the mammalian testis. *Endocr. Rev.* 1:132–39

114. Purvis, J. L., Canick, J. A., Latif, S. A., Rosenbaum, J. H., Hologgitas, J., Menard, R. H. 1973. Lifetime of microsomal cytochrome P-450 steroidogenic enzymes in rat testis as influenced by human chorionic gonadotropin. *Arch. Biochem. Biophys.* 159:39–49

115. Purvis, J. L., Canick, J. A., Mason, J. I., Estabrook, R. W., McCarthy, J. L. 1973. Lifetime of adrenal cytochrome P-450 as influenced by ACTH. *Ann. NY Acad. Sci.* 212:319–43

116. Reed, K. C., Ohno, S. 1976. Kinetic properties of human placental aromatase. Application of an assay measuring ^3H_2O release from $1\beta,2\beta$-^3H-androgens. *J. Biol. Chem.* 251:1625–31

117. Rich, B. H., Rosenfield, R. L., Lucky, A. W., Helke, J. C., Otto, P. 1981. Adrenarche: changing adrenal response to adrenocorticotropin. *J. Clin. Endocrinol. Metab.* 52:1129–36

118. Rommerts, F. F., Brinkman, A. O. 1981. Modulation of steroidogenic activities in testis Leydig cells. *Mol. Cell. Endocrinol.* 21:15–28

119. Rothchild, I. 1981. The regulation of the mammalian corpus luteum. *Rec. Prog. Horm. Res.* 37:183–298

120. Ryan, K. J., Engel, L. L. 1957. Hydroxylation of steroids at carbon 21. *J. Biol. Chem.* 225:103–14

121. Samuels, L. T., Uchikawa, T., Zain-ul-Abedin, M., Huseby, R. A. 1969. Effects of diethylstibestrol on enzymes of cryptorchid mouse testes. *Endocrinology* 85:96–102

122. Sano, Y., Suzuki, K., Avai, K., Okinaga, S., Tamaoki, B. 1981. Changes in enzyme activities related to steroidogenesis in human ovaries during the menstrual cycle. *J. Clin. Endocrinol. Metab.* 52:994–1001

123. Schiebinger, R. J., Albertson, B. D., Barnes, K. M., Cutler, G. B. Jr., Loriaux, D. L. 1981. Developmental changes in rabbit and dog adrenal function: a possible homologue of adrenarche in the dog. *Am. J. Physiol.* 240: E694–99

124. Schiebinger, R. J., Albertson, B. D., Cassorla, F. G., Bowyer, D. W., Geelhoed, G. W., Cutler, G. B. Jr., Loriaux, D. L. 1981. The developmental changes in plasma adrenal androgens during infancy and adrenarche are associated with changing activities of adrenal microsomal 17-hydroxylase and 17,20-desmolase. *J. Clin. Invest.* 67:1177–82

125. Schoen, E. J., Samuels, L. T. 1965. Testicular androgen biosynthesis following corticotrophin and human chorionic gonadotrophin administration. *Acta Endocrinol. (Copenhagen)* 50:365–78

126. Schreiber, J. R., Nakamura, K., Erickson, G. F. 1980. Progestins inhibit FSH-stimulated steroidogenesis in cultured rat granulosa cells. *Mol. Cell. Endocrinol.* 19:165–73

127. Schreiber, J. R., Nakamura, K., Erickson, G. F. 1981. Progestins inhibit FSH-stimulated granulosa estrogen production at a post-cAMP site. *Mol. Cell Endocrinol.* 21:161–70

128. Shikita, M., Hall, P. F. 1967. The action of human chorionic gonadotrophin *in vivo* upon microsomal enzymes of immature rat testes. *Biochim. Biophys. Acta* 136:484–97

129. Shikita, M., Hall, P. F. 1967. Action of human chorionic gonadotrophin *in vivo* upon microsomal enzymes in testes of hypophysectomized rats. *Biochim. Biophys. Acta* 141:433–35

130. Shikita, M., Tamaoki, B. 1965. Testosterone formation by subcellular particles of rat testes. *Endocrinology* 76:563–69

131. Siiteri, P., Thompson, E. A. 1975. Studies of human placental aromatase. *J. Steroid Biochem.* 6:317–22

132. Simpson, E. R. 1979. Cholesterol side-chain cleavage, cytochrome P-450, and the control of steroidogenesis. *Mol. Cell. Endocrinol.* 13:213–27

133. Simpson, E. R., MacDonald, P. C. 1981. Endocrine physiology of the placenta. *Ann. Rev. Physiol.* 43:163–88

134. Simpson, E. R., Mason, J. I. 1976. Molecular aspects of the biosynthesis of adrenal steroids. *Pharmacol. Ther. B* 2:339–69

135. Sire, O., Depeche, J. 1981. *In vitro* effect of a fish gonadotropin on aromatase and 17β-hydroxysteroid dehydrogenase activities in the ovary of the

rainbow trout (*Salmo gairdneri Rich.*). *Reprod. Nutr. Dev.* 21:715–26

136. Slaga, T. J., Krum, A. A. 1973. Modification of rabbit adrenal steroid biosynthesis by prolonged ACTH administration. *Endocrinology* 93:517–26

137. Slanina, S. M., Fevold, H. R. 1982. The enzyme specificity of ACTH stimulation of rabbit adrenal microsomal 17α-hydroxylase activity. *J. Steroid Biochem.* 16:93–99

138. Smals, A. G. H., Pieters, G. F. F. M., Drayer, J. I. M., Boers, G. H. J., Benraad, Th.J., Kloppenborg, P. W. C. 1980. Tamoxifen suppresses gonadotropin-induced 17α-hydroxyprogesterone accumulation in normal men. *J. Clin. Endocrinol. Metab.* 51:1026–24

139. Soewoto, H., Cheng, H. C., Johnson, D. C. 1977. Evidence for macromolecular synthesis in stimulation of the estrogen synthesizing system of the immature rat ovary by PMS. *Steroids* 29:349–61

140. Stone, D., Hechter, O. 1954. Studies on the ACTH action in perfused bovine adrenals: the site of action of ACTH in corticosteroidogenesis. *Arch. Biochem. Biophys.* 51:457–69

141. Suzuki, K., Tamaoki, B. 1979. Enzymological studies of rat luteinized ovaries in relation to acute reduction of aromatizable androgen formation and stimulated production of progestins. *Endocrinology* 104:1317–23

142. Suzuki, K., Tamaoki, B. 1980. Postovulatory decrease in estrogen production is caused by diminished supply of aromatizable androgen to ovarian aromatase. *Endocrinology* 107:2115–16

143. Tait, J. F., Tait, S. A. S., Bell, J. B. G. 1980. Steroid hormone production by mammalian adrenocortical dispersed cells. *Essays Biochem.* 16:99–174

144. Talawar, G. P. 1979. Human chorionic gonadotropin and ovarian and placental steroidogenesis. *J. Steroid Biochem.* 11:27–34

145. Tcholakian, R. K., Steinberger, A. 1979. In vitro metabolism of testoster-

one by cultured Sertoli cells and the effect of FSH. *Steroids* 33:495–526

146. Thornton, M., Hughes, E. R., Kelley, V. C., Ely, R. S. 1962. Influence of age on plasma adrenocorticosteroids in rats, rabbits, and guinea pigs. *Am. J. Physiol.* 202:392–94

147. Valladares, L. E., Payne, A. H. 1979. Induction of testicular aromatization by luteinizing hormone in mature rats. *Endocrinology* 105:431–36

148. Valladares, L. E., Payne, A. H. 1979. Acute stimulation of aromatization in Leydig cells by human chorionic gonadotropin in vitro. *Proc. Natl. Acad. Sci. USA* 76:4460–63

149. Van Bohemen, C. G., Lambert, J. G. D. 1981. Estrogen synthesis in relation to estrone, estradiol and vitellogenin plasma levels during the reproductive cycle of the female rainbow trout, *Salmo gairdneri. Gen. Comp. Endocrinol.* 45:105–14

150. Vinson, G. P. 1967. Role of 21-hydroxypregnenolone in the synthesis of corticosterone from pregnenolone by sheep adrenal tissue in vitro. *Gen Comp. Endocrinol.* 9:154–60

151. Wang, C., Hsueh, A. J. W., Erickson, G. F. 1980. Prolactin inhibition of estrogen production by cultured rat granulosa cells. *Mol. Cell. Endocrinol.* 20:135–44

152. West, C. D., Atcheson, J. B., Rallison, M. L., Chavré, V. J., Tyler, F. H. 1979. Multiple or single 21-hydroxylases in congenital adrenal hyperplasia? *J. Steroid Biochem.* 11:1413–19

153. Yudaev, N. A., Morozova, M. S. 1965. The activity of 21- and 11β-hydroxylases in the adrenal glands of rabbits subjected to repeated ACTH administration. *Probl. Endokrinol. Gormonterap.* No. 1:81–87

154. Yudaev, N. A., Pankov, Yu. A. 1964. The biosynthesis of 17-hydroxy- and 17-deoxycorticosteroids by pig adrenal cortex homogenate from progesteron-4-¹⁴C, pregnenolone-21-¹⁴C, and pregnenolone-4-¹⁴C. *Biokhimiya* 29:707–15

Ann. Rev. Physiol. 1983. 45:37–50

SEXUAL DIMORPHISM IN THE LIVER

Arun K. Roy[1] and Bandana Chatterjee[2]

Hormone Research Laboratory, Departments of Biological Sciences[1] and Chemistry,[2] Oakland University, Rochester, Michigan 48063

INTRODUCTION

The liver plays a central role in the biochemical coordination of various physiological processes, and because of the different metabolic needs for male and female reproduction the hepatic tissue shows considerable sexual dimorphism. Although the origin of sexual dimorphism is genetic in nature, beginning at fertilization with the formation of either XX or XY karyotype, the available evidence indicates that its phenotypic expression is mediated via the sex hormones (41). Early studies showed that estrogen causes a sex reversal of the XY embryo of the fish *Orzias latipes,* and certain marsupials eliminate a sex chromosome from most of their extragonadal cells to become XO but continue to maintain sexual dimorphism (25, 35). These findings clearly demonstrate the irrelevancy of the male and female karyotypes in the development of secondary sexual characteristics. The current concept of the developmental basis of sexual dimorphism in the mammal (25, 33, 41, 100) is presented in Figure 1. The most important component of the scheme is the discovery of the "H-Y antigen," a protein coded by the genes present on the Y chromosome. After fertilization, irrespective of the karyotype, the gonads and other reproductive structures begin to develop as female. In the case of the XY karyotype, at an early stage of development the "H-Y antigen" induces the indifferent gonad to form fetal testes instead of ovaries. The formation of testes results in the synthesis and release of the male sex hormone testosterone, which in the ovary is converted to estradiol (59). These two sex hormones play pivotal roles in sexual differentiation during both pre- and post-natal development. Exposure of differentiating organs during morphogenesis to high levels of either testosterone or es-

0066-4278/83/0315-0037$02.00

tradiol not only produces easily distinguishable morphological alterations in the reproductive tissues but also results in subtle changes within the somatic cells, causing them to react differently to subsequent hormonal stimuli. The molecular basis of this early "imprinting" is not clearly understood. However, recent findings in gene regulation indicate that the organization of the chromatin structure is an important determinant in the differential sensitivity of specific genes to various regulatory signals (61). It is possible that pre- and neonatal "imprinting" by the sex steroids involve conformational rearrangement of the chromatin structure in the target cells that allows them to respond differentially to hormonal signals during later life.

Although certain aspects of the sex difference in gene expression in nonreproductive tissues are imprinted by pre- and neonatal exposure to sex steroids (primarily androgens), a large part of sexual dimorphism at the adult stage is regulated by the action of these hormones themselves (3, 28). The action of sex hormones is considerably modified by differential steroid metabolism in the male and female liver. Sex differences in the steroid metabolizing enzymes are described in the review by Gustafsson et al in this volume. In this chapter we review the sexual dimorphism of the hepatic proteins and enzymes not directly involved in steroid hormone metabolism.

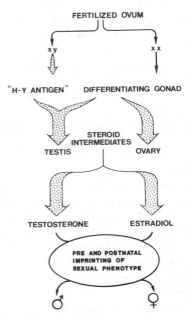

Figure 1 Scheme for the developmental basis of sexual dimorphism.

SEX-SPECIFIC PROTEINS IN THE RODENT LIVER

Much information has recently become available concerning the effects of sex hormones on the synthesis of certain major hepatic proteins in the rodent (76). Among more than 250 newly synthesized rat hepatic proteins separated by two-dimensional gel electrophoresis followed by autoradiography, at least 12 show a considerable degree of sexual dimorphism (A. K. Roy, T. S. Nath, unpublished). Many of these sex-specific proteins are only beginning to be explored; those that have been studied in considerable detail are described below.

Bond's Protein in the Rat

Evidence for a sex-associated protein in the liver of the male rat was first provided in 1960 by Bond (7), who described a major cytoplasmic protein in the liver of the male rat that was absent in the female. This intracellular protein has a sedimentation coefficient of 2.6 ($S_{20,w}$) and in the mature male rat is estimated to comprise no more than 3.2% of the total soluble proteins of the liver. Only trace amounts of this protein are found in the immature male rat, but an abrupt increase was noted between 40 and 60 days of age. Its synthesis in the male could be inhibited by estradiol treatment or castration, while it could be induced in the female by both testosterone or progesterone treatment (8). Adrenalectomy had no effect on the androgenic induction of this protein. Essentially similar results have been reported by Barzilai & Pincus (5).

Rat α_{2u} Globulin

Another male-specific protein in the rat liver is α_{2u} globulin (Mr 18,000), which accounts for more than 50% of the male urinary proteins (84, 86, 87). α_{2u} Globulin has no structural or antigenic relationship to the protein described by Bond (53). α_{2u} Globulin was so named because of its electrophoretic mobility with the α_2 globulins of rat serum and its preponderance in the urine (83). The adult male excretes more than 20 mg of this protein in its urine per day, and the messenger RNA for α_{2u} Globulin comprises 1–2% of the total hepatic mRNA (14, 85). The corresponding cDNA for α_{2u} globulin mRNA has been cloned in E. coli. (78, 95). α_{2u} Globulin is a family of proteins, each member of the family differing slightly either in isoelectric point or in the number of amino acid residues (30, 31, 54, 77, 86). Two molecular weight variants of α_{2u} globulin differing in approximately five amino acids and three isoelectric variants have been identified (B. Chatterjee, N. Motwani, A. K. Roy, unpublished). α_{2u} Globulin is coded by approximately 18 individual genes on the haploid genome (48).

Only trace amounts ($\sim$ 4 ng mg^{-1} hepatic protein) of α_{2u} globulin can be detected in the liver of prepubertal male rats. A rapid rise in its synthesis is associated with puberty, resulting in about 1000-fold higher level at maturity than in the prepubertal state (12, 73, 82). On the other hand, female rats synthesize only trace or undetectable amounts of this protein, but both α_{2u} globulin and its mRNA can be induced in the ovariectomized female with androgen treatment (14, 85). We have identified an unusual form of a cytoplasmic androgen receptor in rat liver which binds both androgenic and estrogenic steroids (60, 82). Androgenic induction of α_{2u} globulin seems to be mediated through this hepatic androgen receptor. Both androgenic induction and estrogenic inhibition of the hepatic synthesis of α_{2u} globulin are mediated through corresponding changes in the hepatic concentration of the messenger RNA for this protein (14, 49, 81).

Pre- and neonatal "imprinting" of sexual characteristics seem to modify the androgen-dependent synthesis of α_{2u} globulin in the adult, since androgenic induction of α_{2u} globulin in the ovariectomized female rat does not bring the level equal to that of the normal male (85). In addition, withdrawal of androgen treatment from ovariectomized females leads to a decline in α_{2u} synthesis faster than that observed in castrated males after androgen withdrawal. This rapid "turnoff" rate in the female after hormone withdrawal can be considerably slowed by neonatal androgen treatment to these animals (97).

Another interesting aspect of the synthesis of α_{2u} globulin is its dependence on pituitary secretions (47, 72). Hypophysectomy in the adult male rat causes a rapid decline and loss of α_{2u} globulin within 3 days. Total reversal of this effect requires simultaneous treatment with androgen, glucocorticoid, growth hormone, and thyroxine (40, 62, 72). Insulin is also required for the androgen-dependent synthesis of α_{2u} globulin, and induction of experimental diabetes causes a more than 80% reduction in its synthesis, again mediated through corresponding changes in the messenger RNA for this protein (79). Both the steroid and the peptide hormones influence the hepatic synthesis of α_{2u} globulin through corresponding changes in the hepatic concentration of the mRNA for this protein (57, 77, 78, 80, 81). Thyroxine, which was thought initially to exert a direct effect on the mRNA for this protein (18, 50, 72, 88), has recently been shown to regulate α_{2u} mRNA via increased secretion of pituitary growth hormone (77).

Senescence Marker Proteins -1 & -2 in the Rat

Recently, we identified two other proteins in the rat liver that depend on sex hormones (13). These proteins were discovered while investigating the age-dependent changes in specific protein synthesis and mRNA content of the male rat. One of these proteins (Mr 28,500) appears at puberty, is synthesized at a high level during adulthood, and declines at senescence and has been designated as senescence marker protein-1 (SMP-1). The other protein is called senescence marker protein-2 (SMP-2) and has an age-dependence opposite to that of SMP-1. Thus SMP-2 (Mr 26,300) and its mRNA are found in high concentrations in the prepubertal male rats, disappear after puberty, and reappear at senescence. Unlike SMP-1, SMP-2 is an androgen repressible protein and is normally expressed in the female rat. Thus the hepatic synthesis of these two senescence marker proteins are coupled to age-dependent changes in the sensitivity of the liver to sex hormones.

MUP in the Mouse

Mature male mice excrete a group of immunochemically related urinary proteins called Major Mouse Urinary Proteins (MUPs) (20, 89). Similar to rat a_{2u} globulin, the MUP is also of hepatic origin, coded by a multigene family, and its synthesis is under hormonal regulation (34). One interesting difference between MUP and a_{2u} globulin is that postpubertal female mice synthesize a considerable amount of MUP (4, 15). However, the relative rate of synthesis in the male mice it still approximately 4 times that in the female. Three electrophoretic variants of MUP are found in the wild type mouse and a genetic difference in the proportion of these three variant forms of MUP has also been observed (92, 93). Because of the availability of various mutant strains of mice, the MUP system is a useful model for the study of both mammalian genetics and hormone action at the molecular level.

HEPATIC SYNTHESIS OF EGG YOLK PROTEINS

In the case of sexually mature females of oviparous animals, a large proportion of the hepatocytic function is occupied by the synthesis of vitellogenin, the precursor of the egg yolk proteins, phosvitin and lipovitellin (24, 26, 94, 98, 99). Vitellogenin in Xenopus laevis is initially synthesized as a dimer of two subunits of approximately 200,000 daltons each, while in the chicken it is synthesized as a large polypeptide with a molecular weight of 240,000 (24, 98). After its synthesis, the protein undergoes extensive posttranslational modifications such as lipidation, glycosylation, and phosphorylations, before it is secreted out of the hepatocytes and transported to the ovary. The massive rate of synthesis of vitellogenin in the egg-laying animal causes considerable ultrastructural changes in the liver cells, which are characterized by extensive proliferation of the rough endoplasmic reticulum and the Golgi apparatus. Normally, vitellogenin is not synthesized in the immature or male animal. However, estrogen treatment of mature males results in a rapid induction of this protein, and within hours after hormone administration vitellogenin mRNA can be detected in the liver of *X. laevis* (42, 90).

The estrogen-dependent synthesis of vitellogenin is mediated through the hepatic estrogen receptor (6, 27). Similar to the androgen receptor in rat liver, the appearance of the hepatic estrogen receptor in the chicken and the frog is developmentally regulated. In the developing chicken liver, appearance of the estrogen receptor in the 13-day embryo correlates with the estrogen inducibility of vitellogenin while in *Xenopus* larva, the estrogen receptor first appears at metamorphic stage 53 and vitellogenin is induced by estrogen at stage 63. Acquisition of the estrogen sensitivity in the amphibian larva is regulated by the thyroid hormone. The inducible state can be held in abeyance by arresting metamorphosis of the tadpole (38, 98). Another similarity between the androgenic induction of α_{2u} globulin in rat liver and the estrogenic induction of vitellogenin is the nature of the primary and secondary inductive response and its correlation with an increased level of the hormone receptor brought about by the action of its own ligand (24, 55). Initial exposure to estrogen results in the induction of both vitellogenin and the hepatic estrogen receptor, while withdrawal of the hormone is associated with a gradual decrease of the vitellogenin synthesis to a base-line level. Nevertheless, an increased level of the estrogen receptor persists in the liver and exposure to a second stimulus by the hormone produces an enhanced vitellogenic response with a shorter lag period. Changes in chromatin organization after the initial exposure to estrogen may also play some contributing role in the enhanced synthesis of vitellogenin during secondary stimulation. The physiology of insect vitellogenesis is similar to that of the vertebrates except that the nonsteroidal juvenile hormone seems to play a more predominant role than the steroid hormone ecdysone (94).

Besides vitellogenin, two additional vitamin binding proteins—i.e. thiamin and riboflavin binding proteins—are also synthesized in the liver under the influence of the estrogenic hormones (63–66). The riboflavin binding protein present in the hen's egg has a molecular weight of 36,000 and is synthesized and secreted by the liver. It is virtually absent in the adult male and immature animals of both sexes but can be induced by estrogen treatment. The kinetics of estrogenic induction of the riboflavin binding protein in immature male chicks are similar to those of vitellogenin induction, and this system also shows the enhanced secondary response or the "memory effect" noted for other steroid hormone responsive systems (66). Most interestingly, the antiserum against purified chicken riboflavin binding protein was found to cross-react with a similar riboflavin binding protein synthesized by the rat liver under estrogenic stimulation. The rat protein has a molecular weight of 90,000 daltons and like the chicken binder interacts with riboflavin at an equimolar ratio. It is normally absent in the male and in immature rats of both sexes. The important role of this protein in the developing rat embryo is indicated by the fact that within 24 hr after a single intraperitoneal injection of the anti-riboflavin binding serum to a 15-day pregnant rat, termination of pregnancy and resorption of the embryo are observed (63). Estrogenic regulation of the hepatic synthesis of the thiamin binding protein in the chicken has also been reported (64). All of these studies underscore the important role of the liver in oogenesis and embryogenesis, and the need for sexual dimorphism to fulfill this role.

SEX DIFFERENCES IN HORMONE RECEPTORS

As mentioned earlier, the degree of hormone response of hepatic cells is also regulated by the sex-specific differences in the concentration of the hormone receptors. The androgen-dependent synthesis of α_{2u} globulin seems to depend on the presence of a hepatic androgen receptor that not only shows sexual dimorphism but also binds to estradiol. This hepatic androgen binder was first discovered in our laboratory (60, 82) and has since been described by other investigators (16, 19, 46, 91, 94a). This unusual androgen receptor has a sedimentation coefficient of 3.5S and binds to 5α-dihydrotestosterone (DHT) and estradiol-17β with K_d of 4.5 X 10^{-8}M and 3.5 X 10^{-7}M, respectively. It is absent in prepubertal male and female, senescent, and $X^{Tfm}Y$ rats—all of which are insensitive to androgenic induction of α_{2u} globulin (60, 82). In mature male rats, the receptor appears at puberty, reaching its peak around 65 days of age. The hepatic levels of the androgen receptor show direct correlation with the synthesis of α_{2u} globulin. Because of the bifunctional nature of this hepatic androgen receptor, initial treatment of ovariectomized female rats with either androgenic or estrogenic steroids can induce α_{2u} globulin. Continued exposure to the androgen results in the induction of α_{2u} globulin as well as an increase in the hepatic level of androgen receptor. On the other hand, estrogen treatment to normal male rats, which contain a high level of the androgen receptor, causes a gradual decline and ultimate loss of the receptor activity; these animals then also become temporarily insensitive to the androgenic induction of α_{2u} globulin (75, 82). It is of interest to note that estrogenic induction of its own receptor in the chicken liver with enhanced induction of vitellogenin has also been reported (55, 94). Cyproterone acetate, a competitive inhibitor of androgen action, which normally binds to the androgen receptors of the reproductive tissues, neither binds to the hepatic androgen receptor nor inhibits the synthesis of α_{2u} globulin in the mature male rats (74, 96). Similarly, another synthetic anti-androgen, flutamide, also does not bind to the hepatic androgen receptor and does not inhibit the hepatic synthesis of α_{2u} globulin in mature male rats (A. K. Roy, unpublished). Despite the strong correlation between the hepatic concentration and ligand specificity of this cytoplasmic androgen receptor and the synthesis of α_{2u} globulin, the absence of in vitro nuclear uptake of the pre-labeled cytoplasmic receptor still remains an enigma (76). Although the hepatic androgen receptor binds estradiol-17β, it can easily be distinguished from the estrogen receptor of rat liver by its inability to bind the synthetic estrogen DES (76). The androgen receptors in mouse fibroblasts and in mouse mammary tumor cells are also known to bind estradiol-17β but not DES (43). A bifunctional hepatic androgen-estrogen binding protein involved in the induction of vitellogenin in a marine teleostean fish (*Gobius niger*) has also been described (56).

Separate existence of a hepatic estrogen receptor that binds to both natural and synthetic estrogen has been reported (2, 17, 58, 69). This hepatic estrogen receptor is found in the liver of both male and female rats. Its level is low prior to puberty, but increases after maturation. Hypophysectomy causes a significant reduction in its concentration. At least three hormones—i.e. glucocorticoid, prolactin, and growth hormone—are known to be involved in the regulation of this receptor (69).

While the role of prolactin in the regulation of hepatic function is not well-understood, considerable sexual dimorphism in its hepatic binding has been reported (29, 36, 45, 67, 68, 71). Normally, the female liver contains a much higher level of the prolactin receptor than the male liver. Estrogen treatment of either male or female rats causes a significant rise in the number of prolactin binding sites whereas androgen administration causes an opposite effect (45). The sex hormones modulate lactogenic receptors in the liver through the pituitary gland (67). Hypophysectomy in the female reduces the hepatic "lactogenic sites" to the level of male rats. Injection of somatostatin into female rats causes about a 60% reduction of the prolactin receptor in the female liver (68). Conversely, passive immunization through multiple injection of antisomatostatin immune serum to male rats elevates the hepatic content of this receptor. Transplanting the pituitary under the renal capsule or transplantation of a growth hormone–producing tumor can cause an increase in the hepatic level of the prolactin receptors in the hypophysectomized rats (21). It is therefore likely that the effect of sex hormones on the hepatic prolactin receptor is mediated through pituitary growth hormone and somatostatin.

SEXUAL DIMORPHISM OF THE HEPATIC ENZYMES

In addition to the presence of male- and female- specific proteins in the liver, there are many other cases of sexual dimorphism involving hepatic enzymes. The foremost example is the group of steroid metabolizing enzymes, which will not be considered here. Another interesting example of a sexually dimorphic enzyme in the rat liver is the sulfonamide-resistant isozyme of carbonic anhydrase (CA-III) (11, 22, 23). This enzyme is normally found in the liver of mature male rats and can be induced in the female with androgenic hormones. On the other hand, the female-specific carbonic anhydrase (CA-II) is inducible by the estrogenic hormones. The induction and repression of these two isozymes serve as valuable markers for the study of the finer aspects of gene regulation in the mammalian liver. Glutathione S-transferase can also serve as a model for studying the molecular mechanism of sex hormone action (32). One of the isozymes, glutathione S-transferase B (also known as ligandin) (51) is three times as active in the male as in the female liver, but hypophysectomy eliminates this difference. Therefore, besides sex hormones, certain pituitary hormones appear to be involved in the regulation of this enzyme. Cloning of the cDNA for this enzyme has recently been reported (44).

In the egg-laying animals, vitellogenesis in the female is associated with increased production of vitellogenin, which places a greater demand on the hepatic cells for the synthesis of lipid components of the lipovitellin and the proliferating endoplasmic reticulum. Thus the rate-limiting enzymes in cholesterol and fatty acid synthesis are also regulated by the sex hormones. Two of these estrogen-inducible enzymes in the liver of *X. laevis* that have received considerable attention are HMG-CoA reductase, involved in cholesterol biosynthesis, and acetyl CoA carboxylase, the initial enzyme in fatty acid synthesis (70). A two- to three-fold higher hepatic level of HMG CoA reductase is not only limited to the oviparous females, but is also found in the liver of female rats. As in the frog, liver enzyme in the rat can be induced with estrogen (10).

The hepatic tissue of the adult male rat contains a concentration of the amino acid metabolizing enzyme histidase approximately 3 times that in the female. Estrogenic induction of this enzyme shows certain similarities with the androgen-dependent synthesis of α_{2u} globulin—i.e. both proteins are insensitive to the inducing steroids before puberty, and the pituitary secretions play a permissive role in their induction by estrogen (1, 52). Hepatic monoamine oxidase (MAO), the enzyme that modulates the action of neurotransmitters such as norepinephrine and serotonin, also shows considerable sexual dimorphism. The activity of this enzyme in the adult female rat is about 50% higher than the adult male. Castration of the adult male increases MAO activity to a level comparable to that of the normal female (39). Neonatal imprinting of the androgen responsiveness of this enzyme by the presence of androgen at an early stage has also been reported. Unlike MAO, two isozymes of aldehyde oxidase (AOX-1 and AOX-2) are found in much higher concentrations in the liver of the male than in that of the female mouse. Both isozymes are reduced after castration and are increased following androgen treatment (37). Finally, an interesting case of sexual dimorphism is exhibited by ethylmorphine demethylase of the mouse liver. In one strain of mouse (BALB/cJ) the activity is greater in the male than in the female, while in another strain (CRL:CD-1) the female liver contains about a 50% higher demethylase activity than the male (9). The physiological basis for this curious example of inverted sexual dimorphism in two strains of mouse is not known.

SUMMARY AND CONCLUSION

That the liver in oviparous females supplies the major part of the egg yolk proteins requires a marked degree of sexual dimorphism of this organ. In addition to vitellogenin, several minor components (e.g. vitamin binding proteins) are supplied by the liver to the oocyte in oviparous animals and to the developing embryo in viviparous females. Other metabolic adjustments to maintain reproductive competency of the female (e.g. increased lipid synthesis, detoxification of the waste products of the developing embryo, and reproductively sensible steroid metabolism) are some of the physiological bases for the differences between the female and male liver. Sex-differences in several other hepatic proteins, enzymes, and hormone receptors have also been established. α_{2u} Globulin, Bond's protein, and carbonic anhydrase are clear examples of the sex specificity of rat liver. Differential expression of the genes for the male- and female-specific proteins in the liver is brought about by the androgenic and estrogenic hormones. The hepatic receptors for these hormones also show a marked degree of sexual dimorphism. During development and aging, these receptors seem to appear when the need for these hormones is most critical. The timely appearance of the hepatic estrogen and androgen receptor and the facilitated action of these hormones are mediated through "pre- and neonatal imprinting" by the sex hormones, especially androgen. Exploration of the physiological and molecular basis of this "imprinting" mechanism remains an exciting area of contemporary endocrinology.

ACKNOWLEDGMENTS

We thank Drs. M. V. Riley and B. S. Winkler for their comments. The work in our laboratory is supported by the NIH Grant AM-14744

Literature Cited

1. Armstrong, E. G., Feigelson, M. 1980. Effects of hypophysectomy and triiodothyronine on de novo biosynthesis, catalytic activity, and estrogen induction of rat liver histidase. *J. Biol. Chem.* 620:167-71

2. Aten, R. F., Dickson, R. B., Eisenfeld, A. J. 1979. Female and male green monkey liver estrogen receptor. *Biochem. Pharmacol.* 28:2445-50

3. Bardin, C. W., Catterall, J. F. 1981. Testosterone: A major determinant of extragenital sexual dimorphism. *Science* 211:1285-94

4. Barth, R. K., Grass, K. W., Gremke, L. C., Hastie, N. D. 1982. Developmentally regulated mRNAs in mouse liver. *Proc. Natl. Acad. Sci. USA* 79:500-4

5. Barzilai, D., Pincus, G. 1965. Sex dependent protein component of rat liver. *Proc. Soc. Exp. Biol. Med.* 118:57-59

6. Bergink, E. W., Witliff, J. L. 1975. Molecular weights of estrogen and androgen binding proteins in the liver of *Xenopus laevis. Biochemistry* 14:3115-21

7. Bond, H. E. 1960. A sex-associated protein in liver tissue of male rat. *Biochem. Biophys. Res. Commun.* 3:53-55

8. Bond, H. E. 1966. Sex-associated protein in liver tissue of the rat. *Nature* 209:1026

9. Brown, T. R., Bardin, C. W., Green, F. E. 1978. Mouse liver N-demethylase activity. Sex differences and androgen responsiveness. *Pharmacology* 16:159-69

10. Carlson, S. E., Mitchell, A. D., Carter, M. L., Goldfarb, S. 1980. Evidence that physiologic levels of circulating estrogens and neonatal sex-imprinting modify postpubertal hepatic microsomal 3-hydroxy-3-methylglutaryl coenzyme reductase activity. *Biochim. Biophys. Acta* 633:154-61

11. Carter, N. D., Hewett-Emmett, D., Jeffrey, S., Tashian, R. E. 1981. Testosterone-induced, sulfonamide-resistant carbonic anhydrase isozyme of rat liver is indistinguishable from skeletal muscle carbonic anhydrase III. *FEBS Lett.* 128:114-18

12. Chatterjee, B., Hopkins, J., Dutchak, D., Roy, A. K. 1979. Super-induction of α_{2u} globulin by actinomycin D: Evidence for the drug mediated increase in α_{2u} mRNA. *Proc. Natl. Acad. Sci. USA* 76:1833-37

13. Chatterjee, B., Nath, T., Roy, A. K. 1981. Differential regulation of the messenger RNA for three major senescence marker proteins in male rat liver. *J. Biol. Chem.* 256:5939-41

14. Chatterjee, B., Roy, A. K. 1980. Messenger RNA for α_{2u} globulin in rat liver: Purification, partial characterization of the mRNA and synthesis of a Hae-III restriction fragment as its cDNA probe. *J. Biol. Chem.* 255:11607

15. Derman, E. 1981. Isolation of a cDNA clone for mouse urinary proteins: Age- and sex-related expression of mouse urinary protein genes is transcriptionally controlled. *Proc. Natl. Acad. Sci. USA* 78:5425-29

16. Dickson, R. B., Aten, R. F., Eisenfeld, A. J. 1978. An unusual sex steroid-binding protein in mature male rat liver cytosol. *Endocrinology* 103:1636-46

17. Dickson, R. B., Eisenfeld, A. J. 1979. Estrogen receptor in liver of male and female rats: Endocrine regulation and molecular properties. *Biol. Reprod.* 21:1105-14

18. Dillman, W. H., Silva, E., Surks, M. I., Oppenheimer, J. H. 1977. Studies of a thyroid hormone and androgen dependent protein in rat liver cytosol. *Acta Endocrinol.* 84:548-58

19. Eagon, P. K., Porter, L. E., Gavaler, J. S., Egler, K. M., Van Thiel, D. H. 1981. Effect of ethanol feeding upon levels of a male-specific hepatic estrogen-binding protein: A possible mechanism for feminization. *Alcoholism* 5:183-87

20. Finlayson, J. S., Patter, M., Schinnick, C. S., Smithies, O. 1974. Components of major urinary protein complex of inbred mice. Determination of NH_2-terminal sequence and comparison with homologous components from wild mice. *Biochem. Genet.* 11:325-34

21. Furuhashi, N., Fang, V. S. 1978. Hormone receptors in livers of GH3 tumor-bearing rats: The predominant effect of growth hormone and testosterone. *Endocrinology* 103:2053-60

22. Garg, L. C. 1974. The effect of sex hormones on rat liver carbonic anhydrase. *J. Pharmacol. Exp. Ther.* 189:557-62

23. Garg, L. C. 1975. Induction of hepatic carbonic anhydrase by estrogen. *J. Pharmacol. Exp. Ther.* 192:297-302

24. Goldberger, R. F., Deeley, R. G. 1980. The effect of estrogen on gene expression in avian liver. In *Gene Regulation by Steroid Hormones,* ed. A. K. Roy, J. H. Clark, pp. 32-57. NY: Springer. 316 pp.

25. Gordon, J. W., Ruddle, F. H. 1981. Mammalian gonadal determination and gametogenesis. *Science* 211:1265-71

26. Gruber, M., Bos, E. S., Ab, G. 1976. Hormonal control of vitellogenin synthesis in avian liver. *Mol. Cell. Endocrinol.* 5:41–50

27. Gschwendt, M. 1975. A cytoplasmic oestrogen-binding component in chicken liver. *Hoppe-Seylers Z. Physiol. Chem.* 356:157–65

28. Gustafsson, J. Å. 1974. Androgen responsiveness of the liver of the developing rat. *Biochem. J.* 144:225–29

29. Gustafsson, J. Å., Eneroth, P., Hokfelt, T., Mode, A., Norstedt, G., Skett, P. 1980. Central control of hepatic steroid metabolism and "lactogenic" receptor. *J. Steroid Biochem.* 12:1–15

30. Haars, L. J., Pitot, H. C. 1980. Characteristics of the carbohydrate moiety and the intermolecular associations of the high-molecular-weight forms of α_{2u} globulin. *Eur. J. Biochem.* 107:539–45

31. Haars, L. J., Pitot, H. C. 1980. Hormonal and developmental regulation of glycosylated α_{2u} globulin synthesis. *Arch. Biochem. Biophys.* 201:556–63

32. Hales, B. F., Neims, A. H. 1976. A sex difference in hepatic glutathione S-transferase B and the effect of hypophysectomy. *Biochem. J.* 160:223–29

33. Haseltine, F. P., Ohno, S. 1981. Mechanisms of gonadal differentiation. *Science* 211:1272–78

34. Hastie, N. D., Held, W. A., Toole, J. J. 1979. Multiple genes coding for the androgen-regulated major urinary proteins of the mouse. *Cell* 17:449–57

35. Hayman, D., Martin, P. 1965. Sex chromosome mosaism in the marsupial genera *Isoodon* and *Perameles.* *Genetics* 52:1201–6

36. Herington, A. C., Burger, H. G., Veith, N. M. 1976. Binding of human growth hormone to hepatic lactogenic binding sites: Regulation by oestrogens and androgens. *J. Endocrinol.* 70:473–84

37. Holmes, R. S. 1979. Genetics, ontogeny, and testosterone inducibility of aldehyde oxidase isozymes in the mouse: Evidence for two genetic loci (AOX-1 and AOX-2) closely linked on chromosome 1. *Biochem. Genet.* 17:517–27

38. Huber, S., Ryffel, G. U., Weber, R. 1979. Thyroid hormone induces competence for oestrogen-dependent vitellogenin synthesis in developing *Xenopus laevis* liver. *Nature* 278:65–67

39. Illsley, N. P., Kita, E., Lamartiniere, C. A. 1980. Role of the pituitary in modulating hepatic monoamine oxidase activity. *Endocrinology* 106:798–804

40. Irwin, J. F., Lane, S. E., Neuhaus, O. W. 1971. Synergistic effect of glucocorticoids and androgens on the biosynthesis of a sex-dependent protein in the male rat. *Biochim. Biophys. Acta* 252:328–34

41. Jost, A. 1953. Problem of fetal endocrinology: The gonadal and hypophyseal hormones. *Rec. Prog. Horm. Res.* 8:379–418

42. Jost, J. P., Ohno, T., Panyim, S., Scheurch, A. R. 1978. Appearance of vitellogenin mRNA sequences and rate of vitellogenin synthesis in chicken liver following primary and secondary stimulation by 17β-estradiol. *Eur. J. Biochem.* 84:355–61

43. Jung-Testas, I., Bayard, F., Baulieu, E. E. 1976. Two sex steroid receptors in mouse fibroblasts in culture. *Nature* 259:136–38

44. Kalinyak, J. E., Taylor, J. M. 1982. Rat glutathione S-transferase-cloning of double-stranded cDNA and induction of its mRNA. *J. Biol. Chem.* 257:523–30

45. Kelly, P. A., LeBlanc, G., Gerland, L., Labrie, F., DeLean, A. 1977. Androgen inhibition of basal and estrogen-stimulated prolactin binding in rat liver. *Mol. Cell. Endocrinol.* 9:195–204

46. Kondratev, I., Smirnov, A. N., Smirnova, O. V. 1980. Multicomponent system of estrogen-binding proteins of the liver. Isolation and comparative properties of 4-5S and other rat liver high molecular weight proteins, which specifically bind estradiol. *Biokhimiia* 45:2065–75

47. Kumar, M., Roy, A. K., Axelrod, A. E. 1969. Androgenic induction of α_{2u} globulin in the rat: Requirement of an intact pituitary. *Nature* 223:399

48. Kurtz, D. T. 1981. Rat α_{2u} globulin is encoded by a multigene family. *J. Mol. Appl. Genet.* 1:29–38

49. Kurtz, D. T., Sippel, A. E., Ansah-Yiadom, R., Feigelson, P. 1976. Effects of sex hormones on the level of the messenger RNA for the rat hepatic protein α_{2u} globulin. *J. Biol. Chem.* 251:3594–98

50. Kurtz, D. T., Sippel, A. E., Feigelson, P. 1976. Effect of thyroid hormones on the level of the hepatic mRNA for α_{2u} globulin. *Biochemistry* 15:1031–36

51. Litwack, G., Ketterer, B., Arias, A. 1971. Ligandin: A hepatic protein which binds steroids, bilirubin, carcinogens and a number of exogenous organic anions. *Nature* 234:466–67

52. Lamartiniere, C. A. 1979. Neonatal estrogen treatment alters sexual differentiation of hepatic histidase. *Endocrinology* 105:1031–35

53. Lane, S. E., Neuhaus, O. W. 1972. Further studies on the isolation and characterization of a sex-dependent protein from the urine of male rats. *Biochim. Biophys. Acta* 257:461–70

54. Lane, S. E., Neuhaus, O. W. 1972. Multiple forms of α_{2u}, a sex-dependent urinary protein of the adult male rat. *Biochim. Biophys. Acta* 263:433–40

55. Lazier, C. 1975. (^{3}H)-estradiol binding by chick liver nuclear extracts: Mechanism of increase in binding following estradiol injection. *Steroids* 26:281–98

56. LeMenn, F., Rochefort, H., Garcia, M. 1980. Effect of androgen mediated by the estrogen receptor of fish liver: Vitellogenin accumulation. *Steroids* 35:315–28

57. Lynch, K. R., Dolan, K. P., Nakhashi, H. L., Unterman, R., Feigelson, P. 1982. The role of growth hormone in α_{2u} globulin synthesis: A reexamination. *Cell* 28:185–89

58. Mataradze, G. D., Rukaiia, M. K. H., Smirnov, A. N., Rozen, V. B. 1979. Multi-component system of estrogen binding proteins from the liver: Characterization of binding properties of high molecular weight protein from rat liver similar to uterine estradiol receptors. *Biokhimiia* 44:1484–92

59. Milewich, L., George, F. W., Wilson, J. D. 1977. Estrogen formation by the ovary of the rabbit embryo. *Endocrinology* 100:187–97

60. Milin, B., Roy, A. K. 1973. Androgen receptor in rat liver: Cytosol receptor deficiency in the pseudohermaphrodite male rats. *Nature New Biol.* 248:50

61. Minty, A., Newmark, P. 1980. Gene regulation: New, old and remote controls. *Nature* 288:210–11

62. Motwani, N. M., Unakar, N. J., Roy, A. K. 1980. Multiple hormone requirement for the synthesis of α_{2u} globulin by monolayer of rat hepatocytes in long term primary culture. *Endocrinology* 107:1606–13

63. Muniyappa, K., Adiga, P. R. 1980. Occurrence and functional importance of a riboflavin-carrier protein in the pregnant rat. *FEBS Lett.* 110:209–12

64. Muniyappa, K., Adiga, P. R. 1980. Oestrogen-induced synthesis of thiamin-binding protein in immature chicks. *Biochem. J.* 198:201–10

65. Murthy, U. S., Adiga, P. R. 1978. Estrogen-induced synthesis of riboflavin-binding protein in immature chicks: Kinetics and hormonal specificity. *Biochem. Biophys. Acta* 538:364–74

66. Murthy, U. S., Adiga, P. R. 1978. Oestrogen induction of riboflavin-binding protein in immature chicks. *Biochem. J.* 170:331–35

67. Norstedt, G., Mode, A. 1982. On the primary site of action of estrogens and androgens in regulation of hepatic prolactin receptors. *Endocrinology.* In press

68. Norstedt, G., Mode, A., Hokfelt, T., Eneroth, P., Labrie, F., Ferland, L., Gustafsson, J. Å. 1982. Possible role of somatostatin in regulation of the sexually differentiated steroid metabolism and prolactin receptor in rat liver. *Endocrinology* In press

69. Norstedt, G., Wrange, O., Gustafsson, J. Å. 1981. Multihormonal regulation of the estrogen receptor in rat liver. *Endocrinology* 103:1190–95

70. Philipp, B. W., Shapiro, D. J. 1981. Estrogen regulation of hepatic 3-hydroxy-3-methylglutaryl coenzyme A reductase and acetyl-CoA carboxylase in *Xenopus laevis. J. Biol. Chem.* 256:2922–27

71. Posner, B. I., Josefsberg, Z., Bergeron, J. J. M. 1979. Intracellular polypeptide hormone receptors. *J. Biol. Chem.* 254:12494–99

72. Roy, A. K. 1973. Androgen dependent synthesis of α_{2u} globulin in rat: Role of the pituitary gland. *J. Endocrinol.* 56:295–301

73. Roy, A. K. 1973. Androgenic induction of α_{2u} globulin in rat: Androgen insensitivity in prepubertal animals. *Endocrinology* 92:957–60

74. Roy, A. K. 1976. Effect of cyproterone acetate on the androgen dependent synthesis of α_{2u} globulin in the rat. *J. Endocrinol.* 70:189–95

75. Roy, A. K. 1977. Early events in the steroidal regulation of α_{2u} globulin in rat liver: Evidence for both androgenic and estrogenic induction. *Eur. J. Biochem.* 73:537–43

76. Roy, A. K. 1979. Hormonal regulation of the hepatic synthesis of α_{2u} globulin. In *Biochemical Actions of Hormones,* ed. G. Litwack, 6:481–517. NY: Academic. 530 pp.

77. Roy, A. K. 1982. Role of thyroid hormone in the expression of α_{2u} globulin and other multihormonally regulated genes. In *Molecular Basis of Thyroid Hormone Action,* ed. J. H. Oppenheimer, H. H. Samuels. NY: Academic. In press

78. Roy, A. K., Chatterjee, B., Demyan, W. F., Nath, T. S., Motwani, N. M. 1982. Pretranslational regulation of α_{2u} globulin in rat liver by growth hormone. *J. Biol. Chem.* 257:7834–38

79. Roy, A. K., Chatterjee, B., Prasad, M. S. K., Unakar, N. J. 1980. Role of insulin in the regulation of the hepatic messenger RNA for α_{2u} globulin in diabetic rats. *J. Biol. Chem.* 255:11614–18

80. Roy, A. K., Dowbenko, D. J. 1977. Role of growth hormone in the multihormonal regulation of messenger RNA for α_{2u} globulin in the liver of hypophysectomized rats. *Biochemistry* 16:3918–22

81. Roy, A. K., Dowbenko, D. J., Schiop, M. J. 1977.Studies on the mode of oestrogenic inhibition of hepatic synthesis of α_{2u} globulin and its corresponding messenger RNA in rat liver. *Biochem. J.* 164:91–97

82. Roy, A. K., Milin, B. S., McMinn, D. M. 1974. Androgen receptor in rat liver: Hormonal and developmental regulation of the cytoplasmic receptor and its correlation with the androgen dependent synthesis of α_{2u} globulin. *Biochim. Biophys. Acta* 354:213–32

83. Roy, A. K., Neuhaus, O. W. 1966. Identification of rat urinary proteins by zone and immunoelectrophoresis. *Proc. Soc. Exp. Biol. Med.* 121:894–99

84. Roy, A. K., Neuhaus, O. W. 1966. Proof of the hepatic synthesis of a sex dependent protein in the rat. *Biochem. Biophys. Acta* 127:82–87

85. Roy, A. K., Neuhaus, O. W. 1967. Androgenic control of a sex dependent protein in the rat. *Nature* 214:618–20

86. Roy, A. K., Neuhaus, O. W., Harmison, C. R. 1966. Preparation and characterization of a sex dependent rat urinary protein. *Biochim. Biophys. Acta* 127:72–81

87. Roy, A. K., Raber, D. L. 1972. Immunofluorescent localization of α_{2u} globulin in the hepatic and renal tissues of rat. *J. Histochem. Cytochem.* 20: 89–96

88. Roy, A. K., Schiop, M. J., Dowbenko, D. J. 1976. The role of thyroxine in the regulation of the translatable messenger RNA for α_{2u} globulin. *FEBS Lett.* 64:396–99

89. Rumke, P. H., Breekveldt-Kielich, J. C., Van Den Broecke-Siddre, A. 1970. Sex-associated urinary protein in the rat. *Biochim. Biophys. Acta* 200:275–83

90. Ryffel, G. U., Wahli, W., Weber, R. 1977. Quantitation of vitellogenin messenger RNA in the liver of male *Xenopus* toads during primary and secondary stimulation by estrogen. *Cell* 11:213–21

91. Smirnov, A. N., Smirnova, O. V., Rozen, V. B. 1977. Detection and preliminary characterization of a particular estrogen-binding protein in the liver of male rats. *Biokhimiia* 42:560–71

92. Szoka, P. R., Paigen, K. 1979. Genetic regulation of MUP production in recombinant inbred mice. *Genetics* 93:173–81

93. Szoka, P. R., Paigen, K. 1978. Regulation of mouse major urinary protein production by the MUP-A gene. *Genetics* 90:597–612

94. Tata, J. R. 1979. Control by oestrogen of reversible gene expression: The vitellogenin model. *J. Steroid Biochem.* 11:361–71

94a. Thompson, C., Powell-Jones, W., Lucier, G. W. 1981. Sex differences in hepatic oestrogen-binding proteins. *Biochem. J.* 194:1–8

95. Unterman, R. D., Lynch, K. R., Nakhashi, H. L., Dolan, K. P., Hamilton, J. W., Kohn, D. V., Feigelson, P. 1981. Cloning and sequence of several α_{2u} globulin cDNAs. *Proc. Natl. Acad. Sci. USA* 78:3478–82

96. Vandoren, G., Heyns, W., Verhoeven, G., DeMoor, P. 1978. Sexual difference in the effect of cyproterone acetate and glucocorticoids on α_{2u} globulin in gonadectomized rats. *J. Endocrinol.* 79: 135–36

97. Vandoren, G., Vanbaelen, H., Verhoeven, G., DeMoor, P. 1978. Relationship between the pituitary gland and gonadal steroids: Involvement of a hypophysial factor in reduced α_{2u} globulin and increased transcortin concentration in rat serum. *J. Endocrinol.* 78:31–38

98. Wahli, W., Dawid, I. B., Ryffel, G. U., Weber, R. 1981. Vitellogenesis and the vitellogenin gene family. *Science* 212:298–304

99. Wangh, L. J., Knowland, J. 1975. Synthesis of vitellogenin in cultures of male and female frog liver regulated by estradiol treatment *in vitro*. *Proc. Natl. Acad. Sci. USA* 72:3172–75

100. Wilson, J. D., George, F. W., Griffin, J. E. 1981. The hormonal control of sexual development. *Science* 211:1278–84

Ann. Rev. Physiol. 1983. 45:51–60

SEX STEROID INDUCED CHANGES IN HEPATIC ENZYMES

J.-Å. Gustafsson[1], A. Mode[1], G. Norstedt,[1] and P. Skett[2]

[1]Department of Medical Nutrition, Karolinska Institute, Huddinge University Hospital F69, S–141 86 Huddinge, Sweden; and [2]Department of Pharmacology, The University of Glasgow, Glasgow G12 8QQ, Scotland

INTRODUCTION

In this review we summarize the literature regarding hormonal control of hepatic steroid and drug metabolism with special emphasis on the possible existence of a new hormonal axis operating in this control.

It has long been known that the duration of action of a number of drugs in the rat is sex-dependent (1) and that this is related to differences in rate of metabolism of the drugs (2, 3). Such sex differences in hepatic metabolism of drugs have been shown for ethylmorphine (4–6), aniline (7, 8), p-nitroanisole (9), lidocaine and imipramine (10), as well as for steroid hormones (11–19). Hepatic steroid and drug metabolism in humans has also been shown to be sex-dependent (20, 21), but the differences do not seem to be as marked as in the rat. Thus it is of both scientific and clinical interest to ascertain the mechanism of control of the sex differences noted.

STEROID METABOLISM

Androgenic Control

In 1958, Yates et al (22) indicated that androgens were involved in the regulation of steroid metabolism; castration increased the activity of the steroid 5α-reductase whereas testosterone treatment reduced the activity back to the normal male level. These findings were confirmed by our own group using 4-androstene-3,17-dione and 5α-androstane-3α,17β-diol as

51

0066-4278/83/0315-0051$02.00

substrates (23, 24) where several hydroxylase activities show a marked reduction after castration (a move towards a more female level) and are subsequently restored to normal activity by testosterone treatment. Such a pattern of regulation is also seen for the phase II metabolism of steroids— e.g. sulfurylation (19).

Of particular interest in this respect is the 15β-hydroxylase active on steroid sulfates (e.g. 5α-androstane-3α,17β-diol 3,17-disulfate). This enzyme is a predominantly female enzyme (male concentration is < 0.03% of that in the female) (25, 26) and, although castration of male animals has little effect, testosterone treatment of female animals suppressed the activity of the enzyme. The simple androgen dependency of a number of steroid-metabolizing enzymes is obviously not applicable to all sex-dependent enzymes in the liver. At least three groups of enzymes can be distinguished on the basis of their androgen dependence. Group I is entirely dependent on androgens, group II is partially dependent, group III is independent of androgens (23, 24, 27, 28). For the group II enzymes it was shown that castration of adult males caused a partial feminization, but neonatal castration caused a total feminization that could not be reversed by androgen treatment in adulthood. Treatment of castrated neonates with testosterone restored the enzyme level to that found in an adult-castrated animal and also restored the androgen responsiveness in the adult animal. Neonatal androgen's affecting the enzyme level and androgen responsiveness of the enzyme in the adult period is referred to as "imprinting." It is also seen for the group I enzymes, whose androgen responsiveness also disappears following neonatal castration. This "imprinting" process has also been described by other groups (29, 30) using androgens and corticosteroids as substrates. "Imprinting" of liver enzymes has been reviewed recently (31).

It was first suggested that the subsequent lack of response to androgen in the neonatally castrated animal could be due to the failure of induction of a hepatic androgen receptor. It was proposed that neonatal androgen might "imprint" the liver to produce a receptor in the adult period (28). No evidence for any sex-dependent androgen receptor has, however, been found. In fact, the androgen receptor seen is equivalent in both sexes (32). It is now accepted that most, if not all, of the androgen effects on liver steroid metabolism are mediated via another androgen-sensitive endocrine organ.

The nature of this organ can be deduced from experimental evidence. In the rat, sex differences in steroid metabolism are not seen before 30 days of age and are not complete until 42 days of age, a period that matches that of puberty and of the maturation of the pituitary gland (33–36). Androgens are known to affect pituitary secretion (37–39), and the hypothalamo-pituitary axis may be the androgen-sensitive organ in question. This possibility was supported by the finding that hypophysectomized male animals were unable to respond to androgen in the adult period (40).

Estrogenic Control

The involvement of estrogens in the control of hepatic steroid metabolism is less clear than that of androgens. Ovariectomy has little effect on the hepatic metabolism of 4-androstene-3,17-dione and 5α-androstane-3α, 17β-diol (23), indicating that estrogens are not necessary for the maintenance of the female type metabolism. Treatment of male animals with estrogens, however, causes a marked shift towards a female-type metabolism (23, 25, 41). It was also found that neonatal "imprinting" could be reversed by the continuous presence of estrogen (42, 43). The effects of estrogens could not, however, be observed in hypophysectomized animals (40).

The information gained from work on sex-hormone control of steroid metabolism indicates that control by androgens and estrogens does indeed exist but is not a direct effect of the sex hormone on the liver. A more complex control involving the hypothalamo-pituitary axis is involved through which the sex hormones exhibit their effects.

Pituitary Control

In 1974, Denef (44) and our own group (45) independently presented data indicating that the pituitary gland was essential for the maintenance of the female-type steroid metabolism. Hypophysectomy of male and female animals abolished the sex differences. These observations were confirmed by data from the metabolism of corticosteroids (46) and other androgens (29).

The important question then to be answered was: What is (are) the pituitary hormone(s) involved in the sex difference in hepatic steroid metabolism? A number of reports have been published showing effects of various purified pituitary hormone preparations. Our own group has shown the effects of LH, FSH, and prolactin (47, 48), indicating that FSH slightly masculinizes hepatic steroid metabolism whereas LH and prolactin have little effect. This was confirmed by Colby et al (49), who used corticosterone as substrate, and was further substantiated by Lax et al (50), who investigated the effect of prolactin on reductive metabolism. Colby et al (49) indicated that a mixture of GH and ACTH could decrease reductive metabolism (an effect similar to hypophysectomy) whereas GH alone increased it (51). All of these studies, however, were performed with heterologous hormones—bovine hormones in the case of LH, FSH, and GH; and the ovine hormone in the case of prolactin. This could lead to results that are open to misinterpretation; caution should be employed when examining these data owing to the marked species specificities of the pituitary hormones. In addition, all of the effects noted were small when compared to the effects of, say, hypophysectomy.

Therefore, in order to further investigate the role of pituitary hormones new methods of study are needed. One promising line of investigation is the continuous subcutaneous infusion of homologous hormones using the Alzet® osmotic minipump (52). The pump is filled with hormone solution and then inserted under the skin of the animal at the nape of the neck. The pump will deliver 1 μl/hr^{-1} for one week. After one week the animal is killed and the effect of the hormone on hepatic steroid metabolism investigated.

Of the pituitary hormones tested only GH (both of human and rat origin) caused a marked feminization when infused in hypophysectomized male animals; infusion resulted in a significant decrease in the activities of the 6β- and 16α-hydroxylases and an increase in 5α-reductase activity (53). Thus GH may be the pituitary "feminizing factor" (54) thought to be responsible for the maintenance of the female type of hepatic steroid metabolism in the rat. These results seemed puzzling in view of the apparent lack of correlation between "femininity" of liver steroid metabolism and serum levels of GH. Recently a possible explanation of this anomaly has been found. The *pattern* of secretion of GH is sex-dependent (55, 56). The male exhibits a highly pulsatile secretory pattern (peaks every 3–4 hr and very low GH levels between peaks), the female a more constant GH level with irregular peaks but higher interpeak GH levels. Experiments in which GH injections at 3–, 6–, and 12-hour intervals were compared to continuous infusion have indicated that this may indeed be the reason for the effects of GH. Continuous infusion and the injections at shorter time intervals (mimicking the female GH pattern) gave feminization, whereas injections at longer time intervals (mimicking the male GH pattern) did not give feminization, although the total amount of GH given was identical in all cases (57, 58).

Hypothalamic Control

In view of the role of GH in control of hepatic steroid metabolism it was of interest to study the possible involvement of somatostatin in regulation of liver function. Electrolytic lesions in male rats localized in the anterior hypothalamic periventricular area caused a "feminization" of hepatic steroid metabolism. Following periventricular lesions, histochemical analysis revealed a decrease in somatostatin-like immunoreactive cell bodies in the periventricular area. Also, the number of immunoreactive somatostatin fibers in the median eminence was dramatically reduced. Somatostatin levels in the median eminence, as measured by radioimmunoassay, were reduced to approximately 2–10% of control values after periventricular lesions. Large lesions in the amygdaloid complex in male rats caused a partial "feminization" of hepatic steroid metabolism. Passive immunization during four days by multiple injections of an antiserum generated against somatostatin resulted in a partial "feminization" of the male rat liver (Norstedt, G., Mode, A., Hökfelt, T., Eneroth, P., Ferland, L., Labrie, F., Gustafsson, J.-Å., submitted for publication).

These results indicate that the anterior periventricular hypothalamic area is important in the control of the sexually differentiated steroid metabolism in the liver and that the amygdaloid complex also may have regulatory influences on this system. Somatostatin or a related compound may be a central neuroendocrine mediator of these sex differences in the liver.

Site of Action of Sex Steroids in Control of Hepatic Metabolism

With the increasing body of evidence that the somatostatin–growth hormone system is involved in regulation of liver metabolism we have recently attempted to study more directly the site of action of gonadal steroids in control of hepatic metabolism. The technique of intracranial implantation of crystalline steroids was used to seek the site of estrogen control of hepatic steroid metabolism. Implantation of cholesterol served as a control experiment to estimate the nonspecific effects of the implantation procedure. Cholesterol implants placed in the paraventricular or pituitary regions of male rats had comparatively small effects on the metabolism of 4-androstene-3,17-dione in liver. Furthermore, subcutaneous implantation of estrogen did not influence hepatic metabolism of 4-androstene-3,17-dione in male rats, suggesting that the estrogen dose given by the implants did not cause systemic effects. However, implantation of estradiol benzoate in the pituitary region of male rats caused a complete feminization of hepatic metabolism of 4-androstene-3,17-dione. Estrogen implanted in the paraventricular region appeared to be slightly less effective in causing feminization.

The synthetic androgen methyltrienolone (R 1881) has a strong androgenic potency and was used in attempts to localize the site of action of androgen when affecting liver metabolism. Administration of R 1881 to normal female rats led to a change of hepatic 4-androstene-3,17-dione metabolism in a masculine direction. However, R 1881 was without effect when administered to hypophysectomized male rats or to deafferentated male rats.

In summary, the following conclusions can be drawn concerning estrogenic and androgenic control of hepatic steroid metabolism:

1. Estrogen feminizes hepatic steroid metabolism via an action at the hypothalamo-pituitary level, possibly directly on the pituitary.

2. An intact hypothalamo-pituitary unit is required for the masculinizing action of R 1881. It is possible that the site of action of androgens is in the rostral hypothalamus or in adjacent areas of the brain.

3. It is suggested that the hypothalamo-pituitary control of the sexually differentiated hepatic steroid metabolism is mediated via GH or a peptide similar to GH.

XENOBIOTIC METABOLISM

Sex differences in metabolism by the rat liver have been shown for a large number of xenobiotics including the model substrates, 7-propoxycoumarin (59) and 1,2,3,4,9,9-hexachloro-1,4,4a,5,6,7,8, 8a-ocatahydro-6,7-dimethyl-6,7-epoxy-1,4-methanonaphthalene (DME) (60), and the clinically important drugs lidocaine (61), diazepam (61, 62), and imipramine (61). The existence of sex differences in xenobiotic metabolism is not unique to the rat. Such differences have been shown in the mouse (the opposite of that found in the rat) (63–65), human (21, 66), and even the trout (similar to that found in the rat) (67).

Gonadal Control

How are these often large sex differences in xenobiotic metabolism regulated? The very nature of the problem leads one to suspect the gonads and gonadal hormones. Indeed, much evidence is now available to suggest that the testes via secretion of androgens play a vital role in the control of hepatic xenobiotic metabolism. El Defrawy el Masry & Mannering (7), studying ethylmorphine N-demethylation, showed that castration decreased the enzyme activity to the female level and subsequent testosterone treatment could restore the full male activity. This sequence of events has also been shown in the mouse (68).

Recently, gonadal control of lidocaine, imipramine, and diazepam metabolism has been shown. Lidocaine N-deethylase, imipramine N-demethylase, and imipramine N-oxidase activities are all decreased by castration towards the female level of enzyme (10), effects that can be partially reversed by testosterone treatment. In the case of diazepam metabolism, results from this laboratory confirm the sex differences previously reported (62) and show an important role of the testes in the control of diazepam metabolism with a significant decrease in 3-hydroxylation (taken as the total of 3-hydroxydiazepam and oxazepam production) and N-demethylation (total of N-desmethyldiazepam and oxazepam production) activities towards the female level following castration of male rats.

In marked contrast to the importance of the testes in regulating hepatic xenobiotic metabolism, little influence of the ovaries (via estrogen secretion) is evident. No effect of ovariectomy is seen when investigating lidocaine, imipramine, or diazepam metabolism (10). It is, however, interesting to note that chronic estrogen treatment of male animals can lead to a more feminine type of metabolism (7, 79). This indicates that although estrogens are not necessary for the maintenance of a feminine type of metabolism, they can under certain circumstances change a masculine to a feminine pattern.

A consistent feature of these studies has been the inability of castration to cause a fully feminine pattern of metabolism. A significant shift is always seen, but in many cases the resulting enzyme activities are in between the male and the female values. It has been suggested that the discrepancy lies in the secretion of androgens by the adrenal gland. Data from studies on steroid metabolism tends to support this theory. However, results obtained using lidocaine and imipramine as substrates do not substantiate this claim. Combined adrenalectomy/castration has no more effect than castration alone and does not change the enzyme activities to female levels. Therefore, the simple androgen dependency of xenobiotic metabolizing enzymes does not hold true.

The neonatal period also seems to be an important time in the regulation of xenobiotic metabolism by androgens. Chung et al (70, 71) have shown that the ethylmorphine N-demethylase in male rats deprived of neonatal androgen responds much less than that in control rats to androgens administered in the adult period. Such imprinting or programming of androgen responsiveness—first reported for steroid metabolism (28)—has also been reported for DME metabolism (72), uridine diphosphoglucuronyltransferase (73) and histidase (74) activities—representing phase I, phase II (conjugation), and endogenous substrate metabolism. Also of interest from a toxicological point of view is the sex difference in cadmium toxicity in the rat (male < female) that is regulated by androgens in the perinatal period (75). Male animals are rendered less sensitive to the hepatotoxicity of cadmium by neonatal diethylstilbestrol (estrogen) treatment.

Pituitary Control

It is now accepted that most, if not all, of the androgen effects on xenobiotic metabolism are indirect, mediated by another androgen-sensitive organ. This is consistent with several previous findings: (a) The pituitary does not mature in the rat until 30 days of age, and xenobiotic metabolism is not sex-differentiated until after 30 days of age (33–36, 76, 77); (b) androgens and estrogens influence xenobiotic metabolism and pituitary hormone secretion (10, 39, 64, 78); and (c) xenobiotic metabolism and pituitary hormone secretion are both imprinted (31, 79–81).

The vital role of the pituitary gland in the control of hepatic xenobiotic metabolism has subsequently been demonstrated. Kramer et al (82) showed that ethylmorphine N-demethylase activity no longer responded to androgen treatment following hypophysectomy. This phenomenon has also been found by our own group (83) as well as by Finnen & Hassal (84) using model substrates. In our own studies on lidocaine and imipramine metabolism (10) we have found that hypophysectomy in the male acts as castration (an effect not unexpected considering the pituitary control of gonadal secretion) but that in the female, although ovariectomy is without effect, hypophysectomy has a marked effect, leading to a more masculine type of metabolism. In fact, the enzyme activities of hypophysectomized females are very similar to those of male castrated animals. This indicates that androgens (acting via the pituitary gland) are the major influence on xenobiotic metabolism in the male, whereas in the female the pituitary gland itself is the major control organ.

What hormone(s) is (are) responsible for maintaining the feminine type of xenobiotic metabolism?

Previous work, notably the extensive studies of Wilson (85–89), has indicated that growth hormone (somatotropin, GH) and adrenocorticotropin (ACTH) are the most active. GH alone decreased the metabolism of ethylmorphine and aminopyrine (85) whereas GH and ACTH in combination decreased the metabolism of N-hydroxy-N-2-fluorenylacetamine (90, 91). Kramer et al (92) have shown an increase in ethylmorphine N-demethylation in female animals following lutropin (LH) and follitropin (FSH) treatment. However, all of the experiments using hormone injections were performed with heterologous hormones and thus could lead to misinterpretation of results considering the high species specificity of peptide hormones (See above). Osmotic minipumps were used in our laboratory to test all of the available rat pituitary hormones [kindly donated by the National Institute of Arthritis, Metabolic and Digestive Diseases (NIAMDD)]. It was shown (93) that a pituitary extract infused by minipump could cause a shift towards a feminine type of metabolism, but none of the purified hormones tested mimicked these effects in all instances. The hormone that most resembled the pituitary extract was GH. This closely resembles the situation found for steroid metabolism in the rat liver as discussed in a previous section.

SUMMARY

Sex differences exist in steroid and xenobiotic metabolism in the liver of a number of species. In the rat, the differences are regulated through the hypothalamo-pituitary axis. The previously postulated "feminizing factor" responsible for a female-type liver metabolism appears to be identical to growth hormone. The different effects of this peptide on hepatic metabolism in male and female rats may be related to the sexual dimorphism of the growth hormone secretory pattern; serum levels of growth hormone do not fluctuate as markedly in female as in male rats and may be simulated by administration of the hormone via osmotic minipumps, a procedure resulting in "feminization" of liver metabolism of male or hypophysectomized rats. This newly discovered system, the hypothalamo-pituitary-liver axis, represents a novel concept in endocrinology.

ACKNOWLEDGMENT

This work was supported by a grant from the Swedish Medical Research Council (No. 13X-2819) as well as by the University of Glasgow Medical Research Funds.

Literature Cited

1. Nicholas, G. S., Barran, D. H. 1932. *J. Pharmacol. Exp. Ther.* 46:125–29
2. Crevier, M., D'Iorio, A., Robillard, E. 1950. *Rev. Can. Biol.* 9:336
3. Pellerin, J., D'Iorio, A., Robillard, E. 1954. *Rev Can. Biol.* 13:257
4. Castro, J. A., Gillette, J. R. 1967. *Biochem. Biophys. Res. Commun.* 28: 426–30
5. Davies, D. S., Gigon, P. L., Gillette, J. R. 1968. *Biochem. Pharmacol.* 17:1865
6. Gram, T. E., Guarino, A. M., Schroeder, D. H., Gillette, J. R. 1969. *Biochem. J.* 113:681–85
7. El Defrawy el Masry, S., Mannering, G. J. 1974. *Drug Metab. Disp.* 2:279–84
8. Quinn, G. P., Axelrod, J., Brodie, B. B. 1958. *Biochem. Pharmacol.* 1:152–59
9. Bell, J. U., Ecobichon, D. J. 1974. *Can. J. Biochem.* 53:433–37
10. Skett, P., Mode, A., Rafter, J., Sahlin, L., Gustafsson, J. -Å. 1980. *Biochem. Pharmacol.* 29:2759–62
11. Hübener, H. J., Amelung, D. 1953. *Hoppe-Seylers Z. Physiol. Chem.* 293: 137–41
12. Forchielli, E., Dorfman, R. I. 1956. *J. Biol. Chem.* 223:443–48
13. Leybold, K., Staudinger, H. 1959. *Biochem. Z.* 331:389–98
14. Conney, A. H., Schneidman, K., Jacobson, M., Kuntzman, R. 1965. *Ann. NY Acad. Sci.* 123:98–109
15. Gustafsson, J. -Å., Eriksson, H. 1971. *Eur. J. Biochem.* 20:231–36
16. Eriksson, H., Gustafsson, J. -Å., Pousette, Å. 1972. *Eur. J. Biochem.* 27: 327–34
17. Gustafsson, J. -Å. 1973. *Biochim. Biophys. Acta* 296:179–88
18. Einarsson, K., Gustafsson, J. -Å., Goldman, A. S. 1972. *Eur. J. Biochem.* 31: 345–53
19. Carlstedt-Duke, J. 1973. *Eur. J. Biochem.* 36:172–77
20. Pfaffenberg, C. D., Horning, E. C. 1977. *Anal. Biochem.* 80:329–43
21. MacLeod, S. M., Giles, H. G., Bengert, B., Liu, F. F., Sellers, E. M. 1979. *J. Clin. Pharmacol.* 19:15–19
22. Yates, F. E., Herbst, A. L., Urquhart, J. 1958. *Endocrinology* 63:887–902
23. Berg, A., Gustafsson, J. -Å. 1973. *J. Biol. Chem.* 248:6559–67
24. Einarsson, K., Gustafsson, J. -Å., Stenberg, Å. 1973. *J. Biol. Chem.* 248: 4987–97
25. Gustafsson, J. -Å., Ingelman-Sundberg, M. 1974. *J. Biol. Chem.* 249:1940–45
26. Gustafsson, J. -Å., Ingelman-Sundberg, M. 1975. *J. Biol. Chem.* 250:3451–58
27. Gustafsson, J. -Å., Stenberg, Å. 1974 *J. Biol. Chem.* 249:711–18
28. Gustafsson, J. -Å., Stenberg, Å. 1974. *J. Biol. Chem.* 249:719–23
29. Lax, E. R., Hoff, H. -G., Ghraf, R., Schroeder, E., Schriefers, H. 1974. *Hoppe-Seylers Z. Physiol. Chem.* 355: 1325–31
30. Denef, C., de Moor, P. 1968. *Endocrinology* 83:791–98
31. Skett, P., Gustafsson, J. -Å. 1979. *Rev. Biochem. Toxicol.* 1:27–52
32. Gustafsson, J. -Å., Pousette, Å., Stenberg, Å., Wrange, Ö. 1975. *Biochemistry* 14:3942–48
33. Döhler, K. D., Wuttke, W. 1974. *Endocrinology* 94:1003–8
34. Eneroth, P., Gustafsson, J. -Å., Skett, P., Stenberg, Å. 1975. *J. Endocrinol.* 65:91–98
35. Simpkins, W., Bruni, J. F., Mioduszewski, R. J., Meites, J. 1976. *Endocrinology* 98:1365–69
36. Ojeda, S. R., McCann, S. M. 1974. *Endocrinology* 95:1499–1505
37. Gay, V. L., Bogdanove, E. M. 1969. *Endocrinology* 84:1132
38. Swerdloff, R. D., Walsh, P. C., Odell, W. D. 1972. *Steroids* 20:13
39. Mallampati, R. S., Johnson, D. C. 1973. *J. Endocrinology* 59:209–16
40. Gustafsson, J. -Å., Stenberg, Å. 1976. *Proc. Natl. Acad. Sci. USA* 73:1462–65
41. Einarsson, K., Ericsson, J. L. E., Gustafsson, J. -Å., Sjövall, J., Zietz, E. 1974. *Biochim. Biophys. Acta* 369:278–93
42. Stenberg, Å. 1975. *Acta Endocrinol.* 78: 294–301
43. Denef, C., deMoor, P. 1969. *Endocrinology* 85:259–69
44. Denef, C. 1974. *Endocrinology* 94: 1577–82

45. Gustafsson, J. -Å., Stenberg, Å. 1974. *Endocrinology* 95:891–96
46. Carlstedt-Duke, J., Gustafsson, J. -Å., Gustafsson, S. A. 1975. *Biochemistry* 14:639–48
47. Gustafsson, J. -Å., Stenberg, Å. 1975. *Acta Endocrinol.* 78:545–53
48. Gustafsson, J. -Å., Stenberg, Å. 1975. *Endocrinology* 96:501–4
49. Colby, H. D., Gaskin, J. H., Kitay, J. I. 1974. *Steroids* 24:679–86
50. Lax, E. R., Ghraf, R., Schriefers, H., Herrmann, M., Petutschnigk, D. 1976. *Acta Endocrinol.* 82:774–84
51. Kramer, R. E., Colby, H. D. 1976. *J. Endocrinol.* 71:449–54
52. Theeuwes, F., Yum, S. I. 1976. *Ann. Biomed. Eng.* 4:343–53
53. Mode, A., Norstedt, G., Simic, B., Eneroth, P., Gustafsson, J. -Å. 1981. *Endocrinology* 108:2103–8
54. Gustafsson, J. -Å., Mode, A., Norstedt, G., Hökfelt, T., Sonnenschein, C., Eneroth, P., Skett, P. 1980. *Biochem. Act. Horm.* 7:47–89
55. Terry, L., C., Saunders, A., Aadet, J., Willoughby, J., Brazeau, P., Martin, J. 1977. *Clin. Endocrinol.* 6:195–285
56. Edén, S. 1979. *Endocrinology* 105: 555–60
57. Mode, A., Norstedt, G., Eneroth, P., Hökfelt, T., Gustafsson, J. -Å. 1981. In *Steroid Hormone Regulation of the Brain*, ed. K. Fuke, J. -Å. Gustafsson, L. Wetterberg, pp. 61–70. Oxford/NY: Pergamon. 406 pp.
58. Mode, A., Gustafsson, J. -Å., Jansson, J. -O., Edén, S., Isaksson, O. 1982. *Endocrinology.* In press
59. Kamataki, T., Ando, M., Yamazoe, Y., Ishii, K., Kato, R. 1980. *Biochem. Pharmacol.* 29:1015–22
60. Hassall, K. A., Adalla, S. A. 1979. *Biochem. Pharmacol.* 28.3199–3203
61. Skett, P., Mode, A., Gustafsson, J. -Å. 1980. *Biochem Soc. Trans.* 8:342–43
62. Nau, H., Liddiard, C. 1980. *Biochem. Pharmacol.* 29:447–49
63. van den Berg, A. P., Noordhoek, J., Savenije-Chapel, E. M., Koopman-Kool, E. 1978. *Biochem. Pharmacol.* 27:627–33
64. Brown, T. R., Greene, F. E. 1980. *Arch. Int. Pharmacodyn. Ther.* 248:13–24
65. Watanabe, M., Tamwa, Y., Abe, T. 1980. *Toxicol. Lett.* 5:55–60
66. Gindicelli, J. F., Tillement, J. P. 1977. *Clin. Pharmacokin.* 2:157–66
67. Stegeman, J. J., Chevion, M. 1980. *Biochem Pharmacol.* 29:553–58
68. Noordhoek, J., van den Berg, A. P.,

Savenije-Chapel, E. M., Koopman-Kool, E. 1978. *Xenobiotica* 8:515–22
69. Al-Turk, W. A., Stohs, S. J., Roche, E. B. 1980. *Drug Metab. Disp.* 8:143–46
70. Chung, L. W. K., Raymond, G., Fox, S. 1975. *J. Pharmacol. Exp. Ther.* 193: 621–30
71. Chung, L. W. K. 1977. *Biochem. Pharmacol.* 26:1979–84
72. Finnen, M. J., Hassall, K. A. 1980. *Biochem. Pharmacol.* 29:3133–37
73. Lamartiniere, C. A., Dieringer, C. S., Kita, E., Lucier, G. W. 1979. *Biochem. J.* 180:313–18
74. Lamartiniere, C. A., Lucier, G. W. 1978. *J. Steroid Biochem.* 9:595–98
75. Lui, E. M. K., Lucier, G. W. 1980. *J. Pharmacol. Exp. Ther.* 212:211–16
76. Skett, P., Eneroth, P., Gustafsson, J. -Å . 1978. *Mol. Cell. Endocrinol.* 10:21–27
77. Mukhtar, H., Philpot, R. M., Bend, J. R. 1978. *Drug Metab. Disp.* 6:577–83
78. Ramirez, V. D., McCann, S. M. 1965. *Endocrinology* 76:412–17
79. Barraclough, C. A. 1961. *Endocrinology* 78:62–67
80. Harris, G. W. 1964. *Endocrinology* 75: 627–48
81. Korenbrot, C. C., Paup, D. C., Gorski, R. A. 1975. *Endocrinology* 97:709–17
82. Kramer, R. E., Greiner, J. W., Canady, W. J., Colby, H. O. 1975. *Biochem. Pharmacol.* 24:2097–99
83. Burke, M. D., Orrenius, S., Gustafsson, J. -Å. 1978. *Biochem. Pharmacol.* 27:1125–28
84. Finnen, M. J., Hassall, K. A. 1980. *Biochem. Pharmacol.* 29:3139–42
85. Wilson, J. T. 1968. *J. Pharmacol. Exp. Ther.* 160:179–88
86. Wilson, J. T. 1968. *Biochem. Pharmacol.* 17:1449–57
87. Wilson, J. T. 1968. *Proc. Soc. Exp. Biol. Med.* 128:445–48
88. Wilson, J. T. 1969. *J. Natl. Cancer Inst.* 43:1067–72
89. Wilson, J. T. 1970. *Nature* 225:861–63
90. Shirasu, Y., Grantham, P. H., Yamamoto, R. S., Weisburger, J. H. 1966. *Cancer Res.* 26:600–6
91. Shirasu, Y., Grantham, P. H., Weisburger, E. K., Weisburger, J. H. 1967. *Cancer Res.* 27:81–87
92. Kramer, R. E., Greiner, J. W., Colby, H. D. 1977. *Biochem. Pharmacol.* 26: 66–68
93. Skett, P., Young, C. 1980. In *Biochemistry, Biophysics and Regulation of Cytochrome P-450*, ed. J. -Å. Gustafsson, J. Carlstedt-Duke, A. Mode, J. Rafter, pp.195–98. Amsterdam: Elsevier/North-Holland

Ann. Rev. Physiol. 1983. 45:61–72

AROMATIC HYDROXYLATION
OF ESTROGENS

Jack Fishman[1]

The Rockefeller University, New York, NY 10021

INTRODUCTION

The metabolism of an endogenous steroid hormone has traditionally been viewed as a means of terminating its activity and facilitating its excretion. In recent years, however, examples have accumulated (18, 50, 76) in which such biotransformations have been shown to have activating rather than inactivating functions, placing the role of metabolism in the expression of hormonal action into a new context. The mammalian metabolism of the female sex hormone is almost exclusively oxidative in nature and is dominated by three pathways, of which the largest and fastest is the oxidation of the 17 β-hydroxy function to the 17 ketone (23). This process in reversible, but the equilibrium greatly favors the oxidized estrone form, which is the principal substrate for the other two main oxidative transformations, hydroxylation at the C-2 or C-16α positions of the molecule. The 16α-hydroxylative pathway, whose most noted product is estriol, was recognized early (59), but the hydroxylation at the C-2 position of the aromatic ring has been detected only relatively recently (52). This biotransformation of estrogens and the even more recently discovered hydroxylation at the isomeric C-4 position (83) have attracted much interest and have generated a substantial literature. The nature of these transformations and the biological properties of their polyphenolic products, the catechol estrogens, are reviewed in this chapter. This review is selective. The reader seeking more detailed information is directed to an exhaustive survey of the field (6), which covers the available information through 1979.

[1]Work supported by grant CA 22795 from the National Cancer Institute.

0066-4278/83/0315-0061$02.00

CATECHOL ESTROGEN FORMATION IN VIVO

Although biological hydroxylation of estrogens at the C-2 position had been already hypothesized in 1940 (82), the actual existence of this reaction was first established by the isolation and identification of 2-methoxyestrone as a metabolite of estradiol in the human (20, 52). Its logical precursor, 2-hydroxyestrone, was identified as a metabolic product soon thereafter (25). Other 2-hydroxylated metabolites, such as 2-hydroxyestradiol and 2-hydroxyestriol and their corresponding 2-methyl ethers, were subsequently identified in body fluids (1, 27), but while 2-hydroxyestrone proved to be the major metabolite of estradiol (21) these catechol estrogens were of much lesser quantitative importance. Measurement of all of these substances was greatly complicated by their exceptional instability, and only the development of special protective procedures (37) permitted their quantitation in body fluids. Measurements of 2-hydroxyestrone in urine confirmed (8) that it was the dominant estrogen metabolite in normal women and men, but the plasma content of this substance is in dispute. Employing a radioimmunoassay without prior separation, Yoshizawa & Fishman found the plasma concentration of 2-OHE$_1$ to be comparable to that of estrone and estradiol (84). Similar values were obtained using a different antibody and prior separation of the plasma extract (3), but other investigators reported much lower or undetectable levels of this material in normal human plasma (62). At the present time the issue remains unresolved, but the high clearance rate of this substance in the human (58, 62) suggests that the lower plasma content is more viable.

The initial studies of the formation of 2-hydroxyestrogens in vivo depended on either the urinary excretion of radiolabeled catechol estrogens following the administration of labeled estrogen precursors (21) or the isolation of endogenous 2-hydroxylated substances (4). Measurement of the extent of the reaction by these methods was compromised by an incomplete knowledge of the proportion of the products excreted by other than urinary routes, or excreted in urine as further transformed unidentified forms. A radiometric method was therefore developed in which the reaction could be followed by the incorporation of ^{3}H from 2^{3}H-estradiol into body water (28), a procedure that did not require the isolation of the catechol estrogen product and therefore bypassed the above difficulties. The reaction was shown to proceed without an isotope effect or an NIH shift, but the amount of ^{3}H$_2$O formed exceeded substantially the 2-hydroxylated products that were measurable in urine. By this method, 2-hydroxylation of estrogen was shown to be the dominant transformation ($>$ 30%) of the female sex hormone in humans and to exhibit a sex difference, the reaction being substantially greater in women than in men (24). An analogous method employing a 4[3]H-estradiol substrate provided the first evidence of the presence of 4-hydroxylation in humans (83), although the magnitude of this reaction was only a fraction of the more massive transformation at the isomeric ortho 2-position. Examination of changes in the 2-hydroxylation of estradiol by the various procedures, in a number of pathological conditions, showed the extent of this transformation to be significantly and consistently diminished in hypothyroidism (29), cirrhosis (85), systemic lupus erythematosus (54, 55), and obesity (22). The reaction was elevated in hyperthyroid individuals (29) and in anorexia nervosa (22). Because the biological properties of the 2-hydroxylated estrogens are distinctive, these metabolic alterations could have physiological consequences. The in vivo formation of catechol estrogens has also been reported in other mammalian species (16, 56, 81), particularly the rat (10, 47, 67) in which it is of major quantitative significance. Its absence has been noted in some species (2), but this could have been due to methodological difficulties in isolating the catechol estrogen products, which are subject to rapid biological and nonbiological transformation. Thus this reaction may be a universal one.

CATECHOL ESTROGEN FORMATION IN VITRO

Demonstration of 2-hydroxylation of estrogens in vitro followed soon after the discovery of the in vivo reaction. The formation of the catechol estrogens in tissue and subcellular fraction incubations was described in numerous publications, most of which were concerned with the liver as the transforming tissue (6). The presence of the reaction was also established in the placenta (15, 26) and in the brain (5, 9, 32, 72). The latter site is particularly significant and is therefore discussed in a separate section of this review. In addition to the above tissues, 2-hydroxylation of estrogens was also found in the lung, kidney, testes, adrenals, muscles, and uterus (9, 43, 45). From these in vitro studies the liver appeared to be the most active tissue; the brain was second. The importance of the in vitro studies lay not only in identifying the organs in which this metabolic transformation takes place but also in the opportunity they provided to study the enzyme involved. The nature and kinetic characteristics of the liver, brain, and placental enzymes have been studied in various degrees. The most information has been acquired about the liver enzyme.

Three different methods have been used in measuring estrogen hydroxylase activity. One is the radiometric procedure in which the displacement of ^3H from 2^3H-estradiol and its incorporation into water serves as the gauge of 2-hydroxylase activity (33). This method, while simple and sensitive, suffers from the disadvantage of being an indirect assay in which nonspecific ^3H release may be spuriously interpreted as enzyme activity.

Another is the product isolation technique in which the amount of 2-hydroxylated products obtained from inert or stably labeled precursors is measured by different procedures. This is a specific and direct method which, however, must contend with the problem of severe losses of the very labile end products before they can be quantitated. Finally, there is a radioenzymatic procedure (71) in which the catechol estrogen product is trapped in a labeled form by incorporating a radiolabeled methyl group by means of the catechol-0-methyl transferase enzyme, a method successfully employed in the measurement of the structural analogs, the biogenic catecholamines. In general, the three procedures yield congruent results insofar as the liver enzyme is concerned, and in several instances they served to cross-validate each other (14, 69). The early observation that the liver estrogen-2-hydroxylase belongs to the family of cytochrome P-450 monooxygenases (49) has been abundantly confirmed in later work (72). There is now litle question that the enzyme in the liver is a NADPH-dependent cytochrome P-450 linked monooxygenase, although some very recent work suggests that an NADH-dependent enzyme also participates in this transformation in the liver. The NADPH-linked liver enzyme exhibits substrate saturation and classic Michaelis-Menten kinetics. A sexual difference is apparent; greater activity is observed in male rat liver; the female liver shows either less activity or possibly a different enzymatic composition (14). The liver enzyme is modulated by testosterone; castration reduces activity in the male and androgen replacement therapy increases it (9, 43). Alcohol ingestion also reduces liver estrogen-2-hydroxylase activity (42), but unlike the case in the human, both hyper- and hypothyroidism in the rat resulted in reduced activity of the liver enzyme (43).

In liver incubations hydroxylation of estradiol at positions 2 and 4 was observed but invariably that at C-2 was greater by a factor of 10 or so (5). It is not known at this time whether these two reactions are mediated by the same or by different enzymes. In view of the quite different biological properties of the 2- and 4-catechol estrogens (60) the presence of two separate enzymes would be physiologically more reasonable, but there is no evidence that this is indeed so.

CATECHOL ESTROGEN FORMATION IN THE BRAIN

The initial demonstration that the brain is capable of transforming estrogens to 2-hydroxyestrogens was obtained by means of the radiometric assay (33). At the same time the nature of the product was confirmed by the isolation of ^{14}C-labeled 2-hydroxyestrone from a ^{14}C-labeled substrate. No quantitative correlation between ^{3}H released from the C-2 position and the yield of ^{14}C product was found, and the discrepancy was assumed to be due to the exceptionally short life of the catechol estrogen products in the brain homogenate. The enzymatic activity was shown to be present in the microsomal fraction by both the radiometric and radioenzymatic assays and was preferentially localized in the hypothalamus.

The possibility that this transformation had important physiological consequences prompted the studies of the formation of catechol estrogens in the brain using other assay procedures. From product isolation it appeared that unlike the liver, the brain formed equal amounts of 2- and 4-hydroxylated estrogens (5, 7). This suggested that either two different enzymes mediated these two reactions, or, if a single enzyme was involved, that the one in the brain exhibited a different substrate specificity from that in the liver and hence was presumably different.

Much of the current information on brain estrogen-2-hydroxylase has been obtained using the radioenzymatic procedure (72). However, measurement of brain catechol estrogen content by this method yields concentrations greater by an order of magnitude than those of the plasma (70). These results could not be confirmed by other independent methods (30), suggesting that a nonspecific component may interfere in the radioenzymatic assay.

Measurement of the activity of the brain enzyme by the radiometric procedure provided evidence of large changes in its activity in the course of the rat estrus cycle; peak levels were attained at proestrus and estrus (35). In addition, the activity in male rat brains was significantly influenced by the administration of opiate agonists and antagonists to the intact animal (34). These changes in the brain enzyme activity provided a scheme by which these metabolites formed in situ in the CNS could function in the regulation of the hypothalamic-pituitary axis by estrogens.

Recently, other investigators concerned that the ^{3}H release from 2[3]H-estradiol exceeded the isolated catechol estrogen products in brain incubations (40) resorted to studying the reaction by a modified product isolation procedure. Results obtained using detergent activation and specific conditions designed to preserve the catechol estrogen product indicated subcellular localization of the enzyme quite different from those reported previously with use of the radiometric and radioenzymatic methods (41).

Thus three different techniques for assessing the estrogen-2-hydroxylase activity, which in general provide similar results with the liver enzyme, produce quite different results when applied to the brain enzyme. The issue is an important one since the previous reports provided the foundation for the hypothesis that catechol estrogen formation in the CNS is an important element in the central functions of the female sex hormone, including its regulation of pituitary hormone release. At this time the question remains unresolved, but it is appropriate to consider possible reasons for the discrepancies in the brain studies. The C-2 and C-4 positions ortho to the phenolic hydroxyl at C-3 are nucleophilic and are subject to attack by activated oxygen, whether the activation is chemical or enzyme induced. In the case of the liver the specific enzymatic 2-hydroxylase reaction is dominant. The peripheral oxidative processes add little to the overall results and thus do not compromise the enzymatic measurements. In brain tissue such a specific enzymatic transformation is very small and can easily be confounded by the nonspecific processes. It is therefore possible that some of the reported brain catechol estrogen formation is an artifact of in vitro incubation. Assays of the brain enzyme should exhibit several characteristics to establish its physiological relevance. The process must demonstrate substrate saturation, an essential criterion of enzyme participation, and any Michaelis-Menten kinetics should exhibit apparent Km values conforming to the potential physiological substrate levels. Furthermore, because of the widely divergent biological properties of the 2- and 4-hydroxyestrogens it would be reasonable to expect that physiologically relevant transformations in the CNS should be regulated differently insofar as these products are concerned. None of the published studies of the brain enzyme to date report the presence of all, if any, of the above criteria, and the question of the physiological role of the brain estrogen-2-hydroxylation must remain speculative until these conflicts are resolved.

BIOLOGICAL PROPERTIES OF CATECHOL ESTROGENS

The biological properties of catechol estrogens received only a modest amount of attention in the years immediately following their discovery as biological products. Pharmacological investigation of 2-hydroxyestrone and its metabolite, 2-methoxyestrone, indicated that they were ineffective in the uterotropic assay but exhibited a relatively greater hypocholesteremic effect (39). 4-Hydroxy estrogen, however, is a much more potent estrogen agonist, in agreement with studies of estrogen receptor binding (uterus, hypothalamus, pituitary) that indicate that the 2-hydroxy estrogens and their O-methylated derivatives exhibit at best only a modest affinity for the receptor, with the corresponding 4-hydroxy estrogens being more effective ligands (17, 60, 61). The uterotropic ineffectiveness of 2-hydroxy estrone may therefore be secondary to (a) its intrinsic properties or (b) its inability to reach target tissue because of its prior O-methylation by erythrocyte catechol-O-methyl transferase (COMT), for which it is a highly effective substrate. [This is also true for both liver and brain COMT (11, 12, 13).] An intriguing observation was that the totally nonuterotropic 2-methoxyestrone proved to have a high affinity for the human sex hormone binding globulin, being by far the best estrogen ligand and exceeding even the affinity of testosterone for this carrier protein (19, 31). The physiological relevance of this enzymatic interaction becomes apparent from studies of the metabolic clearance rates of the 2-hydroxyestrogen in the rat (51) and the human (62). In both species the MCR of these metabolites exceed that of the parent hormone by a factor of 50 or 100; a significant part of the clearance occurred in the blood compartment via O-methylation. Thus, irrespective of the reasons, 2-hydroxyestrone, a major hepatic metabolite of estradiol, must be considered as a nonuterotropic estrogen. As such its formation serves to terminate that aspect of hormonal action. The extraordinarily high MCR of the material also suggests that the hepatic product is unlikely to reach CNS sites intact and cannot participate in neuroendocrine events.

The reported biological responses to exogenous catechol estrogens can be divided into two categories. One category consists of responses commensurate with the estrogen receptor affinity of the test substance, taking its metabolism into consideration. These actions reflect, therefore, estrogen agonist properties of the catechol metabolites; such agonist properties in general are less significant than those of the primary estrogen. The second category of effects elicited by catechol estrogens either exhibit a dissociation of conventional estrogenic activities, provide evidence of estrogen antagonist properties, or include actions not exhibited by the parent estrogen. This category of responses may be more significant because it may reflect physiological mechanisms by which the large variety of female sex hormone actions are expressed or modulated.

These actions of the 2-hydroxyestrogens need not be mediated through the estrogen receptor. As already noted, these metabolites are effective inhibitors of catecholamine O-methylation and have also been shown to inhibit tyrosine hydroxylase, the rate-limiting enzyme of catecholamine biosynthesis (57). Even though these interactions require supraphysiological concentrations, such could be achieved in highly localized brain regions. Another possible mechanism of action is suggested by the report that 2-hydroxyestradiol competes for the pituitary dopamine receptor (77) and also binds to what appear to be specific catechol estrogen receptors in the brain (78). Covalent binding of catechol estrogens to macromolecules (53, 68) also represents another possible mode of action. Finally, the recent report of stimulation of synthesis of a specific prostaglandin by 2-hydroxyestrone (48) presents yet another avenue by which these metabolites may exert their action without involving classical estrogen receptors. A considerable number of such "nonestrogenic" activities have now been described, although some of the reported results have not been reproduced and remain controversial. Most of the reports in this category are concerned with the effect of the catechol estrogens on pituitary hormone secretion in the rodent (38) and human. Positive feedback effects on gonadotropin secretion are suggested by the observations that injections of 2-hydroxyestrone into 35 day old male rats produced large rises in serum LH six hours later (66) and that increased serum FSH and LH surges were apparent in estradiol benzoate primed ovariectomized rats after administration of this catechol estrogen (60). It should be noted that in other studies under similar but not identical conditions, *chronic* 2-hydroxyestrone administration failed to reproduce the LH augmentation (44, 74). Because of the considerable time lag in the positive feedback responses, it is possible that these result from an initial suppression followed by a rebound. The variable timing of the latter may then be responsible for the inconsistencies in observing the gonadotropin rise.

A similar argument has been used to explain the recent demonstration that 2-hydroxyestrone given to male rats with an estradiol implant results in large Prl increase 4 hours after injection (80), the rise being considered a rebound following the initial suppression. These observations suggest that 2-hydroxyestrone functions as an estrogen antagonist. Support for this concept is provided by reports that this catechol estrogen can inhibit estradiol-stimulated cAMP formation in the hypothalamus (73) and estradiol-induced vasodilation in the sheep uterus (75), and that its acute administration can block the preovulatory surge of Prl and LH in the intact cycling rat when it is administered at a time coincident with rising endogenous estrogen levels (46). The putative estrogen antagonist properties of 2-hydroxyestrone could explain the effects of this material on prolactin secretion in the human. It has been reported that administration of 2-hydroxyestrone to estrogen primed hypogonadal women (79) and to normal premenopausal subjects (36) suppressed plasma prolactin levels in most of the subjects. Conversely, the plasma Prl levels of men (63) and of either normal (64) unprimed hypogonadal postmenopausal (79) or hypoprolactinemic women (57) were not influenced by this metabolite. More recently a small series of normal young women also failed to show Prl suppression under the influence of this catechol estrogen. The discrepancy between the two studies of normal young women (36, 64) could be due to a fortuitous separation of estrogen-induced and estrogen-independent prolactin secretory episodes.

Two questions are posed by these activities of exogenous 2-hydroxyestrogens. First, are the effects specific to the catechol estrogens or do they reflect nonspecific actions of the catechol structural component? Second, are these responses solely pharmacological in nature or do they reflect physiological roles? Answers to the first question can be obtained by studying the effects of other catechols unrelated to the estrogens or of catechol estrogens with a stereochemistry known to abolish conventional hormonal activity (65). An answer to the second question will be more difficult. The exceptionally rapid MCR of the catechol estrogens makes it probable that any significant physiological role for these substances is limited to those formed in situ in specific target tissues. Clear evidence of such formation in these tissues and of the modulation of this formation would constitute important circumstantial evidence for such a physiological function. Administration of exogenous catechol estrogens in physiological concentrations to highly localized sites in target tissues will also serve to test the hypothesis. Inhibition of either the formation or activity of the endogenous catechol estrogens can also help to reveal their physiological role. Clearly much further work is necessary before specific physiological functions for these labile metabolites of estradiol can be securely established. At the present time judgment as to their role in estrogen physiology must be reserved.

Literature Cited

1. Axelrod, L. R., Rao, P. N., Goldzieher, J. W. 1961. The conversion of 2-hydroxyestradiol-17β to 2-hydroxy and 2-methoxy metabolites in human urine. *Arch. Biochem. Biophys.* 94:265–68
2. Balikian, H., Southerland, J., Howard, C. M., Preedy, J. R. K. 1968. Estrogen metabolism in the male dog. Uptake and disappearance of specific radioactive estrogens in tissues and plasma following estrone 6,7-³H administration. Identification of estriol-16α,17α in tissues and urine. *Endocrinology* 82:500–10
3. Ball, P., Emons, G., Haupt, O., Hoppen, H. -O., Knuppen, R. 1978. Radioimmunoassay of 2-hydroxyestrone. *Steroids* 31:249–58
4. Ball, P., Gelbke, H. P., Knuppen, R. 1975. The excretion of 2-hydroxyestrone during the menstrual cycle. *J. Clin. Endocrinol. Metab.* 40:406–8
5. Ball, P., Haupt, M., Knuppen, R. 1978. Comparative studies on the metabolism of oestradiol in the brain, the pituitary and the liver of the rat. *Acta Endocrinol.* 87:1–11
6. Ball, P., Knuppen, R. 1980. Catecholestrogens. *Acta Endocrinol.* 93:1–127
7. Ball, P., Knuppen, R. 1978. Formation of 2- and 4-hydroxyestrogens by brain, pituitary, and liver of the human fetus. *J. Clin Endocrinol. Metab.* 47:732–37
8. Ball, P., Reu, G., Schwab, J., Knuppen, R. 1979. Radioimmunoassay of 2-hydroxyestrone and 2-methoxyestrone in human urine. *Steroids* 33:563–76
9. Barbieri, R. L., Canick, J. A., Ryan, K. J. 1978. Estrogen-2-hydroxylase: activity in rat tissues. *Steroids* 32:529–38
10. Bartke, A., Steele, R. E., Williams, J. G., Williams, K. I. H. 1971. Biliary metabolites of ¹⁴C-estrone and ¹⁴C-estradiol from the rat. *Steroids* 18:303–11
11. Bates, G. W., Edman, C. D., Porter, J. C., MacDonald, P. C. 1977. Metabolism of catechol estrogen by human erythrocytes. *J. Clin. Endocrinol. Metab.* 45:1120–23
12. Breuer, H., Köster, G. 1974. Interaction between oestrogens and neurotransmitters at the hypophysial-hypothalamic level. *J. Steroid Biochem.* 5:961–67
13. Breuer, H., Lubrich, W., Knuppen, R. 1968. Wirkung von phenolischen Steroiden auf die Methylierung mit Brenzkatechinaminen. *Hoppe-Seylers Z. Physiol. Chem.* 349:3–9
14. Brueggemeier, R. W. 1981. Kinetics of rat liver microsomal estrogen-2-hydroxylase. *J. Biol. Chem.* 256:10239–42
15. Chao, S. T., Omiecinski, C. J., Namkung, M. J., Nelson, S. D., Dvorchik, B. H., Juchau, M. R. 1981. Catechol estrogen formation in placental and fetal tissues of human, macaques, rats, and rabbits. *Dev. Pharmacol. Ther.* 2:1–16
16. Collins, D. C., Williams, K. I. H., Layne, D. S. 1967. Metabolism of radioactive estrone and estradiol by the golden hamster. *Endocrinology* 80:893–95

17. Davies, I. J., Naftolin, F., Ryan, K. J., Fishman, J., Siu, J. 1975. The affinity of catechol estrogens for estrogen receptors in the pituitary and anterior hypothalamus of the rat. *Endocrinology* 97:554–57

18. DeLuca, H. F., Schnoes, H. K. 1976. Metabolism and mechanism of action of vitamin D. *Ann. Rev. Biochem.* 45: 631–66

19. Dunn, J. F., Merriam, G. R., Eil, C., Kono, S., Loriaux, D. L., Nisula, B. C. 1980. Testosterone-estradiol binding globulin binds to 2-methoxyestradiol with greater affinity than to testosterone. *J. Clin. Endocrinol. Metab.* 51: 404–6

20. Engel, L. L., Baggett, B., Carter, P. 1957. In vivo metabolism of estradiol-17β-16-C¹⁴ in the human being: isolation of 2-methoxyestrone-C¹⁴. *Endocrinology* 61:113–14

21. Fishman, J. 1963. Role of 2-hydroxyestrone in estrogen metabolism. *J. Clin. Endocrinol. Metab.* 23:207–10

22. Fishman, J., Boyar, R. M., Hellman, L. 1975. Influence of body weight on estradiol metabolism in young women. *J. Clin. Endocrinol. Metab.* 41:989–91

23. Fishman, J., Bradlow, H. L., Gallagher, T. F. 1960. Oxidative metabolism of estradiol. *J. Biol. Chem.* 235:3104–7

24. Fishman, J., Bradlow, H. L., Schneider, J., Kappas, A. 1980. Radiometric analysis of oxidation in man: sex differences in estradiol metabolism. *Proc. Natl. Acad. Sci. USA* 77:4957–60

25. Fishman, J., Cox, R. I., Gallagher, T. F. 1960. 2-Hydroxyestrone: a new metabolite of estradiol in man. *Arch. Biochem. Biophys.* 90:318–19

26. Fishman, J., Dixon, D. 1967. 2-Hydroxylation of estradiol by human placental microsomes. *Biochemistry* 6: 1683–87

27. Fishman, J., Gallagher, T. F. 1958. 2-Methoxyestriol: a new metabolite of estradiol in man. *Arch. Biochem. Biophys.* 77:511–13

28. Fishman, J., Guzik, H., Hellman, L. 1970. Aromatic ring hydroxylation of estradiol in man. *Biochemistry* 9: 1593–98

29. Fishman, J., Hellman, L., Zumoff, B., Gallagher, T. F. 1962. Influence of thyroid hormone on estrogen metabolism in man. *J. Clin. Endocrinol. Metab.* 22:389–92

30. Fishman, J., Martucci, C. 1979. Absence of measureable 2-hydroxyestrone in the rat brain: evidence for rapid turnover. *J. Clin. Endocrinol. Metab.* 49: 940–42

31. Fishman, J., Martucci, C. 1980. Dissociation of biological activities in metabolites of estradiol. In *Estrogens in the Environment,* ed. J. A. McLachlan, pp. 131–45. NY: Elsevier North Holland

32. Fishman, J., Naftolin, F., Davies, I. J., Ryan, K. J., Petro, Z. 1976. Catechol estrogen formation by the human fetal brain and pituitary. *J. Clin. Endocrinol. Metab.* 42:177–80

33. Fishman, J., Norton, B. I. 1975. Catechol estrogen formation in the central nervous system of the rat. *Endocrinology* 96:1054–59

34. Fishman, J., Norton, B. I., Hahn, E. F. 1980. Opiate regulation of estradiol-2-hydroxylase in brains of male rats: mechanism for control of pituitary hormone secretion. *Proc. Natl. Acad. Sci. USA* 77:2574–76

35. Fishman, J., Norton, B. I., Krey, L. 1980. 2-Hydroxylation of estrogens in the brain participates in the initiation of the preovulatory LH surge in the rat. *Biochem. Biophys. Res. Commun.* 93: 471–77

36. Fishman, J., Tulchinsky, D. 1980. Suppression of prolactin secretion in normal young women by 2-hydroxyestrone. *Science* 210:73–74

37. Gelbke, H. P., Knuppen, R. 1972. A new method for preventing oxidative decomposition of catechol estrogens during chromatography. *J. Chromatogr.* 71:465–71

38. Gethmann, U., Knuppen, R. 1976. Effect of 2-hydroxyoestrone on lutropin (LH) and follitropin (FSH) secretion in the ovariectomized primed rat. *Hoppe-Seylers Z. Physiol. Chem.* 357:1011–13

39. Gordon, S., Cantrall, E. W., Cekleniak, W. P., Albers, H. J., Maurer, S., Stolar, S. M., Bernstein, S. 1964. Steroid and lipid metabolism. The hypocholesteremic effect of estrogen metabolites. *Steroids* 4:267–71

40. Hersey, R. M., Gunsalus, P., Lloyd, T., Weisz, J. 1981. Catechol estrogen formation by brain tissue: a comparison of the release of tritium from (2-³H)estradiol and (6,7-³H)2-hydroxyestradiol formation from (6,7-³H) estradiol by rabbit hypothalamic tissue in vitro. *Endocrinology* 109:1902–11

41. Hersey, R. M., Williams, K. I. H., Weisz, J. 1981. Catechol estrogen formation by brain tissue: characterization of a direct product isolation assay for estrogen-2- and 4-hydroxylase and its

application to studies of 2- and 4-hydroxyestradiol formation by rabbit hypothalamus. *Endocrinology* 109: 1912–20

42. Hoffman, A. R., Majchrowicz, E., Poth, M. A., Paul, S. M. 1981. Ethanol reduces hepatic estrogen-2-hydroxylase activity in the male rat. *Life Sci.* 29:789–94

43. Hoffman, A. R., Paul, S. M., Axelrod, J. 1980. Estrogen-2-hydroxylase in the rat. Distribution and response to hormonal manipulation. *Biochem. Pharmacol.* 29:83–87

44. Jellinck, P. H., Krey, L., Davis, P. G., Kamel, F., Luine, V., Parsons, B., Roy, E. J., McEwen, B. S. 1981. Central and peripheral action of estradiol and catecholestrogens administered at low concentration by constant infusion. *Endocrinology* 108:1848–54

45. Jellinck, P. H., Norton, B. I., Fishman, J. 1980. Formation of ^3H_2O from (2-^3H) estradiol by rat uterine *in vitro*. Possible role of peroxidase. *Steroids* 35:579–89

46. Katayama, S., Fishman, J. 1982. 2-Hydroxyestrone suppresses and 2-methoxyestrone augments the preovulatory prolactin surge in the cycling rat. *Endocrinology* 110:1448–50

47. Keith, W. B., Williams, K. I. H. 1970. Metabolism of radioactive estrone by rats. *Biochim. Biophys. Acta* 210: 328–32

48. Kelly, R. W., Abel, M. H. 1980. Catechol estrogens stimulate and direct prostaglandin synthesis. *Prostaglandins* 20:613–26

49. King, R. J. B. 1961. Metabolism of oestriol in vitro. Cofactor requirements for the formation of 2-hydroxyoestriol and 2-methoxyoestriol. *Biochem. J.* 79: 361–69

50. King, R. J. B., Mainwaring, W. I. P. 1974. *Steroid Cell Interactions*, pp. 41–101. Baltimore: University Park Press

51. Kono, S., Brandon, G. R., Merriam, G. R., Loriaux, D. L., Lipsett, M. B. 1981. Metabolic clearance rate and uterotropic activity of 2-hydroxyestrone in rats. *Endocrinology* 108:40–43

52. Kraychy, S., Gallagher, T. F. 1957. 2-Methoxyestrone, a new metabolite of estradiol-17β in man. *J. Biol. Chem.* 229:519–26

53. Kuss, E. 1969. Wasserlösliche Metabolite des Östradiols-17β. III. Trennung und Identifizierung der 1- and 4-Glutathionthioäther von 2,3-Dihydroxy-östratrienen. *Hoppe-Seylers Z. Physiol. Chem.* 350:95–97

54. Lahita, R. G., Bradlow, H. L., Kunkel, H. G., Fishman, J. 1981. Increased 16α-hydroxylation of estradiol in systemic lupus erythematosus. *J. Clin. Endocrinol. Metab.* 53:174–78

55. Lahita, R. G., Bradlow, H. L., Kunkel, H. G., Fishman, J. 1979. Alterations of estrogen metabolism in systemic lupus erythematosus. *Arth. Rheum.* 22: 1195–98

56. Leung, K., Merkatz, I., Solomon, S. 1972. Metabolism of ^{14}C-estradiol-17β injected intravenously into the pregnant baboon (*Papio cynocephalus*). *Endocrinology* 91:523–28

57. Lloyd, T., Weisz, J. 1978. Direct inhibition of tyrosine hydroxylase activity by catechol estrogens. *J. Biol. Chem.* 253:4841–43

58. Longcope, C., Ferrino, A., Flood, C., Williams, K. I. H. 1982. Metabolic clearance rate and conversion ratios of (^3H)2-hydroxyestrone in normal men. *J. Clin. Endocrinol. Metab.* 54: 374–80

59. Marrian, G. F. 1930. The chemistry of oestrin. III. An improved method of preparation and the isolation of active crystalline material. *Biochem. J.* 24: 435–40

60. Martucci, C., Fishman, J. 1979. Impact of continuously administered catechol estrogens on uterine growth and LH secretion. *Endocrinology* 105:1288–92

61. Martucci, C., Fishman, J. 1976. Uterine estrogen receptor binding of catechol estrogens and of estetrol (1,3,5,(10)-estratriene-3,15α, 16α,17β-tetrol). *Steroids* 27:325–33

62. Merriam, G. R., Brandon, D. D., Kono, S., Davis, S. E., Loriaux, D. L., Lipsett, M. B. 1980. Rapid metabolic clearance of the catechol estrogen 2-hydroxyestrone. *J. Clin. Endocrinol. Metab.* 51: 1211–13

63. Merriam, G. R., Kono, S., Keiser, H. R., Loriaux, D. L., Lipsett, M. B. 1981. Effects of catechol estrogen infusion upon gonadotropin and prolactin concentrations in men. *J. Clin. Endocrinol. Metab.* 53:784–87

64. Merriam, G. R., Kono, S., Loriaux, D. L., Lipsett, M. B. 1982. Does 2-hydroxyestrone suppress prolactin in women? *J. Clin. Endocrinol. Metab.* 54:753–56

65. Merriam, G. R., MacLusky, N. J., Johnson, L. A., Naftolin, F. 1980. 2-Hydroxyestradiol-17α and 4-hydroxyestradiol-17α, catechol estrogen analogs with reduced estrogen receptor affinity. *Steroids* 36:13–20

66. Naftolin, F., Morishita, H., Davies, I. J., Todd, R., Ryan, K. J., Fishman, J.

1975. 2-Hydroxyestrone induced rise in serum luteinizing hormone in the immature male rat. *Biochim. Biophys. Res. Commun.* 64:905–10

67. Nambara, T., Ishiguro, J., Kawarada, Y., Tajima, H. 1974. Isolation and characterization of biliary metabolites of estriol in the rat. *Chem. Pharmacol. Bull. (Tokyo)* 22:889–93

68. Nelson, S. D., Mitchell, J. R., Dybing, E., Sasame, H. A. 1976. Cytochrome P-450 mediated oxidation of 2-hydroxyestrogens to reactive intermediates. *Biochem. Biophys. Res. Commun.* 70:1157–65

69. Numagawa, M., Kiyono, Y., Nambara, T. 1980. A simple radiometric assay for estradiol-2-hydroxylase activity. *Anal. Biochem.* 104:290–95

70. Paul, S. M., Axelrod, J. 1977. Catechol estrogens: presence in brain and endocrine tissues. *Science* 197:657–59

71. Paul, S. M., Axelrod, J. 1977. A rapid and sensitive radioenzymatic assay for catechol estrogens in tissues. *Life Sci.* 21:493–502

72. Paul, S. M., Axelrod, J., Diliberto, E. J. 1977. Catechol estrogen-forming enzyme of brain: demonstration of a cytochrome P 450 mono-oxygenase. *Endocrinology* 101:1604–10

73. Paul, S. M., Skolnik, P. 1977. Catechol estrogens inhibit estrogen elicited accumulation of hypothalamic cyclic AMP suggesting role as endogenous antiestrogens. *Nature* 266:559–61

74. Rodriguez-Sierra, J. F., Blake, C. A. 1980. Lack of stimulation of phasic LH release by catechol estrogens in the rat. *Life Sci.* 26:743–48

75. Rosenfeld, C. R., Jackson, G. M. 1982. Induction and inhibition of uterine vasodilation by catechol estrogen in oophorectomized, nonpregnant ewes. *Endocrinology* 110:1333–39

76. Ryan, K. J., Naftolin, F., Reddy, V., Flores, F., Petro, Z. 1973. Estrogen formation in the brain. *Am. J. Obstet. Gynecol.* 114:454–60

77. Schaeffer, J. M., Hsueh, A. J. W. 1979. 2-Hydroxyestradiol interaction with dopamine receptor binding in rat anterior pituitary. *J. Biol. Chem.* 254:5606–8

78. Schaeffer, J. M., Stevens, S., Smith, R. G., Hsueh, A. J. W. 1980. Binding of 2-hydroxyestradiol to rat anterior pituitary cell membranes. *J. Biol. Chem.* 255:9838–43

79. Schinfeld, J. S., Tulchinsky, D., Schiff, I., Fishman, J. 1980. Suppression of prolactin and gonadotropin secretion in postmenopausal women by 2-hydroxyestrone. *J. Clin. Endocrinol. Metab.* 50:408–10

80. Shin, S. H., Bates, L., Jellinck, P. H. 1981. Temporal and other effects of catechol estrogens on prolactin secretion in the rat. *Neuroendocrinology* 33:352–57

81. Terqui, M. 1972. Metabolism des oestrogenes chez la brebis gravide. *Ann. Biol. Anim. Biochim. Biophys.* 12:47–56

82. Westerfeld, W. W. 1940. The inactivation of oestrone. *Biochem. J.* 34:51–58

83. Williams, J. G., Longcope, C., Williams, K. I. H. 1974. 4-Hydroxyestrone: a new metabolite of estradiol-17β from humans. *Steroids* 24:687–701

84. Yoshizawa, I., Fishman, J. 1971. Radioimmunoassay of 2-hydroxyestrone in human plasma. *J. Clin. Endocrinol. Metab.* 32:3–6

85. Zumoff, B., Fishman, J., Gallagher, T. F., Hellman, L. 1968. Estradiol metabolism in cirrhosis. *J. Clin. Invest.* 47:20–25

Ann. Rev. Physiol. 1983. 45:73–82

NEUROPEPTIDES AND THE BLOOD-BRAIN BARRIER

William M. Pardridge

Department of Medicine, Division of Endocrinology, UCLA School of
Medicine, Los Angeles, California 90024

INTRODUCTION

Receptors for circulating peptides of gut or neural origin (the neuropeptides) are largely located on the plasma membrane of target tissues (62). Owing to the aqueous pores in capillary walls (46), small peptides (e.g. MW 5,000 or less) readily gain access to the interstitial space and to the receptors on the plasma membrane of the target cells. Unlike the capillaries in any other organ, the microvessels in brain of all vertebrates are characterized by high resistance, epithelial-like tight junctions that essentially cement brain endothelia together (6). The barrier formed by the endothelial tight junctions, the blood-brain barrier (BBB), prevents all water-soluble substances from entering the brain interstitium from blood (31). Indeed, the BBB has all the properties of a cell membrane and may be regarded as a second-order cell membrane for the entire brain. Owing to the presence of the BBB, circulating molecules may gain access to brain interstitium by only one of two mechanisms: (*a*) lipid-mediation or free diffusion through the endothelial plasma membranes, and (*b*) carrier-mediation or transport via specific, enzyme-like carriers located within the endothelial luminal and antiluminal membranes. The steroid hormones traverse the BBB by lipid-mediation; these transport processes have been recently reviewed (39). The thyroid hormones and essential nutrients for brain metabolism (e.g. glucose, amino acids, choline, purines, ketone bodies) penetrate the BBB via carrier-mediation; these transport systems (Table 1) have also been recently reviewed (38, 39). The present summary addresses the current evidence for mechanisms of peptide transport between blood and brain. In addition, evidence for endothelial peptide degrading enzymes and peptide receptors on the BBB is reviewed.

Table 1   Blood-brain barrier transport systems (9, 33, 35, 36)

Transport system	Representative substrate	K_m (mM)	V_{max} (nmol min^{-1}g^{-1})
Hexose	Glucose	9	1600
Monocarboxylic acid	Lactate	1.9	120
Neutral amino acid	Phenylalanine	0.12	30
Amine	Choline	0.44	10
Basic amino acid	Lysine	0.10	6
Purine	Adenine	0.027	1
Nucleoside	Adenosine	0.018	0.7
Acidic amino acid	Glutamate	0.04	0.4
Thyroid hormone	T_3	0.001	0.1

PEPTIDE TRANSPORT BETWEEN BLOOD AND BRAIN

Blood-CSF Barrier: Blood to CSF Transport

About a half-dozen tiny areas of brain that line the ventricles have no BBB (60). These circumventricular organs (CVOs) include the choroid plexus, the median eminence and the organum vasculosum of the lamina terminalis (OVLT) of the hypothalamus, the subfornical organ at the roof of the third ventricle, and the area postrema at the base of the fourth ventricle. In addition to the presence of porous and fenestrated capillaries at the CVOs, the ependyma of these regions that line the ventricles have low-resistance tight junctions (6). Normally, the ependyma lining the ventricles do not have tight junctions or any barrier function, as these areas are perfused by capillaries with tight junctions of the BBB (6). The presence of the CVOs in brain have at least two major functions with regard to peptide entry into the brain. First, the absence of the BBB allows circulating peptides rapidly to enter brain interstitium in these areas and reach the plasma membrane of nerve endings terminating in the CVOs. Van Houten, Posner, and associates (57, 58) have provided evidence for receptors for peptides such as insulin, prolactin, angiotensin II, calcitonin, and ACTH on nerve endings in the median eminence. Second, the absence of the BBB in the CVOs permits circulating substances slowly to enter nonCVO parts of brain. After distribution in the interstitial space of the CVOs, peptides may slowly reach other brain regions by diffusion laterally into adjacent areas with no blood-cerebrospinal fluid (CSF) barrier and then by convection due to bulk flow of CSF. This route, which is nonspecific, is probably how all substances in plasma eventually gain access to the CSF. Since the surface area of capillaries comprising the BBB is at least 5000-fold greater (10) than the surface area of the capillaries perfusing the CVOs, the nonspecific route of entry into brain is slow, with a half-time on the order of several hours (50).

Circulating substances may slowly and nonspecifically enter brain at the CVOs and nonspecifically leave the brain via absorption of CSF at the superior sagittal sinus. Therefore, substances with the same MW should have nearly identical CSF/plasma concentration ratios. After a constant infusion, the CSF/plasma ratio of inulin, an extracellular space marker of MW = 5000, is approximately 2–3% (14). The CSF/plasma ratio of albumin (MW = 68,000) is about 0.3% (15), which is consistent with an inverse relationship between MW and the CSF/plasma ratio. If the CSF/plasma ratio is greater than the ratio expected on the basis of MW, then there must be either (a) direct neurosecretion of the peptide into CSF, or (b) selective transport of the peptide from blood into CSF either at the BBB or the blood-CSF barrier (40). In the case of vasopressin, the CSF/plasma ratio is nearly 1 (26), but there is no correlation between diurnal rhythms in CSF or blood (47). Therefore, CSF vasopressin is probably largely of CNS origin. Similarly, the CSF/plasma ratio of angiotensin II is nearly 1, but there is no correlation between blood and CSF levels (54). Therefore, angiotensin II is probably made in the brain. Controversy exists over the proposal that angiotensin II is synthesized in brain (44). However, assuming that CSF immunoreactivity of angiotensin II reflects CSF peptide concentration, the reported observations on CSF/plasma antiotensin ratios suggest a neural origin of the peptide.

The CSF/plasma ratio of insulin is about 0.25 or about 10-fold the expected value, since inulin and insulin have comparable MW. Since recent evidence indicates brain does not synthesize insulin (16), it is probable that CSF insulin originates only from plasma. If so, then the high CSF/plasma ratio suggests the peptide is selectively transported into brain (40). Since insulin does not cross the BBB (19), it is possible the selective transport of insulin occurs at the ependyma lining the blood-CSF barrier of the CVOs. No in vivo evidence to date is available to support the hypothesis of peptide transport systems at the CVOs (41a). Nevertheless, it is clear that certain peptides—e.g. insulin (61) or, in the developing brain, fetuin or α-feto-protein (15)—selectively enter CSF at rates that exceed the nonspecific pathways of entry.

Arachnoid Villi: CSF to Blood Transport

While peptides *slowly* gain access to CSF from the blood via transport through the CVOs, peptides injected into the CSF may *rapidly* (50) enter blood via absorption into the superior sagittal sinus at the arachnoid villi. The CSF is continually produced and absorbed. In humans the volume of CSF is 140 ml, and this fluid is cleared at a rate of 0.5 ml min^{-1} or a half-time of about 180 min (12). The half-time of clearance of CSF is much lower in small animals; CSF is cleared with a half-time of 28 and 109 min in rats and rabbits, respectively (12). The rapid clearance of CSF should be evaluated in experimental studies in which extra-CNS peptide action is studied following central (ventricular) peptide administration. The studies of Yamada and co-workers (41) have shown that cholecystokinin (CCK_8) and other peptides enter plasma in rabbits with a half-time of 13 min following ventricular administration via a bolus injection. These studies emphasize the importance of measuring plasma peptide levels in any study that measures peripheral peptide action following central peptide administration.

Blood-Brain Barrier: Blood to Brain Transport

Numerous studies have purported to provide evidence for transport of peptides through the BBB. However, a critical review of these studies leads to the following conclusions: (a) Specific transport systems for peptides, similar to systems known to occur for nutrients or thyroid hormone (Table 1), have not thus far been shown to exist at the BBB; and (b) the permeability of the BBB to peptides is low and on the order of that to other putative neurotransmitters that exist in the circulation. Cornford et al (8) showed that the first-pass extraction of the enkephalins or thyrotropin releasing hormone (TRH) was only 1–2%, similar to the extraction for the monoamines or acetylcholine (28). Rapoport et al (43) reported that the permeability of the BBB to enkephalinamide peptides was "moderate," but conversion of permeability constants (cm sec^{-1}) reported by Rapoport et al (43) into extraction fractions indicates the permeability of the BBB to peptides is not moderate. The extraction observed by Rapoport et al is 2% (40), and these data actually confirm the initial studies of Cornford et al (8). In addition to enkephalin and TRH, other studies have shown that insulin, angiotensin II, and vasopressin do not cross the BBB (17, 19, 47).

BLOOD-BRAIN BARRIER PEPTIDE DEGRADATION

The previous section emphasized the view that the permeability of the BBB to peptides is low and on the order of that to other putative neurotransmitters (37, 40). One function of the BBB is the rapid enzymatic inactivation of neuro-active substances—e.g. of monoamines by monoamine oxidase (22), or of acetylcholine by cholinesterase (45). Brain endothelia rapidly degrade peptides, as they do the monoamines and acetylcholine. Brain capillaries have a high aminopeptidase activity, which rapidly cleaves N-terminus tyrosine from enkephalins (37). In addition, enkephalins are degraded by a second capillary enzyme that is probably a peptidyl dipeptidase (37). The latter may be either a dipeptidase specific for enkephalin, which is present in brain (20), or angiotensin converting enzyme. Converting enzyme is known to be present in brain capillaries and to be inhibited by nM concentrations of Captopril (5).

With regard to the peptidases present in brain capillaries, more studies are needed in this important field, since it now appears that peptidase activity is the major way by which centrally released peptides are inactivated (53). If the peptidases in brain capillaries are located on the antiluminal membrane, then brain endothelial metabolism of peptides may be an important site of peptide inactivation.

The aminopeptidase activity of brain capillaries should be considered in the design of experiments of peptide transport in brain. Several peptides are labeled in the N-terminus amino acid—e.g. tyrosine, a neutral amino acid that readily crosses the BBB via carrier-mediated transport (Table 1). Aminopeptidase cleavage of the peptide results in the formation of free tyrosine, which can then be transported into brain in vivo (25) or in vitro in isolated endothelia (37). This effect can be blocked by the co-administration of unlabeled tyrosine, which saturates the BBB neutral amino acid carrier and prevents the uptake of the ^{3}H- or ^{125}I-tyrosine cleaved from the N-terminus of the peptide.

BLOOD-BRAIN BARRIER PEPTIDE RECEPTORS

The evidence currently available indicates peptides slowly enter CSF via transport at the CVOs but are prevented from rapidly reaching brain interstitium owing to the absence of specific transport systems within the BBB. However, if one views the BBB as the cell membrane of the brain, and considers that peptides act by binding cell membrane receptors, then it seems reasonable to suggest that peptide receptors may exist on the luminal side of the BBB. If so, then a circulating peptide could bind the receptor and generate a metabolic signal that could be conveyed rapidly to brain cells (40). This highly speculative hypothesis gained support with the observation that specific receptors for insulin exist on the luminal side of brain capillaries in vivo (56) and on isolated brain endothelia in vitro (18). The BBB insulin receptor has characteristics typical of peripheral insulin receptors; the dissociation constant (K_D) of the high-affinity receptor is 0.4 nM (18). The ratio of receptor capacity to K_D (the binding index) is high for the BBB insulin receptor, and it is likely the brain capillary is a site of sequestration in brain of circulating insulin. If it is assumed that the high-affinity receptor is 50% occupied, and that the brain capillaries comprise 5% of brain weight, then approximately 2–3 ng insulin per g brain may be sequestered by the brain capillary insulin receptor (18). This value approximates the levels recorded by Yalow and associates (16) and is consistent with the view that brain insulin originates from the circulation.

An important area of future research is the characterization of other BBB peptide receptors and the putative second messengers generated by peptide action on the brain capillary endothelia.

PEPTIDE-INDUCED CHANGES IN BLOOD-BRAIN BARRIER PERMEABILITY

Several studies have addressed the problem of alterations in BBB permeability caused by peptides. Insulin is probably the most likely peptide to cause changes in BBB transport, since the brain capillary is known to have an insulin receptor. However, to date there is no evidence to support a physiologic role for insulin in regard to barrier phenomena. The initial report that insulin increases potassium influx into brain of rabbits (1) has not been confirmed in either mice or rabbits (55). Quantitative studies in the dog and rat have shown insulin has no effect on BBB glucose transport (2, 11). However, a recent report in humans suggests insulin may increase BBB glucose transport (23) by as much as 50%. However, the plasma insulin level used in this study, 1400 μU ml^{-1}, is more than 10-fold greater than a high postprandial insulin level. Therefore it is not clear whether physiologic levels of insulin modulate BBB glucose transport in humans. Since brain glycolysis is not limited by transport in brain (38), an insulin-mediated increase in glucose transport would not be expected to accelerate glycolysis in brain. However, insulin has been shown to increase glycogen synthesis in brain (11); and the acceleration of BBB glucose transport by insulin, if this occurs, may be linked to cerebral glycogen synthesis. Another apparent action of peripheral insulin on at least the developing brain is an increase in brain ornithine decarboxylase (49).

While some studies have suggested insulin increases BBB amino acid transport (13), the increase in brain uptake of aromatic amino acids caused by insulin is likely secondary to a branched chain hypoaminoacidemia (34). Insulin increases cellular amino acid transport by increasing the activity of the alanine on the A-preferring amino acid system (48). The A-system is not present on the luminal side of the BBB (34). This is consistent with the failure of studies to show an increase in BBB amino acid transport due to a direct action of insulin on the BBB.

Intracisternal adrenocorticotropin (ACTH) has been shown to increase the CSF concentrations of substances and this may be due either to an increase in the permeability of the blood-CSF barrier or to a decrease in the efflux due to bulk flow of substances out of CSF (51). Since ACTH only increased the CSF concentration of substances that are cleared by bulk flow—e.g. protein, mannitol, inulin—it is likely the effect of the peptide is to decrease bulk flow of CSF. In another study, the peripheral administration of α-melanocyte stimulating hormone (MSH) resulted in an increase in brain uptake of pertechnetate (52). However, the brain uptake of pertechnetate or any substance may be enhanced either by increasing BBB permeability or by decreasing peripheral clearance. Without measurements of the integral of plasma specific activity over the time course of study, the analysis of brain radioactivity alone cannot be used unequivocally as a measure of BBB permeability.

There is indirect evidence that parathyroid hormone (PTH) may alter BBB transport of calcium. Brain calcium is doubled in patients with acute renal failure and elevated plasma PTH, despite a decrease in plasma calcium (7). Although indirect, this study suggests the need for evaluating the presence of PTH receptors on brain capillaries.

Vasopressin when administered intraventricularly has been shown to increase BBB permeability to water (42). In addition, central noradrenergic stimulation causes the same effect (21). Therefore, it is not clear whether vasopressin acts directly on brain endothelia to enhance microvessel transport of water or indirectly via a noradrenergic mechanism. The role of vasopressin, or any other peptide, in the regulation of BBB permeability would be clarified by the demonstration of the presence of specific, high-affinity receptors for the peptide on brain endothelia. Thus far, the only BBB peptide receptor documented is the insulin receptor (18).

STRATEGIES FOR PEPTIDE DELIVERY TO BRAIN

The lipid solubility of native peptides is low, and peptide transport systems are absent within the BBB. Therefore, with the exception of the CVOs, it is not currently possible rapidly to deliver peptides to brain interstitial space following systemic administration. Actually the problem of peptide delivery to brain is similar to the issue of how water-soluble drugs might penetrate the BBB. There are three general approaches to peptide or drug delivery to brain: (a) Opening the BBB, (b) intrathecal administration, and (c) latentiation. Neuwelt and associates (27) have designed protocols for delivery of systemically administered enzymes—e.g. hexosaminidase A—to brain following transient osmotic opening of the BBB. The intracarotid infusion of 25% mannitol for 30 sec results in opening of the BBB and distribution of the enzyme into brain. However, the neurotoxicity of opening the BBB is likely to restrict severely the clinical use of this regimine. Peptides may be delivered to brain via intrathecal administration. However, this approach will only achieve a high level of peptide distribution to the layers of cells surrounding the ventricles.

The most promising, yet least evaluated, strategy for increasing peptide (or drug) delivery to brain is latentiation. The chemical conversion of a water-soluble compound to a lipid-soluble molecule can result in log order increases in BBB permeability (29, 59). Ideally, the chemical modification of the peptide should be a reversible one, so that the native peptide may be regenerated in the brain. The classic example of drug latentiation is morphine. The two hydroxyl groups on morphine can be acetylated to form heroin, which crosses the BBB at a log order faster rate than morphine (30). Once inside the brain, heroin is converted back to morphine via pseudocholinesterase hydrolysis of the acetyl groups. Similarly, other types of reversible chemical modifications have increased BBB permeability to drugs (3, 4). One type of chemical modification of peptides that should be explored in more detail is the formation of diketopiperazines. Cyclization of the C-terminus of oxytocin, Leu-Gly, results in the formation of diketopiperazine, cyclo (Leu-Gly), and this compound appears to cross the BBB (24). The condensation of the dipeptide to form the diketopiperazine would be expected to increase the lipid solubility of the compound by more than a log order of magnitude. Until rational chemical strategies for latentiation of peptides are devised, it is unlikely that significant distribution within the CNS of systemically administered peptides will be achieved.

ACKNOWLEDGMENTS

Work in the author's laboratory is supported by NIH grant NS-17701 and by RCDA AM-00783. The author is indebted to Larry Mietus for superior technical assistance and to Dr. Tadataka Yamada for numerous and valuable discussions.

Literature Cited

1. Arieff, A. I., Doerner, T., Zelig, H., Massry, S. G. 1974. Mechanisms of seizures and coma in hypoglycemia. Evidence for a direct effect of insulin on electrolyte transport in brain. *J. Clin. Invest.* 54:654–63
2. Betz, A. L., Gilboe, D. D., Yudilevich, D. L., Drewes, L. R. 1973. Kinetics of unidirectional glucose transport into the isolated dog brain. *Am. J. Physiol.* 225:586–92
3. Bodor, N., Shek, E., Higuchi, T. 1975. Delivery of a quaternary pyridinium salt across the blood-brain barrier by its dihydropyridine derivative. *Science* 190:155–56
4. Bodor, N., Farag, H. H., Brewster, M. E. III. 1981. Site-specific, sustained release of drugs to the brain. *Science* 214:1370–72
5. Brecher, P., Tercyak, A., Gavras, H., Chobanian, A. V. 1978. Peptidyl dipeptidase in rabbit brain microvessels. *Biochim. Biophys. Acta* 526:537–46
6. Brightman, M. W. 1977. Morphology of blood-brain interfaces. 1977. *Exp. Eye Res.* 25:1–25 (Suppl.)
7. Cooper, J. D., Lazarowitz, V. C., Arieff, A. I. 1978. Neurodiagnostic abnormalities in patients with acute renal failure. *J. Clin. Invest.* 61:1448–55
8. Cornford, E. M., Braun, L. D., Crane, P. D., Oldendorf, W. H. 1978. Blood-brain barrier restriction of peptides and the low uptake of enkephalins. *Endocrinology* 103:1297–303
9. Cornford, E. M., Braun, L. D., Oldendorf, W. H. 1978. Carrier mediated blood-brain barrier transport of choline and certain choline analogs. *J. Neurochem.* 30:299–308
10. Crone, C. 1971. The blood-brain barrier —facts and questions. In *Ion Homeostasis of the Brain*, ed. B. K. Siesjo, S. C. Sorensen, pp. 52–62. Copenhagen: Munksgaard
11. Daniel, P. M., Love, E. F., Pratt, O. E. 1975. Insulin and the way the brain handles glucose. *J. Neurochem.* 25:471–76
12. Davson, H. 1969. The cerebrospinal fluid. *Handb. Neurochem.* 2:23–48
13. De Montis, M. G., Olianas, M. C., Haber, B., Tagliamonte, A. 1978. Increase in large neutral amino acid transport into brain by insulin. *J. Neurochem.* 30:121–24

14. Dziegielewska, K. M., Evans, C. A. N., Malinowska, D. H., Møllgard, K., Reynolds, J. M., Reynolds, M. L., Saunders, N. R. 1979. Studies of the development of brain barrier systems to lipid insoluble molecules in fetal sheep. *J. Physiol.* 292:207–31

15. Dziegielewska, K. M., Evans, C. A. N., Fossan, G., Lorsheider, F. L., Malinowska, D. H., Møllgard, K., Reynolds, M. L., Saunders, N. R., Wilkinson, S. 1980. Proteins in cerebrospinal fluid and plasma of fetal sheep during development. *J. Physiol.* 300:441–55

16. Eng, J., Yalow, R. S. 1980. Insulin recoverable from tissues. *Diabetes* 29:105–9

17. Fitzsimons, J. T. 1978. Angiotensin, thirst, and sodium appetite: retrospect and prospect. *Fed. Proc.* 37:2669–75

18. Frank, H. J., Pardridge, W. M. 1981. A direct in vitro demonstration of insulin binding to isolated brain microvessels. *Diabetes* 30:575–61

19. Goodner, C. J., Berrie, M. A. 1977. The failure of rat hypothalamic tissues to take up labeled insulin in vivo or to respond to insulin in vitro. *Endocrinology* 101:605–12

20. Gorenstein, C., Snyder, S. H. 1980. Enkephalinases. *Proc. R. Soc. London Ser. B* 210:123–32

21. Grubb, R. L. Jr., Raichel, M. E., Eichling, J. O. 1978. Peripheral sympathetic regulation of brain water permeability. *Brain Res.* 144:204–7

22. Hardebo, J. E., Emson, P. C., Falck, B., Owman, C., Rosengran, E. 1980. Enzymes related to monoamine transmitter metabolism in brain microvessels. *J. Neurochem.* 35:1388–93

23. Hertz, M. M., Paulson, O. B., Barry, D. I., Christiansen, J. S., Svendsen, P. A. 1981. Insulin increases glucose transfer across the blood-barrier in man. *J. Clin. Invest.* 67:597–604

24. Hoffman, P. L., Walter, R., Bulat, M. 1977. An enzymatically stable peptide with activity in the central nervous system: its penetration through the blood-CSF barrier. *Brain Res.* 122:87–94

25. Houghten, R. A., Swann, R. W., Li, C. H. 1980. β-Endorphin: stability, clearance behavior, and entry into the central nervous system after intravenous injection of the tritiated peptide in rats and rabbits. *Proc. Natl. Acad. Sci. USA* 77:4588–91

26. Jenkins, J. S., Mather, H. M., Ang, V. 1980. Vasopressin in human cerebrospinal fluid. *J. Clin. Endocrinol. Metabol.* 50:364–67

27. Neuwelt, E. A., Barranger, J. A., Brady, R. O., Pagel, M., Furbish, F. S., Quirk, J. M., Mook, G. E., Frenkel, E. 1981. Delivery of hexosaminidase A to the cerebrum after osmotic modification of the blood-brain barrier. *Proc. Natl. Acad. Sci. USA* 78:5835–41

28. Oldendorf, W. H. 1971. Brain uptake of radiolabeled amino acids, amines, and hexoses after arterial injection. *Am. J. Physiol.* 221:1629–39

29. Oldendorf, W. H. 1974. Blood-brain barrier permeability to drugs. *Ann. Rev. Pharmacol.* 14:239–48

30. Oldendorf, W. H., Hyman, S., Braun, L., Oldendorf, S. Z. 1972. Blood-brain barrier: penetration of morphine, codeine, heroin, and methadone after arterial injection. *Science* 178:984–88

31. Oldendorf, W. H. 1975. Permeability of the blood-brain barrier. In *The Nervous System*, ed. D. B. Tower, 1:279–89. NY:Raven

32. Deleted in proof

33. Pardridge, W. M., Oldendorf, W. H. 1977. Transport of metabolic substrates through the blood-brain barrier. *J. Neurochem.* 28:5–12

34. Pardridge, W. M. 1979. The role of blood-brain barrier transport of tryptophan and other neutral amino acids in the regulation of substrate-limited pathways of brain amino acid metabolism. *J. Neural Trans.* Suppl. 15:43–54

35. Pardridge, W. M. 1979. Regulation of amino acid availability to brain: selective control mechanisms for glutamate. In *Glutamic Acid: Advances in Biochemistry and Physiology*, ed. L. J. Filer Jr., et al, pp. 125–37. NY:Raven

36. Pardridge, W. M. 1979. Carrier-mediated transport of thyroid hormones through the rat blood-brain barrier: primary role of albumin-bound hormone. *Endocrinology* 105:605–12

37. Pardridge, W. M., Meitus, L. J. 1981. Enkephalin and blood-brain barrier: studies of binding and degradation in isolated brain microvessels. *Endocrinology.* 109:1138–43

38. Pardridge, W. M. 1981. Transport of nutrients and hormones through the blood-brain barrier. *Diabetologia* 20:264–54

39. Pardridge, W. M. 1981. Transport of protein-bound hormones into tissues in vivo. *Endocrine Rev.* 2:103–23

40. Pardridge, W. M., Frank, H. J. L., Cornford, E. M., Braun, L. D., Crane, P. D., Oldendorf, W. H. 1981. Neuropeptides and the blood-brain barrier. In *Neurosecretion and Brain Peptides*, ed.

J. B. Martin, S. Reichlin, K. L. Bick, pp. 321–28. NY:Raven

41. Passaro, E. Jr., Debas, H., Oldendorf, W., Yamada, T. 1982. Rapid appearance of intraventricularly administered neuropeptides in the peripheral circulation. *Brain Res.* 241:338–40

41a. Pilgrim, C. 1978. Transport function of hypothalamic tancyte ependyma: how good is the evidence? *Neuroscience* 3:277–83

42. Raichel, M. E., Grubb, R. L. Jr. 1978. Regulation of brain water permeability by centrally-released vasopressin. *Brain Res.* 143:191–94

43. Rapoport, S. I., Klee, W. A., Pettigrew, K. D., Ohno, K. 1980. Entry of opioid peptides into the central nervous system. *Science* 207:84–86

44. Reid, I. A. 1979. The brain renin-angiotensin system: a critical analysis. *Fed. Proc.* 38:2255–59

45. Renkawek, K., Murray, M. R., Spatz, M., Klatzo, I. 1976. Distinctive histochemical characteristics of brain capillaries in organotype culture. *Exp. Neurol.* 50:194–206

46. Renkin, E. M. 1978. Transport pathways through capillary endothelium. *Microvasc. Res.* 15:123–35

47. Reppert, S. M., Artman, H. G., Swaminathan, S., Fisher, D. A. 1981. Vasopressin exhibits a rhythmic daily pattern in cerebrospinal fluid but not in blood. *Science* 213:1256–57

48. Riggs, T. R. 1970. Hormones and transport across cell membranes. In *Biochemical Actions of Hormones,* ed. G. Litwack, 1:157–208. NY:Academic

49. Roger, L. J., Fellows, R. E. 1980. Stimulation of ornithine decarboxylase activity by insulin in developing rat brain. *Endocrinology* 106:619–25

50. Rothman, A. R., Freireich, E. J., Gaskins, J. R., Patlak, C. S., Rall, D. P. 1961. Exchange of inulin and dextran between blood and cerebrospinal fluid. *Am. J. Physiol.* 201:1145–48

51. Rudman, D., Kutner, M. H. 1978. Melanotropic peptides increase permeability of plasma/cerebrospinal fluid barrier. *Am. J. Physiol.* 234:E327–32

52. Sankar, R., Domer, F. R., Kastin, A. J. 1981. Selective effects of α-MSH and MIF-1 on the blood-brain barrier. *Peptides* 2:345–47

53. Schwartz, J. C., Malfroy, B., De La Baume, S. 1981. Biological Inactivation of enkephalins and the role of enkephalin-dipeptidylcarboxypeptidase ("enkephalinase") as neuropeptidase. *Life Sci.* 29:1715–40

54. Severs, W. B., Changaris, D. G., Keil, L. C., Summy-Long, J. Y., Klase, P. A., Kapsha, J. M. 1978. Pharmacology of angiotensin-induced drinking behavior. *Fed. Proc.* 37:2699–702

55. Thurston, J. H., Hauhart, R. E., Dirgo, J. A., McDougal, D. B. 1977. Insulin and brain metabolism. Absence of direct action of insulin on K^+ and Na^+ transport in normal rabbit brain. *Diabetes* 26:1117–19

56. Van Houten, M., Posner, B. I. 1979. Insulin binds to brain blood vessels in vivo. *Nature* 282:623–25

57. Van Houten, M., Posner, B. I., Kopriwa, B. M., Brawer, J. R. 1979. Insulin-binding sites in the rat brain: in vivo localization to the circumventricular organs by quantitative radioautography. *Endocrinology* 105:666–73

58. Van Houten, M., Khan, M. N., Khan, R. J., Posner, B. I. 1981. Blood-borne adrenocorticotropin binds specifically to the median eminence-arcuate region of the rat hypothalamus. *Endocrinology* 108:2385–87

59. Verbiscar, A. J., Abood, L. G. 1970. Carbamate ester latentiation of physiologically active amines. *J. Med. Chem.* 13:1176–79

60. Weindl, A. 1973. Neuroendocrine aspects of circumventricular organs. In *Frontiers in Neuroendocrinology,* ed. W. F. Ganong, L. Martini, pp. 3–32. NY: Oxford Univ. Press

61. Woods, S. C., Porte, D. Jr. 1977. Relationship between plasma and cerebrospinal fluid insulin levels in dogs. *Am. J. Physiol.* 233:E331–34

62. Zeleznik, A. J., Roth, J. 1978. Demonstration of the insulin receptor in vivo in rabbits and its possible role as a reservoir for the plasma hormone. *J. Clin. Invest.* 61:1363–74

Ann. Rev. Physiol. 1983. 45:83–94

GONADOTROPIN RELEASING HORMONE:
Extrapituitary Actions and Paracrine Control Mechanisms

Aaron J. W. Hsueh and Phillip B. C. Jones

Department of Reproductive Medicine, University of California San Diego, La Jolla, California 92093

INTRODUCTION

After the purification of gonadotropin releasing hormone (GnRH), many laboratories have investigated the effects of GnRH and its agonists on various reproductive functions. In both males and females, administration of GnRH or its potent agonists results in sustained increases in serum gonadotropins. Since pituitary gonadotropins are essential for normal gonadal functions, and since hypothalamic GnRH was believed to act solely on the pituitary gland, treatment with high doses of GnRH and its agonists had been predicted to be a potential means for enhancing fertility.

Paradoxically, long-term administration of pharmacological doses of GnRH or potent GnRH agonists was shown to decrease a variety of female and male reproductive functions (22). In females, the reported paradoxical actions of GnRH include: inhibition of ovarian steroidogenesis and gonadotropin receptor content; inhibition of follicle maturation and ovulation; delays in ovum transport and ovum implantation; termination of pregnancy; decreases in uterine growth; and ovarian-dependent mammary tumorigenesis. Similarly, in males, long-term administration of high doses of GnRH or GnRH agonists results in decreases of testicular weight, steroidogenesis, and gonadotropin receptor content; inhibition of spermatogenesis; and arrest of male accessory sex organ growth.

0066-4278/83/0315-0083$02.00

POSSIBLE MECHANISMS INVOLVED IN THE PARADOXICAL INHIBITION OF REPRODUCTIVE FUNCTIONS BY GnRH

To explain the action of GnRH and its agonists in inhibiting female and male reproductive functions, one can propose at least three possible mechanisms.

1. Chronic stimulation of anterior pituitary by high doses of GnRH or its agonists may cause "desensitization" of the gonadotrophs (5), with resulting decreased circulating gonadotropins and subsequent atrophy of female and male reproductive organs.

2. Treatment with pharmacological doses of GnRH or its agonists may stimulate the release of high levels of luteinizing hormone (LH) which, in turn, results in LH-induced "desensitization" of gonadal cells to subsequent LH action (9, 17, 39).

3. In contrast to classical concepts of the neuroendocrine regulation of gonadal functions, GnRH may exert an extrapituitary, direct inhibitory action upon gonadal cells.

Chronic treatment with high doses of GnRH can initially cause a transient increase in serum gonadotropins, but the increase is followed by a period of pituitary refractoriness to subsequent GnRH treatment. However, since several studies indicate that high doses of GnRH agonists decrease testicular functions without concomitant decreases in serum gonadotropin levels (40, 43), it is unlikely that the pituitary desensitization mechanism can fully explain the paradoxical inhibitory effect of GnRH or its agonists.

The inhibitory effect of GnRH on gonadal functions has also been attributed to LH-induced desensitization of the gonads to subsequent LH. Although the administration of a *single* high dose of LH or human chorionic gonadotropin (hCG) decreases testicular steroidogenic responsiveness to subsequent gonadotropin stimulation (17), *repeated* administration of LH to male rats decreases testicular LH receptor content but increases testicular steroidogenic responsiveness to LH (47). Thus the observed decrease in testicular steroidogenic responsiveness following a single dose of LH or hCG probably cannot fully explain the inhibitory effect of prolonged treatment with *multiple* doses of GnRH and GnRH agonists.

We have tested the third hypothesis—i.e. that GnRH and GnRH agonists may directly inhibit gonadal functions. Using an ovarian primary cell culture (10, 11), we tested the third hypothesis and reported, for the first time, a direct inhibitory action of GnRH and its agonists in cultured ovarian granulosa cells (18, 20).

DIRECT CONTROL OF GONADAL FUNCTIONS BY GnRH

Ovarian Granulosa and Luteal Cells

Maturation of the ovarian follicles is accompanied by profound changes in the hormonal responsiveness and steroidogenic capacity of the granulosa cells. Ovarian granulosa cells obtained from preantral follicles of immature hypophysectomized rats respond in vitro to follicle-stimulating hormone (FSH) with the production of estrogen and progestins. Concomitant treatment with increasing concentrations of GnRH causes a dose-dependent inhibition of the FSH stimulation of estrogen and progesterone production with ED_{50} values of 5×10^{-10} and $1.5 \times 10^{-9}M$, respectively (18, 20). In cultures containing FSH and a maximal inhibitory dose ($10^{-8}M$) of GnRH, concomitant addition of increasing concentrations of a GnRH antagonist, [D-pGlu^1,D-Phe^2,D-Trp^{3,6}]-GnRH, results in a dose-dependent blockage of GnRH action by preventing the GnRH inhibition of estrogen and progesterone production (20). These results demonstrate the direct inhibition of ovarian steroidogenesis by GnRH and further suggest that the actions of GnRH and its antagonist may involve stringent stereospecific interactions of these peptides with ovarian recognition sites.

FSH also stimulates LH and prolactin (PRL) receptor formation by these cultured granulosa cells (12, 36, 45). Concomitant treatment with GnRH or its agonists inhibits FSH stimulation of LH and PRL receptor formation, whereas the inhibitory effect of GnRH is blocked by the GnRH antagonist (20, 21, 36).

FSH treatment of cultured granulosa cells in vitro not only induces functional LH and PRL receptors but also increases the responsiveness of granulosa cells to β_2-adrenergic agents (1). These FSH-treated granulosa cells acquire many characteristics similar to those of luteal cells. We tested the direct effect of GnRH and its antagonist on various functional parameters of these FSH-primed "granulosa-luteal" cells. Treatment of the granulosa-luteal cells with LH increases estrogen and progestin production (46). In contrast, treatment with PRL or β_2-adrenergic agents stimulates progesterone production without affecting aromatase (1, 45, 46). Concomitant treatment with GnRH inhibits LH stimulation of estrogen production (29). Similarly, GnRH treatment also inhibits progesterone production stimulated by LH, PRL or β_2-adrenergic agents (24, 29). All of these inhibitory effects of GnRH are blocked by concomitant treatment with a potent GnRH antagonist.

Furthermore, PRL treatment of cultured granulosa-luteal cells increases LH receptor content, whereas GnRH treatment inhibits the PRL action.

Concomitant treatment of these cells with PRL and a GnRH antagonist blocks the inhibitory effect of GnRH on PRL action (29). These studies conclusively demonstrated the potent inhibitory actions of GnRH on the differentiation of granulosa cells and the GnRH suppression of granulosa-luteal cell responsiveness to luteotrophic hormones.

We extended our in vitro studies to in vivo experiments using immature hypophysectomized rats to study the effect of GnRH and its agonists on follicular maturation (18, 21, 29). Treatment with FSH increases ovarian weight, granulosa cell aromatase activity and LH receptor content in hypophysectomized rats. Concomitant administration of high doses of GnRH or GnRH agonists inhibits the FSH stimulation of ovarian weight (21). GnRH or its agonists also suppress FSH-induced increases in granulosa cell aromatase activity and LH receptor content. These inhibitory effects are blocked by in vivo treatment with a potent GnRH antagonist (29).

In vivo and in vitro demonstrations of the extrapituitary actions of GnRH and its agonists on ovarian functions in rats were also provided by other investigators (4, 7, 13, 35). Recently, a direct inhibitory effect of a GnRH agonist on human granulosa cell steroidogenesis was also demonstrated in vitro (44).

A possible direct effect of GnRH on luteal functions in vivo was also studied in immature hypophysectomized rats (27) that were injected sequentially with FSH, LH, and PRL to induce functional corpora lutea. Treatment with GnRH or its agonist results in a dose-dependent inhibition of PRL-stimulated increases in ovarian weight, serum progesterone levels, and ovarian LH/hCG receptor content. That GnRH treatment may inhibit luteal functions in vivo through extrapituitary mechanisms has also been suggested in studies using hypophysectomized pregnant or pseudopregnant rats (14, 34).

Following the demonstration of a direct inhibitory effect of GnRH on cultured granulosa cells, several groups have demonstrated specific uptake (35) and high-affinity binding of ^{125}I-labeled GnRH agonists to GnRH receptor sites in ovarian granulosa (26, 38) and luteal (7) cells. Using an ^{125}I-labeled GnRH agonist, we demonstrated that the agonist binds to the ovarian cell membrane in a saturable manner with a dissociation constant of ~10^{-10}M (26). The direct actions of GnRH on granulosa cells are believed to be mediated by these receptors.

Testicular Leydig Cells

Following the demonstration of direct inhibitory effects of GnRH and its agonists on ovarian granulosa cells, we further studied the extrapituitary action of GnRH on testis functions in male rats (3, 19). Using immature hypophysectomized male rats, we demonstrated that in vivo treatment with high doses of GnRH or GnRH agonists for 5 days decreases the FSH-maintenance of testis weight, LH/hCG receptor content, and Leydig cell androgen biosynthesis. Other investigators (2) have also reported that treatment with a potent GnRH agonist for 7 days decreases LH/hCG receptor content in immature and adult hypophysectomized rats. We further demonstrated that treatment with FSH, PRL, and growth hormone in hypophysectomized immature and adult rats maintains testis weight, LH receptor content, and steroidogenic responsiveness, while concomitant treatment with GnRH or its agonists inhibits the action of the pituitary hormones (3). The decrease in testicular steroidogenesis is associated with a decrease in the activities of the testicular enzyme 17α-hydroxylase (3).

Since one cannot rule out the possibility that GnRH and its agonists may act on extragonadal sites to cause a secondary inhibition of the Leydig cell functions, we pursued in vitro studies to test the direct inhibitory effect of GnRH on cultured testicular cells (16, 23). Treatment with hCG substantially stimulates androgen production in cultured testicular cells obtained from immature or adult hypophysectomized rats. Concomitant treatment with GnRH or GnRH agonists results in a dose-dependent inhibition of androgen production. Furthermore, the inhibitory effect of GnRH is blocked by concomitant treatment with a potent GnRH antagonist (16), suggesting that the actions of these peptides are probably mediated through stereospecific testicular recognition sites.

The direct inhibitory effect of GnRH on testicular Leydig cell functions was reinforced by the demonstration of specific high-affinity ($K_d = \sim 10^{-10}$ M) binding sites for GnRH agonists in testicular Leydig cells (6, 8, 33). In contrast, no specific binding of GnRH was detected in Sertoli cells.

Mechanisms of GnRH Action

GnRH and its agonists presumably act on specific gonadal binding sites to directly modulate gonadal functions. GnRH regulation of various steroidogenic enzymes was studied in cultured granulosa cells in order to understand the mechanisms by which GnRH inhibits gonadotropin stimulation of progesterone production (28, 31). GnRH-induced decreases in progesterone production may result from the inhibition of progesterone biosynthesis and/or the stimulation of progesterone conversion to inactive metabolites.

FSH treatment in vitro markedly stimulates the activity of 3β-hydroxysteroid dehydrogenase (3β-HSD), which converts the precursor pregnenolone to progesterone (10, 31). FSH treatment also causes a slight increase in the activity of 20α-hydroxysteroid dehydrogenase (20α-HSD), which metabolizes progesterone to its inactive metabolite, 20α-hydroxy-pregn-4--en-3-one (28). Concomitant treatment with GnRH partially inhibits the stimulatory effect of FSH on 3β-HSD activity (31) but further enhances FSH stimulation of 20α-HSD activity (28), thereby decreasing the conversion of pregnenolone to progesterone and increasing the metabolism of progesterone. Furthermore, measurement of pregnenolone biosynthesis in granulosa cells treated with cyanoketone (an inhibitor of 3β-HSD activity) shows that FSH stimulates pregnenolone production and GnRH inhibits the FSH action, suggesting that GnRH may affect additional steroidogenic enzymes (such as side-chain cleavage enzymes) prior to pregnenolone production (24). The mechanisms by which GnRH inhibits FSH-stimulated progesterone production are summarized in Figure 1. Similar mechanisms are involved in the GnRH inhibition of progesterone production induced by PRL and β-adrenergic agonists.

Treatment of cultured granulosa cells with GnRH alone also stimulates 20α-HSD activity in the absence of gonadotropins (30). GnRH treatment for 2 days in vitro stimulates 20α-HSD activity in a dose-dependent manner with an ED_{50} value of 8.9 × 10^{-9} M. The stimulatory effect of GnRH is inhibited by concomitant treatment with a GnRH antagonist ([D-pGlu¹, D-Phe²-D,Trp³·⁶]GnRH), whereas treatment with the GnRH antagonist alone does not affect the enzyme activity. The GnRH stimulation of 20α-HSD activity requires a latent period of 12 hr and can be blocked by a protein synthesis inhibitor (30). The finding of the stimulatory effect of GnRH is in direct contrast to other studies consistently demonstrating the direct inhibitory effects of GnRH on gonadal functions. Thus GnRH does not exert an overall inhibition of ovarian functions but rather causes specific

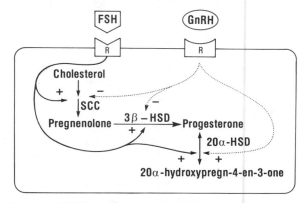

Figure 1   Mechanisms of GnRH action at the ovarian level. R: receptors; scc = side-chain cleavage enzyme; 3β-HSD = 3β-hydroxysteriod dehydrogenase; 20α-HSD = 20α-hydroxysteroid dehydrogenase.

stimulation of the progesterone metabolizing enzyme. These results further suggest that GnRH not only modulates gonadotropin actions but also exerts an independent effect at the ovarian level. Similarly, a direct stimulatory effect of GnRH and its agonists in the induction of oocyte maturation and ovulation has also been demonstrated in hypophysectomized rats (21) and in isolated preovulatory follicles (15). The significance of these findings remains to be elucidated.

The requirement of a prolonged exposure of ovarian cells to GnRH for the inhibitory action of GnRH is in direct contrast to the rapid (within minutes) releasing action of GnRH at the pituitary level. This finding stresses the importance of the frequency of administration of GnRH or its agonists in the design of treatment protocols for pro- or anti-fertility studies. Treatment with high doses of GnRH for prolonged periods (or treatment with long-acting GnRH agonists) is more likely to result in direct gonadal inhibition than is pulsatile administration of "physiological" doses of degradable GnRH (but not GnRH agonists).

In contrast to studies on the ovarian cells, limited results are available regarding the mechanism of action of GnRH on the testicular Leydig cells. Our unpublished studies in cultured testicular cells suggest that GnRH treatment does not affect cAMP production induced by LH/hCG but preferentially inhibits the activities of 17α-hydroxylase and 17-20-desmolase in the Leydig cells, leading to decreases in Leydig cell testosterone production.

EXTRAPITUITARY ACTIONS OF GnRH IN OTHER TISSUES AND POSSIBLE PARACRINE CONTROL MECHANISMS

GnRH and its agonists not only directly affect ovarian and testicular functions but also affect the functions of several other reproductive and nonreproductive organs through extrapituitary mechanisms. Studies from various laboratories are summarized in Table 1.

GnRH agonists inhibit the growth of female and male accessory sex organs such as uterus, ventral prostate, and seminal vesicle in hypophysectomized, castrated rates (42). In addition, GnRH-like peptide was found in the human placenta (32), and GnRH stimulates the release of placental hCG. Furthermore, neurotransmitter role for a GnRH-like peptide was demonstrated in the sympathetic ganglia of the frog (25).

Radioligand binding studies indicate the presence of GnRH binding sites in gonadal and placental tissues. Furthermore, several of the extrapituitary actions of GnRH can be blocked by GnRH antagonists, also suggesting the mediation through stereospecific recognition sites (Table 1).

Table 1 Extrapituitary actions of GnRH and the presence of GnRH-like substance outside the central nervous system

	GnRH effects	GnRH "receptors"[a]	Presence of GnRH-like peptide
1. Ovary			
a. Granulosa cells	yes	yes	?
b. Luteal cells	yes	yes	?
c. Theca and/or interstitial cells	yes	yes	?
d. Oocytes	yes	?	?
2. Testis			
a. Leydig cells	yes	yes	?
b. Sertoli cells	no	no	yes
3. Male accessory sex organs	yes	?	?
4. Female accessory sex organs	yes	?	?
5. Placenta	yes	yes	yes
6. Mammary tissue	?	?	yes
7. Sympathetic ganglia (frog)	yes	yes	yes
8. Adrenal	?	yes	?
9. Pancreas	?	?	yes
10. Fat cells	yes	?	?

[a] The use of the term "receptor" here designates tissues in which ^{125}I-GnRH agonist binding has been demonstrated or the observed direct actions of GnRH have been shown to be blocked by GnRH antagonists.

Demonstration of widespread extrapituitary actions of GnRH and its agonists in various tissues, coupled with the identification of stereospecific GnRH binding sites in gonadal, placental, and other tissues, raises intriguing questions concerning the physiological significance of these findings. In a strict sense, GnRH is different from most classical hormones in that the circulation of this neuropeptide is restricted to the portal vessels. The observed extrapituitary actions of GnRH and its agonists may simply represent an evolutionary vestigial function that is only of pharmacological significance. Or, more likely, the extrapituitary GnRH binding sites may recognize GnRH-like peptides secreted locally by gonadal or other extrahypothalamic tissues.

Evidence for the gonadal production of GnRH-like substances was provided by studies in male rats (37, 41). In testicular interstitial fluid, a GnRH-like substance was shown to compete in a radioligand receptor assay for GnRH and to stimulate LH release by hemipituitaries in vitro (41). The presence of similar GnRH-like peptide was confirmed by immunocytochemical staining of testis cells (37). Although these studies suggest the local production of gonadal GnRH-like peptides, further studies are needed to elucidate their physiologic relevance. Furthermore, several groups have identified GnRH or GnRH-like peptide in the human placenta, frog sympathetic ganglia, and other tissues (Table 1).

SUMMARY

The puzzling and paradoxical inhibitory effect of GnRH and its agonists led endocrinologists to discover an extrapituitary effect of GnRH—a direct inhibitory action of the hypothalamic releasing hormone at the gonadal level. GnRH and its agonists inhibit steroidogenesis in in vitro cultures of ovarian granulosa and luteal cells, and in testicular Leydig cells. These direct gonadal actions of GnRH are blocked by concomitant treatment with GnRH antagonists. Furthermore, studies in other reproductive tissues suggest extrapituitary actions of GnRH on male and female sex organs and on the placenta. The finding of the direct action of GnRH on gonadal cells was followed by the demonstration of stereospecific, tissue-specific, high-affinity and low-capacity gonadal binding sites for GnRH. These discoveries serve to explain the paradoxical inhibitory effect of GnRH and its agonists on female and male reproductive functions and raise intriguing questions regarding a possible local production of endogenous ligand(s).

The possible paracrine role of GnRH or GnRH-like peptides was reinforced by the demonstration of the production of GnRH in human placental tissues and a neurotransmitter function of a GnRH-like peptide in frog sympathetic ganglia. Recent preliminary results suggest the possible production of a GnRH-like peptide(s) by testicular Sertoli cells. Since the maturation of the individual ovarian follicles and testicular seminiferous tubules represents a highly integrated function, controlled in part by factors in the microenvironment, future studies on the local control of gonadal functions by a GnRH-like factor may provide further clues regarding the regulation of germ cell maturation and release as well as the fine tuning of gonadal steroidogenesis.

ACKNOWLEDGMENTS

We thank Ms. Kayle Watts for typing the manuscript. Research in the authors' laboratory is supported by NIH grants HD-14084 and HD-12303. A.J.W.H. is the recipient of NIH Research Career Development Award HD-00375.

Literature Cited

1. Adashi, E. Y., Hsueh, A. J. W. 1981. Stimulation of β_2-adrenergic responsiveness by follicle stimulating hormone in rat granulosa cells *in vitro* and *in vivo*. *Endocrinology* 108:2170–78

2. Arimura, A., Serafini, P., Talbot, S., Schally, A. V. 1979. Reduction of testicular luteinizing hormone/human chorionic gonadotropin receptors by [D-Trp⁶]-luteinizing hormone releasing hormone in hypophysectomized rats. *Biochem. Biophys. Res. Commun.* 90: 687–93

3. Bambino, T. H., Schreiber, J. R., Hsueh, A. J. W. 1980. Gonadotropin-releasing hormone and its agonist inhibit testicular luteinizing hormone receptor and steroidogenesis in immature and adult hypophysectomized rats. *Endocrinology* 107:908–17

4. Behrman, H. R., Preston, S. L., Hall, A. K. 1980. Cellular mechanism of the antigonadotropic action of luteinizing hormone-releasing hormone in the corpus luteum. *Endocrinology* 107: 656–64

5. Belchetz, P. E., Plant, T. M., Nakai, T., Keogh, E. J., Knobil, E. 1978. Hypophysial responses to continuous and intermittent delivery of hypothalamic gonadotropin-releasing hormone. *Science* 202:631–32

6. Bourne, G. A., Regiani, S., Payne, A. H., Marshall, J. C. 1980. Testicular GnRH receptors—characterization and localization on interstitial tissue. *J. Clin. Endocrinol. Metab.* 51:407–9

7. Clayton, R. N., Harwood, J. P., Catt, K. J. 1979. Gonadotropin-releasing hormone analogue binds to luteal cells and inhibits progesterone production. *Nature* 282:90–92

8. Clayton, R. N., Katikineni, M., Chan, V., Dufau, M. L., Catt, K. J. 1980. Direct inhibition of testicular function by gonadotropin-releasing hormone: mediation by specific gonadotropin-releasing hormone receptors in interstitial cells. *Proc. Natl. Acad. Sci. USA* 77: 4459–63

9. Conti, M., Harwood, J. P., Hsueh, A. J. W., Dufau, M. L., Catt, K. J. 1976. Gonadotropin-induced loss of hormone receptors and desensitization of adenylate cyclase in the ovary. *J. Biol. Chem.* 251:7729–31

10. Dorrington, J. H., Armstrong, D. T. 1979. Effects of FSH on gonadal functions. *Rec. Prog. Horm. Res.* 35:301–412

11. Erickson, G. F., Hsueh, A. J. W. 1978. Stimulation of aromatase activity by follicle stimulating hormone in rat granulosa cells *in vivo* and *in vitro*. *Endocrinology* 102:1275–82

12. Erickson, G. F., Wang, C., Hsueh, A. J. W. 1979. FSH induction of functional LH receptors in granulosa cells cultured in a chemically defined medium. *Nature* 279:336–37

13. Gore-Langton, R. E., Lacroix, M., Dorrington, J. H. 1981. Differential effects of luteinizing hormone–releasing hormone on follicle-stimulating hormone–dependent responses in rat granulosa cells and Sertoli cells *in vitro*. *Endocrinology* 108:812–19

14. Harwood, J. P., Clayton, R. N., Chen, T. T., Knox, G., Catt, K. J. 1980. Ovarian gonadotropin-releasing hormone receptors. II. Regulation and effects on ovarian development. *Endocrinology* 107:414–21

15. Hillensjö, T., LeMaire, W. J. 1980. Gonadotropin-releasing hormone agonists stimulate meiotic maturation of follicle-enclosed rat oocytes *in vitro*. *Nature* 287:145–46

16. Hsueh, A. J. W. 1982. Direct effects of gonadotropin releasing hormone on testicular Leydig cell function. *Ann. NY Acad. Sci.* 383:249–71

17. Hsueh, A. J. W., Dufau, M. L., Catt, K. J. 1977. Desensitization of testicular responses—negative control of LH/hCG receptors, cAMP production and steroidogenesis by exogenous hCG *in vivo*. *Proc. Natl. Acad. Sci. USA* 74: 592–95

18. Hsueh, A. J. W., Erickson, G. F. 1979. Extrapituitary action of gonadotropin-releasing hormone: direct inhibition of ovarian steroidogenesis. *Science* 204: 854–55

19. Hsueh, A. J. W., Erickson, G. F. 1979. Extra-pituitary inhibition of testicular function by luteinising hormone releasing hormone. *Nature* 281:66–67

20. Hsueh, A. J. W., Ling, N. C. 1979. Effect of an antagonistic analog of gonadotropin releasing hormone upon ovarian granulosa cell function. *Life Sci.* 25:1223–30

21. Hsueh, A. J. W., Wang, C., Erickson, G. F. 1980. Direct inhibitory effect of gonadotropin-releasing hormone upon follicle-stimulating hormone induction of luteinizing hormone receptors and aromatase activity in rat granulosa cells. *Endocrinology* 106: 1697–705

22. Hsueh, A. J. W., Jones, P. B. C. 1981. Extrapituitary actions of gonadotropin-releasing hormone. *Endocrine Rev.* 2: 437–61

23. Hsueh, A. J. W., Schreiber, J. R., Erickson, G. F. 1981. Inhibitory effect of gonadotropin releasing hormone upon cultured testicular cells. *Mol. Cell. Endocrinol.* 21:43–49

24. Hsueh, A. J. W., Jones, P. B. C. 1982. Direct hormonal modulation of ovarian granulosa cell maturation: effect of gonadotropin releasing hormone. In *Follicular Maturation and Ovulation,* ed. R. Rolland, E. V. VanHall, S. G. Hillier, K. P. McNatty, J. Schoemaker, pp. 19–33. Amsterdam/Oxford/Princeton: Excerpta Medica

25. Jan, Y. N., Jan, L. Y., Kuffler, S. W. 1979. A peptide as a possible transmitter in sympathetic ganglia of the frog. *Proc. Natl. Acad. Sci. USA* 76: 1501–5

26. Jones, P. B. C., Conn, P. M., Marian, J., Hsueh, A. J. W. 1980. Binding of gonadotropin releasing hormone agonist to rat ovarian granulosa cells. *Life Sci.* 27:2125–32

27. Jones, P. B. C., Hsueh, A. J. W. 1980. Direct inhibitory effect of gonadotropin releasing hormone upon luteal LH receptor and steroidogenesis in hypophysectomized rats. *Endocrinology* 107:1930–36

28. Jones, P. B. C., Hsueh, A. J. W. 1981. Direct stimulation of ovarian progesterone metabolizing enzyme by gonadotropin-releasing hormone in cultured granulosa cells. *J. Biol. Chem.* 256: 1248–54

29. Jones, P. B. C., Hsueh, A. J. W. 1981. Direct effect of gonadotropin releasing hormone and its antagonist upon ovarian functions stimulated by FSH, prolactin, and LH. *Biol. Reprod.* 24:747–59

30. Jones, P. B. C., Hsueh, A. J. W. 1981. Regulation of ovarian 20α-hydroxy-steroid dehydrogenase by gonadotropin releasing hormone and its antagonist *in vivo* and *in vitro. J. Steroid. Biochem.* 14:1169–75

31. Jones, P. B. C., Hsueh, A. J. W. 1982. Regulation of ovarian 3β-hydroxy-steroid dehydrogenase by gonadotropin-releasing hormone and follicle-stimulating hormone in cultured rat granulosa cells. *Endocrinology* 110: 1663–71

32. Khodr, G. S., Siler-Khodr, T. M. 1980. Placental luteinizing hormone releasing factor and its synthesis. *Science* 207: 315–17

33. Lefebvre, F.-A., Reeves, J. J., Séguin, C., Massicotte, J., Labrie, F. 1980. Specific binding of a potent LHRH agonist in rat testis. *Mol. Cell. Endocrinol.* 20:127–34

34. Macdonald, G. J., Beattie, C. W. 1979. Pregnancy failure in hypophysectomized rats following LH-RH administration. *Life Sci.* 24:1103–10

35. Mayar, M. R., Tarnovsky, G. K., Reeves, J. J. 1979. Ovarian growth and uptake of iodinated D-Leu⁶,des-Gly,NH₂¹⁰-LHRH ethylamide in hCG treated rats. *Proc. Soc. Exp. Biol. Med.* 161:216–18

36. Navickis, R. J., Jones, P. B. C. 1982. Modulation of prolactin receptors in cultured rat granulosa cells by FSH, LH and GnRH. *Mol. Cell. Endocrinol.* 27:77–88

37. Paull, W. K., Turkelson, C. M., Thomas, C. R., Arimura, A. 1981. Immunohistochemical demonstration of a testicular substance related to luteinizing hormone–releasing hormone. *Science* 213:1263–64

38. Pieper, D. R., Richards, J. S., Marshall, J. C. 1981. Ovarian gonadotropin-releasing hormone (GnRH) receptors: characterization, distribution, and induction by GnRH. *Endocrinology* 108: 1148–55

39. Rao, M. C., Richards, J. S., Midgley, A. R., Reichert, L. E. 1977. Regulation of gonadotropin receptors by luteinizing hormone in granulosa cells. *Endocrinology* 101:512–23

40. Rivier, C., Vale, W. 1979. Hormonal secretion in male rats chronically treated with [D-Trp⁶,Pro⁹,NEt]-LRF. *Life Sci.* 25:1065–74

41. Sharpe, R. M., Fraser, H. M. 1980. HCG stimulation of testicular LHRH-like activity. *Nature* 287:642–43

42. Sundaram, K., Cao, Y.-Q., Wang, N.-G., Bardin, C. W., Rivier, J., Vale, W. 1981. Inhibition of the action of sex steroids by gonadotropin-releasing hormone (GnRH) agonists: A new biological effect. *Life Sci.* 28: 83–88

43. Tcholakian, R. K., De La Cruz, A., Chowdhury, M., Steinberger, A., Coy, D. H., Schally, A. V. 1978. Unusual anti-reproductive properties of the analog [D-Leu⁶,DES-Gly-NH₂¹⁰]-luteinizing hormone-releasing hormone ethylamide in male rats. *Fertil. Steril.* 30: 600–3

44. Tureck, R. W., Mastroianni, L., Blasco, L., Strauss, J. F. 1982. Inhibition of human granulosa cell progesterone secretion by a gonadotropin-releasing hormone agonist *J. Clin. Endocrinol. Metab.* 54:1078–80

45. Wang, C., Hsueh, A. J. W., Erickson, G. F. 1979. Induction of functional prolactin receptors by follicle stimulating hormone in rat granulosa cells *in vivo* and *in vitro*. *J. Biol. Chem.* 254: 11330–36

46. Wang, C., Hsueh, A. J. W., Erickson, G. F. 1981. LH stimulation of aromatase activity in cultured granulosa cells. *Mol. Cell. Endocrinol.* 24:17–28

47. Zipf, W. B., Payne, A. H., Kelch, R. P. 1978. Dissociation of lutropin-induced loss of testicular lutropin receptors and lutropin-induced desensitization of testosterone synthesis. *Biochim. Biophys. Acta* 540:330–36

Ann. Rev. Physiol. 1983. 45:95–107
Copyright © 1983 by Annual Reviews Inc. All rights reserved

CNS PEPTIDES AND GLUCOREGULATION

Lawrence A. Frohman

Division of Endocrinology and Metabolism, Department of Medicine, University of Cincinnati College of Medicine, Cincinnati, Ohio 45267

INTRODUCTION

The role of the central nervous system (CNS) in glucoregulation and metabolic homeostasis has been recognized for more than 100 years—ever since the classic experiments of Bernard, in which puncture (*picure*) of the floor of the fourth ventricle produced transient glycosuria. Subsequent studies provided evidence for the participation of the autonomic nervous system, the adrenals, the endocrine pancreas, and the liver (20, 35). Because of the limited techniques available for studing the CNS components of this system, initial efforts focused on characterizing the peripheral or extraneural components. More recently, however, with the availability of stereotaxic, microiontophoretic, and single-unit recording techniques, and the advances in monoamine and peptide chemistry and pharmacology, assessment of the CNS role has received greater attention.

The CNS utilizes two mechanisms for communication with peripheral effector organs: (*a*) direct neurotransmission involving monoamines and peptides that serve as chemical messengers between nerve terminals and peripheral cells, and (*b*) neurohormonal means involving the release of amines or peptides from nerve terminals into a regional or systemic circulation. Within the past decade the distinction between these processes has become blurred with respect to the definition of neurotransmitters, neurohormones, and hormones.

This review provides a description of the role of the CNS in glucoregulation, an assessment of the participating peptidergic neurotransmitters, and an overall hypothesis of the integrative role of neuropeptides in glucoregulation. It emphasizes processes involved in short-term regulation rather than food intake and caloric homeostasis.

95

0066-4278/83/0315-0095$02.00

ROLE OF THE AUTONOMIC NERVOUS SYSTEM

Neuroanatomic Basis for Glucoregulation

The hypothalamus is the critical CNS locus for metabolic integration. Both the ventromedial (VMH) and ventrolateral (VLH) hypothalamic areas participate in glucoregulation by virtue of the presence of glucose sensitive neurons, the electrical activity of which is modified by changes in ambient glucose concentration. The specific connections of the glucoreceptor neurons themselves remain to be fully clarified, though the terminations of the pathways involved are generally known.

The pathways responsible for glucoregulation involve the autonomic nervous system. Glucose-sensitive neurons in the VMH respond to hypoglycemia by activating the sympathetic nervous system through pathways that travel caudally and laterally from the hypothalamus through the midbrain and pons, interact with neurons residing in the floor of the fourth ventricle, and continue through the medulla by polysynaptic pathways to the intermediolateral column of the spinal cord and the splanchnic nerves. The fibers connect directly with the adrenal medulla and, after reaching the celiac ganglia, with hepatocytes, the pancreatic islets, and hormone-secreting cells in the gastrointestinal tract. Neurons in the VLH travel through the dorsal motor nucleus of the vagus to the gastrointestinal tract, the pancreatic islets and the liver. Sympathetic and parasympathetic nerve fibers become integrated in terminal nerve branches and enter the organs in association with their blood supply.

The two systems exhibit reciprocal effects on glucoregulation, though the responses of individual pancreatic hormones are not entirely specific. The neurometabolic response to a single signal is also not all-inclusive. Thus activation of one component of the system, such as direct neural stimulation of hepatic glycogenolysis, may be unassociated with effects on the endocrine pancreas or the adrenal medulla. Consequently, it has not always been possible to differentiate neurons that activate the liver from those that stimulate the pancreatic A and B cells and thereby differentiate primary (hepatic) from secondary (pancreatic or adrenal medullary) effects on blood glucose regulation.

Effects on the Liver

The most immediate effects of neural control of blood glucose involve the liver (49). Stimulation of the VMH causes a rapid rise in hepatic glucose output and a reduction in liver glycogen content whereas VLH stimulation leads to hepatic glycogenesis. VMH stimulation produces a rise in phosphorylase A and in glucose-6-phosphatase, but no change in glycogen synthetase I while VLH stimulation increases synthetase I activity without affecting phosphorylase A activity. The responses to hypothalamic stimulation can be reproduced by sympathetic or vagus nerve stimulation in the absence of the pancreas and adrenals, indicating that the effects occur directly at the liver. Furthermore, the responses induced by neural stimulation occur much more rapidly than do those produced by administration of glucose or insulin. The VMH and VLH also regulate hepatic gluconeogenesis in a reciprocal manner.

Microinjections of norepinephrine in the VMH increase hepatic phosphorylase A levels through beta-adrenergic mechanisms and mimic the changes observed after electrical stimulation. Microinjections of acetylcholine in the VLH increase hepatic synthetase I activity through muscarinic receptors. Systemic injection of N-methylatropine, which does not penetrate the blood brain barrier, also inhibits the stimulatory effects of acetylcholine, demonstrating that both central and peripheral components of the pathway are under cholinergic control. Nerve terminals in the liver also contain peptidergic as well as aminergic neurotransmitters, and both are likely involved in these processes.

Effects on the Endocrine Pancreas

Neural stimulation of insulin secretion is mediated by both parasympathetic and sympathetic fibers (35). Nerve terminals can be identified within the islets in juxtaposition to A, B, and D cells in association with cell borders and in relation to gap junctions. Vagal stimulation increases and vagotomy decreases insulin secretion, indicating the existence of a tonic effect of the CNS. The responses are acetylcholine-mediated and can be inhibited by atropine. Sympathetic nerve fibers inhibit insulin secretion through alpha-adrenergic receptors on the B cell, which may also be activated by epinephrine and norepinephrine. Neural stimulation constitutes an important regulatory mechanism in all species examined, while that of circulating catecholamines exhibits species variability. Beta-adrenergic receptors are also present on B cells and enhance insulin secretion. Their role appears less important than that of alpha receptors since almost every physiologic or pathologic condition associated with sympathetic nervous system activation results in predominance of the alpha receptor–mediated inhibitory effect. The CNS locus responsible for the sympathetic effects is the VMH. Electrical stimulation of this locus or the microinjection of epinephrine and norepinephrine inhibits insulin secretion even during hyperglycemia. Destruction of the VMH results in increased insulin secretion in response to hyperglycemia, indicating a tonic effect of this locus under normal physiologic circumstances. Microinjection of epinephrine into the VLH results in a selective increase in insulin secretion (50), and at low concentrations epinephrine exhibits a direct stimulatory effect on the B cell.

The control of glucagon secretion by the autonomic nervous system is in many ways reciprocal to that of insulin. At peripheral sites norepinephrine (through both alpha and beta$_2$ receptors) and acetylcholine stimulate glucagon release. The contribution of adrenal catecholamines is less important than for insulin secretion. Centrally, the VMH is the stimulatory locus for glucagon secretion. It is not known whether there are discrete neurons responsible for the hepatic and pancreatic effects or whether individual neurons activate both pathways. Epinephrine, acetylcholine, and to a lesser extent norepinephrine injected into the VMH stimulate glucagon secretion. Neither electrical nor chemical stimulation of the VLH influences glucagon secretion, though activation of glucoreceptor neurons in this locus stimulate glucagon release through parasympathetic pathways in some species.

Somatostatin secretion by pancreatic D cells is stimulated by both beta-adrenergic and cholinergic receptors (1). Gamma-aminobutyric acid receptors on D cells mediate inhibitory effects on somatostatin secretion. Although the effect of hypothalamic stimulation on somatostatin secretion is not known, somatostatin release in response to nutrient stimulation is increased following VMH destruction (21).

NEUROPEPTIDE EFFECTS ON GLUCOREGULATION

A large number of peptides common to the brain, gastrointestinal tract, and pancreas constitute the messengers of what has been termed the Diffuse Neuroendocrine System (44). Many have been implicated in the control of nutrient homeostasis and glucoregulation primarily as the result of experiments involving their systemic administration or their addition to in vitro systems. In this manner, more attention has been given to their hormonal than to their neurotransmitter effects. Antiserum to individual neuropeptides has been administered systemically, and effects of circulating neuropeptide deficiencies have been demonstrated. However, this technique is incapable of distinguishing between endocrine and paracrine effects. Inasmuch as individual neuropeptidergic transmitters are present in multiple areas involved in glucoregulation (CNS, pancreatic islets, and GI tract) it is tempting to propose that their functions at each site are integrated with one another and that they form an overall system analogous to that of the monoamine neurotransmitters.

It is now fairly certain that CNS neuropeptidergic transmitters must exert their effects on glucoregulation primarily as neurotransmitters and by paracrine rather than hormonal actions. For example, although CNS somatostatin is released into the hypothalamic-pituitary portal circulation, somatostatin in the peripheral circulation appears to originate from the GI tract and the pancreas (47). Thus any effects of CNS somatostatin on peripheral target organs and on glucoregulation must be mediated by changes in neurotransmission within the CNS rather than by neurosecretion. The same conclusions can be made for other brain peptides. However, the extent to which individual neuropeptides are utilized to modulate specific homeostatic systems is still unknown.

Somatostatin

Somatostatin was initially isolated from the hypothalamus. However, it is also present in many areas of the CNS and in the stomach and pancreas, providing the potential for effects on glucoregulation (1). In the pancreatic islets somatostatin has been identified in the peripherally located D cells. Exogenously administered somatostatin exerts an inhibitory effect on many hormones involved in glucose homeostasis, including insulin, glucagon, pancreatic polypeptide, gastrin, gastric inhibitory peptide, and secretin. In addition, somatostatin decreases splanchnic blood flow, gastrointestinal motility, glucose absorption from the gut, and hepatic glucose output. The latter effect appears secondary to the inhibition of pancreatic hormone secretion.

The most profound effects of somatostatin are on the inhibition of glucagon and insulin secretion. This effect is believed due to interference with a cAMP-related process, possibly by inhibition of adenylate cyclase (7), or to impairment of calcium transport (40).

Considerable evidence also exists for a role of endogenous pancreatic somatostatin in the inhibition of insulin and glucagon secretion. Administration of antisomatostatin serum in vivo results in increases in insulin levels (46), and exposure of isolated islets in vitro to antisomatostatin serum increases both insulin and glucagon release (27), implying a paracrine effect. Measurements of somatostatin secretion into the hepatic portal circulation, taken as an index of its paracrine activity, have raised questions concerning the physiologic importance of these effects. For example, nutrients such as glucose (which stimulates insulin release) and amino acids (which stimulate insulin and glucagon release) both enhance somatostatin secretion as well (25). Furthermore, VMH destruction results in heightened responses not only of insulin and glucagon but also of somatostatin to the above stimuli (21). While the postulated paracrine action of somatostatin predicts that enhancement of its secretion would result in suppression of insulin and glucagon release, the above examples demonstrate the opposite effect. In contrast, somatostatin responses to nutrient stimuli are increased in diabetes and restored to normal by insulin administration. The enhanced secretion thus appears to be secondary to insulin deficiency rather than to a primary hormonal disturbance. Pancreatic somatostatin content is also increased in experimental and genetic diabetes in animals and in insulin-dependent diabetes in humans (42, 43). Examination of the temporal relationships of pancreatic somatostatin to the disturbances in carbohydrate metabolism supports the concept that changes in pancreatic somatostatin represent a response to rather than a cause of hypoinsulinemia (2).

Excessive production of somatostatin in humans, associated with somatostatin-producing tumors of the pancreas (31), is associated with mild carbohydrate intolerance and relative hypoinsulinemia. These effects are mediated by circulating somatostatin released from the tumor. In infants with nesidioblastosis (a disorder characterized by beta cell hyperplasia, the presence of beta cell clusters throughout the exocrine pancreas, and severe hypoglycemia) the number of somatostatin-containing D cells in the islets is reduced (5). However, it is unclear whether this represents a pathogenetic mechanism or an effect secondary to excessive insulin production.

Preliminary evidence suggests that CNS somatostatin also exhibits an effect on glucoregulation. Central administration of somatostatin has no effect on plasma glucose levels under basal conditions. However, when administered in association with beta-endorphin or bombesin, the hyperglycemia produced by each of these agents is abolished (11, 52). Similar and even more potent effects can be demonstrated with an octapeptide derivative of somatostatin (11) that also exhibits the growth hormone-, insulin-, and glucagon-inhibiting effects of somatostatin. This analog inhibits the plasma catecholamine responses to central glucopenia and to central administration of carbachol and bombesin (19). It has not been possible to demonstrate these effects with native somatostatin, raising the possibility that the effect is mediated by a CNS receptor unrelated to somatostatin. Alternatively, the analog could have greater penetrability than does somatostatin from the cerebrospinal fluid to the specific CNS locus involved.

The possibility of distinct somatostatin receptors in various brain regions is supported by the recent reports of other forms of somatostatin within the CNS and gastrointestinal tract (somatostatin-28 and somatostatin-25) that contain somatostatin-14 at the C-terminal end of the molecule. Somatostatin-28 exhibits greater potency than does somatostatin-14 with respect to inhibition of insulin as compared to glucagon secretion (12). Centrally administered somatostatin-28 is also more potent than somatostatin-14 in inhibiting bombesin-induced hyperglycemia.

If the central actions of somatostatin on glucoregulation are indeed physiologic, it might be expected that alterations in glucose availability within the CNS would influence endogenous somatostatin content or release. Although no alterations in hypothalamic somatostatin content have been found in experimental and genetic diabetes, somatostatin release by the hypothalamus but not the cerebral cortex is stimulated by central gluco-penia and suppressed by elevations in glucose concentrations (3). These findings may serve to explain the decreases in growth hormone levels in the rat in response to hypoglycemia, but they do not explain the elevations in growth hormone seen in humans under similar circumstances.

Neurotensin

Neurotensin is a tridecapeptide first identified in bovine hypothalamus (16) and subsequently in the gastrointestinal tract. Systemic injection of neuro-tensin produces transient hyperglycemia, a decrease in hepatic glycogen, an increase in phosphorylase activity (15), an increase in glucagon, and an inhibition of insulin release (14, 38). Whereas the increase in glucagon release likely represents a direct effect of neurotensin on the A cells, the inhibition of insulin secretion is mediated through the stimulation of epi-nephrine. Many of the effects of systemic neurotensin may be mediated by histamine and can be blocked by pretreatment with H_1-, and to a lesser extent, H_2-histamine receptor antagonists (39). Administration of neuroten-sin into the pancreatoduodenal artery stimulates both glucagon and insulin release in dogs (28) and can be blocked by propranolol, suggesting participa-tion of the beta-adrenergic receptor. In the presence of basal glucose con-centrations, neurotensin stimulates the release of insulin, glucagon, and somatostatin in vitro whereas in the presence of stimulatory concentrations of glucose or arginine, the effects of neurotensin are inhibitory (17).

Two lines of evidence argue against a possible role of circulating neuro-tensin as a mediator of CNS glucoregulation. First, administration of an-tineurotensin serum in a quantity sufficient to inhibit the hyperglycemic response to neurotensin does not impair the hyperglycemic response to central administration of 2-deoxyglucose, a potent stimulator of sympa-thetic nervous system–mediated hyperglycemia (39). Second, systemic infu-sion of neurotensin in quantities sufficient to simulate circulating neurotensin-like immunoreactivity levels in plasma observed after a mixed meal (6) are without effect on plasma glucose, insulin, or glucagon concen-trations. However, neurotensin may exhibit paracrine effects on islet hor-mones. Although attempts to identify neurotensin in pancreatic islets using immunohistochemical techniques have thus far been unsuccessful, the pep-tide has been identified immunologically and is increased in both experi-mental (18) and genetic (4) diabetes. As with somatostatin, however, it appears that the changes in neurotensin are secondary rather than primary.

There has been no evidence to suggest that neurotensin within the CNS participates in glucoregulation. In contrast to the effects of peripherally administered neurotensin, injection of this peptide into the CNS is without effect on plasma glucose, insulin, or glucagon levels (38).

Substance P

Substance P is widely distributed in the CNS, peripheral nerve plexuses, and endocrine cells of the intestinal tract. Systemic administration of substance P results in a hyperglycemia, hyperglucagonemia, and suppression of insulin secretion (14). Intrapancreatic infusion of substance P in the dog increases portal insulin and glucose concentrations as well as pancreatic blood flow (28). The effects are not blocked by baclofen, a gamma-aminobutyric acid analog that suppresses the depolarizing effects of the peptide on spinal reflexes. Thus the effects on the islets are unlikely to be mediated by enhanced autonomic nervous system synaptic transmission. As with neurotensin, the quantity of substance P required to produce hyperglycemia and hyperglucagonemia is in the microgram range, suggesting that this neuropeptide is unlikely to exert physiologic effects on carbohydrate metabolism as a hormone. However, the possibility that substance P may function as a neurotransmitter in components of the autonomic nervous system involved in glucoregulation cannot be excluded by these results. To date there is no evidence for an action within the CNS on glucoregulation or carbohydrate metabolism.

Bombesin

Bombesin is a tetradecapeptide isolated from the skin of the frog. Its mammalian counterpart appears to be a 27 amino acid peptide present in gastrointestinal tract and hypothalamus that exhibits extensive homology in the C-terminal region (45). Systemic bombesin administration produces hyperglycemia. However, when administered intracisternally the peptide exhibits much greater potency (10). Mammalian "bombesin" also exhibits hyperglycemic activity after central administration but appears to be only 10–20% as active as the tetradecapeptide (9). The effects are blocked by adrenalectomy but not by hypophysectomy, and are associated with an immediate release of epinephrine (13). The stimulatory effects of bombesin can be inhibited by a somatostatin analog but not by somatostatin itself.

Endorphins and Enkephalins

The hyperglycemic effect of morphine has been recognized for many years and a number of different effects of endorphins and enkephalins on glucoregulation have recently been described. In the perfused dog pancreas, beta-endorphin stimulates glucose and insulin secretion and concomitantly inhibits somatostatin release (26). In high concentrations met-enkephalin also stimulates insulin and glucagon release (24). The effects of both peptides are reversible by naloxone. When islets are exposed to beta-endorphin in vitro, insulin and glucagon release are inhibited (29). The large concentrations of peptide required for the demonstration of these effects, however, leaves their physiologic significance uncertain.

Administration of beta-endorphin intracisternally produces hyperglycemia in the rat. On a molar basis, the effect of beta-endorphin is less than that of bombesin (11). The effects are blocked by naloxone and by adrenal denervation, indicating a stimulation of sympathetic outflow (52). Intracerebral hemicholinium and somatostatin also block the hyperglycemic effect. Beta-endorphin inhibits dopamine turnover, but concomitant administration of apomorphine, a dopamine agonist, does not inhibit the hyperglycemic response, indicating an absence of dopamine mediation. Glucoreceptor neurons in the VMH are excited by enkephalins whereas glucosensitive neurons in the VLH are inhibited by the peptide (41). Thus the VMH may serve as a locus that mediates the hyperglycemic response to endorphins.

Beta-lipotropin (beta-LPH) stimulates insulin secretion in rabbits by a non-endorphin-mediated mechanism (48). Its effects may be related to the heptapeptide sequence shared with ACTH since the N-terminal portion of ACTH exhibits potent insulin-releasing activity.

Thyrotropin Releasing Hormone

Thyrotropin releasing hormone (TRH) is widely distributed throughout the CNS and is also present in the gastrointestinal tract and pancreas (34). Systemic administration of TRH to fasted rabbits increases glucose, insulin, and glucagon levels. The hyperglycemia is not due to the increases in glucagon and insulin secretion since it occurs in fed animals where the hormonal responses cannot be demonstrated (30). The responses are slightly delayed, suggesting that the effects are not directly on the pancreatic islets. The effects have not been observed in any other species, including humans, and TRH does not exhibit a direct stimulatory effect on glucagon or insulin release in the isolated rat pancreas (37).

Central administration of TRH increases plasma glucose, glucagon, epinephrine, and norepinephrine levels (8). The rises in both glucagon and glucose are not observed in adrenalectomized animals, confirming the mediating role of catecholamine secretion. In contrast to bombesin, TRH stimulation of catecholamine secretion is not inhibited by analogs of somatostatin. As with several of the other peptides, the dose of TRH required is large and the physiologic significance of its effect remains uncertain.

Other Structurally Identified Neuropeptides

Several additional peptides common to the brain and either the gastrointestinal tract or pancreas have systemic effects on glucoregulation either directly or indirectly, most prominent being vasoactive intestinal polypeptide

(VIP), secretin, insulin, and glucagon. VIP and secretin affect the secretion of insulin and glucagon by hormonal mechanisms subsequent to their release from the gastrointestinal tract. The effects of insulin and glucagon are central to the entire process of glucoregulation, and a discussion of their actions is beyond the scope of this chapter.

Administration of insulin into the cerebrospinal fluid decreases pancreatic insulin secretion (53), suggesting the presence of an insulin-sensitive CNS locus. Neurons in the VMH exhibit electrophysiologic changes in response to insulin, and there is evidence for insulin uptake and localization in this region (51). Insulin is present in many brain areas (22) though its role in glucoregulation is uncertain since the levels are unaltered by physiologic and pathologic states in which marked changes in pancreatic insulin occur—i.e. fasting and experimental diabetes.

Effects of Other Neural Factors

Several structurally uncharacterized hypothalamic peptides have been reported to affect insulin and glucagon secretion and blood glucose levels. These studies have utilized models in which crude or partially purified extracts of hypothalamic tissue have served as stimuli for evaluating hormone release from pancreatic islets.

A perfusate of mouse VLH has been reported to stimulate insulin release by isolated islets in vitro (23), and similar results have been obtained with extracts of rat and bovine hypothalamus (32, 33). Insulin-releasing activity could be demonstrated in rat plasma but disappeared following bilateral destruction of the VLH. It is uncertain whether the biologic activity observed in plasma is related to that in the hypothalamus.

Rat VMH contains a peptide that is released into incubation medium and inhibits the secretion of insulin (36). This factor is distinct from other hypothalamic peptides known to have direct effects on insulin release such as somatostatin, neurotensin, and substance P. Direct neurosecretion into the blood stream, while possible, appears unlikely in view of the evidence from studies with other neuropeptides. By analogy, the peptide might also be present in the islets and thus be capable of exhibiting a paracrine effect.

A glucagon-releasing peptide distinguishable from neurotensin and substance P has also been identified in rat VMH (36) and appears distinct from the insulin release–inhibiting peptide.

SUMMARY

The regulation of blood glucose is a complex process involving the integration of the CNS with both hormonal and neural mechanisms. Although neuropeptide participation in the process is only partly understood at present, several conclusions are evident. First, neuropeptides are present in various portions of the autonomic nervous system from the central components in the hypothalamus to the peripheral ganglia and the adrenal medulla. Their mediation of neural impulses involved with glucoregulation is unquestionable, though their interaction with monoaminergic neurotransmitters requires further study. Second, many of these peptides are also present in the gastrointestinal tract and the endocrine pancreas. The results of studies involving the systemic administration of the various peptides and the measurement of their endogenous circulating levels indicate that their effects are produced not by a classical hormonal mechanisms—i.e. secretion into the blood stream—but by direct cell to cell (paracrine) actions or neurotransmitter actions in the pancreas, adrenal medulla, and liver. Third, a pattern is beginning to emerge in which specific neuropeptides appear to exert an integrative role in a specific homeostatic system at different anatomic locations. For example, somatostatin is involved in glucose absorption from the gastrointestinal tract, in pancreatic hormone secretion, and in hepatic glucose production, and somatostatin secretion from the hypothalamus is stimulated by glucopenia. Whether these actions are interrelated through a CNS control mechanism or represent evolutionary developments from a single neuropeptide-mediated process in a more primitive species remains to be elucidated. In either case, a fuller understanding of the role of neuropeptides in glucoregulation should provide new insights into disorders of carbohydrate metabolism.

Literature Cited

1. Berelowitz, M. 1982. Somatostatin and diabetes mellitus. In *Diabetes Mellitus and Obesity,* ed. S. Bleicher, B. Brodoff. Baltimore: Williams & Wilkins. In press
2. Berelowitz, M., Coleman, D. L., Frohman, L. A. 1980. Temporal relationship of tissue somatostatin-like immunoreactivity to metabolic changes in genetically obese and diabetic mice. *Diabetes* 29:717–23
3. Berelowitz, M., Dudlak, D., Frohman, L. A. 1982. Release of somatostatin-like immunoreactivity from incubated rat hypothalamus and cerebral cortex: Effects of glucose and glucoregulatory hormones. *J. Clin. Invest.* 69:1293–1301
4. Berelowitz, M., Nakawatase, C., Frohman, L. A. 1983. Pancreatic immunoreactive neurotensin (IR-NT) in obese (ob) and diabetic (db) mutant mice: A longitudinal study. *Diabetes* In press
5. Bishop, A. E., Polak, J. M., Garin Chesa, P., Timson, C. M., Bryant, M. G., Bloom, S. R. 1981. Decrease of pan-

creatic somatostatin in neonatal nesidioblastosis. *Diabetes* 30:122–26
6. Blackburn, A. M., Fletcher, D. R., Adrian, T. E., Bloom, S. R. 1980. Neurotensin infusion in man: Pharmacokinetics and effect on gastrointestinal and pituitary hormones. *J. Clin. Endocrinol. Metab.* 51:1257–60
7. Borgeat P., Labrie, F., Drouin, J., Belanger A., Immer, H., Sestanj, K., Nelson, V., Gotz, M., Schally, A. V., Coy, D. H., Coy, E. J. 1974. Inhibition of adenosine 3',5'-monophosphate accumulation in anterior pituitary gland in vitro by growth hormone-release inhibiting hormone. *Biochem. Biophys. Res. Commun.* 56:1052–59
8. Brown, M. 1981. Thyrotropin releasing factor: A putative CNS regulator of the autonomic nervous system. *Life Sci.* 28:1789–95
9. Brown, M., Marki, W., Rivier, J. 1980. Is gastrin releasing peptide mammalian bombesin? *Life Sci.* 27:125–28
10. Brown, M., Rivier, J., Vale, W. W. 1977. Bombesin affects the central ner-

vous system to produce hyperglycemia in rats. *Life Sci.* 21:1729–34

11. Brown, M., Rivier, J., Vale, W. 1979. Somatostatin: Central nervous system actions on glucoregulation. *Endocrinology* 104:1709–15

12. Brown, M., Rivier, J., Vale, W. 1980. Somatostatin-28: Selective action on the pancreatic β-cell and brain. *Endocrinology* 108:2391–93

13. Brown, M., Tache, Y., Fisher, D. 1979. Central nervous system action of bombesin: Mechanism of induced hyperglycemia. *Endocrinology* 105:660–65

14. Brown, M., Vale, W. 1976. Effects of neurotensin and substance P on plasma insulin, glucagon and glucose levels. *Endocrinology* 98:819–22

15. Carraway, R. E., Demers, L. M., Leeman, S. E. 1976. Hyperglycemic effect of neurotensin, a hypothalamic peptide. *Endocrinology* 99:1452–62

16. Carraway, R. E., Leeman, S. E. 1973. The isolation of a new hypotensive peptide, neurotensin, from bovine hypothalami. *J. Biol. Chem.* 248:6854–61

17. Dolais-Kitabgi, J., Kitabgi, P., Brazeau, P., Freychet, P. 1979. Effect of neurotensin on insulin, glucagon, and somatostatin release from isolated pancreatic islets. *Endocrinology* 105:256–60

18. Fernstrom, M. H., Mirski, M. A. Z., Carraway, R. E., Leeman, S. E. 1981. Immunoreactive neurotensin levels in pancreas: Elevation in diabetic rats and mice. *Metabolism* 30:853–55

19. Fisher, D. A., Brown, M. R. 1980. Somatostatin analog: Plasma catecholamine suppression mediated by the central nervous system. *Endocrinology* 107:714–18

20. Frohman, L. A. 1982. Integrating actions of the central nervous system. See Ref. 1, In press

21. Goto, Y., Carpenter, R. G., Berelowitz, M., Frohman, L. A. 1980. Effect of ventromedial hypothalamic lesions on the secretion of somatostatin, insulin, and glucagon by the perfused rat pancreas. *Metabolism* 29:986–90

22. Havrankova, J., Schmechel, D., Roth, J., Brownstein, M. 1978. Identification of insulin in rat brain. *Proc. Natl. Acad. Sci. USA* 75:5737–41

23. Idahl, L.-A., Martin, J. M. 1971. Stimulation of insulin release by a ventro-lateral hypothalamic factor. *J. Endocrinol.* 51:601–2

24. Ipp, E., Dhorajiwala, J. M., Moossa, A. R., Rubenstein, A. H. 1980. Enkephalin stimulates insulin and glucagon release

in vivo and accentuates hyperglycemia in diabetic dogs. *Clin. Res.* 28:396A

25. Ipp, E., Dobbs, R. E., Arimura, A., Vale, W., Harris, V., Unger, R. H. 1977. Release of immunoreactive somatostatin from the pancreas in response to glucose, amino acids, pancreozymin-cholecystokinin, and tolbutamide. *J. Clin. Invest.* 60:760–65

26. Ipp, E., Dobbs, R., Unger, R. H. 1978. Morphine and β-endorphin influence the secretion of the endocrine pancreas. *Nature* 276:190–91

27. Itoh, M., Mandarino, L., Gerich, J. E. 1980. Antisomatostatin gamma globulin augments secretion of both insulin and glucagon in vitro. *Diabetes* 29:693–96

28. Kaneto, A., Kaneko, T., Kajinuma, H., Kosaka, K. 1978. Effect of substance P and neurotensin infused intrapancreatically on glucagon and insulin secretion. *Endocrinology* 102:393–401

29. Kanter, R. A., Ensinck, J. W., Fujimoto, W. Y. 1980. Disparate effects of enkephalin and morphine upon insulin and glucagon secretion by islet cell cultures. *Diabetes* 29:84–86

30. Knudtzon, J. 1981. Thyrotropin-releasing hormone increases plasma levels of glucagon, insulin, glucose and free fatty acids in rabbits. *Horm. Metab. Res.* 13:371–75

31. Krejs, G. J., Orci, L., Conlon, J. M., Ravazzola, M., Davis, G. R., Raskin, P., Collins, S. M., McCarthy, D. M., Baetens, D., Rubenstein, A., Aldor, T. A. M., Unger, R. H. 1979. Somatostatinoma syndrome. Biochemical, morphologic and clinical features. *N. Eng. J. Med.* 301:285–92

32. Lockhart-Ewart, R. B., Mok, C., Martin, J. M. 1976. Neuroendocrine control of insulin secretion. *Diabetes* 25:96–100

33. Martin, J. M., Mok, C. C., Penfold, J., Howard, N. J., Crowne, D. 1973. Hypothalamic stimulation of insulin release. *J. Endocrinol.* 58:681–82

34. Martino, E., Lernmark, A., Seo, H., Steiner, D. F., Retetoff, S. 1978. High concentrations of thyrotropin releasing hormone in pancreatic islets. *Proc. Natl. Acad. Sci. USA* 75:4265–67

35. Miller, R. E. 1981. Pancreatic neuroendocrinology: Peripheral neural mechanisms in the regulation of the islets of Langerhans. *Endocrine Rev.* 2:471–94

36. Moltz, J. H., Fawcett, C. P., McCann, S. M., Dobbs, R. E., Unger, R. H. 1975. The hypothalamo-pancreatic axis. Evidence for a neurohormonal pathway in the control of the release of insulin and

glucagon. *Endocrinol. Res. Commun.* 2:537–48

37. Morley, J. E., Levin, S. R., Pehlevanian, M., Adachi, R., Pekary, A. E., Hershman, J. M. 1979. The effect of thyrotropin releasing hormone on the endocrine pancreas. *Endocrinology* 104:137–39

38. Nagai, K., Frohman, L. A. 1976. Hyperglycemia and hyperglucagonemia following neurotensin administration. *Life Sci.* 19:273–80

39. Nagai, K., Frohman, L. A. 1978. Neurotensin hyperglycemia: Evidence for histamine mediation and assessment of a possible physiologic role. *Diabetes* 27:577–82

40. Oliver, J. R. 1976. Inhibition of calcium uptake by somatostatin in isolated rat islets of Langerhans. *Endocrinology* 99:910–13

41. Ono, T., Oomura, Y., Nishino, H., Sasaki, K., Muramoto, K., Yano, I. 1980. Morphine and enkephalin effects on hypothalamic glucoresponsive neurons. *Brain Res.* 185:208–12

42. Orci, L., Baetens, D., Rufener, C., Amherdt, M., Ravazzola, M., Studer, P., Malaisse-Lagae, F., Unger, R. H. 1976. Hypertrophy and hyperplasia of somatostatin-containing D-cells in diabetes. *Proc. Natl. Acad. Sci. USA* 73:1338–42

43. Patel, Y. C., Orci, L., Bankier, A., Cameron, D. P. 1976. Decreased pancreatic somatostatin (SRIF) concentration in spontaneously diabetic mice. *Endocrinology* 99:1415–18

44. Pearse, A. G. E. 1977. The diffuse neuroendocrine system and the APUD concept: Related "endocrine" peptides in brain, intestine, pituitary, placenta, and anuran cutaneous glands. *Med. Biol.* 55:115–25

45. Polak, J. M., Hobbs, R., Bloom, S. R., Solcia, E., Pearse, A. G. E. 1976. Distri-bution of a bombesin-like peptide in human gastrointestinal tract. *Lancet* 1:1109–10

46. Schusdziarra, V., Zyznar, E., Rouiller, D., Boden, G., Brown, J. C., Arimura, A., Unger, R. H. 1980. Splanchic somatostatin: A hormonal regulator of nutrient homeostasis. *Science* 207:530–32

47. Schusdziarra, V., Zyznar, E., Rouiller, D., Harris, V., Unger, R. H. 1980. Free somatostatin in the circulation: Amounts and molecular sizes of somatostatin-like immunoreactivity in portal, aortic, and vena caval plasma of fasting and meal-stimulated dogs. *Endocrinology* 107:1572–76

48. Schwandt, P., Richter, W. O., Kerscher, P., Bottermann, P. 1981. β-Lipoprotein increases plasma insulin immunoreactivity. *Life Sci.* 29:345–49

49. Shimazu, T. 1981. Central nervous system regulation of liver and adipose tissue metabolism. *Diabetologia* 20:343–56

50. Shimazu, R., Ishikawa, K. 1981. Modulation by the hypothalamus of glucagon and insulin secretion in rabbits: Studies with electrical and chemical stimulations. *Endocrinology* 108:605–11

51. van Houten, M., Posner, B. I., Kopriwa, B. M., Brawer, J. R. 1979. Insulin-binding sites in the rat brain: In vivo localization to the circumventricular organs by quantitative radioautography. *Endocrinology* 105:666–73

52. Van Loon, G. R., Appel, N. M. 1981. β-Endorphin-induced hyperglycemia is mediated by increased central sympathetic outflow to adrenal medulla. *Brain Res.* 204:236–41

53. Woods, S. C., Porte, D. 1975. Effect of intracisternal insulin on plasma glucose and insulin in the dog. *Diabetes* 24:905–9

Ann. Rev. Physiol. 1983. 45:109-27

NEUROENDOCRINE CONTROL OF PROLACTIN SECRETION

Denis A. Leong, L. Stephen Frawley, and Jimmy D. Neill

Department of Physiology and Biophysics, University of Alabama in Birmingham, Birmingham, Alabama 35294

INTRODUCTION

Prolactin is the most versatile of pituitary hormones in both the number and diversity of physiologic processes it regulates (107). In mammals, prolactin plays a decisive role in the preparation and maintenance of the mammary gland for milk secretion during lactation. Indeed, prolactin is essential to the survival of most mammalian young after birth. During lactation, the stimulus for prolactin secretion is triggered as the young suckle the mother's nipple. Neural impulses generated by suckling are conveyed to the central nervous system and impinge upon specialized neurons located in the hypothalamus. From the nerve endings of such neurons the hypophysiotropic hormones are released that reach the anterior pituitary via the hypophysial portal vessels. Thus the neurogenic message of suckling is finally conveyed to the pituitary by the action of hypophysiotropic hormones that in the classical sense stimulate or inhibit prolactin secretion. Here we consider recent developments in our understanding of the pituitary gland with particular regard to the hypophysiotropic control of suckling-induced prolactin secretion. Earlier authoritative accounts of the literature are available (85, 103, 104).

THE PITUITARY GLAND

The prospect that prolactin is not a single substance but rather a family of molecular variants is receiving increasing notice. Each form may be a hormone with a different physiologic action, a view that distributes the burden of the perplexing number of functions ascribed to prolactin. Using analytical gel electrophoresis techniques, Sinha & Gilligan (138) have elegantly demonstrated that pituitary extracts contain a mixture of four differ-

109

0066-4278/83/0315-0109$02.00

ent prolactin variants. The possibility that these variants are produced as an artifact of proteolytic degradation was, in part, mitigated by the demonstration that three of these variants were secreted into the medium from pituitary tissue maintained in vitro. During the first hour of incubation, the predominant variant released was a prolactin form with potent bioactivity or disc gel electrophoresis activity (densitometry assay) yet little or no immunoreactivity. The detection of different forms of prolactin appears to explain the puzzling discrepancy (especially evident in dynamic states of prolactin secretion) among bioassay, disc gel electrophoresis densitometry, and radioimmunoassay estimates of prolactin in blood and tissues (4, 5, 79, 80, 108). Analysis of prolactin variants in serum suggests that preferential release of different prolactin forms occurs in pathological states (137, 142) or in situations contrasted by high or low secretory rates (38, 47). In one report, the circulating form of prolactin was different depending on whether prolactin secretion was stimulated by TRH or serotonin (75). Suggestive evidence that the existence of different prolactin forms is indeed related to function has been provided by Mittra, who showed that a cleaved 16K form of prolactin, but not the predominant 22K form, possesses potent mitogenic activity when tested on the mammary gland (95, 96).

These considerations suggest new ways of interpreting old findings. Suckling or mammary nerve stimulation have been reported to induce a large depletion in pituitary prolactin stores, a finding consistently observed by investigators using bioassays or disc electrophoretic assays (57, 58, 92, 106, 108). Paradoxically, the marked depletion in prolactin stores does not appear to be matched by the parallel release of large amounts of prolactin. Rather, the pattern of prolactin release, as determined by radioimmunoassay, suggests a steadier minute-to-minute mode of release with a secretory rate of 500–600 ng min^{-1} (59–61). Based on this discrepancy, Nicoll (106) and Grosvenor and associates (61) have proposed that the proportion of prolactin depleted during suckling does not escape the gland but is transformed into a form that is potentially more releasable and no longer detected by bioassay or disc electrophoresis. This concept of a two-phase prolactin secretory process has been extended to show differential phase responsiveness to inhibiting (63) and releasing (62) hormones and has been reviewed elsewhere (93, 94). An alternative interpretation of the data is that suckling induces both depletion and release of a prolactin form recognized by bioassay and disc electrophoresis but not radioimmunoassay. This form of prolactin, described by Sinha & Gilligan (138), could be immediately released into the circulation and escape detection by radioimmunoassay. This simple view is supported by the finding that a depletion of pituitary prolactin stores during suckling cannot be detected by radioimmunoassay (J. D. Neill et al, unpublished information).

There is also a hint that the prolactin cells of the pituitary are heterogeneous in morphology and function. Lactotropes do not conform to a single morphologic stereotype. In a recent study, immunocytochemically identified lactotropes were categorized into four different types distinguished by the contour of the cells and by the size and shape of the secretory granules (109). Furthermore, the particular morphologic profile of a lactotrope population may change depending on the physiologic or developmental conditions (125). An important new concept of functional heterogeneity within the population of lactotropes has been advanced by Walker & Farquhar (152). They report that newly synthesized prolactin is preferentially released during spontaneous prolactin secretion using normal pituitary cells in culture. On the other hand, TRH stimulated the release of older stored prolactin without altering the release of newly synthesized prolactin. Some heterogeneity arose because different cell types were involved in prolactin release. Apparently, one cell type is not responsive to TRH but preferentially releases newly synthesized prolactin at a very fast rate. A second sub-population of lactotropes responds to TRH with the release of older stored prolactin. The possible relationship between the molecular diversity of prolactin species on the one hand and the cellular diversity of lactotropes on the other is nothing more than suggestive at this time.

The pulsatile pattern of tonic prolactin release in vivo has been recognized for some time (76, 126). Apparently the pituitary releases prolactin in a series of discrete bursts. Pulsatile prolactin release is thought to reflect overlying hypophysiotropic control, as has been recently demonstrated in a preliminary report linking pulsatile GnRH release and pulsatile gonadotropin release (81). The report of synchrony between pulsatile prolactin and gonadotropin release in vivo further supports this view (16). On the other hand, Shin & Reifel (135) reported evidence suggesting that prolactin pulses can originate within the pituitary. Rapidly fluctuating prolactin levels were observed in the serum of hypophysectomized male rats bearing renal grafts of adenohypophysial tissue. This finding suggests that the adenohypophysis can secrete prolactin in a pulsatile fashion and implies the existence of a communicating network of lactotropes. One mode of communication may be through gap junctions demonstrated among homologous but not heterologous pituitary cells (40). Indeed, gap junctions between lactotropes are abundant, and some are electronically coupled (40). However, communication via cellular intimacy is probably limited since lactotropes are distributed evenly throughout the adenohypophysis. [On occasion small clusters of 5–10 lactotropes are formed (109).]

Firmer evidence of cellular communication between pituitary cells has been reported in preliminary form. Denef (31) has shown that GnRH did not alter prolactin release in a population of lactotropes enriched using the technique of unit gravity sedimentation. In contrast, GnRH stimulated marked prolactin increases when a gonadotrope fraction was mixed and cocultured with the lactotropes. In the absence of gap junctions, Denef postulated a paracrine mode of communication to explain the ability of gonadotropes to alter prolactin responsiveness to a hypophysiotropic hormone. These findings, which require confirmation, are especially interesting in the light of persistent reports that lactotropes and gonadotropes are found closely associated in situ (101, 109, 125). These collective findings suggest that the adenohypophysis is far from a simple bag of stereotyped cells responding mechanically to regulatory stimuli. Rather, we are beginning to see that the pituitary may process information in the sophisticated manner of neurons, a view consistent with the assertion that neurons and endocrine cells share a common embryological origin (112).

INHIBITION OF PROLACTIN SECRETION BY THE HYPOTHALAMUS

The unusual ability of the pituitary to secrete prolactin spontaneously for prolonged periods is vigorously expressed when the pituitary is transplanted to a distant site or cultured in vitro. Prolactin secretion appears to be severely restrained in vivo since prolactin is maintained at low levels in the absence of prolactin releasing stimuli. Maneuvers such as pituitary stalk section or median eminence lesions, which permit the expression of spontaneous prolactin release in vivo, established that the prevailing hypothalamic influence over pituitary prolactin is inhibitory (see 103). The impulse to secrete prolactin spontaneously is held firmly in check by the action of hypothalamic prolactin inhibiting factor(s) reaching the pituitary. The large body of work establishing the importance of dopamine in this regard has been well reviewed elsewhere (10, 85, 104). In brief, spontaneous prolactin secretion is inhibited by dopamine (12, 84) acting in small amounts (132, 144); dopamine receptors are found on pituitary membranes (14, 24), in particular those membranes of lactotropes (2, 50); and dopamine is found in hypophysial stalk plasma (9, 115) in amounts sufficient to inhibit prolactin release (49).

There is growing skepticism of the view that dopamine is the sole prolactin inhibiting factor mediating tonic hypothalamic inhibition. The concentration of dopamine measured in hypophysial stalk plasma will significantly, but not completely, suppress spontaneous prolactin release. That is to say, dopamine does not seem to be provided in sufficient amounts to account for all of the prolactin inhibiting activity exerted by the hypothalamus. This conclusion has been reached after several studies in which hypothalamic inhibition was removed by median eminence lesion (49) or diminished by treatment with α-methyl-p-tyrosine (a dopamine synthesis blocker). In both of these experimental preparations, a constant infusion of dopamine, at a rate adjusted to mimic the level of dopamine measured in hypophysial stalk plasma resulted in a 40–70% suppression of spontaneous prolactin release. The studies using α-methyl-p-tyrosine are consistent with previous suggestions that dopamine tonically stimulates the secretion of an unidentified prolactin inhibiting factor (49, 85, 118). This possibility provides a further dimension in interpreting the abundant pharmacologic data demonstrating the potent prolactin releasing activity of drugs that meddle with the biosynthesis or action of dopamine (85). Similar quantitative evidence that dopamine is not the sole prolactin inhibiting factor is the observation that the concentration of dopamine required for full suppression of α-methyl-p-tyrosine stimulated prolactin release was five times higher than is normally present in hypophysial stalk plasma (26, 104). The above studies were performed in urethane-anesthetized rats. Still greater amounts of dopamine must be infused to suppress α-methyl-p-tyrosine stimulated prolactin secretion in conscious lactating rats (78). New findings suggest that the problem of dopamine is even more evident in male rats. Cultured pituitary cells obtained from males are significantly less responsive to dopamine inhibition than those from females (M. T. Hoefer, N. Ben-Jonathan, personal communication). Yet it is well-established that dopamine levels in hypophysial stalk plasma are 5–7 times lower in males than in females (9, 66). The dilemma for the male is that more dopamine is required to inhibit spontaneous prolactin release but he is provided with less.

A possible solution to the problem is that the levels of dopamine in the hypophysial stalk plasma may not account for the total amount of dopamine reaching the pituitary. Ben-Jonathan (10) has proposed that the posterior pituitary provides a second source of dopamine. Accumulating observations of rapid transport of blood (110) and substances (6) from the posterior to the anterior lobe lend credence to the hypothesis. Peters et al (11, 113) reported that posterior lobe extracts contained significant prolactin inhibiting activity that could be attributed to dopamine since inhibition was reversed by cotreatment with a dopamine antagonist. Moreover, posterior lobectomy acutely increased prolactin levels in the male urethane-anesthetized rat. In contrast, prolactin secretion was not altered by posterior lobectomy in a more chronic study where conscious females were used and a recovery period after surgery was allowed (37). Whatever the reason for this discrepancy, the prolactin increases reported after posterior lobectomy are small when compared with the huge rises evoked when the hypothalamic connections to the pituitary are severed. Thus the potential contribution of posterior lobe dopamine to the prevailing inhibition of prolactin secretion might in turn be small.

If this analysis is correct, then to account for the prevailing inhibition of prolactin release we must invoke the existence of an additional prolactin inhibiting factor. A number of candidates have been proposed. One factor for which evidence has rapidly accumulated is gamma aminobutyric acid (GABA). Schally and co-workers (128) reported that, while dopamine was responsible for a large part of the prolactin inhibiting activity of porcine median eminence extracts, a significant part was associated with GABA. The median eminence is rich in GABA-containing neurons (149), GABA directly inhibits spontaneous prolactin release in vitro (34, 120, 128), and GABA receptors are found on pituitary membranes (54, 55). On the other hand, large amounts of GABA are required to inhibit prolactin release (34, 120). Furthermore, hypophysial stalk plasma from diestrous rats contains low levels of GABA not significantly different from circulating levels in peripheral plasma (100). Recognizing the possibility that unidentified hypophysiotropic factors may increase prolactin responsiveness to GABA (22, 56), it is difficult to view GABA as a tonic prolactin inhibiting factor if it is not a secretory product of the median eminence.

Substances with potent prolactin inhibiting activity appear to be formed in the normal course of hypothalamic and pituitary catabolism of TRH and estradiol. Thus the TRH metabolite histidyl-proline diketopiperazine is an inhibitor of spontaneous prolactin release from cultured cells derived from pituitary tumors (8, 90). The suitability of tumor derived cells might be questioned since the dopaminergic mechanism of prolactin inhibition is inadequately expressed in these cells (see 52). Using normal pituitary tissue or cells, discordant findings for (33) or against (74, 119) a direct effect of histidyl-proline diketopiperazine to inhibit spontaneous prolactin secretion have been reported. Similarly, the catechol estrogen 2-hydroxyestradiol was recently shown to inhibit spontaneous prolactin release using an in vitro pituitary superfusion system (83). For all these reports, it remains unlikely that either of these metabolites serves as a *tonic* inhibitor of spontaneous prolactin release. Basal levels of prolactin do not increase in vivo when the levels of their respective precursors are diminished by maneuvers such as ovariectomy (104) or immunization using TRH antiserum (41, 68, 73). Because TRH and estradiol are recognized as stimulators of prolactin secretion, an effect of their respective metabolites to limit or restore stimulated prolactin to baseline levels cannot be ruled out.

STIMULATION OF PROLACTIN SECRETION BY THE HYPOTHALAMUS

The present understanding of the hypothalamic mechanism(s) underlying prolactin increases has been derived in most part from the study of suckling-induced prolactin secretion. Suckling is a powerful stimulus for prolactin release into the circulation. After being separated for a few hours, mothers reunited with young begin to release prolactin in a steady but strikingly increased rate 2–5 min after suckling starts (61). Provided suckling is maintained, prolactin levels 60 times higher than baseline levels accumulate in the circulation within 20–30 min (77, 87). Increases in prolactin secretion are viewed as being superimposed upon the low baseline levels of prolactin, held there by tonic hypothalamic inhibition.

Prolactin Inhibiting Factors

The simplest explanation for increases in prolactin release is that stimuli such as suckling reduce the tonic inhibition exerted by the hypothalamus, freeing the adenohypophysis to express an inherent ability to secrete prolactin spontaneously at a very high rate. This view cannot be evaluated completely at this time since dopamine does not appear to account fully for hypothalamic inhibition, and the identity of the required additional prolactin inhibiting factor is unknown. Nevertheless, the question of whether suckling induces prolactin increases by reducing the secretion rate of dopamine from the median eminence has become a central issue of prolactin research.

The prolactin releasing potential of the withdrawal of dopamine is impressive. Indeed, the process may be accelerated by the paradoxic effect of dopamine at low concentrations to stimulate spontaneous prolactin release still further (19, 30). The effect of dopamine withdrawal on prolactin secretion has been studied recently using an in vitro pituitary superfusion system. A significant, but not complete, inhibition of spontaneous prolactin release was achieved using dopamine in amounts that mimic the levels found in hypophysial stalk plasma. Once dopamine was removed in this dynamic system, prolactin release rapidly ensued achieving a secretory rate comparable with that occurring from the in situ pituitary during suckling (J. D. Peck, J. D. Neill, unpublished observations). In a similar study in vivo, brief interruptions of dopamine infusion led to graded increases in prolactin release in stalk-transected monkeys treated with estrogen (43). These findings confirm the assumption that dopamine withdrawal will permit rapid prolactin release and show that the complete withdrawal of dopamine promotes prolactin release at a rate sufficient to account for the secretory rate established during suckling.

The monkey appears to differ from the rat in some aspects regarding prolactin secretion. The pattern of prolactin release evoked by suckling in monkeys is biphasic (44). In estrogen treated monkeys, dopamine appears to account for most of the inhibition exerted by the hypothalamus (45, 105), though this finding awaits confirmation in models other than stalk-transected monkeys where interpretation may be complicated by the development of dopamine supersensitivity (18, 19). The effectiveness of dopamine inhibition in the monkey is assisted by the in vivo effect of estrogen to increase prolactin responsiveness to dopamine (45, 105). In contrast, the effect of estrogen in vitro in the rat is to decrease prolactin responsiveness to dopamine (121).

Does suckling reduce hypophysiotropic dopamine release? In one series of studies, the technique of electrical stimulation of a mammary nerve trunk was used to evoke prolactin release in anesthetized lactating rats. Using this simulated-suckling stimulus the pattern of hypophysiotropic dopamine release was measured independently by three different methods. Dopamine was measured directly in plasma collected from the hypophysial stalk, via a catecholamine-sensitive electrochemical probe placed in the median eminence, or by labelling dopamine using the [³H]tyrosine precursor and then isolating [³H]dopamine secreted into hypophysial stalk plasma by high-performance liquid chromotography and counting in a liquid scintillation counter. The pattern of hypophysiotropic dopamine remained unchanged during the stimulus except for a transient 60–70% decrease, lasting 3–5 min, associated with the initiation of simulated-suckling (27, 116, 117). The brevity and magnitude of such a decrease in hypophysiotropic dopamine are alone insufficient to account for prolactin rises during suckling (118).

The detailed pattern of hypophysiotropic dopamine release occurring in conscious mothers during suckling has not been resolved. There are numerous reports (20, 91, 97) that the dopamine concentration in the median eminence is depleted by suckling (suggesting that dopamine release is increased during suckling), but others report no change (99, 130, 151). Many of the available histochemical and biochemical techniques that estimate dopaminergic neuronal activity have been applied to this problem; however, the findings are discordant and a definitive picture has yet to emerge. Thus dopaminergic impulse flow in a median eminence is thought to increase (46), remain unchanged (99), or decrease (89, 130, 131) during suckling. Another consideration making interpretation of such findings difficult is that suckling exerts a spectrum of hormonal effects on the pituitary, and it may be naive to correlate every change occurring in the median eminence during suckling with prolactin secretion. In the rat, suckling stimulates prolactin (87, 146), TSH (13, 15), growth hormone (17, 23, 147), and probably ACTH/β-endorphin (67, 150) release; it inhibits the secretion of LH (88, 139) and to a lesser extent FSH (140). Further studies using the catecholamine-sensitive electrochemical probe in conscious suckling mothers may provide the detailed information we require.

Whatever the pattern of hypophysiotropic dopamine release during suckling, more recent evidence suggests that suckling-induced prolactin release cannot be explained solely in terms of an interruption in dopamine release. In conscious lactating rats, experimental control over dopamine levels reaching the pituitary was achieved by pharmacologic suppression of dopamine using α-methyl-p-tyrosine and replacement with a constant infusion of dopamine. When the young were returned to these mothers, suckling-induced prolactin rises of a normal magnitude occurred. Because exogenous dopamine replacement was provided throughout suckling, it was concluded that prolactin release during suckling is not the consequence of an interruption in dopamine release (78). These findings suggest that some hypophysiotropic factor(s) other than dopamine conveys the neurogenic message of suckling to the pituitary.

A variation on the theme is that suckling might antagonize the inhibitory effect of dopamine on prolactin secretion. Although the ability of dopamine to inhibit prolactin release most likely involves a plasma membrane receptor for dopamine, the intracellular mechanism(s) through which dopamine acts on prolactin cells to inhibit prolactin secretion has not been established. Recent studies suggest intriguingly that dopamine is internalized within the lactotrope and that most subcellular dopamine is associated with prolactin secretory granules (64, 102). Gudelsky & Nansel have speculated that the dopamine uptake process constitutes an integral component of the mechanism mediating the inhibitory action of dopamine on prolactin release. This notion requires evaluation in view of the finding that suckling rapidly depletes adenohypophysial dopamine concentration (20), perhaps by suppressing dopamine uptake into lactotropes. Similar falls in adenohypophysial dopamine occur during the afternoon of proestrus (21) and are exaggerated in estrogen treated rats (65). In all these instances such a fall may reflect nothing more than increased extrusion of adenohypophysial dopamine in prolactin secretory granules, to be expected in the states of enhanced prolactin release described above. On the other hand, the newly recognized dopamine uptake process may function as an important locus of control if the inhibitory action of dopamine on the lactotrope depends on it. Further progress rests on an improved understanding of the fundamental interaction between dopamine and the lactotrope.

Prolactin Releasing Factors

Besides an inhibitory mechanism of control for prolactin secretion, the concept of a supporting stimulatory mechanism has enjoyed wide acceptance. Unlike the prolactin inhibitory mechanism, the clear requirement for a prolactin stimulating mechanism has been difficult to demonstrate unambiguously. The concept extends mostly from numerous reports of prolactin releasing activity in purified fractions of hypothalamic extracts (3). A puzzling development in this regard has been the profusion of substances reported to cause prolactin increases by a direct action on the pituitary. The growing list includes: TRH (145), vasoactive intestinal peptide (VIP) (42, 51, 122, 124, 133), serotonin (153), β-endorphin (32, 53), met-enkephalin

(32, 82), leu-enkephalin (82), neurotensin (35, 148), bombesin (154), GnRH (31, 155), angiotensin II (141), vasopressin (136), substance P (72, 148), epidermal growth factor (71, 129), fibroblast growth factor (129), cholecystokinin (86), and estradiol (156). Even though these substances have the capacity to effect the release of prolactin, this fact alone does not establish a physiologic role for the substance as a releasing hormone. On the other hand, many of these candidate releasing hormones are found in the median eminence in high concentrations (111) and a further five have been measured in hypophysial stalk plasma. Even so, it is still difficult to believe that all these substances act as authentic releasing hormones. The difficulty probably lies in the way the question is commonly phrased. The majority of these substances were tested in vitro for their ability to stimulate spontaneous prolactin release. A more appropriate measure of a prolactin releasing hormone might be the capacity to stimulate prolactin release when spontaneous secretion is restrained by the action of dopamine. Indeed, one important corollary of a study described earlier is that the hypophysiotropic hormone responsible for prolactin release during suckling appears to be effective in the presence of dopamine (78).

The evidence establishing that suckling stimulates hypophysiotropic TRH secretion is now complete in the rat. Both suckling and TRH stimulate dual prolactin and TSH secretion (13, 15); TSH secretion is dependent on antecedent TRH rises in physiologic situations (68, 73, 143); and TRH levels in hypophysial stalk plasma are increased after mammary nerve stimulation (28) or suckling (39). In women, the issue of whether TRH acts as a mediator of suckling-induced prolactin secretion is presently controversial owing to conflicting reports about the effect of suckling on TSH levels (25, 48, 70). Although earlier findings questioned the potency of TRH as a prolactin releasing hormone (13, 15), more recent studies have demonstrated that suckling induces a marked increase in prolactin responsiveness to TRH (62, 77). During suckling, remarkably small amounts of TRH—estimated to mimic TRH levels reaching the pituitary during suckling—were sufficient to stimulate significant prolactin increases (77). Furthermore, a similar increase in prolactin (but not TSH) responsiveness to TRH occurs at the time of the proestrus surge of prolactin (29). While Koch et al (73) reported an attenuation of the prolactin surge in proestrous rats passively immunized with TRH antiserum, this finding could not be confirmed by others (68). In summary, there is mounting evidence, more certain during suckling, that increases in prolactin secretion involve a combination of TRH secretion and the development of marked increases in prolactin responsiveness to TRH.

An increasingly studied potential releasing hormone is VIP. First isolated from the small intestine, VIP is present in hypophysial stalk plasma (123, 134); low concentrations of VIP (42, 51, 122, 124, 133) stimulate prolactin release in vitro [although see (86)]; and VIP receptors are found on pituitary membranes (7) and most probably on lactotrope membranes, since VIP-uptake in the pituitary appears exclusively localized to lactotropes (98). When used in large amounts VIP clearly stimulated prolactin release in vivo during suckling; however, smaller doses (comparable on a molar basis with small effective doses of TRH) failed to increase prolactin levels (77). These findings do not rule out VIP as a mediator of prolactin increases in physiologic situations other than suckling.

Prolactin Responsiveness Factors

The underlying mechanism for increases in prolactin responsiveness occurring with prolactin secretion in lactating and proestrous rats has not been identified. In both cases, the increase in prolactin responsiveness is rigidly associated with the onset of the stimulus since TRH treatment before suckling (62, 77) or in advance of the time of the anticipated proestrus surge (29) does not alter prolactin secretion. A self-priming effect, by analogy with that established for GnRH (1), remains to be demonstrated for prolactin secretagogues since pulsatile administration of TRH (29) or hypothalamic extracts (114) did not increase prolactin responsiveness. On the other hand, prolactin responsiveness to TRH can be modulated by the pattern of dopamine reaching the pituitary. Several in vivo studies indicate that a brief fall in dopamine levels (mimicking the brief decrease in hypophysiotropic dopamine occurring immediately after the onset of simulated-suckling) caused an increase in prolactin responsiveness to relatively large amounts of TRH (28, 118). These findings were confirmed in vitro with the use of a pituitary superfusion system where the combined treatment of TRH and a brief fall in dopamine stimulated greater prolactin increases than the sum of each treatment alone (36). While establishing a direct effect at the level of the pituitary, these studies also showed that a brief drop in dopamine in combination with smaller amounts of TRH fell short of achieving the very high secretory rate of prolactin release established during suckling [(36); J. D. Peck, J. D. Neill, unpublished information]. These findings suggest that the prime mediator of increases in prolactin responsiveness to TRH remains to be identified. Parenthetically, the maxim that prolactin secretion represents the simple sum of releasing and inhibiting hormone inputs to the pituitary might be questioned by the finding that a brief decline in the level of an inhibitory factor can determine the potential with which a releasing factor stimulates prolactin secretion. The pituitary's capacity to discriminate such a series of elaborate hypophysiotropic signals suggests that we have underestimated the gland's complexity.

The foundation for the following speculative account of these changes in prolactin responsiveness is the evocative study of Raymond et al (121). These authors showed that prior incubation of cultured pituitary cells with estradiol caused a decrease in prolactin responsiveness to dopamine *in addition to* a marked increase in prolactin responsiveness to TRH. Small amounts of TRH combined with estradiol treatment were sufficient to elicit substantial prolactin increases in the presence of inhibitory amounts of dopamine. By comparison, acute estradiol treatment given alone stimulated a modest increase in spontaneous prolactin release (69, 121), and likewise TRH had no effect on prolactin release in the presence of dopamine. Estradiol may be viewed as a prototype for a new class of prolactin regulators. In this perspective, estradiol might be described as a "prolactin responsiveness factor," defined as a substance with little or no direct influence on prolactin release that rather exerts profound effects on the pituitary by altering prolactin responsiveness to the classical hypothalamic releasing and inhibiting factors. Estradiol as a prolactin responsiveness factor functions by decreasing prolactin responsiveness to dopamine (permitting a measure of spontaneous prolactin release) and, more important, by increasing prolactin responsiveness to TRH. It is tempting to speculate that prolactin secretion, such as that occurring during suckling or at proestrus, may be described in terms of an interaction between dopamine and TRH that is substantively modified by a prolactin responsiveness factor. The permissive effects of estradiol described above may in fact be mediated via pituitary conversion to 2-hydroxyestradiol, a catechol estrogen reported to antagonize [^{3}H]spiroperidol (a dopamine antagonist) binding to the pituitary [(127); see J. Fishman, this volume].

SUMMARY AND CONCLUSIONS

That the pituitary is a gland of unexpected complexity and potential is suggested by some recent studies. By using the single term prolactin we obscure a family of prolactins, each perhaps with a separate physiologic action. The molecular diversity of prolactin is mirrored at the cellular level by lactotrope heterogeneity, both morphologic and functional. Interactions among lactotropes themselves, or between lactotropes and gonadotropes, suggest the existence of intrapituitary pathways of communication. As described by Denef (31), such interactions yield intriguing changes in lactotrope responsiveness to hypothalamic regulators. Progress in elucidation of the neuroendocrine regulatory process may depend upon an improved understanding of the pituitary.

The saga of dopamine continues, for without diminishing its importance as a tonic prolactin inhibiting factor, the requirement for a second inhibitor to account fully for tonic suppression of spontaneous prolactin secretion is emerging. For prolactin increases such as those occurring during suckling or proestrus, there is mounting evidence for the involvement of a classical prolactin releasing hormone such as TRH combined with the development of striking increases in prolactin responsiveness to TRH. Finally, it is speculated that prolactin secretion is also regulated by a new class of hormones coined "prolactin responsiveness factors"—estradiol might be considered a prototype—which could derive from the hypothalamus or the pituitary.

Literature Cited

1. Aiyer, M. S., Chiappa, S. A., Fink, G. 1974. A priming effect of luteinizing hormone releasing factor on the anterior pituitary gland in the female rat. *J. Endocrinol.* 62:573–88
2. Ajika, K., Arai, K., Okinaga, S. 1982. Localization of dopamine in the prolactin cell of the rat anterior pituitary gland: a fluorescence and immuno-electron microscopical study. *Prog. 64th Ann. Meet. Endocr. Soc. San Francisco, Calif.* (Abstr. 367)
3. Arimura, A., Schally, A. V. 1977. Prolactin release inhibiting and stimulating factors in the hypothalamus. In *Hypothalamic Peptide Hormones and Pituitary Regulation*, ed. J. C. Porter, pp. 237–52, NY: Raven Press
4. Asawaroengchai, H., Nicoll, C. S. 1977. Relationships among bioassay, radioimmunoassay and disc electrophoretic assay methods of measuring rat prolactin in pituitary tissue and incubation medium. *J. Endocrinol.* 73:301–8
5. Asawaroengchai, H., Russell, S. M., Nicoll, C. S. 1978. Electrophoretically separable forms of rat prolactin with different bioassay and radioimmunoassay activities. *Endocrinology* 102:407–14
6. Baertschi, A. J. 1980. Portal vascular route from hypophysial stalk/neural lobe to adenohypophysis. *Am. J. Physiol.* 239:R463–69
7. Bataille, D., Peillon, F., Besson, J., Rosselin, G. 1979. Vasoactive intestinal peptide (VIP): recepteurs specifiques et activation de l'adenylate cyclase dans une tumeur hypophysaire humaine a prolactine. *C. R. Acad. Sci. D (Paris)* 288:1315–17
8. Bauer, K., Graf, K. J., Faivre-Bauman, A., Beier, S., Tixier-Vidal, A., Kleinauf, H. 1978. Inhibition of prolactin secretion by histidyl-proline-diketopiperazine. *Nature* 274:174–75
9. Ben-Jonathan, N., Oliver, C., Weiner, H. J., Mical, R. S., Porter, J. C. 1977. Dopamine in hypophysial portal plasma of the rat during the estrous cy-

cle and throughout pregnancy. *Endocrinology* 100:452–58
10. Ben-Jonathan, N. 1980. Catecholamines and pituitary prolactin release. *J. Reprod. Fert.* 58:501–12
11. Ben-Jonathan, N., Peters, L. 1982. Posterior pituitary lobectomy: differential elevation of plasma prolactin and luteinizing hormone in estrous and lactating rats. *Endocrinology* 110:1861–65
12. Birge, C. A., Jacobs, L. S., Hammer, C. T., Daughaday, W. H. 1970. Catecholamine inhibition of prolactin secretion by isolated adenohypophyses. *Endocrinology* 86:120–30
13. Blake, C. A. 1974. Stimulation of pituitary prolactin and TSH release in lactating and proestrous rats. *Endocrinology* 94:503–8
14. Brown, G. M., Seeman, P., Lee, T. 1976. Dopamine/neuroleptic receptors in basal hypothalamus and pituitary. *Endocrinology* 99:1407–10
15. Burnet, F. R., Wakerly, J. B. 1976. Plasma concentrations of prolactin and thyrotropin during suckling in urethane-anaesthetized rats. *J. Endocrinol.* 70:429–37
16. Cetel, N. S., Quigley, M. E., Ropert, J., Yen, S. S. C. 1982. Synchronized pulsatile release of prolactin and luteinizing hormone in normal cycling and hypogonadal women. See Ref. 2, (Abstr. 24)
17. Chen, H. J., Mueller, G. P., Meites, J. 1974. Effects of L-dopa and somatostatin on suckling-induced release of prolactin and GH. *Endocr. Res. Commun.* 1:283–91
18. Cheung, C. Y., Weiner, R. I. 1978. In vitro supersensitivity of the anterior pituitary to dopamine inhibition of prolactin secretion. *Endocrinology* 102:1614–20
19. Cheung, C. Y., Kuhn, R. W., Weiner, R. I. 1981. Increased responsiveness of the dopamine-mediated inhibition of prolactin synthesis after destruction of the medial basal hypothalamus. *Endocrinology* 108:747–51

20. Chiocchio, S. R., Cannata, M. A., Cordero Funes, J. R., Tramezzani, J. H. 1979. Involvement of adenohypophysial dopamine in the regulation of prolactin release during suckling. *Endocrinology* 105:544–47

21. Chiocchio, S. R., Chaufen, S., Tramezzani, J. H. 1980. Changes in adenohypophysial dopamine related to prolactin release. *Endocrinology* 106:1682–85

22. Clemens, J. A., Shaar, C. J. 1981. An endogenous "benzodiazepine-like" substance may regulate the sensitivity of the adenohypophysis to gamma-aminobutyric acid. *Prog. 63rd Ann. Meet. Endocr. Soc. Cincinnati, Ohio.* (Abstr. 931)

23. Collu, R., Tache, Y. 1979. Hormonal effects exerted by TRH through the central nervous system. In *Central Nervous System Effects of Hypothalamic Hormones and Other Peptides,* ed. R. Collu, A. Barbeau, J. R. Ducharme, G. Rochefort, pp. 97–121. NY: Raven Press

24. Creese, I. R., Schneider, P., Snyder, S. H. 1977. ³H-spiroperidol labels dopamine receptors in pituitary and brain. *Eur. J. Pharmacol.* 46:377–81

25. Dawood, M. Y., Khan-Dawood, F. S., Wahi, R. S., Fuchs, F. 1981. Oxytocin release and plasma anterior pituitary and gonadal hormones in women during lactation. *J. Clin. Endocrinol. Metab.* 52:678–83

26. de Greef, W. J., Neill, J. D. 1979. Dopamine levels in hypophysial stalk plasma of the rat during surges of prolactin secretion induced by cervical stimulation. *Endocrinology* 105:1093–99

27. de Greef, W. J., Plotsky, P. M., Neill, J. D. 1981. Dopamine levels in hypophysial stalk plasma and prolactin levels in peripheral plasma of the lactating rat: effects of a simulated suckling stimulus. *Neuroendocrinology* 32:229–33

28. de Greef, W. J., Visser, T. J. 1981. Evidence for the involvement of hypothalamic dopamine and thyrotropin-releasing hormone in suckling-induced release of prolactin. *J. Endocrinol.* 91:213–23

29. De Lean, A., Garon, M., Kelly, P. A., Labrie, F. 1977. Changes of pituitary thyrotropin releasing hormone (TRH) receptor level and prolactin response to TRH during the rat estrous cycle. *Endocrinology* 100:1505–10

30. Denef, C., Manet, D., Dewals, R. 1980. Dopaminergic stimulation of prolactin release. *Nature* 285:243–46

31. Denef, C. 1981. LHRH stimulates prolactin release from rat pituitary lactotrophs co-cultured with a highly purified population of gonadotrophs. *Ann. Endocrinol. (Paris)* 42:65–66

32. Enjalbert, A., Ruberg, M., Arancibia, S., Priam, M., Kordon, C. 1979. Endogeneous opiates block dopamine inhibition of prolactin secretion in vitro. *Nature* 280:595–97

33. Enjalbert, A., Ruberg, M., Arancibia, S., Priam, M., Bauer, K., Kordon, C. 1979. Inhibition of in vitro prolactin secretion by histidyl-proline-diketopiperazine, a degradation product of TRH. *Eur. J. Pharmacol.* 58:97–98

34. Enjalbert, A., Ruberg, M., Arancibia, S., Fiore, L., Priam, M., Kordon, C. 1979. Independent inhibition of prolactin secretion by dopamine and γ-aminobutyric acid in vitro. *Endocrinology* 105:823–26

35. Enjalbert, A., Arancibia, S., Priam, M., Bluet-Pajot, M. T., Kordon, C. 1982. Neurotensin stimulation of prolactin secretion in vitro. *Neuroendocrinology* 34:95–98

36. Fagin, K. D., Neill, J. D. 1981. The effect of dopamine on thyrotropin-releasing hormone-induced prolactin secretion in vitro. *Endocrinology* 109:1835–40

37. Fagin, K. D., Neill, J. D. 1982. Involvement of the neurointermediate lobe of the pituitary gland in the secretion of prolactin and luteinizing hormone in the rat. *Life Sci.* 30:1135–41

38. Farkouh, N. H., Packer, M. G., Frantz, A. G. 1979. Large molecular size prolactin with reduced receptor activity in human serum: high proportion in basal state and reduction after thyrotropin-releasing hormone. *J. Clin. Endocrinol. Metab.* 48:1026–32

39. Fink, G., Koch, Y., Ben-Aroya, N. 1981. Hypophysial portal TRH: turnover, and effects of anaesthetics and suckling. *TRH Satellite Symp. 8th Meet. Int. Soc. Neurochem., Nottingham, United Kingdom.* (Abstr.)

40. Fletcher, W. H., Anderson, N. C. Jr., Everett, J. W. 1975. Intercellular communication in the rat anterior pituitary gland. *J. Cell. Biol* 67:469–76

41. Fraser, H. M., McNeilly, A. S. 1980. Effect of chronic inhibition of thyrotropin releasing hormone on the thyroid hormones and prolactin in the ewe. *J. Endocrinol.* 87:37P–39P (Abstr.)

42. Frawley, L. S., Neill, J. D. 1981. Stimulation of prolactin secretion in rhesus

monkeys by vasoactive intestinal peptide. *Neuroendocrinology* 33:79–83

43. Frawley, L. S., Neill, J. D. 1982. Brief decreases in dopamine result in surges of prolactin secretion in monkeys. *Am. J. Physiol.* Submitted

44. Frawley, L. S., Mulchahey, J. J., Neill, J. D. 1982. Nursing induces a biphasic release of prolactin in rhesus monkeys. *Endocrinology.* Submitted

45. Frawley, L. S., Neill, J. D. 1982. Neuroendocrine regulation of prolactin secretion in primates. In *The Anterior Pituitary Gland,* ed. A. S. Bhatnager. NY: Raven Press. In press

46. Fuxe, K., Hokfelt, T., Nilsson, O. 1969. Factors involved in the control of the activity of tubero-infundibular dopamine neurons during pregnancy and lactation. *Neuroendocrinology* 5:257–70

47. Gala, R. R., Hart, I. C. 1980. Serum prolactin heterogeneity in the cow and goat. *Life Sci.* 27:723–30

48. Gautvik, K. M., Weintraub, B. D., Graeber, C. T., Maloof, F., Zuckerman, J. E., Tashjian, A. H. Jr. 1973. Serum prolactin and TSH: effects of nursing and pyro-Glu-His-ProNH₂ administration in postpartum women. *J. Clin. Endocrinol. Metab.* 37:135–39

49. Gibbs, D. M., Neill, J. D. 1978. Dopamine levels in hypophysial stalk blood in the rat are sufficient to inhibit prolactin secretion in vivo. *Endocrinology* 102:1895–900

50. Goldsmith, P. C., Cronin, M. J., Weiner, R. I. 1979. Dopamine receptor sites in the anterior pituitary. *J. Histochem. Cytochem.* 27:1205–7

51. Gourdji, D., Bataille, D., Vauclin, N., Grouselle, D., Rosselin, G., Tixier-Vidal, A. 1979. Vasoactive intestinal peptide (VIP) stimulates prolactin (PRL) release and cAMP production in rat pituitary cell line (GH3/B6). Additive effects of VIP and TRH on PRL release. *FEBS Lett.* 104:165–68

52. Gourdji, D., Tougard, C., Tixier-Vidal, A. 1982. Clonal prolactin strains as a tool in neuroendocrinology. In *Frontiers in Neuroendocrinology,* ed. W. F. Ganong, L. Martini, pp. 317–57. NY: Raven Press

53. Grandison, L., Guidotti, A. 1977. Regulation of prolactin release by endogenous opiates. *Nature* 270:357–59

54. Grandison, L., Guidotti, A. 1979. γ-Aminobutyric acid receptor function in rat anterior pituitary: evidence for control of prolactin release. *Endocrinology* 105:754–59

55. Grandison, L., Cavagnini, F., Schmid, R., Invitti, C., Guidotti, A. 1982. γ-Amino acid- and benzodiazepine-binding sites in human anterior pituitary tissue. *J. Clin. Endocrinol. Metab.* 54:597–601

56. Grandison, L. 1982. Suppression of prolactin secretion by benzodiazepines in vivo. *Neuroendocrinology* 34:369–73

57. Grosvenor, C. E. 1965. Effect of nursing and stress upon prolactin-inhibiting activity of the rat hypothalamus. *Endocrinology* 77:1037–42

58. Grosvenor, C. E., McCann, S. M., Nallar, R. 1965. Inhibition of nursing-induced and stress-induced fall in pituitary prolactin concentration in lactating rats by injection of acid extracts of bovine hypothalamus. *Endocrinology* 76:883–89

59. Grosvenor, C. E., Whitworth, N. S. 1974. Evidence for a steady rate of secretion of prolactin following suckling in the rat. *J. Dairy Sci.* 57:900–4

60. Grosvenor, C. E., Whitworth, N. S. 1976. Incorporation of rat prolactin into rat milk in vivo and in vitro. *J. Endocrinol.* 70:1–9

61. Grosvenor, C. E., Mena, F., Whitworth, N. S. 1979. The secretion rate of prolactin in the rat during suckling and its metabolic clearance rate after increasing intervals of nonsuckling. *Endocrinology* 104:372–76

62. Grosvenor, C. E., Mena, F. 1980. Evidence that thyrotropin-releasing hormone and a hypothalamic prolactin-releasing factor may function in the release of prolactin in the lactating rat. *Endocrinology* 107:863–68

63. Grosvenor, C. E., Mena, F., Whitworth, N. S. 1980. Evidence that the dopaminergic prolactin-inhibiting factor mechanism regulates only the depletion-transformation phase and not the release phase of prolactin secretion during suckling in the rat. *Endocrinology* 106:481–85

64. Gudelsky, G. A., Nansel, D. D., Porter, J. C. 1980. Uptake and processing of dopamine by cells of the anterior pituitary gland. *Endocrinology* 107:30–34

65. Gudelsky, G. A., Nansel, D. D., Porter, J. C. 1981. Role of estrogen in the dopaminergic control of prolactin secretion. *Endocrinology* 108:440–44

66. Gudelsky, G. A., Porter, J. C. 1981. Sex-related difference in the release of dopamine into hypophysial portal blood. *Endocrinology* 109:1394–98

67. Guillemin, R., Vargo, T., Rossier, J., Minick, S., Ling, N., Rivier, C., Vale,

W., Bloom, F. 1977. β-Endorphin and adrenocorticotropin are secreted concomitantly by the pituitary gland. *Science* 197:1367–69

68. Harris, A. R. C., Christianson, D., Smith, M. S., Fang, S. L., Braverman, L. E., Vagenakis, A. G. 1978. The physiological role of thyrotropin-releasing hormone in the regulation of thyroid-stimulating hormone and prolactin secretion in the rat. *J. Clin. Invest.* 61:441–48

69. Haug, E., Gautvik, K. M. 1976. Effects of sex steroids on prolactin secreting rat pituitary cells in culture. *Endocrinology* 99:1482–89

70. Jeppson, S., Nilsson, K. O., Rannevik, G., Wide, L. 1976. Influence of suckling and of suckling followed by TRH or LH-RH on plasma prolactin, TSH, GH, and FSH. *Acta. Endocrinol.* (*Copenhagen*) 82:246–53

71. Johnson, L. K., Baxter, J. D., Vlodavsky, I., Gospodarowicz, D. 1980. Epidermal growth factor and expression of specific genes: effects on cultured rat pituitary cells are dissociable from the mitogenic response. *Proc. Natl. Acad. Sci. USA* 77:394–98

72. Kato, Y., Chihara, K., Ohgo, S., Iwasaki, Y., Abe, H., Imura, H. 1976. Growth hormone and prolactin release by substance P in rats. *Life Sci.* 19:441–46

73. Koch, Y., Goldhaber, G., Fireman, I., Zor, U., Shani, J., Tal, E. 1977. Suppression of prolactin and thyrotropin secretion in the rat by antiserum to thyrotropin-releasing hormone *Endocrinology* 100:1476–78

74. Lamberts, S. W., Visser, T. J. 1981. The effect of histidyl-proline-diketopiperazine, a metabolite of TRH, on prolactin release by the rat pituitary gland in vitro. *Eur. J. Pharmacol.* 71:337–41

75. Lawson, D. M., Gala, R. R., Chin, M. L., Haislender, D. H. 1980. Size heterogeneity of plasma prolactin in the rat: TRH and serotonin-induced changes. *Life Sci.* 27:1147–51

76. Leighton, P. C., McNeilly, A. S., Chard, T. 1976. Short-term variation in blood levels of prolactin in women. *J. Endocrinol.* 68:177–78

77. Leong, D. A., Neill, J. D. 1982. Regulation of prolactin release in lactating rats: an increase in prolactin secretory responsiveness to TRH and VIP during suckling. *Endocrinology.* Submitted

78. Leong, D. A. 1982. Regulation of suckling-induced prolactin (PRL) release in the lactating rat: the role of hypophysio-

tropic dopamine (DA). *Prog. 15th Ann. Meet. Soc. Study Reprod. Madison, Wis.* (Abstr. 44)

79. Leung, F. C., Russell, S. M., Nicoll, C. S. 1978. Relationship between bioassay and radioimmunoassay estimates of prolactin rat serum. *Endocrinology* 103:1619–28

80. Leung, F. C. 1980. Relationship between radioreceptor assay and radioimmunoassay estimates of prolactin in rat pituitary tissue, incubation medium and serum: effects of dialysis on measurements of the hormone. *Endocrinology* 106:61–67

81. Levine, J. E., Pau, F., Ramirez, V. D., Jackson, G. L. 1981. In vivo LHRH release estimated with push-pull cannulae and simultaneous serum measurement in ovariectomized ewes. *Prog. Ann. Meet. Soc. Neurosci. Los Angeles, Calif.* (Abstr. 10.2)

82. Lien, E. L., Fenichel, R. L., Garsky, V., Sarantakis, D., Grant, N.H. 1976. Enkephalin-stimulated prolactin release. *Life Sci.* 19:837–40

83. Linton, E. A., White, N., Lira de Tineo, O., Jeffcoate, S. L. 1981. 2-Hydroxyoestradiol inhibits prolactin release from the superfused rat pituitary gland. *J. Endocrinol.* 90:315–22

84. MacLeod, R. M., Fontham, E. H., Lehmeyer, J. E. 1970. Prolactin and growth hormone production as influenced by catecholamines and agents that affect brain catecholamines. *Neuroendocrinology* 6:283–94

85. MacLeod, R. M. 1976. Regulation of prolactin secretion. In *Frontiers in Neuroendocrinology,* ed. L. Martini, W. F. Ganong, pp. 169–94. NY: Raven Press

86. Malarkey, W. B., O'Dorisio, T. M., Kennedy, M., Cataland, S. 1981. The influence of vasoactive intestinal polypeptide and cholecystokinin on prolactin release in rat and human monolayer cultures. *Life Sci.* 28:2489–95

87. Mattheij, J. A. M., Gruisen, E. F. M., Swarts, J. J. M. 1979. The suckling-induced rise of plasma prolactin in lactating rats. Its dependence on stage of lactation and litter size. *Horm. Res.* 11:325–36

88. McCann, S. M., Graves, T., Taleisnik, S. 1967. The effect of lactation on plasma LH. *Endocrinology* 68:873–74

89. McKay, D. W., Demarest, K. T., Riegle, G. D., Moore, K. E. 1980. Lactation alters the activity of tuberoinfundibular dopaminergic neurons. *Prog.*

10th Ann. Meet. Soc. Neurosci. Cincinnati, Ohio (Abstr. 152.36)

90. Melmed, S., Carlson, H. E., Hershman, J. M. 1982. Histidyl-proline diketopiperazine suppresses prolactin secretion in human pituitary cell cultures. *Clin. Endocrinol.* 16:97–100

91. Mena, F., Enjalbert, A., Carbonell, L., Priam, M. M., Kordon, C. 1976. Effects of suckling on plasma prolactin and hypothalamic monoamine levels in the rat. *Endocrinology* 99:445–51

92. Mena, F., Pacheco, P., Grosvenor, C. E. 1980. Effect of electrical stimulation of mammary nerve upon pituitary and plasma prolactin concentrations in anesthetized lactating rats. *Endocrinology* 106:458–62

93. Mena, F., Pacheco, P., Whitworth, N. S., Grosvenor, C. E. 1980. Recent data concerning the secretion and function of oxytocin and prolactin during lactation in the rat and rabbit. In *Frontiers of Hormone Research*, ed. C. Valverde, H. Arechiga, pp. 217–49. NY: Karger

94. Mena, F., Grosvenor, C. E. 1980. New concepts concerning the release of prolactin induced by suckling. In *Endocrinology 1980 Proceedings of the VI International Congress of Endocrinology, Melbourne, Australia*, ed. I. A. Cumming, J. W. Funder, F. A. O. Mendelsohn, pp. 194–97. Canberra: Austr. Acad. Sci.

95. Mittra, I. 1980. A novel "cleaved prolactin" in the rat pituitary. Part I. Biosynthesis, characterization and regulatory control. *Biochem. Biophys. Res. Commun.* 95:1750–59

96. Mittra, I. 1980. A novel "cleaved prolactin" in the rat pituitary. Part II. In vivo mammary mitogenic activity of its N-terminal 16K moiety. *Biochem. Biophys. Res. Commun.* 95:1760–67

97. Moore, K. E., Demarest, K. T. 1982. Tuberoinfundibular and tuberohypophyseal dopaminergic neurons. In *Frontiers in Neuroendocrinology*, ed., W. F. Ganong, L. Martini, pp. 161–90. NY: Raven Press

98. Morel, G., Besson, J., Rosselin, G., Dubois, P. M. 1982. Ultrastructural evidence for endogenous vasoactive intestinal peptide-like immunoreactivity in the pituitary gland. *Neuroendocrinology* 34:85–89

99. Moyer, J. A., O'Donohue, T. L., Herrenkohl, L. R., Gala, R. R., Jacobowitz, D. M. 1979. Effects of suckling on serum prolactin levels and catecholamine concentrations and turnover in discrete brain regions. *Brain Res.* 176:125–33

100. Mulchahey, J. J., Neill, J. D. 1982. Gamma amino butyric acid (GABA) levels in hypophyseal stalk plasma of rats. *Life Sci.* 31:453–56

101. Nakane, P. K. 1970. Classification of anterior pituitary cell types with immunoenzyme histochemistry. *J. Histochem. Cytochem.* 18:9–20

102. Nansel, D. D., Gudelsky, G. A., Porter, J. C. 1979. Subcellular localization of dopamine in the anterior pituitary gland of the rat: apparent association of dopamine with prolactin secretory granules. *Endocrinology* 105:1073–77

103. Neill, J. D. 1974. Prolactin: its secretion and control. In *Handbook of Physiology, Sect. 7, Endocrinology*, ed. E. Knobil, W. H. Sawyer, 4(2):469–88. Washington DC: Am. Physiol. Soc.

104. Neill, J. D. 1980. Neuroendocrine regulation of prolactin secretion. In *Frontiers in Neuroendocrinology*, ed. L. Martini, W. F. Ganong, pp. 129–55. NY: Raven Press

105. Neill, J. D., Frawley, L. S., Plotsky, P. M., Tindall, G. T. 1981. Dopamine in hypophysial stalk blood of the rhesus monkey and its role in regulating prolactin secretion. *Endocrinology* 108:489–94

106. Nicoll, C. S. 1972. Some observations and speculation on the mechanism of "depletion" and "repletion" and release of adenohypophyseal hormones. *Gen. Comp. Endocrinol.* (*Suppl.*) 3:86–96

107. Nicoll, C. S. 1974. Physiological actions of prolactin. See Ref. 103, pp. 253–92

108. Nicoll, C. S., Mena, F., Nichols, C. W. Jr., Green, S. H., Tai, M., Russell, S. M. 1976. Analysis of suckling-induced changes in adenohypophyseal prolactin concentration in the lactating rat by three assay methods. *Acta Endocrinol. (Copenhagen)* 83:512–21

109. Nogami, H., Yoshimura, F. 1982. Fine structural criteria of prolactin cells identified immunohistochemically in the male rat. *Anat. Rec.* 202:261–74

110. Page, R. B. 1982. In vivo recording of the direction of porcine pituitary blood flow. See Ref. 2, (Abstr. 10)

111. Palkovits, M. 1980. New aspects of brain-pituitary interrelationships. See Ref. 94, pp. 352–55

112. Pearse, A. G. E. 1977. The diffuse neuroendocrine system and the APUD concept: related "endocrine" peptides in brain, intestine, pituitary, placenta, and anuran cutaneous glands. *Med. Biol.* 55:115–25

113. Peters, L., Hoefer, M. T., Ben-Jonathan, N. 1981. The posterior pituitary: regulation of anterior pituitary prolactin secretion. *Science* 213:659–61

114. Pickering, A. J. M. C., Fink, G. 1979. Do hypothalamic regulatory factors other than luteinizing hormone releasing factor exert a priming effect? *J. Endocrinol.* 81:235–38

115. Plotsky, P. M., Gibbs, D. M., Neill, J. D. 1978. Liquid chromatographic-electrochemical measurement of dopamine in hypophysial stalk blood of rats. *Endocrinology* 102:1887–94

116. Plotsky, P. M., Neill, J. D. 1982. The decrease in hypothalamic dopamine secretion induced by suckling: comparison of voltammetric and radioisotopic methods of measurement. *Endocrinology* 110:691–96

117. Plotsky, P. M., de Greef, W. J., Neill, J. D. 1982. In situ voltammetric microelectrodes: application to the measurement of the median eminence catecholamine release during simulated suckling. *Brain Res.* In press

118. Plotsky, P. M., Neill, J. D. 1982. Interactions of dopamine and thyrotropin releasing hormone (TRH) in the regulation of prolactin release in lactating rats. *Endocrinology* 111:168–73

119. Prasad, C., Wilber, J. F., Akerstrom, V., Banerji, A. 1980. Cyclo (His-Pro): a selective inhibitor of rat prolactin secretion in vitro. *Life Sci.* 27:1979–83

120. Racagni, G., Apud, J. A., Locatelli, V., Cocchi, D., Nistico, G., di Giorgio, R. M., Muller, E. E. 1979. GABA of CNS origin in the rat anterior pituitary inhibits prolactin secretion. *Nature* 281: 575–78

121. Raymond, V., Beaulieu, M., Labrie, F., Boissier, J. 1978. Potent antidopaminergic activity of estradiol at the pituitary level on prolactin release. *Science* 200:1173–75

122. Ruberg, M., Rotsztein, W. H., Arancibia, S., Besson, J., Enjalbert, A. 1978. Stimulation of prolactin release by vasoactive intestinal peptide (VIP). *Eur. J. Pharmacol.* 51:319–20

123. Said, S. I., Porter, J. C. 1979. Vasoactive intestinal polypeptide; release into hypophysial portal blood. *Life Sci.* 24:227–30

124. Samson, W. K., Said, S. I., Snyder, G., McCann, S. M. 1980. In vitro stimulation of prolactin release by vasoactive intestinal peptide. *Peptides* 1:325–32

125. Sato, S. 1980. Postnatal development, sexual difference and sexual cyclic variation of prolactin cells in rats: special

126. Saunders, A., Terry, L. C., Audet, J., Brazeau, P., Martin, J. B. 1976. Dynamic studies of growth hormone and prolactin secretion in the female rat. *Neuroendocrinology* 21:193–203

127. Schaeffer, J. M., Hsueh, A. J. 1979. 2-Hydroxyestradiol interaction with dopamine receptor binding in rat anterior pituitary. *J. Biol. Chem.* 254:5606–8

128. Schally, A. V., Redding, T. W., Arimura, A., Dupont, A., Linthicum, G. L. 1977. Isolation of gamma-aminobutyric acid from pig hypothalami and demonstration of its prolactin release-inhibiting (PIF) activity in vivo and in vitro. *Endocrinology* 100:681–91

129. Schonbrunn, A., Krasnoff, M., Westendorf, J. M., Tashjian, A. H. Jr. 1980. Epidermal growth factor and thyrotropin-releasing hormone act similarly on a clonal pituitary cell strain: modulation of hormone production and inhibition of cell proliferation. *J. Cell Biol.* 85:786–97

130. Selmanoff, M., Wise, P. M. 1981. Decreased dopamine turnover in the median eminence in response to suckling in the lactating rat. *Brain Res.* 212:101–15

131. Selmanoff, M., Gregerson, K. A. 1982. Suckling-induced decreases in dopamine turnover occur in both medial and lateral aspects of the median eminence of the lactating rat. *Fed. Proc.* 41:1100 (Abstr. 4853)

132. Shaar, C. J., Clemens, J. A. 1974. The role of catecholamines in the release of anterior pituitary prolactin in vitro. *Endocrinology* 95:1202–12

133. Shaar, C. J., Clemens, J. A., Dininger, N. B. 1979. Effect of vasoactive intestinal polypeptide on prolactin release in vitro. *Life Sci.* 25:2071–74

134. Shimatsu, A., Kato, Y., Matsushita, N., Katakami, H., Yanaihara, N., Imura, H. 1981. Immunoreactive vasoactive intestinal polypeptide in rat hypophysial portal blood. *Endocrinology* 108: 395–98

135. Shin, S. H., Reifel, C. W. 1981. Adenohypophysis has an inherent property for pulsatile prolactin secretion. *Neuroendocrinology* 32:139–44

136. Shin, S. H. 1982. Vasopressin has a direct effect on prolactin release in male rats. *Neuroendocrinology* 34:55–58

137. Sinha, Y. N. 1980. Molecular size variants of prolactin and growth hormone in mouse serum: strain differences and

alterations of concentrations by physiological and pharmacological stimuli. *Endocrinology* 107:1959–69

138. Sinha, Y. N., Gilligan, T. A. 1981. Identification of a less immunoreactive form of prolactin in the rat pituitary. *Endocrinology* 108:1091–94

139. Smith, M. S., Neill, J. D. 1977. Inhibition of gonadotropin secretion during lactation in the rat: relative contribution of suckling and ovarian steroids. *Biol. Reprod.* 17:255–61

140. Smith, M. S. 1982. Effect of pulsatile gonadotropin-releasing hormone on the release of luteinizing hormone and follicle-stimulating hormone in vitro by anterior pituitaries from lactating or cycling rats. *Endocrinology* 110:882–91

141. Steele, M. K., Negro-Vilar, A., McCann, S. M. 1981. Effect of angiotensin II on in vivo and in vitro release of anterior pituitary hormones in the female rat. *Endocrinology* 109:893–99

142. Suh, H. K., Frantz, A. G. 1974. Size heterogeneity of human prolactin in plasma and pituitary extracts. *J. Clin. Endocrinol. Metab.* 39:928–35

143. Szabo, M., Frohman, L. A. 1977. Suppression of cold-stimulated thyrotropin secretion by antiserum to thyrotropin-releasing hormone. *Endocrinology* 101:1023–33

144. Takahara, J., Arimura, A., Schally, A. V. 1974. Suppression of prolactin release by a purified porcine PIF preparation and catecholamines infused into a rat hypophysial portal vessel. *Endocrinology* 95:462–65

145. Tashjian, A. H. Jr., Barowsky, N. J., Jensen, D. K. 1971. Thyrotropin releasing hormone: direct evidence for stimulation of prolactin production by pituitary cells in culture. *Biochem. Biophys. Res. Commun.* 43:516–23

146. Terkel, J., Blake, C. A., Sawyer, C. H. 1972. Serum prolactin levels in lactating rats after suckling or exposure to ether. *Endocrinology* 91:49–53

147. Terry, L. C., Saunders, A., Audet, J., Willoughby, J., Brazeau, P., Martin, J. B. 1977. Physiologic secretion of growth hormone and prolactin in male and female rats. *Clin. Endocrinol. (Oxford)* 6:19S–28S

148. Vijayan, E., McCann, S. M. 1979. In vivo and in vitro effects of substance P and neurotensin on gonadotropin and prolactin release. *Endocrinology* 105:64–68

149. Vincent, S. R., Hokfelt, T., Wu, J. Y. 1982. GABA neuron systems in the hypothalamus and the pituitary gland. *Neuroendocrinology* 34:117–25

150. Voogt, J. L., Sar, M., Meites, J. 1969. Influence of cycling, pregnancy, labor, and suckling on corticosterone-ACTH levels. *Am. J. Physiol.* 216:655–58

151. Voogt, J. L., Carr, L. A. 1974. Plasma prolactin levels and hypothalamic catecholamine synthesis during suckling. *Neuroendocrinology* 16:108–18

152. Walker, A. M., Farquhar, M. G. 1980. Preferential release of newly synthesized prolactin granules is the result of functional heterogeneity among mammotrophs. *Endocrinology* 107:1095–1104

153. Wehrenberg, W. B., McNicol, D., Frantz, A. G., Ferin, M. 1980. The effects of serotonin on prolactin and growth hormone concentrations in normal pituitary stalk-sectioned monkeys. *Endocrinology* 107:1747–50

154. Westendorf, J. M., Schonbrunn, A. 1982. Bombesin stimulates prolactin and growth hormone release by pituitary cells in culture. *Endocrinology* 110:352–58

155. Wildt, L., Hausler, A., Marshall, G., Knobil, E. 1980. GnRH has prolactin-releasing activity. *Fed. Proc.* 39:374 (Abstr. 552)

156. Zyzek, E., Dufy-Barbe, L., Dufy, B., Vincent, J. D. 1981. Short-term effect of estrogen on release of prolactin by pituitary cells in culture. *Biochem. Biophys. Res. Commun.* 102:1151–57

Ann. Rev. Physiol. 1983. 45:129–35

BIOSYNTHESIS OF VASOPRESSIN AND OXYTOCIN

Michael J. Brownstein

Laboratory of Clinical Science, National Institute of Mental Health, Bethesda, Maryland 20205

INTRODUCTION

In 1964 Sachs and Takabatake (18, 19) suggested that vasopressin (VP) and its associated neurophysin "carrier protein" were produced as parts of a common precursor molecule. Subsequently, it was proposed that oxytocin and its neurophysin were made by a similar mechanism (12). The putative precursors escaped detection until the 1970s, however, when they were identified in the course of pulse-chase studies (2–5). The nucleotide sequence of cloned cDNA encoding the bovine vasopressin/neurophysin precursor (propressophysin) has been determined (7); the structure of the oxytocin/neurophysin precursor (prooxyphysin) remains to be elucidated.

CHARACTERIZATION OF NEUROHYPOPHYSIAL PROHORMONES

Prior to the cloning and sequencing of propressophysin cDNA, a good deal of information had already been obtained about the structure of the propressophysin molecule. Three general strategies were employed for studying this protein. Lauber, Cohen, and their colleagues (8, 10) made bovine neurohypophyseal extracts, separated the proteins in these extracts chromatographically, and assayed for neurophysin- and vasopressin-like molecules by radioimmunoassay. Russell, Gainer, and Brownstein (2–5, 13–16) employed pulse-chase methodology. They infused ^{35}S-cysteine into the brains of rats adjacent to their supraoptic nuclei, and looked for newly formed cysteine-rich molecules that behaved like neurophysin precursors. Finally, Schmale & Richter (20–24) extracted mRNA from bovine brains

129

0066-4278/83/0315-0129$02.00

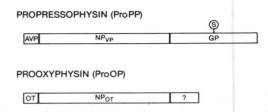

Figure 1   Proposed structural models for propressophysin and prooxyphysin. The heavy lines between the identified peptide components indicate the positions of expected dibasic amino acid residues.

and translated it in vitro. They immunoprecipitated the translation products with antineurophysin, antivasopressin, and antioxytocin antisera.

Based on the above studies, it was generally agreed that the vasopressin/neurophysin precursor was a molecule of about 20,000 daltons; that it was a glycoprotein; and that the vasopressin was found on the N-terminus, the neurophysin in the middle, and the glycopeptide adduct on the C-terminus (see Figure 1).[1]

The nucleotide sequence of the cloned cDNA validates this model (7) (Figure 2). This preprohormone consists of a 19 amino acid "signal peptide," followed by vasopressin. The vasopressin is separated from the amino terminus of neurophysin by a Gly-Lys-Arg sequence (see below). The carboxy terminal region of the precursor contains a naturally occurring glycopeptide (6, 25, 26), 39 amino acids long, which is separated from neurophysin by a single arginine residue. (Glycosylation is coded for by residues 114–116; the Asn is the sugar recipient.)

The oxytocin/neurophysin precursor is similar to propressophysin. It also has oxytocin on its N-terminus, neurophysin next, and an adduct last (Figure 1) (13). The peptide adduct in the case of prooxyphysin is short, however, and is not glycosylated. In a way, this is unfortunate; it makes it hard to imagine the importance of glycosylation to the VP-producing cells.

Now that the structure of the bovine vasopressin/neurophysin prepro-hormone is known, several new questions present themselves. What is the structure of the gene that encodes the preprohormone message? How is message production controlled? How is the preprohormone modified after it is translated? Where does this modification ("processing") occur? How do the preprohormone and its active products make their way from the rough endoplasmic reticulum where translation of mRNA takes place to the secretory granules that store and ultimately release the hormones? No information is available that helps answer the first two questions above, but

[1]Lauber and his colleagues (8) have suggested that a larger neurophysin-containing protein species exists and that it also contains corticotropin and endorphin. This molecule has not been found in pulse-chase studies, and its mRNA has escaped detection thus far (8).

```
5'                                                                                          -50
(NGCACAGUCUACAGAGCACACUGCGCACGUGUGCCCACG) CGUCCAGG   AUG CCC GAC GCC ACA CUG CCC GCC UGC UUC CUC AGC
                                                      MET PRO ASP ALA THR LEU PRO ALA CYS PHE LEU SER
                                                      -19                                                     50
CUG CUG GCC UUC ACC UCU GCU UAC UUC CAG AAC UGC CCA AGG GGC GGG GGG AGG AGG GCC AUG UCC GAC CUG GAG
LEU LEU ALA PHE THR SER ALA CYS TYR PHE GLN ASN CYS PRO ARG GLY GLY GLY ARG ARG ALA MET SER ASP LEU GLU
        -1  1                                                                10
CUG AGA CAG UGU CUC CCC UGC CCC GGG AAA GGC UGC CGC AAG GAG GAG GAG CAA AAC UAC CUG CCC UCG CCC UGC CAG UCC
LEU ARG GLN CYS LEU PRO CYS PRO GLY LYS GLY CYS ARG LYS GLU GLU GLU GLN ASN TYR LEU PRO SER PRO CYS GLN SER
        20                                                      60                              200
CUG GGC UGC UUC GUG GGC ACG GCC GAG GCG CUG CGC UGC GCC GCC GCC GCC AUC UGC UGC CCG UCG CCC CUG CCC UGC CAG UCC
LEU GLY CYS PHE VAL GLY THR ALA GLU ALA LEU ARG CYS ALA ALA ALA ALA ILE CYS CYS PRO SER PRO LEU PRO CYS GLN SER
        150                                              80                    250                          40
GGC CAG AAG CCC UGC GGG AGC GGG GUC GGU UGC GCU CGC GUU CGC CGC GAU GAG AGC AAC GCG AGC GCG GAG GUG GUG ACC
GLY GLN LYS PRO CYS GLY SER GLY VAL GLY CYS ALA ARG VAL ARG ARG ASP GLU SER ASN ALA SER ALA GLU VAL VAL THR
        300                                                                         350
GAG CCC GAG UGC CGG GAA GGU GGC GGG UUC CCC CGC CGC AGG AAC GAC CGG AGC GCG ACC GCG AGC CUG CUG
GLU PRO GLU CYS ARG GLU GLY GLY GLY PHE PRO ARG ARG ARG ASN ASP ARG SER ALA THR ALA SER LEU LEU
100                                                       400
GAC GGG AGC AGC GGG GCC UUG CUG CUG CGG CUG GUG CUG GUG CUG GCG CCG CCG GGG GCG GAG CCC GCC CAG
ASP GLY SER SER GLY ALA LEU LEU LEU ARG LEU VAL LEU VAL LEU ALA PRO PRO GLY ALA GLU PRO ALA GLN
        120                                                                         140
CCC GGC GUC UAC UGA   GGGCGGCCCCCCCCCUCCCCACCCCUGCCCUCGCAGCACGAAAAAUAAACGUUUUAAGGC (A)~150
PRO GLY VAL TYR ***
                147                                              500                     3'
```

Figure 2 Nucleotide sequence of AVP-NpII precursor mRNA from bovine hypothalamus, and deduced amino acid sequence. The nucleotide numbers are shown above the sequence. Nucleotide residues are numbered in the direction 5' → 3' in the mRNA strand, beginning with the first residue in the coding region for arginine vasopressin. The nucleotides upstream from residue 1 are indicated by negative numbers. The predicted amino acid sequence is numbered by designating as 1 the first residue (Cys) of arginine vasopressin. The amino acids constituting the putative signal peptide are indicated by negative numbers; those towards the carboxy terminus of the precursor have positive numbers. The untranslated sequence at the 5' terminus, shown in parentheses, is derived from primer extension sequencing of the mRNA and has not been confirmed by sequencing of cloned DNA. The ³²P-labelled DNA fragments BstNI(-58)-Sau96I(+39)⁺ and DdeI(-23)-Sau96I(+39)⁺ were used as primers. Asterisks indicate the position of the [γ-³²P] label.

in vivo studies of the magnocellular hypothalamic neurons responsible for manufacturing vasopressin and oxytocin have contributed to our understanding of the cell biological aspects of peptide biosynthesis.

PROCESSING
OF NEUROHYPOPHYSIAL HORMONES

Like other peptide precursors, propressophysin and prooxyphysin begin their lives in association with the rough endoplasmic reticulum. There the mRNA that serves as a template for their production is translated by ribosomes. The first part of the message to be translated is its 5-prime end. Thus the first amino acids to emerge from the ribosomal factories are numbers -19 to -1 (see Figure 2). Blobel & Dobberstein have referred to this hydrophobic string of amino acids as the signal sequence. Its job seems to be to bind to and pass through the membrane of the rough endoplasmic reticulum. Soon after the signal sequence penetrates the reticular cisternum it is separated from the nascent protein by a "signalase." Subsequently the remainder of the precursor enters the cisternal space; the motive force that drives this translocation is unknown. Once inside the endoplasmic cisternum, the prohormones are caught there. Proximal glycosylation (9) (in the case of propressophysin) and disulfide bridge formation (1) may help prevent the precursors' escape by making them more globular (11).

The prohormones make their way next to the Golgi apparatus where propressophysin probably undergoes distal glycosylation. The precursors must be present in the Golgi in a very dilute solution, and packaging them into secretory vesicles that bud off the Golgi requires that they be addressed, trapped, and condensed. The fact that the precursors are processed (cleaved enzymatically) during axonal transport (4, 5) suggests that they are packaged in secretory granules along with the appropriate processing enzymes and not broken down in the Golgi. It seems reasonable that the nonvasopressin, nonoxytocin parts of the prohormones are involved in packaging. If so, premature (i.e. intraGolgi) processing of the precursors has to be prevented so that their "zip codes" are not removed before they are delivered to their final destinations. This may be accomplished by maintaining different hydrogen ion concentrations in the Golgi apparatus vs the secretory vesicles. The pH in the Golgi is near neutral; the pH in the granules is about 5.6 (17). The processing enzymes seem to function optimally at a pH of 5.5–6 (Y. P. Loh, V. Hook, personal communication).

The vasopressin precursor is cleaved to yield three principal products: vasopressin, neurophysin, and a glycopeptide. All three of these are present in secretory vesicles, and presumably all three are released when nerve endings are depolarized. At least three enzymes should be involved in the processing of propressophysin or prooxyphysin: a trypsin-like enzyme, a carboxypeptidase B–like enzyme, and an amidating enzyme.

The first of these should split the precursors on the carboxy-terminal side of selected basic residues. The enzyme must cleave certain bonds preferentially because vasopressin is not attacked at the Arg-Gly bond (amino acids 8 and 9, Figure 2) and neurophysin is not cleaved at any of its several internal basic residues (including the Arg-Arg-Val residues, amino acids 105–107, Figure 2).[2] Whether the structure of the precursors dictates the cleavage sites, whether binding of vasopressin to neurophysin protects one or both molecules against further degradation, and whether the tryptic enzyme has a preference for certain amino acid sequences are not known. That a tryptic enzyme is associated with density gradient purified posterior pituitary granules has recently been shown (Y. P. Loh et al, personal communication). This enzyme, as predicted, has a low pH optimum.

The second processing enzyme, a carboxypeptidase B, should trim unwanted basic amino acid residues from the carboxy-terminus of peptides. This enzyme should remove Arg 108 from the end of neurophysin, for example. Whether it acts on vasopressin-Gly-Lys-Arg or vasopressin-Gly-Lys is not known.

The glycine residue in position 10 probably serves as an amino group donor to the glycine (number 9) that precedes it. Amidated peptides seem invariably to be followed by a glycine residue and basic amino acids. Whether the amidating enzymes act on the entire precursor or on partially processed peptide fragments remains to be seen. Thus vasopressin-Gly may or may not be the substrate of the amidating enzyme, and the trypsin- and carboxypeptidase B–like enzymes may or may not operate on the prohormone before the amidating enzyme does.

It appears that the rate of prohormone production and the rate of processing of prohormone can be regulated (5, 16). When rats are given 2% saline to drink, large amounts of vasopressin and neurophysin are released from their posterior pituitaries. Within a few days the hormone content of neurosecretory nerve endings drops to 10% of control values. Evidently, the rate of synthesis of hormone cannot keep up with release, but this is not because the neurons are not trying to compensate for elevated demand. The amount of ^{35}S-cysteine incorporated into vasopressin and oxytocin precursors increases about five-fold in 2% saline treated rats. Similarly, the rate of conversion of the newly synthesized precursors into their products also increases. The mechanism responsible for this phenomenon is unknown.

[2]It is interesting that the precursor is cleaved between residues 108 and 109. Commonly, molecules that are destined to be released from the middle of a precursor are flanked by pairs of basic amino acids.

CONCLUDING REMARKS

Studies of a number of peptide hormone precursors have allowed molecular geneticists and cell biologists to identify elements of their primary structures that undergo posttranslation modification. In addition to the problem of processing a prohormone, the cell faces other problems when it wants to export a hormone. The cell has to move the precursor from the endoplasmic cisternum to the secretory granule where the hormone products, once generated, have to be stored (often in an osmotically inactive state) and whence they have to be released. Identification and characterization of peptide precursors may provide the first clues about how some cells solve these problems.

Literature Cited

1. Anfinson, C. B. 1966. The formation of the tertiary structure of proteins. *Harvey Lect.* 61:95–116
2. Brownstein, M. J., Gainer, H. 1977. Neurophysin biosynthesis in normal rats and in rats with hereditary diabetes insipidus. *Proc. Natl. Acad. Sci. USA* 74:4046–49
3. Brownstein, M. J., Robinson, A. G., Gainer, H. 1977. Immunological identification of rat neurophysin precursors. *Nature* 269:259–61
4. Gainer, H., Sarne, Y., Brownstein, M. J. 1977. Neurophysin biosynthesis: Conversion of a putative precursor during axonal transport. *Science* 195:1354–56
5. Gainer, H., Sarne, Y., Brownstein, M. J. 1977. Biosynthesis and axonal transport of rat neurohypophysial proteins and peptides. *J. Cell Biol.* 73:366–81
6. Holwerda, D. A. 1972. *Eur. J. Biochem.* 28:340–46
7. Land, H., Schutz, G., Schmale, H., Richter, D. 1982. Nucleotide sequence of cloned cDNA encoding bovine arginine vasopressin-neurophysin II precursor. *Nature* 295:299–303
8. Lauber, M., Nicolas, P., Boussetta, H., Fahy, C., Beguin, P., Camier, M., Vaudry, H., Cohen, P. 1981. The Mr 80,000 common forms of neurophysin and vasopressin from bovine neurohypophysis have corticotropin- and β-endorphin-like sequences and liberate by proteolysis biologically active corticotropin. *Proc. Natl. Acad. Sci. USA* 78:6086–90
9. Molnar, J., Robinson, G. B., Winzler, R. J. 1965. Biosynthesis of glycoproteins. IV. The subcellular sites of incorporation of glucosamine-1-¹⁴C into glycoprotein in rat liver. *J. Biol. Chem.* 240:1882–88
10. Nicolas, P., Camier, M., Lauber, M., Masse, M.-J. O., Mohring, J., Cohen, P. 1980. Immunological identification of high molecular weight forms common to bovine neurophysin and vasopressin. *Proc. Natl. Acad. Sci. USA* 77:2587–91
11. Palade, G. 1975. Intracellular aspects of the process of protein synthesis. *Science* 189:347–58
12. Pickering, B. T., Jones, C. W. 1971. The biosynthesis and intraneuronal transport of neurohypophysial hormones: Preliminary studies in the rat. In *Subcellular Organization and Function in Endocrine Tissues*, ed. H. Heller, K. Lederis, pp. 337–51. NY: Cambridge Univ. Press
13. Russell, J. T., Brownstein, M. J., Gainer, H. 1979. Liberation by trypsin of an arginine vasopressin-like peptide and neurophysin from a Mr 20,000 putative common precursor. *Proc. Natl. Acad. Sci.* 76:6086–90
14. Russell, J. T., Brownstein, M. J., Gainer, H. 1980. Biosynthesis of vasopressin, oxytocin and neurophysins: Isolation and characterization of two common precursors (propressophysin and prooxyphysin). *Endocrinology* 107:1880–91
15. Russell, J. T., Brownstein, M. J., Gainer, H. 1981. Timecourse of appearance and release of [³⁵S] cysteine labeled neurophysins and peptides in the neurohypophysis. *Brain Res.* 205:299–311
16. Russell, J. T., Brownstein, M. J., Gainer, H. 1981. Biosynthesis of neurohypophyseal polypeptides: the order of peptide components in pro-pressophy-

sin and pro-oxyphysin. *Neuropeptides* 2:59–66

17. Russell, J. T., Holz, R. W. 1981. Measurement of Δ pH and membrane potential in isolated neurosecretory vesicles from bovine neurohypophyses. *J. Biol. Chem.* 256:5950

18. Sachs, H. 1970. Neurosecretion. In *Handbook of Neurochemistry*, ed. A. Lajtha, pp. 373–428. NY: Plenum

19. Sachs, H., Takabatake, Y. 1964. Evidence for a precursor in vasopressin biosynthesis. *Endocrinology* 75:943–48

20. Schmale, H., Leipold, B., Richter, D. 1979. Cell-free translation of bovine hypothalamic mRNA. *FEBS Lett.* 108:311–16

21. Schmale, H., Richter, D. 1980. In vitro biosynthesis and processing of composite common precursors containing amino acid sequences identified immunologically. *FEBS Lett.* 121:358–62

22. Schmale, H., Richter, D. 1981. Immunological identification of a common precursor to arginine vasopressin and neurophysis II synthesized by in vitro translation of bovine hypothalamic mRNA. *Proc. Natl. Acad. Sci. USA* 78:766–69

23. Schmale, H., Richter, D. 1981. Tryptic release of authentic arginine vasopressin from a composite arginine vasopressin/neurophysin II precursor. *Neuropeptides* 2:47–52

24. Schmale, H., Richter, D. 1981. A direct comparison of the rat and bovine arginine vasopressin/neurophysin II common precursor. *Neuropeptides* 2:151–56

25. Seidah, N. G., Benjannet, S., Chretien, M. 1981. *Biochem. Biophys. Res. Commun.* 100:901-7

26. Smyth, D. G., Massey, D. E. 1979. *Biochem. Biophys. Res. Commun.* 87:1006–10

CARDIOVASCULAR PHYSIOLOGY

Introduction, Loring B. Rowell, *Section Organizer,* and Robert M. Berne, *Section Editor*

The reviewers in this section discuss how the cardiovascular system is regulated during muscular exercise. They focus on six areas that currently receive extensive attention.

Drs. Mitchell, Kaufman, and Iwamoto treat a fundamental question that has plagued physiologists for over a century: What stimuli match cardiovascular responses to the metabolic requirements of skeletal muscle? The authors focus on factors that can elevate blood pressure during exercise. They pursue the idea that certain afferent nerve fibers in skeletal muscle may supply an important link as metabolic- and mechano-sensors in the feedback control of blood pressure.

Of course, control of blood pressure during exercise or any other condition cannot be considered without reference to the actions of regulating reflexes. Dr. Ludbrook discusses how exercise may alter baroreceptor and baroreflex activity. Are the reflexes "reset"? Is their gain or sensitivity altered? Can we assess the separate or synergistic roles of the arterial and cardiopulmonary baroreflexes? Dr. Ludbrook shows that these important reflexes are not blunted or turned off by exercise but rather may play vital roles in establishing proper cardiovascular regulation.

Then there is the matter of how overall sympathetic nervous activity changes during exercise. Drs. Christensen and Galbo have applied the new techniques for measuring concentrations of norepinephrine and epinephrine in plasma to conditions when neuronal leakage of norepinephrine into blood often reflects overall changes in sympathetic nervous activity. These reviewers focus on the circulatory consequences of these changes, contributing as well some sidelights on the importance of augmented sympathetic activity to metabolic function in health and in certain disease states.

The large increases in sympathetic nervous activity during exercise alter vascular resistance and blood flow in many organs. Even with their powerful local metabolic control, coronary blood vessels appear not to be totally exempt from the influences of increased sympathetic vasoconstrictor outflow during exercise. Focusing on the neural aspects of coronary blood flow regulation during exercise, Dr. Stone summarizes the evidence for some reflex modulation of coronary blood flow.

Nor are the blood vessels of the skin excluded from the influence of sympathetic nervous activity during exercise. The skin is on the efferent side of both the thermoregulatory and nonthermoregulatory reflexes that are strongly activated during exercise. Dr. Brengelmann has met the challenge of describing the control of skin blood flow under conditions in which cutaneous and skeletal muscle circulations, whose combined needs cannot be met, compete for flow. Conflicting demands for the regulation of blood pressure and body temperature likewise cannot be satisfied. Dr. Brengelmann also critically analyzes recent ideas about how humans make these difficult adjustments.

Drs. Blomqvist and Saltin discuss how the cardiovascular system adjusts to the chronic high loads associated with physical conditioning. They critically weigh the evidence concerning whether the capacity to consume oxygen is ultimately limited by the cardiovascular system or the metabolic capacity of the working muscle. After they establish that the normal limitation is a cardiovascular one, they identify factors that might be weak links in the oxygen delivery system. These might also be the factors that respond to physical conditioning and permit the increased capacity for transport and consumption of oxygen. The authors provide a well-balanced treatment of how various myocardial and extramyocardial adaptations could contribute to increases in the functional capacity of the cardiovascular system.

Together, these six reviews describe some of the complex interactions that provide tight control of cardiovascular function during exercise, when the "noise" of the resting state is overridden by major demands for oxygen transport. These demands can exceed those of rest by 20–25-fold. We see the central importance of the autonomic nervous system as various homeostatic reflexes are elicited by chemo- and mechano-sensitive nerves in skeletal muscle, by arterial and cardiopulmonary baroreceptors, or by central and peripheral thermoreceptors. All of these influences may be modified by descending motor signals (sometimes called central command) called forth in volitional exercise. In the end, we are left with one of the great unsolved problems in cardiovascular physiology: What are the signals that provide such close matching between oxygen consumption and overall cardiovascular responses?

Ann. Rev. Physiol. 1983. 45:139–53

SYMPATHETIC NERVOUS ACTIVITY DURING EXERCISE

Niels Juel Christensen

Department of Internal Medicine and Endocrinology, Herlev Hospital, 2730 Herlev, Denmark

Henrik Galbo

Department of Medical Physiology B, Panum Institute, University of Copenhagen, Denmark

INTRODUCTION

The sympathetic nervous system controls cardiovascular responses during postural changes and exercise. In addition, norepinephrine and epinephrine have effects on metabolism and hormone secretion that are important during exercise. Norepinephrine, epinephrine and dopamine also function as neurotransmitters within the central nervous system. This review is concerned specifically with sympathetic nervous activity during exercise. After a brief summary of the methods of determining sympathetic nervous activity, we discuss its significance in cardiovascular control, fuel mobilization, and hormone secretion during exercise. We next consider some physiological factors that modify sympathetic nervous activity during exercise. Finally, we emphasize the importance of regulatory mechanisms by noting the changes in sympathetic nervous activity seen in a few pathophysiological conditions.

METHODS

Classically, the function of the sympathetic nervous system has been evaluated indirectly by measuring changes in physiological variables (blood flow, blood pressure, vascular resistance) considered to be controlled by sympathetic activity. A more direct approach is now available. It is now possible to measure norepinephrine and epinephrine concentrations. New radioen-

0066-4278/83/0315-0139$02.00

139

zymatic techniques permit precise measurements in small volumes of plasma (43). Norepinephrine in human plasma is derived from the sympathetic nerve endings. Norepinephrine leaks from nerve terminals into plasma where its concentration reflects its neurotransmitter function (13, 17, 50). In the resting state the plasma norepinephrine concentration is correlated to the number of impulses in the sympathetic nerves to muscle (81). Norepinephrine is rapidly removed from the circulation, its plasma clearance in adult man being approximately 1.5 liter min^{-1} (14).

Sympathetic nervous activity in internal organs may be studied by measuring the release of norepinephrine from these organs into the veins that selectively drain them—e.g. the coronary sinus, renal veins, etc (53, 93). However, to obtain a correct value of individual organ release of norepinephrine the arteriovenous difference has to be corrected for the extraction of norepinephrine across the organ (14, 30, 33).

In animal experiments it is also possible to study the turnover of norepinephrine in single organs: After isotopically labeled norepinephrine is taken up by the organ's nerve terminals or after norepinephrine synthesis is blocked, the disappearance of isotopic label and the decrease in tissue concentration of norepinephrine, respectively, is followed to derive a rate of turnover.

The most direct approach to measuring changes in sympathetic nervous activity is to record impulses within nerve fibers. This procedure has seen longstanding use in anesthetized animals. Recent developments have made it possible to record nerve impulses in superficial sympathetic nerves to skin and muscles in conscious and active human subjects (80).

The function of catecholamines cannot be understood without knowledge of the types of adrenoceptors on the surface of their target cells (alpha- and beta-adrenoceptors and various subtypes). The type and significance of receptors may be studied using various adrenergic antagonists or agonists. The effects of sympathoadrenal activity are not only dependent on the amounts of norepinephrine and epinephrine released, but are also determined by the responsiveness of the tissues to catecholamines. Responsiveness may be altered during various physiological and especially pathophysiological states by changes in number or affinity of receptors. These variables may be examined by radioligand binding techniques (38).

SYMPATHETIC NERVOUS ACTIVITY AND CARDIOVASCULAR CONTROL

The increase in blood flow and oxygen delivery to working muscles is caused by an increase and redistribution of cardiac output. It is well accepted that in humans an increased sympathetic nervous activity is responsible for the redistribution of blood flow away from the splanchnic area, the kidneys, and resting skeletal muscles to the working muscles. The adjustments are proportional to the relative work load (i.e. the fraction of maximal oxygen uptake required during exercise) (65). The skin is also a target of sympathetic vasoconstrictor activity, this activity competing with vasodilator mechanisms activated by the rise in body temperature accompanying exercise (66).

The regulation of cardiac output during exercise is complex. The increase in cardiac output is caused by tachycardia operating in concert with an increased myocardial contractility brought about by the greater sympathetic activity, and also by the Frank-Starling mechanism (9, 57, 82). The initial rise in heart rate is due to withdrawal of vagal tone; thereafter, increments are attributed to an increase in activity to cardiac sympathetic nerves. It is well accepted that beta-adrenergic blockade reduces both the increase in heart rate during exercise and the maximal oxygen uptake. However, because of compensatory increases in both the extraction of oxygen from the blood and in stroke volume, maximal oxygen uptake approached normal values during long-term beta-adrenergic blockade (5, 58, 77).

Plasma concentrations of both norepinephrine and epinephrine increase with the intensity and duration of dynamic exercise (15). During maximal dynamic exercise in normal young subjects, plasma norepinephrine may increase from 1.40 nmol liter^{-1} to 20 nmol liter^{-1} while epinephrine increases from 0.25 to 2 nmol liter^{-1}. These increments are probably almost entirely due to an increased release of catecholamines rather than reduced rates of tissue uptake. Present evidence, though limited and indirect, suggests that plasma clearance of norepinephrine is not altered to any major extent during exercise (29). Approximately 30 nmol min^{-1} of norepinephrine have to be delivered to the circulation to maintain plasma norepinephrine at 20 nmol liter^{-1} (14). In the heart there is a net uptake of epinephrine and a net release of norepinephrine (30). However, during exercise the total amounts of norepinephrine released from the heart and especially from the kidneys are relatively small. Accordingly, the heart is not a major source of norepinephrine (30, 48). The splanchnic area always has a net uptake of norepinephrine. In humans the adrenal medulla is unlikely to be a major source of norepinephrine during exercise. In resting humans the ratio of norepinephrine to epinephrine in the left renal vein is small. Furthermore, during exercise plasma norepinephrine remained unchanged when plasma epinephrine was depressed by glucose (20). In species other than humans a larger proportion of circulating norepinephrine may be derived from the adrenal medulla during exercise (56).

In a neutral thermal environment the only tissue likely to be a major source of plasma norepinephrine during exercise is muscle tissue. Although the peripheral arteriovenous difference for norepinephrine is small both at

rest and during exercise (79), the finding that upper thoracic sympathectomy lowers the norepinephrine concentration in forearm venous blood
shows that a substantial amount of norepinephrine is added to the blood in
peripheral tissues (51). Because plasma norepinephrine concentrations are
high during heavy work involving large muscle groups, norepinephrine
release during heavy exercise can hardly be confined to resting muscles.
Rather, it is likely that there is a uniform increase in sympathetic nervous
activity to many tissues and that during heavy work most of the circulating
norepinephrine is derived from the large working muscle mass. Probably,
in working muscles there is a competition between sympathetic nervous
activity and local vasodilating metabolites. Evidence from studies in both
animals and humans indicates that sympathetic nervous activity may influence blood flow to working muscles (73, 86). In less active muscles sympathetic nervous activity may inhibit the increase in blood flow during as well
as after work. However, in the most active muscles the vasoconstricting
effect is probably completely overridden by vasodilator metabolites. These
hypotheses should be further investigated, especially during exercise involving large muscle groups and at loads eliciting high levels of sympathetic
nervous activity.

   During isometric exercise only small increments in plasma norepinephrine are found (83, 84). Nevertheless, arterial blood pressure rises considerably owing to a rise in cardiac output mediated by both a decrease in
parasympathetic tone and an increase in sympathetic activity. The peripheral vascular resistance is not normally increased by isometric exercise. Still,
arterial blood pressure does increase markedly in subjects with a limited
cardiac reserve, but in these subjects the increase is caused by a rise in
peripheral resistance (70).

   It has been suggested that the observed differences in hemodynamics and
norepinephrine release seen during dynamic as opposed to isometric exercise may stem from the involvement of different muscle masses in these two
types of exercise (3). The muscle mass utilized in isometric exercise is
usually much smaller than that involved in dynamic exercise. However,
relative to oxygen uptake the rise in blood pressure is much larger during
isometric compared to dynamic exercise (1). Differences in muscle mass
might explain some of the differences in response to the two types of
exercise, but not all of them. Neither is the difference in norepinephrine
responses fully explained. One possibility is that during isometric exercise
sympathetic nervous activity is increased predominantly in the heart and
viscera. If so, only a small rise in arterial norepinephrine concentration can
be expected.

   Interestingly, the rise in plasma epinephrine is larger relative to that of
norepinephrine during isometric exercise than during dynamic exercise
(83). This observation has been confirmed in our laboratories (unpublished

results) and is in agreement with the above-mentioned hypothesis that during isometric exercise sympathetic nervous activity is increased in visceral organs rather than in muscle.

Reflex and central mechanisms involved in the integrative control of the cardiovascular system during exercise have recently been summarized (67, 70) and are covered in more detail in Mitchell's review in this volume. Only a few comments concerning the increases in norepinephrine secretion during exercise are given here. The still unanswered question concerns what signals might elicit the increase in sympathetic nervous activity during exercise. Circulatory adjustments to exercise are generally thought to be governed by (*a*) central command and (*b*) chemical stimuli within the working muscle that increase local impulse traffic in afferent nerves to autonomic nerve centers (67, 68). During exercise the baroreceptor reflex is fully operative in the control of blood pressure but its operating point is reset to higher levels (46). It is not known whether central command, reflexes from working skeletal muscle, or baroreflexes function separately, together synergistically, or not at all in stimulating the rise in sympathetic nervous activity during exercise.

In normal subjects as well as in patients with ischemic heart disease, plasma norepinephrine concentration during dynamic exercise is closely correlated to pulmonary arterial oxygen saturation, which may be an index of the aerobic metabolic state in the working muscles (31, 34). Moreover, in normal subjects the increase in plasma norepinephrine during dynamic exercise is attenuated when 100% O_2 is inspired instead of atmospheric air (34). Also, increments in heart rate and plasma epinephrine are reduced during 100% O_2 breathing. Since O_2 breathing only increases the blood concentration of dissolved O_2 and not that of chemically bound O_2 the increase in O_2 delivery to the working muscles will be small. It should be noted, however, that the effect of hyperoxia on the norepinephrine response to heavy exercise may be marked, the reduction being around 25%. These findings suggest that tissue PO_2 or some closely related factor is important for the regulation of norepinephrine release during moderate to heavy dynamic exercise. The mechanism is not known. However, mechanisms not associated with tissue PO_2 levels are undoubtedly involved in the control of norepinephrine release during exercise. Recently, the interplay between central command and intramuscular PO_2 has been discussed (67).

INFLUENCE OF SYMPATHOADRENAL ACTIVITY ON HORMONE SECRETION AND SUBSTRATE TURNOVER

Several lines of evidence suggest that sympathoadrenal activity plays a major role in mobilization of metabolic substrate during exercise. These events provide further evidence that sympathetic nervous activity is increased in proportion to the severity of exercise. In humans, mobilization of fuel depots is probably caused by the direct effects of increased sympathetic nervous activity and its inhibitory influence on insulin release. In accordance with the view that the exercise-induced decrease in insulin release is due to alpha-adrenergic activity, the plasma insulin concentration varies inversely with sympathetic activity. Insulin release decreases with increasing intensity (4, 22, 42) and duration (23, 24, 25) of exercise; the decrease is more pronounced during hypoxia than during normoxia (74), and less pronounced in trained than in untrained subjects (4, 27). Furthermore, insulin concentrations (and release) during exercise are higher after alpha-adrenergic blockade than in controls (21, 42).

In humans the adrenergic activity inhibiting insulin release is probably exerted by sympathetic nerves to the pancreas rather than by epinephrine. This is so since during exercise a decrease in insulin concentrations may be observed when norepinephrine but not epinephrine levels are elevated (23). Furthermore, variations in the concentrations of endogenous epinephrine induced experimentally during exercise are not accompanied by variations in insulin levels (24). Finally, during exercise similar decreases in insulin concentrations are found in adrenalectomized and normal humans (42) whereas insulin levels do not decrease in patients with insulinomas, tumors containing no adrenergic nerve fibers (41). In the rat both sympathetic nerves and epinephrine from the adrenal medulla may contribute to alpha-adrenergic beta-cell inhibition in exercise (59, 60, 64).

In rats the exercise-induced increase in plasma glucagon concentration may be due mainly to increased sympathoadrenal activity (19, 47, 59, 60, 64, 87). In dogs the increase in plasma glucagon during exercise is abolished after selective pancreatic nerve section (28). Also compatible with sympathetic stimulation is the finding that the exercise-induced increase in glucagon concentration is smaller in trained than in untrained rats (27, 90), dogs, and humans (4, 89). In humans, however, it has not been possible to document a major role of sympathoadrenal activity for glucagon secretion in response to exercise (19).

Increased sympathoadrenal activity is probably the major determinant promoting an increase in lipolysis in adipose tissue during exercise. Like sympathoadrenal activity, lipolysis is directly related to the intensity and duration of exercise, is enhanced during hypoxia, and is inversely related both to the plasma glucose concentration existing during exercise and to the insulin concentration existing prior to exercise (19). Furthermore, during exercise lipolysis increases in pancreatectomized, hypophysectomized animals that are probably relying almost entirely on sympathoadrenal activation of lipolysis (54). Destruction of the ventromedial region of the hypothalamus, which may influence efferent sympathetic neuronal activity, is followed by a reduction in the exercise-induced increases in plasma FFA and glycerol concentrations (52). Furthermore, it has been shown that during exercise FFA concentrations in plasma are lower in adrenodemedullated rats (69), chemically sympathectomized rats (69), and immunosympathectomized rats (47) than in controls.

Probably the effect of catecholamines is in part due to direct stimulation of beta-adrenergic receptors on fat cells. Compatible with this view, beta-adrenergic blockade diminishes exercise-induced increases in rate of fat combustion (25), turnover rate of plasma FFA (40), and plasma concentrations of FFA and glycerol (25, 40, 72). The relative importance of circulating catecholamines and sympathetic nervous activity for direct enhancement of lipolysis in exercise is not known, but regional differences may exist (19). Also, the above-mentioned alpha-adrenergic inhibition of insulin secretion probably promotes lipolysis since lipolysis varies inversely with artificially induced acute changes in insulin levels during exercise (19). Finally, changes in sympathoadrenal activity may influence FFA release in exercise by changing adipose tissue resistance and, in turn, perfusion. However, it has recently been argued that during exercise vasodilation in subcutaneous adipose tissue is not an effect of stimulation of vascular beta-receptors but rather is secondary to lipolysis (10).

A definitive understanding of the role of catecholamines for hepatic glucose production in exercise is lacking. Like sympathoadrenal activity, glucose production increases within a few minutes after start of exercise and varies directly with work load (19). In experiments in which rats received chemical sympathectomy and adrenodemedullation, the adrenal medullary hormones may stimulate hepatic glycogenolysis, an effect not entirely secondary to increased secretion of glucagon (19, 59, 60). Evidence has also been presented that these hormones enhance gluconeogenesis in exercising rats (6). Experiments with selective destruction of the sympathetic nerves to the liver have not yet been carried out. The alpha-adrenergic inhibition of insulin secretion probably facilitates glucose production since this varies inversely with artificially induced acute changes in plasma insulin levels during exercise (19). Possibly the sympathetically mediated reduction of hepatic blood flow in humans and, in turn, the reduction in hepatic oxygen tension promotes hepatic glycogenolysis.

Sympathoadrenal activity also influences substrate mobilization in exercising muscle. Thus, beta-adrenergic blockade inhibits exercise-induced depletion of triglyceride stores in rat skeletal muscle (72) (and in heart), and muscular protein depletion may be enhanced after adrenodemedullation (19). Moreover, extensive studies where exogenous epinephrine was substituted after various means of surgical and pharmacological destruction within the sympathoadrenal system were employed have indicated that in the rat epinephrine is essential for glycogenolysis in exercising muscle, whereas noradrenergic nervous activity is of minor importance (59, 60, 64). It has been concluded from experiments with the isolated, perfused rat hindquarter that muscle contractions per se stimulate glycogenolysis only for a brief period, and that a direct effect of epinephrine on muscle is needed for continued glycogenolysis during exercise (62). The latter effect involves beta-adrenergic activation of glycogen phosphorylase and inactivation of synthase, and possibly also some alpha-adrenergic mechanisms (61). In accordance with these in vitro findings, in vivo cAMP may increase in skeletal muscle during exercise (19). Furthermore, breakdown of glycogen within the working muscle and release of lactate may be reduced by beta-adrenergic blockade (19, 25, 40). Besides its acute and direct effects, sympathoadrenal activity may promote glycogen depletion in exercising muscle by depressing insulin secretion since insulin enhances glycogen synthase activity.

FACTORS INFLUENCING THE CATECHOLAMINE RESPONSE TO EXERCISE IN HEALTHY INDIVIDUALS

Plasma concentrations of norepinephrine and epinephrine have been shown to increase during exercise in several mammalian species including small rodents (19). At identical relative work loads (relative to $\dot{V}O_2$) catecholamine levels have been found to be similar in men and women (44, 75). The catecholamine responses are higher relative to the increases in $\dot{V}O_2$ during work with small muscle groups than they are when work is done with large muscle groups (3). Also, catecholamine concentration may increase with age (94). During exercise plasma norepinephrine concentration is increased if receptors sensing heat or cold are stimulated (2, 26). Higher norepinephrine levels are present during exercise in the upright than in the supine position (19) and in sodium depleted as compared to sodium replete conditions (18). These latter observations suggest that cardiovascular pressure receptors may also modulate sympathoadrenal activity in exercise. Accordingly, the decrease in blood volume seen during fasting may explain in part the exaggerated catecholamine response to exercise in this condition (22). Catecholamine responses to exercise are also increased after intake of fat diet (24) and in poorly controlled diabetes, and it has been proposed that the low insulin availability in these states as well as in fasting is of importance for the catecholamine responses.

Glucose sensitive mechanisms are involved in regulation of epinephrine secretion since epinephrine levels vary inversely with artificial changes in glucose levels during exercise (24, 25). Thus a decrease in plasma glucose concentration may constitute an error signal for central sympathetic neuron pools involved in the regulation of metabolism during exercise. Finally, physical training quickly reduces the catecholamine response to exercise (27, 55, 88, 89, 90). This effect is seen when either the trained or untrained muscles are active (79). In this context it should be noted that epinephrine-stimulated lipolysis (71) as well as catecholamine-induced changes in the inotropic (92) and chronotropic (32) state of the heart may be enhanced after physical training. Conflicting results have been presented regarding the effect of training on norepinephrine-induced vasoconstriction (85).

PATHOPHYSIOLOGY IN EXERCISE

Heart Failure

It is generally accepted that in both the basal state and during exercise plasma norepinephrine concentrations are increased in patients with heart failure (8). At identical work loads peripheral resistance is increased more in patients with heart failure than in normal subjects owing to both an increased sympathetic nervous activity and an increased stiffness of the vascular wall (49). During exercise, plasma norepinephrine concentration in this group of patients correlates strongly with pulmonary arterial oxygen saturation and with the degree of left ventricular failure (30, 78). The former relationship is not much different from that observed in normal subjects during exercise (34). During exercise the failing heart probably contributes less to the rise in arterial norepinephrine concentration than the normal heart (30, 48). Thus in contrast to what is normally observed, the increase in sympathetic nervous outflow to peripheral organs in patients with heart failure may be relatively greater than the increase to the heart during exercise. Administration of beta-adrenergic receptor antagonists to these patients may result in a further decline in cardiac function, whereas administration of alpha-adrenergic blocking agents or vasodilators may improve cardiac output during exercise (11).

Diabetes Mellitus

In poorly controlled insulin-dependent diabetics, exercise-induced increments in plasma concentrations of norepinephrine and epinephrine are exaggerated, and consequently so are the increases in heart rate and plasma concentrations of free fatty acids and glucose (12, 76). In contrast, hypoglycemia may develop during or after exercise in better-controlled diabetics. The explanation for this observation is that serum insulin is not suppressed during exercise in diabetes. Accordingly, hepatic glucose production may not increase adequately (63, 91).

In diabetics with autonomic neuropathy, exercise performance is severely impaired. In these patients the resting heart rate is elevated and the initial rise in heart rate at low work loads is less than in diabetics without neuropathy, suggesting a vagal defect (35, 39). Furthermore, because of deficient adrenergic activity, the maximal tolerable work load, the maximal heart rate, and the maximal oxygen uptake as well as the concentrations of catecholamines in plasma during maximal work load are lower than in nonneuropathic diabetic controls (35, 36). Interestingly, when neuropathy is present, the relationship between heart rate and relative work load is identical to that found in normal subjects during combined parasympathetic and beta-adrenergic receptor blockade (35). In diabetics with severe neuropathy, arterial blood pressure actually decreases during exercise (37), a finding in accordance with previous observations in nondiabetic patients with autonomic neuropathy.

Hyperkalemic Familial Periodic Paralysis

In patients with this disease, attacks of paralysis associated with pronounced hyperkalemia occur after exercise. These attacks may be treated or prevented by administration of beta-adrenergic agonists (7, 16). Similarly, in normal subjects beta-adrenergic receptor blockade augments the rise in plasma potassium during short-term exercise (45). Thus beta-adrenergic activity significantly influences exercise-induced changes in plasma potassium.

SUMMARY

At onset of dynamic exercise, central command and afferent impulses from working muscles set a basic pattern of sympathoadrenal activity according to the relative work load. In turn this activity is of major significance for cardiovascular, hormonal, and metabolic responses, and, furthermore, influences thermoregulation, water and electrolyte homeostasis, and muscular performance. During continued exercise, impulses from multiple receptors feed back on sympathetic centers, error signals arising from changes in intravascular pressures, plasma glucose concentration, tissue oxygen tension, body temperatures, and possibly in mechanical performance and extracellular potassium concentration. However, far from fully explored is the exercise-induced basic pattern of impulse distribution within the sympathoadrenal system, and this pattern's dependency on type of exercise—e.g. dynamic versus static, and on the state of the organism—e.g. concerning tissue sensitivity to catecholamines or presence of disease. Much research is needed to clarify the interplay between the various central and peripheral afferent inputs both in the control of sympathoadrenal activity in acute exercise and in the adaptation of this activity to various conditions or procedures (e.g. training).

ACKNOWLEDGMENTS

The authors appreciate the secretarial assistance of Mrs. Ragna Riis. Personal work quoted in the text was supported by the Danish Medical and Sports Research Councils, the Danish Hospital Foundation for Medical Research, Region of Copenhagen, the Faroe Islands and Greenland, and the P. Carl Petersen and Novo Research Foundations.

Literature Cited

1. Asmussen, E. 1981. Similarities and dissimilarities between static and dynamic exercise. *Circ. Res.* 48:(Suppl. I) 3–10
2. Bergh, U., Hartley, H., Landsberg, L., Ekblom, B. 1979. Plasma norepinephrine concentration during submaximal and maximal exercise at lowered skin and core temperatures. *Acta Physiol. Scand.* 106:383–84
3. Blomqvist, C. G., Lewis, S. F., Taylor, W. F., Graham, R. M. 1981. Similarity of the hemodynamic responses to static and dynamic exercise of small muscle groups. *Circ. Res.* 48: (Suppl. I) 87–92
4. Bloom, S. R., Johnson, R. H., Park, D. M., Rennie, M. J., Sulaiman, W. R. 1976. Differences in the metabolic and hormonal response to exercise between racing cyclists and untrained individuals. *J. Physiol.* 258:1–18
5. Bonelli, J., Waldhäusl, W., Magometschnigg, D., Schwarzmeier, J., Korn, A., Hitzenberger, G. 1977. Effect of exercise and of prolonged oral administration of propranolol on haemodynamic variables, plasma renin concentration, plasma aldosterone and c-AMP. *Eur. J. Clin. Invest.* 7:337–43
6. Born, C. K., Spratto, G. R. 1975. The role of the adrenal medulla in the control of gluconeogenesis in the rat. *Res. Commun. Chem. Pathol. Pharmacol.* 12:481–98
7. Bowman, W. C. 1981. Effects of adrenergic activators and inhibitors on the skeletal muscles. In *Handbook of Experimental Pharmacology*, ed. L. Szekeres, 54, II:47–128. Berlin: Springer
8. Braunwald, E. 1980. Alterations in the function of the adrenergic nervous system. In *Heart Disease. A Textbook of Cardiovascular Medicine*, ed. E. Braunwald, 1: 464–71. Philadelphia: W. B. Saunders
9. Braunwald, E., Sonneblick, E. H., Ross, J. Jr., Glick, G., Epstein, S. E. 1967. An analysis of the cardiac response to exercise. *Circ. Res.* 20 & 21: (Suppl. 1) 44–58
10. Bülow, J. 1981. Human adipose tissue blood flow during prolonged exercise. III. Effect of beta-adrenergic blockade, nicotinic acid and glucose infusion. *Scand. J. Clin. Lab. Invest.* 41:415–24
11. Chatterjee, K., Rubin, S. A., Ports, T. A., Parmley, W. W. 1981. Influence of oral prazosin therapy on exercise hemodynamics in patients with severe chronic heart failure. *Am. J. Med.* 71:140–46
12. Christensen, N. J. 1974. Plasma norepinephrine and epinephrine in untreated diabetics, during fasting and after insulin administration. *Diabetes* 23:1–8
13. Christensen, N. J. 1979. Plasma noradrenaline and adrenaline measured by isotope-derivative assay. A review with special reference to diabetes mellitus. *Dan. Med. Bull.* 26:17–36
14. Christensen, N. J. 1983. Sympathetic nervous activity and age. Editorial. *Eur. J. Clin. Invest.* 12:91–92
15. Christensen, N. J., Galbo, H., Hansen, J. F., Hesse, B., Richter, E. A., Trap-Jensen, J. 1979. Catecholamines and exercise. *Diabetes* 28: (Suppl. 1) 58–62
16. Clausen, T. 1981. The hormonal regulation of active electrogenic Na^+-K^+ transport in skeletal muscle. In *Physiology of Non-Excitable Cells*, ed. J. Salanki, 3:209–20. Budapest: Pergamon and Akademiai Kiado
17. Cryer, P. E. 1976. Isotope-derivative measurements of plasma norepinephrine and epinephrine in man. *Diabetes* 25:1071–85
18. Fagard, R., Amery, A., Reybrouck, T., Lijnen, P., Billiet, L., Bogaert, M., Moerman, E., Schaepdryver, A. De. 1978. Effects of angiotensin antagonism at rest and during exercise in sodium-deplete man. *J. Appl. Physiol.* 45:403–7
19. Galbo, H. 1983. *Hormonal and Metabolic Adaptation to Exercise.* Stuttgart: Georg Thieme. In press
20. Galbo, H., Christensen, N. J., Holst, J. J. 1977. Glucose-induced decrease in

glucagon and epinephrine responses to exercise in man. *J. Appl. Physiol.* 42:525–30

21. Galbo, H., Christensen, N. J., Holst, J. J. 1977. Catecholamines and pancreatic hormones during autonomic blockade in exercising man. *Acta Physiol. Scand.* 101:428–37

22. Galbo, H., Christensen, N. J., Mikines, K. J., Sonne, B., Hilsted, J., Hagen, C., Fahrenkrug, J. 1981. The effect of fasting on the hormonal response to graded exercise. *J. Clin. Endocrinol. Metab.* 52:1106–12

23. Galbo, H., Holst, J. J., Christensen, N. J. 1975. Glucagon and plasma catecholamine responses to graded and prolonged exercise in man. *J. Appl. Physiol.* 38:70–76

24. Galbo, H., Holst, J. J., Christensen, N. J. 1979. The effect of different diets and of insulin on the hormonal response to prolonged exercise. *Acta Physiol. Scand.* 107:19–32

25. Galbo, H., Holst, J. J., Christensen, N. J., Hilsted, J. 1976. Glucagon and plasma catecholamines during beta-receptor blockade in exercising man. *J. Appl. Physiol.* 40:855–63

26. Galbo, H., Houston, M. E., Christensen, N. J., Holst, J. J., Nielsen, B., Nygaard, E., Suzuki, J. 1979. The effect of water temperature on the hormonal response to prolonged swimming. *Acta Physiol. Scand.* 105:326–37

27. Galbo, H., Richter, E. A., Holst, J. J., Christensen, N. J. 1977. Diminished hormonal responses to exercise in trained rats. *J. Appl. Physiol.* 43:953–58

28. Girardier, L., Seydoux, J., Berger, M., Veicsteinas, A. 1978. Selective pancreatic nerve section. An investigation of neural control of glucagon release in the conscious unrestrained dog. *J. Physiol. Paris* 74:731–35

29. Hagberg, J. M., Hickson, R. C., McLane. J. A., Ehsani, A. A., Winder, W. W. 1979. Disappearance of norepinephrine from the circulation following strenuous exercise. *J. Appl. Physiol.* 47:1311–14

30. Hansen, J. F., Christensen, N. J., Hesse, B. 1978. Determinants of coronary sinus noradrenaline in patients with ischaemic heart disease: Coronary sinus catecholamine concentration in relation to arterial catecholamine concentration, pulmonary artery oxygen saturation and left ventricular end-diastolic pressure. *Cardiovasc. Res.* 12:415–21

31. Hansen, J. F., Hesse, B., Christensen, N. J. 1978. Enhanced sympathetic nervous activity after intravenous propranolol in ischaemic heart disease: plasma noradrenaline splanchnic blood flow and mixed venous oxygen saturation at rest and during exercise. *Eur. J. Clin. Invest.* 8:31–36

32. Harri, M. N. E., Narvola, I. 1979. Physical training under the influence of beta blockade in rats: Effects on adrenergic responses. *Eur. J. Appl. Physiol.* 41:199–210

33. Henriksen, J. H., Christensen, N. J., Kok-Jensen, A., Christiansen, I. 1980. Increased plasma noradrenaline concentration in patients with chronic obstructive lung disease: relation to haemodynamics and blood gases. *Scand. J. Clin. Lab. Invest.* 40:419–27

34. Hesse, B., Kanstrup, I.-L., Christensen, N. J., Ingemann-Hansen, T., Hansen, J. F., Halkjaer-Kristensen, J., Petersen, F. B. 1981. Reduced norepinephrine response to dynamic exercise in human subjects during O_2 breathing. *J. Appl. Physiol.* 51:176–78

35. Hilsted, J., Galbo, H., Christensen, N. J. 1979. Impaired cardiovascular responses to graded exercise in diabetic autonomic neuropathy. *Diabetes* 28:313–19

36. Hilsted, J., Galbo, H., Christensen, N. J. 1980. Impaired responses of catecholamines, growth hormone, and cortisol to graded exercise in diabetic autonomic neuropathy. *Diabetes* 29:257–62

37. Hilsted, J., Galbo, H., Christensen, N. J., Parving, H- H., Benn, J. 1982. Hemodynamic changes during graded exercise in patients with diabetic autonomic neuropathy. *Diabetologia* 22:318–23

38. Hoffman, B. B., Lefkowitz, R. J. 1980. Radioligand binding studies of adrenergic receptors: New insights into molecular and physiological regulation. *Ann. Rev. Pharmacol. Toxicol.* 20:581–608

39. Hume, L., Ewing, D. J., Campbell, I. W., Reuben, S. R., Clarke, B. F. 1979. Heart-rate response to sustained hand grip: comparison of the effects of cardiac autonomic blockade and diabetic autonomic neuropathy. *Clin. Sci.* 56:287–91

40. Issekutz, B. 1978. Role of beta-adrenergic receptors in mobilization of energy sources in exercising dogs. *J. Appl. Physiol.* 44:869–76

41. Järhult, J., Ericsson, M., Holst, J., Ingemansson, S. 1981. Lack of suppression of insulin secretion by exercise in pa-

tients with insulinoma. *Clin. Endocrinol.* 15:391–94

42. Järhult, J., Holst, J. 1979. The role of the adrenergic innervation to the pancreatic islets in the control of insulin release during exercise in man. *Pflügers Arch.* 383:41–45

43. Johnson, G. A., Kupiecki, R. M., Baker, C. A. 1980. Single isotope derivative (radioenzymatic) methods in the measurement of catecholamines. *Metabolism* 29:1106–13

44. Lehmann, M., Keul, J., Berg, A., Stippig, S. 1981. Plasmacatecholamine und metabolische Veränderungen bei Frauen während Laufbandergometrie. *Eur. J. Appl. Physiol.* 46:305–15

45. Lim, M., Linton, R. A. F., Wolff, C. B., Band, D. M. 1981. Propranolol, exercise, and arterial plasma potassium. *Lancet* 2:591

46. Ludbrook, J., Faris, I. B., Iannos, J., Jamieson, G. G., Russell, W. J. 1978. Lack of effect of isometric handgrip exercise on the responses of the carotid sinus baroreceptor reflex in man. *Clin. Sci.* 55:189–94

47. Luyckx, A. S., Dresse, A., Cession-Fossion, A., Lefebvre, P. J. 1975. Catecholamines and exercise-induced glucagon and fatty acid mobilization in the rat. *Am. J. Physiol.* 229:376–83

48. Manhem, P., Lecerof, H., Hökfelt, B. 1978. Plasma catecholamine levels in the coronary sinus, the left renal vein and peripheral vessels in healthy males at rest and during exercise. *Acta Physiol. Scand.* 104:364–69

49. Mason, D. T., Zelis, R., Longhurst, J., Lee, G. 1977. Cardiocirculatory responses to muscular exercise in congestive heart failure. *Progr. Cardiovasc. Dis.* 19:475–89

50. Mathias, C. J., Christensen, N. J., Corbett, J. L., Frankel, H. L., Spalding, J. M. K. 1976. Plasma catecholamines during paroxysmal neurogenic hypertension in quadriplegic man. *Circ. Res.* 39:204–8

51. Nielsen, S. L., Christensen, N. J., Olsen, N., Lassen, N. A. 1980. Raynaud's phenomenon: Peripheral catecholamine concentration and effect of sympathectomy. *Acta Chir. Scand.* 502:57–62

52. Nishizawa, Y., Bray, G. A. 1978. Ventromedial hypothalamic lesions and the mobilization of fatty acids. *J. Clin. Invest.* 61:714–21

53. Oliver, J. A., Pinto, J., Sciacca, R. R., Cannon, P. J. 1980. Basal norepinephrine overflow into the renal vein; effect

of renal nerve stimulation. *Am. J. Physiol.* 239:F371–77

54. Paul, P. 1971. Uptake and oxidation of substrates in the intact animal during exercise. In *Muscle Metabolism During Exercise*, ed. B. Pernow, B. Saltin, pp. 225–47. NY: Plenum

55. Péronnet, F., Cléroux, J., Perrault, H., Cousineau, D., de Champlain, J., Nadeau, R. 1981. Plasma norepinephrine response to exercise before and after training in humans. *J. Appl. Physiol.* 51:812–15

56. Péronnet, F., Nadeau, R. A., de Champlain, J., Magrassi, P., Chatrand, C. 1981. Exercise plasma catecholamines in dogs: role of adrenals and cardiac nerve endings. *Am. J. Physiol.* 241: H243–47

57. Poliner, L. R., Dehmer, G. J., Lewis, S. E., Parkey, R. W., Blomqvist, C. G., Willerson, J. T. 1980. Left ventricular performance in normal subjects: A comparison of the responses to exericse in the upright and supine positions. *Circulation* 62:528–34

58. Reybrouck, T., Amery, A., Billiet, L. 1977. Hemodynamic response to graded exercise after chronic beta-adrenergic blockade. *J. Appl. Physiol.* 42:133–38

59. Richter, E. A., Galbo, H., Christensen, N. J. 1981. Control of the exercise-induced muscular glycogenolysis by adrenal medullary hormones in rats. *J. Appl. Physiol.* 50:21–26

60. Richter, E. A., Galbo, H., Sonne, B., Holst, J. J., Christensen, N. J. 1980. Adrenal medullary control of muscular and hepatic glycogenolysis and of pancreatic hormonal secretion in exercising rats. *Acta Physiol. Scand.* 108: 235–42

61. Richter, E. A., Ruderman, N. B., Galbo, H. 1983. Alpha and beta adrenergic effects on metabolism in contracting, perfused muscle. *Acta Physiol. Scand.* In press

62. Richter, E. A., Ruderman, N. B., Gavras, H., Belur, E. R., Galbo, H. 1982. Muscle glycogenolysis during exercise: Dual control by epinephrine and contractions. *Am. J. Physiol.* 242:E25–32

63. Richter, E. A., Ruderman, N. B., Schneider, S. H. 1981. Diabetes and exercise. *Am. J. Med.* 70:201–9

64. Richter, E. A., Sonne, B., Christensen, N. J., Galbo, H. 1981. The role of epinephrine for muscular glycogenolysis and pancreatic hormonal secretion in running rats. *Am. J. Physiol.* 240:E526–32

65. Rowell, L. B. 1974. Human cardiovascular adjustments to exercise and thermal stress. *Physiol. Rev.* 54:75–159
66. Rowell, L. B. 1977. Competition between skin and muscle for blood flow during exercise. In *Problems with Temperature Regulation During Exercise,* ed. E. R. Nadel, pp. 49–76. NY: Academic
67. Rowell, L. B. 1980. What signals govern the cardiovascular responses to exercise? *Med. Sci. Sports Exer.* 12:307–15
68. Rowell, L. B., Freund, P. R., Hobbs, S. F. 1981. Cardiovascular responses to muscle ischemia in humans. *Circ. Res.* 48: (Suppl. 1) 37–47
69. Sembrowich, W. L., Ianuzzo, C. D., Saubert, C. W., Shepherd, R. E., Gollnick, P. D. 1974. Substrate mobilization during prolonged exercise in 6-hydroxydopamine treated rats. *Pflügers Arch.* 349:57–62
70. Shepherd, J. T., Blomqvist, C. G., Lind, A. R., Mitchell, J. H., Saltin, B. 1981. Static (isometric) exercise. Retrospection and introspection. *Circ. Res.* 48: (Suppl. 1) 179–88
71. Shepherd, R. E., Noble, E. G., Klug, G. A., Gollnick, P. D. 1981. Lipolysis and cAMP accumulation in adipocytes in response to physical training. *J. Appl. Physiol.* 50:143–48
72. Stankiewicz-Choroszucha, B., Gorski, J. 1978. Effect of beta-adrenergic blockade on intramuscular triglyceride mobilization during exercise. *Experientia* 34:357–58
73. Strandell, T., Shepherd, J. T. 1967. The effect in humans of increased sympathetic activity on the blood flow to active muscles. *Acta Med. Scand.* 472: (Suppl.) 146–67
74. Sutton, J. R. 1977. Effect of acute hypoxia on the hormonal response to exercise. *J. Appl. Physiol.* 42:587–92
75. Sutton, J. R., Jurkowski, J. E., Keane, P., Walker, W. H. C., Jones, N. L., Toews, C. J. 1980. Plasma catecholamine, insulin, glucose and lactate responses to exercise in relation to the menstrual cycle. *Med. Sci. Sports* 12:83–84
76. Tamborlane, W. V., Sherwin, R. S., Koivisto, V., Hendler, R., Genel, M., Felig, P. 1979. Normalization of the growth hormone and catecholamine response to exercise in juvenile-onset diabetic subjects treated with a portable insulin infusion pump. *Diabetes* 28: 785–88
77. Tesch, P. A., Kaiser, P. 1981. Effect of beta-adrenergic blockade on maximal oxygen uptake in trained males. *Acta Physiol. Scand.* 112:351–52
78. Thomas, J. A., Marks, B. H. 1978. Plasma norepinephrine in congestive heart failure. *Am. J. Cardiol.* 41:233–43
79. Trap-Jensen, J., Christensen, N. J., Clausen, J. P., Rasmussen, B., Klausen, K. 1973. Arterial noradrenaline and circulatory adjustment to strenuous exercise with trained and non-trained muscle groups. In *Physical Fitness* (Proc. Satel. Symp. XXV Int. Congr. Physiol. Sci.) Prague: Universita Karlova Press. pp. 414–18
80. Wallin, G. 1981. Neurophysiological methods. *Clin. Physiol.* 1: (Suppl. I) 8–12
81. Wallin, B. G., Sundlöf, G., Eriksson, B.-M., Dominiak, P., Grobecker, H., Lindblad, L. E. 1981. Plasma noradrenaline correlates to sympathetic muscle nerve activity in normotensive man. *Acta Physiol. Scand.* 111:69–73
82. Vatner, S. F., Pagani, M. 1976. Cardiovascular adjustments to exercise. Hemodynamics and mechanisms. *Progr. Cardiovasc. Dis.* 19-91–108
83. Watson, R. D. S., Littler, W. A., Eriksson, B-M. 1980. Changes in plasma noradrenaline and adrenaline during isometric exercise. *Clin. Exp. Pharmacol. Physiol.* 7:399–402
84. Vecht, R. J., Graham, G. W. S., Sever, P. S. 1978. Plasma noradrenaline concentrations during isometric exercise. *Brit. Heart J.* 40:1216–20
85. Wiegman, D. L., Harris, P. D., Joshua, I. G., Miller, F. N. 1981. Decreased vascular sensitivity to norepinephrine following exercise training. *J. Appl. Physiol.* 51:282–87
86. Williams, C. A., Mudd, J. G., Lind, A. R. 1981. The forearm blood flow during intermittent hand-grip isometric exercise. *Circ. Res.* 48: (Suppl. 1) 110–17
87. Winder, W. W., Boullier, J., Fell, R. D. 1979. Liver glycogenolysis during exercise without a significant increase in cAMP. *Am. J. Physiol.* 237:R147–52
88. Winder, W. W., Hagberg, J. M., Hickson, R. C., Ehsani, A. A., McLane, J. A. 1978. Time course of sympathoadrenal adaptation to endurance exercise training in man. *J. Appl. Physiol.* 45:370–74
89. Winder, W. W., Hickson, R. C., Hagberg, J. M., Ehsani, A. A., McLane, J. A. 1979. Training-induced changes in hormonal and metabolic responses to submaximal exercise. *J. Appl. Physiol.* 46:766–71
90. Winder, W. W., Holman, R. T., Garhart, S. J. 1981. Effect of endurance

training on liver cAMP response to prolonged submaximal exercise. *Am. J. Physiol.* 240:R330–34

91. Vranic, M., Berger, M. 1979. Exercise and diabetes mellitus. *Diabetes* 28:147–63

92. Wyatt, H. L., Chuck, L., Rabinowitz, B., Tyberg, J. V., Parmley, W. W. 1978. Enhanced cardiac response to catecholamines in physically trained cats. *Am. J. Physiol.* 234:H608–13

93. Yamaguchi, N., de Champlain, J., Nadeau, R. 1975. Correlation between the response of the heart to sympathetic stimulation and the release of endogenous catecholamines into the coronary sinus of the dog. *Circ. Res.* 36:662–68

94. Ziegler, M. G., Lake, C. R., Kopin, I. J. 1976. Plasma noradrenaline increases with age. *Nature* 261:333–35

Ann. Rev. Physiol. 1983. 45:155–68

REFLEX CONTROL OF BLOOD PRESSURE DURING EXERCISE

J. Ludbrook

Baker Medical Research Institute, Melbourne, Australia.

INTRODUCTION

All forms of exercise result in disturbances of the systemic blood pressure and thus of the mechanisms that tend to maintain blood pressure at a steady level. This review is concerned with the mechanisms that depend on central nervous reflexes, rather than with those that are autoregulatory or independent of central nervous control (72). Heterostatic reflexes (Table 1), which tend to create or exaggerate the blood pressure disturbances that occur during exercise, are considered briefly. Homeostatic reflexes (Table 1) are reviewed in more detail. These comprise first-order reflexes, in which disturbances of blood pressure are directly sensed; and second-order reflexes, in which some other cardiovascular variable is sensed, but which nevertheless often oppose the disturbing influence of exercise on blood pressure. Although the general properties of these homeostatic and heterostatic reflexes have been reviewed recently (24, 26, 44, 54, 69, 71, 78), the specific question of how exercise affects their operations has not been addressed for some time (9, 68, 72, 86).

BEHAVIOR OF BLOOD PRESSURE IN EXERCISE

A number of circulatory responses to exercise have been reviewed elsewhere in this volume. It suffices here to make the distinction between static exercise, in which relatively little of the body's musculature is engaged in a sustained contraction, usually for at most a few minutes; and dynamic exercise, in which a much larger proportion of the body's musculature is usually involved, and in which alternating contraction and relaxation may continue for some hours.

The cardiovascular response to static exercise in normal humans is well defined and reproducible (48, 49, 57). It consists of a rise in blood pressure,

155

0066-4278/83/0315-0155$02.00

Table 1   Reflexes that may affect blood pressure during exercise

	Heterostatic	Homeostatic
First order:	Central command Muscle afferent reflexes	Arterial baroreceptor reflexes Left ventricular reflexes
Second order:	Sympatho-sympathetic reflexes Bainbridge reflex	Atrial reflexes Other cardiopulmonary reflexes
Third order:	Thermoregulatory reflexes	

associated with a parallel rise in heart rate and cardiac output but with little or no change in systemic vascular resistance. These disturbances are caused almost entirely by the alterations in neural output to the cardiovascular effectors that result from the action of the "exercise reflex" (59), to which the stimuli are probably an admixture of central command and the afferent input from contracting muscle. The rise in blood pressure might be termed obligatory. It occurs even if neural control of the heart is impaired, as by beta-adrenoceptor blockade (57, 63, 89), or is absent, as after heart transplantation (38); and it occurs even if the function of the cardiac pump is impaired by myocardial damage (see 63) or by valvular disease (see 34). In these abnormal conditions the blood pressure rise is effected by elevation of systemic vascular resistance rather than by increase in cardiac output. Provided the exercise stimulus is not overpowering, blood pressure appears to rise asymptotically towards a new level (29, 49, 60) which is determined by the vigor of the muscle contraction and to a lesser extent by the mass of contracting muscle (60). This suggests there is a sensory mechanism that indicates when the appropriate level of blood pressure has been attained. There are two main hypotheses about such a negative feedback control mechanism. In the first, receptors (59) in the contracting muscle indicate whether the existing level of blood flow satisfies the metabolic demands of the muscle, and the blood pressure is adjusted accordingly. The evidence for this attractive explanation is regrettably indirect. It is difficult completely to arrest forearm blood flow by voluntary contraction (41), but it is likely that when handgrip is at more than about 20% of maximal the metabolic requirements of the forearm flexors are unsatisfied, if only because ever-increasing effort is necessary to maintain the same strength of contraction (29, 49). Indeed, even at 5% of maximal contraction the O_2 content of the blood draining from the forearm muscles is reduced (5) despite quadrupling of blood flow. The second hypothesis involves homeostatic reflexes that originate from arterial baroreceptors and receptors in the left ventricle. It will be considered in some detail below.

The effects of dynamic exercise on blood pressure are less predictable. The primary exercise stimuli are probably qualitatively similar to those in static exercise (12), but their effects are modified by changes in the magnitude and distribution of blood flow and blood volume. In general the initial rise of blood pressure is in proportion to the work load, but as strenuous exercise continues blood pressure tends to decline while heart rate continues to rise (9, 16, 68). Thus in dynamic exercise it is exceedingly difficult to dissect out the relative contributions of the variables, reflex and other, that determine the level of blood pressure.

HETEROSTATIC REFLEXES

The powerful first-order heterostatic reflexes (Table 1) elicited by the exercise stimulus itself are discussed elsewhere in this volume (59). The third-order thermoregulatory reflexes, which become increasingly important as strenuous exercise is prolonged, are also reviewed in this volume (16) and elsewhere (68). Two second-order heterostatic reflexes deserve special attention here.

Over the past few years a strong body of evidence has been assembled for the existence of sympatho-sympathetic cardiovascular reflexes that operate at a spinal level. Sympathetically innervated receptors have been described (19, 54) that in the heart respond to chemical or mechanical stimuli and that in the descending thoracic aorta respond to distension. The reflex effects of stimulation of these receptors have been shown in anesthetized (51, 54, 76), and more recently in conscious (55, 61), animals to be an increase in heart rate and blood pressure. It is suggested (55) that they provide a positive feedback that can amplify the effects of the exercise stimulus, though there is no direct proof of this.

Another heterostatic reflex of potential importance in exercise is the so-called Bainbridge reflex. In conscious dogs (82) and baboons (87), acute volume loading with dextran or saline solutions causes a striking tachycardia, as does distension of the veno-atrial junctions in anesthetized dogs (50). Medullated vagal afferents appear to be responsible for this latter reflex (43). Both vagal and sympathetic afferents have been implicated in the response to volume loading in dogs and cats (see 86), whereas only vagal afferents appear to be involved in baboons (87). Even in isolated mammalian hearts, stretching of the atrium causes cardioacceleration due to a mechanical effect on the sinoatrial pacemaker (18, 62). It can be argued that these several phenomena that comprise the Bainbridge reflex should contribute to the increase of heart rate and, by extension, of blood pressure, at the onset of dynamic exercise when there is an acute increase in central blood volume and a corresponding increase of pressure within the atria. However, this argument cannot be accepted without question. For instance, cardioacceleration does not accompany acute increase in central venous pressure in all species and circumstances. One potential source of variation is an interspecies difference in innervation of the atrium. For example, the canine atrium seems to be unusually well endowed with receptors innervated by medullated vagal fibers (78). Vatner & Zimpfer (87), having recently reviewed the literature, concluded that the Bainbridge reflex causes tachycardia only when the resting heart rate is low. However, another interpretation of the studies they cite (87), when considered together with those in humans (2, 35, 66, 67) and rabbits (30), is that tachycardia occurs only when hypervolemia is accompanied by hemodilution. Thus judgment must remain suspended whether the Bainbridge reflex is likely to act as a feed-forward mechanism in exercise, or whether it is likely to do so in all species. This reservation of judgment applies especially to humans, in whom ambulatory exercise merely restores central venous pressure to the level that obtains when they are recumbent (9).

HOMEOSTATIC REFLEXES

These can be divided (Table 1) into first-order or second-order depending on whether they are initiated directly by a blood pressure disturbance or tend to correct a blood pressure disturbance by sensing other functions of the circulation.

First-Order Homeostatic Reflexes

ARTERIAL BARORECEPTOR REFLEXES   The steep rise in blood pressure that occurs at the commencement of exercise (particularly static exercise) must cause the arterial baroreceptors to fire at an increased rate, yet despite this the raised blood pressure persists and is accompanied by tachycardia rather than bradycardia. This has led to suggestions that the operation of the arterial baroreceptor reflex could be modified by the exercise stimuli or their consequences.

One hypothesis is that the sensitivity of baroreflex control of blood pressure is greatly depressed by exercise, so that the reflex does not restrain the rise of blood pressure caused by the exercise stimulus. If this were true, then arterial baroreceptor denervation should have little or no effect on the behavior of blood pressure during exercise. This prediction has been tested in five independent studies on dogs that ran for 3–5 min, freely or on a treadmill. The two most recent studies (3, 58) appear to show that the carotid sinus reflex is of major importance in supporting the blood pressure in exercise, whereas the three older studies appear to show that the arterial baroreflexes play little (47) or no (53, 80) part. The origin of this discrepancy deserves examination. In the recent studies it was found that when the carotid baroreceptors, the aortic baroreceptors, and the vagally innervated cardiopulmonary receptors were all excluded, blood pressure fell dramatically from the onset of exercise (3, 58). This blood pressure fall was sustained throughout the period of exercise except, paradoxically, when the exercise was severe (58). However, when the intrathoracic receptors were excluded but the carotid sinus reflex was preserved this fall in blood pressure did not occur (3, 58), thus allowing the conclusion that the carotid sinus reflex is important in exercise. In the three older studies the carotid and aorto-subclavian baroreceptors were excluded, but the vagally innervated cardiopulmonary receptors were preserved (47, 53, 80). The completeness of arterial baroreceptor denervation, not easy to achieve in the dog, was verified in two of these three studies (47, 53) by demonstrating that injection of vasoactive drugs caused almost no change in heart rate. Comparisons were made of the blood pressure during exercise in the baroreceptor-denervated and baroreceptor-intact states. In two of the studies (53, 80) blood pressure rose more or less normally during exercise after baroreceptor denervation. In the third (47), blood pressure fell early in exercise but ultimately rose to the same level as in the baroreceptor-intact state. These results invite a diametrically opposite conclusion (86), namely that the arterial baroreflexes are unimportant in exercise. However, one notable difference between the two sets of experiments is that whereas in the one case the reflexes from vagally innervated cardiopulmonary receptors were preserved (47, 53, 80), in the other case they were rendered inoperative (3, 58) when the effects of baroreceptor exclusion were tested. In the studies where the cardiopulmonary reflexes were preserved, all (47, 53) or most (80) of the arterial baroreceptors had been surgically denervated some days or weeks beforehand. Thus one way of reconciling the conflicting findings is to speculate that chronic baroreceptor denervation renders the cardiopulmonary reflexes more effective as controllers of blood pressure, perhaps as a result of plastic changes within central nervous pathways.

The other approach to establishing whether control of blood pressure by the arterial baroreflexes is affected by exercise has been to make a direct examination of the stimulus-response characteristics of the reflexes. The unconscious animal model with the closest resemblance to isometric exercise is that in which muscle contraction is produced by ventral nerve root stimulation. In one study of this form of static exercise the responses of blood pressure and heart rate to carotid sinus distension were unaffected (21); in another, heart rate responded normally to aortic balloon inflation (75). In humans, the sensitivity of the response of blood pressure to change in carotid sinus transmural pressure has been determined by the variable-pressure neck-chamber technique during exercise. Bevegård & Shepherd (8) found that the depressor response to baroreceptor loading was unaffected by supine bicycling exercise, and our group found later that isometric

handgrip had no effect on the responses of blood pressure to either baroreceptor loading or unloading (52). The depressor effect of carotid sinus nerve
stimulation in dogs has been shown (83) to be unaffected by treadmill
exercise. There have also been two recent studies of the carotid reflex during
treadmill exercise in animals, in which the carotid sinus was able to be
physically (58) or functionally (32) isolated from the remainder of the
circulation. In an elegant set of experiments Melcher & Donald (58) constructed full-range, static, stimulus-response curves for the carotid reflex in
dogs, before and during steady-state exercise at various grades. The form
of the stimulus-response curves for blood pressure was unaffected by exercise, whether the vagi were intact or acutely sectioned. In particular, the
static gain of the reflex was unaffected. In rabbits (32), the dynamic gain
of the carotid reflex with respect to blood pressure was reduced, but only
modestly, during a brief period of treadmill exercise, the effect being attributed to loss of sympathetic control over metabolically dilated muscle
resistance vessels (45). This difference in outcome from Melcher & Donald's
(58) experiments may reflect an effect of species, of the nonsteady-state form
of exercise, or of the fact that the measurement of dynamic rather than
static gain also tests the speed with which a blood pressure disturbance is
corrected. In summary very strong evidence now suggests that the control
of blood pressure by the arterial baroreceptor reflexes—or at any rate by
the carotid baroreceptor reflex—is little affected by either static or dynamic
exercise.

The hypothesis that exercise depresses baroreceptor control of blood
pressure has gained credence because of studies of its effects on baroreceptor
control of heart rate in conscious animals (53) and humans (17, 23, 52, 56).
The experimental data exhibit a good deal of consistency, which is con-
cealed by the two different means employed to express the dependent variable—i.e., sometimes as heart rate, and sometimes as R-R heart interval.
This point has received remarkably scant attention [but see (21, 58, 68)] but
can be put simply: For a given change in heart rate, the corresponding
change in heart interval will be less if the initial heart is high (as in exercise)
than if it is low (as at rest). If the studies are examined in which exercise
was found not to affect the reflex change in heart rate caused by change in
arterial (67) or carotid sinus (8, 58) pressure, conversion of heart rate to
heart interval reveals a marked "depression" of the baroreceptor–heart rate
reflex. Conversely, if the data obtained in humans by vasopressor drug
injection (17, 23) or carotid sinus nerve stimulation (28) are expressed in
terms of heart rate instead of heart interval the effect of exercise on baroreflex sensitivity is rendered less impressive. The same applies to the data we
obtained using the neck-chamber technique (56). Nevertheless, there is
good evidence that very strenuous exercise does attenuate the bradycardia
produced by elevation of blood pressure (17, 24, 53) or of carotid sinus

pressure (56). This effect can be detected at the onset of exercise (17, 56) and coincides with the immediate vagal withdrawal attributable to the effect of the exercise stimuli (40, 57). Considering the absence of a similar effect when ventral root stimulation is used to simulate exercise (21, 75), it seems likely that central command is the main factor responsible, though this has been disputed (40). No corresponding impairment of the rise in heart rate follows baroreceptor unloading (56).

When the effector mechanisms involved in the arterial baroreceptor reflexes are compared with those responsible for the cardiovascular responses to the exercise stimuli, a plausible hypothesis can be advanced to explain the observed effects of exercise on baroreflex control of blood pressure and heart rate. In humans, static exercise causes an immediate withdrawal of vagal drive to the heart (40, 57), whereas carotid baroreceptor stimulation causes a bradycardia almost entirely attributable to increased vagal drive (27, 28). If the two stimuli exert their effects through a common pool of cardiac vagal preganglionic neurons, a lower excitability of this pool in exercise would explain the blunting of the bradycardic response to baroreceptor loading. A similar argument can be used to explain why, during static exercise, the rise in heart rate caused by carotid baroreceptor unloading is preserved (52, 56). The changes in blood pressure that are evoked by altering pressure in the isolated carotid sinus of conscious animals are due chiefly to variations of systemic vascular resistance (31, 44), and therefore of sympathetic drive to resistance vessels (though it must be admitted that in these artificial circumstances the unfavorable changes in afterload may hinder the heart's ability to vary its output). In static exercise there is normally no change in systemic vascular resistance (48, 49, 57), so there is no reason to suppose that the excitability of the pool of sympathetic preganglionic neurons concerned with the resistance vessels is altered, or that baroreceptor control of resistance vessels would be affected at this spinal level. The situation in dynamic exercise is less clear-cut, but such evidence as there is suggests that sympathetic preganglionic pools concerned with many vascular beds are excited, rather than depressed, in humans and baboons, if not so convincingly in dogs (16, 68, 81, 85, 86). Thus it is reasonable to presume that the excitability of the pool of sympathetic preganglionic neurons through which the baroreflex exerts its effect on blood pressure is unaltered or increased by exercise, predicting that baroreflex control of blood pressure would be unaltered, or even enhanced.

A second hypothesis about the arterial baroreflexes in exercise deserves brief discussion. It is that their set point is elevated in proportion to the vigor of the exercise, and that the exercise stimuli produce their cardiovascular effects by utilizing baroreflex pathways. Thus it is proposed that the rises in blood pressure and heart rate that occur in exercise are a direct consequence of elevation of the set point of the baroreflexes. In the case of dynamic exercise there is now good evidence against this. Melcher & Donald (58) found that during treadmill exercise in the dog the location of the sigmoid stimulus-response curves describing the control of blood pressure by the carotid sinus reflex was altered as it would be if baroreflex-independent pathways (46) were responsible for the changes in blood pressure produced by exercise. In static exercise, the stimulus-response relationships for the arterial baroreflexes have not yet been defined over their full ranges, but this may be possible in trained animals (36), and especially in sub-human primates (39), using one of the recently developed methods for characterizing the carotid reflex in conscious animals (31, 73). However, even on present evidence there is reason to believe that nonbaroreflex pathways are responsible for the rise of blood pressure during static exercise, because effector mechanisms are used that are different from those responsible for baroreflex-induced hypertension. In normal humans, static exercise causes little change in systemic resistance (48, 49, 57), but cardiac output rises and ventricular performance is enhanced (22, 37, 63, 64, 65). By contrast, carotid baroreceptor unloading in conscious animals causes a rise in systemic resistance, but with little change in cardiac output (31, 44) or ventricular contractility (44, 84).

Certain properties of the arterial baroreceptor apparatus itself may be relevant to the control of blood pressure in exercise. First, recent work has shown that a passive change of blood pressure is accompanied by a very rapid resetting of the aortic baroreceptors (20, 25) in the direction of that change. This phenomenon would allow the arterial baroreflexes during exercise to maintain their strong dampening effect on short-term disturbances of blood pressure, but to offer much less resistance to slower movements of the mean level of blood pressure than would be the case if the set-point of the reflexes were fixed. Second, the walls of the arteries in which the baroreceptors are located contain sympathetically innervated smooth muscle, so it has been suggested that an increase in sympathetic neural drive or in circulating catecholamines, such as occurs in exercise, may modulate baroreceptor discharge and hence the properties of the reflex. However, the many experiments in anesthetized animals have suggested three different conclusions about this possibility: that increased sympathoadrenal drive (a) excites the baroreceptors directly (15, 44, 79), or (b) mechanically loads (13, 44) or (c) conversely unloads (14, 15, 44, 74) the baroreceptors, depending on whether they are thought of as lying in series or in parallel with smooth muscle fibers. It has not been proven whether the characteristics of the baroreceptor apparatus are altered in any of these ways by exercise.

LEFT VENTRICULAR MECHANORECEPTORS When the arterial baroreceptor reflexes are eliminated, a rise in left ventricular afterload is associated with a reflex fall in heart rate and systemic vascular resistance, which is probably attributable to the engagement of left ventricular receptors innervated by vagal C-fibers (78). This reflex might buffer the blood pressure rise of exercise, but whether it in fact does so is unknown, for the reflex has not yet been studied in conscious animals or humans. In anesthetized animals the receptor discharge-rate correlates well with left ventricular end-diastolic pressure and with the inotropic state of the ventricle, and the reflex effects of graded aortic occlusion correlate well with ventricular end-diastolic volume (78). It is not known whether the rise of blood pressure in exercise is sufficient to cause the threshold of the reflex to be reached.

Vagally innervated chemosensitive receptors, distinguishable from the mechanoreceptors (78), have also been described in the left ventricle. Depressor reflexes are evoked from the heart when a variety of drugs, or natural agents such as bradykinin and prostanoids, are injected into the coronary circulation (19, 78). It has been suggested that the natural stimulus to these receptors is ischemia (19), and indeed powerful, vagally mediated depressor reflexes are evoked by coronary occlusion in anesthetized (33, 77) and conscious (10) animals. Whether the chemosensitive receptors are capable of sensing the subtler changes of myocardial metabolism that occur in exercise is not known.

In future the contribution of left ventricular and other cardiac receptors to blood pressure control in exercise may be studied in conscious animals by using, for instance, pericardial irrigation with local anesthetics to selectively block cardiac autonomic nerves (4, 11, 69).

Second-Order Homeostatic Reflexes

The cardiovascular reflexes described as arising from other vagally innervated intrathoracic receptors are generally depressor (24, 71, 78). Only those dependent on changes in central blood volume, in which the receptors may be the C-fiber innervated atrial net (78), have been studied in the conscious state and in relation to exercise (see above). Others—e.g. in the right ventricle and pulmonary artery (78), and those that respond to pulmonary inflation or pulmonary vascular congestion (71)—may modulate the cardiovascular effects of exercise but have not yet been proven to do so.

There is now some information about the collective role of vagally innervated intrathoracic receptors in exercise, though it has not been possible to separate out the contributions of the individual sets of cardiovascular and pulmonary receptors referred to above. When dogs with intact carotid baroreflexes were studied, acute vagal blockade (3) or section (58) did not cause a marked abnormality of blood pressure during treadmill exercise, though when the carotid reflex was rendered inoperative there was a suggestion that the vagally innervated receptors (including, however, the aort-subclavian baroreceptors) assisted in supporting the blood pressure (58).

In humans, nonhypotensive reduction of central blood volume causes an increase in resistance to blood flow in the forearm muscles and in the splanchnic circulation (1, 42), the former at least being attributable to intrathoracic volume receptors. The reflex appears able to govern forearm resistance vessels during contralateral handgrip exercise in a normal (6, 7) or even an enhanced (88) fashion. It may have an important role during recovery from prolonged strenuous exercise, when blood volume is reduced, vascular capacity is increased, and thermoregulatory reflexes are in play (16).

In recumbent humans, an acute increase in central blood volume has been described to cause reflex vasodilatation in forearm skeletal muscle (70). It has been suggested that, like the Bainbridge reflex, this plays a part in the initiation of the cardiovascular changes of dynamic exercise, but it is doubtful whether its threshold would be reached in the upright posture.

SUMMARY

The exercise stimuli exert a powerful drive to elevate blood pressure. This may be facilitated by spinal sympatho-sympathetic reflexes arising from the heart and aorta. The role of the Bainbridge reflex as a feed-forward mechanism in exercise remains unclear.

Other, homeostatic, reflexes may modulate the pressor effects of the exercise stimuli. The balance of evidence strongly suggests that the arterial baroreceptors are still able to restrain disturbances of blood pressure during exercise, even though their control of heart rate is modified. Vagally innervated cardiopulmonary, and especially left ventricular, receptors may also subserve buffer reflexes in exercise, but whether their thresholds are reached has not been determined.

ACKNOWLEDGMENT

Discussions with Dr. Loring B. Rowell and Dr. Allen M. Scher helped greatly to clarify some of the views expressed in this review.

Literature Cited

1. Abboud, F. M., Eckberg, D. L., Johannsen, U. J., Mark, A. L. 1979. Carotid and cardiopulmonary baroreceptor control of splanchnic and forearm vascular resistance during venous pooling in man. *J. Physiol.* 286:173–84
2. Arborelius, M., Balldin, U. I., Lundgren, C. E. G. 1972. Hemodynamic changes in man during immersion with the head above water. *Aerosp. Med.* 43:592–98
3. Ardell, J. L., Scher, A. M., Rowell, L. B. 1980. Effects of baroreceptor dener-

vation on the cardiovascular response to dynamic exercise. In *Arterial Baroreceptors and Hypertension,* ed. P. Sleight, pp. 311–17. Oxford: Oxford Univ. Press. 540 pp.
4. Arndt, J. O., Pasch, U., Samodelov, L. F., Wiebe, H. 1981. Reversible blockade of myelinated and nonmyelinated cardiac afferents in cats by instillation of procaine into the pericardium. *Cardiovasc. Res.* 15:61–67
5. Baker, P. G. B., Mottram, R. F. 1973. Metabolism of exercising and resting

human skeletal muscle, in the postprandial and fasting states. *Clin. Sci.* 44:479–91

6. Bergenwald, L., Eklund, B., Freyschuss, U. 1977. Effects of withdrawal and infusion of blood on limb circulation at rest and during contralateral isometric handgrip. *Scand. J. Clin. Lab. Invest.* 37:675–81

7. Bergenwald, L., Eklund, B., Freyschuss, U. 1977. Effect of acute blood volume variations in man on the circulatory response to isometric handgrip. *Scand. J. Clin. Lab. Invest.* 37:683–89

8. Bevegård, B. S., Shepherd, J. T. 1966. Circulatory effects of stimulating the carotid arterial stretch receptors in man at rest and during exercise. *J. Clin. Invest.* 45:132–42

9. Bevegård, B. S., Shepherd, J. T. 1967. Regulation of the circulation during exercise in man. *Physiol. Rev.* 47:173–213

10. Bishop, V. S., Peterson, D. F. 1978. The circulatory influences of vagal afferents at rest and during coronary occlusion in conscious dogs. *Circ. Res.* 43:840–47

11. Blix, A. S., Wennergren, G., Folkow, B. 1976. Cardiac receptors in ducks: a link between vasoconstriction and bradycardia during diving. *Acta Physiol. Scand.* 97:13–19

12. Blomqvist, C. G., Lewis, S. F., Taylor, W. F., Graham, R. M. 1981. Similarity of the hemodynamic responses to static and dynamic exercise of small muscle groups. *Circ. Res.* 48:(Suppl. 1) 87–92

13. Bolter, C. P., Ledsome, J. R. 1980. Influence of cervical sympathetic nerve stimulation on carotid sinus baroreceptor afferents. *Experientia* 36:1301–2

14. Brattström, A. 1980. Increasing aortic baroreceptor sensitivity during reflex inhibition of efferent sympathetic activity. *Acta. Biol. Med. Germ.* 39:623–27

15. Brattström, A. 1981. Modification of carotid baroreceptor function by electrical stimulation of the ganglioglomerular nerve. *J. Auton. Nerv. Syst.* 4:81–92

16. Brengelmann, G. 1983. Circulatory adjustments to exercise and heat stress. *Ann. Rev. Physiol.* 45:191–212

17. Bristow, J. D., Brown, E. B., Cunningham, D. J. C., Howson, M. G., Petersen, E. S., Sleight, P. 1971. Effect of bicycling on the baroreflex regulation of pulse interval. *Circ. Res.* 28:582–92

18. Brooks, C. McC., Lu, H-H., Lange, G., Mangi, R., Shaw, R. B., Geoly, K. 1966. Effects of localized stretch of the sinoatrial node region of the dog heart. *Am. J. Physiol.* 211:1197–1202

19. Coleridge, H. M., Coleridge, J. C. G. 1980. Cardiovascular afferents involved in regulation of peripheral vessels. *Ann. Rev. Physiol.* 42:413–27

20. Coleridge, H. M., Coleridge, J. C. G., Kaufman, M. P., Dangel, A. 1981. Operational sensitivity and acute resetting of aortic baroreceptors in dogs. *Circ. Res.* 48:676–84

21. Coote, J. H., Dodds, W. N. 1976. The baroreceptor reflex and the cardiovascular changes associated with sustained muscular contraction in the cat. *Pflügers Arch.* 363:167–73

22. Crawford, M. H., White, D. H., Amon, K. W. 1979. Echocardiographic evaluation of left ventricular size and performance during handgrip and supine bicycling exercise. *Circulation* 59:1188–96

23. Cunningham, D. J. C., Petersen, E. S., Peto, R., Pickering, T. G., Sleight, P. 1972. Comparison of the effect of different types of exercise on the baroreflex regulation of heart rate. *Acta. Physiol. Scand.* 86:444–55

24. Donald, D. E., Shepherd, J. T., 1978. Reflexes from the heart and lungs: physiological curiosities or important regulatory mechanism. *Cardiovasc. Res.* 12:449–69

25. Dorward, P. K., Andresen, M. C., Burke, S. L., Oliver, J. R., Korner, P. I. 1982. Rapid resetting of the aortic baroreceptors in the rabbit and its implications for short-term and longer term reflex control. *Circ. Res.* 50:428–39

26. Downing, S. E. 1979. Baroreceptor regulation of the heart. In *Handbook of Physiology. Sect. 2: The Cardiovascular System, Vol. 1: The Heart,* ed. R. M. Berne, pp. 621–52. Bethesda: Am. Physiol. Soc. 970 pp.

27. Eckberg, D. L., Abboud, F. M., Mark, A. L. 1976. Modulation of carotid baroreflex responsiveness in man: effects of posture and propranolol. *J. Appl. Physiol.* 41:383–87

28. Eckberg, D. L., Fletcher, G. F., Braunwald, E. 1972. Mechanism of prolongation of the R-R interval with electrical stimulation of the carotid sinus nerves in man. *Circ. Res.* 30:131–38

29. Eklund, B., Kaijser, L. 1978. Blood flow in the resting forearm during prolonged contralateral isometric handgrip at maximal effort. *J. Physiol.* 277:359–66

30. Faris, I. B., Iannos, J., Jamieson, G. G., Ludbrook, J. 1981. The circulatory

effects of acute hypervolemia and hemodilution in conscious rabbits. *Circ. Res.* 48:825–34

31. Faris, I. B., Jamieson, G. G., Ludbrook, J. 1981. The carotid sinus-blood pressure reflex in conscious rabbits: the relative importance of changes in cardiac output and peripheral resistance. *Aust. J. Exp. Biol. Med. Sci.* 59:335–41

32. Faris, I. B., Jamieson, G. G., Ludbrook, J. 1982. Effect of exercise on gain of the carotid sinus reflex in rabbits. *Clin. Sci.* 63:115–19

33. Felder, R. B., Thames, M. D. 1979. Interaction between cardiac receptors and sinoaortic baroreceptors in the control of efferent cardiac sympathetic nerve activity during myocardial ischemia in dogs. *Circ. Res.* 45:728–36

34. Fisher, M. L., Nutter, D. O., Jacobs, W., Schlant, R. C. 1973. Haemodynamic responses to isometric exercise (handgrip) in patients with heart disease. *Br. Heart J.* 35:422–32

35. Giuntini, C., Maseri, A., Bianchi, R. 1966. Pulmonary vascular distensibility and lung compliance as modified by dextran infusion and subsequent atropine injection in normal subjects. *J. Clin. Invest.* 45:1770–89

36. Gonyea, W. J., Diepstra, G., Muntz, K. H., Mitchell, J. H. 1981. Cardiovascular response to static exercise in the conscious cat. *Circ. Res.* 48:(Suppl. 1) 63–69

37. Grossman, W., McLaurin, L. P., Saltz, S. B., Paraskos, J. A., Dalen, J. E., Dexter, L. 1973. Changes in the inotropic state of the left ventricle during isometric exercise. *Br. Heart J.* 35:697–704

38. Haskell, W. L., Savin, W. M., Schroeder, J. S., Alderman, E. A., Ingles, N. B., Daughters, G. T., Stinson, E. B. 1981. Cardiovascular responses to handgrip isometric exercise in patients following cardiac transplantation. *Circ. Res.* 48:(Suppl. 1) 156–61

39. Hobbs, S. F., Rowell, L. B., Smith, O. A. 1980. Increased cardiovascular responses to voluntary static exercise after neuromuscular blockade (NMB) in baboons. *Physiologist* 23:120

40. Hollander, A. P., Bouman, L. N. 1975. Cardiac acceleration in man elicited by a muscle-heart reflex. *J. Appl. Physiol.* 38:272–78

41. Humphreys, P. W., Lind, A. R. 1963. The blood flow through active and inactive muscles of the forearm during sustained hand-grip contractions. *J. Physiol.* 166:120–35

42. Johnson, J. M., Rowell, L. B., Niederberger, M., Eisman, M. M. 1974. Human splanchnic and forearm vasoconstrictor responses to reductions of right atrial and aortic pressures. *Circ. Res.* 34:515–24

43. Kappagoda, C. T., Linden, R. J., Sivananthan, N. 1979. The nature of the atrial receptors responsible for a reflex increase in heart rate in the dog. *J. Physiol.* 291:393–412

44. Kirchheim, H. R. 1976. Systemic arterial baroreceptor reflexes. *Physiol. Rev.* 56:100–76

45. Kjellmer, I. 1965. On the competition between metabolic vasodilatation and neurogenic vasoconstriction in skeletal muscle. *Acta Physiol. Scand.* 63:450–59

46. Korner, P. I. 1979. Central nervous control of autonomic cardiovascular function. See Ref. 26, pp. 691–739

47. Krasney, J. A., Levitzky, M. G., Koehler, R. C. 1974. Sinoaortic contribution to the adjustment of systemic resistance in exercising dogs. *J. Appl. Physiol.* 36:679–85

48. Laird, W. P., Fixler, D. E., Huffines, F. D. 1979. Cardiovascular response to isometric exercise in normal adolescents. *Circulation* 59:651–54

49. Lind, A. R., Taylor, S. H., Humphreys, P. W., Kennelly, B. M., Donald, K. W. 1964. The circulatory effects of sustained voluntary muscle contraction. *Clin. Sci.* 27:229–44

50. Linden, R. J. 1976. Reflexes from receptors in the heart. *Cardiology* 61:(Suppl. 1)7–30

51. Lioy, F., Szeto, P. M. 1979. Baroreceptor influence on a spinal cardiovascular reflex. *Can. J. Physiol. Pharmacol.* 57:147–51

52. Ludbrook, J., Faris, I. B., Iannos, J., Jamieson, G. G., Russell, W. J. 1978. Lack of effect of isometric handgrip exercise on the responses of the carotid sinus baroreceptor reflex in man. *Clin. Sci. Mol. Med.* 55:189–94

53. McRitchie, R. J., Vatner, S. F., Boettcher, D., Heyndrickx, G. R., Patrick, T. A., Braunwald, E. 1976. Role of arterial baroreceptors in mediating cardiovascular response to exercise. *Am. J. Physiol.* 230:85–89

54. Malliani, A. 1982. Cardiovascular sympathetic afferent fibers. *Rev. Physiol. Biochem. Pharmacol.* In press

55. Malliani, A., Pagani, M., Bergamaschi, M. 1979. Positive feedback sympathetic reflexes and hypertension. *Am. J. Cardiol.* 44:860–65

56. Mancia, G., Iannos, J., Jamieson, G. G., Lawrence, R. H., Sharman, P. R., Ludbrook, J. 1978. Effect of isometric hand-grip exercise on the carotid sinus baroreceptor reflex in man. *Clin. Sci. Mol. Med.* 54:33–37

57. Martin, C. E., Shaver, J. A., Leon, D. F., Thompson, M. E., Reddy, P. S., Leonard, J. J. 1974. Autonomic mechanisms in hemodynamic responses to isometric exercise. *J. Clin. Invest.* 54:104–15

58. Melcher, A., Donald, D. E. 1981. Maintained ability of carotid baroreflex to regulate arterial pressure during exercise. *Am. J. Physiol.* 241:H838–49

59. Mitchell, J. H. 1983. The Exercise Pressor Reflex: Its Cardiovascular Effects, Afferent Mechanisms, and Central Pathways. *Ann. Rev. Physiol.* 45:229–42

60. Mitchell, J. H., Payne, F. C., Saltin, B., Schibye, B. 1980. The role of muscle mass in the cardiovascular response to static contractions. *J. Physiol.* 309:45–54

61. Pagani, M., Pizzinelli, P., Furlan, R., Guzzetti, S., Rimoldi, O., Malliani, A. 1981. A sympathetic hypertensive reflex from the heart of conscious dogs. *Clin. Sci.* 61:181s–83s

62. Pathak, C. L. 1958. Effects of changes in intraluminal pressure on inotropic and chronotropic responses of isolated mammalian hearts. *Am. J. Physiol.* 194:197–99

63. Perez-Gonzales, J. F., Schiller, N. B., Parmley, W. W. 1981. Direct and noninvasive evaluation of the cardiovascular response to isometric exercise. *Circ. Res.* 48:(Suppl. 1)138–48

64. Quarry, V. M., Spodick, D. H. 1974. Cardiac responses to isometric exercise: comparative effects with different postures and levels of exertion. *Circulation* 49:905–20

65. Quinones, M. A., Gaasch, W. H., Waisser, E., Thiel, H. G., Alexander, J. K. 1974. An analysis of the left ventricular response to isometric exercise. *Am. Heart J.* 88:29–36

66. Risch, W. D., Koubenec, H.-J., Gauer, O. H., Lange, S. 1978. Time course of cardiac distension with rapid immersion in a thermo-neutral bath. *Pflügers Arch.* 374:119–20

67. Robinson, B. F., Epstein, S. E., Kahler, R. L., Braunwald, E. 1966. Circulatory effects of acute expansion of blood volume; studies during maximal exercise and at rest. *Circ. Res.* 19:26–32

68. Rowell, L. B., 1974. Human cardiovascular adjustments to exercise and thermal stress. *Physiol. Rev.* 54:75–159

69. Scher, A. M. 1977. Carotid and aortic regulation of arterial blood pressure. *Circulation* 56:521–28

70. Shepherd, J. T. 1963. *Physiology of the Circulation in Human Limbs in Health and Disease,* pp. 42–72. Philadelphia: Saunders. 416 pp.

71. Shepherd, J. T. 1981. The lungs as receptor sites for cardiovascular regulation. *Circulation.* 63:1–10

72. Smith, E. E., Guyton, A. C., Manning, R. D., White, R. J. 1976. Integrated mechanisms of cardiovascular response and control during exercise in the normal human. *Prog. Cardiovasc. Dis.* 18:421–43

73. Stephenson, R. B., Donald, D. E. 1980. Reflexes from isolated carotid sinuses of intact and vagotomized conscious dogs. *Am. J. Physiol.* 238:H815–22

74. Stinnett, H. O., Sepe, F. J., Mangusson, M. R. 1981. Rabbit carotid baroreflexes after carotid sympathectomy, vagotomy, and β blockade. *Am. J. Physiol.* 241:H600–5

75. Streatfield, K. A., Davidson, N. S., McCloskey, D. I. 1977. Muscular reflex and baroreflex influences on heart rate during isometric contractions. *Cardiovasc. Res.* 11:87–93

76. Szeto, P. M., Lioy, F. 1978. Reflex effects of thoracic aortic wall stretch on regional vascular resistance. *Can. J. Physiol. Pharmacol.* 56:390–94

77. Thorén, P. 1973. Evidence for a depressor reflex elicited from left ventricular receptors during occlusion of one coronary artery in the cat. *Acta Physiol. Scand.* 88:23–34

78. Thorén, P. 1979. Role of cardiac vagal C-fibers in cardiovascular control. *Rev. Physiol. Biochem. Pharmacol.* 86:1–94

79. Tomomatsu, E., Nishi, K. 1981. Increased activity of carotid sinus baroceptors by sympathetic stimulation and norepinephrine. *Am. J. Physiol.* 240:H650–58

80. Vanhoutte, P., Lacroix, E., Leusen, I. 1966. The cardiovascular adaptation of the dog to muscular exercise: role of the arterial pressoreceptors. *Arch. Int. Physiol. Biochim.* 74:201–22

81. Vatner, S. F. 1978. Effects of exercise and excitement on mesenteric and renal dynamics in conscious, unrestrained baboons. *Am. J. Physiol.* 234:H210–14

82. Vatner, S. F., Boettcher, D. H., Heyndrickx, G. R., McRitchie, R. J. 1975. Reduced baroreflex sensitivity with vol-

ume loading in conscious dogs at rest and during exercise. *Circ. Res.* 37:495–503

83. Vatner, S. F., Franklin, D., Van Citters, R. L., Braunwald, E. 1970. Effects of carotid sinus nerve stimulation on blood flow distribution in conscious dogs. *Circ. Res.* 27:495–503

84. Vatner, S. F., Higgins, C. B., Franklin, D., Braunwald, E. 1972. Extent of carotid sinus regulation of the myocardial contractile state in conscious dogs. *J. Clin. Invest.* 51:995–1008

85. Vatner, S. F., Higgins, C. B., White, S., Patrick, T., Franklin, D. 1971. The peripheral vascular response to severe exercise in untethered dogs before and after complete heart block. *J. Clin. Invest.*

50:1950–60

86. Vatner, S. F., Pagani, M. 1976. Cardiovascular adjustments to exercise: hemodynamics and mechanisms. *Prog. Cardiovasc. Dis.* 19:91–108

87. Vatner, S. F., Zimpfer, M. 1981. Bainbridge reflex in conscious, unrestrained, and tranquilized baboons. *Am. J. Physiol.* 240:H164–67

88. Walker, J. L., Abboud, F. M., Mark, A. L., Thames, M. D. 1980. Interactions of cardiopulmonary and somatic reflexes in humans. *J. Clin. Invest.* 65:1491–97

89. Watt, S. J., Thomas, R. D., Belfield, P. W., Goldstraw, P. W., Taylor, S. H. 1981. Influence of sympatholytic drugs on the cardiovascular response to isometric exercise. *Clin. Sci.* 60:139–43

Ann. Rev. Physiol. 1983. 45:169–89

CARDIOVASCULAR ADAPTATIONS TO PHYSICAL TRAINING

C. Gunnar Blomqvist

Weinberger Laboratory for Cardiopulmonary Research and the Harry S. Moss Heart Center, Departments of Internal Medicine and Physiology, University of Texas Health Science Center, Dallas, Texas 75235

Bengt Saltin

August Krogh Institute, University of Copenhagen, Copenhagen, Denmark

The principal features of the cardiovascular responses to endurance training in normal subjects were well documented by the late 1960s (2, 23, 35, 84, 88) and are illustrated in Table 1. They include an increase in maximal oxygen uptake, stroke volume, and cardiac output with no change or a small decrease in maximal heart rate. Systemic vascular conductance increases and there is also an increase in the maximal systemic arteriovenous oxygen difference. Cardiac output at submaximal levels of work does not change significantly but the increase in stroke volume is associated with a relative bradycardia at rest and at any given submaximal level of oxygen uptake. These cardiovascular changes are produced by a complex set of central and peripheral mechanisms operating at multiple levels—e.g. structural, metabolic, and regulatory (13, 14, 97). Our understanding of how these adaptations combine to extend aerobic capacity is still incomplete.

The classical concept that maximal oxygen uptake is limited by the oxygen transport capacity of the cardiovascular system (37) was challenged during the early 1970s (46) and the oxidative capacity of skeletal muscle was then by some considered to be the primary limiting mechanism. More recent work has reinforced the conclusion that functional capacity of the cardiovascular system is the principal limiting factor. Here we review the interaction between training-induced adaptations affecting the heart, the

169

0066-4278/83/0315-0169$02.00

Table 1 Cardiovascular and pulmonary functional capacities determined during maximal exercise in college students and Olympic athletes[a]

	Students			Olympic athletes
	Control	After bedrest	After training	
Maximal oxygen uptake, liters/min	3.30	2.43	3.91	5.38[b]
Maximal voluntary ventilation, liters/min	191	201	197	219
Transfer coefficient for O_2, (ml/min)/(mmHg)	96	83	86	95
Arterial O_2 capacity, vol %	21.9	20.5	20.8	22.4
Maximal cardiac output, liters/min	20.0	14.8	22.8	30.4[b]
Stroke volume, ml	104	74	120	167[b]
Maximal heart rate, beats/min	192	197	190	182
Systemic arteriovenous O_2 difference, vol %	16.2	16.5	17.1	18.0

[a] Mean values, n = 5 and 6. Age, height, and weight similar. Modified after Johnson (44). Data from Saltin et al (88) and Blomqvist et al (8).
[b] Significantly different from college students after training, p < 0.05.

peripheral vasculature, skeletal muscle, and the autonomic nervous system. The various steps involved in the utilization and transport of oxygen provide a convenient framework.

MECHANISMS LIMITING MAXIMAL OXYGEN UPTAKE

Oxidative Capacity of Skeletal Muscle and Substrate Utilization

Maximal oxygen uptake could theoretically be limited by the intrinsic oxidative capacity of skeletal muscle or by the availability of substrate and oxygen for energy transformation. Endurance training produces large increases in the activities of the oxidative enzymes of skeletal muscle. There is little or no effect on the enzymes of the glycolytic pathway (32). Saltin & Rowell (92) and Gollnick & Saltin (31) have recently reviewed the physiological implications of these metabolic adaptations. They noted that both longitudinal and cross-sectional studies on endurance training have demonstrated much larger and more rapid effects on the oxidative enzymes than on maximal oxygen uptake. Thus there is little evidence for a direct causal link. However, the increased oxidative capacity following training is associated with an increased endurance capacity, defined as time to exhaustion at submaximal work load levels. This was well documented in a recent study in the rat (21). The change in endurance was quantitatively related to the enhanced capacity for oxidation. Mitochondrial volume in skeletal muscle doubled after training. Maximal oxygen uptake increased but not in proportion to the enlarged mitochondrial capacity.

Lack of substrate (glycogen) is a performance-limiting factor only during prolonged exercise at high but still submaximal intensities (4). The training-induced cellular adaptations, including increased mitochondrial volume and increased levels of mitochondrial enzymes (e.g. carnitine acyltransferase and the enzymes in the β-oxidation pathway), favor entry into the citric acid cycle of acetyl units derived from fatty acids (31). The overall effects are an increased use of fats as substrate during exercise and a decrease in both aerobic and anaerobic utilization of carbohydrates, particularly muscle glycogen. These changes have no effect on maximal oxygen uptake, but the preferential use of fats improves endurance by postponing the development of performance limitations due to glycogen depletion and/or lactate accumulation. The greater use of fats occurs without any changes in the plasma levels of fatty acids (48).

Oxygen Transport

The rate of oxygen transfer from ambient air to the tissue could be limited at any of several steps in the oxygen transport chain (44). Pulmonary transport includes ventilation, diffusion into blood, and chemical reaction with hemoglobin. Cardiac or aortic transport capacity is equal to the product of maximal cardiac output and arterial oxygen capacity. The final links include distribution of cardiac output and diffusion to sites of tissue utilization. Table 1, modified after Johnson (44), details average pulmonary and cardiovascular functional capacities in a group of young college students before and after bed rest followed by a two-month training program (88) and in a group of Olympic athletes (8). Training produced a significant increase ($+18.5\%$) in maximal oxygen uptake in the group of students but their final level corresponded to only 73% of the mean value for the athletes. The large residual difference presumably reflects the combined effects of different genetic backgrounds (51, 52) and the prolonged intensive training in the athletes.

Measurements relating to pulmonary function were similar in both groups. Further analysis demonstrated that the overall capacity for pulmonary oxygen transport also was similar, 5.6 liters/min in the students after training and 6.2 liters/min in the athletes. Most of the difference in maximal oxygen uptake was accounted for by different capacities for cardiovascular oxygen transport, 4.0 and 5.8 liters/min. The data show that variations in physical activity have little effect on pulmonary function. They also indicate that cardiovascular and pulmonary oxygen transport capacity are closely matched in champion athletes whereas sedentary normal subjects utilize only about two thirds of their pulmonary capacity. Thus the conventional concept that pulmonary function is of no consequence as a limiting factor does not apply to superior athletes. Pulmonary diffusion generally becomes limiting at sea level when maximal oxygen uptake reaches about 6 liters/ min (44) and athletes are likely to have relatively larger declines in performance at altitude than average subjects. The magnitude of the decrease is a function of the ratio between sea level maximal oxygen uptake and pulmonary diffusing capacity (8). Pulmonary diffusing capacity is not affected by prolonged exposure to hypoxia and high altitude in adult life, but recent studies (R. L. Johnson, Jr., personal communication) have demonstrated a large increase in dogs raised at 3100 m from the age of 2 months to adulthood.

Data on the systemic arteriovenous oxygen difference (Table 1) suggest that the final step in the oxygen transport chain, distribution of cardiac output and/or the extraction by the tissues, is more efficient in well-trained subjects. A more efficient distribution of cardiac output can be achieved by an increase in vascular conductance in active tissue. An increased systemic A-V O_2 difference after training has been a consistent finding in longitudinal studies of sedentary young men and patients with ischemic heart disease but not in women or older men (13, 14, 87, 97). A more efficient utilization of available oxygen, reflected by decreased venous oxygen content in the absence of significant changes in arterial oxygen levels, may account for as much as one half of the improvement in maximal oxygen uptake produced by a short-term training program in young men (Table 1).

The training-induced widening of the systemic arteriovenous oxygen difference has been attributed to an increase in mitochondrial volume in skeletal muscle (97). However, it is unlikely that changes in mitochondrial volume are crucial. Immobilization causes a decrease of the aerobic capacity of skeletal muscle with no change or a decrease in mitochondrial volume (80, 88), but the maximal systemic A-V O_2 difference is maintained or increases slightly after bed rest (88) (Table 1). Myoglobin levels are elevated after training in rodents (73). This may contribute to an improved oxygen utilization, but human studies have failed to demonstrate any significant variations in myoglobin content (42, 69).

The high systemic A-V O_2 difference after both training and deconditioning can be explained if vascular adaptations are responsible for the efficient oxygen extraction. A wide systemic A-V O_2 difference after bed rest may reflect a relative prolongation of the mean transit time through skeletal muscle capillaries. Maximal cardiac output, and, presumably, maximal skeletal muscle blood flow are significantly reduced after a bed rest period of less than a month whereas there is little or no short-term change in capillary density (88, 90).

Increased usage of muscle causes a proliferation of the capillary bed (40) with an increase in the number of capillaries (41, 72, 90) and their dimensions (68)—i.e. an increase in capillary blood volume. A larger muscle blood flow following training can therefore be accommodated with little or no change in the capillary transit time. Furthermore, oxygen extraction is facilitated by the increased capillary density and the decreased diffusion distances. However, primary control of perfusion is exerted at the arteriolar level.

The improved utilization of the systemic capacity for oxygen transport only accounts for a small fraction of the large difference in maximal oxygen uptake between athletes and sedentary subjects. A superior systemic aerobic capacity clearly requires superior cardiac pump performance with a large stroke volume during exercise.

MYOCARDIAL ADAPTATIONS

The increased stroke volume that is a salient effect of training in normal subjects can be achieved simply by increasing cardiac dimensions or by improving the performance characteristics of the heart. Pump performance may be increased by (a) enhancing the intrinsic contractile properties of the myocardium and the responses to inotropic stimulation and (b) extramyocardial adaptations that have secondary effects on performance—e.g. by increasing ventricular filling or decreasing myocardial work.

Comprehensive analysis of myocardial function includes simultaneous consideration of force, velocity, and fiber length (64). The velocity axis can often be disregarded without serious loss of information in the analysis of the performance of the intact heart. The ventricular pressure-volume relationship (34, 86, 106, 115) provides a useful framework for analysis and a link between muscle mechanics and ventricular function. It is also helpful when considering peripheral or extracardiac factors. The pressure-volume relation defines contractile state as the maximal pressure (or tension) that can be developed at any given volume (or fiber length). Maximal ventricular pressure is normally a linear function of volume. Implicit in the concept is that the amount of shortening or stroke volume that can be achieved from any given diastolic volume or fiber length can be increased only by reducing afterload or by enhancing contractile state. Similarly, an increase in the amount of shortening at a given afterload requires either an increased end-diastolic volume or an increased contractile state. The linear relationship between peak systolic pressure and end-systolic volume closely approximates the relation between maximal tension and volume. End-systolic volume is independent of preload. This model makes it feasible to evaluate intra- and interindividual physiological differences in ventricular contractile performance even if the experimental conditions make it impossible to control preload and afterload. However, the slope and intercept of the systolic pressure-volume relationship are affected both by the basal or intrinsic properties of the myocardium and by the response to neural and humoral inotropic stimulation.

The normal human cardiac response to the demands of exercise with increasing systolic pressure and peak wall tension includes a combination of increased preload or end-diastolic volume—i.e. a Starling effect—and increased contractile state (76). The increased contractile state is manifest as decreasing end-systolic volume and increasing ejection fraction (the ratio stroke volume/end-diastolic volume).

Cardiac Dimensions

There is a large body of older, mainly German and Scandinavian data on the relationship between heart size and physical performance in athletes and normal subjects. In general, total heart size as estimated from bi-plane radiographs has in cross-sectional studies been found to correlate closely with maximal oxygen uptake, cardiac output, and stroke volume (3). The results from longitudinal series are less consistent; they range from a close correlation between changes in maximal oxygen uptake and stroke volume and total heart size in young normal subjects (88) to no correlation in middle-aged men (36, 99). Activity-related dimensional changes can develop within weeks (88) but former endurance athletes, including young women who have trained intensely over several years and later adopted a level of relative inactivity, maintain a large total heart size (25, 39, 77, 89).

Recent studies based on echocardiographic and radionuclear techniques have generated detailed dimensional data, particularly on the left ventricle. The results support the older radiographic observations. Cross-sectional studies comparing sedentary subjects and highly trained young and older athletes have demonstrated significant differences that can be related to the different demands of different forms of athletic activity. Morganroth et al (66) noted that endurance training—i.e. frequent exposure to conditions producing increased ventricular filling with high stroke volume and cardiac output—causes an increase in left ventricular end-diastolic volume without major changes in wall thickness, whereas isometric exercise, which primarily imposes a pressure load, produces an increased wall thickness without any change in left ventricular volume. Their findings have been confirmed by several subsequent studies, reviewed by Péronnet et al (75). The internal left ventricular end-diastolic diameter is about 10% larger in endurance athletes than in sedentary subjects. This corresponds to a ventricular volume difference of about 33%. Recent studies indicate that both dynamic and isometric training cause an increase in absolute left ventricular mass, but only endurance training increases mass normalized with respect to lean or total body mass (49, 61).

Péronnet et al (75) also assembled echocardiographic data from eight short-term longitudinal studies ($\leq$ 20 weeks) of endurance training in sedentary individuals. The gain in maximal oxygen uptake averaged 17%. At least some increase in left ventricular end-diastolic diameter at rest was recorded in most series, but the changes were generally small and were statistically significant in only three studies. The average increase in diameter was 1.3 mm or 2.5%, which approaches the limit of resolution of the method of measurement. However, ventricular volume is a third power function of the linear dimensions. The small average diameter change translates into a volume increase of 16%, which closely matches the change in maximal oxygen uptake. A post-training increase in end-diastolic diameter could reflect ventricular dilatation and be due simply to relative bradycardia, but left ventricular posterior wall thickness did not change or increased slightly in most series, implying a true increase in muscle mass.

Human echocardiographic studies have been limited to providing data on left ventricular dimensions at rest, but Rerych et al (79) recently used radionuclide angiography and demonstrated larger post-training left ventricular end-diastolic volumes during exercise as well as at rest.

Grande & Taylor (33) showed in an extensive review that active mammals generally have a higher heart-weight/body-weight ratio than inactive but otherwise similar breeds or species. Data from experimental longitudinal studies are less consistent, but it is evident that both swimming and running programs can produce at least a moderate degree of hypertrophy if defined as an increase in the heart-weight/body-weight ratio (29, 71, 95, 97). The extent of the hypertrophy is probably directly related to the intensity and duration of the training program and inversely related to age (10, 53, 67). The mode of exercise (e.g. running vs swimming) and the sex of the experimental animals may also be significant determinants of the degree of cardiac hypertrophy, but findings from several studies conflict (67). One problem is that a majority of the experimental studies have been performed in rodents, mainly rats. The rodent heart appears to be less responsive to exercise training than other mammalian hearts. Muntz et al (67) studied the effects of isometric exercise in the cat. Less than three minutes of daily isometric effort over a six month period produced an increase in left ventricular wall thickness and relative heart weight of about 30%. Significant changes in cardiac mass after endurance training have been reported also in the dog (11, 120), cat (121), and horse (101).

The exercise-induced cardiac hypertrophy appears to be global. Left atrial and right ventricular dimensions are consistently increased in subjects with left ventricular hypertrophy (67, 83, 108, 123). Characteristically, the normal heart muscle grows to match the work load imposed on the ventricle, maintaining a constant relationship between systolic pressure and the ratio of wall thickness to ventricular radius, irrespective of ventricular size (27). This means that normally wall tension is kept constant according to the law of Laplace. The weight lifter's increased mass/volume ratio (49, 61, 66) is inappropriate relative to their blood pressure at rest, but the increased wall-thickness is most likely appropriate to the hemodynamic conditions *during* isometric exercise and strength training, which induce a marked pressor response. By similar reasoning, an increase in ventricular volume with a secondary small increase in wall-thickness is in line with the hemodynamic state during large-muscle dynamic exercise.

Dynamic or isometric exercise training causes only a moderate increase in heart size. Cardiac weights higher than 500 g are rarely seen in athletes (59) whereas valvular and myocardial disease may produce weights well above 1000 g. The primary mechanism in both the abnormal and physiological situation is hypertrophy of the individual muscle fiber and serial addition of sarcomere units. No convincing signs of hyperplasia have been described. Dynamic and isometric exercise training as well as experimentally induced hemodynamic overload tend to produce an increase in mean myocardial fiber diameter and an increased variability of fiber sizes (11, 67). An increased heart-weight/body-weight ratio may also be due to a decrease in body weight without any change in fiber diameter (71).

Contractile Performance

A variety of preparations have been used to evaluate training effects on myocardial function. Isolated papillary muscles and isolated perfused hearts have been employed to analyze the effect on intrinsic myocardial contractile properties—i.e. the performance of denervated heart muscle under rigidly controlled conditions. Nutter & Fuller (70) reviewed six studies of the effect of training on the mechanical performance of isolated left ventricular papillary muscles. Passive or diastolic myocardial length-tension relationships did not change. Isometric or isotonic contractile performance was increased in two series, decreased in two, and showed no change in two.

Several investigators have examined the effects of training on the performance of the isolated perfused heart. Scheuer and associates (5, 7, 94, 95) have made a systematic study of the response to different forms of training—i.e. running and swimming in male and female rats. They concluded (94) that both activities produce skeletal muscle adaptations (e.g. increased cytochrome oxidase activity) in both male and female rats and an increased heart-weight/body-weight ratio. Absolute increases in heart weight relative to weight-matched control rats occur only in female swimmers. They found evidence for improved contractile performance (measurements normalized with respect to heart weight and obtained at several levels of left ventricular filling pressure) in male and female swimmers and male runners but not in female runners. These findings correlated closely with increased calcium binding in isolated sarcoplasmic reticulum and increased actomyosin ATPase (95). However, Fuller & Nutter (29), who studied the effects of running in male rats and essentially replicated the methods used by Scheuer and collaborators, were for reasons that are not apparent unable to demonstrate any training effects on contractile performance. Studies of the intact in situ heart of anesthetized rats (19) and in the awake chronically instrumented dog (11) have also failed to demonstrate any significant changes in myocardial performance attributable to training.

Human echocardiographic data from longitudinal and cross-sectional studies provide no evidence for any significant training effects on contractile performance (75). Physical training has the potential of altering not only cardiac dimensions but also autonomic state, preload, and afterload. It is therefore difficult to separate cardiac and extra-cardiac training effects on ventricular performance. If anything, the training-induced bradycardia at rest tends to be associated with a negative inotropic effect, presumably reflecting a decreased sympathetic drive. Data on myocardial performance during exercise are unfortunately scarce. Rerych and associates (79) found no effect on ejection fraction during submaximal and maximal exercise in a longitudinal study.

Thus the overall effects of physical training on intrinsic myocardial function remain uncertain. A large number of experiments, based on a variety of methods applied to humans and animals, have failed to demonstrate any significant training effects that can be attributed to an enhanced intrinsic contractile state—i.e. an improved quality of the myocardium. On the other hand, the careful studies by Scheuer and associates have documented significant improvement of myocardial function in isolated hearts of trained rats with parallel changes in myocardial myosin ATPase and calcium handling. Data on left ventricular performance during maximal exercise in humans (76, 79) suggest that there is little to be gained from an isolated improvement of contractile performance. The ejection fraction is very high and the end-systolic volume is very low in normal subjects irrespective of the state of training.

Several factors complicate the interpretation of the experimental data on myocardial contractile performance. Maximal oxygen uptake has rarely been measured in subhuman species. The rat, the most often used experimental animal, has obvious advantages over larger mammals, particularly in terms of cost, but there are also potentially important disadvantages. Hypertrophy is often only relative—i.e. consists of an increased heart-weight/body-weight ratio that is due to a lower total body weight in the trained animals rather than to an increased absolute heart weight. Body growth normally continues throughout adult life. Furthermore, the rat has myocardial membrane characteristics that differ significantly from those of other mammals (78). Other animal models also present problems in terms of applicability of findings to humans. The dog has a very high native aerobic capacity, often well above the levels recorded in olympic athletes. The heart-weight/body-weight ratio is also about twice as high as in humans—i.e. 8 g/kg body weight vs 4–5 in humans (96). The horse (101) and pig (93) may provide models in which baseline characteristics and responses to training more closely resemble those in humans.

EXTRAMYOCARDIAL ADAPTATIONS

Coronary Blood Flow

Dynamic exercise at graded work load levels causes a progressive increase in myocardial work with increasing heart rate, wall tension, and velocity of fiber shortening—i.e. the principal determinants of myocardial oxygen demand—but there is no indication that exercise produces ischemia in normal subjects. Myocardial ischemia causes left ventricular dysfunction, but performance is normally enhanced during exercise. Tension development and ejection fraction increase progressively and maximal values are reached during maximal exercise (76). Direct measurements of coronary flow in normal human subjects have also demonstrated that a linear relationship between myocardial work and coronary blood flow is maintained during heavy exercise (38, 45). Furthermore, recent studies in the pig (117) have shown that a coronary vasodilator reserve is present also during maximal exercise.

Longitudinal studies (104, 105) have demonstrated that changes in coronary flow patterns occur very early after the onset of a training program, which suggests significant regulatory adaptations. There is also experimental evidence for a training-induced increase in the size of the *coronary vascular bed* (40, 67, 97, 122) with changes involving both capillaries and larger vessels. The extent to which the increase in vascularity exceeds the increase in muscle mass in the normal heart remains to be determined. Schaible & Scheuer (95) have reported increases in coronary flow proportional to the degree of training-induced increase in heart weight. Others (53, 102, 107) have described an increase in the size of the coronary tree after training even in the absence of changes in heart weight. Neogenesis of coronary capillaries is suggested by studies based on light- and electronmicroscopy and autoradiographic techniques (53, 60, 62) as well as by data on the rate of incorporation of ^{3}H-thymidine in myocardial capillaries in young rats exercised by swimming (60). Older animals may be less responsive (109). The larger heart size in wild animals than in domestic sedentary species (33) is also associated with an increased capillary density of the myocardium (112–114).

Eckstein (22) observed that exercise training promotes collateral flow in dogs with experimental coronary artery narrowing. A larger number of subsequent studies have produced conflicting results (17, 96). Multiple studies in the dog and pig indicate that exercise produces no increase in collateralization in the absence of coronary lesions (17, 93).

Peripheral Vascular Adaptations

INCREASED PRELOAD   There is evidence to suggest an increased pre-load during exercise after training. Changes in physical activity and maximal oxygen uptake are paralleled by small but statistically significant changes in total blood volume (88), usually without major changes in hemoglobin concentration or hematocrit. Well-trained athletes have higher cardiac outputs and pulmonary arterial wedge pressures during maximal supine exercise than sedentary normal subjects (6, 24).

Measurements during maximal exercise following volume overload in sedentary and highly trained subjects provide further insights into the role of ventricular filling as a potential primary limiting factor. Robinson et al (82) studied exercise performance in a group of essentially normal subjects (maximal oxygen uptake 3.2 liters/min) before and after autotransfusion of 1.0–1.2 liters whole blood. This was sufficient to cause an increase in central venous pressure of 7 mmHg but there was no significant change in stroke volume or cardiac output during maximal work. Fortney et al (28) examined a group with slightly higher maximal oxygen uptake (3.5 liters/min) and found a small but significant increase in maximal stroke volume after blood volume expansion. Spriet et al (100) reported a large increase in maximal stroke volume (+31%) and cardiac output after reinfusion of 800 ml whole blood in highly trained athletes. Kanstrup & Ekblom (47) also examined a group of subjects with high maximal oxygen uptake (4.4 liters/-min), stroke volume, and cardiac output. Plasma volume expansion averaging 700 ml produced a 20% increase in stroke volume and a 13% increase in maximal cardiac output. The combined data from these four studies seem to indicate a difference between sedentary and well-trained subjects with respect to the cardiovascular response to an acute blood volume increase. Analysis of the pooled individual data demonstrate that there is a strong linear relationship between maximal stroke volume at the control study (SV_0, ml) and the magnitude of the increase (ΔSV, ml) after volume loading ($\Delta SV = 0.51\ SV_0 - 48$, $r^2 = 0.49$). It is tempting to speculate that endurance training alters the apparent ventricular compliance characteristics by modifying right/left ventricular-pericardial interactions. The result is an increase in diastolic reserve capacity. Experimental studies of chronic volume over-load have demonstrated increased effective left ventricular diastolic compli-ance due to pericardial rather than to myocardial adaptations (55). Measurements of left ventricular volumes in sedentary subjects during exer-cise are also consistent with a stroke volume limitation imposed by the effective left ventricular diastolic compliance. Poliner et al (76) obtained scintigraphic measurements of left ventricular volumes during submaximal and maximal exercise and found that left ventricular end-diastolic volume reached a plateau at low–intermediate submaximal work load levels. In-tracardiac pressures were not measured in their study but other investiga-tors have found progressively increasing left ventricular filling pressure with increasing work loads (6, 24). Intrapleural pressures also become increas-ingly negative with increasing ventilation (63). This contributes to a further increase in effective or transmural diastolic pressure which nevertheless fails to produce an increase in volume.

DECREASED AFTERLOAD   Afterload reduction is a crucial component of the integrated cardiovascular responses to training. Based on data from both cross-sectional and longitudinal studies Clausen (13, 14) has demon-strated a strong inverse and curvilinear relationship between maximal oxy-gen uptake and systemic peripheral resistance. The relationship is defined by the equation $y = 11.8 \cdot x^{-.72}$ where y is maximal O_2 uptake in liters/min and x is the ratio mean arterial blood pressure (mmHg)/cardiac output (liters/min).

A marked reduction in peripheral resistance enables the athlete to gener-ate a cardiac output of up to 40 liters/min compared to 20 in the sedentary subject at similar arterial pressures during maximal exercise. Arterial pres-sures would be twice as high in the athlete if systemic resistance did not change and the same cardiac output were attained. However, analysis of the performance characteristics of the normal heart suggests that any potential gain in stroke volume that could be achieved by a training-induced increase in heart size would largely be negated by the increased afterload unless training also induced a decrease in systemic resistance.

The increase in the size of the capillary bed of skeletal muscle is a striking feature of the training response, but by far the largest portion of the resis-tance to systemic blood flow is exerted at the arteriolar level. The primary mechanisms responsible for the reduction in systemic resistance are poorly defined. They are likely to affect the arterioles and to be regulatory rather than anatomical.

Experiments based on exercise and exercise training involving a smaller muscle mass than both legs have demonstrated that blood flow to the working limb is affected by both systemic and local factors. The capacity of the cardiovascular system to deliver oxygenated blood to active tissue exceeds the demand when only a small fraction of the total muscle mass is active. Local vascular conductance is most likely limiting oxygen delivery although blood flow may be quite high also in untrained muscle. Recent studies utilizing thermodilution techniques indicate that maximal exercise with the knee-extensors of one limb produces a muscle flow of at least 200 ml/100 g/min (1).

Measurements in the same individual during one-leg and two-leg maximal exercise shows a significantly lower flow to the active limb during two-leg exercise with little or no difference in arterial pressures—i.e. evidence for an increase in local vasoconstrictor activity when a larger muscle mass is activated and the systemic oxygen demand exceeds the supply (14, 15, 50, 91). Maximal oxygen uptake during one-leg work is normally about 75% of the absolute or two-leg maximum. Plasma norepinephrine levels during maximal work are proportional to the active muscle mass (9).

Training of only one leg (20, 30, 91) or of both legs separately (50) produces a large increase in one-leg maximal oxygen uptake (20% or more), a much smaller increase in two-leg maximum (10% or less), and no change during maximal exercise of the untrained leg. Changes in submaximal heart rates are reciprocal to the changes in maximal oxygen uptake. Maximal oxygen uptake during exercise with the trained leg also represents a larger portion of the two-leg maximum, 85–90% after training. There is a significant post-training increase in leg blood flow and conductance during maximal work with the trained leg but little or no change during two-leg maximal exercise. Analogous results have been reported from experiments in which either the lower or upper limbs have been trained and both pairs tested separately. The most prominent training effects are always evident when exercise is performed with the trained limb(s) (13–16). The combined data from these experiments support the concept that training causes an important increase in the maximal vascular conductance of working skeletal muscle. This increase is limited to the trained limb or limbs—i.e. mediated primarily by local rather than systemic mechanisms.

Older studies based on ^{133}Xe clearance rates have generated conflicting data on the effects of training on maximal flow rates in skeletal muscle (14). However, the ^{133}Xe method severely underestimates flow (1).

The extent to which the increase in the capacity to vasodilate can be translated into an increased maximal oxygen uptake is clearly modified by an opposing vasoconstrictor drive. The strength of this drive is determined by the relation between systemic oxygen demand and transport capacity. Thus changes in systemic oxygen transport capacity and the systemic impact of the local vascular adaptations are interdependent. Local adaptations with increased vascular conductance are prerequisites for effective utilization of a training-induced increase in cardiac capacity due to the inverse relationship between stroke volume and afterload. Similarly, the gain in aerobic capacity of a trained limb contributes effectively to an increased maximal systemic oxygen uptake only if associated with an increase in the capacity for systemic oxygen transport.

The precise manner in which central vasoconstrictor and local vasodilator mechanisms interact in working muscle is still poorly understood. There is no doubt that the metabolic state of muscle is the key factor. However, the metabolic response to exercise has the potential to enhance both vasoconstrictor and vadodilator drives. Several changes in the composition of the extracellular fluid of metabolically active tissues can produce vasodilation by direct inhibitory effects on smooth muscle cells. Some of these conditions—e.g. acidosis, hyperosmolarity, and release of adenosine—also have an inhibitory effect on adrenergic neurotransmission (110). On the other hand, impulses originating in skeletal muscle receptors responding to changes in metabolic state may contribute to the central vasoconstrictor drive whereas the role of reflex-induced β-adrenergic vasodilatation remains uncertain (98).

Autonomic Regulatory Mechanism

The complexity of the training-induced regulatory changes is well illustrated by the effects on heart rate. The normal heart rate response to exercise is mediated by a combination of vagal withdrawal and β-adrenergic stimulation (81). The essentially linear relationship between relative load (actual load as a fraction or percentage of individual maximum) and heart rates during exercise is not altered by training or deconditioning, but sinus bradycardia at rest and decreased heart rate at any absolute level of submaximal oxygen uptake are hallmarks of a cardiovascular training effect. In Scheuer & Tipton's review (97), ample evidence is presented that there is at rest after training an increased parasympathetic activity that causes bradycardia, but the results of various studies performed during exercise conflict. An enhanced parasympathetic drive may still be important at low work loads and heart rates. However, complete vagal blockade in humans will only produce a heart rate of about 130 beats/min. Any increase above this level must be mediated primarily by β-adrenergic mechanisms. Early studies produced inconclusive data on changes in adrenergic responses after training—i.e. reduced, unchanged, and elevated plasma or myocardial epinephrine or norepinephrine levels (97). Recent studies have generated more uniform results. There are no significant changes in myocardial tissue concentrations or in the plasma levels of epinephrine or norepinephrine at rest (12, 18, 74). Plasma concentrations are lower at any absolute submaximal work load after training but there are no differences when comparisons are made on the basis of relative work intensity. The lower post-training plasma levels at any given absolute level of energy expenditure are consistent with the relative bradycardia and decreased vasoconstrictor tone. The sensitivity of the S-A node to exogenous β-adrenergic agonists appears to be unchanged. The same amount of isoproterenol causes similar heart rate increases in unconditioned and well-conditioned men according to Williams et al (119). They also noted that the lymphocyte β-receptor number and affinity are unaffected by training. These data suggest that training reduces the efferent sympathetic neural outflow to the S-A node. Some investigators have after training found a relatively larger increase in myocardial contractile state in response to exogenous β-adrenergic stimulation (103, 121), but others have reported decreased sensitivity; there is no demonstrable change in the number of β-adrenergic receptors in the heart (65, 118).

Nonneural mechanisms may contribute to the relative bradycardia after training. Several studies have demonstrated a significant decrease in intrinsic sinus node rate as measured after combined vagal and β-adrenergic blockade (56, 57). The exact mechanisms are not known. However, all intrinsic cardiac pacemakers respond to stretch with an increased rate of discharge (43). It is conceivable that the frequent exposure to increased atrial pressures during training affects the basic stress-strain relationships of the sinus node. A chronic stress relaxation phenomenon may in the trained state attenuate the chronotropic response to any given amount of stretch.

It may also be argued that the bradycardia is the result of a primary increase in stroke volume. Normal regulatory mechanisms, predominantly baroreflexes at rest and the poorly defined mechanisms that maintain a very tight link between cardiac output and oxygen uptake during exercise (9, 26), have the potential to produce relative bradycardia even in the absence of any autonomic adaptations.

Autonomic function is a major determinant of the acute response to exercise, and it is evident that training induces significant adaptive changes. Nevertheless, training effects can be produced also in the various abnormal autonomic states. Significant changes in maximal oxygen uptake and hemodynamic responses have been observed both in normal subjects and patients with coronary disease who during endurance training were treated with moderately high oral doses of β-blocking agents (54, 111, 116). Training effects have also been induced in a variety of experimental animal models with significantly altered autonomic and metabolic regulation (unilateral vagotomy, sympathectomy, diencephalic lesions, thyroidectomy, adrenalectomy, hypophysectomy, and genetic hypertension) (97).

Two recent reports present an opposing view and emphasize the importance of the β-adrenergic system. Sable et al (85) found that β-adrenergic blockade abolished the training effect in a series of young healthy subjects. Liang et al (58) concluded that the major cardiovascular training effects can be elicited simply by β-adrenergic cardiac stimulation by chronic dobutamine infusion in dogs. However, the method used by Sable et al (85) to determine the intensity of training (equalization of heart rates, expressed as per cent of maximal heart rate measured during β-blockade and placebo treatment) is likely to have produced a lower relative intensity in the experimental group than in the control group. The results reported by Liang et al (58) included a large decrease in cardiac output during submaximal levels of exercise. This finding represents a significant deviation from the hemodynamic effects usually observed after training in normal subjects.

CONCLUSIONS

This review supports the concept that maximal oxygen uptake in general is limited by cardiovascular oxygen transport and that cardiovascular functional capacity can be enhanced by physical training. Cardiac pump performance, the ability to achieve a large stroke volume and cardiac output during exercise, is likely to be the immediate limiting factor. Training causes a moderate increase in cardiac dimensions with little or no change in intrinsic contractile performance—i.e. an increase in the quantity but not in the quality of the myocardium. An increase in diastolic reserve capacity is likely to be a significant factor. Systemic conductance increases in direct proportion to the increase in maximal VO_2 and cardiac output. Analysis of the performance characteristics of the normal heart indicate that an increase in dimensions would be unlikely to produce a significant increase in maximal stroke volume unless associated with an increase in maximal systemic conductance.

Data on skeletal muscle flow strongly suggest that significant vasoconstrictor tone normally is present also during maximal exercise. A release of vasoconstrictor activity is a crucial training-induced adaptation, but the potential for vasodilatation cannot be effectively utilized unless there is a simultaneous improvement in cardiac pump performance. The key to a better understanding of the cardiovascular effects of training is likely to be a better definition of how the local vasodilator and central vasoconstrictor mechanisms interact.

Further improvements of training techniques—yet to be defined—that induce even larger changes in cardiac pump performance and the potential for cardiovascular oxygen transport and delivery to skeletal muscle may unmask pulmonary diffusing capacity as the factor ultimately limiting performance.

Literature Cited

1. Andersen, P. 1982. Maximal blood flow and oxygen uptake of an isolated exercising muscle group in man. *Acta Physiol. Scand.* 114:37A (Abstr.)
2. Andrew, G. M., Guzman, C. A., Becklake, M. R. 1966. Effect of athletic training on exercise cardiac output. *J. Appl. Physiol.* 21:603–8
3. Åstrand, P. O., Rodahl, K. 1977. *Textbook of Work Physiology.* NY: McGraw-Hill. 681 pp. 2nd ed.
4. Bergström, J., Hermansen, L., Hultman, E., Saltin, B. 1967. Diet, muscle glycogen, and physical performance. *Acta Physiol. Scand.* 71:140–50
5. Bersohn, M. M., Scheuer, J. 1977. Effects of physical training on end-diastolic volume and myocardial performance of isolated rat hearts. *Circ. Res.* 40:510–16
6. Bevegård, S., Holmgren, A., Jonsson, B. 1963. Circulatory studies in well-trained athletes at rest and during heavy exercise, with special reference to stroke volume and the influence of body position. *Acta Physiol. Scand.* 57:26–50
7. Bhan, A. K., Scheuer, J. 1972. Effects of physical training on cardiac actomyosin adenosine triphosphatase activity. *Am. J. Physiol.* 223:1486–90
8. Blomqvist, G., Johnson, R. L. Jr., Saltin, B. 1969. Pulmonary diffusing capacity limiting human performance at altitude. *Acta Physiol. Scand.* 76:284–87
9. Blomqvist, C. G., Lewis, S. F., Taylor, W. F., Graham, R. M. 1981. Similarity of the hemodynamic responses to static and dynamic exercise of small muscle groups. *Circ. Res.* 48:(Suppl. I) 187–92
10. Bloor, C. M., Pasyk, S., Leon, A. S. 1970. Interaction of age and exercise on organ and cellular development. *Am. J. Pathol.* 58:185–99
11. Carew, T. E., Covell, J. W. 1978. Left ventricular function in exercise-induced hypertrophy in dogs. *Am. J. Cardiol.* 42:82–88
12. Christensen, N. J., Galbo, H., Hansen, J. F., Hesse, B., Richter, E. A., Trap-Jensen, J. 1979. Catecholamines and exercise. *Diabetes* 28:(Suppl. I) 58–62
13. Clausen, J. P. 1976. Circulatory adjustments to dynamic exercise and effect of physical training in normal subjects and in patients with coronary artery disease. *Prog. Cardiovasc. Dis.* 18:459–95
14. Clausen, J. P. 1977. Effect of physical training on cardiovascular adjustments to exercise in man. *Physiol. Rev.* 57:779–815

15. Clausen, J. P., Klausen, K., Rasmussen, B., Trap-Jensen, J. 1973. Central and peripheral circulatory changes after training of the arms or legs. *Am. J. Physiol.* 225:675–82
16. Clausen, J. P., Trap-Jensen, J., Lassen, N. A. 1970. The effects of training on the heart rate during arm and leg exercise. *Scand. J. Clin. Lab. Invest.* 26:295–301
17. Cohen, M. V., Yipintsoi, T., Scheuer, J. 1982. Coronary collateral stimulation by exercise in dogs with stenotic coronary arteries. *J. Appl. Physiol.* 52:664–71
18. Cousineau, D., Ferguson, R. J., DeChamplain, J., Gauthier, P., Côté, P., Bourassa, M. 1977. Catecholamines in coronary sinus during exercise in man before and after training. *J. Appl. Physiol.* 43:801–6
19. Cutilletta, A. F., Edmiston, K., Dowell, R. T. 1979. Effect of a mild exercise program on myocardial function and the development of hypertrophy. *J. Appl. Physiol.* 46:354–60
20. Davies, C. T. M., Sargeant, A. J. 1975. Effects of training on the physiological responses to one- and two-leg work. *J. Appl. Physiol.* 38:377–81
21. Davies, K. J., Packer, L., Brooks, G. A. 1981. Biochemical adaptation of mitochondria, muscle, and whole-animal respiration to endurance training. *Arch. Biochem. Biophys.* 209:539–54
22. Eckstein, R. W. 1957. Effect of exercise and coronary artery narrowing on coronary collateral circulation. *Circ. Res.* 5:230–35
23. Ekblom, B. 1969. Effect of physical training on oxygen transport system in man. *Acta Physiol. Scand.* (Suppl.) 328:5–45
24. Ekelund, L. G., Holmgren, A. 1967. Central hemodynamics during exercise. *Circ. Res.* 20–21:(Suppl. I) I33–43
25. Eriksson, B. O., Lundin, A., Saltin, B. 1975. Cardiopulmonary function in former girl swimmers and the effects of physical training. *Scand. J. Clin. Lab. Invest.* 35:135–45
26. Faulkner, J. A., Heigenhauser, G. F., Schork, M. A. 1977. The cardiac output–oxygen uptake relationship of men during graded bicycle ergometry. *Med. Sci. Sports* 9:148–54
27. Ford, L. E. 1976. Heart size. *Circ. Res.* 39:297–303
28. Fortney, S. M., Nadel, E. R., Wenger, C. B., Bove, J. R. 1981. Effect of acute alterations of blood volume on circula-

tory performance in humans. *J. Appl. Physiol.: Respir. Environ. Exer. Physiol.* 50:292–98

29. Fuller, E. O., Nutter, D. O. 1981. Endurance training in the rat. II. Performance of isolated and intact heart. *J. Appl. Physiol.* 51:941–47

30. Gleser, M. A. 1973. Effects of hypoxia and physical training on hemodynamic adjustments to one-legged exercise. *J. Appl. Physiol.* 34:655–59

31. Gollnick, P. D., Saltin, B. 1982. Significance of skeletal muscle oxidative enzyme enhancement with endurance training. *Clin. Physiol.* 2:1–12

32. Gollnick, P. D., Sembrowich, W. L. 1977. Adaptations in human skeletal muscle as a result of training. In *Exercise in Cardiovascular Health and Disease*, ed. E. A. Amsterdam, J. H. Wilmore, A. N. DeMaria, pp. 70–94. NY: Yorke Medical Books. 384 pp.

33. Grande, F., Taylor, H. L. 1965. Adaptive changes in the heart, vessels, and patterns of control under chronically high loads. In *Handbook of Physiology*, Sect. 2., *Circulation*, Vol. III, ed. W. F. Hamilton, P. Dow, pp. 2615–78. Washington DC: Am. Physiol. Soc. 2765 pp.

34. Grossman, W., Braunwald, E., Mann, T., McLaurin, L. P., Green. L. H. 1977. Contractile state of the left ventricle in man as evaluated from end-systolic pressure-volume relations. *Circulation* 56:845–52

35. Hanson, J. S., Tabakin, B. S., Levy, A. M., Nedde W. 1968. Long-term physical training and cardiovascular dynamics in middle-aged men. *Circulation* 38:783–99

36. Hartley, L. H., Grimby, G., Kilbom, Å., Nilsson, N. J., Åstrand, I., Bjure, J., Ekblom, B., Saltin, B. 1969. Physical training in sedentary middle-aged and older men. *Scand. J. Clin. Lab. Invest.* 24:335–44

37. Hill, A. V. 1926. *Muscular Activity.* Baltimore: Williams & Wilkins Co. 115 pp.

38. Holmberg, S., Serzysko, W., Varnauskas, E. 1971. Coronary circulation during heavy exercise in control subjects and patients with coronary heart disease. *Acta Med. Scand.* 190:465–80

39. Holmgren, A., Strandell, T. 1959. The relationship between heart volume, total hemoglobin and physical working capacity in former athletes. *Acta Med. Scand.* 163:149–60

40. Hudlická, O. 1982. Growth of capillaries in skeletal and cardiac muscle. *Circ. Res.* 50:451–61

41. Ingjer, F., Brodal, P. 1978. Capillary supply of skeletal muscle fibers in untrained and endurance-trained women. *Eur. J.Appl. Physiol.* 38:291–99

42. Jansson, E., Sylvén, C., Nordevang, E. 1982. Myoglobin in the quadriceps femoris muscle of competitive cyclists and untrained men. *Acta Physiol. Scand.* 114:627–29

43. Jensen, D. 1971. *Intrinsic Cardiac Rate Regulation.* NY: Meredith Corp. 238 pp.

44. Johnson, R. L. Jr. 1977. Oxygen transport. In *Clinical Cardiology*, ed. J. T. Willerson, C. A. Sanders, pp. 74–84. NY: Grune & Stratton. 660 pp.

45. Jorgensen, C. R., Gobel, F. L., Taylor, H. L., Wang, Y. 1977. Myocardial blood flow and oxygen consumption during exercise. *Ann. NY Acad. Sci.* 301:213–23

46. Kaijser, L. 1970. Limiting factors for aerobic muscle performance. *Acta Physiol. Scand.* (Suppl.) 346:1–96

47. Kanstrup, I., Ekblom, B. 1982. Acute hypervolemia, cardiac performance, and aerobic power during exercise. *J. Appl. Physiol.: Respir. Environ. Exer. Physiol.* 52:1186–91

48. Karlsson, J., Nordesjö, L. O., Saltin, B. 1974. Muscle glycogen utilization during exercise after physical training. *Acta Physiol. Scand.* 90:210–17

49. Keul, J., Dickhuth, H. H., Simon, G., Lehmann, M. 1981. Effect of static and dynamic exercise on heart volume, contractility, and left ventricular dimensions. *Circ. Res.* 48:(Suppl.I) I162–70

50. Klausen, K., Secher, N. H., Clausen, J. P., Hartling, O., Trap-Jensen, J. 1982. Central and regional circulatory adaptations to one-leg training. *J. Appl. Physiol.* 52:976–83

51. Klissouras, V. 1971. Heritability of adaptive variation. *J. Appl. Physiol.* 31:338–44

52. Komi, P. V., Viitasalo, J. H. T., Havu, M., Thorstensson, A., Sjödin, B., Karlsson, J. 1977. Skeletal muscle fibers and muscle enzyme activities in monozygous and dizygous twins of both sexes. *Acta Physiol. Scand.* 100:385–92

53. Leon, A. S., Bloor, C. M. 1968. Effects of exercise and its cessation on the heart and its blood supply. *J. Appl. Physiol.* 24:485–90

54. Lester, R. M., Wallace, A. G. 1978. Cardiovascular adaptations to beta-adrenergic blockade during physical training. *Circulation* 57–58: (Suppl. II) 140 (Abstr.)

55. LeWinter, M. M., Pavelec, R. 1982. Influence of the pericardium on left ventricular end-diastolic pressure-segment relations during early and late stages of experimental chronic volume overload in dogs. *Circ. Res.* 50:501–9

56. Lewis, S. F., Nylander, E., Gad, P., Areskog, N-H. 1980. Non-autonomic component in bradycardia of endurance trained men at rest and during exercise. *Acta Physiol. Scand.* 109:297–305

57. Lewis, S., Thompson, P., Areskog, N.-H., Marconyak, M., Vodak, P., DeBusk, R., Haskell, W. L. 1980. Endurance training and heart rate control studied by combined parasympathetic and beta-adrenergic blockade. *Int. J. Sports Med.* 1:42–49

58. Liang, C. S., Tuttle, R. R., Hood, W. B. Jr., Gavras, H. 1979. Conditioning effects of chronic infusions of dobutamine. *J. Clin. Invest.* 64:613–19

59. Linzbach, A. J. 1960. Heart failure from the point of view of quantitative anatomy. *Am. J. Cardiol.* 5:370–82

60. Ljungqvist, A., Unge, G. 1977. Capillary proliferative activity in myocardium and skeletal muscle of exercised rats. *J. Appl. Physiol.* 43:306–7

61. Longhurst, J. C., Kelly, A. R., Gonyea, W. J., Mitchell, J. H. 1981. Chronic training with static and dynamic exercise: Cardiovascular adaptation and response to exercise. *Circ. Res.* 48:(Suppl. I) I171–78

62. Mandache, E., Unge, G., Appelgren, L. E., Ljungqvist, A. 1973. The proliferative activity of the heart tissues in various forms of experimental cardiac hypertrophy studied by electron microscope autoradiography. *Virchows Arch. Abt. B. Zellpathol.* 12:112–22

63. Mead, J., Agostoni, E. 1964. Dynamics of breathing. In *Handbook of Physiology.* Sect. 3, *Respiration,* ed. W. O. Fenn, H. Rahn, 1:411–28. Washington DC: Am. Physiol. Soc. 926 pp.

64. Mitchell, J. H., Hefner, L. L., Monroe, R. G. 1972. Performance of the left ventricle. *Am. J. Med.* 53:481–94

65. Moore, R. L., Riedy, M., Gollnick, P. D. 1982. Effect of training on β-adrenergic receptor number in rat heart. *J. Appl. Physiol.: Respir. Environ. Exer. Physiol.* 52:1133–37

66. Morganroth, J., Maron, B. J., Henry, W. L., Epstein, S. E. 1975. Comparative left ventricular dimensions in trained athletes. *Ann. Intern. Med.* 82:521–24

67. Muntz, K. W., Gonyea, W. J., Mitchell, J. H. 1981. Cardiac hypertrophy in response to an isometric training program in the cat. *Circ. Res.* 49:1092–1101

68. Myrhage, R., Hudlická, O. 1978. Capillary growth in chronically stimulated adult skeletal muscle as studied by intravital microscopy and histological methods in rabbits and rats. *Microvasc. Res.* 16:73–90

69. Nemeth, P. M., Chi, N. M. L., Hintz, C. S., Lowry, O. H. 1982. Myoglobin content of normal and trained human muscle fibers. *Acta Physiol. Scand.* In press

70. Nutter, D. O, Fuller, E. O. 1977. The role of isolated cardiac muscle preparations in the study of training effects on the heart. *Med. Sci. Sports* 9:239–45

71. Nutter, D. O., Priest, R. E., Fuller, E. O. 1981. Endurance training in the rat. I. Myocardial mechanics and biochemistry. *J. Appl. Physiol.* 51:934–40

72. Nygaard, E., Nielsen, E. 1978. Skeletal muscle fiber capillarization with extreme endurance training in man. In *Swimming Medicine,* ed. B. Eriksson, B. Furberg, 4:282–96. Baltimore: Univ. Park Press. 421 pp.

73. Pattengale, P. K., Holloszy, J. O. 1967. Augmentation of skeletal muscle myoglobin by a program of treadmill running. *Am. J. Physiol.* 213:783–85

74. Péronnet, F., Cléroux, J., Perrault, H., Cousineau, D., DeChamplain, J., Nadeau, R. 1981. Plasma norepinephrine response to exercise before and after training in humans. *J. Appl. Physiol.: Respir. Environ. Exer. Physiol.* 51: 812–15

75. Péronnet, F., Ferguson, R. J., Perrault, H., Ricci, G., Lajoie, D. 1981. Echocardiography and the athlete's heart. *Phys. Sports Med.* 9:102–12

76. Poliner, L. R., Dehmer, G. J., Lewis, S. E., Parkey, R. W., Blomqvist, C. G., Willerson, J. T. 1980. Left ventricular performance in normal subjects: A comparison of the responses to exercise in the upright and supine position. *Circulation* 62:528–34

77. Pyörälä, K., Karvonen, M. J., Taskinen, P., Takkunen, J., Kyrönseppä, H., Peltokallio, P. 1967. Cardiovascular studies on former endurance athletes. *Am. J. Cardiol.* 20:191–205

78. Repke, K., Est, M., Portius, H. J. 1965. Über die Ursache der Species-unterschiede in der Digitalisempfindlichkeit. *Biochem. Pharmacol.* 14:1785–1802

79. Rerych, S. K., Scholz, P. M., Sabiston, D. C., Jones, R. H. 1980. Effects of exercise training on left ventricular function in normal subjects: A longitudinal study

by radionuclide angiography. *Am. J. Cardiol.* 45:244–52

80. Rifenberick, D. H., Gamble, J. G., Max, S. R. 1973. Response of mitochondrial enzymes to decreased muscular activity. *Am. J. Phsiol.* 225:1295–99

81. Robinson, B. F., Epstein, S. F., Beiser, G. D., Braunwald, E. 1966. Control of heart rate by the autonomic nervous system. Studies in man on the interrelation between baroreceptor mechanisms and exercise. *Circ. Res.* 19:400–11

82. Robinson, B. F., Epstein, S. E., Kahler, R. L., Braunwald, E. 1966. Circulatory effects of acute expansion of blood volume. Studies during maximal exercise and at rest. *Circ. Res.* 19:26–32

83. Roeske, W. R., O'Rourke, R. A., Klein, A., Leopold, G., Karliner, J. S. 1975. Noninvasive evaluation of ventricular hypertrophy in professional athletes. *Circulation* 53:286–92

84. Rowell, L. B. 1962. *Factors affecting the prediction of the maximal oxygen intake from measurements made during submaximal work with observations related to factors which may limit maximal oxygen intake.* PhD thesis. Univ. Minnesota, Minneapolis. 275 pp.

85. Sable, D. L., Brammell, H. L., Sheehan, M. W., Nies, A. S., Gerber, J., Horwitz, L. D. 1982. Attenuation of exercise conditioning by beta-adrenergic blockade. *Circulation* 65:679–84

86. Sagawa, K. 1978. The ventricular pressure-volume diagram revisited. *Circ. Res.* 43:677–87

87. Saltin, B. 1971. Central circulation after physical conditioning in young and middle-aged men. In *Coronary Heart Disease and Physical Fitness*, ed. O. A. Larsen, E. O. Malmborg, pp. 21–26. Copenhagen: Munksgaard. 277 pp.

88. Saltin, B., Blomqvist, G., Mitchell, J. H., Johnson, R. L. Jr., Wildenthal, K., Chapman, C. B. 1968. Response to exercise after bed rest and after training. *Circulation* 38:(Suppl. 7) 1–78

89. Saltin, B., Grimby, G. 1968. Physiological analysis of middle-aged and old former athletes. Comparison with still active athletes of the same ages. *Circulation* 38:1104–15

90. Saltin, B., Henrikson, J., Nygaard, E., Andersen, P. 1977. Fiber types and metabolic potentials of skeletal muscles in sedentary man and endurance runners. *Ann. NY Acad. Sci.* 301:3–29

91. Saltin, B., Nazar, K., Costill, D. L., Stein, E., Jansson, E., Essén, B., Gollnick, P. D. 1976. The nature of the training response; peripheral and central adaptations to one-legged exercise. *Acta Physiol. Scand.* 96:289–305

92. Saltin, B., Rowell, L. B. 1980. Functional adaptations to physical activity and inactivity. *Fed. Proc.* 39:1506–13

93. Sanders, M., White, F. C., Peterson, T. M., Bloor, C. M. 1978. Effects of endurance exercise on coronary collateral blood flow in miniature swine. *Am. J. Physiol.* 234:H614–19

94. Schaible, T. F., Penpargkul, S., Scheuer, J. 1981. Cardiac responses to exercise training in male and female rats. *J. Appl. Physiol.* 50:112–17

95. Schaible, T. F., Scheuer, J. 1981. Cardiac function in hypertrophied hearts from chronically exercised female rats. *J. Appl. Physiol.* 50:1140–45

96. Schaper, W. 1982. Influence of physical exercise on coronary collateral blood flow in chronic experimental two-vessel occlusion. *Circulation* 65:905–12

97. Scheuer, J., Tipton, C. M. 1977. Cardiovascular adaptations to physical training. *Ann. Rev. Physiol.* 39:221–51

98. Shepherd, J. T., Blomqvist, C. G., Lind, A. R., Mitchell, J. H., Saltin, B. 1981. Static (isometric) exercise. Retrospection and introspection. *Circ. Res.* 48:(Suppl. I) I179–88

99. Siegel, W., Blomqvist, G., Mitchell, J. H. 1970. Effects of a quantitated physical training program on middle-aged sedentary men. *Circulation* 41:19–29

100. Spriet, L. L., Gledhill, N., Froese, A. B., Wilkes, D. L., Meyers, E. C. 1980. The effect of induced erythrocythemia on central circulation and oxygen transport during maximal exercise. *Med. Sci. Sports Exer.* 12:122–23 (Abstr.)

101. Steel, J. D., Beilharz, R. G., Stewart, G. A., Goddard, M. 1977. The inheritance of heart score in racehorses. *Austr. Vet. J.* 53:306–9

102. Stevenson, J. A. F., Feleki, V., Rechnitzer, P., Beaton, J. R. 1964. Effect of exercise on coronary tree size in the rat. *Circ. Res.* 15:265–69

103. Stone, H. L. 1977. Cardiac function and exercise training in conscious dogs. *J. Appl. Physiol.* 42:824–32

104. Stone, H. L. 1977. The unanesthetized instrumented animal preparation. *Med. Sci. Sports* 9:253–61

105. Stone, H. L. 1980. Coronary flow, myocardial oxygen consumption, and exercise training in dogs. *J. Appl. Physiol.* 49:759–68

106. Suga, H., Sagawa, K. 1974. Instantaneous pressure-volume relationships and their ratio in the excised, supported

canine left ventricle. *Circ. Res.* 35: 117–26

107. Tepperman, J., Pearlman, D. 1961. Effects of exercise and anemia on coronary arteries of small animals as revealed by the corrosion-cast technique. *Circ. Res.* 9:576–84

108. Underwood, R. H., Schwade, J. L. 1977. Noninvasive analysis of cardiac function of elite distance runners— Echocardiography, vectorcardiography, and cardiac intervals. *Ann. NY Acad. Sci.* 301:297–309

109. Unge, G., Carlsson, S., Ljungqvist, A., Tornling, G., Adolfsson, J. 1979. The proliferative activity of myocardial capillary wall cells in variously aged swimming-exercised rats. *Acta Pathol. Microbiol. Scand. (A)* 87:15–17

110. Vanhoutte, P. M., Verbeuren, T. J., Webb, R. C. 1981. Local modulation of adrenergic neuroeffector interaction in the blood vessel wall. *Physiol. Rev.* 61:151–247

111. Vetrovec, G. W., Abel, P. M. 1977. Results of exercise conditioning in propranolol and treated patients trained at low heart rates. *Circulation* 55–56:(Suppl. III) 197

112. Wachtlová, M., Poupa, O., Rakušan, K. 1970. Quantitative differences in the terminal vascular bed of the myocardium in the brown bat (*Myotis myotis*) and the laboratory mouse (*Mus musculus*). *Physiol. Bohemoslov.* 19:491–95

113. Wachtlová, M., Rakušan, K., Poupa, O. 1965. The coronary terminal vascular bed in the heart of the hare (*Lepus europeus*) and the rabbit (*Oryctolagus domesticus*). *Physiol. Bohemoslov.* 14: 328–31

114. Wachtlová, M., Rakušan, K., Poupa, O. 1967. The terminal vascular bed of the myocardium in the wild rat (*Rattus norvegicus*) and the laboratory rat (*Rattus*

Norv. Lab.) *Physiol. Bohemoslov.* 16: 548–54

115. Weber, K. T., Janicki, J. S., Shroff, S., Fishman, A. P. 1981. Contractile mechanics and interactions of the right and left ventricles. *Am. J. Cardiol.* 47: 686–95

116. Welton, D. E., Squires, W. G., Hartung, G. H., Miller, R. R. 1979. Effects of chronic beta-adrenergic blockade therapy on exercise training in patients with coronary heart disease. *Am. J. Cardiol.* 43:399 (Abstr.)

117. White, F. C., Sanders, M., Bloor, C. M. 1981. Coronary reserve at maximal heart rate in the exercising swine. *J. Cardiac Rehab.* 1:31–50

118. Williams, R. S. 1980. Physical conditioning and membrane receptors for cardioregulatory hormones. *Cardiovasc. Res.* 14:177–82

119. Williams, R. S., Eden, R. S., Moll, M. E., Lester, R. M., Wallace, A. G. 1981. Autonomic mechanisms of training bradycardia: β-adrenergic receptors in humans. *J. Appl. Physiol.: Respir. Environ. Exer. Physiol.* 51:1232–37

120. Wyatt, H. L., Mitchell, J. H. 1974. Influences of physical training on the heart of dogs. *Circ. Res.* 35:883–89

121. Wyatt, H. L., Chuck, L., Rabinowitz, B., Tyberg, J. V., Parmley, W. W. 1978. Enhanced cardiac response to catecholamines in physically trained cats. *Am. J. Physiol.* 234:H608–13

122. Wyatt, H. L., Mitchell, J. H. 1978. Influences of physical conditioning and deconditioning on coronary vasculature of dogs. *J. Appl. Physiol.* 45:619–25

123. Zoneraich, S., Rhee, J. J., Zoneraich, O., Jordan, D., Appel, J. 1977. Assessment of cardiac function in marathon runners by graphic noninvasive techniques. *Ann. NY Acad. Sci.* 301:900–17

Ann. Rev. Physiol. 1983. 45:191–212

CIRCULATORY ADJUSTMENTS TO EXERCISE AND HEAT STRESS

G. L. Brengelmann

Department of Physiology and Biophysics, University of Washington, Seattle, Washington 98195

INTRODUCTION

Students of this complex field have excellent resources available. A comprehensive 1965 chapter by Thauer (89) gives access to the earlier literature and provides a synthesis of knowledge regarding both central and peripheral cardiovascular adjustments to thermal stress. Rowell's 1974 review (75) and forthcoming handbook chapter (78) continue this tradition of comprehensive and analytical treatment of the subject, including the major advances in understanding of how cardiac output and its distribution are controlled when the stresses of exercise and heat are combined. Useful recent books include *Man And Animals in Hot Environments* (42), a systematic development that will help to introduce the field; a group of essays (6) emphasizing the control mechanisms involved in temperature regulation; a general overview of thermal physiology (41), with chapters devoted to particular cardiovascular aspects; and a compilation of papers from a symposium on temperature regulation during exercise (60). A major component of the cardiovascular response to heat stress in humans is discussed in a recent review of the subject of active cutaneous vasodilatation (77).

Riedel & Iriki (1979) discuss autonomic nervous system activity associated with integration of thermal and other afferent signals into a final common neural outflow that governs cardiovascular effectors (72). Sciaraffa et al (81) have compiled literature (1968–1977) on acclimatization to heat. A still useful reference on the disorders that accompany hyperthermia is the 1964 book by Liethead & Lind (53). Finally, papers from a number of informative symposia have been published in *Federation Proceedings,* including two that will bring scholars up to date on the neurophysiology of

191

0066-4278/83/0315–0191$02.00

temperature regulation and present concepts of the central neurotransmitters involved (5, 69); one on regulation in physiological systems during exercise, which includes two articles specifically relevant to the present topic (57, 61, 80); and one on fever and hyperthermia (58) in which Stitt (87) contrasts the hyperthermias associated with fever and exercise.

Many papers relevant to the topic of this review have been published in recent years. I have given them unequal treatment. A particular subset of papers with a common conceptual approach seemed ripe for a critical appraisal: those on control of skin blood flow (SkBF) in exercising humans. A major section of the chapter is devoted to this relatively small number of papers. Thereafter follow brief comments on a wider spectrum of papers relevant to the general subject of cardiovascular responses to exercise and thermal stress in human and nonhuman subjects.

CONTROL OF SKIN BLOOD FLOW

General Background

One has only to compare the heat capacity of the body with the metabolic heat production of exercise to appreciate the necessity of powerful effector mechanisms for heat dissipation. Lethal temperatures would be reached in a fraction of an hour of severe exercise if all the heat produced were stored in the body. Skin blood flow (SkBF) transfers heat to the body surface at the rate of several kilocalories for each liter that leaves the cutaneous capillaries equilibrated with skin temperature (T_{sk}), provided that T_{sk} is kept well below internal temperature (T_c).

When T_{sk} is kept low by cool environmental conditions or through evaporation of sweat, stable T_c can be maintained and the cardiovascular adjustments required for maintenance of thermal balance are relatively minor. If T_{sk} cannot be kept low, however, more SkBF is required for the same heat transport. Several liters per minute of cardiac output can be diverted to skin through active cutaneous vasodilatation, a process somehow linked with sweating (9, 27, 76). Thus an effector of the temperature regulation system has major impact on cardiovascular regulation. Alternatively, thermal balance is upset when SkBF is the target of cardiovascular reflexes—e.g. as part of a response to progressive diminution of central blood volume that may accompany exercise.

Therefore, control of SkBF deserves emphasis within the general subject of circulatory adjustments to exercise and heat stress. In fact, this is one area in which better quantitative information has been obtained from humans than from experimental animals, notwithstanding the relative ease of manipulating independent variables in the latter. See (46, 47, 78) for methodological background on the prevailing assumption that SkBF changes can be determined from forearm plethysmography in exercising humans.

Conceptual Orientation

Figure 1, a summary of findings on SkBF control from various laboratories, reflects a commonly held conceptual orientation [details in (8, 60)]. Effector responses are analyzed in terms of plots in the FBF-T_c plane. The promi-

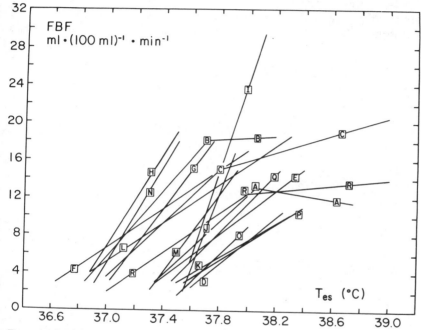

Figure 1 Straight line approximations to data from investigations tabulated in Table 1, coded by letters within squares. Table 1 includes the name of the first author and the date published, workload, T_{sk}, ambient temperature (T_{amb}), and brief notations of experimental conditions. Where workload is tabulated as a percentage, the reference is to the fraction of maximal oxygen uptake; other entries are in watts except for one reference to "moderate." Question marks indicate where T_{sk} was not measured or not reported; ambient temperatures not reported are left blank. Where duplications are indicated by quotation marks, the entries refer to multiple lines from the same paper—e.g. M, N, and O are all from one study. Lines A, B, C, and R have two segments. The remaining lines are all single segments. Note that the squares surrounding the letter labels are touched by the lines to which they belong, avoided by others. All the investigators used esophageal temperature (T_{es}) as their measure of T_c and recorded forearm blood flow (FBF) to determine changes in SkBF.

To aid in sorting out the tangle, Table 1 includes a list of the coordinates of the endpoints and breakpoints of the segments, in the form [Tes, FBF]. Units are, respectively, °C, and (ml)(100 ml)$^{-1}$(min)$^{-1}$. All the coordinates were determined from published illustrations. Most of the lines are actually from linear regressions; their endpoints here extend from the baseline level to the highest FBF in the raw data. A few lines are estimated straight line best fits done by eye from published scatter plots; they also extend from the recorded baseline to the highest FBF in the raw data. Lines A through D are from averages of three or four individuals; all the rest are from that unremarkable creature, the typical subject.

nence given T_c is an implicit assumption that this is the predominant variable in control of effectors that alter thermal balance. Statistical or simple graphical procedures are used to determine contours in the plane for particular values of a second independent variable, such as skin temperature (T_{sk}). Some third variable—e.g. state of acclimatization—may be analyzed in terms of how much it appears to displace these contours.

Contour shifts are described in particular ways. For example, if the T_{sk}

Table 1 Data displayed in Figure 1

Code	First author and date	Workload	T_{sk} (°C)	T_{amb} (°C)	End- or break-points	Conditions
A	Nadel, 1980 (63)	55%	?	35°	[37.35, 3] [38.05, 13] [38.75, 11.5]	Hypohydration Moderately heavy exercise, hea
B	Nadel, 1980 (63)	55%	?	35°	[36.85, 3] [37.70, 18] [38.20, 18.5]	Curve B is average of 4 controls curve A average of 4 hypohydra
C	Nadel, 1979 (62)	40, 70%	35.5°		[37.00, 3.5] [37.80, 15] [39.00, 20.5]	FBF-T_{es} shifted to right by coo T_{sk}, not shifted by workload.
D	Nadel, 1979 (62)	40, 70%	32°		[37.60, 2.4] [38.25, 10.5]	
E	Wenger, 1975 (94)	50%	30.3°		[37.35, 2.9] [38.40, 15]	FBF-T_{es} shifted to right by coo T_{sk}, not shifted by workload
F	Wenger, 1975 (94)	30, 50%	35.5°		[36.64, 2.9] [38.00, 17]	
G	Johnson, 1981 (45)	100–150 W	38°		[37.02, 3.2] [37.75, 18]	Moderate work upright with hea suit versus supine rest. FBF-T_{es}
H	Johnson, 1981 (45)	rest	38°		[36.88. 4] [37.50, 19]	shifted to right by work and/or posture
I	Johnson, 1979 (44)	50–150 W	? ?	24° 24°	[37.59, 5.1] [38.11, 29.4]	FBF-T_{es} not altered over wide range of workloads
J	Johnson, 1975 (46)	100–125 W	?	24°	[37.54, 2.1] [37.90, 16.8]	Prolonged work (HR 130)
K	Johnson, 1974 (47)	moderate	38°		[37.50, 3] [38.30, 10.2]	Upright exercise versus supine r as in G and H. Not shown are in
L	Johnson, 1974 (47)	moderate	38°		[36.88, 3.9] [38.30, 18.6]	mediate effects of exercise per s and posture per se.
M	Roberts, 1980 (73)	40–51%	?	40°	[37.31, 2.2] [37.92, 15]	Hot, upright exercise
N	Roberts, 1980 (73)	40–51%	?	40°	[36.91, 2.9] [37,50, 15]	Hot, supine exercise
O	Roberts, 1980 (73)	40–51%	?	15°	[37.50, 1.6] [38.00, 9]	Cool, upright exercise (overlaps supine)
P	Roberts, 1977 (74)	60–70%	33°	25°	[37.55, 3] [38.00, 9]	Pre-training, (post-training near overlaps line P)
Q	Roberts, 1977 (74)	60–70%	33°	25°	[37.46, 3.2] [38.22, 15]	Post acclimatization, leftward s
R	Brengelmann, 1977 (10)	150 W	38°		[37.00, 2] [38.00, 12.5] [39.00, 14]	Prolonged moderate upright exe cise in heated suit, slope attenua tion at high T_{es}

contours were shifted to the left by acclimatization without change in slope, the modification of the basic relationship would typically be described as a change of "threshold." If T_{sk} contours were altered in slope but not in origin, the change would be described as a change of "gain." In general, "gain" is taken as synonymous with the slope of Response-T_c contours, and "threshold" as that T_c above which first elevations in response are seen. Another term in use is "set-point." In actual experimental results, contours are often found to be altered in slope as well as displaced laterally, so reference is made to changes in both gain and threshold(s) or set-point(s).

The terminology in use and analyses of data tend to be based loosely on a linear model. For example, a linear relationship of the form:

$$(R - R_o) = a(T_c - T_{co}) + b(T_{sk} - T_{so}) \qquad\qquad 1.$$

where R refers to response and Ro, T_{co}, and T_{so} are constants, would describe a system of uniformly spaced T_{sk} contours of identical slope. Of course, this leaves out nonlinear details such as some representation of the fact that $(R - R_o)$ cannot take on negative values and specifics of whether the other terms can in fact take on negative values. Leaving these nonlinearities aside (a convenience indulged to excess), one should note that a change in just one of the two "threshold" constants of equation 1 would shift all the contours laterally—i.e. simple lateral contour shifts can be modelled numerically by appropriate adjustment of either T_{co} or T_{so}. However, reference is made to multiple thresholds in interpretation of lateral shifts—i.e. as if it were proper to describe the contour shifts as alteration of multiple distinct T_c thresholds. This is convenient, and similar terminology will be used here; but all that is denoted by the term "threshold" in such treatments is "that T_c above which effector response distinguishable from baseline is seen for a given set of conditions." In other words, "threshold" is taken to mean simply the intercept of a given contour with baseline rather than the more general meaning associated with a model such as Equation 1.

References to a multiplicative interaction between T_c and other variables are found in the literature. This type of interaction is distinct from that associated with changes in slope—i.e. constants a and/or b in equation 1. The implication is that the partial derivative of the response with respect to T_c would be a function of the other variable (and vice versa). In this type of interaction, each contour in the Response-T_c plane would have a different slope. One has to ask whether curvilinear representations of contours are realistically distinguishable from linear ones. See (11) for further exposition on the subject of critical discriminations between models of effector control systems.

A logical application of the approach described above might be to begin by defining the SkBF-T_c relationship at rest and then to proceed by manipulating other variables systematically. Obvious candidates are T_{sk}, level of exercise, posture, state of conditioning, state of acclimatization, and state of hydration. On the other hand, given a limited life span, experimental programs that would tend to exceed it are impractical. So, one laboratory may look at the influence of T_{sk} against a background of a particular workload and another may examine SkBF-T_c relationships at various workloads. Whether workload would have made a difference in the former or T_{sk} in the latter may be left to the reader. Figure 1 and Table 1 have been prepared in an attempt to aid students of the field in their efforts to synthesize findings reported in the last few years.

Baseline Reference: SkBF Control in Resting Humans

The historical antecedent of all these curves is not shown. Wyss et al (97, 98) heated supine resting men with water-perfused suits. FBF increased in relation to T_{es} with a slope of roughly 10 flow units per °C beyond T_{es} of roughly 36.8°C. This is closely approximated by more recent data from similar experiments (45), represented as line H in Figure 1. The high levels of FBF observed in both studies were necessarily associated with high T_{sk}; one does not find normal resting men with high T_{es} and low T_{sk} except for difficult-to-interpret dynamic periods after the skin of a hot man is cooled (97). From their regression analysis of FBF responses during the early phase of heating (during which brief time T_{sk} ranges upward to the high level at which it is thereafter maintained), Wyss et al (97) reported an FBF : T_{sk} ratio (parameter b in equation 1) on the order of 1 flow unit per °C. According to this, a cooler skin would shift the FBF-T_{es} line to the right. Theoretically, the same FBF would result at 1° higher T_{es} were T_{sk} to drop 10°C. In other words, line H would be shifted rightward to the extreme right margin of the cluster of lines in Figure 1 at higher T_{es}, were T_{sk} to drop from 38° to 28°C. The possible relevance of this lies in the fact that, with exercise in ordinary conditions, high T_{es} occurs with T_{sk} not much above 28°C (see curves O, E, and P). Unless exercise per se modifies the SkBF : T_c : T_{sk} relationship, then, low T_{sk} during exercise may be thought of as inhibitory to SkBF.

Wyss et al (98) did report that T_{sk} influence appeared nonlinear. Increments in T_{sk} contributed less to FBF at higher levels of T_{sk}, but whether the reverse applies down to neutral or cool levels of T_{sk} is not known. I can find no direct FBF-T_c analysis from quasi-steady states at low T_{sk} except a report on data from a single subject by Tam et al (88) in which T_c, measured in the external auditory meatus, was manipulated by ingestion of fluids and immersion of the hands in hot water baths. Unfortunately, the range of T_{sk} reported was only from 32° to 35°C. Also, it is difficult to fit their data into the perspective of Figure 1 since flows ranged only up to 7 units and apparent thresholds are much lower than 37.0°C; the line for the coolest skin temperature would be to the left of line H. Perhaps this is a problem with the site of measurement of T_c (56). On the other hand, the magnitude of the contour shift for a 3°C change in T_{sk} is definitely in proportion to that estimated above. Further experimental investigation of the lower range of the T_{sk} influence on control of SkBF in resting humans with elevated T_c seems a necessary background for clarifying the role of this variable in exercise.

Variables: Posture and Exercise

In 1974, Johnson et al (47) published the first reports of FBF-T_{es} modification by factors related to exercise. They reasoned that posture and exercise could be expected to have independent effects, the latter associated primarily with volume redistribution, and the former with the general elevation of sympathetic nervous system activity in exercise. T_{sk} was held at 38°C in each of four conditions: supine rest, supine exercise, upright rest, and upright exercise. Posture per se had an independent effect; during upright rest, the FBF-T_{es} relationship appeared shifted at least slightly rightward. The effect of exercise per se was a more marked rightward shift. With exercise in the upright posture, the rightward shift was still more marked. Thus the outer margins of the responses they observed were delimited by the responses to supine heating on the left, and upright exercise on the right —e.g. lines L and K in Figure 1. (Line K is among the rightmost cluster.) These examples were chosen from one of six plots for as many subjects. Considerable individual variation was evident. One individual might exhibit different slopes and intercepts from another, but the rightward shifts with posture and exercise were consistently observed in comparisons of the responses of a given subject. The contrast between K and L was interpreted as evidence that exercise per se alters the FBF-T_{es} relationship. An indication of the range of individual variability can be obtained by comparison with data from another study that employed nearly identical methods. Note the marked difference in slope between lines H and L, both from supine resting men heated with T_{sk} at 38°C in water-perfused suits.

More recent experiments have examined effects of posture and/or exercise. Roberts & Wenger (73) compared responses to exercise in the upright versus supine postures in both hot and cool environments. Responses to upright exercise in the heat, line M, appeared shifted rightward with respect to responses to supine exercise in the heat, line N. Lines G and H are from a 1981 study (45) in which the contrast between supine rest and upright exercise was restudied, again with T_{sk} 38°C in water-perfused suits. Exercise still shifts the relationship rightward (to line G) relative to rest (line H), but the effect is not nearly as marked as the shift represented by the transition from line L to line K. In a revisionist mood, the authors reexamined the results of the earlier paper (47) and noted that the latter phase of the response during upright exercise revealed a tendency for the slope to increase so that something more like the comparison between lines G and H would have obtained, had the period of exercise been extended. However, line K is actually from the subject for whom they made that assertion. Plotting the results on the same scale reveals that the authors overlooked the large difference in apparent thresholds between the two papers.

Nonetheless, a general agreement on the effect of exercise and posture at high T_{sk} can be seen in Figure 1. Assumption of upright posture and exercise each cause rightward shifts. Together, they probably contribute something like the sum of their parts. Again, individual variation is considerable: Compare H and G relative to N and M. Line H is from supine rest. Presumably, the same subject would have exhibited a rightward shift with assumption of the upright posture, still at rest. The shift from rightward of H to G is much smaller than that from N to M, though corresponding to the same stimulus—i.e. imposition of exercise. It is intriguing that in each of the three comparisons, G to H, L to K, and M to N, slope seems unaffected. Also intriguing is the implication that the control system actually operates differently during exercise—i.e. for the same T_{sk} and T_{es}, effector output is reduced during exercise. This relates to the old notion of "set point" elevation by exercise and is expanded upon below in the summary.

Also shown in Figure 1 is line O, which represents data obtained when responses to supine versus upright exercise in a cool environment were compared (73). Assumption of upright posture was again associated with a rightward shift, but the difference is so slight that line O can be taken to represent exercise data for both upright and supine posture. The contrast of interest is between line O and line M. Evidently, low T_{sk} in exercising humans causes a rightward shift and slope attenuation of the FBF-T_{es} relationship.

Variable: Workload

Evidently, the intensity of exercise does not shift the FBF-T_{es} relationship for a given T_{sk}. This was first reported (94) in 1975. Exercise at 30% or 50% of maximal oxygen consumption was performed in different environments. FBF fell on line E (Figure 1) regardless of exercise intensity in thermal conditions such that T_{sk} was 35.5°. Data were also obtained with T_{sk} at 30°C, shown in Figure 1 as line F. These were all associated with the higher workload in a cool environment. Again, lower T_{sk} was associated with a rightward FBF-T_{es} shift.

Findings of Wenger et al (94) were confirmed by Nadel et al (62) (curves C and D in Figure 1). FBF elevation fell on line C with both high and moderate levels of exercise and T_{sk} at 35.5°C (except that no FBF data points from the lower workload fell on the segment of curve C beyond the break point). In a cooler environment, T_{sk} was 32°C. FBF elevation associated with both levels of exercise fell on line D, although in point of fact only small FBF elevation occurred with the lower workload, as was to be expected from the thermal conditions. In other words, most of the range of FBF, line D, is associated with only the higher level of exercise. The strongest evidence for the workload-independence of SkBF control is in the initial segment of curve C on which data from a moderate and high workload overlap. Also confirmed is the rightward shift associated with reduction in T_{sk}.

Another confirmation of workload-independence was contributed by Johnson (44). Workload was altered as upright subjects pedaled on a bicycle ergometer in a neutral environment. Over the whole range from 50–150 W, FBF data fell close to line I. The strength of this confirmation that exercise intensity does not alter the FBF-T_{es} relationship lies in the fact that the protocol was so different from that employed in the two studies previously mentioned. Johnson did not report T_{sk} in this study so we cannot be sure which of two possible pairs of lines from other studies are appropriate for comparison. Do we compare line I with lines C and F, the closely corresponding results from varied workloads at T_{sk} approximately 35°C, or with lines D and E, associated with cooler T_{sk}, 32° and 30°C, respectively? However, recall that Nielsen (64) found that T_{sk} took on nearly identical levels near 30°C over a wide range of exercise levels in a neutral environment similar to that used by Johnson. Assuming then, that T_{sk} was close to 30°C in Johnson's experiments, the appropriate comparison is between line I and lines D and E. Note that all three are associated with relatively high threshold.

Johnson's data (line I) stand out in Figure 1 because exceptionally high flows were recorded and the slope exceeds those obtained by others, both in experiments with similar T_{sk} (lines E, D) and also in experiments in which exercise was combined with high T_{sk} (lines G, B, C, F, and R). Note the close parallel with line I of line J, results obtained when men pedaled for a prolonged period at a fixed workload at 24°C T_{amb} (46). It is not clear why the apparent sensitivity of SkBF to T_{es} elevation is so much higher in these experiments.

In summary, the SkBF response for a given T_{sk} and T_{es} appears independent of workload. This statement must at present be limited to the range of T_{sk} and workloads over which it has been tested (T_{sk} 30° to 35°C, workload approximately 40–70% of maximal oxygen consumption). How this relates to the conclusion that exercise per se alters the SkBF associated with a particular T_{es} and T_{sk} is discussed below.

Variable: Skin Temperature

Inhibition of SkBF in exercising humans by low T_{sk} seems clearly established (compare lines D, E, I, J, O, P with lines associated with higher T_{sk}). The evidence is much stronger than that for inhibition of SkBF by low T_{sk} in resting humans. The magnitude of the effect is comparable to that expected, if not specifically shown, for resting individuals. On the basis of parameters mentioned above in the discussion of SkBF control in resting heat-stressed humans, one might crudely estimate T_{sk} changes to be roughly one tenth as effective as T_c changes—i.e. T_{sk} contours associated with 30° and 35°C would be separated on the T_{es} axis by 0.5°C. This is close to the actual comparisons that can be made on Figure 1 (C–D, EB–F) and, indeed, the general grouping of the lines suggests that the subjects in cooler environments tended to exhibit onset of FBF elevation at a T_{es} roughly 0.5°C higher than individuals in hotter environments.

Variables: Acclimatization, Physical Condition

Lines P and Q in Figure 1 are from the study of Roberts et al (74). Subjects were acclimatized to heat after a period of training. Physical condition per se had little influence on the FBF-T_{es} relationship they observed. Line P, which is based on their pre-training data, would be nearly overlapped by their post-training data (all experimental tests were carried out with ambient temperature at 25°C). This is of interest in relation to the established finding that T_c elevation during exercise is a function of the fraction of maximal oxygen uptake attained. Roberts et al adjusted for the increase in maximal uptake as their subjects trained, so that the pre-training and post-training data were obtained at the same fractional workload. Thus the overlap of pre- and post-training data on line P implies that the same SkBF results for the same T_{es} at a higher absolute level of oxygen consumption. How, then, is the additional heat dissipated? Exercise tests were performed in neutral environments, so lower T_{sk} associated with higher post-training sweat rates may be the answer.

Acclimatization was associated with a leftward shift in the FBF-T_{es} relationship (line P to line Q, both with 25°C T_{amb}) and a somewhat increased slope as well. Skin temperatures happened to be 35°C both before and after acclimatization (note that both P and Q lie in a grouping generally associated with lower T_{sk}).

Response Attenuation at High T_{es}

The lines that extend into the extreme high range of T_{es} in Figure 1—i.e. A,C, and R—are all two-segment lines. This was first noted in a 1977 study (10) in which men exercised in suits perfused with hot water for a prolonged interval. Much smaller increments per unit T_{es} increment were associated with the upper portion of the T_{es} range. This was confirmed in another laboratory (62, 63) in men pedaling in a hot environment.

Obviously, SkBF cannot increase without bound; temperature regulation does not have exclusive rights to this effector. Nadel et al (62) made measurements of cardiac output as well (carbon dioxide rebreathing technique) and obtained direct evidence that cardiac output increase is indeed attenuated along with SkBF.

Variable: Hydration

Nadel et al (63) showed that state of hydration markedly alters SkBF control (Figure 1, line A hypohydrated, line B, controls). Subjects pedaled in a moderately hot environment, T_{amb} 35°C. Note that line B falls among others associated with exercise in upright posture in hot conditions but contrasts with others in its marked attenuation of SkBF increase at higher T_{es}. Hypohydration, induced by a five-day course of diuretics (2.7% body weight loss, 11% blood volume reduction), was associated with a rightward shift, to line A. Note the tendency for SkBF to decrease at higher T_{es}. Hyperhydration (vasopressin administration followed by ingestion of 2.0 liters of water) had relatively little effect on plasma volume nor on the FBF-T_{es} relationship; data virtually overlap line B.

Overall Summary

After studying the literature and Figure 1, one can unequivocally state that SkBF tends to rise along with internal temperature whether that elevation be the result of exposure to heat, or exercise, or both. It is hard to be much more definite.

The indication that the level of exercise does not alter SkBF for a given T_{sk} and T_{es} is puzzling if one accepts the evidence reviewed above, which indicates that exercise per se does alter the relationship. Why doesn't more exercise alter it more? Yet two different lines of evidence say that a wide range of workload does not push FBF off certain T_{sk} contours. The thought occurs when focusing on line I in Figure 1 that, after all, perhaps the range of workloads associated with this contour would include zero workload and that low T_{sk} is the reason for the displacement of this contour to the right relative to, say, line H, a contour for high T_{sk} in resting humans. Is line I the basic FBF-T_{es} relationship that would be found in upright resting humans made visible at low T_{sk} by virtue of the high T_{es} that develops during exercise? From this perspective, exercise per se and T_{sk} interact nonlinearly; in conditions permitting low T_{sk}, exercise per se does not inhibit SkBF, but T_{sk} does. Consequent heat storage results in a high T_c–T_{sk} gradient; more heat is transferred to the body surface for a given SkBF. The advantage for cardiac output economy is obvious. Sudomotor function is evidently not inhibited by exercise per se [see Johnson & Park's demonstration of fixed sudomotor versus variable vasomotor thresholds (45)], so this effector can carry the burden of dissipation of heat despite low T_{sk}. All this occurs in the heat, provided evaporation is sufficient to maintain low T_{sk} in the face of resultant convective heat uptake from the environment as well as endogenous heat production. When heat production is too high or humidity interferes, T_{sk} must rise, T_c stability is lost, and these combined signals call for more SkBF and the central circulation must adjust. As T_{sk} rises and SkBF escapes the inhibitory influence of low T_{sk}, a change in control properties occurs, and exercise per se asserts an inhibitory influence.

The inhibitory role of low T_{sk} seems clearly established, though the range tested has not been wide. Upward drift in T_{sk} must tend to enhance SkBF in exercise. When FBF is measured in controlled environmental conditions rather than with control of T_{sk} this may operate to increase the apparent FBF-T_{es} slope. In particular, those lines in Figure 1 for which no T_{sk} is listed in Table 1 may be affected by this factor.

If one could remove two lines from memory, Figure 1 would include two groups distinguished by T_{sk}. The grouping of lines with origins near 37.0°C (F,H,N,B,L,C,G, and R) are all associated with elevated T_{sk}. The remainder are grouped to the right. This includes curve A, associated with high T_{sk} but with the marked inhibitory influence of hypohydration. Lines E, Q,O,D,I and J are all associated with lower T_{sk}. This would promote a focus on T_{sk} as the influence elevating the apparent T_{es} threshold, with other variables contributing details like relatively minor slope changes and diminished response at high T_{es}. But, alas, lines M and K are solidly implanted in the same grouping and both involve elevated T_{sk}. Would these two have been displaced rightward a few tenths of a degree by lowered T_{sk}? Obviously this cannot be resolved in the library. Nor can we dump incongruities in the dustbin of individual variability. Humans do regulate internal temperature very close to 37.0°C, and a contour displacement of a few tenths of a degree represents a substantial change.

Do the data in Figure 1 resolve the issue of set point elevation in exercise? The pattern of T_c elevation observed by Nielsen (64) and interpreted in terms of relative oxygen consumption by Saltin & Hermansen (79) has been observed repeatedly (3, 12, 17, 18, 32, 84), even during a marathon race (55). When conditions are too hot or cold, T_c does not stabilize (2, 4, 17, 25, 39, 50, 55). Clearly, maintenance of a stable T_c is possible within a certain range of environmental conditions and workload.

In that range of conditions in which T_c stability is maintained, it is not proper to refer to the T_c elevation as a mere load error if it is, in fact, partly due to an alteration in control properties. Control properties—i.e. the SkBF: T_{es}: T_{sk} interrelationship—are clearly changed by posture, acclimatization, volume depletions, and high T_{es} (or high SkBF) itself; these variables can legitimately be thought of as modifiers of the "set point" for thermoregulation. In fact, if the implication can be drawn from the studies on hypohydration that the plasma volume decrement during acute exercise (see below) shifts the SkBF-T_{es} relationship rightward in the course of an ordinary bout of exercise, then one could say that the "set point" drifts up progressively as part of the whole "cardiovascular drift" phenomenon (75).

Ironically, only in the very conditions from which the idea of set point elevation originated is it unclear that control properties are altered. Whether SkBF: T_{es}: T_{sk} triplets in the realm of low T_{sk} are different in exercise and rest remains to be seen.

Of course, the important question is not whether some definable "set point" is changed. Rather, the field needs to focus on further quantitative resolution of the interactions among the various variables that are active during exercise with a particular need for more comparisons of SkBF and sweat rate control. Besides further analyses like those touched on here, the whole subject of dynamic behavior—e.g. possible lead and lag characteristics both in "input" and "output" variables—as yet virtually untouched, will challenge the ingenuity of those who hope to understand cardiovascular and thermal regulation during exercise.

OTHER VARIABLES IN CIRCULATORY ADJUSTMENTS TO EXERCISE IN THE HEAT

The relatively small body of literature discussed in the previous section can leave one confused about SkBF control despite the common conceptual outlines and limited number of variables manipulated. A much larger body of literature has accumulated in the past few years in which consequences for the cardiovascular system of exercise and heat stress have been studied under conditions in which it is inherently much more difficult to single out a particular variable of interest. Acclimatization to heat may take a different course depending upon the particular type of environment—i.e. hot and dry versus hot and humid. The processes of conditioning and acclimatization interact. These are just two examples of the complications encountered when acclimatization, conditioning, state of hydration, age, sex, and so on are among the experimental variables. Even a brief treatment of the literature would exceed the space limitations of this review by a factor of two; only an annotated list can be given. Unless otherwise noted, humans were the subjects of all the studies listed.

Acclimatization

Wyndham et al (96) recorded stroke volume (SV) and heart rate (HR) as well as thermal variables over the course of a 10-day acclimatization in a hot, humid environment. Adaptations of the central circulation were attributed to accompanying alterations in body fluid volumes; the authors emphasized that thermal and cardiovascular changes occurred independently.

Frye & Kamon (28) could find no difference between men and women in exercise responses in a hot, dry environment, once they had been acclimatized; lack of sex-related differences was confirmed in hot, humid conditions (4). Fortney & Senay (26) inferred that improved cardiovascular fitness observed in nine acclimatized women was due to maintenance of a larger central blood volume even though plasma volume was not increased.

Sex

Nunneley (65) reviewed the literature on physiological responses of women to thermal stress in 1978 and concluded that sex per se is at most a small factor in determining thermal responses, since confirmed for acclimatization by the studies just noted (4, 28) and for heavy exercise in three different environments (21). The six subjects of the blood volume study (24) discussed below included one female, but her responses were evidently unexceptional. Jurkowski et al (48) found the same cardiovascular responses through the menstrual cycle except that performance at 90% of maximal was impaired in the luteal phase. Shapiro et al (84) did find higher HR, rectal temperature, and sweat rate (SR) in women who exercised in varied hot conditions, but found no cardiovascular basis for the differences.

Body Fluid Volumes and Composition

Exercise in the heat involves another perturbation of cardiovascular system volume besides the gravitational redistribution associated with assumption of the upright posture. Sweating spends fluid at a rate on the order of liters per hour, with associated extracellular and intracellular volume decrements proportioned according to sweat tonicity—i.e. isotonic fluid loss would be completely at the expense of extracellular fluid volume, whereas pure water loss would be from both compartments in proportion to their sizes. High SkBF associated with high SR undoubtedly increases capillary filtration via increased capillary pressures. The washout of cutaneous interstitial space may result in altered tissue oncotic pressure and altered lymphatic uptake. These factors were analyzed by Senay (82) in an editorial that includes a useful summary of the literature through 1978 and a provocative analysis of the intriguing fact that volume changes with heat stress are accompanied by changes in ionic composition that could alter hypothalamic control of thermoregulation (59). The basic response pattern seems straightforward. Plasma volume (PV) falls during exercise, particularly in the heat, and hemoconcentration occurs (37). In the long term, PV changes with acclimatization and conditioning. Harrison et al (37) found that baseline PV was higher after acclimatization to heat and that the PV decrement during an actual exercise session was greater. However, the problem is complex. Different volume changes occur with different levels of exercise, different types of heat exposure, and different postures (15, 19, 29, 33, 35, 83). Lines of investigation naturally lead to questions about the renin-angiotensin system, vasopressin, and the control of blood protein quantity (14, 16, 33, 34, 51, 92). See Rowell (78) for a synthesis of the literature.

Body fluid volumes have been manipulated through partial immersion (34, 49), but note that Peterson et al (67) found evidence in monkeys that immersion and volume expansion bring into play different mechanisms and are not equivalent volume stimuli.

Relevant studies on animal subjects include the demonstration (20) that cats, like humans, exhibit greater T_c increase in hot conditions after dehydration, and the description of acclimation in rhesus monkey (66). Also see (22, 23, 40, 68).

For details of some of the critical methods and calculations employed in determining PV changes, see (31, 91).

Effector Control after Acute and Chronic Volume Changes

In 1981 Fortney et al (25) manipulated blood volume (BV) with diuretics or isotonic serum albumin infusions. They observed that BV decrements and decrements in SR sensitivity to T_c were graded in relation to initial BV—e.g. BV decrements and SR sensitivity were least with hypovolemia. Increments in T_{es} were graded inversely; hypovolemic subjects exhibited the highest T_{es} after exercise. In other words, when less fluid is available, conservation occurs through inhibition of SR, but the price is reduced tolerance of thermal stress.

To determine consequences of volume changes for regulation of the central and peripheral cardiovascular effector systems, Fortney et al (24) altered BV by withdrawal of 10% of subjects' BV and subsequent reinfusion two weeks later. One day prior to and one hour after the BV changes, subjects pedaled in a 30°C environment. Rapid recovery of BV blunted the effect of withdrawal on SV and CO, but the FBF: T_{es} relation was nonetheless shifted rightward and decreased in slope in terms of the analyses described above with respect to Figure 1. Reinfusion increased cardiac output (CO) and HR substantially. The FBF: T_{es} relation was shifted leftward and increased somewhat in slope; in Figure 1, their data would fall close to but within lines A and B (63), respectively, from hypohydrated and euhydrated exercising men, and have similar breaks in slope. Clearly, acute BV changes alter SV, presumably through altered filling pressure, and reflex inhibition of SkBF is among the compensatory responses that would tend to bolster SV. See also Bonde-Peterson et al (7) for descriptions of cardiovascular adaptations to gravitational stress. Various perturbations of volume distribution were accomplished and the tendency for FBF increase to diminish at high T_{es} was reversed by centralward displacement of BV.

The implication of the picture (63) recalled in the previous paragraph— i.e. reduced FBF : T_{es} associated with long-term rather than acute volume depletion—is that these reflex adjustments persist. Perhaps this implication requires further study. Do the reduced filling forces persist? A direct test of central blood volume and central venous pressure following long-term PV increments (acclimatization, hyperhydration) or decrements (hypohydration) would be illuminating.

Cutaneous Vascular Compliance and Volume Redistribution

In an effort to determine how volume redistribution may relate to compliance changes, Wenger et al (93) measured forearm vascular volume (FVV) with a biceps cuff inflated to 32 torr relative to a baseline obtained with the cuff deflated and the arm presumably drained by virtue of the above-venostatic location of the measurement region. Their FVV : T_{es} relationships appear somewhat similar to FBF : T_{es} lines in Figure 1. FVV rose linearly with T_{es} with T_{sk} at 35°C, and was shifted rightward with lower T_{sk}; exercise shifted the relationship further to the right.

These findings were interpreted in terms of venomotor response—e.g. that venoconstriction caused the FVV decrements. If the pressure profile throughout the venous system of the forearm were the same with each cuff congestion, FVV would indeed reflect compliance. In a separate study, pressure in a superficial vein was found to be 19 torr with cuff pressure at 32 torr. But, even assuming that venous pressure would have been 19 torr in all their experiments (despite wide variations in FBF), pressure in the small vein and venule system of the cutaneous bed must have been a function of flow. Significant resistance to flow lies between the venous end of capillaries and large superficial veins. This venule–small vein portion of the cutaneous vasculature has by far the greatest share of the cutaneous vascular volume and compliance (13, 95). Therefore, congested FVV must be a function of FBF (as uncongested FVV may also, depending upon the flow-dependent point where the "waterfall" at venostatic level begins). The low values of FVV associated with low T_{sk} and during exercise may, therefore, simply be the consequence of low FBF.

The results of Wenger et al (93) are valid only if somehow pressure in the part of the vascular system of interest cooperated by remaining consant despite major flow changes. It is attractive to take the apparent venomotor changes as evidence that volume distribution is controlled so that central-ward displacement of BV occurs during exercise and that an inappropriate venodilatation compounds adaptation to heat stress by allowing peripheral-ward displacement. However, some validation is required to show that the changes were not passive (though nonetheless beneficial or problematic—e.g. the inhibition of SkBF during upright exercise in the heat at high T_{sk} shown in Figure 1 automatically results in centralward distribution of blood by virtue of reduced pressures immediately downstream of cutaneous capil-laries).

Experiments on Animals

I have found only a few recent papers with results from animal experiments that are relevant to the present topic. Potential advantages to be gained from animal preparations are offset when the preparation requires anesthesia, particularly when thermal balance is a concern. Temperature regulation is notoriously deranged by anesthesia, with disturbance of peripheral vasomo-tor control a major part of the problem. Disturbances of cardiovascular control by general anesthetics was the subject of a recent symposium (1). One exception to the rule, evidently, is Telazol, recently found to leave temperature regulation unimpaired, vasomotor control in particular, in rhesus monkey (38).

Relevant studies in nonexercising preparations include those that are essentially neurophysiological (72, 85), including, particularly, new discov-eries of sources of afferent information: a finding of a marked influence on systemic arterial pressure of the temperature of blood perfusing isolated pulmonary arteries (52), and a demonstration that cardiac output was altered by both spinal cord and hypothalamic temperatures (30). Discovery of an active vasodilator mechanism in dog tongue (90) may be a foundation for discovery of the unknown transmitter substance of this phenomenon.

The opportunity to manipulate internal and surface temperatures inde-pendently is a great advantage of animal preparations. This has been accom-plished in unanesthetized, relatively unrestrained animals (43, 86). Only a few studies have applied this approach to analysis of cardiovascular re-sponses to thermal stress.

Proppe (71) used extracorporeal heat exchangers in a chronic femoral arteriovenous shunt. When T_{sk} was elevated by means of T_{amb} control, blood flow in the iliac artery was much higher for a given T_c. To what extent this included an SkBF response to local T_{sk} is not clear, but the response fits the pattern of SkBF increase with T_c and T_{sk} in resting humans. Lynch et al (54) controlled pre-optic hypothalamic temperature in squirrel mon-keys with chronically implanted thermodes and used T_{amb} to manipulate

T_{sk}. They found that hypothalamic temperature and T_{sk} influences on vasomotor thresholds (tail and foot skin vasodilatation inferred from local T_{sk} responses) interacted approximately according to a linear model.

Two recent studies of cardiovascular responses in intact animals are of interest. Grimditch et al (36) trained dogs to run at exhausting levels. Rectal temperatures rose above 42°C (possibly the factor limiting exercise), although T_{amb} was not elevated. On the basis of cardiac output and arterial pressure, the authors concluded that myocardial performance was not depressed when dogs were at exhaustion.

Proppe (70) found that the reduction of flow in the mesenteric artery that develops in heat-stressed baboons was nearly completely blocked by alpha-receptor blockade, indicating that this vasoconstrictor response is mediated by the sympathetic alpha system.

ACKNOWLEDGMENTS

The exchange of literary bruises with Dr. Loring B. Rowell in the course of preparation of this manuscript was, as usual, an educational experience for which I am most grateful. Thanks to Ms. Pam Stevens for bibliographic assistance. Dr. Brengelmann's research support: USPHS HL-16910 from NHLBI.

Literature Cited

1. Altura, B. M. 1980. Cardiovascular actions of general anesthetics. *Fed. Proc.* 39:1574–75
2. Araki, T., Matsushita, K., Umeno, K., Tsujino, A., Toda, Y. 1981. Effect of physical training on exercise-induced sweating in women. *J. Appl. Physiol.: Respir. Environ. Exerc. Physiol.* 51: 1516–32
3. Aulick, L. H., Robinson, S., Tzankoff, S. P. 1981. *J. Appl. Physiol.: Respir. Environ. Exerc. Physiol.* 51:1092–97
4. Avellini, B. A., Kamon, E., Krajewski, J. T. 1980. Physiological responses of physically fit men and women to acclimation to humid heat. *J. Appl. Physiol.: Respir. Environ. Exerc. Physiol.* 49: 254–61
5. Blatteis, C. M. 1981. Hypothalamic substances in the control of body temperature. *Fed. Proc.* 40:2735–40
6. Bligh, J., Moore, R., eds. 1972. *Essays on Temperature Regulation.* Amsterdam/London: North-Holland. 186 pp.
7. Bonde-Petersen, F., Christensen, N. J., Henriksen, O., Nielsen, B., Nielsen, C., Norsk, P., Rowell, L. B., Sadamoto, T., Sjogaard, G., Skagen, K., Suzuki, Y. 1980. Aspects of cardiovascular adaptation to gravitational stresses. *The Physiologist* 23(Suppl.):S7–10
8. Brengelmann, G. L. 1977. Control of sweating rate and skin blood flow. See Ref. 60, pp. 27–48
9. Brengelmann, G. L., Freund, P. R., Rowell, L. B., Olerud, J. E., Kraning, K. K. 1981. Absence of active cutaneous vasodilation associated with congenital absence of sweat glands in man. *Am. J. Physiol.* 240 (*Heart Circ. Physiol.* 9):H571–75
10. Brengelmann, G. L., Johnson, J. M., Hermansen, L., Rowell, L. B. 1977. Altered control of skin blood flow during exercise at high internal temperatures. *J. Appl. Physiol.: Respir. Environ. Exerc. Physiol.* 43:790–94
11. Brown, A. C., Brengelmann, G. L. 1970. The interaction of peripheral and central inputs in the temperature regulation system. In *Physiological and Behavioral Temperature Regulation,* ed. J. D. Hardy, A. P. Gagge, J. A. J. Stolwijk. Springfield, IL: Charles C. Thomas. 944 pp.
12. Chappuis, P., Pittet, P., Jequier, E. 1976. Heat storage regulation in exercise during thermal transients. *J. Appl. Physiol.* 40:384–92

13. Conrad, M. C. 1971. *Functional Anatomy of the Circulation to the Lower Extremities.* Chicago: Year Book Medical Publishers. 190 pp.

14. Convertino, V. A., Brock, P. J., Keil, L. C., Bernauer, E. M., Greenleaf, J. E. 1980. Exercise training-induced hypervolemia: role of plasma albumin, renin, and vasopressin. *J. Appl. Physiol.: Respir. Environ. Exerc. Physiol.* 48:665–69

15. Convertino, V. A., Greenleaf, J. E., Bernauer, E. M. 1980. Role of thermal and exercise factors in the mechanism of hypervolemia. *J. Appl. Physiol.: Respir. Environ. Exerc. Physiol.* 48:657–64

16. Convertino, V. A., Keil, L. C., Bernauer, E. M., Greenleaf, J. E. 1981. Plasma volume, osmolality, vasopressin, and renin activity during graded exercise in man. *J. Appl. Physiol.: Respir. Environ. Exerc. Physiol* 50:123–28

17. Davies, C. T. M. 1979. Influence of skin temperature on sweating and aerobic performance during severe work. *J. Appl. Physiol.: Respir. Environ. Exerc. Physiol.* 47:770–77

18. Davies, C. T. M., Brotherhood, J. R., ZeidiFard, E. 1976. Temperature regulation during severe exercise with some observations on effects of skin wetting. *J. Appl. Physiol.* 41:772–76

19. Diaz, F. J., Bransford, D. R., Kobayashi, K., Horvath, S. M., McMurray, R. G. 1979. Plasma volume changes during rest and exercise in different postures in a hot humid environment. *J. Appl. Physiol.: Respir. Environ. Exerc. Physiol.* 47:798–803

20. Doris, P. A., Baker, M. A. 1981. Effect of dehydration on thermoregulation in cats exposed to high ambient temperatures. *J. Appl. Physiol.: Respir. Environ. Exerc. Physiol.* 51:46–54

21. Drinkwater, B. L., Denton, J. E., Raven, P. B., Horvath, S. M. 1976. Thermoregulatory response of women to intermittent work in the heat. *J. Appl. Physiol.* 41:57–61

22. Eisman, M. M., Rowell, L. B. 1977. Renal vascular response to heat stress in baboons—role of renin-angiotensin. *J. Appl. Physiol.: Respir. Environ. Exerc. Physiol.* 43:739–46

23. El-Nouty, F. D., Elbanna, I. M., Davis, T. P., Johnson, H. D. 1980. Aldosterone and ADH response to heat and dehydration in cattle. *J. Appl. Physiol.: Respir. Environ. Exerc. Physiol.* 48:249–55

24. Fortney, S. M., Nadel, E. R., Wenger, C. B., Bove, J. R. 1981. Effect of acute alterations of blood volume on circulatory performance in humans. *J. Appl.*

Physiol.: Respir. Environ. Exerc. Physiol. 50:292–98

25. Fortney, S. M., Nadel, E. R., Wenger, C. B., Bove, J. R. 1981. Effect of blood volume on sweating rate and body fluids in exercising humans. *J. Appl. Physiol.: Respir. Environ. Exerc. Physiol.* 51:1594–1600

26. Fortney, S. M., Senay, L. C. Jr. 1979. Effect of training and heat acclimation on exercise responses of sedentary females. *J. Appl. Physiol.: Respir. Environ. Exerc. Physiol.* 47:978–84

27. Freund, P. R., Brengelmann, G. L., Rowell, L. B., Engrav, L., Heimbach, D. M. 1981. Vasomotor control in healed grafted skin in man. *J. Appl. Physiol.: Respir. Environ. Exerc. Physiol.* 51:168–71

28. Frye, A. J., Kamon, E. 1981. Responses to dry heat of men and women with similar aerobic capacities. *J. Appl. Physiol.: Respir. Environ. Exerc. Physiol.* 50:65–70

29. Gaebelein, C. J., Senay, L. C. Jr. 1980. Influence of exercise type, hydration, and heat on plasma volume shifts in men. *J. Appl. Physiol.: Respir. Environ. Exerc. Physiol.* 49:119–23

30. Gobel, D., Martin, H., Simon, E. 1977. Primary cardiac responses to stimulation of hypothalamic and spinal cord temperature sensors evaluated in anesthetized paralyzed dogs. *J. Therm. Biol.* 2:49–52

31. Greenleaf, J. E., Convertino, V. A., Mangseth, G. R. 1979. Plasma volume during stress in man: osmolality and red cell volume. *J. Appl. Physiol.: Respir. Environ. Exerc. Physiol.* 47:1031–38

32. Greenleaf, J. E., Reese, R. D. 1980. Exercise thermoregulation after 14 days of bed rest. *J. Appl. Physiol.: Respir. Environ. Exerc. Physiol.* 48:72–78

33. Greenleaf, J. E., Sciaraffa, D., Shvartz, E., Keil, L. C., Brock, P. J. 1981. Exercise training hypotension: implications for plasma volume, renin, and vasopressin. *J. Appl. Physiol.: Respir. Environ. Exerc. Physiol.* 51:298–305

34. Greenleaf, J. E., Shvartz, E., Kravik, S., Keil, L. C. 1980. Fluid shifts and endocrine responses during chair rest and water immersion in man. *J. Appl. Physiol.: Respir. Environ. Exerc. Physiol.* 48:79–88

35. Greenleaf, J. E., van Beaumont, W., Brock, P. J., Morse. J. T., Mangseth, G. R. 1979. Plasma volume and electrolyte shifts with heavy exercise in sitting and supine positions. *Am. J. Physiol.* 236

(*Regul. Integr. Comp. Physiol.* 5):R206–14

36. Grimditch, G. K., Barnard, R. J., Duncan, H. W. 1981. Effect of exhaustive exercise on myocardial performance. *J. Appl. Physiol.: Respir. Environ. Exerc. Physiol.* 51:1098–1102

37. Harrison, M. H., Edwards, R. J., Graveney, M. J., Cochrane, L. A., Davies, J. A. 1981. Blood volume and plasma protein responses to heat acclimatization in humans. *J. Appl. Physiol.: Respir. Environ. Exerc. Physiol.* 50:597–604

38. Holmes, K. R., Hunter, W. S. 1980. Thermoregulation in Telazol (CI-744)–anesthetized rhesus monkey (*Macaca mulatta*). *Am. J. Physiol.* 239 (*Regul. Integr. Comp. Physiol.* B): R241–47

39. Hong, S.-I., Nadel, E. R. 1979. Thermogenic control during exercise in a cold environment. *J. Appl. Physiol.: Respir. Environ. Exerc. Physiol.* 47:1084–89

40. Horowitz, M., Samueloff, S. 1979. Plasma water shifts during thermal dehydration. *J. Appl. Physiol.: Respir. Environ. Exerc. Physiol.* 47:738–44

41. Houdas, Y., Guieu, J. D., eds. 1978. *New Trends in Thermal Physiology.* Paris: Masson. 204 pp.

42. Ingram, D. L., Mount, L. E. 1975. *Man and Animals in Hot Environments*, ed. K. E. Shaefer. NY: Springer. 185 pp.

43. Jessen, C. 1981. Independent clamps of peripheral and central temperatures and their effects on heat production in the goat. *J. Physiol.* 311:11–22

44. Johnson, J. M. 1979. Responses of forearm blood flow to graded leg exercise in man. *J. Appl. Physiol.: Respir. Environ. Exerc. Physiol.* 46:457–62

45. Johnson, J. M., Park, M. K. 1981. Effect of upright exercise on threshold for cutaneous vasodilation and sweating. *J. Appl. Physiol.: Respir. Environ. Exerc. Physiol.* 50:814–18

46. Johnson, J. M., Rowell, L. B. 1975. Forearm skin and muscle vascular responses to prolonged leg exercise in man. *J. Appl. Physiol.* 39:920–24

47. Johnson, J. M., Rowell, L. B., Brengelmann, G. L. 1974. Modification of the skin blood flow-body temperature relationship by upright exercise. *J. Appl. Physiol.* 37:880–86

48. Jurkowski, J. E. H., Jones, N. L., Toews, C. J., Sutton, J. R. 1981. Effects of menstrual cycle on blood lactate, O₂ delivery, and performance during exercise. *J. Appl. Physiol.: Respir. Environ. Exerc. Physiol.* 51:1493–99

49. Khosla, S. S., DuBois, A. B. 1981. Osmoregulation and interstitial fluid pressure changes in humans during water immersion. *J. Appl. Physiol.: Respir. Environ. Exerc. Physiol.* 51:686–92

50. Kobayashi, K., Horvath, S. M., Diaz, F. J., Bransford, D. R., Drinkwater, B. L. 1980. Thermoregulation during rest and exercise in different postures in a hot humid environment. *J. Appl. Physiol.: Respir. Environ. Exerc. Physiol.* 48:999–1007

51. Kosunen, K., Pakarinen, A., Kuoppasalmi, K., Naveri, H., Rehunen, S., Standerskjold-Nordenstam, C. G., Harkonen, M., Adlercreutz, H. 1980. Cardiovascular function and the renin-angiotensin-aldosterone system in long-distance runners during various training periods. *Scand. J. Clin. Lab. Invest.* 40:429–36

52. Ledsone, J. R., Kan, W. O., Bolter, C. P. 1980. Respiratory and cardiovascular responses to temperature changes in the perfused pulmonary arteries of the dog. *Can. J. Physiol. Pharmacol.* 59: 493–99

53. Liethead, C. S., Lind, A. R. 1964. *Heat Stress and Heat Disorders.* Philadelphia, PA: F. A. Davis. 304 pp.

54. Lynch, W. C., Adair, E. R., Adams, B. W. 1980. Vasomotor thresholds in the squirrel monkey: effects of central and peripheral temperature. *J. Appl. Physiol.: Respir. Environ. Exerc. Physiol.* 48:89–96

55. Maron, M. B., Wagner, J. A., Horvath, S. M. 1977. Thermoregulatory responses during competitive marathon running. *J. Appl. Physiol.: Respir. Environ. Exerc. Physiol.* 42:909–14

56. McCaffrey, T. V., McCook, R. D., Wurster, R. D. 1975. Effect of head skin temperature on tympanic and oral temperature in man. *J. Appl. Physiol.* 39:114–18

57. Mitchell, J. M. 1980. Regulation in physiological systems during exercise. *Fed. Proc.* 39:1479–80

58. Musacchia, X. J. 1979. Fever and hyperthermia. *Fed. Proc.* 38:27–29

59. Myers, R. D., Gisolfi, C. V., Mora, F. 1977. Role of brain Ca²⁺ in central control of body temperature during exercise in the monkey. *J. Appl. Physiol.: Respir. Environ. Exerc. Physiol.* 43: 689–94

60. Nadel, E. R., ed. 1977. *Problems with Temperature Regulation During Exercise.* NY: Academic. 141 pp.

61. Nadel, E. R. 1980. Circulatory and

thermal regulations during exercise. *Fed Proc.* 39:1491–97

62. Nadel, E. R., Cafarelli, E., Roberts, M. F., Wenger, C. B. 1979. Circulatory regulation during exercise in different ambient temperatures. *J. Appl. Physiol.: Respir. Environ. Exerc. Physiol.* 46: 430–37

63. Nadel, E. R., Fortney, S. M., Wenger, C. B. 1980. Effect of hydration state on circulatory and thermal regulations. *J. Appl. Physiol.: Respir. Environ. Exerc. Physiol.* 49:715–21

64. Nielson, M. 1938. Die Regulation der Körpertemperatur bei Muskelarbeit. *Skand. Arch. Physiol.* 79:193–230

65. Nunneley, S. 1978. Physiological responses of women to thermal stress: a review. *Med. Sci. Sports* 10:250–55

66. Oddershede, I. R., Elizondo, R. S. 1980. Body fluid and hematologic adjustments during resting heat acclimation in rhesus monkey. *J. Appl. Physiol.: Respir. Environ. Exerc. Physiol.* 49:431–37

67. Peterson, T. V., Gilmore, J. P., Zucker, I. H. 1980. Initial renal responses of nonhuman primate to immersion and intravascular volume expansion. *J. Appl. Physiol.: Respir. Environ. Exerc. Physiol.* 48:243–48

68. Phillips, C. J., Coppinger, R. P., Schimel, D. S. 1981. Hyperthermia in running sled dogs. *J. Appl. Physiol.: Respir. Environ. Exerc. Physiol.* 51:135–42

69. Poulos, D. A. 1981. Neurophysiology of temperature regulation. *Fed. Proc.* 40: 2803

70. Proppe, D. W. 1980. α-Adrenergic control of intestinal circulation in heat-stressed baboons. *J. Appl. Physiol.: Respir. Environ. Exerc. Physiol.* 48:759–64

71. Proppe, D. W. 1981. Influence of skin temperature on central thermoregulatory control of leg blood flow. *J. Appl. Physiol.: Respir. Environ. Exerc. Physiol.* 50:974–78

72. Riedel, W., Iriki, M. 1970. Autonomic nervous control of temperature homeostasis. In *Integrative Functions of the Autonomic Nervous System*, ed. C. McC. Brooks, K. Koizumi, A. Sato, 30:394–401. Tokyo: Univ. Tokyo Press

73. Roberts, M. F., Wenger, C. B. 1977. Control of skin blood flow during exercise by thermal reflexes and baroreflexes. *J. Appl. Physiol.: Respir. Environ. Exerc. Physiol.* 48:717–23

74. Roberts, M. F., Wenger, C. B., Stolwijk, J. A. J., Nadel, E. R. 1977. Skin blood flow and sweating changes following exercise training and heat acclimation. *J.*

Appl. Physiol.: Respir. Environ. Exerc. Physiol. 43:133–37

75. Rowell, L. B. 1974. Human cardiovascular adjustments to exercise and thermal stress. *Physiol. Rev.* 54:75–159

76. Rowell, L. B. 1977. Reflex control of the cutaneous vasculature. *J. Invest. Dermatol.* 69:154–66

77. Rowell, L. B. 1980. Active neurogenic vasodilatation in man. In *Vasodilatation*, ed. P. M. Vanhoutte, I. Leusen, pp. 1–17. NY: Raven Press. 536 pp.

78. Rowell, L. B. 1982. Cardiovascular adjustments to thermal stress. In *Handbook of Physiology. Peripheral Circulation and Organ Blood Flow*, ed. J. T. Shepherd, F. M. Abboud. Bethesda, MD: Am. Physiol. Soc. In press

79. Saltin, B., Hermansen, L. 1966. Esophageal, rectal, and muscle temperature during exercise. *J. Appl. Physiol.* 21: 1757–62

80. Saltin, B., Rowell, L. B. 1980. Functional adaptations to physical activity and inactivity. *Fed. Proc.* 39:1506–13

81. Sciaraffa, D., Fox, S. C., Stockmann, R., Greenleaf, J. E. 1980. Human acclimatization and acclimatization to heat: A compendium of research— 1968–1978. *NASA Tech. Memo. 81181.* Moffett Field, CA: NASA, Ames Res. Cent. 102 pp.

82. Senay, L. C. Jr. 1979. Temperature regulation and hypohydration: a singular view. *J. Appl. Physiol.: Respir. Environ. Exerc. Physiol.* 47:1–7

83. Senay, L. C. Jr., Rogers, G., Jooste, P. 1980. Changes in blood plasma during progressive treadmill and cycle exercise. *J. Appl. Physiol.: Respir. Environ. Exerc. Physiol.* 49:59–65

84. Shapiro, Y., Pandolf, K. B., Avellini, B. A., Pimental, N. A., Goldman, R. A. 1980. Physiological responses of men and women to humid and dry heat. *J. Appl. Physiol.: Respir. Environ. Exerc. Physiol.* 49:1–8

85. Simon, E. 1981. Effects of CNS temperature on generation and transmission of temperature signals in homeotherms— a common concept for mammalian and avian thermoregulation. *Pflügers Arch.* 392:79–88

86. Smiles, K. A., Elizondo, R. S., Barney, C. C. 1976. Sweating responses during changes of hypothalamic temperature in the rhesus monkey. *Am. J. Physiol.* 40:653–57

87. Stitt, J. 1979. Fever versus hyperthermia. *Fed. Proc.* 38:39–43

88. Tam, H.-S., Darling, R. C., Cheh, H.-Y., Downey, J. A. 1978. The dead

zone of thermoregulation in normal and paraplegic man. *Can. J. Physiol. Pharmacol.* 56:976–83

89. Thauer, R. 1965. Circulatory adjustments to climatic requirements. In *Handbook of Physiology. Circulation,* Sect. 2, Vol. III, ed. W. F. Hamilton, P. Dow, 55:1921–66. Washington DC: Am. Physiol. Soc. 1786 pp.

90. Thomson, E. M., Pleschka, K. 1980. Vasodilatory mechanisms in the tongue and nose of the dog under heat load. *Pflügers Arch.* 387:161–66

91. van Beaumont, W., Underkofler, S., van Beaumont, S. 1981. Erythrocyte volume, plasma volume, and acid-base changes in exercise and heat dehydration. *J. Appl. Physiol.: Respir. Environ. Exerc. Physiol.* 50:1255–62

92. Wade, C. E., Claybaugh, J. R. 1980. Plasma renin activity, vasopressin concentration, and urinary excretory responses to exercise in men. *J. Appl. Physiol.: Respir. Environ. Exerc. Physiol.* 49:930–36

93. Wenger, C. F., Roberts, M. F. 1980. Control of forearm venous volume during exercise and body heating. *J. Appl. Physiol.: Respir. Environ. Exerc. Physiol.* 49:114–19

94. Wenger, C. B., Roberts, M. F., Stolwijk, J. A. J., Nadel, E. R. 1975. Forearm blood flow during body temperature transients produced by leg exercise. *J. Appl. Physiol.* 38:58–63

95. Wiedeman, M. P. 1963. Dimensions of blood vessels from distributing artery to collecting vein. *Circ. Res.* 12:375–78

96. Wyndham, C. H., Rogers, G. G., Senay, L. C., Mitchell, D. 1976. Acclimatization in a hot, humid environment: cardiovascular adjustments. *J. Appl. Physiol.* 40:779–85

97. Wyss, C. R., Brengelmann, G. L., Johnson, J. M., Rowell, L. B., Niederberger, M. 1974. Control of skin blood flow, sweating and heart rate: role of skin versus core temperature. *J. Appl. Physiol.* 36:726–33

98. Wyss, C. R., Brengelmann, G. L., Johnson, J. M., Rowell, L. B., Silverstein, D. 1975. Altered control of skin blood flow at high skin and core temperatures. *J. Appl. Physiol.* 38:839–45

Ann. Rev. Physiol. 1983. 45:213–27
Copyright © 1983 by Annual Reviews Inc.

CONTROL OF THE CORONARY CIRCULATION DURING EXERCISE

H. Lowell Stone

Department of Physiology and Biophysics, The University of Oklahoma at Oklahoma City, Health Sciences Center, Oklahoma City, Oklahoma 73190

INTRODUCTION

The cardiovascular response to exercise is typified by increases in heart rate, cardiac output, inotropic state of the cardiac chambers, whole body oxygen consumption, and blood flow to the active skeletal muscles. In most animals, some form of vasoconstriction occurs in the splanchnic region and inactive skeletal muscles. In the dog, splanchnic vasoconstriction does not occur; but contraction of the spleen does occur with exercise, and this increases the oxygen carrying capacity of the blood. The response of each organ system (e.g. heart, splanchnic organs, and skeletal muscle) is an equilibrium between the metabolic demand for oxygen by the organ and the neural control of organ blood flow exerted by the autonomic nervous system. The efferent autonomic nervous system activity (principally sympathetic nervous system) is increased during exercise to the heart, inactive skeletal muscle, and splanchnic region.

The control of the coronary circulation during exercise appears to involve a combination of neural and metabolic events. Recent reviews have dealt with the metabolic control of the coronary circulation in great detail (5, 40), so this topic is not covered extensively here. Other topics reviewed recently are cardiovascular adjustments during exercise (57), coronary vascular receptors (45), coronary reflexes (27), and control of coronary flow (29). With these reviews as background, the major focus here is the relationship between the increasing autonomic nervous system activity and the control of coronary blood flow during exercise. Recent publications suggest that, like the changes in organ blood flow to active and inactive regions of the body, the neural regulation of coronary blood flow may represent an important component of the adjustment to exercise. The major role of the neural regulation of the coronary circulation during exercise may be to limit the

213

0066–4278/83/0315–0213$02.00

metabolic vasodilation to ensure adequate myocardial blood flow distribution.

INNERVATION AND PHARMACOLOGY OF THE CORONARY ARTERIES

In 1926 Woollard (61) reported that the coronary arteries received the richest innervation of all the vessels he had examined. He found that by methylene blue staining he could distinguish both vagal and sympathetic nerves. More recent studies (15, 33) indicate that the innervation of the coronary vessels extends to vessels proximal to the capillaries and may indirectly influence capillary function by alterations in precapillary vessels. Denn et al (12) used histochemical techniques to demonstrate that vagal and sympathetic nerve fibers coursed through the adventitial layer of the major coronary vessels. Both types of fibers supplied small branches to the vicinity of the smooth muscle layer of the vessel wall. The sympathetic nerve fibers innervating the coronary vessels of the left ventricle originated from the left stellate ganglion. The parasympathetic fibers on the same vessels appeared to originate from the cardiac plexus at the base of the aorta (26). This dual efferent innervation may contribute to the physiological regulation of coronary blood flow during stresses such as exercise (1). Abundant afferent nerve endings in the heart have been described traveling with the sympathetic and parasympathetic nerves. The characteristics of these afferent fibers are summarized in a recent review (8).

The reactivity of the coronary vessels depends in part upon the type or types of receptors located on the smooth muscle cell membrane. These vascular smooth muscle cells have been shown by pharmacological activation to contain alpha-adrenergic and beta$_2$-adrenergic receptors (46). Activation of the former receptor type causes vasoconstriction, and of the latter, vasodilation.

The distribution of the adrenergic receptors between large and small coronary vessels was investigated in anesthetized dogs by several groups (20, 25, 32). Malindzak et al (32) found that norepinephrine increased resistance in large vessels but decreased it in small vessels. Electrical stimulation of cardiac sympathetic nerves had the same effect. Alpha-adrenergic blockade abolished the large vessel response, and beta-adrenergic blockade reversed the resistance change in the small vessels. The latter finding suggested that the small vessels were responding mainly to the increased metabolism of the surrounding myocardium. Zuberbuhler & Bohr (62) obtained similar results using isolated strips of large (1.5–2.4 mm in diameter) and small (0.25–0.50 mm in diameter) blood vessels. Another study (52) indicates that the coronary vascular response to receptor activation was dependent on extracellular calcium, which may be a unique feature of these vessels. Hamilton & Feigl (20) investigated the type of coronary beta-adrenergic receptors and their physiological role by using sympathetic stimulation, catecholamine infusion, and adrenergic blockade. Isoproternol infusion caused a dose-dependent increase in flow ($+72$ ml min^{-1} 100 g^{-1}) and a decrease of coronary sinus Po$_2$ (-14 mm Hg) with respect to control values. Beta$_1$-adrenergic blockade under the same conditions resulted in an increase of coronary flow and sinus Po$_2$ with isoproterenol infusion. The authors concluded that the coronary beta-adrenergic receptors were similar to peripheral beta-adrenergic receptors (beta$_2$) and that little if any physiological activation of these receptors occurred in the coronary vascular system. Using an intact anesthetized dog preparation, Kelly & Feigl (25) compared the changes in total coronary and large coronary vessel resistance following beta-adrenergic blockade using the bolus injection of norepinephrine and sympathetic nerve stimulation. The results from this study suggested that large vessel coronary resistance only contributed an average of 60% of the total increase in resistance under these experimental conditions and further suggest that alpha-adrenergic receptors are located in small coronary vessels.

Direct measurement of the diameter of large epicardial coronary vessels in conscious dogs during activation of alpha-adrenergic receptor showed a decrease in internal cross-sectioned area that represented active vasoconstriction (58).

Activation of the vagus nerve after beta-adrenergic blockade results in a decrease in coronary resistance that can be blocked by atropine (14). The physiological role of such a mechanism is unclear, but presynaptic inhibition of the release of norepinephrine from adrenergic nerve terminals by the parasympathetic nervous system may contribute to coronary vasodilation (31).

VASOCONSTRICTION AND AUTONOMIC REFLEXES

Alpha-Adrenergic Vasoconstriction

The major factor regulating the coronary circulation under physiological conditions is the metabolism of the surrounding myocardium, but the activation of alpha-adrenergic receptors by norepinephrine released from sympathetic nerves on the coronary vessels modulates the overall effect of metabolism.

The coronary blood flow to any area of the myocardium and the oxygen delivery will be the result of the relationship between these two factors. Feigl (13) investigated the question of modulation of myocardial oxygen tension by the activation of the alpha-adrenergic receptors. In the vagoto-mized anesthetized dog, sympathetic nerve stimulation resulted in an in-crease in coronary flow, heart rate, and blood pressure, and a decrease in coronary sinus Po_2 from 19 to 15 mm Hg. Following beta-adrenergic blockade in the same animals, the positive inotropic and chronotropic responses were blunted and an alpha-adrenergically mediated vasoconstric-tion occurred causing coronary sinus Po_2 to fall from 17 to 11 mm Hg. The decrease in coronary sinus Po_2 was a result of coronary vasoconstriction and could be diminished by alpha-adrenergic blockade. These results sug-gested that myocardial oxygen tension might be regulated by sympatheti-cally mediated coronary vasomotion. In a subsequent study (36), sympathetically mediated vasoconstriction competed with metabolic vasodilation so as to reduce the metabolically linked increase in blood flow by about 30%. Under these experimental conditions oxygen extraction by the myocardium increased. Thus a strict one-to-one relationship between an increase in myocardial oxygen consumption and oxygen delivery did not occur. In another study (9), coronary vasoconstriction could still be ob-tained in the presence of an approximate 70% stenosis of a coronary vessel. This implies that the vasoconstrictor response was not abolished in a condi-tion of limited coronary flow. Mudge et al (37) studied coronary artery resistance in patients with normal coronary arteries and patients with coro-nary artery disease using the cold pressor test. They found a decreased coronary resistance in the former patients and an increased coronary resis-tance in the latter. These authors concluded that an alpha-adrenergic vaso-constriction was responsible for the increased resistance in the patients with coronary artery disease. These studies in dogs and humans indicate that the alpha-adrenergic vasoconstriction can limit the metabolic increase in coro-nary flow and thus potentially cause myocardial ischemia under appropriate conditions.

Coronary vasoconstriction has been observed during reflex activation of the sympathetic nerves to the heart. However, these studies did not deter-mine the level of resting sympathetic tone in the coronary vessels. Evidence (22, 41, 48, 54) suggests the presence of a tonic vasoconstrictor tone in the coronary vessels of both dogs and humans at rest. The range of change in coronary vascular resistance with removal or blockade of the sympathetic nervous system was found to be 12–40%. However, evidence against the presence of a vasoconstrictor tone at rest in awake dogs was recently pre-sented (10). The differences between these studies are not readily apparent, but the results do not change the concept that vasoconstrictor activity in the coronary vessels may be reflexly mediated during physiological condi-tions such as exercise.

During exercise, the metabolic activity of the heart increases almost in a linear fashion with increasing workload. With a large metabolic signal for coronary vasodilation can a tonic vasoconstrictor tone still be present? Occlusion of a major coronary artery for several seconds will result in a large coronary vasodilation (reactive hyperemia) as a result of the build-up of vasoactive metabolites in the extracellular space of the tissue. Using the reactive hyperemic response to a 10 sec coronary artery occlusion, Schwartz & Stone (48) found that removal of the left stellate ganglion increased the hyperemic response to a 10 sec occlusion from 476% to 622%. This same result could be obtained following alpha-adrenergic blockade with phentolamine. Beta-adrenergic blockade reduced the RH response while removal of the right stellate ganglion had no effect. Removal of the left stellate ganglion permitted an increase in the coronary dilation that was not a result of an increase in sensitivity to circulating catecholamines (49). The study demonstrated the ability of a tonic vasoconstrictor tone to compete with a large metabolic signal and the ensuing vasodilation.

Baroreceptor Reflex

The control of arterial pressure by baroreceptor reflexes involves alteration of the autonomic nervous system activity to both the heart and peripheral vascular beds. Baroreceptor-mediated changes in coronary resistance have been reported by several investigators (39, 43, 54). Vatner et al (54) stimulated the carotid sinus nerve of conscious dogs and found that coronary resistance decreased. This response could be blocked by phenoxybenzamine but was not affected by atropine or propranolol. Further stimulation of the carotid sinus nerve during exercise caused coronary resistance to decrease an additional 18% below the control level during exercise. These results not only indicate a reflex modulation of coronary flow but also reveal the potential existence of a vasoconstrictor action on the coronary vessels during exercise. Powell et al (43) vagotomized anesthetized dogs, treated them with propranolol, and isolated their carotid sinus regions. When the pressure in both carotid sinuses was decreased to 40 mm Hg, coronary resistance increased by 21%. Myocardial oxygen extraction increased simultaneously with this increase in resistance. The increases in both coronary resistance and extraction could be blocked by alpha-adrenergic antagonists. Murray et al (39) examined the response of the right coronary circulation to a reduction in carotid sinus pressure. The right ventricle would not be exposed to an increased afterload. With heart rate held constant in conscious dogs, bilateral carotid occlusion caused a 33% increase in arterial pressure and a 32% increase in right coronary resistance. The increase in right coronary resistance could not be mimicked by a similar increase in aortic pressure. Thus coronary autoregulation could not explain the results. Alpha-adrenergic blockade eliminated the increase in right coronary resistance in response to a reduction in carotid sinus pressure.

Thus reflex coronary vasoconstriction can occur in the face of metabolic changes that should lead to vasodilation and may influence coronary flow during exercise.

Pulmonary Inflation Reflex

The increase in respiration during exercise is the result of a change in central neurogenic control of respiration. An increase in the depth of respiration in the conscious dog can be achieved by the intracarotid injection of cyanide (56). This maneuver activated a potent chemoreceptor reflex and resulted in a decrease in coronary resistance. The major component responsible for the decrease in resistance, from 1.62 ± 0.08 to 0.78 ± 0.06 mm Hg ml·min^{-1}, was the inflation of the lungs. Control of ventilation during activation of the chemoreceptor reflex dramatically reduced the coronary resistance response. The decrease in coronary resistance could be almost entirely prevented by alpha-adrenergic blockade.

Skeletal Muscle Reflex

Activation of skeletal muscle afferent fibers can result in changes in heart rate and arterial pressure. Such an activation would normally occur with both static and dynamic exercise. Kniffki et al (30) suggest that the muscle group III and group IV (unmyelinated) afferent fibers may transmit from the working muscle to the central nervous system those impulses that result in the cardiovascular changes. Crayton et al (11) found in dogs that myocardial blood flow rose little during static hind limb contractions in the face of an increase in heart rate and blood pressure that would cause an increased oxygen demand by the myocardium. Using the same dog preparation as Crayton et al (11), Aung-Din et al (2) determined that alpha-adrenergic vasoconstriction in the heart attends simulated static exercise. They observed a 29.6% increase in coronary flow with no change in coronary resistance. Following beta-adrenergic blockade, coronary flow decreased by 30% and resistance increased by 53% during simulated static exercise.

CONTROL DURING EXERCISE

Coronary flow can increase four to five times above the resting values during exercise and has been shown (57) to increase in an almost linear fashion with increasing myocardial oxygen consumption. During exercise at any work load, heart rate, contractility, and arterial pressure are increased to varying degrees. The increase in all of these variables contributes to an increase in myocardial oxygen consumption (7). The linear increase of coronary flow with increasing oxygen demand results from a large metabolic signal acting on the coronary resistance vessels and reflex modulation of the neural control of the coronary resistance vessels. Capillary recruitment during states of increased myocardial metabolic demand (51) may also be important during exercise and would be influenced by the upstream resistance vessels.

Coronary blood flow and myocardial oxygen consumption have been measured during exercise in both dogs and humans. In an early study on exercising dogs, Van Citters & Franklin (53) recorded coronary flow and heart rate in sled dogs as they pulled a load over a familiar course for up to an hour. With the initiation of exercise, heart rate accelerated to over 300 bpm and usually was maintained around a value of 300 bpm for the duration of the run. This heart rate may be near maximum for the dog. Van Citters & Franklin (53) found that coronary flow increased approximately five-fold and was generally sustained at this level during the remainder of the running period. Stone (51) measured coronary blood flow and myocardial oxygen consumption in dogs exercising on a motor-driven treadmill. The peak heart rate obtained during exercise was 238 ± 8 bpm. Coronary flow increased to three times the coronary flow value obtained with the dog standing on the treadmill prior to exercise. Coronary flow increased in an almost linear fashion with increasing work load. Extraction of oxygen across the heart increased with exercise (69% to 80%), while the coronary sinus oxygen content decreased (0.053 ml O_2 to 0.042 ml O_2). Coronary arteriovenous oxygen difference increased throughout the exercise period. Von Restorff et al (59) found similar results in dogs exercised on a treadmill at higher heart rates. Two additional observations (59) deserve comment: (a) Initiation of exercise resulted in a rapid decrease in sinus oxygen saturation, which was followed by an increase and then a subsequent decline. (b) At the highest work load, maximum coronary vasodilation was not achieved since coronary flow could still increase after a transient occlusion of the coronary artery. The authors concluded that these findings were consistent with the concept of an alpha-adrenergic vasoconstrictor tone restricting coronary flow even during high levels of exercise. In studies on normal human subjects, measurements of coronary sinus blood flow or coronary blood flow indexes during exercise have shown an almost linear increase in flow with increasing myocardial oxygen consumption and widening of the arteriovenous oxygen difference across the heart (6, 24, 28).

In summary, coronary blood flow increases in an almost linear fashion with increasing myocardial oxygen demand. The increase in flow is accompanied by a widening of the arteriovenous oxygen difference across the heart, which may be explained by capillary recruitment and/or a change in the distribution of blood flow across the myocardial wall. Even with near-maximal exercise in dogs, some vasodilator capacity was still present in the coronary vascular bed.

MYOCARDIAL BLOOD FLOW DISTRIBUTION

Distribution of blood flow across the wall of the ventricle is discussed primarily in reference to the thick-walled left ventricle. Today myocardial blood flow and its distribution have been measured by means of the injection of radioisotope labelled microspheres of either 9 or 15 μm in diameter. It has become common practice to compare changes in the endocardial to epicardial flow (endo/epi ratio) as an index of the distribution of flow.

With exercise, as discussed in previous sections, coronary blood flow increases with increasing work load. Ball et al (3) have reported regional myocardial flows measured in 9 dogs during various intensities of exercise; the highest level of exercise elicited a heart rate of 240 ± 6 bpm. Resting coronary flow averaged 0.94 ± 0.09 ml min^{-1}g^{-1} with endocardial flow exceeding epicardial flow. The endo/epi ratio varied from 1.12 to 1.33; both values were significantly different from 1. During the highest level of exercise, as specified above, coronary flow averaged 3.90 ± 0.26 ml min^{-1}g^{-1} and the endo/epi ratio was 0.98. Coronary blood flow increased to all layers of the myocardium. The decrease in the endo/epi ratio (from 1.33 to 0.98) occurred at a level of exercise lower than the highest level used and did not change with further increased work load. It should be noted that while flow increased to all layers of the left ventricle, the gradient in the flow between the endocardium and epicardium was abolished with exercise. This would indicate a preferential increase in epicardial flow over endocardial flow during exercise. In another study (4), the ability of the coronary vascular bed to dilate during exercise was determined using the injection of microspheres. Barnard et al (4) measured regional coronary flow in ten dogs at rest, during exercise, and during exercise following the injection of dipyridamole (0.75 mg kg^{-1}). Heart rate at rest was 81 ± 6 bpm and increased to 271 ± 8 bpm during exercise. Heart rate and exercise work load were similar following the injection of dipyridamole. Coronary flow at rest was 0.91 ± 0.06 ml min^{-1}g^{-1} and increased to 4.24 ± 0.30 ml min^{-1}g^{-1} with exercise. Following dipyridamole injections and during exercise, coronary flow rose to 6.20 ± 0.35 ml min^{-1}g^{-1}. The endo/epi ratio decreased from rest to exercise; the decrease was not altered by dipyridamole treatment. Evidence based on a transmural electrocardiogram suggested a lack of any endocardial ischemia. These two studies clearly indicate that near-maximal exercise does not exhaust the coronary dilator capacity and, further, that the altered transmural distribution of flow does not result in endocardial ischemia. The mechanism for the redistribution of coronary blood flow is not clear at the present time.

Since all of the studies cited in this section have shown an almost linear increase in both coronary blood flow and myocardial oxygen demand with increasing work load, this might suggest a purely metabolic regulation of coronary flow. Watkinson et al (60) measured the pericardial fluid concentration of adenosine at rest and during exercise in four dogs. Using a chronic pericardial catheter, fluid could be introduced and removed in these animals. The underlying assumption in this study is that the concentration of adenosine in the pericardial fluid reflects the extracellular fluid concentration of adenosine, which affects the vascular smooth muscle. Adenosine concentration increased from an average value of 95.5 $\pm$ 7.6 pmol ml^{-1} at rest to 263 $\pm$ 19.1 pmol ml^{-1} during exercise at a heart rate of 204 $\pm$ 4 bpm. This suggests that extracellular adenosine plays a role in the metabolic control of coronary flow during exercise. The relative importance of its role is reflected by the recent finding that approximately one third of the maximum coronary flow during reactive hyperemia could be explained by cellular release of adenosine (47). In the anesthetized dog, endogenous adenosine did not appear to exert any influence on resting flow (47). Rembert et al (44) infused several doses of adenosine intravenously into conscious dogs and measured the alteration in myocardial blood flow with microspheres. Myocardial blood flow increased with all doses of adenosine but the response of the endo/epi ratio was not uniform for different doses. With intermediate doses of adenosine, the endo/epi ratio increased. With the highest dose of adenosine (1 mg kg^{-1}) the endo/epi ratio decreased below the control value. This indicated to the authors a possible preferential effect of adenosine on the endocardial vessels at the lower doses. The change in the endo/epi ratio with adenosine infusion and the role played by adenosine in maximum dilation of the coronary vascular bed may indicate that other factors are operating also to control the coronary circulation during exercise.

Electrical stimulation of the sympathetic nerves to the heart cause a coronary vasoconstriction when propranolol is used to block the cardiac beta-adrenergic receptors (23). Adenosine infusion always causes coronary vasodilation. Adenosine infusion plus electrical stimulation of the sympathetic nerves to the heart during beta-adrenergic blockade will result in a vasoconstriction of the coronary vessels that reduces coronary flow below that with adenosine infusion alone. A surprising finding in this study (23) was the alteration in the endo/epi ratio. The infusion of adenosine and the ensuing coronary vasodilation resulted in a decrease in the endo/epi ratio from 1.26 $\pm$ 0.12 to 0.77 $\pm$ 0.10, but the electrical stimulation of the sympathetic nerves caused the endo/epi ratio to increase from 0.77 $\pm$ 0.10 to 1.25 $\pm$ 0.12. There was an apparent preferential effect of sympathetic nerve stimulation on the epicardial vessels under these conditions. The authors concluded that the results could be explained best by a differential effect of adenosine on the prejunctional neural membranes that would affect the release of norepinephrine. Adenosine may have a differential vasodilator role in the heart (endo vs epi) [as suggested by Rembert et al (44)] and simultaneously a differential prejunctional effect on neural membranes. In either case, endocardial blood flow may be preserved to a greater extent under physiological conditions by reducing the epicardial vasodilation. During exercise with the increased myocardial oxygen demand reflex modulation of vasodilation in the epicardium would be very important.

SIGNIFICANCE OF NEURAL CONTROL DURING EXERCISE

Schwartz et al (48) studied the effect of removal of either the left or right stellate ganglion or both ganglia on the coronary flow response to exercise. In nine dogs, the response to exercise was studied before and after left stellate ganglion removal. Heart rate at the highest work load studied was 243 ± 10 bpm and increased to 258 ± 6 bpm following left stellectomy. Coronary blood flow increased an average of 14 ± 4% following left stellectomy. The increase in coronary blood flow could be a result of the increased heart rate response to exercise (increased metabolic demand), the removal of a tonic alpha-adrenergic vasoconstrictor tone, or an increased sensitivity to circulating catecholamines. The latter mechanism has been ruled out by a subsequent study (50). In the group of six animals in which both stellate ganglia had been removed, coronary flow was not different from the intact animal's coronary flow during exercise despite a reduced heart rate and left ventricular inotropic response. This would suggest that the removal of a tonic vasoconstrictor activity was responsible for the increase in coronary flow in the animals following removal of the left stellate ganglion.

Results from two studies have indicated that a vasoconstrictor tone was present on the coronary vessels during submaximal and maximal exercise (17, 38). Murray & Vatner (38) found an increase in coronary flow during maximal exercise following alpha-adrenergic blockade in dogs. This increase in coronary flow seemed to be independent of change in any of the factors that would cause an increase in myocardial oxygen consumption. Gwirtz et al (17) found similar results during submaximal exercise in dogs. Again the increase in coronary blood flow was greater than could be explained by the increase in myocardial oxygen consumption. From these studies it seems clear that the alpha-adrenergic vasoconstriction can effectively compete with the increase in metabolic vasodilation during exercise as shown by Mohrman et al (36) in the anesthetized dog. Heyndrickx et al (21) measured coronary blood flow and myocardial oxygen consumption in dogs during exercise before and after beta-adrenergic blockade with propranolol. Coronary blood flow and myocardial oxygen consumption were both decreased, when compared to the responses in the unblocked animals, but the coronary sinus oxygen content decreased more and arteriovenous oxygen difference was further increased following beta-adrenergic blockade. The authors concluded that the attenuated metabolic vasodilation during exercise after blockade was probably caused by a sympathetic vasoconstrictor tone on the vessels, this tone being unopposed by the degree of metabolic vasodilation normally present during exercise. Recent evidence suggests that during severe exercise the heart does not contribute to the increase in plasma norepinephrine but in fact may actually take up norepinephrine (42). This implies that the cardiac sympathetic efferent fiber activity, reuptake, receptor binding, and catecholamine metabolism are in equilibrium during exercise.

The effect of norepinephrine on the coronary vasculature in conscious dogs has been reported to be a biphasic response (18, 19, 54). The initial response to norepinephrine was a vasodilation followed by a vasoconstriction. The vasodilation could be blocked by either propranolol or a specific beta$_1$-adrenergic antagonist. Alpha-adrenergic blockade and general anesthesia would eliminate the vasoconstrictor response. Hypercholesterolemia was found to potentiate the vasoconstrictor response to norepinephrine in the coronary vascular bed (44) of conscious dogs. The authors postulated that the effect of a high cholesterol diet was to increase the number of alpha-adrenergic receptors on the vascular smooth muscle.

Coronary blood flow and myocardial oxygen consumption were measured by Gregg et al (16) in five animals during exercise following total extrinsic cardiac neural ablation. They found that the coronary flow and myocardial oxygen consumption were lower in the denervated dogs than in normally innervated dogs during exercise. The rate of increase in coronary flow at the onset of exercise was slower in the denervated dogs. This might be explained by the delayed increase in heart rate and fall in arterial blood pressure and by a lack of reflex control of the coronary circulation.

Mean arterial pressure increases during exercise. As mentioned previously, this could contribute to a coronary vasodilation through a reduced vasoconstrictive tone on the coronary vessels. McRitchie et al (34) studied the response to exercise in dogs before and after sinoaortic baroreceptor denervation. Total baroreceptor denervation did not alter the changes in heart rate or total peripheral resistance in response to exercise. At rest, injection of an alpha-adrenergic agonist caused a bradycardia but during exercise it had no effect on heart rate. This study suggests that the baroreceptor reflex was turned off during exercise. On the other hand, Melcher & Donald (35) found that the control of arterial pressure by the carotid sinus baroreceptors was reset to higher pressure levels during exercise. These authors suggest that the variance with the previous study (32) was the result of adaptations taking place in the chronically denervated animals. If the baroreceptor mechanism is reset to higher pressure levels during exercise, the reflex effect on the coronary vascular system should not be important. Reflexes originating from cardiopulmonary receptors independent of arterial pressure control could influence coronary blood flow during exercise. The pulmonary inflation reflex, or reflexes initiated by skeletal muscle receptors, could also be important in controlling coronary flow during dynamic exercise. No experimental evidence is available upon which to base a firm conclusion about any of these possibilities at this time.

SUMMARY

This review has focused on the potential for neural control of the coronary circulation during exercise and has presented evidence that neural reflexes can alter coronary blood flow independent of any metabolic signal for vasodilation in the heart. Coronary reserve is not exhausted during near-maximal exercise, and cardiac ischemia does not occur under these conditions. From the evidence presented it appears that a vasoconstrictor tone can restrict coronary flow by approximately 30% even during maximal exercise. Thus the major factor (approximately 70%) resulting in coronary vasodilation during exercise is a metabolic signal associated with the increased myocardial metabolism.

Reflexes originating in the active skeletal muscle could contribute to an increase in the vasoconstriction of the coronary vessels during exercise; this increase can be eliminated by alpha-adrenergic blockade. Additionally, cardiopulmonary reflexes may contribute to the modulation of coronary resistance, since removal of the left stellate ganglion altered the coronary flow response to exercise. Two elements are worth considering in ascribing to neural control a more active role in the initial response of coronary flow to exercise. The first (55) is the transient decrease in coronary sinus oxygen saturation with the initiation of exercise. The second (15) is the slow response of the coronary flow change in totally denervated hearts. The transient reduction in coronary sinus oxygen content may be a result of coronary vasoconstriction. Subsequently, vasodilation occurs with increasing metabolic demand and modulation of the vasoconstrictor tone of the vessels. In the absence of neural reflexes, the transient effects on coronary flow disappear and vasodilation is reduced because of a reduced metabolic signal. Capillary recruitment may be differentially affected between the epicardium and endocardium by vasoactive metabolic products resulting in a greater increase in coronary flow to the epicardium as compared to the endocardium. Modulation of coronary resistance by the sympathetic nervous system may result in a redistribution of myocardial blood flow to ensure adequate endocardial perfusion during exercise.

ACKNOWLEDGMENT

The author thanks Ms. Irene McMichael and Ms. Shirley Wood for editing and typing the manuscript. A portion of the research cited from the author's laboratory was supported by NIH grant No. 22154.

Literature Cited

1. Armour, J. A., Hopkins, D. A. 1981. Localization of sympathetic postganglionic neurons of physiologically identified cardiac nerves in the dog. *J. Comp. Neurol.* 202:169–84
2. Aung-Din, R., Mitchell, J. H., Longhurst, J. C. 1981. Reflex alpha-adrenergic coronary vasoconstriction during hindlimb static exercise in dogs. *Circ. Res.* 48:502–9
3. Ball, R. M., Bache, R. J., Cobb, F. R., Greenfield, J. C. Jr. 1975. Regional myocardial blood flow during graded treadmill exercise in the dog. *J. Clin. Invest.* 55:43–49
4. Barnard, R. J., Duncan, H. W., Livesay, J. J., Buckberg, G. D. 1977. Coronary vasodilator reserve and flow distribution during near-maximal exercise in dogs. *J. Appl. Physiol: Respir. Environ. Exer. Physiol.* 43:988–92
5. Berne, R. M., Rubio, R. 1979. Coronary circulation. In *Handbook of Physiology, Sect. 2, Vol. 1. The Heart*, ed. R. M. Berne, N. Sperelakis, S. R. Geiger, pp. 873–952. Bethesda, MD: Am. Physiol. Soc.
6. Bertrand, M. E., Carre, A. G., Ginestet, A. P., Lefebvre, J. M., Desplanque, L. A., Lekieffre, J. P. 1977. Maximal exercise in normal subjects. *Eur. J. Cardiol.* 5/6:481–91
7. Braunwald, E. 1971. Control of myocardial oxygen consumption. Physiologic and clinical considerations. *Am. J. Cardiol.* 27:416–32
8. Brown, A. M. 1979. Cardiac reflexes. See Ref. 5, pp. 677–89
9. Buffington, C. W., Feigl, E. O. 1981. Adrenergic coronary vasoconstriction in the presence of coronary stenosis in the dog. *Circ. Res.* 48:416–23
10. Chilian, W. M., Boatwright, R. B., Shoji, T., Griggs, D. M. Jr. 1981. Evidence against significant resting sympathetic coronary vasoconstrictor tone in the conscious dog. *Circ. Res.* 49:866–76
11. Crayton, S. C., Aung-Din, R., Fixler, D. E., Mitchell, J. H. 1979. Distribution of cardiac output during induced isometric exercise in dogs. *Am. J. Physiol.* 236:H218–24

12. Denn, M. J., Stone, H. L. 1976. Autonomic innervation of dog coronary arteries. *J. Appl. Physiol.* 41:30–35
13. Feigl, E. O. 1975. Control of myocardial oxygen tension by sympathetic coronary vasoconstriction in the dog. *Circ. Res.* 37:88–95
14. Feigl, E. O. 1975. Reflex parasympathetic coronary vasodilation elicited from cardiac receptors in the dog. *Circ. Res.* 37:175–82
15. Forbes, M. S., Rennels, M. L., Nelson, E. 1977. Innervation of myocardial microcirculation; terminal autonomic axons associated with capillaries and postcapillary venules in mouse heart. *Am. J. Anat.* 149:71–92
16. Gregg, D. E., Khouri, E. M., Donald, D. E., Lowensohn, H. S., Pasyk, S. 1972. Coronary circulation in the conscious dog with cardiac neural ablation. *Circ. Res.* 31:129–44
17. Gwirtz, P. A., Stone, H. L. 1981. Coronary blood flow and myocardial oxygen consumption after alpha adrenergic blockade during submaximal exercise. *J. Pharmacol. Exp. Ther.* 217:92–98
18. Gwirtz, P. A., Stone, H. L. 1981. Norepinephrine and the coronary vascular bed in the conscious dog. *Basic Res. Cardiol.* 76:518–23
19. Gwirtz, P. A., Stone, H. L. 1982. Coronary blood flow changes following activation of adrenergic receptors in the conscious dog. *Am. J. Physiol.* In press
20. Hamilton, F. N., Feigl, E. O. 1976. Coronary vascular sympathetic beta-receptor innervation. *Am. J. Physiol.* 230:1569–76
21. Heyndrickx, G. R., Pannier, J.-L., Muylaert, P., Mabilde, C., Leusen, I. 1980. Alteration in myocardial oxygen balance during exercise after beta-adrenergic blockade in dogs. *J. Appl. Physiol: Respir. Environ. Exer. Physiol.* 49:28–33
22. Holtz, J., Mayer, E., Bassenge, E. 1977. Demonstration of alpha-adrenergic coronary control in different layers of canine myocardium by regional myocardial sympathectomy. *Pflügers Arch.* 372:187–94

23. Johannsen, U. J., Mark, A. L., Marcus, M. L. 1982. Responsiveness to cardiac sympathetic nerve stimulation during maximal coronary dilation produced by adenosine. *Circ. Res.* 50:510–17

24. Jorgensen, C. R., Wang, K., Wang, Y., Gobel, F. L., Nelson, R. R., Taylor, H. 1973. Effect of propranolol on myocardial oxygen consumption and its hemodynamic correlates during upright exercise. *Circulation* 48:1173–82

25. Kelley, K. O., Feigl, E. O. 1978. Segmental alpha-receptor-mediated vasoconstriction in the canine coronary circulation. *Circ. Res.* 43:908–17

26. Kent, K. M., Epstein, S. E., Cooper, T., Jacobowitz, D. M. 1974. Cholinergic innervation of the canine and human ventricular conducting system. *Circulation* 50:948–55

27. Kirchheim, H. R. 1976. Systemic arterial baroreceptor reflexes. *Physiol. Rev.* 56:100–76

28. Kitamura, K., Jorgensen, C. R., Gobel, F. L., Taylor, H. L., Wang, Y., Olds, D. P. 1972. Hemodynamic correlates of myocardial oxygen consumption during upright exercise. *J. Appl. Physiol* 32:516

29. Klocke, F. J., Ellis, A. K. 1980. Control of coronary blood flow. *Ann. Rev. Med.* 31:489–508

30. Kniffki, K.-D., Mense, S., Schmidt, R. F. 1981. Muscle receptors with fine afferent fibers which may evoke circulatory reflexes. *Circ. Res.* 48(Part II):I25–31

31. Levy, M. N., Blattberg, B. 1976. Effect of vagal stimulation on the overflow of norepinephrine into the coronary sinus during cardiac sympathetic nerve stimulation in the dog. *Circ. Res.* 38:81–85

32. Malindzak, G. S. Jr., Kosinski, E. J., Green, H. D., Yarborough, G. W. 1978. The effects of adrenergic stimulation on conductive and resistive segments of the coronary vasular bed. *J. Pharmacol. Exp. Ther.* 206:248–58

33. Malor, R., Griffin, C. J., Taylor, S. 1973. Innervation of the blood vessels in guinea-pig atria. *Cardiovasc. Res.* 7:95–104

34. McRitchie, R. J., Vatner, S. F., Boettcher, D., Heyndrickx, G. R., Patrick, T. A., Braunwald, E. 1976. Role of arterial baroreceptors in mediating cardiovascular response to exercise. *Am. J. Physiol.* 230:85–89

35. Melcher, A., Donald, D. E. 1981. Maintained ability of carotid baroreflex to regulate arterial pressure during exercise. *Am. J. Physiol.* 241:H838–49

36. Mohrman, D. E., Feigl, E. O. 1978. Competition between sympathetic vasoconstriction and metabolic vasodilation in the canine coronary circulation. *Circ. Res.* 42:79–86

37. Mudge, G. H. Jr., Goldberg, S., Gunther, S., Mann, T., Grossman, W. 1979. Comparison of metabolic and vasoconstrictor stimuli on coronary vascular resistance in man. *Circulation* 59:544–50

38. Murray, P. A., Vatner, S. F. 1979. Alpha-adrenergic attenuation of the coronary vascular responses to severe exercise in the conscious dog. *Circ. Res.* 45:654–60

39. Murray, P. A., Vatner, S. F. 1981. Carotid sinus baroreceptor control of right coronary circulation in normal, hypertrophied, and failing right ventricles of conscious dogs. *Circ. Res.* 49:1339–49

40. Olsson, R. A. 1981. Local factors regulating cardiac and skeletal muscle blood flow. *Ann. Rev. Physiol.* 43:385–95

41. Orlick, A. E., Ricci, D. R., Alderman, E. L., Stinson, E. B., Harrison, D. C. 1978. Effects of alpha adrenergic blockade upon coronary hemodynamics. *J. Clin. Invest.* 62:459–67

42. Peronnet, F., Nadeau, R. A., de Champlain, J., Magrassi, P., Chatrand, C. 1981. Exercise plasma catecholamines in dogs: role of adrenals and cardiac nerve endings. *Am. J. Physiol.* 241:H243–47

43. Powell, J. R., Feigl, E. O. 1979. Carotid sinus reflex coronary vasoconstriction during controlled myocardial oxygen metabolism in the dog. *Circ. Res.* 44:44–51

44. Rembert, J. C., Boyd, L. M., Watkinson, W. P., Greenfield, J. C. Jr. 1980. Effect of adenosine on transmural myocardial blood flow distribution in the awake dog. *Am. J. Physiol.* 239:H7–13

45. Rosendorff, C., Hoffman, J. I. E., Verrier, E. D., Rouleau, J., Boerboom, L. E. 1981. Cholesterol potentiates the coronary artery response to norepinephrine in anesthetized and conscious dogs. *Circ. Res.* 48:320–29

46. Ross, G. 1976. Adrenergic responses of the coronary vessels. *Circ. Res.* 39:461–65

47. Saito, D., Steinhart, C. R., Nixon, D. G., Olsson, R. A. 1981. Intracoronary adenosine deaminase reduces canine myocardial reactive hyperemia. *Circ. Res.* 49:1262–67

48. Schwartz, P. J., Stone, H. L. 1977. Tonic influence of the sympathetic nervous system on myocardial reactive

hyperemia and on coronary blood flow distribution in dogs. *Circ. Res.* 41: 51–58

49. Schwartz, P. J., Stone, H. L. 1979. Effects of unilateral stellectomy upon cardiac performance during exercise in dogs. *Circ. Res.* 44:637–45

50. Schwartz, P. J., Stone, H. L. 1982. Left stellectomy and denervation supersensitivity in conscious dogs. *Am. J. Cardiol.* 49:1185–90

51. Stone, H. L. 1980. Coronary flow, myocardial oxygen consumption, and exercise training in dogs. *J. Appl. Physiol: Respir. Environ. Exer. Physiol.* 49: 759–68

52. Van Breemen, C., Siegel, B. 1980. The mechanism of alpha-adrenergic activation of the dog coronary artery. *Circ. Res.* 46:426–29

53. Van Citters, R. L., Franklin, D. L. 1969. Cardiovascular performance of Alaska sled dogs during exercise. *Circ. Res.* 24:33–42

54. Vatner, S. F., Franklin, D., Van Citters, R. L., Braunwald, E. 1970. Effects of carotid sinus nerve stimulation on the coronary circulation of the conscious dog. *Circ. Res.* 27:11–21

55. Vatner, S. F., Higgins, C. B., Braunwald, E. 1974. Effects of norepinephrine on coronary circulation and left ventricular dynamics in the conscious dog. *Circ. Res.* 34:812–23

56. Vatner, S. F., McRitchie, R. J. 1975. Interaction of the chemoreflex and the pulmonary inflation reflex in the regulation of cornary circulation in conscious dogs. *Circ. Res.* 37:664–73

57. Vatner, S. F., Pagani, M. 1976. Cardiovascular adjustments to exercise: hemodynamics and mechanisms. *Prog. Cardiovasc. Dis.* 19:91–108

58. Vatner, S. F., Pagani, M., Manders, W. T., Pasipoularides, A. D. 1980. Alpha adrenergic vasoconstriction and nitroglycerin vasodilation of large coronary arteries in the conscious dog. *J. Clin. Invest.* 65:5–14

59. Von Restorff, W., Holtz, J., Bassenge, E. 1977. Exercise induced augmentation of myocardial oxygen extraction in spite of normal coronary dilatory capacity in dogs. *Pflügers Arch.* 372: 181–85

60. Watkinson, W. P., Foley, D. H., Rubio, R., Berne, R. M. 1979. Myocardial adenosine formation with increased cardiac performance in the dog. *Am. J. Physiol.* 236:H13–21

61. Woollard, H. H. 1926. The innervation of the heart. *J. Anat.* 60:345–73

62. Zuberbuhler, R. C., Bohr, D. F. 1965. Responses of coronary smooth muscle to catecholamines. *Circ. Res.* 16:431–40

Ann. Rev. Physiol. 1983. 45:229–42

THE EXERCISE PRESSOR REFLEX: Its Cardiovascular Effects, Afferent Mechanisms, and Central Pathways

Jere H. Mitchell, Marc P. Kaufman, and Gary A. Iwamoto

Weinberger Laboratory for Cardiopulmonary Research and the Harry S. Moss Heart Center, Departments of Internal Medicine, Physiology, and Cell Biology, The University of Texas Health Science Center, Dallas, Texas 75235

INTRODUCTION

The neural control mechanisms responsible for the cardiovascular response to exercise are not yet completely understood. Experimental evidence suggests two theories about the initiation and maintenance of this response. The first, called "central command," is that neural impulses, arising from the central activity that recruits motor units, excite medullary and spinal neuronal circuits that cause the cardiovascular changes during exercise (26, 67, 72). The second is that muscle contraction stimulates afferent endings within the skeletal muscle which in turn reflexly evoke the cardiovascular changes (15, 50, 67). These two theories are not mutually exclusive; substantial evidence suggests that both are applicable (54).

The "exercise pressor reflex," broadly defined, comprises all of the cardiovascular changes reflexly induced from contracting skeletal muscle that are responsible for the increase in arterial blood pressure. Here we describe the cardiovascular changes that occur during induced muscular contractions and examine the skeletal muscle afferents and central pathways responsible for this reflex. Recently an exercise depressor reflex has been reported in rabbits (75), but controversy exists over whether the decrease in arterial blood pressure is due to a reflex (54, 58).

The most direct method to study the exercise pressor reflex is to use anesthetized animals in which the cut peripheral ends of the ventral roots

229

are electrically stimulated to cause muscular contraction. This preparation completely prevents central command from participating in the cardiovascular responses to contraction; therefore, any observed response is due to the exercise pressor reflex.

Results obtained from anesthetized animals form the basis of this review. Experiments done in conscious animals and in humans are extremely important to the study of neural control mechanisms during exercise; however, it is frequently difficult to interpret their results in terms of specific central and peripheral neural control mechanisms.

CARDIOVASCULAR ADJUSTMENTS DURING THE EXERCISE PRESSOR REFLEX

Arterial Blood Pressure, Cardiac Output, and Peripheral Vascular Resistance

In cats and dogs a sustained tetanic contraction of muscle induced by spinal ventral root stimulation causes an increase in arterial blood pressure (15, 18, 22, 50, 53, 58). Recently the pressor response has been found to occur during a sustained tetanic contraction of fast-twitch fibers but not during the sustained tetanic contraction of cat soleus muscle, which contains only slow-twitch fibers (59, 60, 61). It was also shown that an electrically induced sustained contration of the cat's medial gastrocnemius muscle, which contains both slow- and fast-twitch muscle fibers, caused a marked pressor response that could be reduced by administration of either decamethonium or curare (59). More importantly, however, the increase in mean blood pressure at similar muscle tensions was less after decamethonium administration, which tends to block preferentially the fast-twitch muscle fibers, than it was after the administration of curare, which tends to block preferentially the slow-twitch fibers. The reason for this difference in blood pressure response to induced sustained contractions of slow- and fast-twitch fibers is not known. It may be due to differences in blood flow, metabolism, or the distribution and sensitivity of Group III and Group IV afferent nerve endings between the slow- and fast-twitch fibers.

The effect of a sustained tetanic contraction on cardiac output and peripheral vascular resistance has been studied in dogs by means of both ventral root stimulation (18, 22) and direct muscle activation (13). In one study (18) cardiac output increased 26%, mean arterial pressure increased 13%, and total peripheral vascular resistance did not change significantly. In another study (13), cardiac output increased 24%, mean arterial pressure increased 17% and total peripheral vascular resistance did not change significantly. After section of the appropriate dorsal roots to eliminate the afferent limb of the exercise pressor reflex, induced static contractions caused a significant decrease in mean arterial pressure and peripheral vascular resistance with no significant change in cardiac output (18).

Heart Rate and Contractile State of the Left Ventricle

During a sustained tetanic contraction there is a small but significant increase in heart rate. In addition to the reflex increase in heart rate during simulated static exercise, there is also an increase in the contractile state of the left ventricle (22, 53). The maximal rate of left ventricular pressure development increases during a sustained tetanic contraction (22, 53). In the study of Mitchell et al (53) the effect of simulated static exercise on the relationship between left ventricular rate of pressure development and the developed pressure (total left ventricular pressure minus left ventricular end-diastolic pressure) was determined before and after β-adrenergic receptor blockade. Before blockade the higher rate of pressure development at any given developed pressure during simulated static exercise indicates an increase in the contractile state of the left ventricle. After β-adrenergic receptor blockade this relationship did not change from rest to simulated exercise.

Distribution of Cardiac Output

Crayton et al (18) and Clement & Pannier (13) have both determined the distribution of cardiac output during induced sustained contraction of muscle by utilizing the radioactive microsphere technique. Blood flow increased to the contracting muscles and decreased to the kidneys. In addition a decrease in flow was found to the resting muscle, skin, and gut (13), and no change in flow was found to the liver (hepatic artery), spleen, brain, and myocardium (18). After section of the appropriate dorsal roots the changes in flow were abolished except for the increase in flow to the exercising muscle (18). The decrease in renal blood flow during simulated static exercise was abolished by α-adrenergic receptor blockade; however, the increase in flow to the exercising limb was not affected by either α- or β-adrenergic receptor blockade (18).

The lack of an increase in coronary blood flow during an induced sustained contraction when heart rate, arterial blood pressure, and the contractile state of the left ventricle are increased is of interest and has been studied in detail (5, 46). After β-adrenergic blockade, simulated static exercise increased systolic arterial pressure and the double product (heart rate X systolic arterial pressure), and at the same time decreased blood flow to the left and to the right ventricle and increased coronary vascular resistance. Following combined β- and α-adrenergic receptor blockade the reduction in coronary blood flow and the increase in coronary vascular resistance were both abolished. These findings suggest that simulated static exercise can cause an α-adrenergic receptor mediated coronary vasoconstriction by a reflex from skeletal muscle (5, 46).

SKELETAL MUSCLE AFFERENT MECHANISMS THAT MAY CAUSE THE EXERCISE PRESSOR REFLEX

Classification of Afferent Fibers from Skeletal Muscle

The classification of afferent fibers with endings in skeletal muscle has been based both on anatomical and electrophysiological measurements (49, 54). Four groups of muscle afferents have been identified by these two methods. Group I have fiber diameters of 12–20 μm and conduct impulses at 71–120 m sec^{-1}. Group II have fiber diameters of 2–16 μm and conduct impulses at 31–70 m sec^{-1}. Group III (Aδ) have diameters of 1–6 μm and conduct at 2.5–30 m sec^{-1}, while group IV (C) have diameters of 1 μm or less and conduct at 2.5 m sec^{-1} or less. Groups I, II, and III muscle afferents are myelinated; group IV afferents are unmyelinated (54).

Two lines of evidence have shown that groups III and IV, but not groups I and II, are responsible for evoking the "exercise pressor reflex." First, electrical stimulation of the central cut ends of group I and II afferents had little or no effect on heart rate and arterial blood pressure, whereas activation of group III and IV afferents markedly increased these variables (16, 33, 42, 69). Second, anodal blockade of the L_7–S_1 dorsal roots blocked firing from group I and II afferents but did not block the exercise pressor reflex. On the other hand, topical application of lidocaine to the dorsal roots did not block firing from group I and II afferents but did block the exercise pressor reflex (50).

Attempts have been made to categorize some of the group III and IV muscle afferents into two groups, ergoreceptors and nociceptors. Ergoreceptors are those group III and IV afferents that cause the exercise pressor reflex and therefore should be stimulated by static contraction of skeletal muscle (32). Nociceptors are those group III and IV afferents that transduce the sensation of muscle pain and therefore should be stimulated by algesic chemicals and by vigorous pinching of the muscle (38). These two categories are likely to represent two poles of a continuum, with most of the group III and IV afferents lying somewhere in between. A similar continuum has been used previously to describe the discharge properties of afferent vagal C-fibers with endings in the heart (6).

Possible Involvement of Group III Afferents in the Exercise Pressor Reflex

Paintal (57) was among the first to examine the discharge properties of group III muscle afferents. He reported that they were stimulated by both static muscular contraction and noxious pressure. Moreover, they were stimulated by injecting a 6% NaCl solution directly into the muscle, a maneuver that produces severe pain in humans. Mense (51) also reported that group III afferents have discharge properties similar to those of the afferents described by Paintal (57).

However, another type of group III afferent appears to function solely as an ergoreceptor. In addition to being activated by muscular contraction, induced by stimulation either of a muscle nerve (51) or a ventral root (35), these afferents were activated by gentle stroking of their receptive fields, a maneuver barely perceptible when applied to the skin of the investigators. Because of their marked sensitivity to light touch, these group III ergoreceptors were unlikely to transduce the sensation of pain.

Most of the group III muscle afferents that appear to function solely as ergoreceptors are very mechanosensitive (35, 38). Three lines of evidence support this suggestion. First, these group III afferents were stimulated by stretching the muscle (35, 51). Second, their response to muscular contraction increases as the tension developed by the contracting muscle increases (35, 51). Third, they are stimulated by nonnoxious probing of their receptive fields (34, 35, 51).

Possible Involvement of Group IV Afferents in the Exercise Pressor Reflex

Many group IV afferents appear capable of functioning both as ergoreceptors and as nociceptors. When probing the triceps surae, investigators have been able to fire many of these afferents only by vigorously pinching their receptive fields; indeed some could not be stimulated even by this noxious maneuver. Most of these group IV ergoreceptors were stimulated by at least one of several algesic substances, including bradykinin, serotonin, potassium, capsaicin, and hyperosmolar lactate and phosphate (35, 37).

Other group IV afferents may function only as ergoreceptors. These afferents were discharged by gently squeezing their receptive fields, a stimulus which when applied to the investigators was perceived as pressure but not as pain. Nevertheless, some of these group IV afferents were stimulated by algesic substances such as bradykinin and capsaicin (35, 37).

Finally, a subset of group IV muscle afferents have been described that may function only as nociceptors. These were stimulated by algesic substances but not by muscular contraction (35, 37). These group IV afferents may have discharge properties similar to those of the group IV afferents described recently by Mense (52), who reported that both prostaglandin E_2 and serotonin enhanced the sensitivity of group IV afferents to bradykinin.

The discharge patterns of the group IV afferents stimulated by muscular contraction may indicate whether these afferents were responding to mechanical or metabolic events in the muscle. One type of group IV afferent responded to contraction within 2 sec of the onset of this manuever (35, 37). In fact, some of these afferents, having receptive fields located at the junction of the calcaneal tendon and the triceps surae, responded to contraction almost instantaneously (37). Therefore, these group IV ergoreceptors were likely to be responding to mechanical events occurring in the contracting skeletal muscle.

A second type of discharge pattern of group IV afferents responding to contraction has been described. These afferents were stimulated by contraction after a delay, the onset of which was often 5 to 15 sec after the start of contraction (35, 37). In addition these afferents, when stimulated by contraction, gradually increased their firing rates as the exercise period progressed (35). The discharge patterns of these group IV afferents suggested that they were likely to be stimulated by metabolic factors occurring in the contracting skeletal muscle.

Central Projections of Groups III and IV Muscle Afferents

Little is known about the central projections of the afferents causing the exercise pressor reflex. For example, the effect of static muscular contraction on the impulse activity of interneurons in the spinal cord and brainstem, which receive input from groups III and IV muscle afferents, has yet to be examined. However, the anatomical projections of these afferents have recently been determined. These investigations (described below) are likely to provide a basis for future descriptions of the central pathway and integrating mechanisms of the exercise pressor reflex.

Most group III and IV fibers enter the spinal cord via the dorsal root. However, in the cat at least 15% of the ventral root axons are sensory; one third of these have receptive fields in the skin or muscle (14). A significant pressor response has been elicited via ventral root afferent fibers both by stimulating the central cut end of the sciatic nerve and by injecting capsaicin into the arterial supply of the skinned hindlimb even though the appropriate dorsal roots were cut (47).

Kalia et al (31) injected horseradish peroxidase into the triceps surae of the cat in order to determine the terminations of afferent fibers innervating this muscle group. Terminal labeling was found in laminas I through V of the spinal cord with heaviest labeling in laminas I (marginal zone) and II (substansia gelatinosa). In addition, labeling was found both in the dorsal column nuclei and in the nucleus of the solitary tract. It was not known, however, whether this terminal labeling arose from groups I, II, III, or IV muscle afferents.

Light & Perl (43) applied horseradish peroxidase to the lumbar dorsal roots of cats, rats, and monkeys and found ipsilateral terminal labeling in laminas I, II, III and contralateral labeling in lamina III. In addition, they combined the horseradish peroxidase technique with partial section of the dorsal roots to determine the terminations of thick and thin diameter afferents. Lamina I received input from "intermediate or smaller myelinated fibers," whereas lamina II received input from the "very finest fibers."

CENTRAL PATHWAYS OF THE EXERCISE PRESSOR REFLEX

Little is known about the central nervous system pathways of the exercise pressor reflex. Much of the related information is based on the characteristics of reflexes evoked by stimulation of peripheral nerves at various intensities—the somatosympathetic reflexes. This information may or may not be totally applicable to the exercise pressor reflex since numerous types of afferents other than those from muscle have often been included with electrical stimulation of peripheral nerves. In addition, actual cardiovascular changes must often be inferred, as neural activity is measured as the efferent arm of the reflex. Furthermore, investigations of these reflexes have been limited since few experiments have attempted to localize precisely the brain components necessary for the reflex, indicating only that medulla, pons, or midbrain levels may be involved.

Evidence for Multiple Levels of Integration

Several levels of integration may exist in the exercise pressor reflex. The early studies of Ranson (62) and later Brooks (8) showed that peripherally stimulated pressor responses seemed to depend upon an intact rostral neuraxis and that the spinal cord by itself played a minor role. Investigators using lumbar sympathetic discharge as a monitor of reflex activity have confirmed that a supraspinal and a spinal component appear to exist. Since activation of group I and II afferents causes no appropriate cardiovascular response, we discuss largely the reflexes of group III and IV afferents thought to mediate the exercise pressor reflex. For a more complete treatment including the effects of lower threshold afferents, see (70).

A number of reflex components that may be involved in the exercise pressor reflex have been identified, each with its own characteristics. Both an "early" (latency 25–50 msec) and a "late" (80–120 msec) somatosympathetic reflex may be observed in the intact animal (71) in response to stimulation of nerve fibers with group II and III diameters. This dual pattern of reflex activity is preserved even when only an intact medulla and spinal cord remain, but following spinal transection at C_1 or T_8, the "late" reflex is abolished. Thus the late reflex requires mediation by the caudal brainstem. Despite the well-known cardiovascular reflexes found in animals with chronic spinal transections (74) it has been reported that the "late" reflex of groups II and III never reappears (39). The spinal reflex is most demonstrable at spinal segments at or adjacent to the afferent entry level. Since the exercise pressor reflex is usually evoked by stimuli lasting several seconds it should be noted that a supraspinally mediated "very late" reflex (latency 300–350 msec) to group III stimulation may also be obtained (70).

Group IV fibers give rise to two reflexes, one complete at spinal levels, the other supraspinally mediated (68). Latency of the combined reflexes is ~ 250–500 msec, with the long delay due primarily to the conduction time of the unmyelinated afferent (73). Again, the spinal portion of the reflex is most clearly demonstrated at the segmental level of the afferent input. A group IV intersegmental reflex, while not present in the intact animal or just after spinal cord transection, appears several weeks post-transection, thus explaining the cardiovascular reflex activity of the chronic animal (68).

It is unclear whether or not the reflex responses of the isolated spinal cord are operative during the exercise pressor reflex. These responses are expressed only after many weeks post-transection; they may not be functional in the intact animal and therefore may play no role in the exercise pressor reflex. We have adopted this view despite the fact that the large pressor reflexes of the long-term post-transection spinal animals (74) are generally referred to as classic examples of cardiovascular function localized in the isolated spinal cord. At the present time, however, one cannot exclude that at least the segmental responses of the isolated spinal cord may have some effect on the expression of the reflex through sympathetic outflow at the spinal levels innervating the limbs, since this reflex does not require a long post-transection period to be expressed.

The exercise pressor reflex is present in decerebrate animals and thus does not require the rostral brain (telencephalon and diencephalon) for its expression (15, 50). However, the supraspinal structures involved have not been identified completely.

In summary, many identifiable responses are known to be evoked by the stimulation of group III and IV afferents utilizing supraspinal, segmental, and intersegmental reflex pathways. The supraspinal path relays primarily through the medulla. It would be unwise at this time to rule out completely a contribution by any of these reflex components, except perhaps that of the isolated spinal cord appearing many weeks post-transection.

Ascending and Descending Spinal Cord Pressor Pathways

Recent evidence suggests that the region surrounding the dorsolateral sulcus (including the dorsolateral funiculus and fasiculus) contains most of the ascending and descending funicular (white matter) axon trajectories mediating the somatic afferent cardiovascular reflexes. Reflexes mediated by myelinated fibers appear to ascend bilaterally via the dorsolateral funiculus (DLF) (11), while the unmyelinated fibers appear to ascend bilaterally via a region surrounding the dorsolateral sulcus (DLS) (10, 40).

The cardiovascular responses to treadmill exercise by all four limbs are reduced with DLF-DLS lesions, but not the adjustments to exercise by the hindlimbs. This is opposite to the expected result based on current thought. This finding suggests that alternative pressor pathways to the brainstem may exist (40), and thus may be important in elucidating the nature of the central pathways of the exercise pressor reflex. Information concerning which spino-reticular projections are critical for the reflex is not well-developed, although numerous anatomical pathways exist (7, 36, 66).

Many agree that the pathway for the descending components of the pressor reflexes is through the dorsolateral spinal cord (19, 24, 25). The supraspinal origins of the pathway are not known with certainty (9, 76). Therefore, it is appropriate to discuss the anatomical evidence for possible sites of supraspinal origin caudal to the midcollicular level, since the reflex is thought to be complete below this level (15, 50). Loewy and co-workers (44, 45) have studied projections of various brainstem nuclei to the intermediolateral cell column (ILC) using autoradiographic and retrograde horseradish peroxidase transport techniques. These studies and a recent retrograde transport study by Amendt and co-workers (3) have indicated that the A5 cell group (noradrenaline containing), the raphe nuclei (serotonergic), the nucleus of the solitary tract, the Kölliker-Fuse nucleus, and the ventrolateral rostral medulla including the rostral prolongation of the lateral reticular nucleus (LRN) all project directly to the spinal cord ILC. Ross et al (65) used immunocytochemical and retrograde transport techniques and found that the C-1 (adrenaline containing) cell groups also project to the spinal cord. These areas are all linked with cardiovascular reflex function and therefore may play a role in the exercise pressor reflex.

Brainstem Structures that May Mediate the Exercise Pressor Reflex

Until now few experiments have been performed to identify the brainstem structures subserving the exercise pressor reflex. The brainstem has long been implicated in the control of cardiovascular responses, since it was first partitioned into various "pressor" and "depressor" regions (reviewed in 2).

However, recent investigations suggest that the paramedian reticular nucleus (55) as well as the caudal raphe nuclei (1) and the nucleus gigantocellularis (41) correspond well to the posteromedial depressor region described by Alexander (2). The lateral reticular nucleus, nucleus parvocellularis (27), and rostral raphe nuclei (1) can be identified with the lateral and rostral brainstem pressor sites.

Likely candidates for the brainstem relay nuclei mediating the exercise pressor reflex are any that (a) receive appropriate spinal afferent information, (b) project directly or indirectly to the spinal cord's intermediolateral nucleus, or (c) produce pressor responses when stimulated directly. Only one example will be discussed, though the possibilities are numerous.

Experiments indicate that the lateral reticular nucleus (LRN) is one key brainstem site in producing a pressor response to somatic afferent stimulation since ipsilateral lesions of the nucleus abolish pressor responses to sciatic nerve stimulation (12). These findings suggest that by virtue of the lateral reticular nucleus's known muscle afferent response characteristics (63, 64), pressor effect on stimulation (12), and heavy spinobulbo projection (17, 28) it represents a logical potential relay in the exercise pressor reflex. Recent experiments have shown that bilateral lesions of the lateral reticular nuclei of the cat abolish the exercise pressor reflex (29) even though the cat can still demonstrate a pressor response to brain stimulation. Furthermore, labeling of brainstem cell groups with 2-deoxyglucose during a sustained exercise pressor reflex has indicated that the lateral reticular nucleus is active during the response (30). Thus evidence to date indicates that the lateral reticular nucleus and not fibers "en-passage" in the area are probably responsible for the mediation of the exercise pressor reflex.

Efferent connections of the lateral reticular nucleus are also of interest. The main cell groups of the lateral reticular nucleus apparently do not project to the spinal cord ILC directly (3). Despite this, there is ample anatomical and physiological evidence that the efferent information from the (LRN) reaches the cerebellum (63, 64), and the efferent projections supply the cerebellar cortex and the fastigial nucleus (48), the latter a well known pressor site (55). Furthermore, evidence indicates that the information, following integration, may be relayed back to various brainstem nuclei related to cardiovascular function, including paramedian reticular nucleus (4, 55, 56), nucleus gigantocellularis (4, 56), and the region of the A5 catecholamine area (20), as well as the locus coeruleus, nucleus parvocellularis, and LRN (56). Thus although shorter spino-bulbo-spinal arrangements may exist, connections of the lateral reticular nucleus with the cerebellum make the possibility of a spino → bulbo → cerebellar → bulbo → spinal reflex arc for the exercise pressor reflex an attractive hypothesis.

Certainly, the cerebellum is involved with the cardiovascular circuitry supporting exercise since a reduction in the pressor response has been observed in exercising conscious dogs with lesions in the fastigial nucleus (21, 23). The evidence, while at present circumstantial, suggests the overlap of a central neural mechanism ("central command") (26) with a peripheral neural mechanism (exercise pressor reflex), the coordinating function being served by the cerebellum (21).

Although the exercise pressor reflex appears to be relayed through the lateral reticular nucleus and its connections, we do not discount the existence of other parallel pathways. The loss of the LRN may simply reduce the general excitation of all the pressor circuitry to the point at which the response may no longer be easily obtained. To mention just one other candidate for a key role in the reflex, the raphe nuclei (e.g. raphe magnus) may also subserve some function in the reflex by virtue of their known pressor effects (1) when stimulated and their requisite anatomical relationships (3, 7).

CONCLUSIONS

Contraction of skeletal muscle can reflexly cause changes in the efferent sympathetic and parasympathetic outputs to the cardiovascular system that are in turn responsible for increases in arterial blood pressure, heart rate, contractile state of the left ventricle, cardiac output, and changes in the distribution of blood flow. Our knowledge of the afferent mechanisms involved in the exercise pressor reflex is incomplete. However, a specific subset of group III and group IV muscle afferents may serve as ergoreceptors activated by either mechanical or metabolic perturbations. Little is known about the central neural pathway of the exercise pressor reflex, though it appears that the lateral reticular nucleus may be an important site of integration. Among several other areas in the brainstem that may be involved are the fastigial nucleus and raphe nuclei. We do not know the precise role of the exercise pressor reflex in the overall changes in the cardiovascular system during exercise in the conscious animal. All these areas are now under extensive investigation.

ACKNOWLEDGMENTS

Supported in part by NIH Program Project Grant #HL06296 and the Lawson and Rogers Lacy Research Fund in Cardiovascular Diseases. We greatly appreciate the assistance of Ms. Jan Wright in preparing this manuscript.

Literature Cited

1. Adair, J. R., Hamilton, B. L., Scappaticci, K. A., Helke, C. J., Gillis, R. A. 1977. Cardiovascular responses to electrical stimulation of the medullary raphe area of the cat. *Brain Res.* 128:141–45
2. Alexander, R. S. 1946. Tonic and reflex functions of medullary sympathetic cardiovascular centers. *J. Neurophysiol.* 9:205–17
3. Amendt, K., Czachurski, J., Dembowsky, K., Seller, H. 1979. Bulbospinal projections to the intermediolateral cell column; a neuroanatomical study. *J. Auton. Nerv. Syst.* 1:103–17
4. Andrezik, J. A., Dormer, K. J., Foreman, R. D., Gower, M. D. 1982. Fastigial nucleus projections to the brain stem in beagles. *Fed. Proc.* 4:1517
5. Aung-Din, R., Mitchell, J. H., Longhurst, J. C. 1981. Reflex α-adrenergic coronary vasoconstriction during hindlimb static exercise in dogs. *Circ. Res.* 48:502–9
6. Baker, D. G., Coleridge, H. M., Coleridge, J. C. G. 1979. Vagal afferent C fibres from the left ventricle. In *Cardiac Receptors*, ed. R. Hainsworth, C. Kidd, R. J. Linden, pp. 117–37. Oxford: Cambridge Univ. Press
7. Brodal, A., Walberg, F., Taber, E. 1960. The raphe nuclei of the brain stem in the cat III. Afferent connections. *J. Comp. Neurol.* 114:261–81
8. Brooks, C. McC. 1933. Reflex activation of the sympathetic system in the spinal cat. *Am. J. Physiol.* 106:251–66
9. Chung, K., Chung, J. M., LaVelle, F. W., Wurster, R. D. 1979. The anatomical localization of descending pressor pathways in the cat spinal cord. *Neurosci. Lett.* 15:71–75
10. Chung, J. M., Webber, C. L. Jr., Wurster, R. D. 1979. Ascending spinal pathways for the somatosympathetic A and C reflexes. *Am. J. Physiol.* 237: H342–47
11. Chung, J. M., Wurster, R. D. 1976. Ascending pressor and depressor pathways in the cat spinal cord. *Am. J. Physiol.* 231:786–92
12. Ciriello, J., Calaresu, F. R. 1977. Lateral reticular nucleus: a site of somatic and cardiovascular integration in the cat. *Am. J. Physiol.* 233:R100–9
13. Clement, D. L., Pannier, J. L. 1980. Cardiac output distribution during induced static muscular contractions in the dog. *Eur. J. Appl. Physiol.* 45:199–207
14. Clifton, G. L., Coggeshall, R. E., Vance, W. H., Willis, W. D. 1976. Receptive fields of unmyelinated ventral root afferent fibres in the cat. *J. Physiol.* 256:573–600
15. Coote, J. H., Hilton, S. M., Perez-Gonzalez, J. F. 1971. The reflex nature of the pressor response to muscular exercise. *J. Physiol.* 215:789–804
16. Coote, J. H., Perez-Gonzalez, J. F. 1970. The response of some sympathetic neurones to volleys in various afferent nerves. *J. Physiol.* 208:261–78
17. Corvaja, N., Grofova, I., Pompeiano, O., Walberg, F. 1977. The lateral reticular nucleus in the cat. I. An experimental anatomical study of its spinal and supraspinal afferent connections. *Neuroscience* 2:537–53
18. Crayton, C. S., Aung-Din, R., Fixler, D. E., Mitchell, J. H. 1979. Distribution of cardiac output during induced isometric exercise in dogs. *Am. J. Physiol.* 236:H218–24
19. Dembowsky, K., Czachurski, J., Amendt, K., Seller, H. 1980. Tonic descending inhibition of the spinal somatosympathetic reflex from the lower brain stem. *J. Auton. Nerv. Syst.* 2:157–82
20. Dormer, K. J., Foreman, R. D., Andrezik, J. A., Person, R. J. 1982. Brain stem lesions modulate the fastigial nucleus pressor response in anesthetized beagles. *Neurosci. Abstr.* In press
21. Dormer, K. J., Stone, H. L. 1982. Fastigial nucleus and its possible role in the cardiovascular response to exercise. In *Circulation, Neurobiology and Behavior*, ed. O. A. Smith, R. M. Galosy, S. M. Weiss, pp. 201–15. Amsterdam: Elsevier. pp. 346
22. Fisher, M. L., Nutter, D. O. 1974. Cardiovascular reflex adjustments to static muscular contractions in the canine hindlimb. *Am. J. Physiol.* 226:648–55
23. Foreman, R. D., Dormer, K. J., Ohata, C. A., Stone, H. L. 1980. Neural control of the heart during arrhythmias and exercise. *Fed. Proc.* 39:2519–25
24. Foreman, R. D., Wurster, R. D. 1973. Localization and functional characteristics of descending sympathetic spinal pathways. *Am. J. Physiol.* 225:212–17
25. Gebber, G. L., Taylor, D. G., Weaver, L. C. 1973. Electrophysiological studies on organization of central vasopressor pathways. *Am. J. Physiol.* 224:470–81
26. Goodwin, G. .M, McCloskey, D. I., Mitchell, H. J. 1972. Cardiovascular and respiratory responses to changes in central command during isometric ex-

ercise at constant muscle tension. *J. Physiol.* 226:173–90

27. Henry, J. L., Calaresu, F. R. 1974. Excitatory and inhibitory inputs from medullary nuclei projecting to spinal cardioacceleratory neurons in the cat. *Exp. Brain Res.* 20:485–504

28. Hrycyshyn, A. R., Flumerfelt, D. A. 1981. A light microscopic investigation of the lateral reticular nucleus in the cat. *J. Comp. Neurol.* 197:477–502

29. Iwamoto, G. A., Kaufman, M. P., Botterman, B. R., Mitchell, J. H. 1982. Effects of lateral reticular nucleus lesions on the exercise pressor reflex in cats. *Circ. Res.* 51:400–3

30. Iwamoto, G. A., Parnavelas, J. P., Kaufman, M. P. Botterman, B. R., Mitchell, J. H. 1983. Identification of brainstem cell groups activated during the exercise pressor reflex. *Fed. Proc.* In press

31. Kalia, M., Mei, S. S., Kao, F. F. 1981. Central projections from ergoreceptors (C fibers) in muscle involved in cardiopulmonary responses to static exercise. *Circ. Res.* 48 (Suppl. I):I48–62

32. Kao, F. F. 1963. An experimental study of the pathway involved in exercise hyperpnea employing cross-circulation technique. In *The Regulation of Human Respiration*, ed. D. J. C. Cunningham, B. B. Lloyd, pp. 461–502. Oxford: Blackwell

33. Katz, S., Perryman, J. H. 1965. Respiratory and blood pressure responses to stimulation of peripheral afferent nerves. *Am. J. Physiol.* 208:993–99

34. Kaufman, M. P., Iwamoto, G. A., Longhurst, J. C., Mitchell, J. H. 1982. Effects of capsaicin and bradykinin on afferent fibers with endings in skeletal muscle. *Circ. Res.* 50:133–39

35. Kaufman, M. P., Longhurst, J. C., Rybicki, K. J., Wallach, J. H., Mitchell, J. H. 1982. Effect of muscular contraction on thin fiber muscle afferents in cats. *Fed. Proc.* 41:1604

36. Kevetter, G. A., Yezierski, R. P., Willis, W. D. 1981. Cells of origin of the spinoreticular pathway in the monkey. *Anat. Rec.* 199:138A

37. Kniffki, K.-D., Mense, S., Schmidt, R. F. 1978. Responses of group IV afferent units from skeletal muscle to stretch, contraction and chemical stimulation. *Exp. Brain Res.* 31:511–22

38. Kniffki, K.-D., Mense, S., Schmidt, R. F. 1981. Muscle receptors with fine afferent fibers which may evoke circulatory reflexes. *Circ. Res.* 48 (Suppl. I): I25–31

39. Koizumi, K., Sato, A., Kaufman, A., Brooks, C. McC. 1968. Studies of sympathetic neuron discharges modified by central and peripheral excitation. *Brain Res.* 11:212–24

40. Kozelka, J. W., Chung, J. M., Wurster, R. D. 1981. Ascending spinal pathways mediating somato-cardiovascular reflexes. *J. Auton. Nerv. Syst.* 3:171–75

41. Kuo, J. S., Hwa, Y., Chai, C. Y. 1979. Cardioinhibitory mechanisms in the gigantocellular reticular nucleus of the medulla oblongata. *Brain Res.* 178: 221–32

42. Laporte, Y., Bessou, P., Bouissett, S. 1960. Action reflexe des differents types de fibres afferents d'orogine musculaire sur la pression sanguine. *Arch. Ital. Biol.* 98:206–21

43. Light, A. R., Perl, E. R. 1979. Reexamination of the dorsal root projection to the spinal dorsal horn including observations on the differential termination of coarse and fine fibers. *J. Comp. Neurol.* 186:117–31

44. Loewy, A. D. 1981. Descending pathways to sympathetic and parasympathetic preganglionic neurons. *J. Auton. Nerv. Syst.* 3:265–75

45. Loewy, A. D., McKellar, S. V. 1980. The neuroanatomical basis of central cardiovascular control. *Fed. Proc.* 39: 2495–2503

46. Longhurst, J. C., Aung-Din, R., Mitchell, J. H. 1981. Static exercise in anesthetized dogs, a cause of reflex alpha-adrenergic coronary vasoconstriction. *Basic Res. Cardiol.* 76:530–35

47. Longhurst, J. C., Mitchell, J. H., Moore, M. B. 1980. The spinal cord ventral root: an afferent pathway of the hind-limb pressor reflex in cats. *J. Physiol.* 301:467–76

48. Matsushita, M., Ikeda, M. 1976. Projections from the lateral reticular nucleus to the cerebellar cortex and nuclei in the cat. *Exp. Brain Res.* 24:403–21

49. Matthews, P. B. C. 1972. *Muscle Receptors and Their Central Actions.* London: Arnold

50. McCloskey, D. I., Mitchell, J. H. 1972. Reflex cardiovascular and respiratory responses originating in exercising muscle. *J. Physiol.* 224:173–86

51. Mense, S. 1978. *Muskelreceptoren mit dünnen markhaltigen und marklosen afferenten Fasern: Receptive Eigenschaften und mögliche Function.* Kiel: Christian-Albrechts-Universität

52. Mense, S. 1981. Sensitization of group IV muscle receptors to bradykinin by

5-hydroxytryptamine and prostaglandin E$_2$. *Brain Res.* 225:95–105
53. Mitchell, J. H., Reardon, W. C., McCloskey, D. I. 1977. Reflex effects on circulation and respiration from contracting skeletal muscle. *Am. J. Physiol.* 233:H374–78
54. Mitchell, J. H., Schmidt, R. F. 1982. Cardiovascular reflex control by afferent fibers from skeletal muscle receptors. In *Handbook of Physiology.* Washington DC: Am. Physiol. Soc. In press.
55. Miura, M., Reis, D. J. 1969. Cerebellum: a pressor response elicited from the fastigial nucleus and its efferent pathway in the brainstem. *Brain Res.* 13:595–99
56. Moolenaar, G. M., Rucker, H. K. 1976. Autoradiographic study of brain stem projections from fastigial pressor areas. *Brain Res.* 114:492–96
57. Paintal, A. S. 1960. Functional analysis of group III afferent fibers of mammalian muscles. *J. Physiol.* 152:250–70
58. Perez-Gonzalez, J. F. 1981. Factors determining the blood pressure responses to isometric exercise. *Circ. Res.* 48(Suppl. I): I76–86
59. Petrofsky, J. S., Lind, A. R. 1980. The blood pressure response during isometric exercise in fast and slow twitch skeletal muscle in the cat. *Eur. J. Appl. Physiol.* 44:223–30
60. Petrofsky, J. S., Phillips, C. A., Lind, A. R. 1981. The influence of fiber composition, recruitment order and muscle temperature on the pressor response to isometric contractions in skeletal muscle of the cat. *Circ. Res.* 48(Suppl. I): I32–36
61. Petrofsky, J. S., Phillips, C. A., Sawka, M. N., Hanpeter, D., Lind, A. R., Stafford, D. 1981. Muscle fiber recruitment and blood pressure response to isometric exercise. *J. Appl. Physiol.* 50:32–37
62. Ranson, S. W. 1916. New evidence in favour of a chief vasoconstrictor center in the brain. *Am. J. Physiol.* 42:1–8
63. Rosen, I., Scheid, P. 1972. Cutaneous afferent responses in neurons of the lateral reticular nucleus. *Brain Res.* 43:259–63
64. Rosen, I., Scheid, P. 1973. Patterns of afferent input to the lateral reticular nucleus of the cat. *Exp. Brain Res.* 18:242–55

65. Ross, C. A., Armstrong, D. M., Ruggiero, D. A., Pickel, V. M., Joh, T. H., Reis, D. J. 1981. Adrenaline neurons in the rostral ventrolateral medulla innervate thoracic spinal cord: a combined immunocytochemical and retrograde transport demonstration. *Neurosci. Lett.* 25:257–62
66. Rossi, G. F., Brodal, A. 1957. Terminal distribution of spinoreticular fibers in the cat. *Arch Neurol. Psychiatr. Chicago* 78:439–53
67. Rowell, L. B., Freund, P. R., Hobbs, S. F. 1981. Cardiovascular responses to muscle ischemia in humans. *Circ. Res.* 48 (Suppl. I):I37–47
68. Sato, A. 1973. Spinal and medullary reflex components of the somato-sympathetic reflex discharges evoked by stimulation of the group IV somatic afferents. *Brain Res.* 51:307–18
69. Sato, A., Sato, Y., Schmidt, R. F. 1981. Heart rate changes reflecting modifications of efferent cardiac sympathetic outflow by cutaneous and muscle afferent volleys. *J. Auton. Nerv. Syst.* 4:231–47
70. Sato, A., Schmidt, R. F. 1973. Somatosympathetic reflexes: afferent fibers, central pathways, discharge characteristics. *Physiol. Rev.* 53:916–47
71. Sato, A., Tsushima, N., Fujimori, B. 1965. Reflex potentials of lumbar sympathetic trunk with sciatic nerve stimulation in cats. *Jpn. J. Physiol.* 15:532–39
72. Schibye, B., Mitchell, J. H., Payne, F. C. III, Saltin, B. 1981. Blood pressure and heart rate response to static exercise in relation to electromyographic activity and force development. *Acta Physiol. Scand.* 113:61–66
73. Schmidt, R. F., Weller, E. 1970. Reflex activity in the cervical and lumbar sympathetic trunk induced by unmyelinated somatic afferents. *Brain Res.* 24:207–18
74. Sherrington, C. S. 1906. *The Integrative Action of the Nervous System.* New Haven: Yale Univ. Press
75. Tallarida, G., Baldoni, F., Peruzzi, G., Raimondi, G., Massaro, M., Sangiorgi, M. 1981. Cardiovascular and respiratory reflexes from muscles during dynamic and static exercise. *J. Appl. Physiol.* 50:784–91
76. Wurster, R. D. 1977. Spinal sympathetic control of the heart. In *Neural Regulation of the Heart,* ed. W. C. Randall, pp. 211–46. NY: Oxford Univ. Press. 440 pp.

COMPARATIVE AND INTEGRATIVE PHYSIOLOGY

Introduction, James E. Heath, *Section Editor*

Most species of plants and animals live in habitats that never or rarely approach the freezing point of water. A few organisms have developed methods to exploit those climates and habitats that regularly experience daily or seasonal temperatures below freezing.

Avoidance of exposure is a general category not considered here. It includes such diverse behavioral and physiological mechanisms as body temperature regulation, migration, hibernation, and selection of microhabitats (such as caves, deep underground burrows, and deep waters of lakes and ponds) that do not freeze even in winter.

A second category is composed of organisms that tolerate freezing. These have developed resistance to extreme cold and the concomitant biological problems of ice formation and elevated salinity. Here we find sessile intertidal invertebrates that may experience daily temperature variation from –20°C to above freezing as well as insects with resistant stages tolerating –20°C for months.

A final group comprises organisms, largely aquatic, that live seasonally or indefinitely at temperatures near but below the freezing point of their tissues. These organisms carry on the full cycle of life under such circumstances.

For the latter two categories, we have come to recognize important new groups of glycoproteins and glycopeptides that operate as either antifreeze agents or as nucleating agents controlling the location and extent of ice formation in the tissues. Three chapters (DeVries; Duman & Horwath; and Murphy) chronicle recent advances in this fascinating field, from which may come important applications in tissue preservation. These chapters incidentally convey the degree of frontier hardiness displayed by investigators working in arctic and antarctic conditions.

The other chapter takes up the role of peptides in the neural organization of invertebrates. In a highly critical essay, Greenberg & Price review the occurrence and function of neuropeptides in invertebrates. They propose an irrelation between neuropeptide structure and apparent function in the vertebrates or invertebrates.

These four essays reveal what comparative physiology is about. It is the documentation of the modes of adaptation and function of various kinds of organisms.

Ann. Rev. Physiol. 1983. 45:245–60

ANTIFREEZE PEPTIDES AND GLYCOPEPTIDES IN COLD-WATER FISHES

A. L. DeVries

The University of Illinois, Urbana, Illinois 61801

INTRODUCTION

During the winter season the polar oceans and the near-shore waters of the north temperate oceans are at the freezing point of seawater (–1.9°C), a temperature well below the freezing point of a typical marine teleost (–0.8°C) (5). This one degree difference between environment and body fluid freezing point is large enough to result in freezing because supercooling in the presence of ice cannot occur (74). Freezing of the body fluids or tissues of fishes has been shown in all cases to lead to death, although several hours may intervene between thawing and death. Two different strategies by which fishes avoid freezing when their habitats are cooled below their freezing points are recognized. The first concerns behavioral responses. Some shallow-water summer inhabitants migrate offshore to warm water (15) while others move into deep (100 m) cold water and overwinter at a temperature of –1.9°C in a supercooled state. One degree of supercooling is small and appears to be metastable at these depths where the waters are ice free.

In the shallow ice-laden waters of the polar oceans many fishes spend their entire lives beneath thick ice cover (11, 12, 14) yet do not appear to freeze. In fact some even use the ice crystal formations associated with the year-round thick ice cover as a habitat in which to forage for food yet appear to be immune to freezing (3, 16). The body fluids of such fishes will not freeze until the temperature is lowered below –2°C (16). Lowering of the environmental temperature below –2°C in the presence of ice results in freezing and death (16, 74).

In most temperate marine fishes, sodium chloride is the principle electrolyte present in the blood and is responsible for 85% of the freezing-point

0066-4278/83/0315-0245$02.00

depression (40). The remainder of the freezing-point depression is due to small amounts of potassium, calcium, urea, glucose, and the free amino acids (67). In fishes inhabiting freezing environments, concentrations of sodium chloride in the body fluids are elevated relative to temperate forms (30, 32, 59). They are, however, not high enough to account for the low freezing points. In fact they are responsible for only 40–50% of the observed freezing-point depression (15, 30, 32, 59). Concentrations of other ions and small organic solutes are nearly the same as those found in temperate-water fishes (15). In these cold-water fishes over half of the freezing-point depression has been shown to be associated with the colloidal fraction of the blood, and it is retained by a dialysis membrane with a cutoff of 3000 daltons (15, 16). The large freezing-point depression associated with the colloidal fraction indicates that relatively large molecules are involved and also implies that they exert their effect by a noncolligative mechanism. In most antarctic fishes and many north-temperate fishes these molecules are glycopeptides, while in some arctic and north-temperate fishes they are peptides (43). These glycopeptides and peptides range between 2,400 and 34,000 daltons (14, 27, 29). On a weight basis they appear to be as effective as sodium chloride in depressing the freezing point of water (19). On a molal basis they depress the freezing point 200–300 times more than expected on the basis of colligative relationships (13). These colloidal solutes can be characterized as having "antifreeze" properties where it is stressed that the freezing point is lowered in a noncolligative manner with little effect on the melting point of the solid phase.

BIOLOGICAL ANTIFREEZES

Glycopeptides

The glycopeptide antifreezes were first isolated from the blood of notothen-iid fishes inhabiting McMurdo Sound, Antarctica (19). They make up approximately 3.5% (W/V) of the blood, and electrophoretic analyses indicate 8 separate glycopeptides in the blood of most of the antarctic nototheniids (13, 18, 20). They range from 2400 to 34,000 daltons. Glyco-peptides 1–5 are composed of repeating units of glycotripeptides in which the disaccharide β-D-galactopyranosyl-(1→3)-2-acetamido-2-deoxy-α-D-galactospyranose is linked to the threonine residue of the tripeptide, alanyl-threonyl-alanine (21, 49, 78, 79). Glycopeptides 6, 7, and 8 differ from 1–5 in that the amino acid proline replaces some of the alanines beginning at position seven and appears at every third position until the C-terminal is reached (52, 56). Glycopeptide 8 appears to be a mixture of three identical-sized molecules in which the prolines occupy different positions in the polypeptide (52, 56). The same 8 glycopeptides have been isolated from the

BIOLOGICAL ANTIFREEZE AGENTS 247

northern gadids including the Greenland cod, *Gadus ogac* from Labrador (83), the arctic polar cod, *Boreogadus saida* (62), and the Atlantic cod from Newfoundland, *Gadus morhua* (47). The positions occupied by proline in glycopeptide 8 in some of these forms differ from those reported for the antarctic nototheniids (36, 47, 61). The saffron cod, *Eleginus gracilis,* from the Bering Sea and the Atlantic tomcod, *Microgadus tomcod,* also have glycopeptide antifreezes that differ slightly (15, 36, 71). The antifreezes in the saffron cod and rock cod are both glycopeptides but they differ substantially in composition and size, indicating considerable variability in the same family. No variability among families has been noted in the glycopeptides of three antarctic nototheniid families studied so far. It appears remarkable that fishes belonging to unrelated families inhabiting opposite hemispheres have evolved identical antifreeze glycopeptides (83) while sympatric species of the same family have evolved glycopeptides that show considerable variation in composition and size.

Peptides

Peptide antifreezes have been identified in and isolated from several north-temperate and arctic fishes (Table 1). They vary in size and composition, and only a few have been completely characterized. Three separate peptides have been isolated from the winter flounder, *Pseudopleuronectes americanus.* They are composed of 8 amino acids in which alanine accounts for 60% of the residues (23, 25). Most of the remainder are polar residues such as aspartate, glutamate, lysine, serine, and threonine. A partial sequence of each of the three peptides shows a repeat pattern of the two polar residues aspartic and threonine separated by two alanines with each polar sequence separated by 7 nonpolar residues, usually a leucine and 6 alanines (17). The Alaskan plaice, *Pleuronectes quadritaberulatus,* has evolved peptide antifreezes similar to those of the winter flounder and possesses a similar polar sequence separated by long stretches of alanine (15). In this peptide, the positions of threonine and aspartate are conserved but leucine is absent (15). Antifreeze peptides have also been isolated from the Bering Sea sculpin, *Myoxocephalus verrucosus* (71); the several electrophoretic variants may, however, be of similar size. The composition of these peptides resembles that of those isolated from the short horn sculpin, *M. scorpius,* from the waters of Newfoundland and Ellsmere Island (34, 46). This is not entirely unexpected since these species are taxonomically almost indistinguishable. Like the flounder peptides, these contain about 60% alanine and are rich in the polar residues aspartate, threonine, glutamate, and lysine. They differ in that they contain the nonpolar amino acids isoleucine, glycine, methionine, and proline (34, 46). The peptide isolated from the polar eel pout, *Lycodes polaris,* is similarly rich in polar residues, but some of the alanines have been replaced by nonpolar residues such as leucine and valine (15). Recently an antifreeze peptide has been isolated from the sea raven, *Hemitripterus americanus*, which differs substantially from the other peptide antifreezes. It has less alanine and relatively large amounts of glycine and some of the aromatic amino acids (81). None of the other peptide antifreezes contains the aromatic amino acids and the large amounts of glycine. Their functional role is unexplained. The only antarctic fish that possesses a peptide antifreeze is the eel pout, *Rhigophila dearborni*. This peptide contains twelve amino acids (primarily alanine); in addition to the nonpolar residues mentioned above, it contains valine (15).

CONFORMATION   Only limited information about the secondary structure of the antifreezes exists. Dialysis, viscosity, and circular dichroism measurements indicate that both the glycopeptide and peptide antifreezes are expanded molecules (20, 39, 72). X-ray diffraction, detailed circular dichroism studies, and natural abundance C-13 nuclear magnetic resonance (NMR) studies have not given definitive information on the secondary structure of the glycopeptides (1, 4, 8). Circular dichroism studies and viscosity measurements indicate that the peptide antifreezes that have been studied thus far are helical rods (2, 72). The significance of this conformation is that the polar residues aspartic and threonine, which are generally separated by two alanine residues, are separated by a distance of 4.5 Å (17). The existence of this repeat spacing of these polar residues in the peptide is of paramount importance for recognition of the ice lattice and the binding to the oxygen atoms in it (17).

Colligative Freezing Points

The freezing point of a solution is defined as the temperature at which the vapor pressure over the liquid phase is equal to that over the solid phase (64). If the system is in thermal equilibrium, then by definition the freezing point of the solution will be the same as the melting point of the solid phase. In practice this "equilibrium freezing point" can be estimated by determining the melting temperature of a small seed ice crystal in a small volume of the solution. In such a system, raising the temperature by 0.01°C or lowering it by 0.01°C results in melting of the solid phase and freezing of a small amount of the liquid, respectively. Thus the melting point and freezing point can be assumed to be the same. In order to obtain the freezing point in salt solutions and biological solutions under conditions approaching thermal equilibrium the size of the ice crystal must be kept small relative to the volume of the solution. In addition, the rate of warming or cooling necessary to observe melting or freezing must be slow so that the system approaches thermal equilibrium. These rates are on the order of 0.01°C per

Table 1 Comparison of sugar and amino acid content of antifreezes in northern and antarctic fishes[a]

Amino acid or sugar	Pagothenia borchgrevinki (20) Boreogadus saida (62) Gadus morhua (47) Gadus ogac (83)	Eleginus gracilis (71) Microgadus tomcod (15, 36)	Pseudo-pleuronectes americanus	Pleuronectes quadrita-berculatus (15)	Myoxo-cephalus verrucosus (71)	Myoxo-cephalus scorpius (46)	Lycodes polars (15)	Hemi-tripterus americanus (81)
Aspartic acid			3	3	3	3	3	4
Threonine	8	7	6	6	3	4	3	3
Serine			1	1	1	1	1	1
Glutamic acid			1	1	3	2	5	2
Glycine					1			6
Proline	3					2	2	1
Alanine	18	16	32	34	31	38	28	12
Half-cystine								6
Methionine					1	1	1	4
Isoleucine					1	1	2	1
Leucine			2		3	2	5	4
Tyrosine								1
Phenylalanine								1
Lysine			1	1	1	1	2	1
Histidine								1
Tryptophan								2
Arginine	1		1	1	1	1	1	1
N-acetylgalac-tosamine	8	7						
Galactose	8	7						

[a] Values are number of residues per 5,000 grams antifreeze.

2 min for one-microliter samples. Since the depression of the freezing point of body fluids lacking antifreeze is dependent on the number of particles in solution, an indirect estimate of this freezing point can be obtained by determining the vapor pressure lowering, or by determining the freezing point with a freezing osmometer (15). The latter device has a strong dependance on the rate of freezing and therefore must be standardized against known freezing points. With such a device it is assumed that the unknowns freeze the same way the standards do.

Noncolligative Freezing Points

Because relatively large molecules in the blood of polar fishes produce a substantial depression of the freezing point, the depression must occur via a noncolligative mechanism. Determinations of the equilibrium freezing points of the blood and solutions of the purified antifreezes have revealed a most unusual freezing-melting behavior. The melting point of the solid phase (seed ice crystal) occurs at a temperature predicted by colligative relationships; however, the freezing point (temperature of ice crystal propagation) is much lower than the melting point (13, 28, 70, 73, 82). In antarctic nototheniid blood serum, the seed crystal melts at approximately $-1.0°C$ while ice begins to propagate rapidly from the face of the seed at $-2.2°C$ (13, 42). Ice in a 2% glycopeptide or peptide antifreeze solution will melt at $-0.02°C$ and will not propagate from the face of the seed until the temperature is lowered below $-1.2°C$. Growth, then, as in the blood, is in the form of long thin spicules (Figure 1) (13, 70). Most of the glycopeptide and peptide antifreezes exhibit the same depression of the freezing point of water on a weight basis except for some of the smaller glycopeptides isolated from the antarctic nototheniids (52) and northern cods (36, 61). Solutions of the low-molecular-weight glycopeptides produce only about half the noncolligative lowering of the freezing point than the larger glycopeptides and peptides do when compared on a weight basis (15). Even though some of the lower-molecular-weight antifreezes of the same size have occasional arginines substituted for threonines, the activity is the same (77). When compared on a molar basis this antifreeze effect of the various antifreezes increases with the size (77). The antifreezes also affect the crystal habit. When the seed crystal grows, spicules form parallel to the c-axes (70). The size of the seed crystal does not change at temperatures intermediate between melting and freezing (68).

Freezing-point estimates obtained under conditions where substantial supercooling (4–6°C) occurs results in very different freezing points (14, 69). With the northern hemisphere cods that possess glycopeptide antifreezes, estimates of the blood freezing points, obtained with a modified freezing-point osmometer (80), are much higher than those obtained by

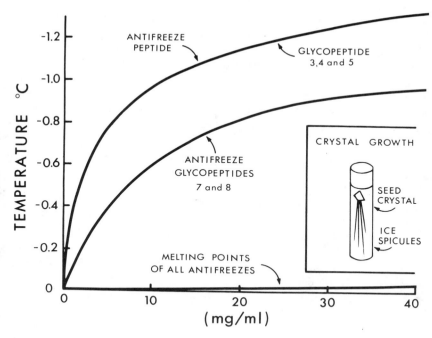

Figure 1   Freezing and melting points of aqueous solutions of the peptide and glycopeptide antifreezes as a function of concentration. The high-molecular-weight glycopeptides and peptides have essentially the same antifreeze activity while the low-molecular-weight glycopeptides have much less. The melting points are the same for all sizes. The inset shows the spicular ice growth that propagates from the seed crystal when freezing occurs.

determining the temperature of crystal growth in the same fishes (14, 15). Use of the freezing-point osmometer where glycopeptide solutions are supercooled by 4°C before freezing is initiated reduces the freezing point depression of glycopeptides 1–5 by 25%; in glycopeptides 7 and 8 the depression is reduced to values expected on the basis of colligative relationships (14, 75). Addition of small amounts of the large glycopeptides to the small ones leads to a significant increase in the freezing-point depression of the small ones and has been referred to as a potentiation (57, 63). However, when freezing points are determined in the presence of a small seed crystal and the freezing point is approached slowly (0.01°C/min), no potentiation of the antifreeze activity of the small by the large glycopeptides is observed (75). Thus prevention of supercooling prior to freezing is of the utmost importance because freezing points obtained in this manner give misleading results. Evidence for this interpretation comes from examination of the biological role of the antifreezes. Fishes that inhabit freezing oceans experience only small changes in temperature when the water is freezing. Slow freezing conditions employed for freezing-point determination more closely approximate those observed in nature. Thus the distinction between active and inactive antifreeze components (29, 63) is an artifact of the method and does not accurately describe the freezing behavior of glycopeptides 7 and 8. The facts that they have recently been shown to be the only antifreeze components present in intestinal fluid of antarctic fishes and that they lower the fluid's freezing point to $-2°C$ (60) support this thesis.

MECHANISM OF ANTIFREEZE ACTIVITY

Water Structuring

The expanded structures of the antifreeze and the abundance of side chains rich in hydroxyls and polar groups suggest that these peptides may structure the water that surrounds them. However, recent NMR studies (41) indicate that the amount of water bound is small. Isopiestic determinations of water binding under equilibrium conditions reveal that these peptides bind only slightly more water than other proteins of a similar size when in solution (26). It would appear that the amount of "bound" water is much too small to explain the antifreeze effect.

ADSORPTION   Considerable information indicates that adsorbed impurities can inhibit the crystallization or the growth of small crystals (7). Such inhibitors are usually characterized by a specificity for a particular kind of crystal, and large polymers composed of repeating units are more effective than small nonrepetitive ones. It is currently thought that adsorption of an impurity inhibits crystal growth by interfering with the propagation of steps across the face of the crystal. In many cases, adsorption of impurities also causes a change in the type of crystal growth, or habit, observed when the supersaturation point is exceeded (9). The inhibition of the freezing of water in the presence of the antifreezes, at temperatures below the expected freezing point when the system is in thermal equilibrium, appears to be another example of the adsorption-inhibition phenomenon.

Studies of the freezing behavior of solutions of the glycopeptide and peptide antifreezes indicate that they adsorb to ice (22, 48, 70, 82). At very low concentrations the antifreezes (a) alter the direction in which water freezes fastest on the faces of an ice crystal and (b) prevent recrystallization (48). Thus the mechanism of antifreeze activity involves the ice-water interface. The affinity of these peptides for ice varies with molecular weight; the small molecules bind less than the large (70). The affinity for ice disappears if these molecules are chemically modified and their antifreeze activity is then lost as well (22, 78). In the case of glycopeptides, alteration of the hydroxyls of the carbohydrate moiety leads to loss of activity (54) as well as limited cleavage of the polypeptide backbone (49). Reduction in the size of the glycopeptides by sequential degradation results in decreased binding and antifreeze activity (77). This is consistent with the observation that large polymers made up of repeating subunits are better inhibitors of crystallization than is the subunit alone. Modifications of the carboxyl groups of the aspartic and glutamic acid residues of the peptides result in loss of activity (25) and, presumably, of binding. Specific modification of the sculpin peptide antifreeze by attachment of fluorocene to its 4 lysine residue results in complete loss of activity (76). Loss of antifreeze activity resulting from modification of polar side chains appears to be correlated with a loss in the affinity for ice (70). Since all of the polar side chains are potential hydrogen bonders, it would appear that the antifreezes probably attach to ice through hydrogen bonding between the polar side chains and water molecules in the ice lattice. In order for maximal hydrogen bonding to occur it can be predicted that the potential hydrogen bonding residues should occupy positions in the molecule that would align them opposite the oxygens in the ice lattice.

Space-filling models of the glycopeptides reveal that many of the hydroxyls of the disaccharide side chain are spaced approximately 4.5 Å apart, a distance that also separates the oxygens in the ice lattice parallel to the a-axis. The secondary structure of the glycopeptides remains to be elucidated (4, 27). However it is instructive to speculate how the spacings of the hydroxyl groups and other hydrogen bonding groups in the various glycopeptide conformations might lead to binding with ice. The carbohydrate moieties might keep the polypeptide backbone of the antifreeze in a completely extended conformation. In such a conformation, alternate carbonyl groups project from the same side of the polypeptide; in the completely extended conformation they are separated by ~ 7.3 Å (15, 65). This distance also separates alternate oxygens along the c-axis in the ice lattice (38). This 7.36 Å spacing of the oxygens in the lattice is also a repeat spacing. Some evidence for the existence of a completely extended conformation exists (39) but is not overwhelming. With the glycopeptides, the presence of a repeat spacing may not be necessary for binding. The important requirement may be the presence of several groups on the glycopeptides that can attach to several oxygens in the ice lattice, which may not necessarily be regularly arranged. Within the disaccharide side chain, for example, many of the hydroxyl groups are separated by distances that closely approximate the 4.5 Å spacing between the oxygens of the water molecules in the ice lattice, as well as other spacings such as 7.36 Å.

Sequence studies of the flounder antifreeze peptides indicate the presence of clusters of polar amino acids separated by long sequences of nonpolar alanine residues (Figure 2). The polar clusters usually contain threonine and aspartate separated by two alanines (17, 45). In the Alaskan plaice peptide, a similar arrangement of polar and nonpolar residues is present (15). Physical-chemical studies indicate that these peptides are all α-helixes (2, 70). In such a conformation, the polar side chains are located on one side of the helix while the nonpolar side chains face the other side. Aspartate and threonine residues in such a conformation are separated by 4.5Å, a repeat distance that also separates adjacent oxygens in the prism faces of hexagonal ice that are parallel to the a-axes. This lattice match between the polar residues and the oxygens in the ice lattice suggests that the peptides orient themselves on the lattice and bind to it through hydrogen bonding. Figure 3 illustrates how the flounder peptide might be aligned parallel to one of the a-axes of the lattice and how they might hydrogen-bond to it. In such a model, every third row of oxygens does not participate in hydrogen bonding. This may be important because an uninterrupted 4.5Å repeat spacing of the polar residues might result in nucleation.

Thus far complete sequences have been determined for a winter flounder and an Alaskan plaice antifreeze peptide. The repeat spacing of the polar threonines and aspartates found in the flounder peptide are conserved in that of the plaice. Preliminary sequences of fragments of the sculpin peptides also indicate the presence of threonines or serines separated from either aspartate or glutamate by 4.5Å.

Recently it has been suggested that the polar clusters participate in β-turns between the helical segments of alanine (55). In such turns, a

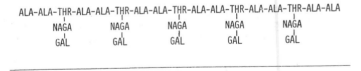

Figure 2   The primary structure of glycopeptides 1–5 isolated from the antarctic nototheniid, *Dissostichus mawsoni*. The basic glycotripeptide is repeated in the different sizes except glycopeptides 6, 7, and 8 where prolines replace some of the alanines. The lower panel shows the structure of one of the antifreeze peptides isolated from the blood of the winter flounder, *Pseudopleuronectes americanus*. In the conformation of an α-helix, the aspartic and threonine residues are separated by 4.5 Å, a distance that also separates the oxygens along the a-axes of the ice lattice.

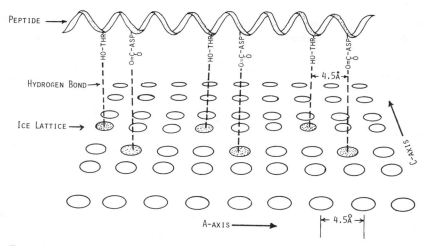

Figure 3   Model of flounder antifreeze hydrogen bonded to prism face of hexagonal ice, parallel to the a-axes. Darker circles represent oxygens in the ice lattice that participate in hydrogen bond formation with the hydroxyl of the threonine residue and carboxyl of the aspartic acid residue. These two residues are separated by 4.5 Å, a distance that also separates the oxygens in the ice lattice parallel to the a-axes.

4.5Å spacing between aspartate and threonine could still be conserved; however, recent fluorescence polarization studies indicate that the peptides are rigid rods and therefore probably lack β-turns (76). Further studies are needed in order to verify the underlying structural requirements necessary for binding to ice.

INHIBITION   Anomalously low freezing points of water in gels and tissues have been explained on the basis of increases in surface free energy resulting from a high ratio of surface area to volume. In gels, physical constraints result in the formation of microcrystals with high surface free energies (6, 50). For freezing to occur in such systems, energy must be removed from the system. This is done by lowering the temperature. The appearance of microcrystals at the lower temperature would show that in effect the freezing point of the water in which they formed had been lowered.

Adsorption of the antifreezes to ice crystals could lead to an increase in surface area with only a small increase in volume and could result in a lowered freezing point. The evidence for this hypothesis and the mathematical analysis are reviewed in depth elsewhere (68); only a qualitative overview is set forth here, where it is assumed that the adsorption of the antifreeze to ice leads to an increase in surface free energy of the ice crystal resulting in depression of the freezing point. Ice crystal growth occurs as water molecules join the crystal at steps on the basal planes. It is thought that adsorbed antifreeze molecules force growth to occur in the regions between them. The small distances between the adsorbed antifreezes result in the growth of many highly curved individual fronts with a large surface area compared to their volume and as a consequence a high surface free energy. Growth between the molecules stops when the ratio of surface area to volume exceeds a critical point. This point is related to the radius of curvature of the front. When the radius is equal to one half of the spacing between two adsorbed adjacent antifreeze molecules, growth stops. If the spacing between the antifreeze molecules is reduced then the under-cooling required to allow the step to propagate through the spacing must be increased. Stated another way, the freezing point of water is lowered.

The spacing between the antifreeze molecules appears to be a function of their concentration and size (68). If certain assumptions are made about the density and randomness of the antifreeze molecules on the crystal face, the undercooling (or freezing-point depression) is proportional to the square root of the concentration. Good agreement exists between freezing point depression curves obtained experimentally and those derived from the above relationship (70).

SEASONAL OCCURRENCE OF ANTIFREEZES

Compared to the high latitude waters of the antarctic and arctic, those of the north-temperate regions show extreme temperature variation. As a consequence, blood levels of antifreeze in the winter flounder, Atlantic cod, tomcod, and short horned sculpin all show seasonal changes (23, 24, 30, 32, 33, 37, 66). Antifreeze is synthesized in the liver during the autumn; its biosynthesis is apparently controlled at the level of transcription and possibly translation (10, 45, 51, 53). Seasonal changes in the level of antifreeze are correlated with temperature (24, 32, 33, 66), and photoperiod may be involved (24, 32). There is some evidence for an endogenous cycle (32, 33) with some pituitary influence (31, 35, 44).

Antarctic and high arctic waters are near their freezing point throughout the year and their fishes always have high levels of antifreeze in their blood (14–16). The antifreeze is synthesized by the liver (58). Warm acclimation at +4°C for 60 days does not alter the levels of glycopeptide antifreeze in these fishes (16), indicating that temperature has little effect on the control of its synthesis. The control of the annual cycle of antifreeze production deserves further attention.

ACKNOWLEDGMENTS

Much of the research described here was supported by NSF PCM 77-25166 and NSF DPP 78-23462 to ALD.

Literature Cited

1. Ahmed, A. I., Feeney, R. E., Osuga, D. T., Yeh, Y. 1975. Antifreeze glycoproteins from an antarctic fish. *J. Biol. Chem.* 250:3344–47
2. Ananthanaryanan, V. S., Hew, C. L. 1977. Structural studies on the freezing point–depressing protein of the winter flounder *Pseudopleuronectes americanus. Biochem. Biophys. Res. Commun.* 74:685–89
3. Andriashev, A. P. 1970. Cryopelagic fishes in the Arctic and Antarctic and their significance in polar ecosystems. In *Antarctic Ecology,* ed. M. W. Holdgate, 1:297–304. London: Academic
4. Berman, E., Allerhand, A., DeVries, A. L. 1980. Natural abundance carbon 13 nuclear magnetic resonance spectroscopy of antifreeze glycoproteins. *J. Biol. Chem.* 255:4407–10
5. Black, V. S. 1951. Some aspects of the physiology of fish. II. Osmotic regulation in teleost fishes. *Univ. Toronto Biol. Ser. 59.* 71:53–89
6. Block, R., Walter, D. H., Kuhn, W. 1963. Structurally caused freezing point depression of biological tissues. *J. Gen. Physiol.* 46:605–15
7. Buckley, H. E. 1952. *Crystal Growth.* NY: Wiley. 339 pp.
8. Bush, A., Feeney, R. E., Osuga, D. T., Ralapati, S., Yeh, Y. 1981. Antifreeze glycoprotein. *J. Peptide Protein Res.* 17:125–29
9. Butchard, A., Whetstone, J. 1949. The effect of dyes on crystal habits on some oxy-salts. *Disc. Faraday Soc.* 5:254–61
10. Davies, P. L., Hew, C. L. 1980. Isolation and characterization of the antifreeze protein messenger RNA from the winter flounder. *J. Biol. Chem.* 255: 8729–34
11. DeVries, A. L. 1970. Freezing resistance in Antarctic fishes. In *Antarctic Ecology,* ed. M. W. Holdgate, 1:320–38. London: Academic
12. DeVries, A. L. 1971. Freezing resistance in fishes. In *Fish Physiology,* ed. W. S. Hoar, D. J. Randall, 6:157–90 NY: Academic
13. DeVries, A. L. 1971. Glycoproteins as biological antifreeze agents in antarctic fishes. *Science* 172:1152–55
14. DeVries, A. L. 1974. Survival at freezing temperatures. In *Biochemical and Biophysical Perspectives in Marine Biology,* ed. J. S. Sargent, D. W. Mallins, 1:289–330. London: Academic
15. DeVries, A. L. 1980. Biological antifreezes and survival in freezing environments. In *Animals and Environmental Fitness,* ed. R. Gilles, pp. 583–607. Oxford/NY: Pergamon
16. DeVries, A. L., Lin, Y. 1977. The role of glycoprotein antifreezes in the survival of antarctic fishes. In *Adaptations within Antarctic Ecosystems,* ed. G. A. Llano, pp. 439–58. Houston: Gulf Publ.
17. DeVries, A. L., Lin, Y. 1977. Structure of a peptide antifreeze and mechanism of adsorption to ice. *Biochim. Biophys. Acta* 495:388–92
18. DeVries, A. L., Somero, G. N. 1971. The physiology and biochemistry of low temperature adaptation in antarctic marine organisms. In *Antarctic Ice and Water Masses,* ed. Sir G. Deacon, pp. 101–13. Cambridge: Sci. Comm. Antarct. Res.
19. DeVries, A. L., Wohlschlag, D. E. 1969. Freezing resistance in some antarctic fishes. *Science* 163:1074–75
20. DeVries, A. L., Komatsu, S. K., Feeney, R. E. 1970. Chemical and physical properties of freezing point-depressing glycoproteins from antarctic fishes. *J. Biol. Chem.* 245:2901–13
21. DeVries, A. L., Vandenheede, J., Feeney, R. E. 1971. Primary structure of freezing point-depressing glycoproteins. *J. Biol. Chem.* 246:305–8
22. Duman, J. G., DeVries, A. L. 1972. Freezing behavior of aqueous solutions of glycoproteins from the blood of antarctic fish. *Cryobiology* 9:469–72
23. Duman, J. G., DeVries, A. L. 1974. Freezing resistance in winter flounder. *Pseudopleuronectes americanus. Nature* 247:237–38
24. Duman, J. G., DeVries, A. L. 1974. The effects of temperature and photoperiod on the production of antifreeze in cold water fishes. *J. Exp. Zool.* 190:89–97
25. Duman, J. G., DeVries, A. L. 1976. Isolation, characterization and physical properties of protein antifreezes from the winter flounder, *Pseudopleuronectes*

258 DEVRIES

americanus. *Comp. Biochem. Physiol.*
53B:375–80
26. Duman, J. G., Patterson, J. L., Kozak,
J. J., DeVries, A. L. 1980. Isopiestic
determination of water binding by fish
antifreeze glycoproteins. *Biochim. Biophys. Acta* 626:332–36
27. Feeney, R. E. 1982. Penguin egg-white
and polar fish blood-serum proteins.
Int. J. Peptide Protein Res. 19:215–32
28. Feeney, R. E., Hofmann, R. 1973. Depression of freezing point by glycoproteins from an Antarctic fish. *Nature*
243:357–59
29. Feeney, R. E., Yeh, Y. 1978. Antifreeze
proteins from fish bloods. *Adv. Protein
Chem.* 32:191–282
30. Fletcher, G. L. 1977. Circannual cycles
of blood plasma freezing point and
Na+ and Cl- concentrations in Newfoundland winter flounder (*Pseudopleuronectes americanus*) correlation
with water temperature and photoperiod. *Can J. Zool.* 55:789–95
31. Fletcher, G. L. 1979. The effects of
hypophysectomy and pituitary replacement on the plasma freezing point depression, Cl-, glucose and protein antifreeze in the winter flounder. *Comp.
Biochem. Physiol.* 63A:535–37
32. Fletcher, G. L. 1981. Effects of temperature and photoperiod on the plasma
freezing point depression, Cl- concentration, and protein "antifreeze" in winter flounder. *Can. J. Zool.* 59:193–201
33. Fletcher, G. L., Smith, J. C. 1980. Evidence for permanent population differences in the annual cycle of plasma "antifreeze" levels of winter flounder. *Can.
J. Zool.* 58:507–12
34. Fletcher, G. L., Addison, R. F., Slaughter, D., Hew, C. L. 1982. Antifreeze
proteins in the arctic shorthorn sculpin
(*Myoxocephalus* scorpius). *Arctic.* In
press
35. Fletcher, G. L., Campbell, C. M., Hew,
C. L. 1978. The effects of hypophysectomy on seasonal changes in plasma
freezing-point depression, protein 'antifreeze,' and Na+ and Cl- concentrations
on winter flounder (*Pseudopleuronectes
americanus*). *Can. J. Zool.* 56:109–13
36. Fletcher, G. L., Hew, C. L., Joshi, S. R.
1982. Isolation and characterization of
antifreeze glycoproteins from the
frostfish, *Microgadus tomcod. Can. J.
Zool.* 60:348–55
37. Fletcher, G. L., Slaughter, D., Hew, C.
L. 1982. Seasonal changes in the plasma
levels of glycoprotein antifreeze, Na+,
Cl-, and glucose in Newfoundland At-

lantic cod (*Gadus morhua*). *Can. J.
Zool.* 60:1851–54
38. Fletcher, N. H. 1970. *The Chemical
Physics of Ice.* Cambridge, England:
Cambridge Univ. Press. 111 pp.
39. Franks, F., Morris, E. R. 1978. Blood
glycoprotein from Antarctic fish. *Biochim. Biophys. Acta* 540:346–56
40. Gordon, M. S., Andur, B. N., Scholander, P. F. 1962. Freezing resistance
in some northern fishes. *Biol. Bull.*
122:52–62
41. Haschemeyer, A. E. V., Guschlbauer,
W., DeVries, A. L. 1977. Water binding
by antifreeze glycoproteins from Antarctic fish. *Nature* 269:87–88
42. Hargens, A. R. 1972. Freezing resistance in polar fishes. *Science* 176:
184–86
43. Hew, C. L. 1981. Biochemical adaptations to the freezing environment—antifreeze proteins in the marine fishes.
Bull. Can. Biochem. Soc. 18:41–46
44. Hew, C. L., Fletcher, G. L. 1979. The
role of the pituitary in regulating antifreeze protein synthesis in the winter
flounder. *FEBS Lett.* 99:337–39
45. Hew, C. L., Yip, C. 1976. The synthesis
of freezing-point-depressing protein of
the winter flounder *Pseudopleuronectes
americanus* in *Xenopus laevis* oocytes.
Biochem. Biophys. Res. Commun. 71:
845–50
46. Hew, C. L., Fletcher, G. L., Ananthanarayanan, V. S. 1980. Antifreeze
proteins from the shorthorn sculpin,
Myoxocephalus scorpius: isolation and
characterization. *Can. J. Biochem.*
58:377–83
47. Hew, C. L., Slaughter, D., Fletcher, G.
L., Joshi, S. B. 1981. Antifreeze glycoproteins in the plasma of Newfoundland
Atlantic cod (*Gadus morhua*). *Can. J.
Zool.* 59:2186–92
48. Knight, C. A., DeVries, A. L. 1982.
Effect of an "antifreeze protein" on the
growth of ice from supercooled water.
Presented at Int. Symp. Physics and
Chemistry of Ice, Rolla, Mo.
49. Komatsu, S. K., DeVries, A. L.,
Feeney, R. E. 1970. Studies of the structure of freezing point-depressing glycoproteins from an antarctic fish. *J. Biol.
Chem.* 245:2901–8
50. Kuhn, W. 1956. Über die durch ano-
male Kristallgestalt sowie durch
Limitierung der Kristallgrosse bedingte
Gefrierpunktserniedrigung. *Helv.
Chim. Acta* 39:1071–86
51. Lin, Y. 1979. Environmental regulation
of gene expression. *J. Biol. Chem.*
254:1422–26

52. Lin, Y., Duman, J. G., DeVries, A. L. 1972. Studies on the structure and activity of low molecular weight glycoproteins from an antarctic fish. *Biochem. Biophys. Res. Commun.* 46: 87–92

53. Lin, Y., Long, D. J. 1980. Purification and characterization of winter flounder antifreeze peptide messenger ribonucleic acid. *Biochemistry* 19:1111–16

54. Lin, Y., Raymond, J. A., Duman, J. G., DeVries, A. L. 1976. Compartmentalization of NaCl in frozen solutions of antifreeze glycoproteins. *Cryobiology* 13:334–40

55. Loucheux-LeFebvre, M. 1978. Predicted β-turns in peptide and glycopeptide anti-freezes. *Biochem. Biophys. Res. Commun.* 81:1352–56

56. Morris, H. R., Thompson, M. R., Osuga, D. T., Ahmed, A. I., Chan, S. M., Vandenheede, J. R., Feeney, R. E. 1978. Antifreeze glycoproteins from the blood of an Antarctic fish. *J. Biol. Chem.* 253:5155–62

57. Mulvihill, D. M., Geoghegan, K. F., Yeh, Y., DeRemer, K., Osuga, D. T., Ward, F. C., Feeney, R. E. 1980. Antifreeze glycoproteins from polar fish. *J. Biol. Chem.* 255:659–62

58. O'Grady, S. M., Clarke, A., DeVries, A. L. 1982. Characterization of glycoprotein antifreeze biosynthesis in isolated hepatocytes from *Pagothenia borchgrevinki. J. Exp. Zool.* 220:179–89

59. O'Grady, S. M., DeVries, A. L. 1982. Osmotic and ionic regulation in polar fishes. *J. Exp. Mar. Biol. Ecol.* 57:219–28

60. O'Grady, S. M., Ellory, J. C., DeVries, A. L. 1982. Protein and glycoprotein antifreezes in the intestinal fluid of polar fishes. *J. Exp. Biol.* In press

61. O'Grady, S. M., Schrag, J. D., Raymond, J. A., DeVries, A. L. 1982. Comparison of antifreeze glycopeptides from arctic and antarctic fishes. *J. Exp. Zool.* In press

62. Osuga, D. T., Feeney, R. E. 1978. Antifreeze glycoproteins from Arctic fish. *J. Biol. Chem.* 253:5338–43

63. Osuga, D. T., Ward, F. C., Yeh, Y., Feeney, R. E. 1978. Cooperative functioning between antifreeze glycoproteins. *J. Biol. Chem.* 253:6669–72

64. Pauling, L. 1953. *General Chemistry.* San Francisco: W. H. Freeman. pp. 345–47. 2nd ed.

65. Pauling, L., Corey, R. B., Branson, H. R. 1951. The structure of proteins: Two hydrogen-bonded helical configurations

of the polypeptide chain. *Proc. Natl. Acad. Sci. USA* 37:193–94

66. Petzel, D. H., Reisman, H. M., DeVries, A. L. 1980. Seasonal variation of antifreeze peptide in the winter flounder, *Pseudopleuronectes americanus. J. Exp. Zool.* 211:63–69

67. Potts, W. T. W., Parry, G. 1964. *Osmotic and Ionic Regulation in Animals.* Vol. 19. Oxford: Pergamon. 171 pp.

68. Raymond, J. A. 1976. *Adsorption inhibition as a mechanism of freezing resistance in polar fishes.* PhD thesis. Univ. Calif., San Diego. 169 pp.

69. Raymond, J. A., DeVries, A. L. 1972. Freezing behavior of fish blood glycoproteins with antifreeze properties. *Cryobiology* 9:541–47

70. Raymond, J. A., DeVries, A. L. 1977. Adsorption inhibition as a mechanism of freezing resistance in polar fishes. *Proc. Natl. Acad. Sci. USA* 74:2589–93

71. Raymond, J. A., Lin, Y., DeVries, A. L. 1975. Glycoproteins and protein antifreeze in two Alaskan fishes. *J. Exp. Zool.* 193:125–30

72. Raymond, J. A., Radding, W., DeVries, A. L. 1977. Circular dichroism of protein and glycoprotein fish antifreeze. *Biopolymers* 16:2575–78

73. Scholander, P. F., Maggert, J. E. 1971. Supercooling and ice propagation in blood from arctic fish. *Cryobiology* 8:371–74

74. Scholander, P. F., VanDam, L., Kanwisher, J. W., Hammel, H. T., Gordon, M. S. 1957. Supercooling and osmoregulation in arctic fish. *J. Cell Comp. Physiol.* 49:5–24

75. Schrag, J. D., DeVries, A. L. 1982. The effects of freezing rate on the cooperativity of antifreeze glycopeptides. *Comp. Biochem. Physiol.* In press

76. Schrag, J. D., DeVries, A. L. 1982. Fluorescent depolarization of glycopeptide antifreezes. Presented at 19th Ann. Meet. Soc. Cryobiol., Houston, Texas

77. Schrag, J. D., O'Grady, S. M., DeVries, A. L. 1982. Relationship of amino acid composition and molecular weight of antifreeze glycopeptides to non-colligative freezing point depression. *Biochim. Biophys. Acta.* In press

78. Shier, W. T., Lin, Y., DeVries, A. L. 1972. Structure and mode of action of glycoproteins from an antarctic fish. *Biochim. Biophys. Acta* 263:406–13

79. Shier, W. T., Lin, Y., DeVries, A. L. 1975. Structure of the carbohydrate of antifreeze glycoproteins from an antarctic fish. *FEBS Lett.* 54:135–38

80. Slaughter, D., Hew, C. L. 1981. Improvements in the determination of antifreeze protein activity using a freezing point osmometer. *Anal. Biochem.* 115:212–18

81. Slaughter, D., Fletcher, G. L., Ananthanarayanan, V. S., Hew, C. L. 1981. Antifreeze proteins from the sea raven, *Hemitripterus americanus*. *J. Biol. Chem.* 256:2022–26

82. Tomimatsu, Y., Scherer, J., Yeh, Y., Feeney, R. E. 1976. Raman spectra of a solid antifreeze glycoprotein and its liquid and frozen aqueous solutions. *J. Biol. Chem.* 251:2290–98

83. Van Voorhies, W. V., Raymond, J. A., DeVries, A. L. 1978. Glycoproteins as biological antifreeze agents in the cod *Gadus ogac* (Richardson). *Physiol. Zool.* 51:347–53

Ann. Rev. Physiol. 1983. 45:261-70

THE ROLE OF HEMOLYMPH PROTEINS IN THE COLD TOLERANCE OF INSECTS

J. Duman and K. Horwath

Biology Department, University of Notre Dame, Notre Dame, Indiana 46556

INTRODUCTION

Insects that overwinter in areas where they may be exposed to subzero temperatures must behaviorally select overwintering sites that are thermally buffered and/or adapt physiologically either by becoming freeze tolerant (able to survive ice formation in their extracellular body fluids) or by depressing the freezing and supercooling points of their body fluids to temperatures below those to which they will be exposed during winter. General reviews of this topic have recently been published (1, 5, 35, 37). During winter many insects produce high concentrations (several molar) of polyhydroxy alcohols (e.g. glycerol, sorbitol, and mannitol) that function either as cryoprotectants to help prevent freeze damage in freeze-tolerant insects or as antifreezes in freeze-susceptible species. However, more recently hemolymph proteins have been found to function in subzero temperature tolerance. Antifreeze proteins that produce a thermal hysteresis (a difference between the freezing and melting points of an aqueous solution) similar to that of the antifreeze proteins and glycoproteins of polar marine teleost fishes (6) (see also the review by DeVries in this volume) have been found in a number of overwintering insects (8, 11, 14, 23, 29, 32). Also, the hemolymph of many freeze-tolerant insects contains ice nucleating proteins that inhibit supercooling and ensure that ice will form in the extracellular fluid at comparatively high temperatures, thereby minimizing the formation of lethal intracellular ice (48). Here we review these hemolymph proteins and their role in insect cold tolerance.

0066-4278/83/0315-0261$02.00

THERMAL HYSTERESIS PROTEINS

Ramsay (20, 33), in his classical studies of the cryptonephridial rectal complex in larvae of the beetle *Tenebrio molitor*, first described thermal hysteresis. He found that in fluid samples from the hemolymph, mid-gut, and especially the perinephric space the melting and freezing points differed by as much as several degrees. The proteins responsible for the thermal hysteresis were partially purified, but their function was not determined. In subsequent years the antifreeze nature of the fish proteins and glycoproteins with thermal hysteresis activity became well established (6). However, the function of the insect thermal hysteresis proteins (THPs) remained unknown.

In 1977 (8, 9) it was reported that the overwintering larvae of another Tenebrionid beetle, *Meracantha contracta*, produce THPs. These THPs are found only in the winter, and they lower the freezing point of the hemolymph to ~-5°C, approximately 4°C below the melting point. In addition, the supercooling points of the larvae are depressed. Because *Meracantha* do not proliferate polyols in winter it was proposed that the THPs depress the supercooling point. This is important because it has generally been assumed that the temperature to which a freeze-susceptible insect can be supercooled before spontaneous nucleation occurs is a critical ecological parameter for such a species.

Tenebrio molitor larvae, as Ramsay had earlier determined, have low levels (0.75°C) of thermal hysteresis in their hemolymph when they are held under summer conditions (24°C, long photoperiod) at a high relative humidity. However, acclimation to low temperatures, a short photoperiod, or a low relative humidity induces a significant increase in thermal hysteresis that coincides with a lowered supercooling point (29). Like *Meracantha*, *Tenebrio* do not concentrate polyols under these conditions. Consequently, it appears that the supercooling points, and therefore the lower lethal temperatures, of these freeze-susceptible insects are depressed by the THPs. It is perhaps risky to speculate on the significance of such studies in an insect such as *Tenebrio*, which has been reared in the laboratory for countless generations. However, *Tenebrio* originated in the cold climate of central Europe (26).

The presence of THPs in the hemolymph of overwintering insects is apparently common. To date, 14 species of insects have been reported to have THPs. Many of these are beetles [families Tenebrionidae, Elateridae, Cucujidae, Pyrochroidae, Lampyridae, and Coccinellidae (8, 11, 14, 29)], but other orders are also represented, such as the Orthoptera [a wood roach, *Parcoblatta pennsylvanica* (11); the milkweed bug, *Oncopeltus fasciatus* (32)] and Mecoptera [a scorpionfly, *Boreus westwoodi* (23)]. In addition, J.

A. Husby and K. E. Zachariassen (personal communication) have identified several Norwegian insects with THPs. THPs are also found in certain overwintering spiders (12, 23). Typically in these animals the THPs are present only during the winter, or if low levels are present in the summer the amount of thermal hysteresis increases several fold in the winter (9, 11, 12, 13), thus lowering both the freezing and supercooling points of the insects by several degrees. Some species, such as *Meracantha* and *Tenebrio*, do not concentrate polyols along with the THPs; however, many species do. Overwintering adults of the Tenebrionid beetle *Uloma impressa* belong to this group. *Uloma* have low levels of THPs in summer, but these are increased approximately four-fold in winter. The THPs plus high concentrations of glycerol combine to lower the freezing point of the insects to ~-14°C while the supercooling point is depressed from -6°C in summer to -22°C in winter (11).

Although most of the insects and all the spiders in which THPs have been found are freeze-susceptible, THPs are also present in a few freeze-tolerant species (11, 13). It is not apparent why insects physiologically adapted to survive freezing should have an antifreeze. One likely possibility is that during the early fall and late spring, when these insects are not freeze-tolerant, the THPs function to prevent freezing during the occasional sub-zero temperatures. Freeze-tolerant larvae of the beetle *Dendroides canadensis* during the winter 1978–1979 produced THPs that along with glycerol and sorbitol depressed the freezing point of the hemolymph to ~-11°C (13). Because of the presence of ice nucleating proteins (see below) the larvae did not supercool. With lower lethal temperatures of -25 to -30°C for most of the winter, the larvae were freeze-hardy. However, during a late winter thaw the larvae temporarily lost freeze tolerance. The presence of the THP antifreeze at this point may have been critical to their survival, especially because of the continued presence of the nucleator during this period. During January (the coldest on record in northern Indiana) and February of 1982, *Dendroides* were collected after long periods of very cold temperatures. These larvae were not freeze-tolerant, and they supercooled to -25 to -30°C, presumably because of the absence of the nucleator and the presence of the THPs and polyols (K. L. Horwath, J. G. Duman, unpublished observations). This is the first description of an insect that switched its mechanism of adapting to subzero temperatures.

Control of THP Levels

THP concentrations increase in early autumn and decrease in spring. Consequently, one would expect that environmental factors signaling seasonal changes would control the annual cycle of THP production and loss in insects. Acclimation to low temperatures and/or short photoperiods induces THP production in *Meracantha* (10), *Tenebrio* (29), and *Dendroides* [(22) and K. L. Horwath, J. G. Duman, unpublished observations]. The critical temperature for induction of THPs in *Dendroides* is between 10 and 15°C, while the critical photoperiod is between 10L/14D and 11L/13D at 20°C (K. L. Horwath, J. G. Duman, unpublished observations). "Resonance" experiments in which *Dendroides* were acclimated to environmental light cycles of 8L/16D, 8L/28D, 8L/40D, 8L/52D, and 8L/64D indicated that circadian rhythmicity is involved in the photoperiodic timing mechanism that controls THP levels in *Dendroides* (22). Only larvae held on light cycles of 24 hrs or multiples thereof (48 and 72 hrs) produced THPs; those held on cycles of 36 and 60 hrs did not produce THPs, even though they were exposed to a normally inductive period of 8 hrs of light during each cycle. Photoperiod is a much more reliable seasonal cue than temperature. It also allows the insect to "anticipate" changes in temperature. Consequently, it is not surprising that photoperiodic cues control THP production in insects.

Likewise, in the spring both temperature and photoperiod may be involved in regulating the loss of THPs. High temperatures (20–23°C) induce THP loss in *Tenebrio* (K. L. Horwath, J. G. Duman, unpublished observations) and in the spider *Philodromus* (12), regardless of the photoperiod. However, in *Meracantha* a combination of high temperature and long photoperiod is required to induce THP loss, thus providing a failsafe system ensuring that THPs are not lost in the spring until the danger of freezing is past (10).

Initial studies concerning the hormonal control of THP levels have shown that treatment of *Dendroides* larvae with juvenile hormone induces THP production (K. L. Horwath, J. G. Duman, unpublished observations). Likewise, treatment of larvae with precocene, an anti-juvenile hormone drug (4), prevents THP production in *Dendroides* acclimated to conditions (short photoperiod) that would otherwise initiate THP production.

THP Function

Insect THPs, like those of fishes, function primarily as antifreezes. In approximately half of the insect species in which they have been found the THPs are present only in winter, while in species with low THP levels in summer the THPs increase several fold in winter. By mid-winter the THPs generally lower the hemolymph freezing point by ~5°C, although some individuals may have 8–10°C of thermal hysteresis. Although insect cuticle has generally been thought to prevent seeding of the hemolymph by external ice, such inoculative freezing may be a greater problem than was previously supposed (38, 43). The extra freezing point depression provided by THPs would reduce the likelihood of inoculative freezing.

In the absence of inoculative freezing, an insect supercools until spontaneous nucleation occurs. This ability to supercool then becomes critical to a freeze-susceptible insect. With the exception of freeze-tolerant insects that produce ice nucleating agents, the supercooling points of insects are significantly depressed when THPs proliferate. This correlation is not proof of causation. However, purified *Tenebrio* THPs do depress the temperature of certain types of heterogeneous nucleation (45). The mechanism by which THPs might lower the supercooling point is unknown but may be related to the noncolligative mechanism by which they depress the freezing point (6, 34). As water is supercooled below its freezing point the size of molecular aggregates increases with decreasing temperature. Eventually a critical radius is reached and an "embryo crystal" seeds the solution (24). In biological systems these embryo crystals typically form around nonwater motes, thus resulting in heterogeneous nucleation (39). In the absence of heterogeneous nucleation pure water supercools to $\sim -40°C$, where homogeneous nucleation occurs. The proven ability of THPs to adsorb to the surface of ice crystals (15, 34) and thus disturb their role as seeds is critical to the proposed mechanism by which THPs lower the freezing point of water. Likewise, if THPs were to bind to embryo crystals, or more probably to heterogeneous nucleation sites, then the temperature of spontaneous nucleation would be lowered.

Water in a supercooled state is a metastable system. Consequently, as the period increases during which an insect remains supercooled, the probability of spontaneous nucleation also increases. Recent unpublished studies by K. E. Zachariassen (personal communication) indicate that THPs may function to stabilize the supercooled state.

Ramsay's original studies on *Tenebrio* showed that THPs were present in mid-gut fluid (33). This possibility has not been investigated in other THP-producing insects, but the presence of THPs in this fluid could be important since it is known that gut contents can act as a nucleation site in feeding insects (40, 43). Therefore THPs in the gut may allow the insects to feed later in the autumn and earlier in the spring than would otherwise be the case.

The advantage of THPs over polyols or other possible antifreeze agents is that the THPs function by means of a noncolligative mechanism (6, 34). Glycerol and other solutes, at concentrations required to lower significantly the freezing and supercooling points, drastically increase the osmotic pressure of the body fluids and can therefore be toxic, especially at above-freezing temperatures when the insects become active. Such problems may preclude the proliferation of polyols in the autumn in anticipation of impending cold and in the spring when temperatures have warmed but when subzero temperatures are still probable. Overwintering insects generally lose polyols within 1–2 days, or even a few hours, after being placed at room temperature. In contrast, THPs are typically produced in early autumn and are maintained until late spring.

The presence of low levels of THPs in some species during the summer may indicate that these proteins have a secondary function(s) in addition to their involvement in cold tolerance. The concentration of THPs in the perinephric space in *Tenebrio* led Ramsay to speculate that they may be involved in water balance (20). Studies showed that *Tenebrio* acclimated to conditions that induced THP production (low temperatures, short photoperiods, or low relative humidities) were much better able to survive subsequent low humidities (29). Gradual acclimation to low humidities would be expected to induce physiological adjustments to desiccation, but it is not obvious that acclimation to low temperatures or short photoperiods should do so. The higher THP levels may somehow enhance water balance. However, it should be remembered that overwintering insects, because they do not eat or drink for long periods, may face a considerable water balance problem. Consequently, the acclimation to short photoperiods or low temperatures may have induced normal water balance adaptations for the onset of winter. NMR and isopiestic studies (18, 21) with fish antifreeze glycoproteins have shown that while these glycoproteins bind more water than other proteins (such as hemoglobin) this effect is not large enough to allow them to be linked to a water balance function in *Tenebrio*. However, similar experiments have not been conducted with *Tenebrio* THPs.

Another possibility is that the THPs function as storage proteins. Overwintering hemolymph THP levels are on the order of 30–50 mg ml^{-1} or higher. It seems logical that the amino acids in these THPs would be reprocessed into other proteins upon the breakdown of the THPs and that the THPs may be maintained until the need for these amino acids arises (such as during food deprivation, molting, or gamete production). Preliminary work has shown that late winter *Dendroides* larvae lose the THPs more quickly upon acclimation to high temperatures and long photoperiods if they are deprived of food. In addition, although summer-collected *Dendroides* larvae have THPs (at levels considerably lower than in winter), the adults do not (K. L. Horwath, J. G. Duman, unpublished observations).

Compositions of Insect THPs

Compared with the structural information available on the fish THPs, our understanding of the structure-function relationships of the insect THPs is minimal. However, THPs have been purified from three species of insects, and some generalizations may be appropriate. Several different THPs with molecular weights ranging between 9,000 and 17,000 have been purified from *Tenebrio* (30, 31, 41, 46). In addition, a THP from the milkweed bug,

Oncopeltus fasciatus (32), and one from *Dendroides,* with a molecular weight of 14,500, (J. Duman, J. Morris, unpublished observations) have been purified. None of these has a carbohydrate component and therefore the glycoprotein antifreeze found in many fish species have not yet been found in insects. Another basic difference concerns the alanine content of the THPs. With a single known exception (42), alanine accounts for over 60% of the amino acid residues of the fish protein and glycoprotein anti-freezes. Alanine comprises a much smaller percentage of the insect THPs (6.8–14%). The side-chains of hydrophilic amino acids are essential for the activity of fish noncarbohydrate containing THPs, as these provide the sites for hydrogen bonding to the ice lattice (7, 16). In general, the insect THPs have more hydrophilic amino acids than do those of the fish. In the winter flounder THPs approximately 33% of the amino acids are hydrophilics (16) while in the insect THPs hydrophilics account for 40–61% of the amino acids present. The milkweed bug THP, which contains 30.5% serine, is particularly interesting in this regard (32). Because the primary structures of the insect THPs are undetermined, it is not known if the hydrophilic amino acids have the regular spacing found in the winter flounder THP (7).

Interesting THPs with high cysteine contents have been found in two insects, *Tenebrio* and *Dendroides.* Schneppenheim & Theede (41) isolated from *Tenebrio* an impure fraction (containing 6 proteins) with thermal hysteresis activity; it had a cysteine content of 12%. The activity of this fraction was eliminated by treatment with dithiothreitol, indicating that at least some of the cysteines are involved in disulfide bridges and that these are essential for activity. Two THPs with cysteine contents of 15.4 and 28.0 mol % have been purified from *Tenebrio* (31). Also, a THP of 22% cysteine has been purified from *Dendroides* (J. Duman, J. Morrison, unpublished observations). The function of these extremely high levels of cysteine is currently unknown. However, the higher-order structure of THPs is critical to their activity (6), and it is possible that disulfide bridges are involved in maintaining this structure.

Studies to investigate the primary and higher-order structures of insect THPs and their relationship to thermal hysteresis activity are badly needed. The reason for the great diversity of THP present in *Tenebrio* (30, 31, 41, 46) should also be investigated.

ICE NUCLEATOR PROTEINS

When a tissue freezes ice is generally confined to the extracellular fluid, unless the tissue has been extensively supercooled and/or frozen rapidly (19). Because intracellular freezing is lethal, it is critical to the survival of freeze-tolerant insects that they do not supercool extensively. In 1976 Zachariassen & Hammel (48) observed ice nucleating factors in the hemolymph of several species of freeze-tolerant beetles. Addition of hemolymph containing the nucleator (5% of final volume) to aqueous solutions of various concentrations of NaCl or glycerol raised the supercooling point of the solution to a temperature 5.3°C below the freezing point. The ice nucleator therefore inhibits extensive supercooling and thereby ensures that ice is formed in the extracellular fluid at fairly high temperatures. The nucleator may also conserve energy stores since at a given subzero temperature an insect uses less energy if it is frozen than if supercooled (3). Consequently, the more time an insect spends frozen over the course of the winter, the less energy it uses.

Subsequent studies have shown that most [but not all (37)] freeze-tolerant insects have ice nucleating factors (1–3, 11, 13, 17, 27, 28, 35–37, 44, 47, 48) that generally cause them to freeze a few degrees below the hemolymph freezing point (generally above –10°C). In mid-winter, freeze-tolerant larvae of *Dendroides canadensis* supercool less than 1°C below the freezing point (13).

The ice nucleating factors of the insects studied by Zachariassen & Hammel (48) were inactivated by heat. In addition, the nucleators of *Vespula maculata* and *Dendroides* are heat sensitive, nondialyzable, and inactivated by a proteolytic enzyme (13, 17). Thus these insect ice nucleators are apparently proteins. Preliminary purification attempts have shown that *Vespula* has 3–6 proteins with nucleator activity in the hemolymph, while *Dendroides* has only 1–2 (J. G. Duman, unpublished observations). The ice nucleating agent from an Afro-alpine plant seems to be a high-molecular-weight polysaccharide (25). The structure-function relationship of the insect ice nucleators should prove interesting.

FUTURE STUDIES

The importance of long-neglected studies on the role of high-molecular-weight hemolymph solutes in insect cold tolerance has been realized over the past few years. Thermal hysteresis antifreeze proteins and proteinaceous ice nucleators are both common and critical adaptations to subzero temperatures in many insects. Such studies remind us of our dearth of knowledge in the physiology and biochemistry of insect cold tolerance and should spur work on the possible involvement of other hemolymph proteins.

The study of antifreeze proteins and ice nucleator proteins is relatively new, and many questions remain to be answered. How widespread are these proteins among overwintering insects and other terrestrial poikilotherms? What are the structure-function relationships of these proteins? Virtually nothing is known of the composition and structure of the nucleators. Determinations of the primary and higher-order structure of the insect THPs would allow comparisons to be made with the fish THPs. How much and by which mechanisms do the THPs and nucleators affect the supercooling of water? Progress has been made in understanding the factors that control production of these proteins, but much remains to be done.

ACKNOWLEDGMENT

This work was supported in part by NSF grant PCM-8109708.

Literature Cited

1. Baust, J. G. 1981. Biochemical correlates of cold hardening in insects. *Cryobiology* 18:186–98
2. Baust, J. G., Edwards, J. S. 1979. Mechanisms of freeze tolerance in an Antarctic midge, *Belgica antarctica*. *Physiol. Entomol.* 4:1–5
3. Baust, J. G., Grandee, R., Condon, G., Morrissey, R. E. 1979. The diversity of overwintering strategies utilized by separate populations of gall insects. *Physiol. Zool.* 52:572–80
4. Bowers, W. S. 1981. How anti-juvenile hormones work. *Am. Zool.* 21:737–42
5. Danks, H. V. 1978. Modes of seasonal adaptation in the insects: I. Winter survival. *Can. Entomol.* 110:1167–1205
6. DeVries, A. L. 1980. Biological antifreezes and survival in freezing environments. In *Animals and Environmental Fitness*, ed. R. Gilles, 1:583–607. NY: Pergamon. 619 pp.
7. DeVries, A. L., Lin, Y. 1977. Structure of a peptide antifreeze and mechanism of adsorption to ice. *Biochim. Biophys. Acta* 495:388–92
8. Duman, J. G. 1977. The role of macromolecular antifreeze in the darkling beetle, *Meracantha contracta*. *J. Comp.- Physiol.* 115:279–86
9. Duman, J. G. 1977. Variations in macromolecular antifreeze levels in larvae of the darkling beetle, *Meracantha contracta*. *J. Exp. Zool.* 201:85–92
10. Duman, J. G. 1977. Environmental effects on antifreeze levels in larvae of the darkling beetle, *Meracantha contracta*. *J. Exp. Zool.* 201:333–37
11. Duman, J. G. 1979. Thermal hysteresis factors in overwintering insects. *J. Insect Physiol.* 25:805–10
12. Duman, J. G. 1979. Subzero temperature tolerance in spiders: The role of thermal hysteresis factors. *J. Comp. Physiol.* 131:347–52
13. Duman, J. G. 1980. Factors involved in the overwintering survival of the freeze

tolerant beetle, *Dendroides canadensis*. *J. Comp. Physiol.* 136:53–59
14. Duman, J. G. 1982. Antifreeze agents in terrestrial arthropods. *Comp. Biochem. Physiol.* In press
15. Duman, J. G., DeVries, A. L. 1972. Freezing behavior of aqueous solutions of glycoproteins from the blood of an Antarctic fish. *Cryobiology* 9:469–72
16. Duman, J. G., DeVries, A. L. 1976. Isolation, characterization and physical properties of protein antifreezes from the winter flounder, *Pseudopleuronectes americanus*. *Comp. Biochem. Physiol.* 54B:375–80
17. Duman, J. G., Patterson, J. L. 1978. The role of ice nucleators in the frost tolerance of overwintering queens of the bald-faced hornet. *Comp. Biochem. Physiol. A.* 59:69–72
18. Duman, J. G., Patterson, J. L., Kozak, J. J., DeVries, A. L. 1980. Isopiestic determination of water binding by fish antifreeze glycoproteins. *Biochim. Biophys. Acta* 626:332–36
19. Farrant, J. 1980. General observations on cell preservation. In *Low Temperature Preservation in Medicine and Biology*, ed. M. J. Ashwood-Smith, J. Farrant, pp. 1–18. Baltimore: University Park Press. 323 pp.
20. Grimstone, A. V., Mullinger, A. M., Ramsay, J. A. 1968. Further studies on the rectal complex of the mealworm, *Tenebrio molitor* (Coleoptera, Tenebrionidae). *Philos. Trans. R. Soc. Ser. B* 253:343–82
21. Haschemeyer, A. E. V., Guschlbauer, W., DeVries, A. L. 1977. Water binding by antifreeze proteins from Antarctic fish. *Nature* 269:87–88
22. Horwath, K. L., Duman, J. G. 1982. Involvement of the circadian system in photoperiodic regulation of insect antifreeze proteins. *J. Exp. Zool.* 219:267–70

23. Husby, J. A., Zachariassen, K. E. 1980. Antifreeze agents in the body fluid of winter active insects and spiders. *Experientia* 36:963–64

24. Knight, C. A. 1967. *The Freezing of Supercooled Liquids.* NY: Van Nostrand. 145 pp.

25. Krog, J. O., Zachariassen, K. E., Larsen, B., Smidsrod, O. 1979. Thermal buffering in Afro-alpine plants due to nucleating agent-induced water freezing. *Nature* 282:300–1

26. Metcalf, C. L., Flint, W. P. 1951. *Destructive and Useful Insects.* NY: McGraw-Hill. 1071 pp.

27. Miller, L. K. 1978. Physical and chemical changes associated with seasonal alterations in freezing tolerance in the adult Tenebrionid, *Upis cerambroides. J. Insect Physiol.* 24:791–96

28. Morrissey, R. E., Baust, J. G. 1976. The ontogeny of cold tolerance in the gall fly, *Eurosta solidagensis. J. Insect Physiol.* 22:431–37

29. Patterson, J. L., Duman, J. G. 1978. The role of the thermal hysteresis factor in *Tenebrio molitor. J. Exp. Biol.* 74:37–45

30. Patterson, J. L., Duman, J. G. 1979. Composition of a protein antifreeze from larvae of the beetle, *Tenebrio molitor. J. Exp. Zool.* 210:361–67

31. Patterson, J. L., Duman, J. G. 1982. Purification and composition of protein antifreezes with high cysteine contents from larvae of the beetle, *Tenebrio molitor. J. Exp. Zool.* 219:381–84

32. Patterson, J. L., Kelly, T. J., Duman, J. G. 1981. Purification and composition of a thermal hysteresis producing protein from the milkweed bug, *Oncopeltus fasciatus. J. Comp. Physiol.* 142:539–42

33. Ramsay, J. A. 1964. The rectal complex of the mealworm, *Tenebrio molitor* L. (Coleoptera, Tenebrionidae). *Philos. Trans. R. Soc. Ser. B.* 248:279–314

34. Raymond, J. A., DeVries, A. L. 1977. Adsorption inhibition as a mechanism of freezing resistance in polar fishes. *Proc. Natl. Acad. Sci. USA* 74:2589–93

35. Ring, R. A. 1980. Insects and their cells. See Ref. 19, pp. 187–217

36. Ring, R. A., Tesar, D. 1980. Cold-hardiness of the Arctic beetle, *Pytho americanus* Kirby Coleoptera, Pythidae (Salpingidae). *J. Insect Physiol.* 26:763–74

37. Ring, R. A., Tesar, D. 1981. Adaptations to cold in Canadian Arctic insects. *Cryobiology* 18:199–211

38. Salt, R. W. 1963. Delayed innoculative freezing of insects. *Can. Entomol.* 95:1190–1202

39. Salt, R. W. 1966. Factors influencing nucleation in supercooled insects. *Can. J. Zool.* 44:117–33

40. Salt, R. W. 1967. Location and quantitative aspects of ice nucleators in insects. *Can. J. Zool.* 16:329–33

41. Schneppenheim, R., Theede, H. 1980. Isolation and characterization of freezing point depressing peptides from larvae of *Tenebrio molitor. Comp. Biochem. Physiol. B.* 67:561–68

42. Slaughter, D., Fletcher, G. L., Ananthanarayanan, V. S., Hew, C. L. 1981. Antifreeze proteins from the sea raven, *Hemitripterus americanus. J. Biol. Chem.* 256:2022–26

43. Sömme, L. 1981. Cold tolerance of alpine, Arctic and Antarctic collembola and mites. *Cryobiology* 18:212–20

44. Sömme, L., Conradi-Larsen, E. M. 1979. Nucleating agents in the hemolymph of third instar larvae of *Eurosta solidagensis* (Fitch) (Dipt. Tephritidae). *Norw. J. Entomol.* 25:187–88

45. Tomchaney, A. P. 1981. *The purification and characterization of a thermal hysteresis protein from the larvae of* Tenebrio molitor. Master's thesis. Univ. Notre Dame

46. Tomchaney, A. P., Morris, J. P., Kang, S. H., Duman, J. G. 1982. Purification, composition and physical properties of a thermal hysteresis "antifreeze" protein from larvae of the beetle, *Tenebrio molitor. Biochemistry* 21:716–21

47. Zachariassen, K. E. 1980. The roles of polyols and nucleating agents in cold hardy beetles. *J. Comp. Physiol.* 140:227–34

48. Zachariassen, K. E., Hammel, H. T. 1976. Nucleating agents in the hemolymph of insects tolerant to freezing. *Nature* 262:285–87

Ann. Rev. Physiol. 1983. 45:271–88

INVERTEBRATE NEUROPEPTIDES: NATIVE AND NATURALIZED

M. J. Greenberg and D. A. Price

C. V. Whitney Laboratory, University of Florida, St. Augustine, FL 32084

INTRODUCTION

There are actually two independent sets of invertebrate neuropeptides. Those in the first group are native to the invertebrates. They have been identified by their ability to modify or regulate known physiological or biochemical processes, and their effects, formalized as bioassays, have directed their purification. Many such neuropeptides have been discovered in invertebrate nervous tissues during the past three or four decades (reviewed in 42, 58). At this writing, however, only seven of them have been completely characterized—i.e. sequenced and synthesized (Table 1), and their phyletic distribution is not well known.

The invertebrate peptides of the second kind are naturalized. They were discovered more recently and are being identified primarily by their binding to antisera raised to known vertebrate peptides. To date, immunoreactive analogs of some 16 vertebrate peptides have been detected in the brains and guts of about 60 species from 10 invertebrate phyla (Table 2). None of these analogs has been sequenced, and for only a handful has biological activity been demonstrated.

This essay is an attempt to reconcile the two sets of data. To that end, we first examine the relationships among the structures, functions, and occurrences of the native invertebrate peptides, and then evaluate the standing of the immunoreactive, naturalized ones. Naturalized peptides seem to be ubiquitous in invertebrates and biologically active, but their physiological roles are uncertain and different from those of the native peptides.

271

0066-4278/83/0315-0271$02.00

NATIVE INVERTEBRATE PEPTIDES

Peptide Families

All of the invertebrate neuropeptides for which a sequence could possibly be written, and a few selected, characterized, glandular products related to neuropeptides, are listed in Table 1. Altogether, there are only 14 of them in three phyla, mostly molluscs and arthropods.

The small sample size notwithstanding, some of these peptides are emerging as members of extensive families, varying somewhat in amino acid composition but retaining those portions of the sequence necessary for binding to a complementary set of receptor sites. Thus family members are recognized by similarities in chemical behavior and biological activity. The conserved active site of a peptide family emerges, in practice, from the similarity of its structure-activity relations (SAR) on some set of biological or radioimmunological assay systems. Although the SAR of individual invertebrate peptides have been studied (Table 1), the small number of identified members in most families has precluded investigations of cross-reactivity.

Since no invertebrate peptide family has been thoroughly studied, generalizations about their characteristics must be synthesized from patches of information gleaned from one or another of them.

Conservation of Structure but not Function

The crustacean red pigment–concentrating hormone (RPCH) and the locust adipokinetic hormone (AKH) represent a large peptide family. Both hormones have similar amino acid sequences (Table 1), and the potentially charged residues, including the terminals, are blocked. Therefore neither peptide reacts with ninhydrin, and both are electrophoretically immobile.

The complementary receptor sites for RPCH and AKH are also similar; the SARs are alike (reviewed in 80), and the peptides are cross-reactive (e.g. 78). Interestingly, the intracellular mechanisms underlying the adipokinetic and erythrophore concentrating responses may also be the same. Thus the effect of AKH (and RPCH) on locust fat body is mediated by a cyclic AMP–activated protein kinase (reviewed in 86). In *Uca*, cyclic AMP inhibits erythrophore dispersion (94); thus it may mediate concentration by RPCH.

These features can be taken as characteristic of the family and can be helpful in identifying and determining the structures of new peptides. For example, two products of corpora cardiaca (CC)—locust compound II (21) and cockroach neurohormone D (6)—both have clear chemical affinities to AKH and RPCH: They are electrophoretically immobile, have blocked N-terminals, and their aspartyl residues are apparently amidated (6, 21).

Compound II also has biological affinities to AKH and RPCH. It is one of two peaks of adipokinetic activity identified in extracts of locust CC; the other is AKH itself (21). Compound II also has both red pigment–concentrating (21) and hyperglycemic activity (124). Moreover, its amino acid composition resembles that of RPCH more than AKH (21). The sequence of compound II proposed in Table 1 reflects those considerations as well as the relative potencies of AKH and RPCH at producing hyperlipemia in locusts and hyperglycemia in cockroaches (78) and neck-ligated locusts (71).

The amino acid composition of neurohormone D is also similar to that of AKH and RPCH, although tryptophan was not determined. However, the cardioexcitor activity of locust CC has been ascribed to AKH, which requires a Trp^8 for activity (80). Therefore we have included Trp in the sequence proposed in Table 1.

In contrast to their structural similarities, the actions of the RPCH-AKH family are diverse (Table 1). In insects, these peptides produce lipid mobilization, hyperglycemia, related metabolic effects, and cardioexcitation. However, their physiological roles, particularly those of the various hyperglycemic factors, may lie elsewhere (79). In crustaceans, RPCH is probably one of a group of related peptides, each having maximal effectiveness on a different set of pigment cells (reviewed in 87, 93). No extrapigmentary roles for the chromatophorotropins, including RPCH, have been demonstrated as yet in crustaceans (93). However, the neurodepressing hormone is electrophoretically immobile and has a blocked N-terminal (5), so it may also be a homolog of RPCH (87).

That a single peptide or a close homolog may produce different effects at each of its receptive tissues is a common observation in comparative endocrinology and pharmacology, and it has, for example, been described in regard to FMRFamide (47). Of course, the range of effects of a family of peptides within a major phylum should be very large.

Nonneuronal Secretion of Neuropeptides

Vertebrate peptide families include the secretory products of exocrine and endocrine glands of the skin and gut, as well as neurons (e.g. 123). Invertebrate peptides appear to be similarly distributed.

Primary examples are peptides A and B and egg-releasing hormone (ERH). These peptides occur in the atrial gland, a nonneural structure located on the hermaphroditic duct of *Aplysia californica*, or in the duct wall in other species (Table 1). Overwhelming morphological and physiological evidence suggests that the atrial gland is exocrine in function and that the roles of the peptides in its secretion are to be sought within the large hermaphroditic duct (4,7). Nevertheless, since the atrial gland peptides are

Table 1 Identified native invertebrate peptides

Phylum / Neuropeptide Sequence[a]	Source[b] (Ref.)	Action (Ref.)	SAR[c] (Ref.)
Coelenterata			
Head Activator Hormone pQPPGGSKVILF	1° *Hydra attenuata, Anthopleura elegantissima* (10, 101) 2° Human & bovine hypothalamus: rat intestine(s) (14)	Hydra regeneration: increased rate (tentacle number) Increase in bud outgrowth (102, 103)	(10)
Mollusca			
FMRFamide FMRF-NH₂	1° *Macrocallista nimbosa*; ganglia (89, 90) 2° Vertebrate CNS & gut (*c, r*) *Hydra attenuata* (*c, r*) (47, 52)	Cardioexcitation; -inhibition; cAMP increase Muscle: contraction; relaxation Nerve: hyper-; depolarization Vertebrate blood pressure: incr.; vasc. smooth muscle: dilation (47–49)	(31, 32, 85, 91, 127)
pQNFIRFa pQNFIRF-NH₂*	1° *Helix aspersa*, ganglia (88)	Cardioexcitation; muscle contraction (49)	
Egg-Laying Hormone (ELH) I S I N Q D L K A I T D M L L T E Q I R E R Q R Y L A D L R Q R L L E K	1° *Aplysia californica*, bag cells only (23) 2° *A. vaccaria, A. braziliana, A. dactylomela, A. braziliana*, bag cells only (*b, c*) (24)	Stereotyped behavior; egg-release; egg extrusion Other effects on muscle, ducts, heart, nerve (11, 117)	
Egg-Releasing Hormone (ERH) I Ṣ I V S L F K A I T D M L L T E Q I Y A N Y F S T P R L R F Y P I	1° *Aplysia californica*, atrial gland (106, 107) 2° *A. braziliana*, large hermaphroditic duct (*b*) (13)	Stimulates bag cell afterdischarge; mimics ELH in absence of bag cells; stimulates heart & small hermaphroditic duct (4, 12, 13)	

Proteins A and B

(A) A V K L S S D G N Y P F D L S K E D G A Q P Y F M T P R L R F Y P I

(B) A — S — Y E K ——————— I

Name / Sequence	Source	Actions
Eledoisin pQPSKDAFIGLM-NH₂	1° *Eledone moschata*, posterior salivary glands (37) 2° Analogs are frog tachykinins & substance P (s, c, r, b) (36, Table 2)	Molluscs: contracts the clam rectum (29) Vertebrates: lowers blood pressure; stimulates smooth muscle & salivary secretion (36)	(2)
Arthropoda			
Adipokinetic Hormone (AKH) pQLNFTPNWGT-NH₂	1° *Locusta migratoria* & *Schistocerca gregaria*, corpus cardiacum glandular lobe (17, 114)	Locust: lipid mobilization Cockroach: hyperglycemia Other pharm. actions (28, 79, 80)	(115)
Compound II pQLNFSTGW-NH₂*	1° *Schistocerca americana gregaria*, corpus cardiacum glandular lobe (21) 2° *Apis mellifera*, brain & corpora cardiaca/corpora allata (b) (124)	Mimics AKH Locust (ligated), cockroach: hyperglycemia (21, 43, 124)	
Neurohormone D pQVNFSPN(W)-NH₂*	1° *Periplaneta americana*, corpora cardiaca (6)	Cockroach heart: acceleration (6)	
Red Pigment–Concentrating Hormone (RPCH) pQLNFSPGW-NH₂	1° *Pandalus borealis*, eyestalks (38, 40) 2° *Leander adspersus*, eyestalks (s) (20)	Decapod erythrophores: conc. Other pharmacological actions (93)	(25, 26)
Distal Retinal Pigment Hormone (DRPH) NSGMINSILGIPRVMTEA-NH₂	1° *Pandalus borealis*, eyestalks (39)	Ommatidial distal pigment cells (decapods): proximal migration; Somatic pigment cells: dispersion (93)	(98)
Proctolin RYLPT	1° *Periplaneta americana*, whole body (110) 2° Many insects, whole body; *Periplaneta*, identified neuron (b, c, r) (18, 60, 84) *Cardisoma, Homarus*, pericardial organs (b, c, r) (109, 118)	Arthropod heart, visceral & somatic muscle, nerve: increased excitability, contraction (45)	(111, 118)

[a] Sequences: One-letter abbreviations of amino acids approved by IUPAC-IUB Comm. on Biochem. Nomenclature (*Pure Appl. Chem.* 31: 641, 1972). pQ, pyroGlu. Sequences are aligned within families to show common residues.

[b] Source: 1° (primary): first sequence and synthesis; 2° additional localizations by the techniques indicated: (c), immunocytochemistry; (r), radioimmunoassay; (b), bio-assay; (s), sequenced.

[c] SAR: structure activity relations.

* Speculative sequences: Only amino acid composition in ref. Tryptophan (W), not determined in neurohormone D (6). Speculations explained in text.

structurally and pharmacologically related to the egg-laying hormone (ELH) in the bag cells of *Aplysia* (12, 13), they are exocrine members of the ELH family (Table 1).

A second nonneural peptide, eledoisin, was identified from the posterior salivary glands of the octopus *Eledone* (37). It represents a family of related peptides, including the vertebrate neuropeptide, substance P (36), which was finally characterized a decade after eledoisin. Immunoreactive substance P also occurs in molluscs [Table 2; (83, 108)].

Nonneuronal secretion of a neuropeptide has been demonstrated experimentally in *Hydra*. Normally, head activator hormone is produced primarily in nerve and stored in neurosecretory granules (reviewed in 100). However, nerve-free hydras contain about 8 times more head activator than controls, all of it perforce produced by myoepithelial cells (102).

The Scope of a Peptide Family

FMRFamide has only been identified unequivocally in the ganglia of a single species of bivalve mollusc. A second peptide, extracted from the ganglia of *Helix aspersa,* has biological and immunological activity similar to, but distinct from, authentic FMRFamide (31, 32, 49). The preliminary sequence, based on amino acid composition and FMRFamide SAR (85), was: pGlu-Asx-Phe-Ile-Arg-Phe-NH$_2$ (88). Of the two possible analogs (-Asn^2- and -Asp^2-), both now synthesized, the peptide containing an asparagine residue better mimics the chemical, immunological, and biological activities of the extracts (D. A. Price, unpublished experiments). This substance (pQNFIRFa) is likely to be the FMRFamide-like peptide of *Helix,* and its sequence is therefore listed in Table 1.

In addition to FMRFamide and pQNFIRFa, immunoreactive analogs have been detected in the Mollusca and other phyla [(47); see below]. Some of these studies show how the sensitivity and specificity of the assay system used can determine the extent of a family of peptides.

EXTRA-MOLLUSCAN IMMUNOREACTIVE FMRFamide   Immunoreactive (IR) FMRFamide has now been localized in ectodermal neurons of *Hydra attenuata* (52) and in the CNS, pancreas, and gut, variously, of fish, frog, chicken, and seven species of mammals, including humans (16, 31, 32, 127). In both the coelenterate and vertebrate extracts, the IR-FMRFamide could be detected by radioimmunoassay (RIA), but gel and ion exchange chromatography showed that the immunoreactive substances were not authentic FMRFamide, and the concentrations detected were low.

The three antisera used in these studies, insofar as they were characterized [(16, 31, 32, 127); D. A. Price, personal communication], were similar in specificity to each other and to molluscan tissue receptors (85). That is, they all required a C-terminal amide for full immunoreactivity and were tolerant of N-terminal elongated analogs. But all three antisera were also less selective than the tissue receptors.

Among the substances that might have interfered in the immunological determination of FMRFamide in vertebrate extracts are the pancreatic polypeptides (PP), all of which end in -Arg-Tyr-NH$_2$. Indeed, an antiserum raised to the C-terminal hexapeptide of PP had the same immunocytochemical distribution as FMRFamide in chicken pancreas, and both peptides were demonstrated in the same cells in dog ileum (31, 32, 122). In mammals, the distribution of FMRFamide immunoreactivity did not parallel that of authentic mammalian PP, which occurs in pancreas; rather, it followed the distribution of immunoreactive PP in intestine and brain (32, 122). The peptides of mammalian brain and gut seem to resemble avian pancreatic polypeptide more than bovine in both immunoreactivity (70) and amino acid composition (120). This similarity may explain the failure to find any significant cross-reactivity of antisera to FMRFamide with the C-terminal hexapeptide of pancreatic polypeptide (32). Of course, these brain and intestinal PP-like peptides may also have FMRFamide-like biological activity, even though bovine PP has none (91).

In summary, the scope of a peptide family might be greatly enhanced by the application of a suitably unspecific assay system, or reduced by an overly specific one. The following case is the extreme example of the latter possibility.

THE FMRFamide-ENKEPHALIN CONNECTION   Met-enkephalin-Arg[6] Phe[7] (YGG-FMRF), at once an enkephalin and a FMRFamide analog, was discovered in chromaffin cells of adrenal medulla and in the striatum of mammals (113). Since YGG-FMRF lacks the requisite C-terminal amide, it is virtually unrecognized by bioassays and most RIAs specific for FMRFamide (27, 29, 46, 126, 127). Moreover, no immunohistochemical FMRFamide-like immunoreactivity is demonstrable in the adrenal medulla or striatum (31, 32); and antisera to FMRFamide and to YGG-FMRF do not react with the same neurons (127). In fact, in various pharmacological and receptor binding assays, in three phyla, YGG-FMRF has never been shown to be more than a potent opioid agonist [(29, 61); G. B. Stefano, personal communication]. Finally, the formation of a C-terminal amide by post-translational processing would require that the phenylalanyl residue be followed by a glycine (16a, 66). But in the nucleotide sequence for preproenkephalin, the codon for YGG-FMRF is followed immediately by the termination codon (81). Hence, there is no tissue in which this gene can give rise to YGG-FMRFamide. In summary, even assuming that the tetrapeptide fragment FMRF in Met-enkephalin-Arg[6]Phe[7] is an ancient, conserved sequence, it has become, in the course of evolution, a vestigial homolog capable of no functional association with any of the FMRFamide receptors that may occur in mammals (47).

An entirely separate question is whether FMRFamide and Met-enkephalin-Arg[6]Phe[7] are homologous peptides. No analogs of these peptides have been sequenced outside of the molluscs and vertebrates, respectively; therefore this question cannot be answered in structural terms at present. Since FMRFamide and YGG-FMRF are not functional analogs, their similarity could be due to convergent evolution. But the more heuristic view is that *both* FMRFamide and the enkephalins diverged from an ancestral sequence, Tyr-Gly-Gly-Phe-Met-Arg-Phe-NH$_2$, which acted at a single receptor having a pair of binding sites, each complementary to one end of the peptide. Experimental findings supporting this notion have been reviewed (47).

Summary and Two Remarks

Invertebrate peptides are similar to vertebrate ones in that they occur in families identified by longer or shorter homologous sequences critical for activity; their effects are likely to be diverse; and they are secreted by tissues other than nerves, including glands and epithelia.

Unexpectedly, there appears to be as yet no clear relationship between the structural similarity of two homologous peptides and the phyletic relatedness of the organisms containing them. For example, RPCH and AKH are no more dissimilar than FMRFamide and pQNFIRFa; and the corresponding relationships, between crustaceans and insects and between bivalves and pulmonates, are about the same. Eledoisin has half of its residues in common with substance P, but so has physalaemin from the skin of a frog (36). Most remarkable is that the *Hydra* head activating hormone occurs in mammalian brain and gut with its sequence intact (14).

Finally, among native invertebrate peptides, only the synthesis of ELH as a fragment of a large precursor molecule that is then processed has been studied (3). The genetic basis of the ELH/ERH family was recently established by means of recombinant DNA techniques (104). At least 5 RNA transcripts encoding ELH were found, but only in the bag cells and atrial gland. One bag cell clone was analyzed; it included the complete sequence of ELH, as well as that of peptide B.

VERTEBRATE PEPTIDES IN INVERTEBRATES

The distribution of vertebrate neuropeptides among the invertebrate phyla is set out in Table 2. The data, from about 60 reports, are concentrated in the molluscs and insects; but 4 vertebrate peptides have been detected in

Table 2 Distribution and characterization of vertebrate peptides in invertebrates

Phylum or class (no. species)	Peptides[a]													
	Gastrin/ CCK	Sub-stance P	Bombesin	Neuro-tensin	Enkephalin/ Endorphin	AVP/OT/ AVT	Soma-tostatin	PP	Insulin	Glucagon family[b]	ACTH/ α-MSH	TRH	Calci-tonin	Systematic references[d]
Porifera (1)				r										22
Coelenterata (3)	c, r[c]	c, r, b	c, r	c, r										50, 51, 52, 53, 54
Platyhelminthes (3)				r	b		c				c			22, 105, 125
Mollusca (13)	(c)c, r	c, r		r	(c)c, b	c, r, b	c	c	c, b	c	c(c)	r, b	c	47, 75, 108
Annelida (4)	r	r		r	c	(c)	c	c	r, b	c				67, 96, 99, 132
Crustacea (4)		c		r, b	c		c							22, 73, 74
Insecta (23)	c, r	c			c, r, b	c, r	c	c, r, a	c, r, b, a	r, b				30, 34, 35
Echinodermata (2)				c										22
Hemichordata (1)				c										22
Urochordata (4)	c, b	c	c	c, r			c		c					41, 95, 121
Peptide references[d]	9, 30, 33, 54, 99, 121	50, 83	53	22, 95	47, 73, 96, 112, 125, 132	75, 77, 92	74	34	64, 67, 68	108, 119, 123	15, 75	56, 57	108	108, 123*

[a] Peptides: CCK, cholecystokinin; AVP, Arg-vasopressin; OT, oxytocin; AVT, Arg-vasotocin; PP, pancreatic polypeptide; TRH, thyrotropin releasing hormone.

[b] Glucagon family: glucagon, secretin, vasointestinal polypeptide (VIP), gastric inhibiting peptide (GIP).

[c] Characterizations: c, immunocytochemistry; r, radioimmunoassay; b, bioassay; a, amino acid analysis; ( ), negative result.

[d] References: Selected for currency and bibliographic access to all data.

* General references.

Hydra attenuata. Two key groups, the crustaceans and echinoderms, have received little attention.

Most of the vertebrate peptides were identified by immunocytochemistry (c in Table 2) or radioimmunoassay (r). Biological activity (b) has been studied in a few cases, but there has been little chemical characterization. In fact, no homolog of a vertebrate peptide (except eledoisin) has yet been fully identified in an invertebrate.

Biological Activity of Vertebrate Peptides on Invertebrates

The following list includes most of the recent observed effects of vertebrate peptides on an assortment of invertebrate systems. Synthetic peptides were used in the majority of experiments.

Compelling evidence [summarized in (47)] suggests that enkephalin-like neuropeptides play a physiological role in molluscs. A demonstrated action is to regulate the release of transmitter from dopaminergic nerves (112). Stereospecific opioid binding sites (65) have been identified, but no molluscan enkephalin has been isolated.

Both Arg-vasotocin (AVT) and Arg-vasopressin (AVP) suppress the gill withdrawal reflex in *Aplysia californica.* Moreover, when superfused over the abdominal ganglion, AVT increased the bursting activity of neuron R_{15} but decreased the activity of bursters L_3-L_6 (72, 77). AVT also increased the amplitude and rate of beat of the *Aplysia* heart; threshold was very low, and the effect persisted for hours after washout (129). IR-AVT was detected in the left pleural ganglion and was purified by HPLC (77), but the immunoreactive fractions were not assayed, so the notion that AVT is an active neurosecretory product in *Aplysia* is not yet substantiated.

Immunoreactive thyrotropin-releasing hormone (TRH) was detected in the brain of the pulmonate *Lymnaea stagnalis* only when the snails were kept in 0.05% NaCl (55). Synthetic TRH reduced the net flux of Na^+ into *Helisoma carabaceum* (57) and variously altered the cyclic AMP levels of *Lymnaea* ganglia (56).

High doses of porcine cholecystokinin, perfused into the gastric blood spaces of *Styela* (Urochordata) via the cardiostomaic vessel caused protein and acid phosphatase to be secreted into the cavity of the stomach (9).

In a few cases, immunoreactive homologs of vertebrate hormones were purified from invertebrate tissue and tested. For example, one of the multiple peaks of IR-glucagon was purified from *Manduca* corpus cardiacum–corpus allatum complex. This factor reduced fat-body glycogen, but it had no effect on blood trehalose levels. Bovine glucagon was less effective (119).

In a similar vein, purified immunoreactive insect insulins (*Manduca; Calliphora*) variously lowered hemolymph trehalose levels, displaced bovine insulin from fat body, and increased glucose incorporation into rat fat-cells (33a, 119). The hypertrehalosemia produced by removing the median neurosecretory cells of *Calliphora* was also reversed by IR-insulin (119). Among other uncertainties, bovine insulin had no effect in *Manduca* (119), although porcine insulin lowered hemolymph lipid levels in the locust (82). Recently, however, a convincing amino acid analysis of a porcine-like IR-insulin from the hemolymph of *Manduca* (64) was reported. This analysis, plus one for an ovine-like IR-pancreatic polypeptide from the brain of *Calliphora vomitoria* (34), represent the most advanced characterizations of vertebrate peptides in invertebrates.

In summary, vertebrate peptides are active in invertebrate systems. Moreover, in the cases of insulin and glucagon, the characteristic vertebrate effects have been demonstrated. Of course, the physiological role of all of these naturalized peptides remains unknown.

Immunocytochemistry and Radioimmunoassay

The problems inherent in detecting and purifying neuropeptides by RIA or immunocytochemical procedures have been reviewed (e.g. 19, 130). These difficulties are increased when the peptide sought has a structure different from that of the reference antigen, which is true of nearly every immunoreactive peptide listed in Table 2.

The immunological techniques employed varied. In about half of the experiments, multiple antibodies were used, and they were relatively well characterized (e.g. 33, 50). Some antibodies were directed toward the biologically active end of the molecule (e.g. 22). Others would react with only one of a set of closely related peptides (e.g. 1) and were therefore directed toward an antigenic determinant far from the biologically active site. Some immunochemical evidence was particularly convincing. For example, two laboratories, using different orthopterans and different antibodies, both localized IR-vasopressin to only two cells in the ventral portion of the subesophageal ganglion (97, 116).

COMPARISON OF NATIVE AND NATURALIZED INVERTEBRATE PEPTIDES

The sets of native and naturalized invertebrate peptides are virtually nonoverlapping, and each leads to a different general conclusion about invertebrate peptides.

First, although most of the immunological and some of the biological findings about the naturalized peptides (Table 2) are contestable, the overwhelming majority point to the same conclusion (which we accept for argument's sake), that each vertebrate peptide family is represented by one or more active structural homologs in all invertebrate animals.

In opposition to this conclusion and its contributory findings, is the common observation that whenever an endogenous invertebrate regulatory factor is finally characterized, it never turns out to be a homolog of a vertebrate peptide. Examples abound. The gonad stimulating substance from starfish nerve is a peptide, but it is similar neither to *Aplysia* ELH nor to any conceivable mammalian egg-laying hormone (62). Again, the pigment dispersing chromatophorotropin of crustaceans (DRPH, Table 1) is completely dissimilar in structure to its vertebrate analog, α-MSH. Finally, the species-specific hyperglycemic hormones (HGH) of crustaceans differ from the various native hyperglycemic factors in insects that have been characterized; and none of them is glucagon (e.g. 44, 63, 69, 131).

Such results lead to the second conclusion that analogous physiological roles in different classes or phyla are rarely carried out by homologous peptides. This notion is an extension of the idea of peptide family diversity discussed earlier.

The curious irrelation between the native and naturalized peptides seems to stem from the approaches to their detection. That is, native invertebrate peptides are sought, identified, and characterized on the basis of their functions, whereas the naturalized vertebrate peptides are detected and localized with reference to their structures. That the approach can determine the type of peptide observed is demonstrated clearly by a recent report that 15 vertebrate peptides were localized by immunocytochemistry to particular sets of neurons in *Lymnaea stagnalis* (108). Most of the localizations were *not* to the previously described neurosecretory cells (128), some of which have been implicated in physiological processes [references in (8)]. Therefore, the secretions of those neurosecretory cells must be different from the vertebrate peptides recently discovered, and the functions of the two sets of substances should also differ.

CONCLUSIONS

Vertebrate peptide families have homologs distributed throughout the invertebrate phyla. These naturalized peptides have biological activity, but their physiological roles are obscure. Certainly these roles are not those of the native peptides of known invertebrate neurosecretory systems. Conversely, there must still be a large number of native peptide families, not yet identified in any vertebrate, hidden away in each of the major invertebrate phyla. Therefore, concerted searches for invertebrate neuropeptides, and then for their analogs in vertebrates, would probably increase the roster of known peptides in higher organisms. The interesting task will be finding out what they do.

Literature Cited

1. Alumets, J., Håkanson, R., Sundler, F., Thorell, J. 1979. Neuronal localization of immunoreactive enkephalin and β-endorphin in the earthworm. *Nature* 279:805–6

2. Amino acid sequence, physical and biological properties of natural and related synthetic oligopeptides. Eledoisin group. In *Handbook of Biochemistry*, ed. H. A. Sober, pp. C204–22. Cleveland: CRC Press. 1973.

3. Arch, S. 1983. Neuropeptide chemistry and physiology in a "simple" system. In *Current Methods in Cellular Neurobiology*, Vol. 2, ed. J. Barker, J. McKelvy. NY: Wiley. In press

4. Arch, S., Lupatkin, J., Smock, T., Beard, M. 1980. Evidence for an exocrine function of the *Aplysia* atrial gland. *J. Comp. Physiol.* 141:131–37

5. Arechiga, H., Huberman, A. 1980. Peptide modulation of neuronal activity in crustaceans. In *The Role of Peptides in Neuronal Function*, ed. J. L. Barker, T. G. Smith Jr., pp. 318–49. NY: Marcel Dekker

6. Baumann, E., Gersch, M. 1982. Purification and identification of neurohormone D, a heart accelerating peptide from the corpora cardiaca of the cockroach *Periplaneta americana*. *Insect Biochem.* 12:7–14

7. Beard, M., Millecchia, L., Masuoka, C., Arch, S. 1982. Ultrastructure of secretion in the atrial gland of *Aplysia californica*. *Tissue Cell* 14:297–308

8. Benjamin, P. R., Slade, C. T., Soffe, S. R. 1980. The morphology of neurosecretory neurones in the pond snail, *Lymnaea stagnalis*, by the injection of Procion Yellow and horseradish peroxidase. *Philos. Trans. R. Soc. London Ser. B* 290:449–78

9. Bevis, P. J. R., Thorndyke, M. C. 1981. Stimulation of gastric enzyme secretion by porcine cholecystokinin in the ascidian *Styela clava*. *Gen. Comp. Endocrinol.* 45:458–64

10. Birr, C., Zachmann, B., Bodenmüller, H., Schaller, H. C. 1981. Synthesis of a new neuropeptide, the head activator from hydra. *FEBS Lett.* 131:317–21

11. Blankenship, J. E. 1980. Physiological properties of peptide-secreting neuroendocrine cells in the marine mollusc *Aplysia*. In *The Role of Peptides in Neuronal Function*, ed. J. L. Barker, T. G. Smith Jr., pp. 160–87. NY: Plenum

12. Blankenship, J. E., Rock, M. K., Robbins, L. C., Livingston, C. A., Lehman, H. K. 1983. Atrial gland peptides, but not copulation, cause egg laying in *Aplysia*. *Fed. Proc.* 42. In press

13. Blankenship, J. E., Rock, M. K., Schlesinger, D. H. 1982. Structure and function of peptides from a neuroendocrine system controlling egg-laying behavior in Aplysia. In *Proteins in the Nervous System: Structure and Function*, ed. B. Haber, R. J. Perez-Polo, J. D. Coulter, pp. 159–77. NY: Alan R. Liss, Inc.

14. Bodenmüller, H., Schaller, H. C. 1981. Conserved amino acid sequence of a neuropeptide, the head activator, from coelenterates to humans. *Nature* 293: 579–80

15. Boer, H. H., Schot, L. P. C., Roubos, E. W., ter Maat, A., Lodder, J. C., Reichelt, D., Swaab, D. F. 1979. ACTH-like immunoreactivity in two electrotonically coupled giant neurons in the pond snail *Lymnaea stagnalis*. *Cell Tissue Res.* 202:231–40

16. Boer, H. H., Schot, L. P. C., Veenstra, J. A., Reichelt, D. 1980. Immunocytochemical identification of neural elements in the central nervous systems of a snail, some insects, a fish, and a mammal with an antiserum to the molluscan cardio-excitatory tetrapeptide FMRF-amide. *Cell Tissue Res.* 213:21–27

16a. Bradbury, A. F., Finnie, M. D. A., Smyth, D. G. 1982. Mechanism of C-terminal amide formation by pituitary enzymes. *Nature* 298:686–88

17. Broomfield, C. E., Hardy, P. M. 1977. The synthesis of locust adipokinetic hormone. *Tetrahed. Lett.* 25:2201–4

18. Brown, B. E. 1977. Occurrence of proctolin in six orders of insects. *J. Insect Physiol.* 23:861–64

19. Busby, W. H., Youngblood, W. W. Jr., Humm, J., Kizer, J. S. 1981. A review of the methods used for the measurement of thyrotropin-releasing hormone (TRH). *J. Neurosci. Meth.* 4:305–14

20. Carlsen, J., Christensen, M., Josefsson, L. 1976. Purification and chemical structure of the red pigment–concentrating hormone of the prawn *Leander adspersus*. *Gen. Comp. Endocrinol.* 30: 327–31

21. Carlsen, J., Herman, W. S., Christensen, M., Josefsson, L. 1979. Characterization of a second peptide with adipokinetic and red pigment–concentrating activity from the locust corpora cardiaca. *Insect Biochem.* 9:497–501

22. Carraway, R., Ruane, S. E., Kim, H.-R. 1982. Distribution and immunochemical character of neurotensin-like material in representative vertebrates and in-

vertebrates: apparent conservation of the COOH-terminal region during evolution. *Peptides* 1:115–23

23. Chiu, A. Y., Hunkapiller, M. W., Heller, E., Stuart, D. K., Hood, L. E., Strumwasser, F. 1979. Purification and primary structure of the neuropeptide egg-laying hormone of *Aplysia californica*. *Proc. Natl. Acad. Sci. USA* 76:6656–60

24. Chiu, A. Y., Strumwasser, F. 1981. An immunohistochemical study of the neuropeptidergic bag cells of *Aplysia*. *J. Neurosci.* 1:812–26

25. Christensen, M., Carlsen, J., Josefsson, L. 1978. Structure-function studies on red pigment–concentrating hormone. The significance of the terminal residues. *Hoppe-Seyler's Z. Physiol. Chem.* 359:813–18

26. Christensen, M., Carlsen, J., Josefsson, L. 1979. Structure-function studies on red pigment–concentrating hormone, II. The significance of the C-terminal tryptophan amide. *Hoppe-Seyler's Z. Physiol. Chem.* 360:1051–60

27. Cottrell, G. A. 1982. FMRFamide neuropeptides simultaneously increase and decrease K^+ currents in an identified neurone. *Nature* 296:87–89

28. Dallmann, S. H., Herman, W. S., Carlsen, J., Josefsson, L. 1981. Adipokinetic activity of shrimp and locust peptide hormones in butterflies. *Gen. Comp. Endocrinol.* 43:256–58

29. Doble, K. E., Greenberg, M. J. 1982. The clam rectum is sensitive to FMRFamide, the enkephalins and their common analogs. *Neuropeptides* 2:157–67

30. Dockray, G. J., Duve, H., Thorpe, A. 1981. Immunochemical characterization of gastrin/cholecystokinin-like peptides in the brain of the blowfly, *Calliphora vomitoria*. *Gen. Comp. Endocrinol.* 45:491–96

31. Dockray, G. J., Vaillant, C., Williams, R. G. 1981. New vertebrate brain-gut peptide related to a molluscan neuropeptide and an opioid peptide. *Nature* 293:656–57

32. Dockray, G. J., Vaillant, C., Williams, R. G., Gayton, R. J., Osborne, N. N. 1981. Vertebrate brain-gut peptides related to FMRFamide and Met-enkephalin Arg[6]Phe[7]. *Peptides* 2 (Suppl. 2): 25–30

33. Duve, H., Thorpe, A. 1981. Gastrin/cholecystokinin (CCK)-like immunoreactive neurones in the brain of the blowfly, *Calliphora erythrocephala*

(Diptera) *Gen. Comp. Endocrinol.* 43:381–91

33a. Duve, H., Thorpe, A., Lazarus, N. R. 1979. Isolation of material displaying insulin-like immunological and biological activity from the brain of the blowfly *Calliphora vomitoria*. *Biochem. J.* 184:221–27

34. Duve, H., Thorpe, A., Lazarus, N. R., Lowry, P. J. 1982. A neuropeptide of the blowfly *Calliphora vomitoria* with an amino acid composition homologous with vertebrate pancreatic polypeptide. *Biochem. J.* 201:429–32

35. El-Salhy, M., Abou-El-Ela, R., Falkmer, S., Grimelius, L., Wilander, E. 1980. Immunohistochemical evidence of gastro-entero-pancreatic neurohormonal peptides of vertebrate type in the nervous system of a dipteran insect, the hoverfly *Eristalis aeneus*. *Regulat. Peptides* 1:187–204

36. Erspamer, V. 1981. The tachykinin peptide family. *Trends Neurosci.* 4:267–69

37. Erspamer, V., Anastasi, A. 1962. Structure and pharmacological actions of eledoisin, the active endecapeptide of the posterior salivary gland of *Eledone*. *Experientia* 181:58–59

38. Fernlund, P. 1974. Structure of the red-pigment–concentrating hormone of the shrimp, *Pandalus borealis*. *Biochim. Biophys. Acta* 371:304–11

39. Fernlund, P. 1976. Structure of a light-adapting hormone from the shrimp, *Pandalus borealis*. *Biochim. Biophys. Acta* 439:17–25

40. Fernlund, P., Josefsson, L. 1972. Crustacean color change hormone: amino acid sequence and chemical synthesis. *Science* 177:173–75

41. Fritsch, H. A. R., Van Noorden, S., Pearse, A. G. E. 1979. Localization of somatostatin-, substance P- and calcitonin-like immunoreactivity in the neural ganglion of *Ciona intestinalis* L. (Ascidiaceae). *Cell Tissue Res.* 202:263–74

42. Frontali, N., Gainer, H. 1977. Peptides in invertebrate nervous systems. In *Peptides in Neurobiology*, ed. H. Gainer, pp. 259–94. NY: Plenum.

43. Gäde, G. 1981. Studies on a phosphorylase-activating factor in the corpora cardiaca of stick insects: characterization and preliminary purification. *Zool. Jahrb. Physiol.* 85:266–77

44. Gäde, G., Lohr, P. 1982. Restricted specificity of a hyperglycemic factor from the corpus cardiacum of the stick insect, *Carausius morosus*. *J. Insect Physiol.* 28:805–11

45. Greenberg, M. J. 1982. Invertebrate cardioactive neuropeptides: FMRFamide and proctolin. In *Proc. Ninth Int. Symp. Comp. Endocrinol.*, ed. B. Lofts. Hong Kong: Univ. Hong Kong Press. In press

46. Greenberg, M. J., Painter, S. D., Price, D. A. 1981. The amide of the naturally occurring opioid [Met]enkephalin-Arg⁶-Phe⁷ is a potent analog of the molluscan neuropeptide FMRFamide. *Neuropeptides* 1:309–17

47. Greenberg, M. J., Painter, S. D., Doble, K. E., Nagle, G. T., Price, D. A., Lehman, H. K. 1983. The molluscan neurosecretory peptide FMRFamide: comparative pharmacology and relationship to the enkephalins. *Fed. Proc.* 42. In press

48. Greenberg, M. J., Price, D. A. 1979. FMRFamide, a cardioexcitatory neuropeptide of molluscs: an agent in search of a mission. *Am. Zool.* 19:163–74

49. Greenberg, M. J., Price, D. A. 1980. Cardioregulatory peptides in molluscs. In *Peptides: Integrators of Cell and Tissue Function*, ed. F. E. Bloom, pp. 107–26. NY: Raven Press

50. Grimmelikhuijzen, C. J. P., Balfe, A., Emson, P. C., Powell, D., Sundler, F. 1981. Substance P–like immunoreactivity in the nervous system of hydra. *Histochemistry* 71:325–33

51. Grimmelikhuijzen, C. J. P., Carraway, R. E., Rökaeus, A., Sundler, F. 1981. Neurotensin-like immunoreactivity in the nervous system of hydra. *Histochemistry* 72:199–209

52. Grimmelikhuijzen, C. J. P., Dockray, G. J., Schot, L. P. C. 1982. FMRFamide-like immunoreactivity in the nervous system of hydra. *Histochemistry* 73:499–508

53. Grimmelikhuijzen, C. J. P., Dockray, G. J., Yanaihara, N. 1981. Bombesinlike immunoreactivity in the nervous system of hydra. *Histochemistry* 73: 171–80

54. Grimmelikhuijzen, C. J. P., Sundler, F., Rehfeld, J. F. 1980. Gastrin/CCK-like immunoreactivity in the nervous system of coelenterates. *Histochemistry* 69: 61–68

55. Grimm-Jørgensen, Y. 1978. Immunoreactive thyrotropin-releasing factor in a gastropod: distribution in the central nervous system and hemolymph of *Lymnaea stagnalis. Gen. Comp. Endocrinol.* 35:387–90

56. Grimm-Jørgensen, Y. 1980. Effect of thyrotropin releasing hormone on the cAMP content in circumesophageal ganglia of *Lymnaea emarginata. Life Sci.* 26:1211–16

57. Grimm-Jørgensen, Y. 1980. Effect of thyrotropin-releasing hormone on ²²Na uptake by the pond snail *Helisoma carabaceum. J. Exp. Zool.* 212:471–73

58. Haynes, L. W. 1980. Peptide neuroregulators in invertebrates. *Prog. Neurobiol.* 15:205–45

59. Heller, E., Kaczmarek, L. K., Hunkapiller, M. W., Hood, L. E., Strumwasser, F. 1980. Purification and primary structure of two neuroactive peptides that cause bag cell afterdischarge and egg-laying in *Aplysia. Proc. Natl. Acad. Sci. USA* 77:2328–32

60. Holman, G. M., Cook, B. J. 1979. The analytical determination of proctolin by HPLC and its pharmacological action in the stable fly. *Comp. Biochem. Physiol.* 62C:231–35

61. Inturrisi, C. E., Umans, J. G., Wolff, D., Stern, A. S., Lewis, R. V., Stein, S., Udenfriend, S. 1980. Analgesic activity of the naturally occurring heptapeptide [Met] enkephalin-Arg⁶-Phe⁷. *Proc. Natl. Acad. Sci. USA* 77:5512–14

62. Kanatani, H. 1973. Maturation-inducing substance in starfish. *Int. Rev. Cytol.* 35:253–98

63. Keller, R., Wunderer, G. 1978. Purification and amino acid composition of the neurosecretory hyperglycemic hormone from the sinus gland of the shore crab, *Carcinus maenas. Gen. Comp. Endocrinol.* 34:328–35

64. Kramer, K. J., Childs, C. N., Spiers, R. D., Jacobs, R. M. 1982. Purification of insulin-like peptides from insect hemolymph and royal jelly. *Insect Biochem.* 12:91–98

65. Kream, R. M., Zukin, R. S., Stefano, G. B. 1980. Demonstration of two classes of opiate binding sites in the nervous tissue of the marine mollusc *Mytilus edulis.* Positive homotropic cooperativity of lower affinity binding sites. *J. Biol. Chem.* 255:9218–24

66. Kreil, G., Suchanek, G., Kindås-Mügge, I. 1977. Biosynthesis of a secretory peptide in honeybee venom glands: intermediates detected in vivo and in vitro. *Fed. Proc.* 36:2081–86

67. Le Roith, D., Lesniak, M. A., Roth, J. 1981. Insulin in insects and annelids. *Diabetes* 30:70–76

68. Le Roith, D., Shiloach, J., Roth, J., Lesniak, M. A. 1980. Evolutionary origins of vertebrate hormones: Substances similar to mammalian insulins are native to unicellular eukaryotes. *Proc. Natl. Acad. Sci. USA* 77:6184–88

69. Leuven, R. S. E. W., Jaros, P. P., Van Herp, F., Keller, R. 1982. Species or group specificity in biological and immunological studies of crustacean hyperglycemic hormone. *Gen. Comp. Endocrinol.* 46:288–96

70. Lorén, I., Alumets, J., Håkanson, R., Sundler, F. 1979. Immunoreactive pancreatic polypeptide (PP) occurs in the central and peripheral nervous system: preliminary immunocytochemical observations. *Cell Tissue Res.* 200:179–86

71. Loughton, B. G., Orchard, I. 1981. The nature of the hyperglycemic factor from the glandular lobe of the corpus cardiacum of *Locusta migratoria. J. Insect Physiol.* 27:383–85

72. Lukowiak, K., Thornhill, J. A., Cooper, K. E., Veale, W. L. 1980. Vasopressin suppresses gill reflex behaviour and evoked synaptic activity in central gill motor neurons of *Aplysia. Can. J. Physiol. Pharmacol.* 58:583–87

73. Mancillas, J. R., McGinty, J. F., Selverston, A. I., Karten, H., Bloom, F. E. 1981. Immunocytochemical localization of enkephalin and substance P in retina and eyestalk neurones of lobster. *Nature* 293:576–78

74. Martin, G., Dubois, M. P. 1981. A somatostatin-like antigen in the nervous system of an isopod *Porcellio dilatatus* Brandt. *Gen. Comp. Endocrinol.* 45:125–30

75. Martin, R., Frösch, D., Voigt, K. H. 1980. Immunocytochemical evidence for melanotropin- and vasopressin-like material in a cephalopod neurohemal organ. *Gen. Comp. Endocrinol.* 42:235–43

76. Miller, M. W., Sullivan, R. E. 1981. Some effects of proctolin on the cardiac ganglion of the Maine lobster, *Homarus americanus* (Milne Edwards). *J. Neurobiol.* 12:629–39

77. Moore, S. J., Thornhill, J. A., Gill, V., Lederis, K., Lukowiak, K. 1981. An arginine vasotocin-like neuropeptide is present in the nervous system of the marine mollusc *Aplysia californica. Brain Res.* 206:213–18

78. Mordue, W., Stone, J. V. 1977. Relative potencies of locust adipokinetic hormone and prawn red pigment–concentrating hormone in insect and crustacean systems. *Gen. Comp. Endocrinol.* 33:103–8

79. Mordue, W., Stone, J. V. 1979. Insect hormones. In *Hormones and Evolution,* ed. E. J. W. Barrington, pp. 215–71. NY: Academic

80. Mordue, W., Stone, J. V. 1981. Structure and function of insect peptide hormones. *Insect Biochem.* 11:353–60

81. Noda, M., Furutani, Y., Takahashi, H., Toyosato, M., Hirose, T., Inayama, S., Nakanishi, S., Numa, S. 1982. Cloning and sequence analysis of cDNA for bovine adrenal preproenkephalin. *Nature* 295:202–5

82. Orchard, I., Loughton, B. G. 1980. A hypolipaemic factor from the corpus cardiacum of locusts. *Nature* 286:494–96

83. Osborne, N. N., Cuello, A. C., Dockray, G. J. 1982. Substance P and cholecystokinin-like peptides in *Helix* neurons and cholecystokinin and serotonin in a giant neuron. *Science* 216:409–11

84. O'Shea, M., Adams, M. E. 1981. Pentapeptide (proctolin) associated with an identified neuron. *Science* 213:567–69

85. Painter, S. D., Morley, J. S., Price, D. A. 1982. Structure-activity relations of the molluscan neuropeptide FMRFamide on some molluscan muscles. *Life Sci.* 31:2471–78

86. Pines, M., Tietz, A., Weintraub, H., Applebaum, S. W., Josefsson, L. 1981. Hormonal activation of protein kinase and lipid mobilization in the locust fat body *in vitro. Gen. Comp. Endocrinol.* 43:427–31

87. Price, D. A. 1983. Crustacean neuropeptides. In *Brain Peptides,* ed. D. T. Krieger, M. Brownstein, J. Martin. NY: Wiley. In press

88. Price, D. A. 1982. The FMRFamide-like peptide of *Helix aspersa. Comp. Biochem. Physiol.* 72c:325–28

89. Price, D. A., Greenberg, M. J. 1977. Purification and characterization of a cardioexcitatory neuropeptide from the central ganglia of a bivalve mollusc. *Prep. Biochem.* 7:261–81

90. Price, D. A., Greenberg, M. J. 1977. The structure of a molluscan cardioexcitatory neuropeptide. *Science* 197:670–71

91. Price, D. A., Greenberg, M. J. 1980. The pharmacology of the molluscan cardioexcitatory neuropeptide FMRFamide. *Gen. Pharmacol.* 11:237–41

92. Proux, J., Rougon-Rapuzzi, G. 1980. Evidence for vasopressin-like molecule in migratory locust. Radioimmunological measurements in different tissues: correlation with various states of hydration. *Gen. Comp. Endocrinol.* 42:378–83

93. Rao, K. R. 1983. Pigmentary effectors.

In *Biology of Crustacea*, ed. D. Bliss, L. Mantel. NY: Academic. In press
94. Rao, K. R., Fingerman, M. 1983. Regulation of release and mode of action of crustacean chromatophorotropins. *Am. Zool.* 23. In press
95. Reinecke, M., Carraway, R. W., Falkmer, S., Feurle, G. E., Forssman, W. G. 1980. Occurrence of neurotensin-immunoreactive cells in the digestive tract of lower vertebrates and deuterostomian invertebrates. A correlated immunohistochemical and radioimmunochemical study. *Cell Tissue Res.* 212: 173-83
96. Rémy, C., Dubois, M. P. 1979. Localisation par immunofluorescence de peptides analogues à l'α-endorphine dans les ganglions infra-oesophagiens du Lombricidé *Dendrobaena subrubicunda* Eisen. *Experientia* 35:137-38
97. Rémy, C., Girardie, J. 1980. Anatomical organization of two vasopressin-neurophysin-like neurosecretory cells throughout the central nervous system of the migratory locust. *Gen. Comp. Endocrinol.* 40:27-35
98. Rhiem, J. P., Rao, K. R. 1982. Structure-activity relationships of a pigment-dispersing crustacean neurohormone. *Peptides* 3:643-47
99. Rzasa, P., Kaloustian, K. V., Prokop, E. K. 1982. Immunochemical evidence for a gastrin-like peptide in the intestinal tissues of the earthworm *Lumbricus terrestris. Comp. Biochem. Physiol.* 71A:631-34
100. Schaller, H. C. 1979. Neuropeptides in *Hydra. Trends Neurosci.* 2:120-22
101. Schaller, H. C., Bodenmüller, H. 1981. Isolation and amino acid sequence of a morphogenetic peptide from hydra. *Proc. Natl. Acad. Sci. USA* 78:7000-4
102. Schaller, H. C., Rau, T., Bode, H. 1980. Epithelial cells in nerve-free hydra produce morphogenetic substances. *Nature* 283:589-91
103. Schaller, H. C., Schmidt, T., Grimmelshuijzen, C. J. P. 1979. Separation and specificity of action of four morphogens from hydra. *Wilhelm Roux's Arch. Dev. Biol.* 186:139-49
104. Scheller, R. H., Jackson, J. F., McAllister, L. B., Schwartz, J. H., Kandel, E. R., Axel, R. 1982. A family of genes that codes for ELH, a neuropeptide eliciting a stereotyped pattern of behavior in *Aplysia. Cell* 28:707-19
105. Schilt, J., Richoux, J. P., Dubois, M. P. 1981. Demonstration of peptides immunologically related to vertebrate neurohormones in *Dugesia lugubris*

(Turbellaria, Tricladida). *Gen. Comp. Endocrinol.* 43:331-35
106. Schlesinger, D. H., Babirak, S. B., Blankenship, J. E. 1981. Primary structure of an egg laying peptide from atrial gland of *Aplysia californica*. In *Neurohypophyseal Peptide Hormones and other Biologically Active Peptides*, ed. D. North Holland, pp. 137-50. NY: Elsevier
107. Schlesinger, D. H., Blankenship, J. E. 1981. Primary structure and synthesis of an egg-releasing peptide (ERH) from the atrial gland of *Aplysia californica*. In *Peptides: Synthesis—Structure—Function*, ed. D. H. Rich, E. Gross, pp. 739-43. NY: Pierce Chemical Co.
108. Schot, L. P. C., Boer, H. H., Swaab, D. F., Van Noorden, S. 1981. Immunocytochemical demonstration of peptidergic neurons in the central nervous system of the pond snail *Lymnaea stagnalis* with antisera raised to biologically active peptides of vertebrates. *Cell Tissue Res.* 216:273-91
109. Schwarz, T. L., Lee, G., Kravitz, E. A. 1981. Proctolin-like immunoreactivity in the nervous system of the lobster *Homarus americanus. Soc. Neurosci. Abstr.* 7:253
110. Starratt, A. N., Brown, B. E. 1975. Structure of the pentapeptide proctolin, a proposed neurotransmitter in insects. *Life Sci.* 17:1253-56
111. Starratt, A. N., Brown, B. E. 1979. Analogs of the insect myotropic peptide proctolin: synthesis and structure-activity studies. *Biochem. Biophys. Res. Commun.* 90:1125-30
112. Stefano, G. B., Hall, B., Makman, M. H., Dvorkin, B. 1981. Opioid inhibition of dopamine release from nervous tissue of *Mytilus edulis* and *Octopus bimaculatus. Science* 213:928-30
113. Stern, A. S., Lewis, R. V., Kimura, S., Rossier, J., Gerber, L. D., Brink, L., Stein, S., Udenfriend, S. 1979. Isolation of the opioid heptapeptide Met-enkephalin [Arg^6, Phe^7] from bovine adrenal medullary granules and striatum. *Proc. Natl. Acad. Sci. USA* 76:6680-83
114. Stone, J. V., Mordue, W., Batley, K. E., Morris, H. R. 1976. Structure of locust adipokinetic hormone, a neurohormone that regulates lipid utilisation during flight. *Nature* 263:207-11
115. Stone, J. V., Mordue, W., Broomfield, C. E., Hardy, P. M. 1978. Structure-activity relationships for the lipid-mobilising action of locust adipokinetic hormone. *Euro. J. Biochem.* 89:195-202

116. Strambi, C., Rougon-Rapuzzi, G., Cupo, A., Martin, N., Strambi, A. 1979. Mise en évidence immunocytologique d'un composé apparenté à la vasopressine dans le système nerveux du grillon *Acheta domesticus. C. R. Acad. Sci. Ser. D* 288:131–33

117. Strumwasser, F., Kaczmarek, L. K., Chiu, A. Y., Heller, E., Jennings, K. R., Viele, D. P. 1980. Peptides controlling behavior in *Aplysia.* See Ref. 49, pp. 197–218

118. Sullivan, R. E. 1979. A proctolin-like peptide in crab pericardial organs. *J. Exp. Zool.* 210:543–52

119. Tager, H. S., Markese, J., Kramer, K. J., Spiers, R. D., Childs, C. N. 1976. Glucagon-like and insulin-like hormones of the insect neurosecretory system. *Biochem. J.* 156:515–20

120. Tatemoto, K., Carlquist, M., Mutt, V. 1982. Neuropeptide Y—a novel brain peptide with structural similarities to peptide YY and pancreatic polypeptide. *Nature* 296:659–60

121. Thorndyke, M. C. 1982. Cholecystokinin (CCK)/gastrin-like immunoreactive neurones in the cerebral ganglion of the protochordate ascidians *Styela clava* and *Ascidiella aspersa. Regulatory Peptides* 3:281–88

122. Vaillant, C., Taylor, I. L. 1981. Demonstration of carboxyl-terminal PP-like peptides in endocrine cells and nerves. *Peptides* 2 (Suppl. 2):31–35

123. Van Noorden, S., Falkmer, S. 1980. Gut-islet endocrinology—some evolutionary aspects. *Invest. Cell Pathol.* 3: 21–36

124. Van Norstrand, M. D., Carlsen, J. B., Josefsson, L., Herman, W. S. 1980. Studies on a peptide with red pigment–concentration and hyperglycemic activity from the cephalic endocrine system of the honeybee, *Apis mellifera. Gen. Comp. Endocrinol.* 42:526–33

125. Venturini, G., Carolei, A., Palladini, G., Margotta, V., Cerbo, R. 1981. Naloxone enhances cAMP levels in planaria. *Comp. Biochem. Physiol.* 69C: 105–8

126. Voigt, K. H., Kiehling, C., Frösch, D., Schiebe, M., Martin, R. 1981. Enkephalin-related peptides: direct action on the octopus heart. *Neurosci. Lett.* 27:25–30

127. Weber, E., Evans, C. J., Samuelsson, S. J., Barchas, J. D. 1981. Novel peptide neuronal system in rat brain and pituitary. *Science* 214:1248–51

128. Wendelaar Bonga, S. E. 1970. Ultrastructure and histochemistry of the neurosecretory cells and neurohaemal areas in the pond snail *Lymnaea stagnalis* (L.). *Z. Zellforsch.* 108:190–224

129. Wernham, S., Lukowiak, K. 1981. Peptide modulation of the isolated *Aplysia* heart. *Soc. Neurosci. Abstr.* 7:316

130. Yalow, R. S., Eng, J. 1981. Peptide hormones in strange places—Are they there? *Peptides* 2:17–23

131. Ziegler, R. 1979. Hyperglycaemic factor from the corpora cardiaca of *Manduca sexta* (L.) (Lepidoptera: Sphingidae). *Gen. Comp. Endocrinol.* 39: 350–57

132. Zipser, B. 1980. Identification of specific leech neurones immunoreactive to enkephalin. *Nature* 283:857–58

Ann. Rev. Physiol. 1983. 45:289-99

FREEZING RESISTANCE IN INTERTIDAL INVERTEBRATES

D. J. Murphy

Department of Toxicology, The Squibb Institute for Medical Research, New Brunswick, New Jersey 08903

INTRODUCTION

Marine organisms inhabiting the intertidal zone are periodically exposed to conditions characteristic of the terrestrial environment. The duration of aerial exposure is dependent on both the pattern of tidal cycles and the vertical distributions of animals on the shore. Along the eastern coast of the United States, intertidal animals living below the mean tidal level are exposed to air twice daily for periods of 0–6 hr, while animals living above this level are exposed from 6 hr to 2 weeks at a time (43). Marine organisms that have colonized the intertidal zone have had to adapt to the desiccation and thermal stresses associated with a terrestrial environment. This is particularly true for low-temperature stress. Organisms continually immersed in seawater are generally not exposed to temperatures below −1.7°C, the freezing point of seawater, whereas intertidal animals in North Temperate regions are exposed to air temperatures from −10 to −20°C during the colder winter months (13, 25). Indeed, the ability of marine animals to tolerate temperatures in this range is restricted to the inhabitants of the intertidal zone (12, 13, 25, 44).

The groups of invertebrates that are most abundant in the intertidal zone during the winter months, and whose freezing resistance has been most thoroughly studied, include species of marine snails (Phylum, Molluska; Class, Gastropoda), barnacles (Phylum, Arthropoda; Class, Crustacea), and bivalves (Phylum, Molluska; Class, Bivalvia). Here I review the freezing resistances of these invertebrates and examine the environmental, physical, and biological factors that influence freezing resistance, the mechanisms of freezing injury, and the physiological mechanisms of freezing resistance.

0066-4278/83/0315-0289$02.00

FACTORS INFLUENCING FREEZING RESISTANCE

Exposure Conditions

Lowering freezing temperature or lengthening freezing time increases the freezing injury of intertidal invertebrates. The quantitative relationship between these two exposure conditions was examined in the marine snail *Littorina littorea*. Over the temperature range of –8 to –13°C, a decrease in freezing temperature is proportional to a decrease in the log of the time required to reach 50% mortality (27). More specifically, for every 1°C drop in temperature, there is a 2.6-fold decrease in the time required to reach 50% mortality. Thus although *L. littorea* can tolerate –8°C for approximately 8 days, survival at –12 and –13°C is possible for only 6 and 2.3 hr, respectively. Since the exposures of intertidal invertebrates to freezing stresses are periodic (ranging from several hours to several weeks), a better understanding of the quantitative relationship between freezing temperature and time is needed to characterize fully the resistance of these animals to freezing.

The rate of cooling during the formation and growth of tissue ice is also an important influence on the freezing resistance of *L. littorea* (27). The cooling rates of these snails are influenced primarily by total body weights and exposure temperatures. When the cooling rates exceed 0.4°C min⁻¹, freezing resistance in reduced. For a population of *L. littorea* exposed to temperatures between –7 and –20°C, cooling rates can range anywhere from 0.06°C min⁻¹ for the largest snails exposed to –7°C, to 1.60°C min⁻¹ for the smallest snails exposed to –20°C (27). Since these values extend above and below 0.4°C min⁻¹, the cooling rate during tissue ice formation may be an important influence on the freezing resistance of *L. littorea*. Indeed, Murphy & Johnson (27) demonstrated that the ability of larger specimens of *L. littorea* to tolerate lower temperatures is due solely to differences in cooling rates during freezing. The effects of cooling rates on the freezing resistances of other intertidal invertebrates have not yet been examined.

Exposure to seawater at temperatures between 0 and 5°C for 1–3 weeks prior to a freezing stress usually increases the freezing resistance of intertidal invertebrates (29, 39), although in some cases it has no effect (5, 25, 29) or even reduces freezing resistance (25). Specimens of *L. littorea* held in seawater at 4°C following freezing and thawing recover with less freezing injury than snails placed into 20°C seawater; this effect is independent of the temperature to which these snails were acclimated prior to freezing (27). Although this response to recovery temperature has also been observed in plants (16) and mammalian cells (20), the explanation for this response remains unknown.

Seasonal Changes

Most intertidal mollusks and barnacles display seasonal changes in freezing resistance, with greater resistances occurring during the colder winter months (6, 12, 34, 39). These changes in freezing resistance are dependent to some extent on changes in ambient temperatures. Intertidal invertebrates collected during the winter months and exposed to temperatures between 0 and 5°C in the laboratory retain their high degree of freezing resistance, while exposures to temperatures between 15 and 25°C reduce this resistance (5, 29, 39). Acclimation to low temperatures during the summer months, however, has no effect on the freezing resistances of either the bivalve *Modiolus demissus* (29) or the barnacle *Balanus balanoides* (5, 6), and neither high- nor low-temperature exposures influence the seasonal changes in the freezing resistance of the snail *L. littorea* (25). Temperature, therefore, is not the only factor influencing seasonal changes in freezing resistance. For *B. balanoides*, a combination of low temperature, low light intensity, and food deprivation increases the freezing resistance of summer animals, whereas the physiological changes associated with the annual breeding cycle have no effect (5, 6). The seasonal changes in the freezing resistance of intertidal mollusks are not influenced by photoperiod (25). The effect of the breeding cycle has not yet been examined in these animals.

Salinity

Species of marine bivalves living in low-salinity environments characteristically possess lower freezing resistances than the same species living at higher salinities (39, 40). Furthermore, exposure of marine bivalves (12, 29, 39, 40, 44), snails (25), and barnacles (5) to higher salinities in the laboratory increases freezing resistance. The physiological changes associated with acclimation to higher salinities, however, do not appear to be the same as those associated with freezing-resistance mechanisms; instead, the increases in freezing resistance result directly from increases in the osmolarity of the tissue fluids following acclimation to higher salinities (5, 29, 44). A change in tissue osmolarity does influence freezing-resistance mechanisms, however, since seasonal changes, species variations, and temperature-induced differences in the freezing resistances of intertidal mollusks are reduced or eliminated at lower salinities (25, 39).

Oxygen Tension

Exposure of the intertidal bivalve *Mytilus edulis* to air causes an increase in tissue fluid osmolarity, a reduction in tissue oxygen levels, and an increase in freezing resistance (39). The increases in tissue osmolarity following exposure to air could not account for the observed changes in freezing resistance. When this bivalve was exposed to seawater with a low oxygen tension, there were even greater increases in freezing resistance with no changes in tissue osmolarity (39). Similarly, when the valves of *M. demissus* were clamped shut to prevent water loss and oxygen uptake, there was an increase in freezing resistance without a significant increase in tissue osmolarity (23). Murphy (23) also found that exposure of *M. demissus* to seawater at temperatures below 10°C results in a shift from an aerobic to an anaerobic metabolism and an increase in freezing resistance. Thus a reduction in tissue levels of oxygen is an important correlate of greater freezing resistance in intertidal mollusks.

MECHANISMS OF FREEZING INJURY

Certain insects (8, 33, 35), fish (7, 9), and terrestrial snails (36) survive exposures to temperatures below the freezing point of their body fluids by preventing the formation of tissue ice. Intertidal invertebrates, on the other hand, withstand the freezing conditions imposed during the winter months by tolerating the presence of tissue ice. Indeed, intertidal mollusks exposed to temperatures of –10 to –22°C survive with 65–80% of their tissue water frozen (13, 25, 29, 32, 44). To define the mechanism of injury resulting from the formation of tissue ice, it is first necessary to establish whether ice crystals occur within cells or are restricted to extracellular spaces.

Intracellular Ice Formation

Ice crystals present within cells at temperatures above –40°C are large enough to cause injury to cells by an apparent mechanical disruption of cellular components (2). A major factor influencing intracellular ice formation in biological systems is the rate of cooling during the freezing process. When the cooling rate exceeds a critical value characteristic of a certain cell type, intracellular ice appears and freezing injury results (18, 19). Cooling rates above 0.4°C min^{-1} increase the freezing injury of *L. littorea* (27), suggesting that intracellular ice is forming at these rates. An important influence on cooling rates in this intertidal invertebrate is total body weight, and the quantitative relationship between cooling rate (y) and total body weight (x) can be expressed by the hyperbolic equation $y = 1/(1.04 + 1.58 x)$ when *L. littorea* is exposed to an air temperature of –10°C (27). Thus in a population of *L. littorea,* individuals with body weights of 1 g or less that are exposed to temperatures of –10°C or lower may be susceptible to intracellular ice formation. Whether the cooling rate at which intracellular ice formation occurs in intertidal invertebrates varies among species, or changes seasonally; and what effects animal aggregations, substrate composition, and wind velocity have on cooling rates in the field are important unanswered questions.

Extracellular Ice Formation

The occurrence of extracellular ice has been demonstrated in a variety of intertidal snails and bivalves but has not yet been examined in intertidal barnacles. Using a freeze-substitution, histological technique, Kanwisher (14) demonstrated that tissues from intertidal snails and bivalves frozen in the field to temperatures of −10 to −15°C possessed large extracellular ice crystals, with no evidence of intracellular ice. During extracellular ice formation, the mole fraction of extracellular water rapidly declines, intracellular water diffuses down its concentration gradient in the extracellular space, and cellular dehydration results (18, 19). Extracellular ice formation, therefore, represents a form of desiccation. In fact, freezing and desiccation resistance are closely related in intertidal mollusks (28, 32), supporting the histological evidence for extracellular ice formation in these invertebrates and suggesting that the mechanism of freezing injury involves a freezing dehydration.

A mechanism accounting for the damage caused by extracellular ice formation has not yet been determined in intertidal invertebrates. However, it has been demonstrated in intertidal mollusks that freezing injury following extracellular ice formation is associated with the loss of a critical amount of cell water, and that cell membranes are a primary target of injury. The relationship between the loss of cell water and freezing injury was determined by examining the effects of salinity acclimation on freezing resistance and extracellular ice formation (29, 44). Acclimation of intertidal mollusks to higher salinities increases the osmolarity of the tissue fluids and lowers the lethal freezing temperature by reducing the amounts of tissue ice formed. The percentage of tissue water frozen at the lethal freezing temperature for each salinity, moreover, remains constant. This demonstrates that injury from extracellular ice formation involves the loss of a critical amount of cell water, not the concentrating of tissue solutes to a toxic level, as occurs in red blood cells (17).

To determine the primary site of freezing injury in intertidal mollusks, Murphy (24) examined the contractile response of foot muscle from $M.$ $demissus$ frozen to different temperatures, thawed, and then exposed to caffeine, acetylcholine, KCl, or $CaCl_2$. The contractile response of the freeze-thawed muscle exposed to caffeine, acetylcholine, and KCl ceased when the exposure temperature approached −10°C, while the response to

$CaCl_2$ continued down to $-13°C$. The loss of response to KCl or acetylcholine [which elicit muscle contraction by plasma membrane depolarization (30)] and caffeine [which causes contraction by eliciting a Ca^{2+} release from either the sarcoplasmic reticulum or plasma membrane (11)] suggests that membrane damage occurred at $-10°C$. In contrast, the persistent response of the freeze-thawed muscle to $CaCl_2$ [which interacts directly with the contractile apparatus (31)] indicates that the intracellular components were still intact.

Theede (39) found that aldolase, a cytosolic enzyme, and acid phosphatase, a lysosomal enzyme, leaked from the isolated gills of *M. edulis* following a freeze-thaw cycle. The amount of leakage was proportional to freezing injury (i.e. the loss of ciliary beating) and preceded histological evidence of cellular damage. The movement of these high-molecular-weight proteins through membranes indicates a disruption of normal membrane permeability and suggests again that cell membranes are the primary targets of freezing damage in intertidal mollusks.

Studies that have defined influences on the freezing injury in intertidal mollusks have demonstrated that the mechanism of freezing injury in these animals, and perhaps in other intertidal invertebrates as well, must involve both membrane damage and the loss of a critical amount of cell water. One hypothesis based on work done with red blood cells proposes that the loss of cell water during extracellular ice formation reduces cell volume below a critical minimum value at the lethal freezing temperature. This cell shrinkage exerts a mechanical force on the membrane, distorting it sufficiently to cause permeability changes and eventual disruption, either during or after the completion of thawing (21). Whether cell volume changes are involved in the mechanism of freezing injury in intertidal invertebrates has yet to be determined.

PHYSIOLOGICAL MECHANISMS OF FREEZING RESISTANCE

Prevention of Intracellular Ice Formation

Freezing resistance in intertidal invertebrates is dependent on mechanisms that prevent the occurrence of intracellular ice and increase resistance to the presence of extracellular ice. Intracellular ice formation in intertidal invertebrates appears to be dependent on cooling rate. Thus physiological mechanisms that increase the rate of cooling needed for intracellular ice to form will reduce the incidence of intracellular ice. Such mechanisms have not been examined in intertidal invertebrates. However, in red blood cells and unicellular organisms such mechanisms involve membrane alterations that increase the rate of water movement into and out of cells during a freeze-thaw cycle (18, 19).

Increased Resistance to Extracellular Ice

Physiological mechanisms that lower the temperatures at which extracellular ice produces injury in intertidal invertebrates must involve a reduction in the amount of tissue ice formed and/or an increase in resistance to greater quantities of tissue ice. The intertidal mussel *M. edulis* can tolerate temperatures as low as –10°C, while the subtidal clam *Venus mercenaria* cannot survive at temperatures below –6°C. When the amounts of tissue ice formed at various freezing temperatures are measured, the amount present in the tissue of *M. edulis* is always lower than that of *V. mercenaria*. (44). Both species die, however, when 64% of their tissue water freezes. The difference between the two lethal freezing temperatures is due to a property of the tissue from the more freezing-resistant species that lowers this threshold temperature. Since the osmolarity of the tissue fluids was identical in both species, Williams (44) proposed that the quantitative differences in tissue ice formation were due to the presence of specific intracellular components in *M. edulis* that "bind" a certain fraction of cellular water, prevent its diffusion to the growing extracellular ice cyrstals, and thus reduce the fraction of cell water lost during the freezing process. This mechanism would increase freezing resistance by lowering the temperature necessary to attain a cell volume small enough to produce freezing injury.

Tissue components that appear to "bind" cellular water have been identified in *M. edulis*. Muscle fibers from *M. edulis*, treated with glycerol to remove all nonstructural components and subsequently placed into an aqueous solution, can prevent a fraction of the water associated with the tissue from being frozen (3). In addition, high-molecular-weight glycoproteins have been isolated from *M. edulis* that can lower the freezing point of water below that predicted by the osmolarity of the solution (41). These high-molecular-weight glycoproteins could produce this effect by making a certain fraction of water inaccessible to the ice crystals (9). Although tissue components that can impede or prevent the growth of ice crystals have been identified in *M. edulis*, a quantitative relationship between the amounts of these components and the degrees of freezing resistance in intertidal invertebrates has not yet been demonstrated. Thus the role of water "binding" components in the freezing resistance of intertidal invertebrates remains to be determined.

Resistance to greater quantities of extracellular ice is a common mechanism for lowering the lethal freezing temperatures for intertidal mollusks. The ability of intertidal snails to tolerate lower freezing temperatures than subtidal snails is due to a resistance to greater quantities of tissue ice (25,

26). Similarily, the seasonal decreases in the lethal freezing temperatures of the snails *L. littorea* and *Nassarius obsoletus* (25) and the bivalve *M. demissus* (29) are due to resistances to greater quantities of tissue ice. The physiological mechanisms of resistance to greater quantities of tissue ice have not yet been investigated in intertidal invertebrates. However, low levels of tissue oxygen are associated with the increased resistance to extracellular ice in intertidal mollusks (23, 39). This association suggests either (*a*) that the mechanism involves structural or tissue solute changes that are dependent on a shift from an aerobic to an anaerobic metabolism, or (*b*) that oxygen is associated with freezing injury, and that increases in freezing resistance involve mechanisms that prevent oxygen-dependent injury.

An increase in the concentration of a tissue solute that is dependent on anaerobic metabolism and that results in a resistance to greater quantities of tissue ice has been demonstrated in *M. demissus* (23, 24). Acclimation to temperatures between 0 and 5°C, or exposure to anaerobic conditions, caused a shift from an aerobic to an anaerobic metabolism and an increase in the concentration of calcium in the blood. This increase in calcium, the only tissue solute change associated with the increased resistance to greater quantities of tissue ice, could account for only 40% of the total increase in freezing resistance, demonstrating that the freezing resistance mechanism involves another important component or components. Since membranes are a primary target of freezing injury in mollusks and calcium increases the freezing resistance of *M. demissus* by interacting with cell membranes (24), an important structural change associated with the freezing resistance mechanism might involve cell membranes. Membrane distortion and subsequent disruption, which occur during extracellular ice formation, might be prevented by structural changes that produce an increase in the fluidity or elasticity of membranes during freezing. Similarily, an increase in tissue levels of glycerol occurs in the barnacle *B. balanoides* during the winter months when freezing resistance is greatest (4). However, we do not yet know whether these changes in glycerol levels are dependent on anaerobic metabolism or whether they indeed influence freezing resistance.

In addition to reductions in tissue levels of oxygen and the physiological changes associated with a shift from an aerobic to an anaerobic metabolism, the mechanism for increasing the resistance of *M. demissus* to greater quantities of tissue ice may also involve factors that reduce the effects of oxygen on freezing injury. Indeed, the possibility that oxygen is associated with injury following extracellular ice formation in intertidal invertebrates deserves further investigation. At present, the evidence for such an influence is indirect. It is based on the findings that reductions in the tissue levels of oxygen are correlated with lower lethal freezing temperatures in intertidal mollusks and that oxygen potentiates freezing injury in bacteria (37, 38). A relationship between oxygen and freezing damage to membranes has also been established by the finding that mitochondrial membranes are damaged following freezing and thawing by an oxygen-dependent process known as lipid peroxidation (42). Thus the physiological mechanism whereby inter-tidal invertebrates resist the formation of extracellular ice may involve increased production of factors that inhibit lipid peroxidation. Lipid peroxidation can be inhibited by antioxidants, and increasing freezing resistance may involve changes in the levels of (a) naturally occurring antioxidants such as alpha-tocopherol (Vitamin E) (22), ascorbic acid (Vitamin C) (15), and uric acid (1), or (b) enzymes such as glutathione peroxidase, catalase, and superoxide dismutase, which protect against lipid peroxidation and other oxidant stresses (10).

SUMMARY

Intertidal invertebrates survive exposures to temperatures as low as $-20°C$ by tolerating the presence of tissue ice. This resistance to freezing is in-fluenced by such factors as the time and temperature of exposure, the rate of cooling during tissue ice formation, the temperature and salinity of the seawater to which the animals have adapted, and the oxygen content of tissues. Freezing injury appears to result primarily from extracellular ice formation, although for certain smaller invertebrates that cool at rates exceeding $0.4°C$ min^{-1} during tissue ice formation, intracellular ice forma-tion may be the cause of freezing injury. Extracellular ice formation is a dehydration stress, and injury resulting from extracellular ice appears to involve membrane damage resulting from the loss of a critical amount of cellular water. Physiological mechanisms that lower the temperatures at which extracellular ice causes injury are dependent on factors that either (a) "bind" a certain fraction of intracellular water and thus reduce the amount of water lost during freezing, or (b) increase the resistance of cells to greater quantities of tissue ice. Certain structural components and glyco-proteins have been isolated from an intertidal mollusk that can impede or prevent the formation of ice. However, a quantitative relationship between these components and freezing resistance has not been established. The resistance to greater quantities of tissue ice appears to be associated with low levels of tissue oxygen and with anaerobic metabolism. A rise in blood calcium concentration following a shift from aerobic to anaerobic metabo-lism can account for part of the increased resistance of an intertidal mollusk to greater quantities of tissue ice, while membrane changes and factors that reduce the toxic effects of oxygen may also be involved. The possibility that oxygen is associated with injury resulting from extracellular ice formation in intertidal invertebrates deserves further investigation.

Literature Cited

1. Ames, B. N., Cathcart, R., Schwiers, E., Hochstein, P. 1981. Uric acid provides an antioxidant defense in humans against oxidant- and radical-caused aging and cancer: A hypothesis. *Proc. Natl. Acad. Sci. USA* 78:6858–62

2. Bank, H. 1973. Visualization of freezing damage. II. Structural alterations during warming. *Cryobiology* 10:157–70

3. Bloch, R., Walters, D. H., Kuhn, W. 1963. Structurally caused freezing point depression of biological tissues. *J. Gen. Physiol.* 46:605–15

4. Cook, P. A., Gabbot, P. A. 1970. Seasonal changes in free glycerol in the body parts of the adult barnacles (*Balanus balanoides*). *Mar. Biol.* 7:11–13

5. Cook, P. A., Lewis, A. H. 1971. Acquisition and loss of cold-tolerance in adult barnacles (*Balanus balanoides*) kept under laboratory conditions. *Mar. Biol.* 9:26–30

6. Crisp, D. J., Ritz, D. A. 1967. Changes in temperature tolerance of *Balanus balanoides* during its life cycle. *Heloländer Wiss. Meeresunters.* 15:98–115

7. DeVries, A. L., Wohlschlag, D. E. 1969. Freezing resistance in some antarctic fishes. *Science* 163:1073–75

8. Duman, J. G. 1977. The role of macromolecular antifreeze in the darkling beetle, *Meracantha contracta. J. Comp. Physiol.* 115:279–86

9. Feeney, R. E. 1974. A biological antifreeze. *Am. Sci.* 62:712–19

10. Halliwell, B. 1974. Superoxide dismutase, catalase and glutathione peroxidase: Solutions to the problems of living with oxygen. *New Phytol.* 73:1075–86

11. Huddart, H., Syson, A. J. 1975. The effect of caffeine on calcium efflux and calcium translocation in skeletal and visceral muscle. *J. Exp. Biol.* 63:131–42

12. Ibing, V. J., Theede, H. 1975. Zur Gefrierresistenz litoraler Mollusken von der deutschen Nordsee Kuste. *Kiel. Meeresforsch.* 31:44–48

13. Kanwisher, J. 1955. Freezing in intertidal animals. *Biol. Bull.* 109:56–63

14. Kanwisher, J. 1959. Histology and metabolism of frozen intertidal animals. *Biol. Bull.* 116:258–64

15. Leung, V., Vang, M. J., Mavis, R. D. 1981. The cooperative interaction between Vitamin E and Vitamin C in suppression of peroxidation of membrane phospholipids. *Biochim. Biophys. Acta* 664:266–72

16. Levitt, J. 1972. *Responses of Plants to Environmental Stresses*, pp. 45–66. NY: Academic. 250 pp.

17. Lovelock, J. E. 1953. The mechanism of the protective action of glycerol against hemolysis by freezing and thawing. *Biochim. Biophys. Acta* 11:28–36

18. Mazur, P. 1963. Kinetics of water loss from cells at subzero temperatures and the likelihood of intracellular freezing. *J. Gen. Physiol.* 47:347–69

19. Mazur, P. 1977. The role of intracellular freezing in the death of cells cooled at supraoptimal rates. *Cryobiology* 14:251–72

20. McGann, L. E., Kruuv, J., Frim, J., Frey, H. E. 1975. Factors affecting the repair of sublethal freeze-thaw damage in mammalian cells. I. Suboptimal temperature and hypoxia. *Cryobiology* 12:530–39

21. Meryman, H. T. 1971. Osmotic stress as a mechanism of freezing injury. *Cryobiology* 8:489–500

22. Molenaar, I., Vos, J., Hommes, F. A. 1972. Effect of Vitamin E. deficiency on cellular membranes. *Vitam. Horm. (NY)* 30:45–82

23. Murphy, D. J. 1977. Metabolic and tissue solute changes associated with changes in the freezing tolerance of the bivalve mollusc *Modiolus demissus. J. Exp. Biol.* 69:1–12

24. Murphy, D. J. 1977. A calcium-dependent mechanism responsible for increasing the freezing tolerance of the bivalve mollusc *Modiolus demissus. J. Exp. Biol.* 69:13–21

25. Murphy, D. J. 1979. A comparative study of the freezing tolerance of the marine snails *Littorina littorea* (L.) and *Nassarius obsoletus* (SAY). *Phys. Zool.* 52:219–30

26. Murphy, D. J. 1979. The relationship between the lethal freezing temperatures and the amounts of ice formed in the foot muscle of marine snails (Mollusca: gastropoda). *Cryobiology* 16:292–300

27. Murphy, D. J., Johnson, L. C. 1980. Physical and temporal factors influencing the freezing tolerance of the marine snail *Littoria littorea* (L.) *Biol. Bull.* 158:220–32

28. Murphy, D. J., McCausland, E. 1980. The relationship between freezing and desiccation tolerance in the marine snail *Ilyanassa obsoleta* (Stimpson). *Estuaries* 3:318–20

29. Murphy, D. J., Pierce, S. K. 1975. The physiological basis for changes in the freezing tolerance of intertidal mol-

luscs. I. Response to subfreezing temperatures and the influence of salinity and temperature acclimation. *J. Exp. Zool.* 193:313–22

30. Prosser, C. L. 1973. Excitable membranes. In *Comparative Animal Physiology,* ed. C. L. Prosser, pp. 457–504. Pennsylvania: W. B. Saunders. 970 pp.

31. Prosser, C. L. 1973. Muscles. See Ref. 30, pp. 730–34

32. Roland, W., Ring, R. A. 1977. Cold, freezing, and desiccation tolerance of the limpet *Acmaea digitalis* (Eschscholtz). *Cryobiology* 14:228–35

33. Somme, L. 1964. Effects of glycerol on cold-hardiness in insects. *Can. J. Zool.* 42:87–101

34. Somme, L. 1966. Seasonal changes in the freezing tolerance of some intertidal animals. *Nytt Mag. Zool.* 13:52–55

35. Somme, L. 1967. The effects of temperature and anoxia on haemolymph composition and supercooling in three overwintering insects. *J. Insect. Physiol.* 13:805–14

36. Stover, H. 1973. Cold resistance and freezing in *Arianta arbustorum* L. (Pulmonata). In *Effects of Temperature on Ectothermic Organisms,* ed. W. Wieser, pp. 281–90. NY: Springer

37. Swartz, H. M. 1970. Effect of oxygen on freezing damage: I. Effect on survival of *Escherichia coli* B/r and *Escherichia coli* Bs-1. *Cryobiology* 6:546–51

38. Swartz, H. M. 1972. Effect of oxygen on freezing damage: II. Physical-chemical effects. *Cryobiology* 8:255–64

39. Theede, H. 1972. Vergleichende ökologisch-physiologische Untersuchungen zur zellularen Kalteresistenz mariner Evertebraten. *Mar. Biol.* 15:160–91

40. Theede, H., Lassig, J. 1967. Comparative studies on cellular resistance of bivalves from marine and brackish waters. *Helgol. Wiss. Meeresunters.* 16:119–29

41. Theede, H., Schneppenheim, R., Beress, L. 1976. Frostschutzglykoproteine bei *Mytilus edulis.* 36:183–89

42. Vladimirov, Y. A., Olenev, V. I., Suslova, T. B., Cheremisina, Z. P. 1980. Lipid peroxidation in mitochondrial membrane. *Adv. Lipid Res.* 17:173–249

43. Weyl, P. K. 1970. *Oceanography: An Introduction to the Marine Environment,* pp. 238–48. NY: Wiley. 535 pp.

44. Williams, R. J. 1970. Freezing tolerance in *Mytilus edulis. Comp. Biochem. Physiol.* 35:145–61

CELL AND MEMBRANE PHYSIOLOGY

Introduction, Joseph F. Hoffman, *Section Editor*

"The calcium ion has an unusual importance in biological phenomena, and the literature concerning its effects is extremely voluminous." That this statement, written more than 30 years ago (1), also describes the situation today was certainly expected if not anticipated by L. V. Heilbrunn, whose text on general physiology highlights the then known numerous and critical roles performed by calcium in living organisms. While progress has surged, we have yet, regardless of appearances, to reach an "Age of Calcium," wherein calcium might be a physiologist's equivalent of DNA. Even so, there have been remarkable advances in detailing many of the molecular processes by which calcium exerts its variety of effects. This year's Cell and Membrane Physiology section surveys not only permeability mechanisms by which the cellular level of calcium is regulated but also some of the actions that calcium has in modifying membrane properties and in modulating cellular functions. Of the following articles, each in its own way emphasizes current aspects and some of the exciting developments that are taking place in the field. While the coverage could not possibly be comprehensive, we hope that in future years this area will be updated as well as expanded.

Literature Cited

1. Heilbrunn, L. V. 1952. *An Outline of General Physiology.* Philadelphia: W. B. Saunders

Ann. Rev. Physiol. 1983. 45:303–12

THE RED CELL CALCIUM PUMP

H. J. Schatzmann

Department of Veterinary Pharmacology, University of Bern, Switzerland

The reader who finds the following chapter exasperatingly brief is referred to more extensive recent reviews (50, 51, 59, 61, 72).

GENERAL PROPERTIES

The ability of the human red cell to extrude Ca^{2+} ions against a gradient by a mechanism that depends directly on ATP (57) was taken at the time of its discovery as a curiosity. However, this Ca pump is an attribute of the plasma membrane not only in red cells from pigs, dogs, cattle, birds, and humans, but probably in all animal cells (59). The following deals with the Ca pump of human red cells.

At saturating Ca^{2+} concentration the cells transport some 10 mmoles per liter of cells per hour, which is 200–1000 times their passive permeability to Ca^{2+} (11, 27a). At the physiological permeability the pump maintains a gradient of almost 10,000 (58), such that the intracellular Ca^{2+} concentration is $< 4 \times 10^{-7}$ M (27a, 63). In membranes isolated in Ca^{2+}-containing media it presents itself as an "ATPase" (requiring free Mg^{2+} ions) that is stimulated by Ca^{2+} with a K^{app}_{Ca} of ~ 1 μM or less (6) depending on the pH; it has 2 ATP-accepting sites of vastly differing affinity (K^{app}_{1} 1–3.5 μM; K^{app}_{2} 120–330 μM) (33–35, 42, 65). The ATP and Mg^{2+} sites are situated on the internal membrane surface, and inorganic phosphate is liberated internally (62).

In Na^+- or K^+-containing media the rate of transport and ATP hydrolysis is 30–50% higher than in tris-Cl or choline-Cl media. The affinities for

0066-4278/83/0315-0303$02.00

this effect are definitely unequal ($K_{Na} = 30$; $K_K = 6$ mM). The sidedness of the Na-K-action is as yet unclear (45, 46, 76).

It was recently shown that Ca^{2+} transport is slowed if no permeant anion is present to accompany Ca^{2+} (18, 74, 75) and that under such conditions Ca^{2+} is exchanged for a suitable cation (49). Taken together these observations can only mean that the system is electrogenic, or that it exchanges Ca^{2+} for protons (37a).

Membrane preparation procedures may cause artefacts by altering accessibility of ligand sites (6, 7). Such may also be the case for the use of EGTA-Ca buffers (35, 51, 59). An elegant way to study ATPase *and* transport is offered by inside-out vesicles (54).

CHEMICAL CONSTITUTION

Lipid Requirement

Any glycerophospholipid in the inner membrane leaflet sustains function (43, 44) in the presence of calmodulin. Acidic lipids can replace calmodulin (see below).

Isolation

The protein is phosphorylated rapidly at 0°C from [γ-^{32}P]–ATP under the influence of Ca^{2+} (24), much as the Na-pump protein is phosphorylated under the influence of Na^+. This property was useful in tracing the protein during successful isolation procedures. Wolf and co-workers (28, 29, 77) isolated three proteins from the bulk of solubilized membranes by gel-filtration chromatography. One of them of mol wt 145,000 showed the characteristic rapid, Ca^{2+}-requiring phosphorylation (28, 29) and displayed Ca^{2+}, Mg^{2+}-ATPase activity with the expected affinities as well. With a similar procedure Haaker & Racker (21) obtained from porcine red cells a protein capable of Ca^{2+} transport.

These achievements were superseded when Niggli et al (5, 36, 37) and Gietzen et al. (15) used Sepharose-4B-coupled calmodulin to trap the solubilized pump protein on a column in the presence of Ca^{2+}, washed off all other proteins, and eluted it with EGTA-solution, having phospholipids present throughout. Both methods yield a more than 90% pure protein which, when combined with phospholipid micelles on the column, functions as ATPase. Occasionally one obtains an additional heavier protein, possibly a dimer, and a 90,000 protein in small quantity that might be the product of proteolytic activity during preparation. The protein is identified as the pump by the monomeric mol wt of 130–140,000; the specific, Ca^{2+}-dependent rapid phosphorylation (28, 29, 37, 65); and its Ca^{2+}, Mg^{2+}-ATPase function, with two sites for ATP (65) and affinities for Ca^{2+} (if calmodulin is added) and Mg^{2+} similar to those found in membranes (65). Finally, it performs ATP-dependent uphill transport of Ca^{2+} when incorporated into artificial lipid vesicles (5, 64).

ATP phosphorylates an acyl group [the product is acid-stable but sensitive to hydroxylamine (29, 40, 77)]. It is probable that the enzyme undergoes conformational changes during the transport cycle since the physiological ligands Ca^{2+}, Mg^{2+}, and ATP modify the inhibitory action of N-ethylmaleimide (NEM) (3, 31) or the efficacy on function of proteolytic attack (3).

Calmodulin Dependence

The cytosol of red cells contains 3–5 μM calmodulin (12). Calmodulin is an acidic, Ca^{2+}-binding, fairly heat-stable, water soluble protein of 16,700 mol wt, apparently present in all living cells. It has four metal-binding sites whose affinity for Ca^{2+} ($K_{Ca} \sim$ a few μM) exceeds that for Mg^{2+} by far.

Bond & Clough (4) early found a proteinaceous activator for the Ca pump in the cytosol of red cells. This activator is calmodulin. Vincenzi and co-workers (19, 25, 72, 73) were first to show that calmodulin can activate the Ca pump. One aspect of activation is an increase in apparent affinity of (one of) the Ca^{2+} sites involved in Ca^{2+} transport. This effect explains the vastly diverging Ca^{2+} affinities reported in the early literature on the Ca pump. Scharff & Foder's work gives short shrift to a confused discussion. They showed that calmodulin lowers K_{Ca}^{app} by a factor of about 30 and at the same time raises V_{max} and that complete removal of calmodulin does not abolish the activation by Ca^{2+} completely (56; see also 34, 35, 78). A basal activity at elevated Ca^{2+} concentration is also observed in the pump protein virtually free of calmodulin [less than 1 molecule for 400 molecules (K. Gietzen, personal communication)] coming from a calmodulin column. Ca-calmodulin undoubtedly binds to the pump protein (15, 23, 36, 37) with a K_{diss} of 2–15 nM at μmolar Ca^{2+} concentrations. Foder & Scharff have shown it probable that there is one binding site for calmodulin on the pump protein (12). It seems that the highest affinity of calmodulin for the pump protein is obtained when calmodulin is occupied by Ca^{2+} at 3 of its 4 metal-binding sites (the fourth being combined with Mg^{2+}) (55). At physiological intracellular Ca^{2+}, Mg^{2+}, and calmodulin concentration the pump-calmodulin complex dissociates (12). Binding of calmodulin seems to be a relatively slow process (7, 35, 56).

Mild trypsin digestion mimics the action of calmodulin (52, 70). Calmodulin no longer binds after digestion, and the molecular weight of the phosphorylated intermediate drops by about 30,000 (9). In the purified protein a single peptide of 30–40,000 is removed and the Ca^{2+}-Mg^{2+}-dependence of the digested preparation is identical to that of the calmodulin-replete system, including that in the inhibitory Ca^{2+} range (66). The inhibition by Ca^{2+} may be due to competition of Ca^{2+} with Mg^{2+} or CaATP with MgATP (35). Thus (a) calmodulin is not required for Ca^{2+} transport; (b) Ca^{2+} bound to calmodulin is not the Ca^{2+} transported; and (c) the inhibitory action of Ca^{2+} is not on calmodulin, but on the main protein. Similar conclusions are borne out by the fact that acidic lipids such as phosphatidylserine, unsaturated fatty acids and cardiolipin (5, 36, 65), and even certain detergents such as Triton X-100 can substitute for calmodulin in conferring high Ca^{2+} affinity to the system. It remains to be seen if the 30–40,000 peptide carries the calmodulin binding site. Be that as it may, its restraining action is abolished by calmodulin.

Recently a second activator protein, distinct from calmodulin, was found (32).

The Cytosolic Inhibitor

Several authors showed that the red cell cytosol also exhibits an inhibitory activity (1, 26, 54, 78). It is associated with a small protein (mol wt 19,000), which has been purified to homogeneity (78). Its action is the mirror image of that of calmodulin, and its calmodulin antagonism is complex (78).

REACTION CYCLE

The reaction cycle is depicted in Figure 1. Phosphorylation-dephosphorylation can be studied at 0°C using $[\gamma^{32}P]$-ATP. Dephosphorylation appears separately if the phosphorylation is stopped by diluting with unlabeled ATP or by removal of Ca^{2+} with EGTA or the like.

Ca^{2+} alone is required for *phosphorylation.* Thus Mg-ATP is not the obligatory substrate. It was recently made probable that MgATP can be the substrate (8, 53), but without Mg^{2+} there is a low ATPase activity (20, 38) sustained by free ATP or CaATP (see also 35). K^{app} for total ATP has been found to be 1.4–2.7 μM (at 2 mM Mg^{2+}) (31, 34) or 2.5 μM (at zero Mg^{2+})(31; see also 33, 42).

ATP at high concentration ($\geq$ 100 μM) accelerates *dephosphorylation.* This is in accord with the finding of two ATP-affinities in the ATPase reaction and in Ca^{2+} transport (see above). The postulate of two conformational forms of the phosphorylated intermediate ($E_1{\sim}P$, $E_2{-}P$) and of the requirement of Mg^{2+} ($K_{Mg} \sim 10$ μM) for their interconversion is based on the observation by Garrahan and Rega (13) that ATP accelerates dephosphorylation only if Mg^{2+} is present or if Mg^{2+} has been present before addition of ATP (they removed Mg^{2+} with CDTA). We find that Mg^{2+} must be present together with ATP (31). We interpret this to mean that in our preparation for some unknown reason MgATP rather than free ATP is required at 0°C, as seems to be the case for the calmodulin replete system at 37°C (35); otherwise the concept of Garrahan & Rega is correct. The reasons for not abandoning the $E_1 \sim P$ Mg^{2+} E_2-P transition are: (a) Function increases with the MgATP concentration with a $K\frac{1}{2} \sim 10 \mu M$ (8) or $\sim 300 \mu M$ (35), which is much higher than K_{MgATP}^{app} at the enzymic site and argues for a requirement of MgATP in dephosphorylation. (b) La^{3+} seems to block precisely at reaction II (Figure 1) for the following reason: With La^{3+} (0.2 mM) dephosphorylation in the forward direction is impossible, but the back reaction (with excess ADP) is rapid (31, 60, 67). If La^{3+} is added after phosphorylation has proceeded in the absence of Mg^{2+}, addition of ATP (0.5 mM) and Mg^{2+} (1 mM) initiates a negligible drop in phosphorylated intermediate. If Mg^{2+} is already present during phosphorylation, the drop in phosphorylated intermediate caused by ATP (+ Mg^{2+}) is not prevented by La^{3+} added prior to ATP (30).

The whole process is reversible. Under a high Ca^{2+} gradient the system produces (slowly) ATP from ADP and phosphate (47, 80).

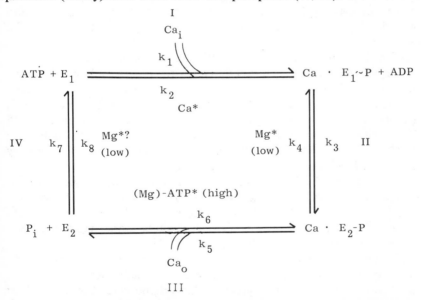

Figure 1   The reaction cycle of the human red cell calcium pump. The protein splits ATP by cycling through two conformational states (E_1 and E_2) in the clockwise direction. Phosphorylation from ATP of E_1 at an acyl group initiates the cycle. This step requires Ca^{2+}. $E_1 \sim P \rightarrow E_2 - P$ requires Mg^{2+}. Dephosphorylation requires high ATP (or MgATP) concentration ($\geqslant 100 \mu M$). Internal Ca^{2+} is bound to the protein before phosphorylation. E_1, therefore, is the form presenting the Ca^{2+}-binding site to the internal membrane surface. Ca^{2+} release into the external medium may occur upon dephosphorylation. Asterisks indicate the requirements of the partial reactions. For concentration dependences see text.

It seems quite possible (but has not been proven directly) that the translocation step for $Ca^{2+}_i \longrightarrow Ca^{2+}_o$ is concomitant with the $E_1 \sim P \longrightarrow E_2-P$ transition: La^{3+} is inhibitory from inside or outside and does not penetrate the membrane (39, 67, 68). It is natural, therefore, to assume that it binds to the Ca^{2+} transport site and blocks transmembrane movement of this site. It also blocks selectively the conformational transition $E_1 \sim P \longrightarrow E_2-P$ (see above)—i.e. some spatial rearrangement. For the sarcoplasmic reticulum it was recently shown that release of Ca^{2+} is concomitant with dephosphorylation (69). This might be similar in the red cell Ca pump and would mean that the reorientation of the Ca^{2+} carrying site and the affinity drop for Ca^{2+} are not simultaneous.

There is good evidence for involvement of 2 Ca^{2+} ions in the cycle (6, 10, 51). However, it is still unclear whether both are transported. Sarkadi found that the stoichiometric ratio (Ca transported: ATP hydrolysed) in inside-out vesicles rises with increasing Ca^{2+} concentration (0.1 – 1 mM) from 0.3 to 2 (51) and Akyempon & Roufogalis (1) reported the opposite behavior at 6.4 mM $MgCl_2$. Direct measurement in resealed ghosts gave a ratio of 1 (58, 62). The transport inhibitable by external La^{3+} has a ratio of 2 (39).

With the help of La^{3+}, reaction I (Figure 1) can be studied as a simple equilibrium (31). From such experiments with whole membranes k_1 seems to be 7.5×10^4, $k_2 = 4 \times 10^6$ ($M^{-1}sec^{-1}$) or $K_{eq} = 1.8 \times 10^{-2}$. Thus $E_1 \sim$ P-formation is endergonic (+ 9 kJ/mole), and $E_1 \sim P \longrightarrow E_2-P \longrightarrow E_2 + P_i$ is consequently strongly exergonic (– 38.6 kJ/mole). A compound $\overleftarrow{k} = 0.38$ for the latter was approximated from the rate of dephosphorylation (with Mg^{2+}), and $\overleftarrow{k} = 1.5 \times 10^{-8}$ was obtained from this and the known energy drop from $E_1 \sim P$ to $E_2 + P_i$. It is likely that the equilibrium II (Figure 1) is poised towards E_2-P (with Mg^{2+} present) (30). At physiological concentrations of ATP, ADP, P_i, and Mg^{2+} (0°C) less than 10% of the enzyme is in the phosphorylated form (31). The apparent acceleration of phosphorylation in the steady-state by Mg^{2+} (13, 31) might be ascribed to acceleration of reaction II [and possibly IV (Figure 1) (35)].

The action of calmodulin is complex. It was observed to increase phosphorylation and dephosphorylation rate about equally in the presence of Mg^{2+} at 0°C (9, 34, 35, 41), which explains its positive effect on V_{max} of the ATPase at all temperatures. It increases the affinity for Ca^{2+} and for ATP at the enzymic site at 37°C (34). With calmodulin at 37°C the system has a requirement for high MgATP concentration at the site accelerating dephosphorylation (34), and CaATP antagonizes MgATP in this function (35); whereas without calmodulin (at 0°C) high *free* ATP in the presence of low (10 μM) Mg^{2+} concentration brings about rapid dephosphorylation (35).

INHIBITORS

For La^{3+}, see above. Vanadate ([VO$_3$(OH)]$^{2-}$) is interesting in being potentiated by Mg^{2+} and K$^+$ (2, 64) and antagonized by external Ca^{2+} (48). It has no effect on dephosphorylation, but reduces the steady-state phosphorylated intermediate (31) and thus might block E$_2$⟶E$_1$ as suggested by its chemical similarity to phosphate. Phenothiazine neuroleptics and butyrophenones that bind to Ca-calmodulin (27) have been claimed to block selectively the calmodulin activation (14, 22); this, however, is not the case [the calmodulin free system activated by trypsin treatment is inhibited at nearly the same concentration of trifluoperazine as the calmodulin replete system (64)]. Vinca alkaloids have a certain specificity for the calmodulin-activated part (17). A novel inhibitor for calmodulin-activated enzymes, calmidazolium (R 24571) (71), is also active on the Ca pump (16). It has at least a 100-fold higher affinity for the Ca pump than for the Na-K pump. Quercetin (79) and phloretin (54) are inhibitory, as are ruthenium red and sulphydryl reagents. [NEM blocks phosphorylation and not the E$_1$~P E$_2$-P transition (31) as in the Na-K pump, and its action is strongly dependent on the physiological ligands Ca^{2+}, ATP, and Mg^{2+} (3, 31).] 4-Chloromercuribenzoic acid is reversibly inhibitory without affecting the affinity for Ca^{2+} or ATP (52). Suramin-Na is equally potent on the Ca pump and on the Na pump (H. J. Schatzmann, unpublished) with a $I_{1/2}$ of ~50 μM.

Literature Cited

1. Akyempon, C. K., Roufogalis, B. D. 1982. The stoichiometry of the Ca^{2+} pump in human erythrocyte vesicles: Modulation by Ca^{2+}, Mg^{2+}, and calmodulin. *Cell Calcium* 3:1–17
1a. Au, K. S., Lee, K. S. 1980. An endogenous inhibitor of erythrocyte (Ca^{2+} + Mg^{2+})-ATPase involved in calcium transport. *Int. J. Biochem.* 11:177–81
2. Barrabin, H., Garrahan, P. J., Rega, A. F. 1980. Vanadate inhibition of the Ca^{2+}-ATPase from human red cell membranes. *Biochim. Biophys. Acta* 600:796–804
3. Bond, G. H. 1972. Ligand-induced conformational changes in the (Mg^{2+} + Ca^{2+})-dependent ATPase of red cell membranes. *Biochim. Biophys. Acta* 288:423–38
4. Bond, G. H., Clough, D. L. 1973. A soluble protein activator of (Ca^{2+} + Mg^{2+})-dependent ATPase in human red cell membranes. *Biochim. Biophys. Acta* 323:592–99

5. Carafoli, E., Niggli, V. 1981. Purification and reconstitution of the calcium, magnesium adenosine triphosphatase of the erythrocyte membrane. *Ann. NY Acad. Sci.* 358:159–68
6. Downes, P., Michell, R. H. 1981. Human erythrocyte membranes exhibit a cooperative, calmodulin-dependent Ca^{2+}-ATPase of high calcium sensitivity. *Nature* 290:270–71
7. Downes, C. P., Simmonds, S. H., Michell, R. H. 1981. Apparent variation in the activation characteristics of human erythrocyte membrane Ca^{2+}-pump ATPase may be caused by variable membrane permeability. *Cell Calcium* 2: 473–82
8. Enyedi, A., Sarkadi, B., Gardos, G. 1982. On the substrate specificity of the red cell calcium pump. *Biochim. Biophys. Acta* 687:109–12
9. Enyedi, A., Sarkadi, B., Szasz, I., Bot, G., Gardos, G. 1980. Molecular properties of the red cell calcium pump II. *Cell Calcium* 1:299–310

10. Ferreira, H. G., Lew, V. L. 1976. Use of ionophore A 23187 to measure cytoplasmic Ca buffering and activation of the Ca pump by internal Ca. *Nature* 259:47–49

11. Ferreira, H. G., Lew, V. L. 1977. Passive Ca transport and cytoplasmic Ca-buffering in intact red cells. In *Membrane Transport in Red Cells*, ed. J. C. Ellory, V. L. Lew, pp. 53–91. NY: Academic

12. Foder, B., Scharff, O. 1981. Decrease of apparent calmodulin affinity of erythrocyte (Ca^{2+} + Mg^{2+})-ATPase at low Ca^{2+} concentrations. *Biochim. Biophys. Acta* 649:367–76

13. Garrahan, P. J., Rega, A. F. 1978. Activation of partial reactions of the Ca^{2+}-ATPase from human red cells by Mg^{2+} and ATP. *Biochim. Biophys. Acta* 513:59–65

14. Gietzen, K., Mansard, A., Bader, H. 1980. Inhibition of human erythrocyte Ca^{2+}-transport ATPase by phenothiazines and butyrophenones. *Biochem. Biophys. Res. Commun.* 94:674–81

15. Gietzen, K., Tejcka, M., Wolf, H. U. 1980. Calmodulin affinity chromatography yields a functional purified erythrocyte (Ca^{2+} + Mg^{2+})-dependent adenosine triphosphatase. *Biochem. J.* 189:81–88

16. Gietzen, K., Wüthrich, A., Bader, H. 1981. R 24571: A new powerful inhibitor of red blood cell Ca^{++} transport ATP-ase and of calmodulin-regulated functions. *Biochem. Biophys. Res. Commun.* 101:418–25

17. Gietzen, K., Wüthrich, A., Mansard, A., Bader, H. 1980. Effects of Vinca alkaloids on calmodulin dependent Ca^{2+} transport ATPase. In *Proc. Int. Vinca Alkaloid Symp.*, ed. W. Brade, G. A. Nagel, S. Seeber, pp. 16–26. Basel: Karger

18. Gimble, J. M., Goodman, D. B. P., Rasmussen, H. 1981. Comparison of the Ca-Mg-ATPase and calcium transport in rat and human erythrocytes: Evidence for an electrogenic mechanism. *Cell Calcium* 2:525–43

19. Gopinath, R. M., Vincenzi, F. F. 1977. Phosphodiesterase protein activator mimics red blood cell cytoplasmic activator of (Ca^{2+} + Mg^{2+})-ATPase. *Biochem. Biophys. Res. Commun.* 77:1203–9

20. Graf, E., Penniston, J. T. 1981. CaATP: The substrate, at low ATP concentrations, of Ca^{2+}-ATPase from human erythrocyte membranes. *J. Biol. Chem.* 256:1587–92

21. Haaker, H., Racker, E. 1979. Purification and reconstitution of the Ca^{2+}-ATPase from plasma membranes of pig erythrocytes. *J. Biol. Chem.* 254:6598–602

22. Hinds, T. R., Raess, B. U., Vincenzi, F. F. 1980. Plasma membrane Ca^{2+} transport: Antagonism by several potential inhibitors. *J. Membr. Biol.* 58:57–65

23. Jarrett, H. W., Kyte, J. 1979. Human erythrocyte calmodulin. Further chemical characterization and the site of its interaction with the membrane. *J. Biol. Chem.* 254:8237–44

24. Knauf, P. A., Proverbio, F., Hoffman, J. F. 1974. Electrophoretic separation of different phosphoproteins associated with Ca-ATPase and Na-K-ATPase in human red cell ghosts. *J. Gen. Physiol.* 63:324–36

25. Larsen, F. L., Vincenzi, F. F. 1979. Calcium transport across the plasma membrane: Stimulation by calmodulin. *Science* 204:306–8

26. Lee, K. S., Au, K. S. 1981. Inhibitor protein of pig erythrocyte membrane (Ca^{2+} + Mg^{2+})-ATPase. *Biochem. Soc. Trans.* 9 (2):132P

27. Levin, R. M., Weiss, B. 1979. Selective binding of antipsychotics and other psychoactive agents to the calcium-dependent activator of cyclic nucleotide phosphodiesterase. *J. Pharmacol. Exp. Ther.* 208:454–59

27a. Lew, V. L., Tsien, R. Y., Miner, C. 1982. The physiological $[Ca^{2+}]_i$ level and pump-leak turnover in intact red cells measured with the use of an incorporated Ca chelator. *Nature* 298:478–81

28. Lichtner, R., Wolf, H. U. 1980. Phosphorylation of the isolated high-affinity (Ca^{2+} + Mg^{2+})-ATPase of the human erythrocyte membrane. *Biochim. Biophys. Acta* 598:472–85

29. Lichtner, R., Wolf, H. U. 1980. Characterization of the phosphorylated intermediate of the isolated high-affinity (Ca^{2+} + Mg^{2+})-ATPase of human erythrocyte membranes. *Biochim. Biophys. Acta* 598:486–93

30. Luterbacher, S., Schatzmann, H. J. 1983. *Experientia.* In press

31. Luterbacher, S. 1982. *Die Teilreaktionen der ATP-Spaltung durch das isolierte Protein der Ca^{2+}-Pumpe aus der Erythrozytenmembran.* Thesis, Univ. Bern

32. Mauldin, D., Roufogalis, B. D. 1980. A protein activator of Mg^{2+}-dependent, Ca^{2+}-stimulated ATPase in human ery-

throcyte membranes distinct from calmodulin. *Biochem. J.* 187:507–13

33. Muallem, S., Karlish, S. J. D. 1979. Is the red cell calcium pump regulated by ATP? *Nature* 277:238–40

34. Muallem, S., Karlish, S. J. D. 1980. Regulatory interaction between calmodulin and ATP on the red blood cell Ca^{2+}-pump. *Biochim. Biophys. Acta* 597:631–36

35. Muallem, S., Karlish, S. J. D. 1981. Studies on the mechanism of regulation of the red cell Ca^{2+}-pump by calmodulin and ATP. *Biochim. Biophys. Acta* 647:73–86

36. Niggli, V., Adunyah, E. S., Penniston, J. F., Carafoli, E. 1981. Purified (Ca^{2+} + Mg^{2+})-ATPase of the erythrocyte membrane: Reconstitution and effect of calmodulin and phospholipids. *J. Biol. Chem.* 256:395–401

37. Niggli, V., Penniston, J. T., Carafoli, E. 1979. Purification of the (Ca^{2+} + Mg^{2+})-ATPase from human erythrocyte membranes using a calmodulin affinity column. *J. Biol. Chem.* 254: 9955–58

37a. Niggli, V., Sigel, E., Carafoli, E. 1982. The purified Ca^{2+}-pump of human erythrocyte membranes catalyzes an electroneutral Ca^{2+}-H^+ exchange in reconstituted liposomal systems. *J. Biol. Chem.* 257:2350–56

38. Penniston, J. T. 1982. Substrate specificity of the erythrocyte Ca^{2+}-ATPase. *Biochim. Biophys. Acta.* 688:735–39

39. Quist, E., Roufogalis, B. D. 1975. Determination of the stoichiometry of the calcium pump in human erythrocytes using lanthanum as selective inhibitor. *FEBS Lett.* 50:135–39

40. Rega, A. F., Garrahan, P. J. 1975. Calcium ion-dependent phosphorylation of human erythrocyte membranes. *J. Membr. Biol.* 22:313–27

41. Rega, A. F., Garrahan, P. J. 1980. Effects of calmodulin on the phosphoenzyme of Ca^{2+}-ATPase of human red cell membranes. *Biochim. Biophys. Acta* 596:487–89

42. Richards, D. E., Rega, A. F., Garrahan, P. J. 1978. Two classes of sites for ATP in the Ca^{2+}-ATPase from human red cell membranes. *Biochim. Biophys. Acta* 511:194–201

43. Roelofsen, B. 1981. The (non)specificity in the lipid requirement of calcium- and (sodium plus potassium)-transporting adenosine triphosphatases. *Life Sci.* 29:2235–47

44. Roelofsen, B., Schatzmann, H. J. 1977. The lipid requirement of the (Ca^{2+} +

Mg^{2+})-ATPase in the human erythrocyte membrane, as studied by various highly purified phospholipases. *Biochim. Biophys. Acta* 464:17–36

45. Romero, P. J. 1981. Active calcium transport in red cell ghosts resealed in dextran solutions. *Biochim. Biophys. Acta* 649:404–18

46. Romero, P. J. 1981. The activation of the calcium pump of human erythrocyte ghosts by external sodium or potassium. *Adv. Physiol. Sci.* 6:189–94

47. Rossi, J. P. F. C., Garrahan, P. J., Rega, A. F. 1978. Reversal of the calcium pump in human red cells. *J. Membr. Biol.* 44:37–46

48. Rossi, J. P. F. C., Garrahan, P. J., Rega, A. F. 1981. Vanadate inhibition of active Ca^{2+}-transport across human red cell membranes. *Biochim. Biophys. Acta* 648:145–50

49. Rossi, J. P. F. C., Schatzmann, H. J. 1982. Is the red cell calcium pump electrogenic? *J. Physiol.* 327:1–15

50. Roufogalis, B. D. 1979. Regulation of calcium translocation across the red blood cell membrane. *Can. J. Physiol.* 57:1331–49

51. Sarkadi, B. 1980. Active calcium transport in human red cells. *Biochim. Biophys. Acta* 604:159–90

52. Sarkadi, B., Enyedi, A., Gardos, G. 1980. Molecular properties of the red cell calcium pump I. *Cell Calcium* 1:287–97

53. Sarkadi, B., Enyedi, A., Gardos, G. 1981. Metal-ATP complexes as substrates and free metal ions as activators of the red cell calcium pump. *Cell Calcium* 2:449–58

54. Sarkadi, B., Szasz, I., Gardos, G. 1980. Characteristics and regulation of active calcium transport in inside-out red cell membrane vesicles. *Biochim. Biophys. Acta* 598:326–38

55. Scharff, O. 1980. Kinetics of calcium-dependent membrane ATPase in human erythrocytes. In *Membrane Transport in Erythrocytes,* ed. U. V. Lassen, H. H. Ussing, J. O. Wieth, pp. 236–48. Copenhagen: Munksgaard

56. Scharff, O., Foder, B. 1978. Reversible shift between two states of Ca^{2+}-ATPase in human erythrocytes mediated by Ca^{2+} and a membrane bound activator. *Biochim. Biophys. Acta* 509: 67–77

57. Schatzmann, H. J. 1966. ATP-dependent Ca^{2+}-extrusion from human red cells. *Experientia* 22:364–68

58. Schatzmann, H. J. 1973. Dependence on calcium concentration and stoichi-

ometry of the calcium pump in human red cells. *J. Physiol.* 235:551–69

59. Schatzmann, H. J. 1982. The plasma membrane calcium pump of erythrocytes and other animal cells. In *Membrane Transport of Calcium,* ed. E. Carafoli, pp. 41–108. NY: Academic

60. Schatzmann, H. J., Bürgin, H. 1978. Calcium in human red blood cells. *Ann. NY Acad. Sci.* 307:125–47

61. Schatzmann, H. J., Bürgin, H., Luterbacher, S., Stieger, J., Wüthrich, A., Rossi, J. P. 1982. How to keep cellular calcium low. The red cell as an example. In *INSERM Eur. Symp. Horm. Cell Regul.,* ed. J. E. Dumont, J. Nunez, G. Schultz, 6:13–25. Amsterdam: Elsevier North Holland Biomedical Press

62. Schatzmann, H. J., Roelofsen, B. 1977. Some aspect of the Ca-pump in human red blood cells. In *Biochemistry of Membrane Transport,* ed. G. Semenza, E. Carafoli, pp. 389–400. NY: Springer

63. Simons, T. J. B. 1982. A method for estimating free Ca within human red blood cells with an application to the study of the Ca-dependent K-permeability. *J. Membr. Biol.* 66:235–47

64. Stieger, J. 1982. *Charakterisierung und Rekonstitution der isolierten (Ca²⁺ + Mg²⁺)-ATPase aus Erythrocytenmembranen.* Thesis, Univ. Bern

65. Stieger, J., Luterbacher, S. 1981. Some properties of the purified (Ca²⁺ + Mg²⁺)-ATPase from human red cell membranes. *Biochim. Biophys. Acta* 641:270–75

66. Stieger, J., Schatzmann, H. J. 1981. Metal requirement of the isolated red cell Ca²⁺-pump ATPase after elimination of calmodulin dependence by trypsin attack. *Cell Calcium* 2:601–16

67. Szasz, I., Hasitz, M., Sarkadi, B., Gardos, G. 1978. Phosphorylation of the Ca²⁺-pump intermediate in intact cells, isolated membranes and inside-out vesicles. *Molec. Cell. Biochem.* 22:147–52

68. Szasz, I., Sarkadi, B., Schubert, A., Gardos, G. 1978. Effects of lanthanum on calcium dependent phenomena in human red cells. *Biochim. Biophys. Acta* 512:331–40

69. Takisawa, H., Makinose, M. 1981. Occluded bound calcium on the phosphorylated sarcoplasmic transport ATPase. *Nature* 290:271–73

70. Taverna, R. D., Hanahan, D. J. 1980. Modulation of human erythrocyte (Ca²⁺ + Mg²⁺)-ATPase activity by phospholipase A₂ and proteases. A comparison with calmodulin. *Biochem. Biophys. Res. Commun.* 94:652–59

71. Van Belle, H. 1981. R 24571: A potent inhibitor of calmodulin-activated enzymes. *Cell Calcium* 2:483–94

72. Vincenzi, F. F., Hinds, T. R. 1980. Calmodulin and plasma membrane calcium transport. In *Calcium and Cell Function,* ed. W. Y. Cheung, 1:127–65. NY: Academic

73. Vincenzi, F. F., Larsen, F. L. 1980. The plasma membrane calcium pump: regulation by a soluble Ca²⁺-binding protein. *Fed. Proc.* 39:2427–31

74. Waisman, D. M., Gimble, J. M., Goodman, D. B. P., Rasmussen, H. 1981. Studies of the Ca²⁺ transport mechanism of human erythrocyte inside-out plasma membrane vesicles. II. Stimulation of the pump by phosphate. *J. Biol. Chem.* 256:415–19

75. Waisman, D. M., Gimble, J. M., Goodman, D. B. P., Rasmussen, H. 1981. Studies of the Ca²⁺ transport mechanism of human erythrocyte inside-out plasma membrane vesicles. III. Stimulation of the Ca²⁺-pump by anions. *J. Biol. Chem.* 256:420–24

76. Wierichs, R., Bader, H. 1980. Influence of monovalent ions on the activity of the (Ca²⁺ + Mg²⁺)-ATPase and Ca²⁺ transport of human red blood cells. *Biochim. Biophys. Acta* 596:325–28

77. Wolf, H. U., Dieckvoss, G., Lichtner, R. 1977. Purification and properties of high-affinity Ca²⁺-ATPase of human erythrocyte membranes. *Acta Biol. Germ.* 36:847–58

78. Wüthrich, A. 1982. Isolation from haemolysate of a proteinaceous inhibitor of the red cell Ca²⁺-pump ATPase. Its action on the kinetics of the enzyme. *Cell Calcium.* 3:201–14

79. Wüthrich, A., Schatzmann, H. J. 1980. Inhibition of the red cell calcium pump by quercetin. *Cell Calcium* 1:21–35

80. Wüthrich, A., Schatzmann, H. J., Romero, P. 1979. Net ATP synthesis by running the red cell Ca-pump backwards. *Experientia* 35:1589–90

Ann. Rev. Physiol. 1983. 45:313–24
Copyright © 1983 by Annual Reviews Inc. All rights reserved

THE CALCIUM PUMP AND SODIUM-CALCIUM EXCHANGE IN SQUID AXONS

R. DiPolo

Laboratorio de Permeabilidad Iónica, Centro de Biofísica y Bioquímica, Instituto Venezolano de Investigaciones Científicas, Apartado 1827, Caracas 1010A, Venezuela

L. Beaugé

División de Biofísica, Instituto M. y M. Ferreyra, Casilla de Correo 389, 5000 Córdoba, Argentina

INTRODUCTION

Most living cells can maintain an exceedingly large Ca electrochemical gradient across their plasma membranes. Since the inwardly directed Ca gradient is expressed as a constant "leak" of Ca into the cells, mechanisms at the membrane must perform the long-term regulation of the $[Ca^{2+}]_i$. The short-term regulation of internal Ca^{2+} requires intracellular systems (organelles, Ca binding proteins, etc) and/or plasma membrane mechanisms able to overcome sudden fluctuations in its concentration (excitation-secretion-contraction).

The study of Ca transport processes in excitable and nonexcitable cells has led to the discovery that Na^+ and ATP are intimately involved in the regulation of the $[Ca^{2+}]_i$. In fact, Na^+ ions are associated with Ca movements in several tissues (see 1–5), and the hypothesis first proposed for cardiac muscle (6) was that dissipation of the energy stored in the Na electrochemical gradient could lead to a net Ca extrusion (Na/Ca countertransport). A different mechanism exists in red blood cells and sarcoplasmic reticulum. There active Ca transport is ATP-dependent and is apparently not coupled to the gradient of a counter-ion (7, 8).

313

0066-4278/83/0315-0313$02.00

At present, much of our knowledge concerning Ca^{2+} extrusion in excitable cells comes from experiments on squid axons. In this preparation Ca extrusion can be associated with the inwardly directed Na gradient (1). Although earlier squid work suggested an involvement of metabolism in Ca extrusion (9, 10), it has been discovered recently that ATP promotes a net outward movement of Ca not related to the existing Na gradient (11). These findings raise two basic questions: (a) Do different mechanisms for Ca extrusion work in parallel to regulate the $[Ca^{2+}]_i$ in excitable cells; and (b) if so, what is the relevance of each?

This review focuses on these questions, emphasizing recent research done in dialyzed squid giant axons. For further information on various aspects of Ca transport see other recent reviews (2, 3, 5).

METHODOLOGICAL CONSIDERATIONS

Internal dialysis has proved to be a powerful technique for measuring solute fluxes in large single cells (12). Its advantages over conventional methods (injection, extrusion) include (a) continuous control of the concentration of intracellular solutes; (b) measurement of solute fluxes under internal steady-state conditions; (c) determination of efflux and influx in the same axon (13); and (d) careful manipulation of intracellular metabolic energy substrates (ATP, ADP, Pi, etc).

An important application of this technique has been in the field of Ca metabolism. The Ca ion is sequestered and bound to intracellular structures (14, 15); it is thus difficult to analyze Ca fluxes properly. Internal dialysis allows the inclusion of the chelating agent EGTA (1–2 mM) to control the $[Ca^{2+}]_i$ effectively (4, 13).

THE INTRACELLULAR IONIZED CA CONCENTRATION

Precise knowledge of the resting Ca_i^{2+} concentration is of paramount importance when studying Ca regulation since it determines the concentration range at which the related physiological mechanisms must be operational. Table 1 shows the values for the resting $[Ca^{2+}]_i$ measured in three different squid species, using different experimental procedures. The validity of the values shown here depends on the choice of the dissociation constant (K_D) of the CaEGTA complex. For the experiments on *Loligo pealei* and *Dorteuthis plei* we used a measured apparent K_D of 0.15 μM [at pH 7.3 and 0.3 ionic strength (16)]. Recently, we have redetermined this value under similar conditions employing the method described by Bers (17), using Ca-selective electrodes. The K_D of 0.168 μM obtained

Table 1 Resting $[Ca^{2+}]_i$ in intact squid axons

	Method (reference)			
Species	Injected (33) aequorin (μM)	Dialysis (16) aequorin (μM)	Injected (16) arsenaro III (μM)	Ca selective (52) electrodes (μM)
L. forbesi	0.1	—	—	—
L. pealei	—	0.02–0.05	0.08	—
D. plei	—	—	—	0.05–0.16

with this procedure (52) is in good agreement with the one previously reported.

The similarity in the resting $[Ca^{2+}]_i$ in these three squid species demonstrates that the $[Ca^{2+}]_i$ of a fresh squid axon is not greater than 0.1 μM. Taking a mean resting Ca^{2+}_i of 70 nM, and given an ionized Ca in the squid hemolymph of about 4 mM (2), the ratio $[Ca^{2+}]_o/[Ca^{2+}]_i$ is near 6 $\times$ 10^4. As discussed below, the presence of Ca^{2+} gradient of about 10^5 across the membrane is the result of a low passive Ca permeability and an active Ca pump mechanism located in the plasma membrane.

THE SODIUM-CALCIUM EXCHANGE

Evidence of a carrier-mediated counter-transport mechanism (Na-Ca exchange) in squid axons is based on observations that (*a*) in injected nerves from *Sepia* a component of Ca efflux depended on external sodium (18, 19) and (*b*) a fraction of the ouabain-insensitive Na efflux depended on external calcium (20). This mechanism was further supported, first, by the finding of both a Na influx activated by internal Ca [(21); R. DiPolo, L. Beaugé, unpublished information] and a Ca influx activated by internal sodium (13, 18); and, second, by the fact that in axons highly loaded with calcium, the total intracellular Ca content depends on the direction of the Na electrochemical gradient (3). For this counter-exchange mechanism to be responsible for the observed low resting $[Ca^{2+}]_i$ ($\leqslant$ 10^{-7} M), theoretical considerations alone require a minimum of four Na ions moving inwardly in exchange for a single Ca ion, (22) thus indicating that this transport mechanism is electrogenic. Although studies on the voltage dependence of the Na_o-dependent Ca efflux favor an electrogenic carrier system (21, 23, 24), at present no definitive experimental data confirm the expected stoichiometry. Further work is needed to clarify this important point.

A simplified view of a classical electrogenic counter-transport system for the case of the Na-Ca exchange in squid axons seems complicated by the demonstration of a marked asymmetry in the forward and backward movement of the cations concerned (Na and Ca). In fact, if we consider the *forward reaction* (Na_o-dependent Ca efflux or its counterpart, the Ca_i-dependent Na influx), we notice that: (*a*) It proceeds in both the presence and absence of ATP (25, 26); nevertheless, ATP increases the affinity of the carrier transport system for external Na (9, 10). (*b*) External Na activates Ca efflux in both the presence and absence of external Ca ions (18, 25, 26). (*c*) Internal Ca^{2+} activates the Na_o-dependent Ca efflux (presence of ATP) with a $K_{1/2}$ between 5 and 10 μM (4, 26). Blaustein (26), has reported a lower $K_{1/2}$ (0.7 μM) in axons dialyzed with a Na_i of 5 mM. However, at more physiological [Na]$_i$ (20–40 mM) (27, 28), this parameter increases up to the micromolar range (26). These characteristics differ from those of the *backward reaction* (Na_i-dependent Ca influx or its counterpart, the Ca_o-dependent Na efflux): (*a*) The backward reaction does not proceed in the absence of ATP up to 1 μM Ca_i (13, 18); (*b*) internal Na activates Ca influx only in the presence of Ca^{2+}_i (13); and (*c*) internal ionized Ca activates the Na_i-dependent Ca influx with a $K_{1/2}$ of about 0.6 micromolar (13, 29). In light of the present experimental data, it remains an open question whether the forward and backward exchange modes are part of a unique, highly asymmetric system or represent the behavior of two different entities.

The high maximal rate of Na_o-dependent Ca efflux (2000–3000 fmoles cm^{-2} sec $^{-1}$)[1] (25) and the relatively low apparent affinity for Ca^{2+} (about 50–100 times higher than the physiological Ca^{2+}_i concentration) allow one to consider this transport mechanism a *high-capacity low-affinity system* (see Figures 1, 2). Similar kinetic properties have been reported recently for the Na-Ca exchange in other preparations (30, 31, 32), thus suggesting this to be a general characteristic of the Na-Ca antiporter.

THE CALCIUM PUMP

As a result of the recent demonstration of a low resting [Ca^{2+}]$_i$ in fresh squid axons (nanomolar range), it was realized that most experiments on Ca transport in this preparation were carried out at exceedingly high [Ca^{2+}]$_i$ (micromolar range). More recent experiments performed in dialyzed and intact axons containing [Ca^{2+}]$_i$ in the physiological range [(24, 34); see Figures 1, 2] show that 80–90% of the total Ca efflux is insensitive to external sodium. This Na-independent efflux of Ca has recently attracted

---

[1] fmole cm^{-2} sec^{-1} = f/CS

much attention because it depends completely on the presence of ATP (11, 34). A crucial piece of evidence regarding a direct involvement of ATP in Ca transport was the demonstration of an ATP-dependent net Ca extrusion in the complete absence of any ionic gradient across the membrane (11). Thus it was postulated (11, 34) that the "residual" efflux of Ca manifests an uncoupled Ca pump of the type present in red blood cells and sarcoplasmic reticulum. The term "uncoupled Ca pump" indicates that the extrusion of Ca is apparently not accompanied by the translocation of any other counter-ion. This is confirmed by the fact that in dialyzed axons, isosmotic substitution of Na_o, Ca_o, and Mg_o together with Tris, choline, lithium, or mannitol causes no effect on this ATP-dependent Ca efflux component [(11); R. DiPolo, L. Beaugé, unpublished observations].

Experiments on the kinetic properties of the proposed Ca pump show that: (a) Intracellular Ca^{2+} activates with high apparent affinity ($K_{1/2} = 0.2$ μM) (4, 34). (b) The maximum rate of Ca efflux is about 200 f/CS (4, 34).

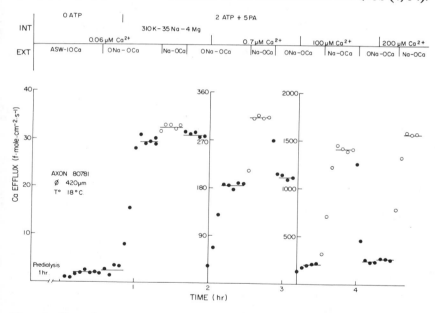

Figure 1   The activation of the ATP-dependent uncoupled and the Na_o-dependent Ca efflux by Ca^{2+}. Ordinate: Ca efflux in fmole $cm^{-2} s^{-1}$. Abscissa: time in hr. ● = Ca efflux in the absence of external Na and Ca (uncoupled component). ○ = Ca efflux in the presence of Na_o (Na_o-dependent component). To observe the activation of the Ca efflux by ATP, the axon was predialyzed for 1 hr with an ATP-free dialysis medium containing 1 mM CN^-. Notice the changes in the ordinate scale at different $[Ca^{2+}]_i$. Total EGTA = 1 mM. A Ca-ATP dissociation constant of 1.4 mM (P. DeWeer, personal communication) was used to determine the Ca^{2+} at 100 and 200 μM. Specie: *Doryteuthis plei*.

(c) Intracellular ATP activates the Ca efflux following a Michaelian function with a Km of about 20 micromolar (4, 34).

In contrast with the already described Na_o-dependent Ca efflux (forward Na-Ca exchange), the Ca pump can be kinetically considered as a *high-affinity low-capacity Ca transport system*. It is important to stress that the $K_{1/2}$ for the activation of the uncoupled Ca pump by Ca^{2+}_i is only twice that of the resting physiological $[Ca^{2+}]_i$ while it is almost one hundred times that

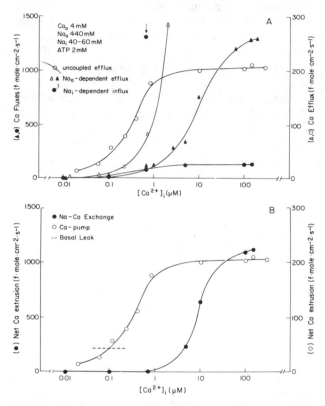

Figure 2   Unidirectional and net Ca fluxes as a function of the $[Ca^{2+}]_i$. Ordinate: Ca fluxes in fmole $cm^{-2} s^{-1}$. Abscissa: $[Ca^{2+}]_i$ in μM. A: Uncoupled Ca efflux (o), Na_o-dependent Ca efflux ($\triangle\blacktriangle$), Na_i-dependent Ca influx (●). Notice that the $K_{1/2}$ for the Na_i-dependent Ca influx is about 0.6 μM whereas that of the Na_o-dependent Ca efflux is 10 μM. The arrow shows the steady-state Na_i-dependent Ca influx in an axon depolarized with 100 mM K_o. B: Net Ca extrusion promoted by the Ca pump and the Na-Ca exchange. Net Ca extrusion by the Na-Ca exchange was calculated by subtracting the Na_i-dependent Ca influx component from the Na_o-dependent Ca efflux. The horizontal broken line corresponds to a resting Ca influx of about 44 f/CS. Open symbols are read on the righthand scale. Closed symbols are read on the left hand scale. The data correspond to experiments in (4, 13, 29, 34).

of the Na-dependent mechanism. Therefore, it appears that in the earlier squid Ca flux experiments the uncoupled Ca efflux component was over-looked owing to the experimental conditions usually employed (excessively high $[Ca^{2+}]_i$) (see Figure 2). In fact, under those circumstances the ATP-dependent uncoupled Ca efflux (200 f/CS at 200 μM) was evidently masked by the ten-fold greater Na_o-dependent Ca efflux component (2000 f/CS at 200 μM Ca^{2+}_i).

A Ca pump of the type postulated here must manifest itself as a mem-brane bound Ca-dependent ATPase activity. In searching for this en-zymatic activity we have used plasma membrane fragments isolated from optical nerves of the squid. This preparation has the advantage of producing a high yield in axolemma with negligible contamination from Schwann cells and intracellular organelles (35). In addition, it has a (Na,K)-ATPase activ-ity with kinetic properties similar to those of the active Na-K transport in squid axons under dialysis conditions (35, 36). It seems fair then to compare the properties of an eventual Ca-dependent ATPase activity with those of the ATP-dependent uncoupled Ca transport in dialyzed axons. Experimen-tal results show that there is indeed a Ca,Mg-ATPase activity with proper-ties almost identical to the transport parameters of the proposed Ca pump: similar $K_{1/2}$ for the activation by Ca ions (0.3 μM) and ATP (18 μM), and an absolute requirement for Mg ions in both cases. Furthermore, while they are insensitive to ouabain and oligomycin, both are completely inhibited by micromolar concentrations of vanadate. The membrane fragments can be phosphorylated from ATP in the presence of Ca and Mg ions showing a fast rate of spontaneous dephosphorylation. The phosphorylated protein is acid stable, suggesting that the fast turnover rate is enzymatically produced.

CALCIUM PUMP AND SODIUM CALCIUM EXCHANGE: TWO SYSTEMS?

Are the Ca pump and the Na-Ca exchange independent or interdependent? Table 2 summarizes the most conspicuous features of the two modalities for Ca transport. The data shown strongly indicate that the two modes are expressions of two different mechanisms. The only qualitative analogy be-tween them is their activation by ATP. For the uncoupled Ca efflux, the evidence points clearly to hydrolysis of ATP (a true Ca pump). For the Na_o-dependent component, the ATP stimulation has been described tradi-tionally as a modulatory effect in which the nucleotide might not be hydro-lyzed (9, 10, 37). However, the finding that only hydrolyzable ATP analogs activate Ca efflux suggests that a phosphorylation step could be involved in the ATP activation of the Na-Ca exchange (49). Another interesting possi-bility is that the ATP-stimulated Na_o-dependent Ca efflux is not

Table 2 Comparison of the ATP-dependent uncoupled and the Na_o-dependent Ca efflux in dialyzed squid axons

	Ca pump	Na-Ca exchange	Reference
Relative magnitude at physiologic conditions[a]	85–95%	5–15%	4, 34
$K_{1/2}$ for Ca_i^{2+}	0.18 μM	10 μM	4, 34, 26
V_{max}	200 f/CS	2000–3000 f/CS	4, 34, 26
Ca_o	Inhibits at high Ca (enhanced by alkaline pH_o)	Activates at high Ca_i^{2+}	47
Na_o	No effect	Stimulates	4, 25, 26, 34
Na_i	No effect	Inhibits	2
Mg_i	Essential	Not required	49, 50
Membrane depolarization	—	Inhibits	21, 33
pH_i	Acid inhibits Alkaline no effect	Acid inhibits Alkaline stimulates	42 48
pH_o	Alkaline inhibits (enhanced by Ca_o)	Alkaline no effect	48
ATP	Required ($K_{1/2}$ 20 μM)	Activates, not essential ($K_{1/2}$ 270 μM)	25, 34
Vanadate	Inhibits ($K_{1/2}$ 7 μM)	No effect without ATP Stimulates at high Ca_i and with ATP	38, 51

[a] Ca_i^{2+} 0.1 μM; Na_i 40–60 mM; Ca_o 4 mM; Na_o 440 mM; pH_i 7.3; pH_o 7.8; Temp. 17–19°C; K_i 310 mM; K_o 10 mM (4, 34).

related at all to the Na-Ca exchange but constitutes a different operational mode of the Ca pump, which at high Ca_i^{2+} becomes further activated by Na_o. A peculiar observation suggesting this idea is that internal vanadate activates the Na_o-dependent Ca efflux only at high $[Ca^{2+}]_i$ and in the presence of ATP (38). Nevertheless, it remains an open question whether there is a real link between the ATP-dependent uncoupled efflux and the ATP-stimulated Na_o-dependent Ca efflux.

THE REGULATION OF THE RESTING INTRACELLULAR IONIZED CA CONCENTRATION: PHYSIOLOGICAL CA FLUXES

Perhaps the most controversial point related to $[Ca^{2+}]_i$ regulation in squid axons (and probably in other preparations as well) regards the relative importances of the Na-Ca exchange and the ATP-driven Ca pump in the maintenance of resting $[Ca^{2+}]_i$. In order to compare these regulators we need reliable information not only about the transmembrane Ca electrochemical gradient but also on the rate at which this gradient is continuously dissipated (Ca influx).

The Resting Ca Influx

The Ca influx measured in intact and dialyzed axons incubated in artificial seawater containing 10 mM Ca averages about 110f/CS (13, 18, 39). Since the activity of Ca^{2+} ions in squid blood is around 4 mM (2), from the well-known linear relationship between Ca influx and external Ca concentration (23, 24, 39) the expected resting entry of Ca at nearly physiological conditions (0.07 μM Ca^{2+}_i; 30 mM Na_i; 4 mM Ca^{2+}_o; 440 mM Na_o) is about 44 f/CS.

How do Ca^{2+} ions enter the axon under resting physiological conditions? In principle, the dissipation of the Ca gradient can be accomplished via multiple pathways. In excitable cells, the existence of fast Ca channels (TTX-sensitive) suggests that at least part of the resting Ca influx could occur through Na channels. Voltage-sensitive, slow, or late Ca channels (D-600-, Co^{2+}-, and Mn^{2+}-sensitive) could also contribute to the resting Ca entry. In addition, backward Na-Ca exchange will add to the dissipation of the Ca gradient. Recent data obtained in squid axons dialyzed under "physiological" conditions show that 70% of the resting Ca influx goes via a TTX-sensitive pathway, about 20% by reversal of the Na-Ca exchange (Na_i-dependent Ca influx), and the remaining 10% penetrates by a route insensitive to Na_i, Ca_i, ATP, TTX, and D-600 (29). The relative contributions of these pathways for Ca entry can change markedly according to the composition of the internal medium. At a constant Na_i and in the presence of ATP, increasing the intracellular Ca^{2+} increases the Ca influx through the Na-Ca exchange system (Na_i-dependent Ca influx) without affecting the other components of Ca influx (13, 29). At 0.1 μM Ca^{2+}_i, the absolute magnitude of the Na_i-dependent Ca influx is about 10 f/CS (from 4 mM Ca_o), whereas at 1 μM Ca^{2+}_i, it becomes 160 f/CS. This *trans* activating effect of Ca^{2+}_i is also reflected in a much larger depolarization-induced Na_i-dependent Ca influx at high $[Ca^{2+}]_i$ [(29); see Figure 2]. As recently proposed, this modulating effect of Ca^{2+} on the backward reaction might have important physiological implications in cardiac muscle contraction and synaptic facilitation (29, 40).

The Balance of the Ca Fluxes

Thermodynamic arguments have usually been employed to indicate that an ideal Na-Ca exchange system (one in which Ca can move across the membrane only via the carrier) working near equilibrium can explain the experimentally observed resting $[Ca^{2+}]_o/[Ca^{2+}]_i$ ratio if a 4 $Na^+/1$ Ca^{2+} stoichiometry is assumed (22). Although thermodynamically correct, these calculations might not reflect the situation prevailing in a real axon, since one should consider not only the magnitude of the physiological Ca gradient but also the values of the resting inwardly and outwardly directed Ca fluxes (kinetic parameters). At nearly physiological conditions, the Na-Ca exchange cannot be working at equilibrium since most of the total Ca influx occurs via resting Na channels and not through the carrier-mediated system. Therefore, in order to attain a steady-state Ca flux balance, the axon must compensate for this steady Ca entry by actively extruding between 40–50 f/CS of Ca ions. The experimental data presented in Figure 2 show that a net Ca extrusion of this magnitude by the Na-Ca exchange (net = forward minus backward reaction) is attained at a $[Ca^{2+}]_i$ near 1 μM, a value more than ten times the actual resting $[Ca^{2+}]_i$. Thus one would expect this system to contribute only marginally to the net Ca extrusion at submicromolar $[Ca^{2+}]_i$. As also shown in Figure 2, the ATP-dependent uncoupled net Ca extrusion (net = uncoupled efflux), owing to its high affinity for Ca^{2+}, is a mechanism better suited to regulate the Ca^{2+} at low $[Ca^{2+}]_i$. In fact, an influx of Ca of the order of 40–50 f/CS can be balanced by the Ca pump at a $[Ca^{2+}]_i$ of about 0.1 μM.

Before accepting the conclusion that ATP is directly associated with Ca extrusion in squid axons, one must consider and explain apparently conflicting evidence. Requena et al (3, 41), analyzing the *total* Ca_i content of squid axons as an indication of net Ca movements, found that axons poisoned or injected with apyrase (ATP-deficient axons) were still able to extrude an imposed *high Ca load* in the presence of external Na. This led these authors to believe that ATP is not an essential substrate in the regulation of the $[Ca^{2+}]_i$. However, far from denying a role of ATP in net Ca extrusion, their data can be explained on the basis that: (*a*) poisoning and Ca loading markedly raise the ionized Ca_i (42, 43), and at these high levels of $[Ca^{2+}]_i$ the Na_o-dependent Ca efflux will certainly contribute to the net Ca extrusion; and (*b*) at the ATP concentration present in their poisoned or apyrase-injected axons the Ca pump would have been about 75% activated. As emphasized in this review (Figures 1, 2; Table 3), the level of the $[Ca^{2+}]_i$ (not the total Ca_i) is the critical variable, since it markedly affects how Ca is extruded from the axon. Therefore, nothing can be inferred from the above-mentioned experiments about Ca extrusion at more physiological $[Ca^{2+}]_i$. More recently, in experiments closely related to those of Requena et al (net Ca extrusion during a high Ca load), Baker & Singh (44) showed that if the $[Ca^{2+}]_i$ is maintained close to its physiological value during the Ca load, net Ca extrusion is mostly ATP-dependent (poison sensitive), Na_o-insensitive, and vanadate-sensitive. This finding further supports our view on the relative importance of the Ca pump in the maintenance of the resting $[Ca^{2+}]_i$.

The presence of two parallel independent systems for Ca translocation across the axon membrane does not seem to be unique to squid nerves. These two systems have recently been proposed to occur in several other excitable tissues, including cardiac muscle (31), smooth muscle (45), mammalian brain (46), intact synaptosomes (47), and cultured neuroblastomes (32).

With respect to the role of the low-affinity–high-capacity Na^+–Ca^{2+} exchange, this system might be important in removing large amounts of Ca^{2+} from the cytosol following transient increases in the $[Ca^{2+}]_i$ during depolarization-repolarization cycles such as those occurring at the nerve terminal and during cardiac muscle contraction. Furthermore, this mechanism, though traditionally thought to be primarily present for Ca extrusion, may prove to be more useful for facilitating the entry of Ca into the cell during membrane depolarization (40).

SUMMARY

Calcium membrane extrusion in squid axons is mediated by two mechanisms able to regulate the Ca^{2+} with different degrees of efficiency. The *ATP driven uncoupled Ca pump* with its high affinity for Ca^{2+}_i will work primarily to balance the physiological Ca leak, hence controlling the $[Ca^{2+}]_i$ at rest. *The Na-Ca exchange system,* although less important in the maintenance of the resting Ca^{2+}_i owing to its large capacity of transport (outward and inward), will certainly be important in physiological and unphysiological conditions in which relatively high $[Ca^{2+}]_i$ concentrations are attained.

ACKNOWLEDGMENT

This work was supported by Grants from CONICIT (S1-1144), Venezuela; CONICET, Argentina; PNUD-UNESCO RLA 78-024, #31/81; and NSF-USA-BNS-8025579.

Literature Cited

1. Baker, P. F. 1970. In *Calcium and Cellular Function,* ed. A. W. Cuthbert, pp. 96–107. London: MacMillan
2. Blaustein, M. P. 1974. *Rev. Physiol. Biochem. Pharmacol.* 70:33–82
3. Requena, J., Mullins, L. J. 1979. *Q. Rev. Biophys.* 12:371–460
4. DiPolo, R., Beaugé, L. 1980. *Cell Calcium* 1:147–69
5. Sulakhe, P. V., St. Louis, P. J. 1981. *Prog. Biophys. Molec. Biol.* 35:135–95
6. Reuter, H., Seitz, N. 1968. *J. Physiol.* 195:451–70
7. Schatzman, H. J., Burgin, H. 1978. *Ann. NY Acad. Sci.* 307:125–47
8. Inesi, G. 1979. *Transport across Single Biological Membranes,* Vol. 2, pp. 357–93. NY: Springer
9. Baker, P. F., Glitsch, H. G. 1973. *J. Physiol.* 233:44p.
10. DiPolo, R. 1974. *J. Gen. Physiol.* 64:503–17

324   DIPOLO & BEAUGÉ

11. DiPolo, R. 1978. *Nature* 274:390–92
12. Brinley, F. J., Mullins, L. J. 1967. *J. Gen. Physiol.* 50:2303–31
13. DiPolo, R. 1979. *J. Gen. Physiol.* 73:91–113
14. Baker, P. F., Schlaepfer, W. W. 1978. *J. Physiol.* 276:103–25
15. Brinley, F. J. 1978. *Ann. Rev. Biophys. Bioeng.* 7:363–92
16. DiPolo, R., Requena, J., Brinley, F. J., Mullins, L. J., Scarpa, A., Tiffert, T. 1976. *J. Gen. Physiol.* 67:433–67
17. Bers, D. M. 1981. *J. Physiol.* 312:2–3p.
18. Baker, P. F., Blaustein, M. P., Hodgkin, A. L., Steinhardt, R. A. 1969. *J. Physiol.* 200:431–58
19. Blaustein, M. P., Hodgkin, A. L. 1969. *J. Physiol.* 200:497–527
20. Baker, P. F. 1968. *J. Gen. Physiol.* 51:1725–95
21. Blaustein, M. P., Russell, J. M., DeWeer, P. 1974. *J. Supramol. Struct.* 2:558–81
22. Mullins, L. J. 1977. *J. Gen. Physiol.* 70:681–95
23. Mullins, L. J., Brinley, F. J. 1975. *J. Gen. Physiol.* 65:135–52
24. Baker, P. F., McNaughton, P. A. 1976. *J. Physiol.* 259:103–44
25. DiPolo, R. 1973. *J. Gen. Physiol.* 62:575–89
26. Blaustein, M. P. 1977. *Biophys. J.* 20:79–111
27. DeWeer, P., Geauldig, D. 1973. *Science* 179:1326–28
28. Caldwell-Violich, M., Requena, J. 1979. *J. Gen. Physiol.* 74:739–52
29. DiPolo, R., Rojas, H., Beaugé, L. 1982. *Cell Calcium* 3:194
30. Reeves, J. P., Sutko, J. L. 1979. *Proc. Natl. Acad. Sci. USA* 76:590–94
31. Caroni, P., Carafoli, E. 1980. *Nature* 283:765–67
32. Kurzinger, K., Stadtkus, C., Hamprecht, B. 1980. *Eur. J. Biochem.* 103:597–611
33. Baker, P. F. 1976. Calcium in biological systems. *Soc. Exp. Biol. Symp.*, 30th, pp. 67–88. Cambridge: Cambridge Univ. Press
34. DiPolo, R., Beaugé, L. 1979. *Nature* 278:271–73
35. Beaugé, L., DiPolo, R., Osses, L., Barnola, F., Campos, M. 1981. *Biochim. Biophys. Acta* 644:147–52
36. Beaugé, L., DiPolo, R. 1981. *J. Physiol.* 314:457–80
37. Baker, P. F. 1978. *Ann. NY Acad. Sci.* 307:250–68
38. DiPolo, R., Beaugé, L. 1981. *Biochim. Biophys. Acta* 645:229–36
39. Hodgkin, A. L., Keynes, R. D. 1957. *J. Physiol.* 128:28–60
40. Mullins, L. J. 1979. *Am. J. Physiol.* 236:103–10
41. Requena, J., Mullins, L. J., Brinley, F. J. 1979. *J. Gen. Physiol.* 73:327–42
42. Baker, P. F., Hodgkin, A. L., Ridgway, E. B. 1971. *J. Physiol.* 218:709–55
43. Brinley, F. J., Teffert, J. T., Scarpa, A. 1978. *J. Gen. Physiol.* 72:101–27
44. Baker, P. F., Singh, R. 1981. *Biochim. Biophys. Acta* 646:450–56
45. Van Breemen, C., Aaronson, P., Loutzenhiser, R. 1979. *Pharmacol. Rev.* 30:167–208
46. Schellemberg, G. D., Swanson, P. 1982. *Biochim. Biophys. Acta* 648:13–27
47. Akerman, K. E. O., Nicholls, D. G. 1981. *J. Biochem.* 117:491–97
48. DiPolo, R., Beaugé, L. 1982. *Biochim. Biophys. Acta* 688:237–45
49. DiPolo, R. 1977. *J. Gen. Physiol.* 69:795–814
50. Requena, J. 1978. *Biochim. Biophys. Acta* 512:452–58
51. DiPolo, R., Rojas, H., Beaugé, L. 1979. *Nature* 281:228–29
52. DiPolo, R., Rojas, H., Vergara, J., Lopez, R., Caputo, C. 1983. *Biochim. Biophys. Acta.* In press

Ann. Rev. Physiol. 1983. 45:325–39
Copyright © 1983 by Annual Reviews Inc. All rights reserved

ENERGETICS AND ELECTROGENICITY OF THE SARCOPLASMIC RETICULUM CALCIUM PUMP

W. Hasselbach

Max-Planck-Institut für Medizinische Forschung, Abteilung Physiologie, Heidelberg, West Germany

H. Oetliker

Physiologisches Institut der Universität Bern, Bern, Switzerland

Introduction

Activity of skeletal muscle is regulated by the free myoplasmic calcium concentration, $[Ca^{2+}]$, which varies from $5 \cdot 10^{-8}$ M at rest to $5 \cdot 10^{-6}$ M during activity. About 90% of activator Ca is contained in the terminal cisternae of the sarcoplasmic reticulum (SR), whence Ca is released by a still unknown mechanism. The SR occupies about 9% of muscle volume and has a surface area (S) of ~ 2 m^2 per gram muscle. Its internal $[Ca^{2+}]$ is in the order of 0.5–2 mM (Table 1). One activation-relaxation cycle requires release and reuptake of ~ 200 nmol Ca per gram muscle (19, 67, 89). This in turn requires a fast release and uptake system. Ca uptake and maintenance of a Ca^{2+}-gradient (1:10^4–10^5) across the SR are responsible for a considerable fraction of muscle metabolism.

In this review we evaluate the energetics of muscular Ca turnover from different view points; (*a*) maintenance and restitution of the resting gradient, (*b*) transformation of chemical into osmotic energy, and (*c*) membrane permeabilities interfering with passive and active Ca movement.

0066-4278/83/0315-0325$02.00

Energy Consumption of the SR Calcium Pump in the Resting and Active Muscle

An estimate of how much energy resting muscle expends for the SR Ca transport requires information about (a) distribution of Ca^{2+} between the myoplasm and SR, (b) the SR surface, and (c) the permeability of SR to Ca^{2+} and other ions. The data in Table 1 are based on the assumption that all or nearly all the different structural entities of the SR participate in Ca transport. This assumption seems justified by the presence of 90 Å membrane particles, characteristic for the Ca-transport protein, in all SR areas (13, 22, 34). An estimate of energy requirement for the Ca pump in 1 g resting muscle is obtained assuming that the membrane's high permeability to small ions prevents buildup of a membrane potential: 2 m^2 for SR surface area; a Ca efflux of 26 nM min^{-1}, as observed in isolated vesicles (20°C, pH 7.0) (25, 33); and either a Ca gradient of 10,000:1 or a Ca/ATP ratio of the pump of 2. Both approaches yield a resting energy requirement of ~ 0.13 cal g^{-1} min^{-1}, which is $\sim 7\%$ of the resting muscle metabolism. The energy required for relaxation, to free the contractile proteins from Ca and to store it in the SR, can be deduced from the amount of Ca^{2+} transported and the $[Ca^{2+}]$ in myoplasm and SR. The amount of Ca^{2+}, needed for contraction, is estimated taking into account the analytically determined Ca-specific binding sites of troponin C and of other Ca-binding proteins (0.1–0.2 μmol g^{-1}) (64, 67). The muscle spends ~ 1 mcal g^{-1} for Ca transport in a single twitch. This is an essential part of total energy output (2–3 mcal g^{-1}) during a contraction-relaxation cycle (30, 42). The energy used for Ca uptake is limited by the concentration of the Ca-transport

Table 1 Sarcoplasmic reticulum characteristics

			Calcium		
			Intraretic		Extraretic
Muscle	Volume fraction (%)	Surface (m^2 ml^{-1})	Total (mM)	Free (mM)	Free (μM)
Frog sartorius	9 (58)[a]–13 (61)	2 (58)–5 (61)	20 (73)	5–10	0.05 (11)–0.3 (35)
Rat, Rabbit cardiac	3.5 (74)	1.5 (74)	10 (92)	2–5	0.1 (11, 45) – 1.0 (10, 20)
Rabbit skeletal	2.5[b]	1.5[b]	—	—	0.01 – 0.1 (63)

[a] Numbers in parentheses are references.
[b] The estimate is based on the maximum extraction yield of 3–4 mg SR membrane protein from 1 g of muscle [(53); unpublished results] and an internal space of 4 μl mg^{-1} (39) of the vesicular membranes. One mg of vesicular protein corresponds to 0.3 m^2 surface at a mean vesicular diameter of 100 nm. The free concentration of calcium is calculated by using the binding parameters for the internal calcium binding sites (27, 57) or osmotic equilibrium data (43).

protein and its turnover number. In the same animal the system seems to be the more developed the faster a muscle contracts and relaxes (81, 82). Furthermore, transport proteins isolated from fast and slow muscle appear to exhibit different specific activities (62, 76, 87).

Attempts to confer turnover rates of transport protein, measured in vitro, to in vivo situations are considerably handicapped by uncertainties about effects of [Ca^{2+}] inside the SR on turnover rates. Inhibition of Ca transport by [Ca^{2+}]$_i$ is well-known (31, 46, 86). Ca^{2+} accumulation of isolated SR is severely suppressed if the [Ca^{2+}]$_i$ reaches values of 0.2–1.0 mM (pH 7.0). As shown in Table 1, [Ca^{2+}]$_i$ in vivo might reach 10 mM. Therefore, if the living system exhibits the same sensitivity for [Ca^{2+}]$_i$, Ca translocation would be so slow that the transport rates could hardly account for the observed speed of relaxation.

The free energy of ATP hydrolysis driving the Ca pump is obtained from the standard free energy (ΔG_o) of ATP, adapted to physiological conditions ($\Delta G_o = 7.4$ kcal mol^{-1}), and the prevailing concentrations of ATP, ADP, and phosphate (84). Chemical analysis yields ATP/ADP·P$_i$ ratios between 10,000 and 30,000 for rat skeletal muscle (84). Thus a free energy of ~ 14 kcal mol^{-1} ATP is available. In vitro it is possible to predetermine the available ΔG. A factor of great importance for overall economy of Ca transport is the molar ratio of Ca^{2+} taken up to ATP hydrolyzed. In most studies a transport ratio of ~ 2 was found (24, 34, 90). Smaller values are obtained at elevated pH or temperatures where the membranes become highly Ca-permeable (25, cf. 69). The finding that the coupling ratio does not decline when the pump rates become smaller indicates that under these conditions Ca leakage can be disregarded (47). A coupling ratio of 2 is observed not only during Ca uptake but also when the system synthesizes ATP from ADP and P$_i$ during Ca efflux—i.e. when the pump cycle is reversed (14, 48). The overall reaction can thus be described as follows

$$2Ca_o + ATP \rightleftharpoons 2Ca_i + ADP + P_i$$

$$\frac{Ca_i{}^2}{Ca_o{}^2} = \frac{K_{eq} \cdot ATP}{ADP \cdot P}$$

where K$_{eq}$ (equilibrium constant) = ATP$_{eq}$/ADP$_{eq}$·P$_{eq}$ = 10^5; and ATP, ADP, and P$_i$ are the actual concentrations of the reactants. At a given ATP/ADP·P$_i$ ratio this relation allows us to estimate the maximal Ca$_i$/Ca$_o$ ratio the pump can achieve. The observed values of 10^4–10^5 in living muscle (Table 1) and of $2\cdot10^3$–$2\cdot10^4$ in experiments with isolated membranes are near the theoretically possible limits [(28, 47); unpublished results]. This indicates that Ca leakage is small compared to the uptake capacity of the pump—i.e. the system works close to its theoretical equilibrium. The latter conclusion is not stringent, because the same concentration ratio would be measured when the pump operates against a significant leak, provided that the transport ratio were reduced from two to one. At such a reduced transport ratio the pump would create much higher [Ca^{2+}] ratios in tight membranes.

Ca-Dependent and Ca-Independent Interaction of ATP, ADP, and P_i with the Transport Protein

In recent years attempts were made to resolve the pump cycle into a sequence of single reaction steps (17, 32, 36, 50). The following steps could be defined and arranged in a closed cycle. (a) Ca^{2+} and ATP bind to sites on the cytoplasmic SR surface. (b) Catalyzed by Ca^{2+} and Mg^{2+} the terminal P-residue at ATP is transferred to the transport protein. (c) Ca^{2+} is translocated from external high- to internal low-affinity sites and released into the SR. (d) The P-residue is hydrolytically cleaved from the transport protein.

This reaction sequence can be reversed, leading to Ca efflux and simultaneous synthesis of ATP from ADP and P_i (48). Analysis of the different transfer reactions together with Ca movement leads to the reaction scheme shown in Figure 1 as the simplest possible mechanism.

Two isomerization steps (4 and 8, Figure 1) are connected to a cycle by two phosphoryl transfer reactions (steps 2–3 and 7–6, Figure 1). Enzyme phosphorylation by NTP, giving rise to EP_1, and transfer of the phosphoryl group of EP_1 to NDP, proceed rapidly compared to the steady-state rates of ATP hydrolysis or Ca transport (23, 68, 85). In native vesicles phosphoprotein formation and Ca-movement appear to occur simultaneously (8, 34, 59). At low [Ca^{2+}]$_o$ and [ATP], two Ca^{2+} simultaneously become inaccessible to external EGTA with incorporation of one P-residue. However, when the external Ca-binding sites were initially saturated with Ca, Ca/P-protein ratios up to 5 were observed when the reaction was started by addition of GTP (21). The unexpectedly high ratios force us to assume that phosphorylation of one transport unit protects Ca^{2+} from EGTA binding in adjacent unphosphorylated protein units. The phosphorylation-induced inaccessibility of Ca to EGTA does not necessarily mean that Ca was translocated across the membranes. In fact, even nonaccumulating membrane preparations can occlude Ca from EGTA chelation (80). Occluded Ca can only be removed from the protein by EGTA when the enzyme is dephosphorylated by ADP or NDP in parallel—i.e. when the first reaction step is reversed (18). Demonstration of the occluded state requires reaction conditions that decelerate the cycle (e.g. low [Mg^{2+}] or high [K^+] to make the lifetime of the first intermediate sufficiently long (80). Under favorable conditions occlusion leads to a small increase of Ca binding (80, 88). If formation of

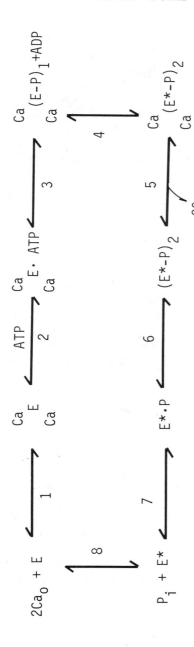

Figure 1 SR Ca pump reaction cycle

EP_1 leads not only to occlusion but also to Ca translocation, an affinity reduction of the protein for Ca^{2+} by three to four orders of magnitude must occur. As a consequence, reaction 1–3 could only proceed in the reverse direction as long as $[Ca^{2+}]$ is high at the internal internal binding sites. This, however, is not the case. The rate of ATP-ADP exchange, indicative for this reaction, remains 2–5-fold faster than Ca translocation at low $[Ca^{2+}]_i$ (68, 81). A direct coupling of phosphoprotein formation, EP_1, and Ca translocation is further difficult to reconcile with an equilibrium constant (K_{eq}) of ~ 1 for the initial transfer reaction catalyzed by Ca-permeable membranes together with the fact that high Ca^{2+} gradients can be created in the presence of equal concentrations of NTP and NDP (54, 85). The K_{eq} of 1 for the first phosphoprotein transfer reaction indicates that EP_1 is a high-energy phosphate compound. The forward reaction requires Mg^{2+} and Ca^{2+}, while the reverse reaction can occur without both ions. Hence, not only Ca^{2+} but also Mg^{2+} must be occluded in EP_1 (51). Reactions 6 and 7 (Figure 1) describe the steps in which P_i leaves or enters the reaction chain depending on the working mode of the pump. Without Ca^{2+} at cytoplasmic binding sites of the enzyme, P_i and Mg^{2+} interact with the enzyme in a random sequence forming at first a noncovalent Mg-P-protein complex that is in equilibrium with a Mg-containing acid-stable acyl-phosphate complex (15, 37, 52, 65). We are apparently dealing with a P-compound EP_2 of low energy of formation. In the presence of Ca^{2+} when the pump runs forward P must be released from this complex. The P-residue of EP_2 cannot be transferred back to ADP to make ATP. P-incorporation or its spontaneous release from the complex occurs slowly compared to the first reaction step (3, 5, 7, 66). P-incorporation leads to formation of a phosphoprotein compound that differs from EP_2 and resembles EP_1 if Ca-filled closed vesicles are phosphorylated by P_i (26, 49, 75). The occupancy of internal low-affinity sites results in a remarkable further increase in apparent affinity of the protein for Mg and P. Although the high apparent affinity of the protein for P indicates that this compound has an even lower free energy of formation than EP_2, the P-residue can easily be transferred to ADP to form ATP. This phosphoprotein, formed by P-incorporation at high $[Ca^{2+}]_i$ and low $[Ca^{2+}]_o$, is evidently identical with the Ca-containing intermediate formed from ATP in the first reaction sequence 1–3. Ca must have entered the complex from inside because the external medium has been depleted of Ca^{2+}. In contrast, EP_2 formed at low $[Ca^{2+}]_i$ and $[Ca]_o$ should be a Ca-free complex. Hence, one has to assume that conversion of EP_1 into EP_2 is the reaction sequence in which Ca is translocated. The transition of EP_1 to EP_2 has been extensively analyzed (71, 77, 78, 79). In nonaccumulating membrane preparations this transition is accompanied by a net Ca release from the protein (32, 88). The latter reaction can best be demonstrated at reduced pH (88). The reverse transition (EP$_2$ to EP$_1$) was convincingly demonstrated by de Meis (16, 17). The purified transport protein, which allows easy access of Ca to internal Ca-binding sites, can transiently be converted into EP$_1$ after it has been phosphorylated by P$_i$ at low [Ca^{2+}] by a rise in [Ca^{2+}] the P-group of EP$_1$ can then be transferred to ADP (41).

Energy Dissipation in the Reaction Cycle Far From and Near Equilibrium

Without knowing in detail the single reaction steps we can obtain information about energy partitioning in the reaction cycle by measuring energy dissipation under steady-state conditions far from or close to transport equilibrium (12). Energy dissipation in the respective reaction sequence is calculated from the ratio of forward- to reverse-reaction rates, obtained from measured rates of ATP hydrolysis, ATP-ADP exchange, and ATP-P$_i$ exchange.

$$G_{Diss} = - RT \cdot \ln(1 + \frac{V_s}{V_e}),$$

where V$_e$ is the rate of ATP-ADP exchange (sequence 2–3, Figure 1) or rate of ATP-P$_i$ exchange (sequence 2–7, Figure 1) and V$_s$ is the rate of ATP hydrolysis.

In closed vesicles at maximal [Ca^{2+}]$_i$/[Ca^{2+}]$_o$, forward- and reverse-rates are comparable (29, 68). Thus little energy is dissipated under these conditions in the respective sequences 2–3, 2–7 (Figure 1). This agrees with the predicted osmotic potential based on the available free energy and a transport ration of 2. On the other hand, in nonvesicular fragments no osmotic work is done and the free energy of ATP is dissipated completely. Under these conditions the pattern of energy dissipation, however, depends on [Ca^{2+}]. At optimal [Ca^{2+}] (1–10 μM), most of the energy is dissipated in sequence 2–7. A completely different pattern results if experiments are performed at millimolar [Ca^{2+}] (68, 70). As in closed vesicles, no energy is dissipated in sequence 2–7. Hence, dissipation must occur in the last reaction step (step 8 in Figure 1). This shows that (a) under all conditions very little energy is dissipated in ATP-ADP exchange and largely excludes energy coupling in this step; and (b) energy dissipation in the subsequent reaction sequence is not confined to a specific step but can occur at any later step depending on [Ca^{2+}].

Localization of Coupling Sequence by Simultaneous Measurement of Ca Movement and P Turnover

The assignment of specific elementary steps of the P-transfer reaction sequence to Ca translocation has further been approached by simultaneous measurements of Ca movement and P turnover after Ca transport has reached steady state or equilibrium (6, 86). When Ca transport is energized by NTPs in the presence of NTP regenerating systems, closed vesicles reach a constant maximum Ca load of approximately 100 nmol mg^{-1} at a persisting Ca turnover. Its rate and Ca-dependent NTP hydrolysis depend on $[Ca^{2+}]_o$ and on the kind of NTP (40, 68, 90). The fact that the same Ca load is maintained at very different rates of Ca turnover suggests coupling between Ca influx and efflux. Since this behavior cannot be explained by passive Ca outflow through membrane leaks, it has been proposed that under these conditions Ca might be carried outward by reaction step 4 (86). When the pump is inactive, this pathway has a very low calcium permeability (P_{Ca}). Supplementing the system with NDP opens another Ca pathway, enabling the partial reactions 1–3 to occur. Ca turnover is increased while NTP hydrolysis is simultaneously reduced (50, 86). This finding allows us to conclude that Ca is released prior to P_1. It does not prove that Ca release is directly coupled to the phosphoryl transfer reaction (72, 76). The nonexisting stoichiometry between Ca turnover and the exchange of P between NTP and NDP rather contradicts such a coupling. The increased Ca turnover by NDP is best explained by assuming that Ca, entering the first P-complex, EP_1, from outside or inside, is released to the external solution coupled with backtransfer of the P residue to NDP. This reaction is indicative of the "occluded state" of Ca in the first phosphoprotein complex, $Ca_2(E-P)_i$. An essential prerequisite for enhanced Ca–Ca exchange is accessibility of the phosphoprotein complex to Ca^{2+}_i. The reaction sequence making the phosphoprotein complex EP_1 accessible to Ca^{2+}_i must be considered to be the translocation step itself. The fact that the NDP-stimulated translocation occurs in the absence of P_i further supports the assumption that when the pump runs forward, translocation occurs before release of P$_i$ from the reaction chain or enters it after P_i when the pump runs backward. This order is also suggested by the fact that the rate of Ca exchange exceeds that of NTP-P_i exchange (sequence 2–7, Figure 1) and that of unidirectional Ca release when the pump runs backward synthesizing ATP (26).

The NDP-induced exchange is additionally stimulated when the system is supplemented with P_i. This stimulated Ca turnover largely exceeds net Ca uptake proceeding in synchrony. The strong stimulation of Ca turnover by P_i indicates that the exchange rate observed without P_i is not limited by the kinetics of the Ca-translocation step. One might assume that P_i enhances the formation of a phosphoprotein that accepts Ca^{2+}_i for translocation. However, we were unable to detect an increased level of stable phosphoprotein after addition of P_i.

Ion Permeability and Electrogenicity

The estimate of the energy requirement for Ca uptake (see above) was based on the assumption that no energy is required to overcome an electrical potential during Ca translocation. However, as in artificial liposomes doped with ion carriers, a high potential across the SR can be created when cation gradients are formed in the presence of impermeable anions (1, 2, 55, 94). If an inside-negative potential is imposed, Ca transport and ATPase activity are activated (1, 55). This demonstrates that Ca transport proceeds electrogenically, producing an inside-positive potential that counteracts unbinding of Ca^{2+} from internal low-affinity transport sites. We think this effect is negligible for the in vivo situation for the following reasons.

Since Ca release is more critically dependent on SR membrane resistance (r_{SR}) for monovalent ions than Ca uptake, it is worthwhile first to calculate the maximal specific membrane resistance, $(R_m)_{max}$, compatible with passive Ca release along the Ca^{2+} gradient. Under the assumption that the resistance for ions other than Ca^{2+} is the same during Ca uptake, an upper limit for the buildup of a membrane potential during Ca uptake can be deduced.

The Ca required to activate 1 g of muscle (200 nmol) corresponds to a current of 8 A if the release lasts 5 msec. Based on a SR surface of 20,000 cm^2 g^{-1} of muscle and a specific membrane capacitance of 1 μF/cm^2, only about 9 nmol of Ca^{2+} can be released without charge compensation before the SR is charged up to the Ca^{2+} equilibrium potential. It can be assumed that $\sim$90% of the Ca^{2+} is released at a gradient of not more than 1000: 1. Under these conditions the available free energy for Ca release and ion flow for charge compensation is RT ln 1000 $\cdot$ 2 $\cdot$ 10^{-7} M $\cong$ 3 $\cdot$ 10^{-3}J, yielding an upper limit for total r_{SR} (Ca release and countercurrent flow) of 1.10^{-2} Ω, deduced from: work (in J) = I^2 $\cdot$ r $\cdot$ t, (I = 8 A, t = 5 msec). Assuming that the longitudinal resistances from Ca-release sites to sites of charge compensation are negligibly small (cf 60) and that the whole SR surface is involved in charge compensation, a $(R_m)_{max}$ of $\sim$ 200 Ωcm^2 is deduced, under the condition that the resistance for Ca^{2+} release is negligibly small. If the SR has indeed such a low R_m, the current, carried by Ca uptake (about 1/10 or less of the release current, $\sim$ 0.8 A) would cause at most an inside positive potential of $\sim$ 8 mV. Equal resistances for both currents (Ca^{2+}-release current and charge compensating current) would reduce the potential to 4 mV and R_m, compatible with Ca release, to 100 Ω cm^2. Morphological restrictions like narrowed parts between longitudinal SR and terminal cisternae would require still lower R_m values.

These values of 200 or 100 Ωcm^2 are substantially lower than all values deduced from shape-change experiments, experiments with optical probes of membrane potential on SR vesicles exposed to different solutes (38), or experiments on whole muscle fibers (4). Resistance values of 500–42,000 Ωcm^2 (see Table 2) would require a larger ΔG as driving force for charge compensation than originally was expended for Ca uptake (100 nmol ATP/200 nmol Ca). On the other hand, these "energetically upper limits" for R_m of 200 Ωcm^2 respectively 100 Ωcm^2 are considerably higher than the values of 3, 17, and 68 Ωcm^2 deduced from direct and independent conductance measurements for Cl^-, K^+, and Na^+ on SR vesicles fused with planar artificial lipid bilayers. While for Cl^- a steady conductance of ~ 3 Ωcm^2 (at 10 mM Cl^-) is found, the conductance for K^+ and Na^+ increases and decreases in discrete steps of $\sim$ 25–100 pS at 0.1 M KCl or NaCl (44). The probability that the K^+/Na^+ channels are in the open configuration is voltage-dependent in such a way that an inside-negative membrane potential increases the channel's mean open time and therefore decreases the shunt resistance, thus preventing the buildup of a substantial membrane potential. Extrapolation to 0 mV potential difference yields a time-averaged $(R_m)_K$ of 17 Ωcm^2. Under these conditions $(R_m)_K$ alone would allow enough counter-current to limit the buildup of an inside-positive membrane potential to $\sim$ 0.7 mV during Ca uptake.

Table 2   Ion permeability of SR membranes[a]

Ions (references)	Measurement	Conditions pH	°C	Permeability (10^{-7} cm s^{-1})	Spec. membrane resistance (R_{SR}) (Ωcm^2)		Assumed activity for calculation of R_{SR} (mM)
K^+ (38)	Turbidity	6.5	23	0.6	42,000	s	100
K^+ (55)	Fluorescence	6.0	20	10–50	2,500–500	s	100
K^+ (44)	Conductivity	7.0	20	—	17	s	(meas. at 100)
Na^+ (38)	Turbidity	6.5	23	0.4	62,500	s	10
Na^+ (44)	Conductivity	7.0	20	—	68	s	(meas. at 100)
Cl^- (38)	Turbidity	6.5	23	30	8,300	s	10
Cl^- (56)	Conductivity	7.3	20	—	3	s	(meas. at 10)
Mg^{2+} (38)	Turbidity	6.5	23	0.02	$2.1 \cdot 10^7$	i	3
Ca^{2+} (38)	Turbidity	6.5	23	0.024	$2.6 \cdot 10^7$	o	2
Ca^{2+} (25)	Efflux	6.5	20	*0.002–0.01	3.1–$0.6 \cdot 10^8$	o	2
Ca^{2+} (25, 38)	Efflux	7.0	20	*0.02–0.1	3.1–$0.6 \cdot 10^7$	o	2
Ca^{2+} (25)	Efflux	7.0	30	*0.06–0.3	10–$2 \cdot 10^6$	o	2
Ca^{2+} (25)	Efflux	8.0	30	*0.12–0.6	5–$1 \cdot 10^6$	o	2
H^+ (55)	Fluorescence	6.2–7.6	15	10^4	$2.5 \cdot 10^6$	s	10^{-4}

[a] All permeability data are derived from studies with isolated SR vesicles. (*) The Ca-permeability has been calculated from observed rates of Ca efflux from Ca-loaded vesicles. Letters behind the values for R_{SR} indicate direction of current for which R_{SR} was calculated: s = symmetrical, i = from myoplasm into SR, o = from SR into myoplasm. Permeability was converted into specific membrane resistance according to Weidmann (91).

Changes in SR membrane potential deduced from optical measurements in muscle fibers during excitation and from isolated SR in vitro are likely to be substantially contaminated by varying interaction of the dyes with the transport protein. [For review and literature see (60).]

A high permeability of the SR for small cations and anions is consistent with the observation that no difference in [Na], [K], and [Cl] between SR lumen and myoplasm are found by electron probe microanalysis (73). After a 1.2 sec tetanus the [Ca] in the internal cisternae is reduced to 40%. [Mg] and [K] are simultaneously increased. However, the observable charge compensation is incomplete by ~56 meq/kg dry wt of terminal cisternae. It was proposed that H$^+$ could compensate for the missing charge; but because of the low [H$^+$] in the myoplasm the H conductance of the SR is substantially lower than the K conductance, even if a permeability coefficient of 30 cm sec^{-1} (corresponding to free diffusion of HCl in water) is assumed (see Table 2). It is therefore highly improbable that H$^+$ cross the SR in response to an electrical potential. The Ca pump may be activated during the 1.2 sec tetanus, generating and releasing H$^+$ into the SR, thereby preventing further uptake of "visible" positive charge carriers (9).

ACKNOWLEDGMENT

H. Oetliker was supported by grants from the Swiss National Science Foundation (No. 3.423-0.78) and the Muscular Dystrophy Association, USA.

Literature Cited

1. Beeler, T. J. 1980. Ca^{2+} uptake and membrane potential in sarcoplasmic reticulum vesicles. *J. Biol. Chem.* 255: 9156–61
2. Beeler, T. J., Farmen, R. H., Martonosi, A. N. 1981. The mechanism of voltage-sensitive dye responses on sarcoplasmic reticulum. *J. Membr. Biol.* 62:113–37
3. Beil, F. U., von Chak, D., Hasselbach, W. 1977. Phosphorylation from inorganic phosphate and ATP synthesis of sarcoplasmic membranes. *Eur. J. Biochem.* 81:151–64
4. Benzanilla, F., Horowicz, P. 1975. Fluorescence intensity changes associated with contractile activation in frog muscle stained with nile blue. *J. Physiol.* 246:709–35
5. Boyer, P. D., de Meis, L., Carvalho, M. G. C., Hackney, P. D. 1977. Dynamic reversal of enzyme carboxyl group phosphorylation as the basis of the oxygen exchange catalyzed by sarcoplasmic

reticulum adenosine triphosphatase. *Biochemistry* 16:136–39
6. Feher, J. J., Briggs, F. N. 1981. The order of calcium and ADP release from the calcium pump of sarcoplasmic reticulum. *Fed. Proc.* 33: Abstr. MPM G1
7. Chaloub, R. M., Guimaraes-Motta, H., Verjovski-Almeida, S., de Meis, L., Inesi, G. 1979. Sequential reactions in P$_i$ utilization for ATP synthesis by sarcoplasmic reticulum. *J. Biol. Chem.* 254:9464–68
8. Chiesi, M., Inesi, G. 1979. The use of quench reagents for resolution of single transport cycles in sarcoplasmic reticulum. *J. Biol. Chem.* 254:10370–77
9. Chiesi, M., Inesi, G. 1980. Adenosine 5' triphosphate dependent fluxes of manganese and hydrogen ions in sarcoplasmic reticulum vesicles. *Biochemistry* 19:2912–18

10. Chiesi, M., Ho, M. M., Inesi, G., Somlyo, A. V., Somlyo, A. P. 1981. Primary role of sarcoplasmic reticulum in phasic contractile activation of cardiac myocytes with shunted myolemma. *J. Cell Biol.* 91:728–42

11. Coray, A., Fry, C. H., Hess, P., McGuigan, J. A. S., Weingart, R. 1980. Resting calcium in sheep cardiac tissue and frog skeletal muscle measured with ion-selective micro-electrodes. *J. Physiol.* 305:60–61

12. Dancker, P. 1980. Tropomyosin-troponin-induced changes in the partitioning of free energy release of actomyosin-catalyzed ATP hydrolysis as measured by ATP-phosphate exchange. *Z. Naturforsch.* 35c:431–38

13. Deamer, D. W., Baskin, R. J. 1969. Ultrastructure of sarcoplasmic reticulum preparations. *J. Cell Biol.* 42:296–307

14. Deamer, D., Baskin, R. J. 1972. ATP synthesis in sarcoplasmic reticulum. *Arch. Biochem. Biophys.* 153:47–54

15. de Meis, L., Masuda, H. 1974. Phosphorylation of the sarcoplasmic reticulum membrane by orthophosphate through two different reactions. *Biochemistry* 13:2057–62

16. de Meis, L., Tume, R. K. 1977. A new mechanism by which an H^+ concentration gradient drives the synthesis of adenosine triphosphate, pH jump, and adenosine triphosphate synthesis by the Ca^{2+}-dependent adenosine triphosphatase of sarcoplasmic reticulum. *Biochemistry* 16:4455-63

17. de Meis, L. 1981. The sarcoplasmic reticulum in transport. In *Life Science,* ed. E. E. Bittar, 2:1–163. NY: Wiley

18. Dupont, Y. 1980. Occlusion of divalent cations in the phosphorylated calcium pump of sarcoplasmic reticulum. *Eur. J. Biochem.* 109:231–38

19. Endo, M. 1977. Calcium release from the sarcoplasmic reticulum. *Physiol. Rev.* 57:71–108

20. Fabiato, A. 1980. Sarcomere length dependence of calcium release from the sarcoplasmic reticulum of skinned cardiac cells demonstrated by differential microspectrophotometry with arsenazo III. *J. Gen. Physiol.* 76:15a

21. Fassold, E., von Chak, D., Hasselbach, W. 1981. Variable Ca^{2+} transport: phosphoprotein ratios in the early part of the GTP-driven calcium-transport reaction of the sarcoplasmic reticulum. *Eur. J. Biochem.* 113:611–16

22. Franzini-Armstrong, C. 1980. Structure of sarcoplasmic reticulum. *Fed. Proc.* 39:2403–9

23. Froehlich, J. P., Taylor, E. W. 1976. Transient state kinetic effects of calcium ion on sarcoplasmic reticulum adenosine triphosphatase. *J. Biol. Chem.* 251:2307–15

24. Hasselbach, W., Makinose, M. 1963. Über den Mechanismus des Calciumtransportes durch die Membranen des sarkoplasmatischen Retikulums. *Biochem. Z.* 339:94–111

25. Hasselbach, W., Fiehn, W., Makinose, M., Migala, A. J. 1969. Calcium fluxes across isolated sarcoplasmic membranes in the presence or absence of ATP. In *The Molecular Basis of Membrane Function,* ed. D. C. Testeson, pp. 299–316. Englewood Cliffs, NJ: Prentice-Hall

26. Hasselbach, W. 1979. The sarcoplasmic calcium pump. A model of energy transduction in biological membranes. In *Topics in Current Chemistry,* ed. M. J. S. Dewar, 78:1–56. Berlin/Heidelberg/NY: Springer

27. Hasselbach, W., Koenig, V. 1980. Low affinity calcium binding sites of the calcium transport ATPase of sarcoplasmic reticulum membranes. *Z. Naturforsch.* 35c:1012–18

28. Hasselbach, W. 1981. Calcium-activated ATPase of the sarcoplasmic reticulum membranes. In *Membrane Transport,* ed. S. L. Bonting, J. J. H. H. M. de Pont, pp. 183–208. NY: Elsevier/North Holland

29. Hasselbach, W., Fassold, E., Migala, A., Rauch, B. 1981. Magnesium dependence of sarcoplasmic reticulum calcium transport. *Fed. Proc.* 40:2657–61

30. Homsher, E., Mommaerts, W. F. H. M., Ricchiuti, N. V., Wallner, A. 1972. Activation heat, activation metabolism and tension-related heat in frog semitendinosus muscle. *J. Physiol.* 220:601–25

31. Ikemoto, N. 1975. Transport and inhibitory Ca^{2+} binding sites on the ATPase enzyme isolated from the sarcoplasmic reticulum. *J. Biol. Chem.* 250:7219–24

32. Ikemoto, N. 1976. Behaviour of the Ca^{2+} transport sites linked with the phosphorylation reaction of ATPase purified from the sarcoplasmic reticulum. *J. Biol. Chem.* 251:7275–77

33. Inesi, G. 1979. Transport across sarcoplasmic reticulum in skeletal and cardiac muscle. In *Membrane Transport in Biology,* ed. G. Giebisch, D. C. Testeson, H. H. Ussing, 2:357–93. Berlin/-Heidelberg/NY: Springer

34. Inesi, G. 1981. The sarcoplasmic reticulum of skeletal and cardiac muscle. In

Cell and Muscle Motility, ed. R. M. Dowben, G. W. Shay, 1:63–97. NY: Plenum

35. Julian, F. J., Moss, R. L. 1981. Effects of calcium and ionic strength on shortening velocity and tension development in frog skinned muscle fibres. *J. Physiol.* 311:179–99

36. Kanazawa, T., Yamada, S., Yamamoto, T., Tonomura, Y. 1971. Reaction mechanism of the Ca²⁺-dependent ATPase of sarcoplasmic reticulum from skeletal muscle. *J. Biochem.* 70:95–123

37. Kanazawa, T., Boyer, P. D. 1973. Occurrence and characteristics of a rapid exchange of phosphate oxygens catalyzed by sarcoplasmic reticulum vesicles. *J. Biol. Chem.* 248:3163–72

38. Kasai, M., Kometani, T. 1979. Ionic permeability of sarcoplasmic reticulum membranes. In *Cation Flux across Biomembranes,* ed. Y. Mukohata, L. Packer, pp. 167–177. NY: Academic

39. Kasai, M. 1980. Inulin exclusion volume of sarcoplasmic vesicles under various solvent conditions. *J. Biochem.* 88:1081–85

40. Katz, A. M., Repke, D. I., Dunnett, J., Hasselbach, W. 1977. Dependence of calcium permeability of sarcoplasmic reticulum vesicles on external and internal calcium ion concentrations. *J. Biol. Chem.* 252:1950–56

41. Knowles, A. F., Racker, E. 1975. Formation of adenosine triphosphate from P_i and adenosine diphosphate by purified Ca²⁺ adenosine triphosphatase *J. Biol. Chem.* 250:1949–51

42. Kobayashi, T., Sugi, H. 1980. Measurement of heat production during summation of isometric contraction in frog skeletal muscle with an infrared radiometer. *Jpn. J. Physiol.* 30:617–29

43. Kometani, T., Kasai, M. 1980. Ion movement accompanied by calcium uptake of sarcoplasmic reticulum vesicles studied through the osmotic volume change by the light scattering method. *J. Membr. Biol.* 56:159–68

44. Labarca, P. P., Miller, C. 1981. A K⁺-selective, three-state channel from fragmented sarcoplasmic reticulum of frog leg muscle. *J. Membr. Biol.* 61:31–38

45. Lee, C. O., Uhm, D. Y., Dresdner, K. 1980. Sodium-calcium exchange in rabbit heart muscle cells: direct measurement of sarcoplasmic Ca²⁺ activity. *Science* 209:699–701

46. Makinose, M., Hasselbach, W. 1965. Der Einfluss von Oxalat auf den Calcium-Transport isolierter Vesikel des sar-

koplasmatischen Retikulum. *Biochem. Z.* 343:360–82

47. Makinose, M., The, R. 1965. Calcium-Akkumulation und Nukleosidtriphosphat-Spaltung durch die Vesikel des sarkoplasmatischen Retikulum. *Biochem. Z.* 343:383–93

48. Makinose, M., Hasselbach, W. 1971. ATP Synthesis by the reverse of the sarcoplasmic reticulum pump. *FEBS Lett.* 12:271–72

49. Makinose, M. 1972. Phosphoprotein formation during osmo-chemical energy conversion in the membrane of the sarcoplasmic reticulum. *FEBS Lett.* 25:113–15

50. Makinose, M. 1973. Possible functional states of the enzyme of the sarcoplasmic calcium pump. *FEBS Lett.* 37:140–43

51. Makinose, M., Boll, W. 1979. The role of magnesium on the sarcoplasmic calcium pump. In *Cation Flux across Biomembranes,* ed. Y. Mukohata, L. Packer, pp. 89–100. NY: Academic

52. Martin, D. W., Tanford, C. 1981. Phosphorylation of calcium adenosine-triphosphatase by inorganic phosphate: van't Hoff analysis of enthalpy changes. *Biochemistry* 20:4597–602

53. Meissner, G., Conner, G. E., Fleischer, S. 1973. Isolation of sarcoplasmic reticulum by zonal centrifugation and purification of Ca²⁺-pump and Ca²⁺-binding proteins. *Biochim. Biophys. Acta* 298:246–69

54. Meissner, G. 1973. ATP and Ca²⁺ binding by the Ca²⁺ pump protein of sarcoplasmic reticulum. *Biochim. Biophys. Acta* 298:906–26

55. Meissner, G. 1981. Calcium transport and monovalent cation and proton fluxes in sarcoplasmic reticulum vesicles. *J. Biol. Chem.* 256:636–43

56. Miller, C., Racker, E. 1976. Ca²⁺-induced fusion of fragmented sarcoplasmic reticulum with artificial planar bilayers. *J. Membr. Biol.* 30:283–300

57. Miyamoto, H., Kasai, M. 1979. Asymmetric distribution of calcium binding sites of sarcoplasmic reticulum fragments. *J. Biochem.* 85:765–73

58. Mobley, B. A., Eisenberg, B. R. 1975. Sizes of components in frog skeletal muscle measured by methods of stereology. *J. Gen. Physiol.* 66:31–45

59. Noack, E., Kurzmack, M., Verjovski-Almeida, S., Inesi, G. 1978. The effect of propanolol and its analogs on Ca2+ transport by sarcoplasmic reticulum vesicles. *J. Pharmacol. Exp. Therap.* 206:281–88

60. Oetliker, H. 1982. An appraisal of the evidence for a sarcoplasmic reticulum potential and its relation to calcium release in skeletal muscle. *J. Muscle Res. Cell Motil.* 3: In press

61. Peachey, L. D. 1965. The sarcoplasmic reticulum and transverse tubulus of the frog's sartorius muscle. *J. Cell Biol.* 25:209–31

62. Pette, D., Heilmann, C. 1979. Some characteristics of sarcoplasmic reticulum in fast- and slow-twitch muscles. *Biochem. Soc. Transact.* 7:765–67

63. Portzehl, H., Zaoralek, P., Grieder, A. 1965. Der Calcium-Spiegel in lebenden und isolierten Muskelfibrillen von Maia Squinado und seine Regulierung durch die sarkoplasmatischen Vesikel. *Pflügers Arch.* 286:44–56

64. Potter, J. D. 1974. The content of tropomin, tropomyosin, actin, and myosin in rabbit skeletal muscle myofibrils. *Arch. Biochem. Biophys.* 162:436–41

65. Punzengruber, C., Prager, R., Kolassa, N., Winkler, F., Suko, J. 1978. Calcium gradient-dependent and calcium gradient-independent phosphorylation of sarcoplasmic reticulum by orthophosphate. The role of magnesium. *Eur. J. Biochem.* 92:349–59

66. Rauch, B., v. Chak, D., Hasselbach, W. 1977. Phosphorylation by inorganic phosphate of sarcoplasmic membranes. *Z. Naturforsch.* 32c: 828–34

67. Robertson, S. D., Johnson, J. S., Potter, J. D. 1981. The time-course of Ca^{2+} exchange with calmodulin, troponin, parvalbumin, and myosin in response to transient increases in Ca^{2+}. *Biophys. J.* 34:559–69

68. Ronzani, N., Migala, A., Hasselbach, W. 1979. Comparison between ATP-supported and GTP-supported phosphate turnover of the calcium-transporting sarcoplasmic reticulum membranes. *Eur. J. Biochem.* 101:593–606

69. Rossi, B., de Assis Leone, G., Gache, C., Lazdunski, M. 1979. Pseudosubstrates of the sarcoplasmic Ca^{2+}-ATPase as tools to study the coupling between substrate hydrolysis and Ca^{2+} transport. *J. Biol. Chem.* 254:2302–7

70. Scofano, H. M., de Meis, L. 1981. Ratio of hydrolysis and synthesis of ATP by the sarcoplasmic reticulum ATPase in the absence of a Ca^{2+} concentration gradient. *J. Biol. Chem.* 256:4282–85

71. Shigekawa, M., Akowitz, A. A. 1979. On the mechanism of Ca^{2+}-dependent adenosine triphosphatase of sarcoplasmic reticulum. *J. Biol. Chem.* 254: 4726–30

72. Sleep, J. A., Smith, S. J. 1981. Actomyosin ATPase and muscle contraction. *Curr. Top. Bioenerg.* 11: 239–86

73. Somlyo, A. V., Gonzalez-Serratos, H., Shuman, H., McLellan, G., Somlyo, A. P. 1981. Calcium release and ionic changes in the sarcoplasmic reticulum of tetanized muscle: An electron probe study. *J. Cell Biol.* 90:577–94

74. Sommer, J. R., Johnson, E. A. 1979. The ultrastructure in cardic muscle. In *Handbook of Physiology, Sect. 2, The Cardiovascular System*, ed. R. M. Berne, 1:113–86. Bethesda: Am. Physiol. Soc.

75. Suko, J., Plank, B., Preis, P., Kolassa, N., Hellmann, G., Conca, W. 1981. Formation of magnesium-phosphoenzyme and magnesium-calcium-phosphoenzyme in the phosphorylation of adenosine triphosphatase by orthophosphate in sarcoplasmic reticulum. *Eur. J. Biochem.* 119:225–36

76. Sumida, M., Wang, T., Mandel, F., Froehlich, J. P., Schwartz, A. 1978. Transient kinetics of Ca^{2+} transport of sarcoplasmic reticulum. *J. Biol. Chem.* 253:8772–77

77. Takakuwa, Y., Kanazawa, T. 1981. Reaction mechanism of (Ca^{2+},Mg^{2+})-ATPase of sarcoplasmic reticulum vesicles. *J. Biol. Chem.* 256:2691–95

78. Takakuwa, Y., Kanazawa, T. 1979. Slow transition of phosphoenzyme from ADP-insensitive froms in solubilized Ca^{2+},Mg^{2+}-ATPase of sarcoplasmic reticulum. *Biochem. Biophys. Res. Commun.* 88:1209–16

79. Takisawa, H., Tonomura, Y. 1979. ADP-sensitive and -insensitive phosphorylated intermediates of solubilized Ca^{2+},Mg^{2+}-dependent ATPase of the sarcoplasmic reticulum from skeletal muscle. *J. Biochem.* 86:425–41

80. Takisawa, H., Makinose, M. 1981. Occluded bound calcium on the phosphorylated sarcoplasmic transport ATPase. *Nature* 290:271–73

81. The, R., Husseini, H. S., Hasselbach, W. 1981. Synthetic monoacylphospholipids as reactivators of the calcium-dependent ATPase of enzymatically delipidated sarcoplasmic membranes. *Eur. J. Biochem.* 118:223–29

82. Tomanek, R. J. 1976. Ultrastructure differentiation of skeletal muscle fibres and their diversity. *J. Ultrastruct. Res.* 55:212–27

83. Van Winkle, W. B., Schwartz, A. 1978. Morphological and biochemical corre-

lates of skeletal muscle contractility in the rat. *J. Cell. Physiol.* 97:99–120

84. Veech, R. L., Lawson, J. W. R., Cornell, N. W., Krebs, H. A. 1979. Cytosolic phosphorylation potential. *J. Biol. Chem.* 254:6538–47

85. Verjovski-Almeida, S., Kurzmack, M., Inesi, G. 1978. Partial reactions in the catalytic and transport cycle of sarcoplasmic reticulum ATPase. *Biochemistry* 17:5006–13

86. Waas, W., Hasselbach, W. 1981. Interference of nucleoside diphosphate and inorganic phosphate with nucleoside-triphosphate-dependent calcium fluxes and calcium-dependent nucleoside-triphosphate hydrolysis in membranes of sarcoplasmic-reticulum vesicles. *Eur. J. Biochem.* 116:601–8

87. Wang, T., Grassi de Gende, A. O., Tsai, L.-I., Schwartz, A. 1981. Influence of monovalent cations on the Ca²⁺-ATPase of sarcoplasmic reticulum isolated from rabbit skeletal and dog cardiac muscle. *Biochim. Biophys. Acta* 637:523–29

88. Watanabe, T., Lewis, D., Nakamoto, R., Kurzmack, M., Fronticelli, C., Inesi, G. 1981. Modulation of calcium binding in sarcoplasmic reticulum adenosinetriphosphatase. *Biochemistry* 20:6617–25

89. Weber, A., Herz, R. 1963. The binding of calcium to actomyosin systems in relation to their biological activity. *J. Biol. Chem.* 238:599–605

90. Weber, A., Herz, R. 1966. Study of the kinetics of calcium transport by isolated fragmented sarcoplasmic reticulum. *Biochem. Z.* 345:329–69

91. Weidmann, S. 1966. The diffusion of radiopotassium across intercalated disks of mammalian cardiac muscle. *J. Physiol.* 187:323–42

92. Wendt-Gallitelli, M. F., Wolburg, H., Schlote, W., Schwegler, M., Holnbarsch, C., Jacob, R. 1980. Prospects of X-ray microanalysis of myocardial contraction. *Basic Res. Cardiol.* 75:66–72

93. Zimniak, P., Racker, E. 1978. Electrogenicity of Ca²⁺ transport catalyzed by the Ca²⁺-ATPase from sarcoplasmic reticulum. *J. Biol. Chem.* 253:4631–37

Ann. Rev. Physiol. 1983. 45:341–58

CALCIUM CHANNELS IN EXCITABLE CELL MEMBRANES

R. W. Tsien

Department of Physiology, Yale University School of Medicine, New Haven, Connecticut 06510

INTRODUCTION

The existence of calcium permeability in excitable cells has been appreciated for 30 years (31)—almost as long as we have known about voltage-dependent permeabilities to sodium and potassium (46, 47). Yet, to this day, our understanding of Ca channels has lagged far behind our knowledge of Na or K channels. This situation is ironic because Ca channels are widely distributed and rival their better-characterized counterparts in diversity of biological function (42). Ca channels play a crucial role in coupling membrane excitation to cellular responses such as secretion or contraction. They are primarily responsible for some specialized but very interesting forms of excitability—e.g. in the nodal regions of the heart (14, 76), the cilia of *Paramecium* (11, 12), or the dendrites (64) or growth cones (6) of certain neurons. Unlike Na channels, Ca channels are often modulated by hormones and neurotransmitters.

For many years, biophysical or biochemical analysis of Ca channels has been seriously hampered by experimental problems (e.g. 42, 81). No preparation has been as suitable and no drug as specific for Ca channels as the squid axon and tetrodotoxin are for Na channels. But the state of the art has improved recently with the development of powerful methods for recording Ca channel activity and of blocking drugs that may interact with Ca channels in a potent and specific manner.

We now know that Ca channels are pores, capable of transferring millions of permeant ions per second, whose voltage-dependent properties clearly distinguish them from pumps or exchange mechanisms described elsewhere in this volume. There is growing appreciation that Ca channels can be

341

0066-4278/83/0315-0341$02.00

classified into various subtypes (42), differing most dramatically in the mechanism of inward current decay during a maintained depolarization. Within an individual subtype, there may be a strong similarity between Ca channel properties in different cells.

Future progress will be speeded by a more cosmopolitan view of Ca channels and better communication between investigators who work on Ca channels in different tissues. In this spirit, I organize this review according to general questions about these channels, rather than preparation by preparation. Restricted in length, but aided by some valuable recent predecessors (20, 42, 55, 67, 81), this article emphasizes exciting developments not previously reviewed.

OLD PROBLEMS, NEW METHODS

Hagiwara & Byerly (42) carefully discussed drawbacks of existing methods for studying Ca currents and set forth some criteria for new approaches. Their arguments can be summarized by a list of features desirable for any preparation to be used for biophysical analysis of the Ca current: (a) The preparation should have a strong Ca current. (b) The voltage clamp should be spatially uniform and rapidly settling. (c) The composition of solutions on both sides of the membrane should be under experimental control. (d) The Ca current should be separable from other ionic currents. (e) The reversal potential should be clearly defined if possible. Corresponding requirements would be met by systems available for studying Na or K channels, but not, until recently, by methods for studying Ca channels. Fortunately, the outlook for Ca channels is improving rapidly.

Intracellular Dialysis or Perfusion

Neurons and heart cells have been subjected to methods that rupture a large area of membrane to gain free access to the intracellular space. The membrane may be disrupted at one place to allow "dialysis" (16, 56, 59) or in two places to permit "perfusion" (32, 57, 60). This general approach allows recording of robust Ca currents, with rapidly settling voltage steps and prompt solution changes, so requirements a–c are readily met. Furthermore, requirements for dissection and reversal of Ca channel current (d and e) seem to be satisfied in dialyzed single ventricular cells (66), as described below.

Gigaseal Recording from Membrane Patches

The patch clamp method of Neher, Sakmann, and colleagues (45) has made it possible to record activity from individual Ca channels. A fine-tipped, fire-polished pipette is filled with a high concentration of permeant ion and then pressed against the outside of an enzymatically treated cell. After application of gentle suction, a "gigaseal" forms between the pipette tip and the membrane surface, so that current flow across the membrane patch and into the pipette can be collected and recorded with high resolution. The method allows unitary Ca channel currents of the order of 0.5–2 pA to be recorded under good voltage control; interference from other channels is usually easy to recognize and eliminate. Thus requirements a, b, and d are readily satisfied. Excision of membrane patches would allow changes in the cytoplasmic solution (requirement c), but in chromaffin cells at least this abolishes Ca channel activity within minutes (34). Outward current through individual Ca channels has not yet been reported.

Gigaseal Recording from Small Cells

Gigaseal pipettes have also been used to record Ca channel activity in whole cells. After gigaseal formation, the application of strong suction ruptures the membrane patch and allows current flow and diffusional exchange between the pipette and the cytoplasm. The method has been used to record unitary Ca channel activity (33, 34) or global Ca channel activity (34, 43); it allows rapid voltage steps and prompt exchange of small ions if the cell is small and the pipette opening relatively large. Reversal of Ca channel current (probably due to Cs efflux) has been obtained in chromaffin cells using this technique (34).

SINGLE CHANNEL CURRENTS

Unitary current pulses associated with the activity of single Ca channels have been recorded in snail neuron (65), bovine adrenal chromaffin cell (33, 34), and cultured ventricular cells of neonatal rat heart (84). A few years ago, it seemed doubtful that such recordings would be possible; now they open up many new possibilities for studying Ca channels. The uniform amplitude of the unitary current pulses supports the assumption that Ca channels have only two distinguishable conductance levels, open and closed; so far, there is no evidence for the intermediate conductance levels sometimes found for other ionic channels. This encourages the practice of representing the global Ca channel current (I) very simply, as $I = \bar{I} \cdot p$, where p is the probability of an individual channel being open and $\bar{I}$ is the current if all the channels are open. The determination of the single channel current (i) allows $\bar{I}$ to be factored further, as $\bar{I} = N \cdot i$, where N is the number of channels in the membrane. Thus,

$$I = N \cdot i \cdot p. \qquad\qquad 1.$$

Directly recorded unitary current amplitudes and values of i obtained from nonstationary fluctuation analysis agree rather well (34). Estimates of the single channel current range between 0.5 and 1.2 pA with 95–100 mM Ba as the external current carrier and V_m near 0 mV (33, 34, 43, 84). Substitution of 50 mM Ca for 50 mM Ba reduces i from 0.75 pA to 0.41 pA in snail neurons (65). At physiological levels of extracellular calcium, i is probably too small to be resolved by direct recordings; nonstationary fluctuation analysis in chromaffin cells near zero membrane potential gives $i = 0.025$ pA in 1 mM Ca_o and $i = 0.06$ pA in 5 mM Ca_o (34).

Earlier estimates of i from stationary fluctuation analysis of current noise in snail neurons (2, 58) are lower than recent values, including those obtained in the same preparation (65). The discrepancy is most striking in the case of Krishtal et al (58), who found that $i = 0.2$ pA in 130 mM Ba_o. One possibility (65) is that i was reduced by the external acidity (pH $= 5.7$) in the Krishtal et al experiments (see 20, 44). Direct measurements of the effect of pH on i would be worthwhile, particularly in heart, since acidification is known to decrease Ca influx and contractility during myocardial ischemia (for review see 20).

Ion Flux per Channel

A single channel current of 1 pA corresponds to a flux of three million divalent cations per second. As in the case of other ionic channels, the high rate of ion transfer puts the channel well beyond the capabilities of known mobile carrier mechanisms and argues that the ion transfer mechanism is a pore.

Number of Ca Channels per Unit Area

Information about the total number of functional Ca channels in a membrane patch or whole cell comes along with estimates of the unitary current. Estimates of channel density range from ~ 1 μm^{-2} in GH_3 pituitary tumor cells (43) and 5–15 μm^{-2} in chromaffin cells, up to 30–60 per μm^{-2} in snail neurons (58). It will be important to compare electrophysiological estimates of channel density with the density of binding sites for radiolabelled Ca channel blockers such as [3H]-nitrendipine (10, 29, 72).

OPEN CHANNEL PROPERTIES

The high throughput rate of single Ca channels raises fundamental questions about how they work. Little is known about how the channel manages to allow so many Ca or Ba ions to permeate while largely rejecting other ions that are far more numerous. The characteristics of the open channel

—its current–voltage relationship, and its dependence on permeant ion concentration—are important, not only as a description of channel performance but also as an expression of ion interaction with channel structure.

There is growing appreciation of ion saturation and block as reflections of binding site(s) within the channel (for review see 42). Unfortunately, there is no general agreement on the form of the current–voltage relationship for open Ca channels. Here, as in some other areas, investigators of neuronal and cardiac membranes have reached divergent conclusions. For neurons, Kostyuk states that "Ca channels are, as a matter of fact, completely rectifying and can pass ions only into the cell" (55), and Hagiwara & Byerly write that "the Ca current appears to be inherently a one-way current" (42). These conclusions are based on considerations of the extreme asymmetry of the Ca ion activities on either side of the membrane and the blocking effect of intracellular Ca. Similar considerations led to suggestions that the open-channel characteristic might show inward-going rectification (slope conductance increasing with hyperpolarization). In the case of cardiac preparations, the prevailing view is very different, owing largely to results of Reuter & Scholz (82). They reported a clearcut reversal potential (which they attributed to K efflux through the Ca channel) and an ohmic open-channel characteristic.

Reversal of Ca Channel Current?

In searching for outward current through the Ca channel in molluscan neurons, most investigators have chosen to replace intracellular K with Cs to avoid outward current through K-specific channels (including those activated by intracellular Ca). Generally, increasing the depolarizing pulse to very positive values suppresses the inward Ca current but does not produce an outward current that can be associated with opening of the Ca channel (1, 3, 16, 56). In some cases, the depolarizations evoke a slowly activating, Cd-sensitive outward current called a nonspecific current, or I_{ns}, because it is not abolished when intracellular K or Cs are replaced by Tris or tetraethylammonium (16, 56).

Struck by the disparity between views of Ca channels in neuron and heart, Kai Lee and I (61) looked for outward movements of monovalent ions through the Ca channel in dialyzed single heart cells. When we followed the strategy of the neuron experiments, and substituted Cs for intracellular K, we also found no clear indication of outward Ca channel current with depolarizations up to +120 mV. However, when the extracellular Ca was replaced by Ba, a rather striking reversal of time-dependent current was found. The apparent reversal potential, E_{rev}, was displaced appropriately by varying extracellular Ba or intracellular Cs. The decaying outward Cs current showed the same inactivation kinetics as inward Ba current. Perhaps most important, block of Ca channels by Cd or D600 reduced inward and outward currents but had no effect on the (time-independent) current recorded at E_{rev}. These observations argued in favor of a genuine reversal of Ca channel current with Ba outside and Cs inside (61). Similar experimental tests were applied to the apparent reversal seen with Ca outside and K inside (82) and provided evidence once again for a bona fide reversal of Ca channel current (66).

Fenwick et al (34) also found a clear-cut reversal of Ca channel current in whole-cell recordings from chromaffin cells bathed in 1 mM or 5 mM Ca_o. In their case, the outward current was attributed to the outflow of Cs since Cs from the pipette was presumed to replace intracellular K.

Do Open Ca Channels Rectify?

The other major question about open Ca channels concerns their voltage dependence at negative potentials. Is $\bar{I}$ ohmic (81) or does it show increasing conductance with hyperpolarization—supralinearity—would be as predicted by constant-field theory (42)? Most evidence suggests that neither of these is the case. The open-channel current seems to fall short of an ohmic voltage dependence (sublinearity) at negative potentials in a number of preparations: sinoatrial node (75), GH₃ cells (43), snail neurons (16, 93), and squid presynaptic terminal (63). In these studies, the "instantaneous" open-channel current was estimated by extrapolating tail currents back to the time of the repolarizing step. This method runs the risk of underestimating the open-channel current if the initial decay of the tail current is obscured by the settling of the voltage clamp; however, the sublinearity was found even in the snail neuron experiments where special pains were taken to achieve rapid voltage control (93). On the other hand, a supralinear open-channel characteristic was found in stick insect skeletal muscle (7) and with a rapidly settling voltage clamp in chromaffin cells (34).

ACTIVATION

Activation refers to the opening of Ca channels in response to a depolarization. In most tissues, it approaches a steady level within a few milliseconds after a depolarizing step, before much inactivation has occurred. Recent recordings from membrane patches and single cells have provided new information about how activation develops with time and how the peak level of activation depends on the level of the depolarization.

Voltage Dependence of Channel Opening

MAXIMAL PROBABILITY   Measurements of global membrane current have suggested that p increases with depolarization from zero up to a saturating level that is generally assumed to be unity, rather than, say, a much lower value. This assumption has now received direct support from recordings of unitary currents (34, 84) and nonstationary fluctuation analysis (34, 43): At strong depolarizations, p does in fact approach one.

VOLTAGE RANGE OF ACTIVATION   Ca channels become activated over a voltage span of about 50 mV in most cases. The position of the activation curve along the voltage axis varies; half-maximal activation usually occurs between −20 and +10 mV, depending on the preparation and the ionic conditions. Determinations of the voltage dependence of peak activation using tail currents or direct recordings of unitary activity show reasonable agreement (34). Either method is much preferable to inferences from the voltage dependence of peak current (57), which results from the strongly opposing voltage dependences of $p(V)$ and $I(V)$.

Time Course of Channel Opening

IS ACTIVATION A FIRST-ORDER PROCESS?   There is growing agreement that activation of Ca channels develops with a sigmoid time course following a step depolarization, not monoexponentially as expected for a first-order process. The evidence is particularly clear in preparations where Ca current leads to secretion (21, 34, 43, 63).

Activation was described as a first-order process in some earlier studies in heart (52, 82), molluscan neurons (3), and tunicate egg (77). This raised the interesting possibility that Ca channels might activate by a simpler mechanism than Na or K channels. However, voltage clamp methods that give more rapidly settling potential changes reveal a distinctly sigmoid onset in molluscan neurons (1, 16, 56, 57, 96) as well as in heart cells (66). The first-order kinetic description in tunicate egg may also be questioned. Here the time course of activation fits an exponential time course, but only after allowance for a 2 msec delay, a longer lag than can be accounted for by the ~1 msec settling time of the egg cell voltage clamp (77).

Patch clamp recordings provide additional evidence against first-order kinetics. Single channel activity often appears as closely spaced bursts of brief unitary current pulses separated by wider intervals (33, 34, 83); also, the mean open time is much shorter than the main activation time constant, contrary to expectations for a first-order open-closed reaction (34, 65, 84).

DOES ACTIVATION OBEY m^x KINETICS?   The sigmoid onset of Ca current has led many investigators to try to fit their results with the same kinetic framework that Hodgkin & Huxley (46) used for Na and K channels (for review see 42). The probability of channel opening is set proportional to a first-order variable (usually called m) raised to an integer power x. This might correspond to x independent, identical first-order processes that controlled the opening of a channel by unanimous vote. In the case where

$x = 2$, the channel would have two closed states, C_1 and C_2, and one open state, O, connected by voltage-dependent rate constants α_m and β_m as follows:

$$C_1 \underset{\beta m}{\overset{2\alpha_m}{\rightleftharpoons}} C_2 \underset{2\beta_m}{\overset{\alpha_m}{\rightleftharpoons}} O \qquad\qquad \text{A.}$$

Recordings of global Ca currents or activity of individual Ca channels show behavior inconsistent with some key predictions of scheme A. First, at very negative potentials Ca current tails associated with channel deactivation consist of more than one exponential component, and not the simple exponential predicted for Hodgkin-Huxley kinetics (16, 34, 93). Second, during small step perturbations in membrane potential the time constant of Ca current relaxation is considerably briefer than the dominant time constant for activation (16, 57).

KINETIC PARAMETERS FROM ANALYSIS OF NOISE AND UNITARY CURRENTS   Fenwick et al (34) described activation in chromaffin cells using the same three states but with four adjustable rate constants instead of just two.

$$C_1 \underset{k_{-1}}{\overset{k_1}{\rightleftharpoons}} C_2 \underset{k_{-2}}{\overset{k_2}{\rightleftharpoons}} O \qquad\qquad \text{B.}$$

They gave the following kinetic parameters for cells in 95 mM Ba_o at -5 mV membrane potential.

$$C_1 \underset{606 \text{ s}^{-1}}{\overset{61 \text{ s}^{-1}}{\rightleftharpoons}} C_2 \underset{1230 \text{ s}^{-1}}{\overset{345 \text{ s}^{-1}}{\rightleftharpoons}} 0 \qquad\qquad \text{C.}$$

The parameters were largely derived from analysis of unitary currents, but they were consistent with fluctuations and global current signals recorded under the same conditions. The main difference with scheme A lies in k_1. Much slower than the other rate constants, k_1 rate-limits activation and largely controls the interval between bursts. Model C points the way toward further kinetic analysis. It is possible that additional closed states may be required to explain how Ca channel kinetics vary with temperature (96) or membrane potential (S. Hagiwara & H. Ohmori, unpublished experiments).

INACTIVATION

Inactivation refers to the decline in Ca conductance seen in many excitable cells during maintained depolarization. When it occurs, Ca channel inactivation is usually much slower than activation, making kinetic separation of activation from inactivation somewhat easier than for sodium channels (see 4). As in the case of other channels, inactivation of Ca channels can be seen not only as a relaxation of inward Ca current during a depolarization but also as a depression of peak I_{Ca} during a subsequent depolarization.

In its common usage, inactivation refers to a property of Ca channels themselves and is not to be confused with slowly increasing outward current through K channels, which can masquerade as inactivation when it overlaps Ca current (e.g. 1, 13, 19, 63). Inactivation may also be distinguished from a decline in Ca current due to a decreased concentration gradient for charge carriers. Such a decline of I_{Ca} can occur, for example, with depletion of Ca from a restricted extracellular space (5, 38). These distinctions reserve the term inactivation for mechanisms that produce a genuine decline in calcium permeability. Two such mechanisms are known: inactivation produced by membrane depolarization as such, and inactivation caused by intracellular calcium. Voltage-dependent inactivation might be analogous to Na channel inactivation as Hodgkin & Huxley described it (46), while Ca_i-dependent inactivation seems to be a more unusual mechanism, one particularly responsive to cellular metabolism and prior activity.

Even a superficial survey shows that Ca channel inactivation is an extremely variable phenomenon from one membrane system to the next. Some excitable cells show little inactivation while others display voltage- or Ca_i-dependent inactivation to different degrees. Two kinds of Ca channels, each with different inactivation properties, seem to coexist in egg cell membranes of starfish (44) and the marine polychaete *Neanthes* (37). In other systems, the wide variation in the mechanism and extent of inactivation may reflect specific adaptations to cellular functions.

Calcium Channels Showing Very Slow or Very Slight Inactivation

Little inactivation has been found so far for Ca channels involved with excitation-secretion coupling. This holds true for depolarizations lasting hundreds of milliseconds in squid synaptic terminals (63), adrenal chromaffin cells (34) and photoreceptor inner segments (21), and to a lesser degree GH_3 pituitary tumor cells (43). A relative lack of inactivation in the Ca channels of photoreceptor inner segments seems to fit nicely with their participation in continual release of transmitter in the dark (21). Inactivation of Ca channels has been reported in rat neurohypophysis, but only for depolarizations lasting many minutes (see 25). On the other hand, rat brain synaptosomes show two components of divalent cation influx: a La-sensitive component that inactivates within 1 sec and a La-resistant component that does not inactivate within 1 min (73).

Inactivation is also minimal during ~1 sec depolarizations in barnacle muscle (54). But the near-absence of inactivation has been most extensively documented for Ca channels of cut skeletal muscle fibers of the frog (5) and type II Ca channels of the *Neanthes* egg (38). Inactivation is so slow in these preparations that depletion of extracellular Ca, not inactivation, is the main factor responsible for Ca current decay during maintained depolarization. One particularly convincing argument for depletion involves manipulation of the total calcium in the extracellular medium; when the reserve of charge carriers is increased while the size of the Ca current is held constant, the current relaxation is appropriately slowed (5, 38).

Inactivation Mediated by Intracellular Ca^{2+}

This mechanism was proposed by Brehm, Eckert & Tillotson (11, 12, 88) on the basis of voltage clamp experiments in *Paramecium* and *Aplysia* neurons (for review see 28). According to their hypothesis, intracellular Ca accumulates as a result of Ca entry and produces a specific inhibitory effect on Ca channel conductance that appears as inactivation. In its strongest form, the hypothesis claims that Ca_i is a necessary as well as sufficient cause of inactivation; a more restricted version states only that Ca_i plays an important role, but does not exclude the participation of membrane depolarization per se.

The idea of Ca_i-mediated inactivation of Ca channels has far-reaching implications for the general question of intracellular Ca regulation. It has already received support in many excitable cells: snail neurons (13, 79), stick insect skeletal muscle (8), heart muscle (15, 35, 50, 68; see also 9, 30, 62), as well as *Paramecium* (11, 12) and *Aplysia* neurons (27, 88). Many experimental arguments have been presented to support Ca_i-dependent inactivation, but since most are rather indirect, questions remain about the validity of the hypothesis and the extent to which it accounts for inactivation.

The hypothesis was founded initially on three basic observations. (*a*) Relaxation of Ca channel current is slowed when extracellular Ca is replaced by Sr or Ba and (*b*) the inactivation left behind by a depolarizing pulse varies directly with the Ca entry during that pulse. These findings were allied with earlier observations in perfused cells, showing that (c) raising intracellular Ca reduces Ca conductance (see 42). More recently, the evidence in favor of Ca_i-dependent inactivation has been strengthened by further manipulations of intracellular Ca (including injection of EGTA) and by additional measurements of Ca current tails and intracellular Ca transients. The major questions about this hypothesis and key experimental answers are summarized below.

DOES THE DECAY OF INWARD CURRENT REFLECT GENUINE INACTIVATION? Slowly developing outward currents carried by voltage-dependent K channels, Ca_i-activated K channels, or nonspecific cation channels could confound measurements of true Ca channel inactivation. However, the genuineness of Ca channel inactivation has been substantiated by different methods for measuring inactivation, using Ca current tails to minimize interference from outward currents (26) or using test pulses to different levels as a check against outward current contamination (79). Measurements of intracellular Ca transients using Arsenazo III [(89); S. J. Smith, unpublished] also seem consistent with earlier two-pulse inactivation experiments (88).

DOES THE INACTIVATION DEPEND ON CA ENTRY PER SE? As the strength of a depolarizing pulse is increased, calcium entry first increases with greater activation and then decreases as the Ca driving force approaches zero. In many experiments, the bell-shaped voltage dependence of Ca entry is mirrored by the bell-shaped voltage dependence of the inactivation the depolarization leaves behind. This has been taken as evidence that calcium entry is the direct cause of the inactivation.

The nonmonotonic voltage dependence of Ca inactivation is somewhat reminiscent of Na channel inactivation in perfused squid axons, which is partially relieved by depolarizations to strongly positive potentials (18). However, the analogy seems strained because of the strong dependence of Ca channel inactivation on the species of divalent cation (1, 8, 11, 68, 70, 88). Furthermore, Eckert & Tillotson (27) and Mentrard et al (70) found that strong depolarizations do not actually remove previous Ca channel inactivation, contrary to the result expected if Ca channels behaved like Na channels (18).

DOES INTRACELLULAR CA ACT THROUGH REDUCTION OF CA DRIVING FORCE? This possibility has been rebutted by two arguments. One argument invokes constant-field theory, which predicts that inward current should be insensitive to intracellular Ca as long as Ca_i remains several orders of magnitude lower than extracellular Ca (see 42). The other argument points out that inactivation of Ba movement through the Ca channel is slight, even though larger changes in driving force are expected for Ba than for Ca (see 28).

MECHANISM OF REDUCED CA CONDUCTANCE   Many questions about Ca_i-mediated inactivation remain open. (a) It is not known whether Ca binds to a regulatory site on the cytoplasmic surface or acts within the pore itself. An action of Ca (but not Ba) within the pore is plausible since the species of permeant ion is known to affect the gating of other channels and perhaps activation of Ca channels as well (34; cf 43). (b) The stoichiometry and kinetics of Ca action could be explored if the site of action lies outside the pore. This problem might be simplified by looking at Ca_i-dependent inactivation in the absence of extracellular Ca, using K or Cs as the permeant species (34, 66). (c) The nature of Ca_i-dependent inactivation is not known at the level of single channels. Patch clamp experiments could determine whether Ca_i-mediated inactivation involves a decrease in p like that found for voltage-dependent inactivation (84).

Calcium Channels Showing Voltage-Dependent Inactivation

In many preparations, inactivation was initially attributed to a voltage-dependent mechanism before tests for Ca_i-mediated inactivation were widely known. More recently, investigators have applied experimental criteria in hopes of deciding between these mechanisms. Arguments for a purely voltage-dependent inactivation mechanism are most persuasive in the case of another class of Ca channels in the *Neanthes* egg, designated type I (36, 37). These may be summarized as follows: (a) Inactivation increased monotonically with increasing depolarization and became significant at depolarizations too weak to activate Ca entry; (b) the time course of inactivation was unchanged by increasing extracellular Ca or replacing it with Sr or Ba; and (c) the degree of inactivation was not lessened with depolarizations approaching the expected equilibrium potentials for Ca, Sr, or Ba (up to +200 mV). In each of these respects, the type I channels of *Neanthes* eggs seem clearly different from channels where Ca_i-mediated inactivation seems dominant. Cota et al (22) have presented similar arguments for Ca channels in intact frog skeletal muscle fibers and used the temperature dependence of the rate of inactivation ($Q_{10} \sim 2.8$) as an additional argument against a simple depletion hypothesis. Striking differences between the behavior of intact muscle in hypertonic solution (22) and that of cut muscle fibers in isotonic solution (5) are only partly explained by differences in the volume of the transverse tubular system (see 22).

Ca Channels Where Both Mechanisms Seem Significant

In snail neurons, there is evidence that Ca channel inactivation is voltage-dependent as well as Ca_i-dependent (13). A similar combination of mechanisms may hold for cardiac tissues as well. All cardiac preparations examined so far show earmarks of Ca_i-dependent inactivation (15, 35, 50, 68). On the other hand, Ca channel inactivation can be produced in the absence of divalent cation influx. In dialyzed heart cells, outward Cs^+ or K^+ movements through the Ca channel show inactivation even in the absence of permeant divalent cations (66); single Ca channels can be partially inactivated by depolarizations too weak to elicit any measurable channel opening (84). Both observations argue against a strict Ca_i-dependence.

How do Ca_i and membrane potential act? Eckert & Tillotson (27) considered the possibility that intracellular Ca binds to the cytoplasmic face of the membrane, changes the surface potential, and acts through a hyperpolarizing displacement of a voltage-dependent gating process. They pointed out that such a displacement of the activation curve would be inappropriate for explaining Ca_i-mediated inactivation. However, another possibility opens up if an intrinsically voltage-dependent inactivation process exists. In this case a voltage shift to negative potentials would be in the right direction to account for Ca_i-promoted inactivation. Calcium-permeable alamethicin channels provide a model system for this type of mechanism (17).

MESSENGERS AND MECHANISMS FOR Ca CHANNEL MODULATION

Heart Cells

Calcium channels in the heart are particularly interesting because they respond to a wide variety of neurohormones and drugs (42, 81, 91, 92). Experiments in multicellular preparations have already described the basic response to agents such as epinephrine (80, 94), acetylcholine (40, 41, 51), digitalis (69, 95), and angiotensin II (53); they have also provided evidence for the participation of cyclic AMP, cyclic GMP, and Ca as intracellular mediators. The development of methods for studying Ca channels at the level of single cells and single channels opens up many new possibilities for understanding the fundamental basis of Ca channel modulation. Recent papers give a preview of what is to come.

Trautwein et al (90) injected cyclic nucleotides into single heart cells and measured changes in action potential attributable to the slow inward Ca current. Cyclic AMP mimicked epinephrine, and cyclic GMP resembled acetylcholine in changing the action potential plateau, as expected from earlier injection experiments in heart muscle bundles that relied on intercellular diffusion of cyclic nucleotide (for review see 91, 92). Furthermore, changes in action potential configuration or Ca current produced by injection of regulatory or catalytic subunits of cyclic AMP-dependent protein kinase (78) provide strong evidence for protein phosphorylation as the mechanism of Ca-channel modulation by β-adrenergic compounds (74, 81, 87, 91).

Until recently, it was widely believed that β-adrenergic agents, acting through cyclic AMP, enhanced Ca current through an increase in the density of channels rather than a change in individual channel properties [(74, 82, 87, 91); but see (92)]. However, recent recordings of single Ca channel activity in cell-attached membrane patches (84) suggest a different mechanism. Isoproterenol did not change the single-channel current (i) as expected, but it also did not noticeably change the number of functional channels in any given patch (84). Increases in average channel activity were brought about by an increased probability of channel activation, seen most clearly as a prolongation of the duration of individual openings but also as a decrease in the interval between clusters of openings [(84); A. Noma, B. Sakmann, and W. Trautwein, unpublished experiments]. These results call for reexamination of earlier evidence that β-adrenergic stimulation leaves the kinetics of Ca channel activation unchanged (83). It will also be interesting to see whether acetylcholine reduces Ca channel currents by diametrically opposing the effect of β-adrenergic agonists at the level of single channels.

Neurons

Calcium channels in vertebrate ganglionic neurons are inhibited by a wide variety of putative transmitters, ranging from norepinephrine (23, 39, 48, 49, 71) to GABA, serotonin, enkephalin, and somatostatin (23, 71). These effects have been proposed as a possible mechanism of presynaptic inhibition (23, 24; see also 85). The question of possible intracellular messengers remains largely open. In perfused dorsal root ganglion cells, application of cyclic AMP temporarily reverses the progressive run-down of a Ca current (32); involvement of cyclic AMP as a messenger remains uncertain, however, since Ca current in similar neurons is decreased by all the neurochemical substances tested so far. It will be interesting to see if the inhibitory effects are mediated by decreased probability of channel opening (the converse of the β-adrenergic response in heart), by a decrease in the number of functional channels (see 86), or by some other effect.

ACKNOWLEDGMENT

I am grateful to R. W. Aldrich, B. P. Bean, K. S. Lee, and M. Nowycky for their helpful discussion, and to the American Heart Association, Marion Laboratories, and Miles Pharmaceuticals for support.

Literature Cited

1. Adams, D. J., Gage, P. W. 1980. Divalent ion currents and the delayed potassium conductance in an *Aplysia* neurone. *J. Physiol.* 304:297–313
2. Akaike, N., Fishman, H. M., Lee, K. S., Moore, L. E., Brown, A. M. 1978. The units of calcium conduction in *Helix* neurones. *Nature* 274:379–81
3. Akaike, N., Lee, K. S., Brown, A. M. 1978. The calcium current of *Helix* neuron. *J. Gen. Physiol.* 71:509–31
4. Aldrich, R. W., Corey, D. P., Stevens, C. F. 1982. Stochastic analysis of the kinetics of single sodium channels. *Soc. Neurosci. Abstr.* 8:727
5. Almers, W., Fink, R., Palade, P. T. 1981. Calcium depletion in frog muscle tubules: the decline of calcium current under maintained depolarization. *J. Physiol.* 312:177–207
6. Anglister, L., Shahar, A., Farber, I. C., Grinvald, A. 1981. Growth cones expand in vitro by depolarization under conditions which permit Ca^{2+} entry. *Soc. Neurosci. Abstr.* 7:548
7. Ashcroft, F. M., Stanfield, P. R. 1980. Calcium and potassium currents in muscle fibres of an insect (*Carausius morosus*). *J. Physiol.* 323:93–115
8. Ashcroft, F. M., Stanfield, P. R. 1981. Calcium dependence of the inactivation of calcium currents in skeletal muscle fibers of an insect. *Science* 213:224–26
9. Bogdanov, K., Zakharov, S., Rozenshtraukh, L. 1980. Changes in cell membrane excitability during guinea pig papillary muscle after-contractions. *Fiziol. Zh. USSR* 66:859–65
10. Bolger, G. T., Gengo, P. J., Luchowski, E. M., Siegel, H., Triggle, D. J., Janis, R. A. 1982. High affinity binding of a calcium channel antagonist to smooth and cardiac muscle. *Biochem. Biophys. Res. Commun.* 104:1604–9
11. Brehm, E., Eckert, R. 1978. Calcium entry leads to inactivation of the calcium channel in *Paramecium*. *Science* 202:1203–6
12. Brehm, P., Eckert, R., Tillotson, D. 1980. Calcium-mediated inactivation of calcium current in *Paramecium*. *J. Physiol.* 306:193–203
13. Brown, A. M., Morimoto, K., Tsuda, Y., Wilson, D. L. 1981. Calcium current-dependent and voltage-dependent inactivation of calcium channels in *Helix Aspersa*. *J. Physiol.* 320:193–218
14. Brown, H. F., Giles, W., Noble, S. J. 1977. Membrane currents underlying activity in frog sinus venosus. *J. Physiol.* 271:783–816

15. Brown, H. F., Kimura, J., Noble, S. 1981. Calcium entry dependent inactivation of the slow inward current in the rabbit sinoatrial node. *J. Physiol.* 320:11P
16. Byerly, L., Hagiwara, S. 1982. Calcium currents in internally perfused nerve cell bodies of *Limnea stagnalis*. *J. Physiol.* 322:503–28
17. Cahalan, M. D., Hall, J. 1982. Alamethicin channels incorporated into frog node of Ranvier. Calcium-induced inactivation and membrane surface charges. *J. Gen. Physiol.* 79:411–36
18. Chandler, W. K., Meves, H. 1965. Evidence for two types of sodium conductance in axons perfused with sodium fluoride solution. *J. Physiol.* 211:653–78
19. Connor, J. A. 1979. Calcium current in molluscan neurones: measurement under conditions which maximize its visibility. *J. Physiol.* 286:41–60
20. Coraboeuf, E. 1980. Voltage clamp studies of the slow inward current. In *The Slow Inward Current and Cardiac Arrhythmias,* ed. D. P. Zipes, J. C. Bailey, V. Elharrar, pp. 25–95. The Hague: Martinus Nijhoff
21. Corey, D. P., Dubinsky, J., Schwartz, E. A. 1982. The calcium current of rodphotoreceptor inner segments recorded with a whole-cell patch clamp. *Soc. Neurosci. Abstr.* 8:944.
22. Cota, G., Siri, L. N., Stefani, E. 1981. Calcium current decay in frog skeletal muscle fibres: inactivation and/or depletion from TTS. *Int. Congr. Biophys. Abstr.*
23. Dunlap, K., Fischbach, G. D. 1978. Neurotransmitters decrease the calcium component of sensory neurone action potentials. *Nature* 276:837–39
24. Dunlap, K., Fischbach, G. D. 1981. Neurotransmitters decrease the calcium conductance activated by depolarization of embryonic chick sensory neurones. *J. Physiol.* 317:519–35
25. Dyball, R. E. J., Shaw, F. D. 1981. Evidence for calcium-induced inactivation of calcium-dependent hormone release from the rat neurohypophysis. *J. Physiol.* 319:104P
26. Eckert, R., Ewald, D. 1981. Ca-mediated Ca channel inactivation determined from tail current measurements. *Biophys. J.* 33:145a
27. Eckert, R., Tillotson, D. 1981. Calcium-mediated inactivation of the calcium conductance in caesium-loaded giant neurones of *Aplysia californica*. *J. Physiol.* 314:265–80

28. Eckert, R., Tillotson, D. L., Brehm, P. 1981. Calcium-mediated control of Ca and K currents. *Fred. Proc.* 40:2226–32
29. Ehlert, F. J., Itoga, E., Roeske, W. R., Yamamura, H. 1982. The interaction of [³H]nitrendipine with receptors for calcium antagonists in the cerebral cortex and heart of rats. *Biochem. Biophys. Res. Commun.* 104:937–43
30. Eisner, D. A., Lederer, W. J., Noble, D. 1979. Caffeine and tetracaine abolish the slow inward calcium current in sheep cardiac Purkinje fibres. *J. Physiol.* 293:76–77P
31. Fatt, P., Katz, B. 1953. The electrical properties of crustacean muscle fibres. *J. Physiol.* 120:171–204
32. Fedulova, S. A., Kostyuk, P. G., Veselovsky, N. S. 1981. Calcium channels in the somatic membrane of the rat dorsal ganglion, effects of cAMP. *Brain Res.* 214:210–14
33. Fenwick, E. M., Marty, A., Neher, E. 1981. Voltage clamp and single-channel recording from bovine chromaffin cells. *J. Physiol.* 319:100P
34. Fenwick, E. M., Marty, A., Neher, E. 1982. Sodium and calcium channels in bovine chromaffin cells. *J. Physiol.* In press
35. Fischmeister, R., Mentrard, D., Vassort, G. 1981. Slow inward current inactivation in frog heart atrium. *J. Physiol.* 320:27–28P
36. Fox, A. P. 1981. Voltage-dependent inactivation of a calcium channel. *Proc. Natl. Acad. Sci. USA* 78:953–56
37. Fox, A. P., Krasne, S. 1981. Two calcium currents in egg cells. *Biophys. J.* 33:145a
38. Fox, A. P., Krasne, S. 1982. Relaxation due to depletion in the egg cell calcium current. *Biophys. J.* 37:20a
39. Galvan, M., Adams, P. 1982. Control of calcium current in rat sympathetic neurons by norepinephrine. *Brain Res.* 244:135–44
40. Giles, W., Noble, S. J. 1976. Changes in membrane current in bullfrog atrium produced by acetylcholine. *J. Physiol.* 261:103–23
41. Giles, W., Tsien, R. W. 1975. Effects of acetylcholine on membrane currents in frog atrial muscle. *J. Physiol.* 246:64–66P
42. Hagiwara, S., Byerly, L. 1981. Calcium channel. *Ann. Rev. Neurosci.* 4:69–125
43. Hagiwara, S., Ohmori, H. 1982. Studies of Ca channels in rat clonal pituitary cells with patch electrode voltage clamp. *J. Physiol.* In press
44. Hagiwara, S., Ozawa, S. A., Sand, O. 1975. Voltage clamp analysis of two inward current mechanisms in the egg cell membrane of a starfish. *J. Gen. Physiol.* 65:617–44
45. Hamill, O. P., Marty, A., Neher, E., Sakmann, B., Sigworth, F. J. 1981. Improved patch-clamp techniques for high-resolution current recording from cells and cell-free membrane patches. *Pflügers. Arch.* 391:85–100
46. Hodgkin, A. L., Huxley, A. F. 1952. A quantitative description of membrane current and its application to conduction and excitation in nerve. *J. Physiol.* 117:500–44
47. Hodgkin, A. L., Katz, B. 1949. The effect of sodium ions on the electrical activity of the giant axon of the squid. *J. Physiol.* 108:37–77
48. Horn, J. P., McAfee, D. A. 1979. Norepinephrine inhibits calcium-dependent potentials in rat sympathetic neurons. *Science* 204:1233–35
49. Horn, J. P., McAfee, D. A. 1980. Alpha-adrenergic inhibition of calcium-dependent potentials in rat sympathetic neurones. *J. Physiol.* 301:191–204
50. Hume, J. R., Giles, W. 1982. Turn-off of a TTX-resistant inward current 'i$_{Ca}$' in single bullfrog atrial cells. *Biophys. J.* 37:240a
51. Ikemoto, Y., Goto, M. 1975. Nature of the negative inotropic effect of acetylcholine on the myocardium. *Proc. Jpn. Acad.* 51:501–5
52. Isenberg, G., Klöckner, U. 1980. Glycocalyx is not required for slow inward calcium current in isolated rat heart myocytes. *Nature* 284:358–60
53. Kass, R. S., Blair, M. L. 1981. Effects of angiotensin II on membrane current in cardiac Purkinje fibres. *J. Mol. Cell Cardiol.* 13:797–809
54. Keynes, R. D., Rojas, E., Taylor, R. E., Vergara, J. 1973. Calcium and potassium systems of a giant barnacle muscle fibre under membrane potential control. *J. Physiol.* 229:409–55
55. Kostyuk, P. G. 1981. Calcium channels in the neuronal membrane. *Biochim. Biophys. Acta* 650:128–50
56. Kostyuk, P. G., Krishtal, O. A. 1977. Separation of sodium and calcium currents in the somatic membrane of mollusc neurones. *J. Physiol.* 270:545–68
57. Kostyuk, P. G., Krishtal, O. A., Pidoplichko, V. I. 1981. Calcium inward current and related charge movements in the membrane of snail neurones. *J. Physiol.* 310:403–21

58. Krishtal, O. H., Pidoplichko, V. I., Shakhovolov, Y. A. 1981. Conductance of the calcium channel in the membrane of snail neurones. *J. Physiol.* 310: 423–34

59. Lee, K. S., Akaike, N., Brown, A. M. 1978. Properties of internally perfused, voltage-clamped isolated nerve cell bodies. *J. Gen. Physiol.* 71:489–507

60. Lee, K. S., Akaike, N., Brown, A. M. 1980. The suction pipette method for internal perfusion and voltage clamp of small excitable cells. *J. Neurosci. Methods* 2:51–78

61. Lee, K. S., Lee, E. W., Tsien, R. W. 1981. Slow inward current carried by Ca^{2+} or Ba^{2+} in single isolated heart cells. *Biophys. J.* 33:143a

62. Linden, J., Brooker, G. 1980. Properties of cardiac contractions in zero sodium solutions: intracellular free calcium controls slow channel conductance. *J. Mol. Cell Cardiol.* 12:457–78

63. Llinas, R., Steinberg, I. Z., Walton, K. 1981. Presynaptic calcium currents in squid giant synapse. *Biophys. J.* 33:289–322

64. Llinas, R., Sugimori, M. 1980. Electrophysiological properties of *in vitro* Purkinje cell dendrites in mammalian cerebellar slices. *J. Physiol.* 305:197–213

65. Lux, H. D., Nagy, K. 1981. Single channel Ca^{2+} currents in *Helix Pomatia* neurons. *Pflügers Arch.* 391:252–54

66. Lee, K. S., Tsien, R. W. 1982. Reversal of current through calcium channels in dialyzed single heart cells. *Nature* 297:498–501

67. McDonald, T. F. 1982. The slow inward calcium current in the heart. *Ann. Rev. Physiol.* 44:425–34

68. Marban, E., Tsien, R. W. 1981. Is the slow inward calcium current of heart muscle inactivated by calcium? *Biophys. J.* 33:143a

69. Marban, E., Tsien, R. W. 1982. Enhancement of calcium current during digitalis inotropy in mammalian heart: positive feedback regulation by intracellular calcium. *J. Physiol.* 329:589–614

70. Mentrard, D., Vassort, G., Fischmeister, R. 1982. Calcium-mediated inactivation of the calcium conductance in calcium-loaded frog atrial cells. Submitted for publication

71. Mudge, A. W., Leeman, S., Fischbach, G. D. 1979. Enkephalin inhibits release of substance P from sensory neurons in culture and decreases action potential duration. *Proc. Natl. Acad. Sci. USA* 76:526–30

72. Murphy, K. M. M., Snyder, S. H. 1982. Calcium antagonist receptor binding sites labelled with [³H]-nitrendipine. *Eur. J. Pharmacol.* 77:201–2

73. Nachsen, D. A. 1981. Influx of Ca, Sr, and Ba through Ca channels in synaptosomes. *Biophys. J.* 33:145a

74. Niedergerke, R., Page, S. 1977. Analysis of catecholamine effects in single atrial trabeculae of the frog heart. *Proc. R. Soc. Lond. Ser. B.* 197:333–62

75. Noma, A., Kotake, H., Kokubun, S., Irisawa, H. 1981. Kinetics and rectification of the slow inward current in the rabbit sinoatrial node cell. *Jpn. J. Physiol.* 31:491–500

76. Noma, A., Yanagihara, K., Irisawa, H. 1977. Inward current of the rabbit sinoatrial node cell. *Pflüger's Arch.* 373:43–51

77. Okamoto, H., Takahashi, K., Yoshii, M. 1976. Two components of the calcium current in the egg cell membrane of the tunicate. *J. Physiol.* 255:527–61

78. Osterrieder, W., Brum, G., Hescheler, J., Trautwein, W., Flockerzi, V., Hofmann, F. 1982. Injection of subunits of cyclic AMP-dependent protein kinase into cardiac myocytes modulates Ca^{2+} current. *Nature.* 298:576–78

79. Plant, T. D., Standen, N. B. 1981. Calcium current inactivation in identified neurones of *Helix aspersa. J. Physiol.* 321:273–85

80. Reuter, H. 1967. The dependence of the slow inward current on external calcium concentration in Purkinje fibres. *J. Physiol.* 192:479–92

81. Reuter, H. 1979. Properties of two inward membrane currents in the heart. *Ann. Rev. Physiol.* 41:413–24

82. Reuter, H., Scholz, H. 1977. A study of the ion selectivity and the kinetic properties of the calcium dependent slow inward current in mammalian cardiac muscle. *J. Physiol.* 264:17–47

83. Reuter, H., Scholz, H. 1977. The regulation of the Ca conductance of cardiac muscle by adrenaline. *J. Physiol.* 264:49–62

84. Reuter, H., Stevens, C. F., Tsien, R. W., Yellen, G. 1982. Properties of single calcium channels in cardiac cell culture. *Nature* 297:501–4

85. Shapiro, E., Castellucci, V. F., Kandel, E. R. 1980. Presynaptic inhibition in *Aplysia* involves a decrease in the Ca^{2+} current of the presynaptic neuron. *Proc. Natl. Acad. Sci. USA* 77:1185–89

86. Siegelbaum, S. A., Camardo, J. S., Kandel, E. R. 1982. Serotonin and cAMP

close single K$^+$ channels in *Aplysia* sensory neurones. *Nature.* 299:413–17

87. Sperelakis, N., Schneider, J. A. 1976. A metabolic control mechanism for calcium ion influx that may protect the ventricular myocardial cell. *Am. J. Cardiol.* 37:1079–85

88. Tillotson, D. 1979. Inactivation of Ca conductance dependent on entry of Ca ions in molluscan neurons. *Proc. Natl. Acad. Sci. USA* 76:1497–1500

89. Tillotson, D. 1980. Ca^{++}-dependent inactivation of Ca^{++} channels. In *Molluscan Nerve Cells: from Biophysics to Behavior,* ed. J. Koester, J. H. Byrne, 1:41–48. Cold Spring Harbor: Cold Spring Harbor Laboratory. 230 pp.

90. Trautwein, W., Taniguchi, J., Noma, A. 1982. The effect of intracellular cyclic nucleotides and calcium on the action potential and acetylcholine response of isolated cardiac cells. *Pflügers Arch.* 392:307–14

91. Tsien, R. W. 1977. Cyclic AMP and contractile activity in heart. *Adv. Cyclic Nucl. Res.* 8:363–420

92. Tsien, R. W., Siegelbaum, S. 1978. Excitable tissues: the heart. In *The Physiological Basis for Disorders of Biomembranes,* ed. T. Andreoli, J. F. Hoffman, D. Fanestil. NY: Plenum. 1122 pp.

93. Tsuda, Y., Wilson, D. L., Brown, A. M. 1982. Calcium tail currents in snail neurons. *Biophys. J.* 37:181a

94. Vassort, G., Rougier, O., Garnier, D., Sauviat, M. P., Coraboeuf, E., Gargouil, Y. M. 1969. Effects of adrenaline on membrane inward currents during the cardiac action potential. *Pflügers Arch.* 309:70–81

95. Weingart, R., Kass, R. S., Tsien, R. W. 1978. Is digitalis inotropy associated with enhanced slow inward calcium current? *Nature* 273:389–92

96. Wilson, D. L., Tsuda, Y., Brown, A. M. 1982. Activation of Ca channels in snail neurons. *Biophys. J.* 37:181a

Ann. Rev. Physiol. 1983. 45:359–74

CA²⁺-ACTIVATED K⁺ CHANNELS IN ERYTHROCYTES AND EXCITABLE CELLS

Wolfgang Schwarz and Hermann Passow

Max-Planck-Institut für Biophysik, 6000 Frankfurt am Main 71, West Germany

INTRODUCTION

The proper execution of many physiological functions, such as the conduction of impulses in nerve and muscle, the activities of cardiac and neuronal pacemakers, light reception, secretion, and fertilization, usually requires accurately timed and selective changes of K^+ permeability. These changes are brought about by the activation of distinct channels that can be divided into two classes: those activated by variations in the membrane potential, and others activated by Ca^{2+} (5, 9, 22, 29, 37, 47, 70, 84a) and modulated by the membrane potential. In nerve axons, only the potential-activated K^+ channels have been found (66). However, in the soma of neurons and in most other types of cells that have been studied so far, Ca^{2+}-activated channels were discovered, either alone or together with the potential-activated channels. The other cells include even nonexcitable cells such as macrophages, L-cells, and erythrocytes. Only the Ca^{2+}-activated K^+-selective channels form the subject of the present review (Table 1).

Ca^{2+}-activated, K^+-selective channels were first discovered in red cells, whose functions do not seem to depend to any extent on variations of K^+ permeability or the associated variations of membrane potential. Observations made by Wilbrandt (99) in the late 1930s showed that the glucolytic inhibitors fluoride and iodoacetate could induce a selective increase of K^+ efflux that exceeded the increment expected to occur after an interruption of the energy supply to the K-Na pump. These observations were confirmed and extended by Gárdos (26), who showed that the inhibition of metabolism must be accompanied by the presence of Ca^{2+} to obtain the response. Later work has shown that the presence of certain drugs [e.g. propranolol (19, 83)] renders the cells sensitive to

0066-4278/83/0315-0359$02.00

Table 1 Certain properties of Ca^{2+}-activated K$^+$ channels[a]

Cell type	Ca concentration range (μM) (Refs.)	Block of Ca channels (Refs.)	Block of K channels (Refs.)	Single-channel conductance (pS) (Refs.)
Red cells	1–4 (83, 93)	Verapamil (10)	Na, Cs, TEA, Ba, Quinine (1, 6, 44, 59, 84)	20 (33)
L-cells		Co (36)	Ba (74)	
Neurons	*Aplysia:* ≤14 (31) *Helix:* 0.1–0.9 (66)	Co, Mn, D600, Verapamil (17, 68)	TEA, Ba, Quinine (13, 28, 39, 68)	20 (63)
Neuroblastoma		Mn (71)	Quinine (23)	
Clonal·anterior pituitary cells	0.01–1.0 (100)		TEA (100)	210 (100)
Skeletal muscle	1.5 (22)		TEA, Ba (21)	
Myotubes	0.01–100 (78)	Co, Mn (5)	Ba (5)	180 (77)
T-tubules vesicles[b]	0.1 (57)		Na, Cs, TEA (57, 96)	226 (57)
Rat brain vesicles[b]	100 (55)		Cs, TEA, Quinine (55)	200–260 (55)
Photoreceptors		Co (9, 18)	TEA (9)	
Tunicate eggs			Na, Cs, Ba (73)	6–10 (72)
B-cells		Co, Mn, D600 (85a)	TEA, Quinine (3, 69)	
Chromaffin cells	0.01–0.2 (65)			180 (65)

[a] Further examples of Ca^{2+}-activated K$^+$ channels are found in neurons (4, 54) and eggs (70) of vertebrates in neurons of leech (48) and insects (95), cardiac Purkinje fibres (46), smooth muscle (97), paramecium (16), electroreceptors (11), and gland cells (47a, 84a) and macrophages (75).
[b] Fused into planar lipid bilayers.

Ca^{2+}, even without causing major changes of the cell metabolism. Finally, incorporation of Ca^{2+} into resealed red cell ghosts (7) and the use of the ionophore A23187 (85) have shown beyond doubt that the entry of Ca^{2+} into the cells is an absolute requirement for the permeability change to occur. More recent work has demonstrated that under suitable conditions even in the absence of the ionophore, Ca^{2+} may produce a considerable, although transient, response (56). In addition, Pb^{2+}, which had also been demonstrated in the 1930s to enhance K$^+$ efflux (76), was found to exert this effect by combination with the same receptor that combines with Ca^{2+} (81). In contrast to Ca^{2+}, Pb^{2+} easily penetrates across the cell membrane, and thus no special treatment of the red cell is required to induce the effect.

Later work has shown that the activation of the system cannot be brought about by internal Ca^{2+} alone; external K$^+$ must also be present (53). Thus strictly speaking, in red cells the K$^+$-selective channels should be called (Ca^{2+} + K$^+$)-activated K$^+$ channels. The synergistic actions of Ca$^{2+}_i$ and K^+_o are antagonized by internal Na$^+$ (6, 53). The effects of the three ion species mentioned are modulated by pH (84) and, at least in certain excitable cells, by the membrane potential (65, 77). In addition, the susceptibility of the system to Ca$^{2+}_i$ + K^+_o is controlled by the metabolic state of the cells. The properties of the activated system are understood in terms of ionic diffusion across aqueous pores that show a considerable selectivity of K$^+$ over Na$^+$. Inhibitors exist, but detailed information on mode of action is available only for a few of them. Thus it is usually unknown whether they block the activated channels or inhibit their activation.

Reviews on the red cell system have appeared at more or less regular intervals since 1963 (41–43, 59, 79, 80, 88). Work on the Ca^{2+}-activated K channels in excitable tissues apparently originated largely independently of the work on red cells. The first comprehensive review dates back to 1978 (67). In this same year appeared a still valuable article by Lew & Ferreira (59) in which the work on erythrocytes and other cells was discussed from a common point of view. In the present paper the two developments are again discussed jointly, although without implying that the channels in the different cells have necessarily an identical biochemical basis. We discuss first the factors responsible for the activation of the channels and then the properties of the activated channels.

ACTIVATION OF THE K$^+$ CHANNELS

The Role of Ca^{2+}

The activation of the channels is brought about by intracellular Ca^{2+}, while extracellular Ca^{2+} is ineffective (7, 65, 77, 90). Under physiological conditions, the cytoplasmic Ca^{2+} concentration is raised to activating levels by the influx of Ca^{2+} through gated channels or by the liberation of Ca^{2+} from intracellular stores. The actual concentration of free Ca^{2+} at the site of action is then determined by the rate of appearance of Ca^{2+}, the Ca^{2+} buffer capacity of the cytoplasm, and the rate at which the Ca pump removes the arriving Ca^{2+}. The ensuing increase of K^+ permeability leads to a hyperpolarization of membrane potential (41, 66, 69, 74, 75). This causes the desired modulation of the physiological functions mentioned in the introduction. The hyperpolarization may also reduce the sensitivity of the K^+-selective channels to Ca^{2+} (65, 77) and thereby counteract the original Ca^{2+}-induced activation (see below, Figure 1A) before the Ca pump could restore the original low intracellular Ca^{2+} concentration.

The experimental study of the effect of Ca^{2+} depends to a large extent on suitable methods for the intracellular application of Ca^{2+}. These methods encompass, besides the use of ionophores and Ca^{2+} buffers, the use of ghosts and of electrophoretic or pressure injection. They are supplemented by measurements of the actual intracellular Ca^{2+} concentrations with Ca^{2+}-sensitive dyes (31, 103) and microelectrodes (45). A particularly important experimental approach was introduced by Neher, Sakmann, and their colleagues in Göttingen in the form of the patch-clamp technique. The most recent version (34) allows one to measure under voltage-clamp conditions the conductance of single channels in cell-free membrane patches. In this system intra- and extrafacial ion concentrations can be varied at will. This new technique and the classical flux measurements will supplement each other most effectively. The incorporation of the channels into artificial membranes will probably assume significance similar to that of the patch-clamp technique. Ca^{2+}-induced single-channel activities have been observed after fusing into preformed bilayers vesicles from T-tubules of rabbit skeletal muscle or from rat brain (see Table 1).

Table 1 shows that the intracellular Ca^{2+} concentrations required to activate the channels are in the micromolar range. However, a considerable variability exists. This may be due to inaccuracies of the determinations of the concentration of free Ca^{2+} at the site of action, but the existence of different types of channels with different susceptibilities to Ca^{2+} cannot be excluded. G. Isenberg (personal communication) believes that he can demonstrate, in the same Purkinje fiber, two different types of Ca^{2+}-activated K^+-selective channels (47) that exhibit different sensitivities to Ca^{2+}. Thus Table 1 may reflect genuine differences between Ca^{2+}-activated K^+ channels in different types of cells.

In red cells (84, 93), in cultured rat muscle cells (78), and in cloned anterior pituitary cells (100), the relationship between intracellular Ca^{2+} concentration and effect appears to be sigmoidal, suggesting the binding of two or more Ca ions per channel. In red cells this accounts for the rather narrow range of Ca^{2+} concentrations over which the effect develops from zero to maximal response. Similar observations have been made when Pb^{2+} is used instead of Ca^{2+} (81, 82). The situation shows an additional complication because different cells in a population respond with different thresholds to the action of a given concentration of Ca^{2+} or Pb^{2+}. If the concentration of the divalent metal ions remains below the threshold value of a given cell, there is little increase of K^+ flux. If the threshold is exceeded, K^+ flux is increased by one or two orders of magnitude. Different cells possess different threshold values, suggesting that the sensitivity of the most sensitive channel in the various cells differs (82, 87, 88). Possibly the response of all the channels in a cell is coupled by as yet unknown factors, e.g. by an association of the channels with the cytoskeleton and different sensitivities of the cytoskeleton in different cells to the action of the divalent ions. The differences of the thresholds observed in different cells in a population must be distinguished from differences of the thresholds of the channels in the same cell. The latter may exist, but have not yet been demonstrated experimentally.

Recently, the analysis of the action of Ca^{2+} was considerably refined by single-channel recordings. It was shown (8, 57, 65, 77) that Ca^{2+} increases the frequency and length of the opening of the individual channels and that, at a given Ca^{2+} concentration, the opening times are reduced by hyperpolarization and increased by depolarization (Figure 1A). On the other hand,

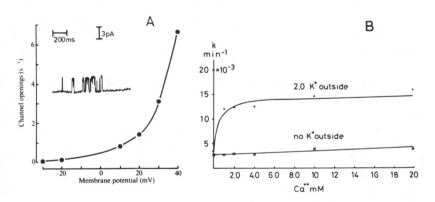

Figure 1 A: Effect of membrane potential on the frequency of channel openings for an isolated membrane patch of rat myotube with 0.5 μM free Ca^{2+} on the intracellular side of the membrane. Depolarization to positive holding potentials increased both the frequency of channel openings and the effective open times. Inset: Recording of channel activation. Membrane potential 0 mV. Taken from (77). Reprinted by permission from *Nature* 293:471-74. Copyright © 1987 Macmillan Journals Limited

B: Rate constants of net K^+ efflux from metabolically exhausted human red cells as a function of external Ca^{2+} concentration in the absence and presence of external K^+. Taken from (53).

when the Ca^{2+} concentration is increased, stronger hyperpolarizations are necessary to inactivate the K channels.

In addition to Ca^{2+}, other divalent cations may activate the K^+ channels. For example, in *Aplysia* neurons (28), injected Sr^{2+}, Mn^{2+}, or Fe^{2+} activate with falling effectiveness. These ions seem to assume the role of Ca^{2+}, and thus behave in a manner similar to that of Pb^{2+} (81) or Sr^{2+} (84, 93) in erythrocytes.

The Role of K^+

The presence of Ca^{2+} inside the red cells does not suffice to open the K^+-selective channels. Only if extracellular K^+ is also present does the activation occur (Figure 1B). At the maximally activating Ca^{2+} concentration inside the cells, the half-maximal response is obtained at a K^+ concentration of about 0.5–0.75 mM (35, 53). If prepared under suitable conditions, red cell ghosts may retain sufficient membrane-bound Ca^{2+} to respond even without added Ca^{2+} in the medium with net K^+ efflux upon exposure to external K^+ (101).

External K^+ is necessary not only to activate the responsive channel but also to maintain the channel in a state in which it can respond to the combined actions of Ca^{2+}_i and K^+_o. In the complete absence of K^+_o, the capacity to respond is lost with a half time of 5–10 min at 37°C. A few tenths of a millimole of K^+_o prevent this irreversible transition (35).

High concentrations of external K^+ (above 5 mM) that exceed those required to induce the response inhibit K^+ efflux slightly. This could not simply be related to a reduction of the driving force for K^+ efflux, but would seem to represent a genuine change of the properties of the K^+ channel (35, 53).

The three different actions of K^+ on the Ca^{2+}-activated channels observed in red cells are summarized in Figure 2. They have not yet been studied systematically in other types of cells. However, certain reports on the voltage-activated K^+ channels in nerve axons describe a requirement for external K^+ for the activation of the channels (14, 49) and an irreversible block of the K^+ conductance after prolonged absence of external as well as internal K^+ (2). The study of the action of K^+ would be a most specific means of establishing similarities between channels in erythrocytes and other types of cells. Latorre and co-workers (personal communication) have observed that the Ca^{2+}-activated K^+ channels in T-tubules do not require external K^+ for activation.

The Role of Na^+

Under physiological conditions besides Ca^{2+} and K^+, Na^+ is always present. In red cells it was observed that the actions of all three ion species

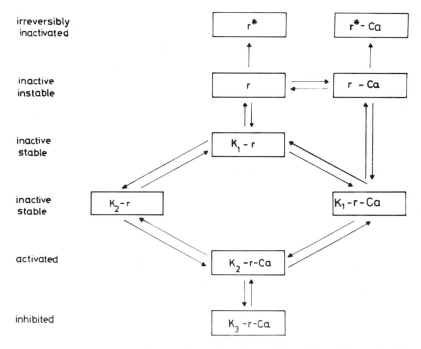

Figure 2   Effects of external K^+ on $(Ca^{2+} + K^+)$-dependent K^+ channels of human red blood cells. Based on (35, 53). Presence of K^+_o (K_1) prevents the channel r from undergoing transition into irreversibly inactivated form r^*. K^+_o maintains r in a state in which, at higher K^+_o concentration (K_2) together with Ca^{2+}_i, the response is elicited. Even higher K^+_o (K_3) produces inhibition. The exact stoichiometries of binding to the various sites of action for K^+_o are unknown.

are interdependent, leading to a complex pattern of behavior that we cannot discuss in detail here [for a brief review, see (42)]. It should be mentioned, however, that one observes separate effects of K^+, Na^+, and Ca^{2+} on the two sides of the membrane, and that the nature of these effects depends on the concentration gradient and probably the potential gradient across the membrane (6, 35, 44, 84, 93). Two observations may suffice to illustrate the problem at hand. The threshold for the induction of a net efflux of KCl under its electrochemical potential gradient is augmented by increasing internal Na^+, whereas external Na^+ has little effect. As a consequence, higher concentrations of K^+_o are needed to elicit the response when internal Na^+ is raised. When the K^+ movements are measured by means of $^{42}K^+$ at equal concentrations of all ion species at both surfaces of the membrane, the effects of Na^+ are altered. At low K^+, Na^+ inhibits; at high K^+, it has no effect or may even accelerate the exchange (6, 53, 84, 93). The interpretation of these data is complicated since a separation of the effects on the activation of the channels and the penetration of K^+ across the activated channels is difficult to achieve with the macroscopical methods employed so far.

The Role of a Loosely Bound Membrane Protein

Many of the observations described above are based on experiments performed with red cell ghosts. When the cell contents are extremely diluted during the ghosting procedure, or when inside-out vesicles are formed in low-ionic-strength solutions, the capability of ghosts or vesicles to respond to internal Ca^{2+} plus external K^+ is lost. This seems to be due to the removal of a water soluble, heat labile, nondialyzable component, probably a protein different from calmodulin, that is loosely bound to the membrane (56, 91). If extensive dilution is avoided, the loss of this protein can be reduced such that even inside-out vesicles retain their susceptibility to Ca^{2+} plus K^+ (91). In cells other than red cells, experiments with excised membrane patches and with vesicles fused into bilayers provided no evidence of such a membrane component (55, 57, 65, 77).

Modulation of Activation

When the metabolism of red cells is inhibited, the balance among passive Ca^{2+} influx, Ca^{2+} buffering by metabolic intermediates, and Ca^{2+} ejection by the Ca pump is disturbed. Ca^{2+} accumulates and elicits the response. It has been suggested, however, that in addition the sensitivity of the channel's response to Ca^{2+} changes considerably (58, 59). This change seems to depend in a complex manner on the mode of inhibition of metabolism, and on the presence of additional agents—e.g. metabolic inhibitors like fluoride, drugs like propranolol—and on the concentration of the ionophore used to increase the intracellular Ca^{2+} concentration (59). Finally, there may exist pathological situations, as in sickle cell anemia, where the sensitivity to the intracellular Ca^{2+} may be greatly reduced (60). More specific studies have shown that the ratios ATP/ADP (89) and NADH/NAD (24, 62) may play a major role in the control of the susceptibility of the channels to activation by Ca^{2+}.

Metabolic depletion or poisoning with NaCN is a prerequisite for the stimulation by Ca^{2+} of a K^+ conductance in skeletal muscle fibers (98). In addition to an increase of Ca^{2+}, an increased sensitivity of the K^+ channels is held responsible for these changes (22). Finally, in nerves, photoreceptors, and beta cells inhibitors like cyanide and uncouplers of oxidative phosphorylation like dinitrophenol enhance the Ca^{2+}-activated K^+ permeability (4, 30, 37, 66).

PROPERTIES OF THE ACTIVATED K⁺ CHANNELS

The Channels are Aqueous Pores

The Ca^{2+}-activated K^+ efflux from the red cells into a medium with a K^+ concentration below that of the cell interior is accompanied by an enormous enhancement of K^+ influx as measured with ^{42}K (6, 80). Until recently, there existed two different interpretations of this effect: (a) the enhanced K^+ influx is the result of a (potential-dependent or potential-independent) carrier-mediated counter-transport, where the high intracellular concentration of ^{39}K replaces the ^{42}K that arrives at the inner membrane surface and thus maintains a gradient of ^{42}K-loaded carriers in a direction opposite to the direction of the concentration gradient of ^{39}K. (b) The alternative explanation first proposed by Glynn & Warner (27) was based on the idea that the anion permeability of the red cell membrane is primarily due to an electrically "silent" exchange mechanism and that the value of the permeability coefficient for Cl⁻ is smaller than that for K^+ seen after the activation of the channels. The ensuing hyperpolarization would then increase the driving force for the influx of $^{42}K^+$ against a considerable concentration difference. Using the patch-clamp technique in single red cells, Hamill (33) recently demonstrated the existence of single channels with a conductance of 20 pS, which are most likely to be responsible for the $(Ca^{2+}+K^+)$-activated K^+ movements. This suggests that the proposition by Glynn & Warner is correct and that the channels are aqueous pores. The flux measurements in red cells obey the Ussing equation quite well (41); therefore, at least under the specific experimental conditions of these measurements the occupancy of the pores is low and there are no major cross effects between activated particles moving in opposite directions. Also for other cells it could be demonstrated that the Ca^{2+}-activated currents result from movements of K^+ through K^+-selective pores. The single-channel conductances (Table 1) sometimes exhibit slight voltage dependences. They can be divided into two groups: channels of normal cells that have conductances not exceeding 20 pS, and channels of cultured cells and reconstituted channels that exhibit conductances of 100 pS and higher. The differences are not correlated to different ion selectivities. This is surprising, but nevertheless in agreement with the observation that a reduction in selectivity can be associated with a decrease in single-channel conductance (51).

The Selectivity of the K⁺ Channels

In most cases the Ca^{2+}-activated channels show a considerable selectivity for K^+ over Na^+ (20, 52, 79, 84, 93, 96, 102). They all [with the exception of the T-tubules (96)] have high permeabilites to Rb^+.

In red cells of chicken and certain species of fish (64), Ca^{2+}-activated channels were found that are selective for cations but do not discriminate between K^+ and Na^+. In Purkinje fibers besides the K^+-selective channels that form the subject of this review, such channels do also exist (12, 92). Further investigation will reveal to what extent the important functional differences between the two types of Ca^{2+}-activated channels are reflections of distinct biochemical units.

INHIBITORS

Inorganic cations as well as many organic compounds produce inhibitory effects that may be useful for the identification and exploration of Ca^{2+}-activated K^+ channels. Some of the more extensively studied inhibitors are listed in Table 1. Several of these (internal TEA, Na^+, Cs^+, Ba^{2+}) are also known to block K^+ currents in voltage-gated channels, where they seem to act as plugs.

A particularly large variety of drugs and other organic compounds have been studied in red cells. They include in addition to TEA, furosemide, ouabain (6), and quinine a number of agents that are capable of combining with calmodulin (56a).

Most effective were oligomycin and a potential-sensitive fluorescent dicarbocyanine derivative called diS-C_3(5) (94). Oligomycin seems to decrease the affinity for Ca^{2+}, to reduce the Hill coefficient for activation by Ca^{2+} from about 2 to about 1, and to decrease the maximal rate of K^+ efflux (84). The carbocyanine dye is most effective when the system is maximally activated, indicating that it blocks primarily the K^+ movements across the open channels rather than the opening of the channels (94).

Among the various inhibitors, TEA and quinine have been applied most extensively in other types of cells and found to be more or less effective. However, the statement that an agent like TEA blocks Ca^{2+}-activated K^+ channels does not imply that the mode of action is necessarily the same in all types of cells. For example, TEA always inhibits the Ca^{2+}-induced K^+ fluxes if applied at the inner membrane surface, but in some cases also when applied to the outer surface (21, 39). This latter behavior is similar to the effect of TEA on the voltage-activated channels. Interesting is the observation that apamin inhibits the Ca^{2+}-activated K^+ efflux from liver cells but not from erythrocytes, indicating differences of the channels in the two cell types (9a). Aminopyridines (18, 21, 38, 92) and ruthenium red (40) are inhibitors that discriminate between Ca^{2+}-activated and voltage-activated K^+ channels.

If the increase in intracellular Ca^{2+} is achieved by an influx of Ca^{2+} from the external medium, K^+ currents can also be inhibited by ions and drugs that block Ca^{2+} channels (Table 1).

BIOCHEMICAL BASIS OF THE K⁺ CHANNELS

The number of channels per erythrocyte seems to be small—probably below about one thousand, and possibly less than a few hundred (25, 61). Selectively binding specific inhibitors that could be used for covalent labelling have not yet been discovered. Thus the chemical nature of the channels is still unknown. However, it has been suggested that the ATPases that accomplish active transport of either alkali ions (6) or Ca^{2+} (56a, 56) may also be able to form channels under the influence of cytoplasmic Ca^{2+}.

The involvement of the K-Na pump was suggested by the finding that in metabolically carefully depleted red cells ouabain was capable of inhibiting the response to Ca^{2+} (6). Against this view was advanced the argument (59) that the red cells of certain species (pig, horse) do not respond to Ca^{2+} or Pb^{2+} but nevertheless contain the alkali ion pump (15, 59). This does not seem a valid objection, since in human red cells the threshold for the response is increased by lowering the temperature. This renders a considerable fraction of the cells refractory against activation, although at 37°C all of the cells in the population show the well-known response (32). Thus in the other species the lipids may maintain the transport protein in a conformation that does not allow the formation of the channels, even at 37°C.

More convincing for a participation of the K-Na pump appeared to be the argument that dog red cells contain less transport ATPase than the potassium-rich cells that respond easily. Nevertheless, the dog red cells do react to the action of Ca^{2+} just as human red cells do, provided the high intracellular Na^+ is exchanged against K^+ prior to eliciting the response (86). Recent work with proteoliposomes shows that reconstitution of the Na-K pump activity is not associated with the appearance of a (Ca^{2+}-K^+)-activated K^+ efflux (50).

The involvement of the Ca ATPase was suggested on the grounds that this transport enzyme may undergo changes of its activity in response to variations of Ca^{2+}, Mg^{2+}, and ATP that resemble in certain respects the behavior of the (Ca^{2+} +K^+)-activated K^+ channels (56). However, the reported linear relationship between the inhibition of the Ca pump and the K^+ movements across the Ca^{2+}-activated channels in the presence of calmodulin inhibiting substances (56a) needs further exploration since conflicting results were obtained elsewhere (A. Rothstein, personal communication). Of course the channels may be independent entities related to none of the known membrane proteins.

In any event, the channels must represent complex structures, probably similar to transport proteins, possibly composed of several subunits (93), since the variety, specificity, and sidedness of the interations among Ca^{2+}, K^+, and Na^+ potential and modulating substances would otherwise be difficult to comprehend.

ACKNOWLEDGMENT

We thank Drs. J. F. Hoffman, H. Ch. Lüttgau, B. Neumcke, and H. Porzig for their comments on the manuscript.

Literature Cited

1. Armando-Hardy, M., Ellory, J. C., Ferreira, H. G., Fleminger, S., Lev, V. L. 1975. Inhibition of the calcium-induced increase in the potassium permeability of human red blood cells by quinine. *J. Physiol.* 250:32p–33p
2. Almers, W., Armstrong, C. M. 1980. Survival of K^+ permeability and gating currents in squid axons perfused with K^+-free media. *J. Gen. Physiol.* 75: 61–78
3. Atwater, I., Dawson, C. M., Ribalet, B., Rojas, E. 1979. Potassium permeability activated by intracellular calcium ion concentration in the pancreatic β-cell. *J. Physiol.* 288:575–88
4. Barrett, E. F., Barrett, J. N. 1976. Separation of two voltage-sensitive potassium currents, and demonstration of a tetrodotoxin-resistant calcium current in frog motoneurons. *J. Physiol.* 255: 737–74
5. Barrett, J. N., Barrett, E. F., Dribin, L. B. 1981. Calcium-dependent slow potassium conductance in rat skeletal myotubes. *Dev. Biol.* 82:258–66
6. Blum, R. M., Hoffman, J. F. 1971. The membrane locus of Ca-stimulated transport in energy-depleted human red blood cells. *J. Membr. Biol.* 6:315–28
7. Blum, R. M., Hoffman, J. F. 1972. Ca-induced K^+ transport in human red cells: Localization of the Ca-sensitive site to the inside of the membrane. *Biochem. Biophys. Res. Commun.* 46: 1146–52
8. Boheim, G., Methfessel, G., Sakmann, B. 1982. Ca^{++} activates a K^+ channel by preventing channel blockade. *Pflügers Arch.* 392 (Suppl): R19 (Abstr.)
9. Bolsover, S. R. 1981. Calcium dependent potassium current in barnacle photoreceptor. *J. Gen. Physiol.* 78: 617–36
9a. Burgess, G. M., Claret, M., Jenkinson, D. H. 1981. Effects of quinine and apamin on the calcium-dependent potassium permeabilities of mammalian hepatocytes and red cells. *J. Physiol.* 317:67–90
10. Carafoli, E. 1982. Vanadate-induced movements of Ca^{2+} and K^+ in red cells. *J. Biol. Chem.* Submitted
11. Clusin, W. T., Bennett, M. V. L. 1979. The ionic basis of oscillatory responses of skate electroreceptors. *J. Gen. Physiol.* 73:703–23
12. Colquhoun, D., Neher, E., Reuter, H., Stevens, C. F. 1981. Inward current channels activated by intracellular Ca in cultured cardiac cells. *Nature* 294: 752–54
13. Connor, J. A. 1979. Calcium current in molluscan neurones: Measurement under conditions which maximize its visibility. *J. Physiol.* 286:41–60
14. Dubois, J. M., Bergman, C. 1977. The steady-state potassium conductance of the Ranvier node at various external K-concentrations. *Pflügers Arch.* 370: 185–95
15. Dunker, E., Passow, H. 1953. Zwei Arten des Anionenaustausches bei den roten Blutkörperchen verschiedener Säugetiere. *Pflügers Arch.* 256:446–56
16. Eckert, R. 1977. Genes, channels and membrane currents in paramecium. *Nature* 268:104–5
17. Eckert, R., Lux, H. D. 1977. Calcium-dependent depression of a late outward current in snail neurons. *Science* 197: 472–75
18. Edgington, D. R., Stuart, A. E. 1981. Properties of tetraethylammonium ion-resistant K^+ channels in the photoreceptor membrane of giant barnacle. *J. Gen. Physiol.* 77:629–46
19. Ekman, A. M., Manninen, V., Salminen, S. 1969. Ion movements in red

cells treated with propranolol. *Acta Physiol. Scand.* 75:333–34

20. Fink, R., Grocki, K., Lüttgau, H. C. 1980. Na/K selectivity, ion conductances and net fluxes of K⁺ and Na⁺ in metabolically exhausted muscle fibres. *Eur. J. Cell. Biol.* 21:109–15

21. Fink, R., Wettwer, E. 1978. Modified K channel gating by exhaustion and the block by internally applied TEA⁺ and 4-amino-pyridines in muscle. *Pflügers Arch.* 374:289–92

22. Fink, R., Hase, S., Lüttgau, H. Ch., Wettwer, E. 1982. The effect of cellular energy reserves and internal Ca²⁺ on the potassium conductance in skeletal muscle of the frog. *J. Physiol.* In press

23. Fishman, M. C., Spector, I. 1981. Potassium current suppression by quinidine reveals additional calcium currents in neuroblastoma cells. *Proc. Natl. Acad. Sci. USA* 78:5245–49

24. Garcia-Sancho, J., Sanchez, A., Herreros, B. 1979. Stimulation of monovalent cation fluxes by electron donors in the human red cell membrane. *Biochim. Biophys. Acta* 556:118–30

25. Garcia-Sancho, J., Sanchez, A., Herreros, B. 1982. All-or-none response of the Ca²⁺-dependent K⁺ channel in inside-out vesicles. *Nature* 296:744–46

26. Gárdos, G. 1958. The function of calcium in the potassium permeability of human erythrocytes. *Biochim. Biophys. Acta* 30:653–54

27. Glynn, I. M., Warner, A. E. 1972. Nature of the calcium dependent potassium leak activated by (+)-propranolol, and its possible relevance to the drug's antiarrythmic effect. *Br. J. Pharmacol.* 44:271–78

28. Gorman, A. L. F., Hermann, A. 1979. Internal effects of divalent cations on potassium permeability in molluscan neurons. *J. Physiol.* 296:393–410

29. Gorman, A. L. F., Hermann, A., Thomas, M. V. 1981. Intracellular calcium and the control of neural pacemaker activity. *Fed. Proc.* 40:2233–39

30. Gorman, A. L. F., McReynolds, J. S. 1974. Control of K⁺ permeability in a hyperpolarising photoreceptor: Similar effects of light and metabolic inhibitors. *Science* 185:620–21

31. Gorman, A. L. F., Thomas, M. V. 1980. Potassium conductance and internal calcium accumulation in a molluscan neuron. *J. Physiol.* 308:287–313

32. Grigarzik, H., Passow, H. 1958. Versuche zum Mecchanismus der Bleiwirkung auf die Kaliumpermeabilität roter Blutkörperchen. *Pflügers Arch.* 267: 73–92

33. Hamill, O. P. 1981. Potassium channel currents in human red blood cells. *J. Physiol.* 319:97P–98P (Abstr.)

34. Hamill, O. P., Marty, A., Neher, E., Sakmann, B., Sigworth, F. J. 1981. Improved patch-clamp techniques for high-resolution current recording from cells and cell-free membrane patches. *Pflügers Arch.* 391:85–100

35. Heinz, A., Passow, H. 1980. Role of external potassium in the calcium-induced potassium efflux from human red blood cell ghosts. *J. Membr. Biol.* 57:119–31

36. Henkart, M. P., Nelson, P. G. 1979. Evidence of an intracellular calcium store releasable by surface stimuli in fibroblasts (L-cells). *J. Gen. Physiol.* 73:655–73

37. Henquin, J. C. 1980. Metabolic control of the potassium permeability in pancreatic islet cells. *Biochem. J.* 186: 541–50

38. Hermann, A., Gorman, A. L. F. 1981. Effects of 4 aminopyridine on potassium currents in a molluscan neuron. *J. Gen. Physiol.* 78:63–86

39. Hermann, A., Gorman, A. L. F. 1981. Effects of tetraethylammonium on potassium currents in a molluscan neuron. *J. Gen. Physiol.* 78:87–110

40. Hermann, A., Gorman, A. L. F. 1982. Ruthenium red blocks Ca²⁺ inward current and Ca²⁺ activated outward current of molluscan neurons. *Biophys. J.* 3:183a (Abstr.)

41. Hoffman, J. F., Yingst, D. R., Goldinger, R. M., Blum, R. M., Knauf, P. A. 1980. On the mechanism of Ca-dependent K transport in human red blood cells. In *Membrane Transport in Erythrocytes,* ed. U. V. Lassen, H. H. Ussing, J. O. Wieth, pp. 178–95. Copenhagen: Munnksgaard

42. Hoffman, J. F., Yingst, D. R. 1981. On calcium-dependent potassium transport in human red blood cells. *Adv. Physiol. Sci.* 6:195–201

43. Hoffman, J. F., Knauf, P. A. 1973. The mechanism of the increased K transport activated by Ca in human red blood cells. In *Erythrocytes, Thrombocytes, Leukocytes: Recent Advances in Membrane and Metabolic Research,* ed. E. Gerlach, K. Moser, E. Deutsch, W. Wilmanns, pp. 66–70. Stuttgart: Georg Thieme

44. Hoffman, J. F., Blum, R. M. 1977. On the nature of the transport pathway used for Ca⁺⁺-dependent K movement

in human red blood cells. In *Membrane Toxicity*, ed. M. W. Miller, A. E. Shamoo, pp. 381–405. NY: Plenum

45. Hofmeier, G., Lux, H. D. 1981. The time courses of intracellular free calcium and related electrical events after injection of CaCl$_2$ into neurons of the snail, *Helix pomatia. Pflügers Arch.* 391:242–51

46. Isenberg, G. 1977. Cardiac Purkinje fibers: Resting, action, and pacemaker potential under the influence of Ca$^{2+}_i$ as modified by intracellular injection techniques. *Pflügers Arch.* 371:51–59

47. Isenberg, G. 1977. Cardiac Purkinje fibres: Ca$^{2+}_i$ controls the potassium permeability via the conductance components g_{K1} and g_{K2}. *Pflügers Arch.* 371:77–85

47a. Iwatzuki, N., Petersen, O. H. 1978. Intracellular Ca^{2+} injection causes membrane hyperpolarization and conductance increase in lacrimal acinar cells. *Pflügers Arch.* 377:185–87

48. Jansen, J. K. S., Nicholls, J. G. 1973. Conductance changes, an electrogenic pump and the hyperpolarization of leech neurons following impulses. *J. Physiol.* 229:635–55

49. Junge, D. 1982. Reduction of outward currents in snail neurons by replacement of extracellular potassium. *Biophys. J.* 37:183a (Abstr.)

50. Karlish, S. J. D., Ellory, J. C., Lew, V. L. 1981. Evidence against Na$^+$-pump mediation of Ca^{++}-activated K$^+$ transport and diuretic-sensitive (Na$^+$/K$^+$)-cotransport. *Biochim. Biophys. Acta* 646:353–55

51. Khodorov, B. I., Neumcke, B., Schwarz, W., Stämpfli, R. 1981. Fluctuation analysis of Na$^+$ channels modified by batrachotoxin in myelinated nerve. *Biochim. Biophys. Acta* 648: 93–99

52. Kregenow, V. M., Hoffman, J. F. 1962. Metabolic control of passive transport and exchange diffusion of Na and K in human red cells. Abstr. Commun. Meet. Biophys. Soc., Washington D.C.

53. Knauf, P. A., Riordan, J. R., Schuhmann, B., Wood-Guth, I., Passow, H. 1975. Calcium-potassium-stimulated net potassium efflux from human erythrocyte ghosts. *J. Membr. Biol.* 25:1–22

54. Krjevic, K., Puil, E., Werman, R. 1978. EGTA and motoneuron afterpotentials. *J. Physiol.* 275:199–223

55. Krueger, B. K., French, R. J., Blaustein, M. B., Worley, J. F. 1982. Incorporation of Ca^{++}-activated K$^+$-chan-

nels, from rat brain, into planar lipid bilayers. *Biophys. J.* 37:170a (Abstr.)

56. Lassen, U. V., Pape, L., Westergaard-Bogind, B. 1980. Calcium-related transient changes in membrane potential of red cells: Experimental observations and a model involving calcium-dependent regulator (CDR). See Ref. 41, pp. 255–73

56a. Lackington, I., Orrega, F. 1981. Inhibition of calcium-activated potassium conductance of human erythrocytes by calmodulin inhibitory drugs. *FEBS Lett.* 133:103–6

57. Latorre, R., Vergara, C., Hildago, C. 1982. Reconstitution in planar lipid bilayers of a Ca^{2+}-dependent K$^+$ channels from transverse tubule membranes isolated from rabbit skeletal muscle. *Proc. Natl. Acad. USA* 79:805–9

58. Lew, V. L., Ferreira, H. G. 1976. Variable Ca^{++} sensitivity of a K-selective channel in intact red cell membranes. *Nature* 263:336–38

59. Lew, V. L., Ferreira, H. G. 1978. Ca^{++}-transport and the properties of a Ca-sensitive K channel in red cell membranes. *Curr. Top. Membr. Transp.* 10:217–71

60. Lew, V. L., Bookchin, R. M., Brown, A. M., Ferreira, H. G. 1980. Ca-sensitivity modulation. See Ref. 41, pp. 196–207

61. Lew, V. L., Muallem, S., Seymour, C. A. 1982. Properties of the Ca-activated K channel in one-step inside-out vesicles from human red cell membranes. *Nature* 296:742–44

62. Lindemann, B., Passow, H. 1960. Versuche zur Aufklärung der Beziehung zwischen Glycolysehemmung und Kaliumverlust bei der Fluoride Vergiftung von Menschenerythrocyten. *Pflügers Arch.* 271:497–510

63. Lux, H. D., Neher, E., Marty, A. 1981. Single channel activity associated with the calcium dependent outward current in *Helix pomatia. Pflügers Arch.* 389: 293–95

64. Marino, D., Sarkadi, B., Gardos, G., Bolis, L. 1981. Calcium-induced alkali cation transport in nucleated red cells. *Molec. Physiol.* 1:295–300

65. Marty, A. 1981. Ca-dependent K channels with large unitary conductance in chromaffin cell membranes. *Nature* 291:497–500

66. Meech, R. W. 1974. The sensitivity of *Helix aspersa* neurons to injected calcium ions. *J. Physiol.* 237:256–77

67. Meech, R. W. 1978. Calcium-dependent potassium activation in nervous tis-

sue. *Ann. Rev. Biophys. Bioeng.* 7:1–18
68. Meech, R. W., Standen, N. B. 1975. Potassium activation in *Helix aspersa* neurons under voltage clamp: A component mediated by calcium influx. *J. Physiol.* 249:211–39
69. Meissner, H. P., Preissler, M. 1979. Glucose-induced changes of the membrane potential of pancreatic B-cells: Their significance for regulation of insulin release. In *Treatment of Early Diabetes,* ed. R. A. Camerini-Davalos, B. Hanover. NY: Plenum
70. Miyazaki, S., Igusa, Y. 1982. Ca-mediated activation of a K current at fertilization of golden hamster eggs. *Proc. Natl. Acad. Sci. USA* 79:931–35
71. Moolenaar, W. H., Spector, I. 1979. The calcium current and the activation of a slow potassium conductance in voltage-clamped mouse neuroblastoma cells. *J. Physiol.* 292:307–23
72. Ohmori, H. 1978. Inactivation kinetics and steady-state current noise in the anomalous rectifier of tunicate egg cell membranes. *J. Physiol.* 281:77–99
73. Ohmori, H. 1980. Dual effects of K ions upon the inactivation of the anomalous rectifier of tunicate egg cell membrane. *J. Membr. Biol.* 53:143–56
74. Okada, Y., Tsuchiya, W., Inouye, A. 1979. Oscillations of membrane potential in L-cells: IV. Role of intracellular Ca²⁺ in hyperpolarizing excitability. *J. Membr. Biol.* 47:357–76
75. Olivera-Castro, G. M., Dos Reis, G. A. 1981. Electrophysiology of phagocytic membranes: III. Evidence for a calcium-dependent potassium permeability change during slow hyperpolarizations of activated macrophages. *Biochim. Biophys. Acta* 640:500–11
76. Ørskov, S. L. 1935. Untersuchungen über den Einfluss von Kohlensäure und Blei auf die Permeabilität der Blutkörperchen für Kalium und Rubidium. *Biochem. Z.* 297:250–61
77. Pallotta, B. S., Magleby, K. L., Barrett, J. N. 1981. Single channel recordings of Ca²⁺-activated K⁺ currents in rat muscle cell culture. *Nature* 293:471–74
78. Pallotta, B. S., Magleby, K. L., Barrett, J. N. 1982. Kinetics of the Ca²⁺-activated K⁺ channel in cultured rat muscle. *Biophys. J.* 37:318a (Abstr.)
79. Passow, H. 1963. Metabolic control of passive cation permeability in human red cells. In *Cell Interface Reactions,* ed. H. D. Brown, pp. 57–107. NY: Scholar's Library
80. Passow, H. 1970. The red blood cell: Penetration, distribution and toxic ac-

tions of heavy metals. In *Effects of Metals on Cells, Subcellular Elements and Macromolecules,* ed. J. Manilof, J. R. Coleman, M. Miller, pp. 291–344. Springfield: Charles G. Thomas
81. Passow, H. 1981. Selective enhancement of potassium efflux from red blood cells by lead. A comparison with the effects of calcium. In *The Function of Red Blood Cells: Erythrocyte Pathobiology,* ed. D. F. H. Wallach, A. R. Liss, pp. 79–104. NY:
82. Passow, H., Tillman, K. 1955. Untersuchungen über den Kaliumverlust bleivergifteter Menschenerythrocyten. *Pflügers Arch.* 262:23–36
83. Porzig, H. 1975. Comparative study of the effects of propranolol and tetracaine on cation movements in resealed human red cell ghosts. *J. Physiol.* 249:27–50
84. Porzig, H. 1977. Studies on cation permeability of human red cell ghosts. *J. Membr. Biol.* 31:317–49
84a. Putney, J. W. 1979. Stimulus-permeability coupling: Role of calcium in the receptor regulation of membrane permeability. *Pharmacol. Rev.* 30:209–45
85. Reed, P. W. 1976. Effects of the divalent cation ionophore A23187 on potassium permeability of rat erythrocytes. *J. Biol. Chem.* 251:3489–93
85a. Ribalet, B., Beigelman, P. M. 1980. Calcium action potential and potassium permeability activation in pancreatic β-cells. *Am. J. Physiol.* 239:C124–33
86. Richardt, H.-W., Fuhrmann, G. F., Knauf, P. A. 1979. Dog red blood cells exhibit a Ca stimulated increase in K permeability in the absence of (Na+K)-ATPase activity. *Nature* 279:248–50
87. Riordan, J. R., Passow, H. 1971. Effects of calcium and lead on potassium permeability of human erythrocyte ghosts. *Biochim. Biophys. Acta* 249:601–5
88. Riordan, J. R., Passow, H. 1973. The effects of calcium and lead on the potassium permeability of human erythrocytes and erythrocyte ghosts. In *Comparative Physiology,* ed. L. Bolis, K. Schmidt-Nielsen, S. H. P. Madrell, pp. 543–81. Amsterdam: North-Holland
89. Romero, P. J. 1978. Is the Ca²⁺-sensitive K⁺ channel under metabolic control in human red cells? *Biochim. Biophys. Acta* 507:178–81
90. Romero, P. J., Whittam, R. 1971. The control by internal calcium of membrane permeability to sodium and potassium. *J. Physiol.* 214:481–507

91. Sarkadi, B., Szebeni, J., Gardos, G. 1980. Effects of calcium on cation transport processes in inside-out red cell membrane vesicles. See Ref. 41, pp. 22–235
92. Siegelbaum, S. A., Tsien, R. W. 1980. Calcium-activated transient outward current in calf cardiac Purkinje fibres. *J. Physiol.* 299:485–506
93. Simons, T. J. B. 1976. Calcium-dependent potassium exchange in human red cell ghosts. *J. Physiol.* 256:227–44
94. Simons, T. J. B. 1979. Actions of a carbocyanine dye on calcium-dependent potassium transport in human red cell ghosts. *J. Physiol.* 288:481–507
95. Thomas, M. V. 1981. Properties of a Ca mediated K conductance in an insect neuron. *J. Physiol.* 320:117P (Abstr.)
96. Vergara, C., Hidalgo, C., Latorre, R. 1981. Incorporation into and properties of a K^+-selective, Ca^{++}-dependent channel in lipid bilayer membranes. *7th Int. Biophys. Congr. & 3rd Pan Am. Biochem. Congr., Mexico City, 1981*, p. 306 (Abstr.)
97. Walsh, J. W., Singer, J. J. 1981. Voltage clamp of single freshly dissociated smooth muscle cells: Current-voltage relationships for three currents. *Pflüg-*

ers Arch. 390:207–10
98. Wettwer, E., Hase, S., Lüttgau, H. C. 1981. The increase in potassium conductance in metabolically poisoned skeletal muscle fibres. *Adv. Physiol. Sci.* 5:262–69
99. Wilbrandt, W. 1940. Die Abhängigkeit der Ionenpermeabilität der Erythrocyten vom glycolytischen Stoffwechsel. *Pflügers Arch.* 243:519–36
100. Wong, S. B., Lecar, H., Adler, M. 1982. Differentiation of the two potassium channels in clonal anterior pituitary cells by the patch clamp technique. *Biophys. J.* 37:318a (Abstr.)
101. Wood, P. G., Rempel, U. 1982. The spontaneous generation of a potassium channel during the preparation of resealed human erythrocyte ghosts. *Biochim. Biophys. Acta.* Submitted
102. Woolum, J. C., Gorman, A. L. F. 1980. The selectivity of the Ca^{2+}-activated K^+ channel for monovalent cations. *Soc. Neurosci.* 6:834 (Abstr.)
103. Yingst, D. R., Hoffman, J. F. 1978. Change of intracellular Ca^{++} as measured by arsenazo III in relation to the K permeability of human erythrocyte ghosts. *Biophys. J.* 23:463–71

Ann. Rev. Physiol. 1983. 45:375–90

CALCIUM TRANSPORT PROTEINS, CALCIUM ABSORPTION, AND VITAMIN D

R. H. Wasserman and C. S. Fullmer

Department of Physiology, New York State College of Veterinary Medicine, Cornell University, Ithaca, NY 14853

INTRODUCTION

The significant, multi-functional roles served by calcium in biology need no emphasis today. A number of the physiological and biochemical reactions influenced by Ca^{2+} was tabulated by Carafoli & Crompton (11); for example, calcium is required for bone and teeth formation, muscle contraction, nerve conduction, neurotransmitter release, blood coagulation, activation of specific enzymes, endocrine secretion, cell differentiation, cell motility, and cell division.

A major function of Ca^{2+} is as a "second messenger," activating and regulating cellular processes and reactions. As emphasized by Kretsinger (44), Ca^{2+} is well suited for this role, coupling a given stimulus to the appropriate response. The conditions allowing for calcium-mediated responses are: (*a*) an extracellular ionic Ca^{2+} at 10^{-3} M; (*b*) cellular mechanisms that maintain intracellular ionic Ca^{2+} at 10^{-7} M or less in the resting state; (*c*) increased leakage of Ca^{2+} into the cytosol upon stimulation, thereby raising cytosolic ionic Ca^{2+} to 10^{-6}–10^{-5} M; (*d*) an intracellular calcium-binding receptor or modulator with a k_a of about 10^6 M^{-1} so that a high proportion of the Ca^{2+} sites are occupied in the stimulated state; (*e*) a rapid return of cytosolic ionic Ca^{2+} to 10^{-7} M or less in the post-stimulatory phase, with the release of Ca^{2+} from the receptor. Calcium-receptor proteins that link the transitory elevation of ionic Ca^{2+} to the stimulated response include troponin C of muscle and the ubiquitous calmodulin (44, 51).

375

0066-4278/83/0315-0375 $02.00

As mentioned, two of the available conditions for stimulus-response coupling by Ca^{2+} are an extracellular Ca^{2+} concentration of 10^{-3} M and a resting, intracellular Ca^{2+} concentration of about 10^{-7} M. The former is assured by processes that maintain serum Ca^{2+} levels in the 10^{-3} M range, and these include the intestinal absorption of Ca^{2+} from dietary sources, the tubular reabsorption of Ca^{2+} by the kidney, and the resorption of Ca^{2+} from bone. Each of these processes is hormonally regulated, involving the parathyroid hormone, the vitamin D_3 hormone(s), calcitonin, and other endocrine factors.

Here we emphasize the intestinal absorption of Ca^{2+} and the proteins and other macromolecules potentially involved in the process. As depicted in Figure 1, the transfer of calcium from lumen to lamina propria can be delineated in distinct steps: the transfer of Ca^{2+} across the brush-border membrane; transfer through the cell interior; and extrusion in the parent-

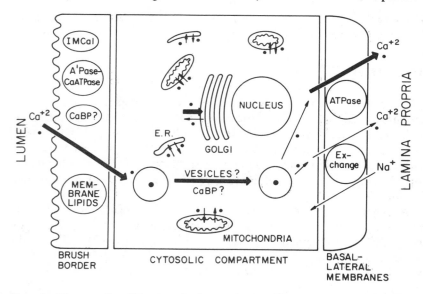

Figure 1   Diagram of possible events in the transfer of Ca^{2+} across the intestinal epithelial cell. Transfer across the brush border is downhill thermodynamically and facilitated by the action of vitamin D. Several factors located in this region, some of which are vitamin D–dependent, could be involved. Transfer through the cell might be in association with CaBP or encased in vesicles. Sequestration of intracellular Ca^{2+} by mitochondria, endoplasmic reticulum, or other organelles or by binding proteins maintains cytosolic Ca^{2+} at nontoxic levels. Extrusion of Ca^{2+} from the cell is against a thermodynamic gradient and is via a high-affinity Ca-activated ATPase and/or by Na^+/Ca^{2+} exchange. IMCal = intestinal membrane calcium-binding protein; A'Pase-CaATPase = alkaline phosphatase = low-affinity Ca-activated ATPase complex; CaBP = vitamin D–dependent calcium-binding protein; E. R. = endoplasmic reticulum; ATPase = Ca-activated ATPase. Heavy arrows indicate processes that appear to be vitamin D–dependent.

eral direction. Physiological data disclose that the total process—i.e. Ca^{2+} transfer from lumen to lamina propria—is by active transport and/or diffusion, the dominating process depending upon the concentration of Ca^{2+} in the luminal compartment (87). At lower levels of Ca^{2+} ($\leqslant$ 5 mM), the process is primarily active transport and, above this value, the diffusional process becomes increasingly significant. The active transport of Ca^{2+} is undoubtedly a transcellular event; the diffusional process might be either transcellular or paracellular.

ASPECTS OF VITAMIN D ACTION

The fact that vitamin D_3 is required for the optimal absorption of calcium has given a strategic advantage in attempts to understand features of the Ca^{2+} absorption process. For example, the injection of vitamin D_3 or its most active metabolite, $1,25(OH)_2D_3$, into rachitic chicks increases duodenal Ca^{2+} absorption by a factor of about 5 (87) and increases the transport of Ca^{2+} across rat everted duodenal sacs by a similar factor (72). This increment in Ca^{2+} absorption allows comparison of the molecular changes due to vitamin D_3 and, by difference, gives an indication of vitamin D_3 -dependent factors that *might* be involved in Ca^{2+} absorption. A sorting-out of vitamin D_3 effects directly related to Ca^{2+} transport from pleiotropic responses or those due secondarily to Ca^{2+} is required for this approach.

A basic premise is that $1,25(OH)_2D_3$ manifests changes in the intestine and other tissues in "typical" steroid fashion—i.e. by the induction, through interaction with the nuclear genetic apparatus, of proteins directly involved in the calcium transport process. There is considerable support for this premise and, as documented in recent reviews (cf 14, 32, 47, 56, 58), the evidence includes the nuclear localization of $1,25(OH)_2D_3$ in intestine, kidney, and other tissues; the identification of a specific receptor for $1,25(OH)_2D_3$ in the cytosol and nucleus in tissues; and the synthesis of a unique vitamin D_3-induced calcium-binding protein (CaBP). The synthesis or biochemical activity of proteins other than CABP is also affected by vitamin D status (81).

The protein synthetic hypothesis of vitamin D action has been questioned. It was reported that the administration of inhibitors of protein synthesis (cycloheximide, actinomycin D) to rachitic chicks did not inhibit Ca^{2+} absorption, whereas the synthesis of CaBP and alkaline phosphatase was inhibited or reduced (2). Cycloheximide pretreatment of chicks did not block the $1,25(OH)_2D_3$-dependent uptake of Ca^{2+} by isolated brush-border vesicles (64). Unfortunately, problems of interpretation accompany in vivo studies done with inhibitors of protein synthesis. Timing of the injection of inhibitor with that of $1,25(OH)_2D_3$ is critical, and these inhibitors have toxic effects beyond their effects on the protein synthetic machinery. Less ambiguous information comes from organ culture experiments with embryonic chick intestine. Inhibitors of protein synthesis clearly inhibited the 1,25(OH)$_2$D$_3$-stimulated transport of calcium (9, 20) and the synthesis of CaBP (9). These differences in conceptualization of the fundamental action of vitamin D obviously require resolution. Vitamin D may perform dual actions on the intestinal cell—one dependent on protein synthesis and the other not, for which there is precedent with other steroid hormones (69).

CALCIUM TRANSPORT ACROSS THE BRUSH BORDER

The transfer of Ca^{2+} across the brush border into the cytoplasm is undoubtedly a "diffusional" event, in the sense that a steep electropotential gradient favors passive transport (10^{-3} M Ca^{2+} → 10^{-7} M Ca^{2+}; $\Delta \psi \approx 30$ mV, inside negative). The presence of vitamin D$_3$ alters in some fashion the properties of the microvillar membrane or brush-border complex to enhance the rate of entrance of Ca^{2+} into the cell.

Several vitamin D–dependent or vitamin D–sensitive responses have been identified in the brush-border–microvillus region of the intestine.

Alkaline Phosphatase–CaATPase Complex

The involvement of alkaline phosphatase–CaATPase in calcium absorption has been proposed frequently. The reason for this is clear: (a) Enzyme activity correlates with the degree of calcium absorption in different parts of the intestinal tract; (b) correlations were observed between enzyme activity and Ca^{2+} transport under different circumstances (17, 73); and (c) the activity of a Ca^{2+},Mg^{2+}-dependent ATPase present in intestinal brush borders was shown to be increased by vitamin D (52). A similar dependency of alkaline phosphatase activity on vitamin D was also reported (33, 59). It was proposed that alkaline phosphatase and brush-border CaATPase are expressions of the same molecule (33, 34, 68), since attempts to separate these activities by various biochemical procedures have not been successful (62). However, there are physiological circumstances in which the activity of alkaline phosphatase and brush-border CaATPase can be separately affected. De Wolff (15) reported that diphenylhydantoin, an anti-convulsant drug, stimulated both Ca absorption and intestinal CaATPase, but slightly inhibited alkaline phosphatase activity in the rat intestine. Lane & Lawson (46) observed that, after 1,25(OH)$_2$D$_3$ injection into rachitic chicks, alkaline phosphatase activity was significantly increased at about 10 hr, plateaued at about 30 hr, and remained at this level of activity for at least 60 hr. CaATPase, on the other hand, responded more rapidly to the 1,25(OH)$_2$ D$_3$ pulse, maximizing at 10 hr and returning to base line at 24 hr. A subsequent injection of 1,25(OH)$_2$D$_3$ at about 24 hr had no effect on alkaline phosphatase, but again stimulated CaATPase activity. Further, Ca absorption, as determined with an in vitro everted ileal sac preparation, was highly correlated with changes in CaATPase activity, but not with alkaline phosphatase activity (46). The above information does not necessarily disprove the molecular identity of alkaline phosphatase and CaATPase, but could be due to the presence of a vitamin D–dependent accessory factor that confers Ca-sensitivity upon the enzyme complex (19, 22, 54).

The alkaline phosphatase–CaATPase complex, with its low affinity for Ca^{2+}, has been distinguished from a high-affinity, Ca-stimulated ATPase associated with the plasma membrane of the intestinal cell (25). The former is present in both brush-border and basal-lateral membranes and is inhibitable by L-phenylalanine; the latter is found primarily in the basal-lateral membranes and is inhibitable by chlorpromazine (25).

A role of alkaline phosphatase in phosphate transport has also been proposed (3, 41).

The 86,000–90,000 M_r Brush-Border Protein

A distinctive vitamin D–responsive brush-border protein in the above molecular weight range was identified by SDS PAGE (66) and by the preferential incorporation of labeled amino acids after 1,25(OH)$_2$D$_3$ treatment of rachitic chicks (91). A hydrophobic glycoprotein of similar molecular weight was also identified by SDS PAGE; and the protein, phosphorylated with either ^{32}P-phosphate or ^{32}P-γ-ATP, was soluble in organic solvents (82). Wilson & Lawson (93) noted that phosphorylation of this protein was Ca^{2+} sensitive, and that the phosphoprotein was hydroxylamine-resistant, distinguishing it from other membrane-bound ATPases.

Recent information suggests that this protein is a monomer or a fragment of alkaline phosphatase (13). Rat basal-lateral membranes contained three proteins phosphorylatable with ^{32}P-γ-ATP (M_r: 64,000; 84,000; 115,000). The two smaller proteins were also phosphorylatable with ^{32}P-phosphate, and this phosphorylation was inhibited by the presence of β-glycerophosphate, indicative of a relation of these smaller proteins to alkaline phosphatase. Also the smaller proteins were present in both brush-border membranes and basal-lateral membranes, their distribution similar to that of alkaline phosphatase. The 115,000 M_r protein is primarily in the basal-lateral membranes, as is the high-affinity CaATPase.

Intestinal Membrane Calcium-Binding Proteins

Kowarski & Schachter (43) have isolated a vitamin D–dependent intestinal membrane calcium-binding protein (IMCal). On initial extraction with deoxycholate or n-butanol, IMCal is associated with the alkaline phosphatase-calcium ATPase complex but is dissociated therefrom by biochemical purification procedures. The quantity of IMCal in intestinal cells varies with the degree of calcium absorption under various physiological and nutritional states, thereby implicating this factor as part of the calcium transport system. The estimated M_r of IMCal, determined by gel filtration in 0.1% Triton X-100, is 200,000 whereas, when SDS PAGE is employed after disassociation in 1% SDS, the monomeric form has a M_r of 20,500. The apparent k_a for Ca^{2+} was estimated at 2.7×10^6 M^{-1}, nearly identical to that of rat CaBP as determined by Bruns et al (5), but different from the value for rat CaBP (4.4×10^5 M^{-1}) determined by Kowarski & Schachter (43). It was proposed that IMCal may mediate Ca^{2+} entry into the cell, possibly by forming a Ca^{2+} channel comprised of the 20,500 M_r subunits.

Miller et al (53) isolated a vitamin D-dependent calcium-binding protein from rat brush borders that was released without detergent treatment. This protein (M_r 18,500) binds Ca^{2+} to the same extent as the soluble rat CaBP and is similar in size to calmodulin, known to be associated with intestinal brush borders (36).

Actin

Stimulation of the synthesis of an actin-like protein in chick intestinal brush borders by $1,25(OH)_2D_3$ was shown via a double-labeling experiment by Wilson & Lawson (91). The synthesis of this 43,000 M_r protein was enhanced 1 hr after $1,25(OH)_2D_3$ administration and represents one of the earliest effects of the vitamin D hormone. The rate of synthesis maximizes at 4 hr and falls to the rachitic baseline level at 10 hr. Later studies provided evidence that these proteins are β- and γ-actin (92). Under different experimental conditions another double-labeling study, in which proteins in intestinal mucosa were separated by 2-dimensional electrophoresis, indicated that the syntheses of β- and γ-actin were reduced after vitamin D_3 repletion (42).

A comparison of rachitic and vitamin D brush-border core proteins did not reveal any significant difference in actin content (35). In view of the increased incorporation of labeled amino acids into actin after $1,25(OH)_2$ D_3 treatment, the above results suggest a greater rate of turnover of actin in the vitamin D–replete intestinal cell.

The existence of a relationship of actin and microfilaments to calcium transport was suggested by observations that cytochalasin B significantly inhibited Ca^{2+} absorption by chick intestine in situ (38). However, another group reported only a slight effect of the same drug on Ca^{2+} transport by chick jejunum in vitro, but there was a substantial inhibitory effect on phosphate transport (23).

Phospholipid Metabolism and the Brush-Border Membrane

The passive permeability of membranes to Ca^{2+} could be influenced by the presence of Ca^{2+} channels, Ca^{2+} ionophoric carriers, or the state of fluidity of membrane lipids. Several years ago, it was noted that the presence of detergents enhanced the rate of Ca^{2+} transport by rachitic intestine in vitro (88), as did filipin, a non-ionophoric polyene antibiotic (60). The site of action of both types of compounds appears to be on the entrance of Ca^{2+} into the intestinal cell—i.e. on the brush-border membrane, and in a sense these compounds mimic one of the actions of vitamin D_3. The investigations with filipin led to the proposal that vitamin D_3 might influence the molecular organization of brush-border membranes and, as a result, directly or indirectly influence Ca^{2+} permeability. The accessibility of membrane proteins to labeling by nonpenetrating, covalent-linking radioactive probes and to proteolytic digestion disclosed differences in the labeling pattern and proteolytic release of proteins from the brush-border membranes derived from rachitic or vitamin D–replete chicks (60). These studies thus suggest that vitamin D affects, in some manner, morphological characteristics of the brush-border membrane.

The potential significance of brush-border phospholipids on Ca^{2+} transport by the intestine was brought into focus by the studies of Rasmussen and his colleagues (65). The administration of $1,25(OH)_2D_3$ to rachitic chicks resulted in an increase in the phosphatidyl choline (PC) content of brush borders and a modification in the number of polyunsaturated acyl chains of PC; the phosphatidyl ethanolamine content of these membranes and their fatty acid composition remained essentially unchanged. These $1,25(OH)_2D_3$-dependent changes were considered to increase membrane fluidity. This could hypothetically alter the rate of Ca^{2+} permeation across the brush-border membrane. This so-called "liponomic" regulation of Ca^{2+} transport was supported by the observation that the direct addition of the methyl ester of cis-vaccenic acid to isolated microvillar membrane vesicles increased Ca^{2+} uptake, whereas the methyl ester of trans-vaccenic acid was inactive; the cis- form increases membrane fluidity and the trans-form tends to have the opposite effect. In this context, O'Doherty (61) reported that $1,25(OH)_2D_3$ enhanced both phospholipase A_2 activity and lysophosphatidyl acyltransferase activity in intestinal cells, thereby implicating the deacylation-acylation cycle of phospholipids in the action of the vitamin D hormone. Alterations in phospholipid metabolism have been associated with other stimulatory factors, and the effect of specific phospholipids on enzyme activation has been reviewed (70).

A possible increase in membrane fluidity due to $1,25(OH)_2D_3$, as suggested from the biochemical data, might be verified by the several physical techniques now available. A preliminary report of an electron spin resonance (ESR) study with 5-nitroxide stearate stated that "vitamin D had no detectable effect on the polarity or fluidity" of the brush-border membrane or of the Golgi and basal-lateral membranes (63). The lack of detection of fluidity changes by ESR is contrary to the proposal of the Rasmussen group (60), and resolution of this discrepancy is required.

Calmodulin

As previously mentioned, the calcium-dependent regulator, calmodulin, is present within the brush-border unit of the intestine and in association with core proteins (27, 36). Calmodulin is also present in the cytosol of the intestinal cell (30, 78), and its concentration is not detectably influenced by the vitamin D (78) status of the animal. Owing to its high concentration in the microvillus and high Ca^{2+} binding affinity ($\sim 10^6$ M^{-1}), calmodulin might protect the integrity of the microvillus structure by preventing the Ca^{2+}-dependent proteolysis of F-actin by villin (27). The role of calmodulin in relation to the activity of the basal-lateral Ca,Mg-ATPase is discussed below.

Brush-Border CaBP

Whereas most of the vitamin D–induced CaBP is localized in the cytosolic compartment of the intestinal cell (67, 76), 5–10% appears to be membrane-bound (18). Highly purified brush-border membranes from vitamin D_3-replete chicks contain significant amounts of Triton X-100 extractable CaBP (74). The function of CaBP in this region of the cell is not known.

INTRACELLULAR PROTEINS AND TRANSPORT

The entrance of Ca^{2+} into the cell is only the first step in the transcellular transport of Ca^{2+}. Once within the cell, Ca^{2+} in some fashion must translocate to the exiting barrier, the basal-lateral membrane. Vitamin D enhances the transfer of Ca^{2+} from the apical region of the cell to the lamina propria (87), and part of this action could very well be on the intracellular transit of Ca^{2+}. Most of the vitamin D–induced CaBP is located within this compartment (39, 49, 67, 76). Effects of vitamin D on mitochondria and the Golgi complex have also been reported.

Vitamin D–Induced CaBP

Perhaps the best-defined molecular expression of vitamin D action is the induction of the vitamin D-induced CaBP (84). CaBP is virtually absent in the intestinal mucosa of the vitamin D-deficient animal and appears within 2–3 hr after the injection of $1,25(OH)_2D_3$ (77, 85). In addition to its vitamin D dependency, the concentration of this protein in the intestine varies directly with the efficiency of intestinal calcium absorption under a wide variety of physiological and nutritional circumstances, as previously reviewed (84). Two general types of CaBP have been identified, the avian-type of 28,000 M_r and the mammalian-type of about 9,000–10,000 M_r. The former binds 4 atoms of Ca^{2+} per molecule and the latter, 2, with high affinity. The apparent k_a of both types is about 2×10^6 M^{-1} (5, 16, 81). The bovine (24) and porcine (33a) intestinal CaBPs have been sequenced and the three-dimensional structure of the bovine CaBP determined crystallographically to 2.3Å (75).

CaBP occurs in several different tissues, both in "traditional" vitamin D targets (intestine, kidney) and "nontraditional" sites (brain, pancreas), and in both epithelial and nonepithelial organs (8, 86). Its function in each type of tissue has not been defined, but in the intestine the evidence is overwhelming for a role in the transcellular movement of Ca^{2+}.

One of several early proposals was that CaBP translocated Ca^{2+} from the apical to the basal region of the intestinal cell (71). This proposal has merit since CaBP, with its high affinity, could decrease or prevent the sequestration of Ca^{2+} by mitochondria and endoplasmic reticulum, maintaining intracellular Ca^{2+} at nontoxic levels during its transcellular passage. Recent evidence has provided support for this model. Bikle et al (1) showed that a rapid response of the rachitic intestine to 1,25(OH)$_2$D$_3$ was an increased entrance of Ca^{2+} into the intestinal cell, accompanied by the accumulation of Ca^{2+} by mitochondria prior to CaBP synthesis. After CaBP had been synthesized in response to the pulse of 1,25(OH)$_2$D$_3$, the accumulation of Ca^{2+} by intestinal mitochondria was less apparent, suggesting that the mitochondrial release of Ca^{2+} and its transfer across the basal-lateral membranes was enhanced by the presence of CaBP. Features of these observations by Bikle et al (1) were verified, in part, by our group (83). The administration of 1,25(OH)$_2$D$_3$ to rachitic chicks stimulated, within 1–2 hr, the uptake of Ca^{2+} by intestinal mucosa, but the epithelial transfer was not yet affected. Only when CaBP appeared at 2–4 hr following the 1,25(OH)$_2$D$_3$ pulse was there an observable increase in calcium absorption. These studies therefore imply that CaBP might provide a Ca^{2+} connection between the two poles of the intestinal cell. Kretsinger (45) recently developed a theoretical model to explain this possible mechanism for CaBP. In addition, the observations of Hamilton & Holdsworth (31) suggest that CaBP can directly stimulate Ca^{2+} efflux from mitochondria beyond its capacity to bind Ca^{2+}.

Intracellular Organelles

A significant increase in Ca^{2+} uptake by vesicles from a Golgi-rich fraction from rat intestinal cells was noted at 15 min after addition of 1,25(OH)$_2$ D$_3$. Uptake peaked at 30 min and declined to the basal value at 8 hr (21,

48). This was followed by a later increase in Ca^{2+} uptake by the Golgi fraction that was still evident at 120 hr after the $1,25(OH)_2D_3$ pulse. The response of the Golgi membranes preceded any change in Ca^{2+} uptake by everted gut sacs and isolated microvillus membranes. The authors (21, 48) proposed that there might be a translocation of $1,25(OH)_2D_3$-modified Golgi membranes to other parts of the cell. A quasi-parallelism between the biphasic change in Ca^{2+} permeability of the Golgi membranes in response to $1,25(OH)_2D_3$ and the biphasic change in cAMP levels in the chick intestine (10, 85) suggested either a direct effect of cAMP on Ca^{2+} permeability or an effect via activation of a cAMP-dependent protein kinase (21, 48). It was later shown that the $1,25(OH)_2D_3$-dependent uptake of Ca^{2+} by the Golgi vesicles was carrier-mediated, inhibitable by cycloheximide, and not dependent upon ATP (90).

Warner & Coleman (80) visualized calcium "packets" within the intestinal cell by electron probe analysis. The possibility that Ca^{2+} moves through the cytosol by "mobile" mitochondria (89) or calcium-containing secondary lysosomes (12, 37) has been suggested. Exit of Ca^{2+} from the cell by the latter mechanism would be by exocytosis, for which there is no evidence.

TRANSFER ACROSS THE BASAL-LATERAL MEMBRANE

Ca Pump

The uphill transfer of Ca^{2+} across the basal-lateral membrane is mediated by an ATP-activated Ca^{2+} pump, most likely identical to a high-affinity Ca^{2+}-dependent ATPase identified in these membranes (13, 25, 57, 79). The activity of this ATPase and basal-lateral Ca transport appear to be increased by $1,25(OH)_2D_3$ (26). The K_m of the basal-lateral CaATPase is 0.3 μM and its V_{max}, is 1.2 $\mu moles$ $P_i/hr/$ mg protein (79). The activity of this enzyme was fully inhibited by phenothiazine, an inhibitor of calmodulin activity (13). Phosphorylation with ^{32}P-γ-ATP in the presence of Ca^{2+} (and Mg^{2+}) yielded a phosphoprotein intermediate of about 115,000 daltons, a reaction inhibited by the phenothiazines.

Vesicles produced from basal-lateral-enriched membranes transported Ca^{2+} in the presence of Mg^{2+} and ATP; the addition of electroplax calmodulin significantly increased the maximal transport rate and the calcium affinity of the transport reaction (57). Chloropromazine inhibited Ca transport by these vesicles in the absence of added calmodulin, suggesting that the isolation of the membranes, even in the presence of EDTA, did not completely disassociate endogenous calmodulin. These studies with the phenothiazines and calmodulin per se imply that Ca^{2+} activation of the

Ca^{2+} pump is mediated by calmodulin, as it is in erythrocyte membranes (29, 40), the cardiac sarcolemma (7), and other membrane-associated Ca pumps (6).

Na$^+$/Ca^{2+} Exchange

The transport of Ca^{2+} across rat intestine in vitro is dependent upon the presence of Na$^+$. It was suggested that Na$^+$ acts at the basal-lateral membrane by increasing Ca^{2+} efflux (50). Birge & Gilbert (4) identified a Na$^+$,Ca^{2+}-dependent phosphatase in basal-lateral membranes that was considered responsible for the Na$^+$ effect.

More recently, a Na$^+$/Ca^{2+} antiport was detected in basal-lateral membranes of rat intestine (55). The ATP-driven uptake of Ca^{2+} by isolated basal-lateral vesicles was considerably reduced in the presence of Na$^+$. Also, the efflux of Ca^{2+} from pre-loaded vesicles was greater when incubated in a Na$^+$-containing buffer as compared to a K$^+$-containing buffer. A similar Na$^+$/Ca^{2+} exchange system occurs in the basal-lateral membranes of renal cells (28). The proposed exchange ratio of Na$^+$/Ca^{2+} is 3 (28, 55) and is therefore rheogenic. As with other cell membranes in which both ATP-dependent extrusion and Na$^+$/Ca^{2+} exchange are present, it was proposed that the Na$^+$/Ca^{2+} exchanger is effective at relatively high concentrations of intracellular Ca^{2+} and the Ca pump, at lower, resting levels of Ca^{2+}.

SUMMARY

A number of proteins and other factors have been proposed as participants in the transfer of calcium from intestinal lumen to the lamina propria. The vitamin D–dependency of many of these molecules and reactions provides their potential connection to vitamin D–dependent Ca^{2+} absorption. The evidence becoming available suggests that vitamin D might have more than one primary effect on the overall absorptive process. This proposal comes from the observations that a pulse of 1,25(OH)$_2$D$_3$ can effect a rapid increase in the influx of Ca^{2+} into the intestinal cell of rachitic animals but that an increase in the total absorptive process takes longer to occur (83). The time required for 1,25(OH)$_2$D$_3$-induced CaBP synthesis corresponds to the second phase. Now that the basal-lateral membrane high-affinity Ca^{2+}, Mg^{2+}-ATPase has been shown to be stimulated by 1,25(OH)$_2$D$_3$, it is possible that the vitamin D hormone affects all three phases of the Ca^{2+} absorptive process—i.e. transfer into the cell, translocation through the cell interior, and extrusion from the intestinal cell. Future experimentation is required to verify this proposal and to provide additional details of the mechanism of Ca^{2+} absorption, both that dependent on and that independent of vitamin D.

ACKNOWLEDGMENTS

The authors appreciate the efforts of Mrs. Norma Jayne in the preparation of manuscript and the suggestions of Mrs. Sharon Meyer. Investigations by the authors cited herein were supported by NIH Grant AM-04652.

Literature Cited

1. Bikle, D. D., Morrissey, R. L., Zolock, D. T. 1979. The mechanism of action of vitamin D in the intestine. *Am. J. Clin. Nutr.* 32:2322–38

2. Bikle, D. D., Zolock, D. T., Morrissey, R. L., Herman, R. H. 1978. Independence of 1,25-dihydroxyvitamin D_3-mediated calcium transport from *de novo* RNA and protein synthesis. *J. Biol. Chem.* 253:484–88

3. Birge, S. J., Avioli, R. C. 1981. Intestinal phosphate transport and alkaline phosphatase activity in the chick. *Am. J. Physiol.* 240:E384–90

4. Birge, S. J., Gilbert, H. R. 1974. Identification of an intestinal sodium and calcium-dependent phosphatase stimulated by parathyroid hormone. *J. Clin. Invest.* 54:710–17

5. Bruns, M. E. H., Fliesher, E. B., Avioli, L. V. 1977. Control of vitamin D-dependent calcium-binding protein in rat intestine by growth and fasting. *J. Biol. Chem.* 252:4145–50

6. Carafoli, E., Niggli, V., Malmstrom, K., Caroni, P. 1980. Calmodulin in natural and reconstituted calcium transporting systems. *Ann. NY Acad. Sci.* 356:258–66

7. Caroni, P., Carafoli, E. 1981. The Ca^{2+}-pumping ATPase of heart sarcolemma. Characterization, calmodulin dependence, and partial purification. *J. Biol. Chem.* 256:3263–70

8. Christakos, S., Norman, A. W. 1980. Vitamin D-dependent calcium-binding protein and its relation to 1,25-dihydroxyvitamin D receptor localization and concentration. In *Calcium-Binding Proteins: Structure and Function*, ed. F. L. Siegel, E. Carafoli, R. H. Kretsinger, D. H. MacLennan, R. H. Wasserman, pp. 371–78. NY: Elsevier-North Holland

9. Corradino, R. A. 1973. 1,25-Dihydroxycholecalciferol: inhibition of action in organ-cultured intestine by actinomycin D and α-amanitin. *Nature* 243:42–43

10. Corradino, R. A. 1974. Embryonic chick intestine in organ culture. In-

teraction of adenylate cyclase system and vitamin D_3-mediated calcium absorptive mechanism. *Endocrinology* 94:1607–14

11. Carafoli, E., Crompton, M. 1978. The regulation of intracellular calcium. *Curr. Top. Memb. Transp.* 10:151–216

12. Davis, W. L., Jones, R. G. 1981. Calcium lysosomes in rachitic and vitamin D_3 replete chick duodenal absorptive cells. *Tissue Cell* 13:381–91

13. DeJonge, H. R., Ghijsen, W. E. J., Van Os, C. H. 1981. Phosphorylated intermediates of Ca^{2+}-ATPase and alkaline phosphatase in plasma membranes from rat duodena epithelium. *Biochem. Biophys. Acta* 647:140–49

14. De Luca, H. F. 1976. Metabolism and mechanism of action of vitamin D. *Ann. Rev. Biochem.* 45:631–66

15. DeWolff, F. A. 1975. Stimulation of vitamin D-dependent Ca-ATPase and of intestinal calcium absorption by diphenylhydantoin. *Eur. J. Pharmacol.* 33:71–79

16. Dorrington, K. J., Hiu, A., Hofman, T., Hitchman, A. J. W., Harrison, J. E. 1974. Porcine intestinal calcium-binding protein. Molecular properties and the effect of binding calcium ions. *J. Biol. Chem.* 249:199–204

17. Feher, J. J., Wasserman, R. H. 1979. Intestinal calcium-binding protein and calcium absorption in cortisol-treated chicks: Effects of vitamin D_3 and 1,25-dihydroxyvitamin D_3. *Endocrinology* 104:547–51

18. Feher, J. J., Wasserman, R. H. 1979. Studies on the sub-cellular localization of the membrane-bound fraction of intestinal calcium-binding protein (CaBP). *Biochem. Biophys. Acta* 585:599–610

19. Fontaine, N. 1981. Alkaline phosphatase and calcium-binding properties in the intestine of the rat. *Arch. Intern. Physiol. Biochim.* 89:207–16

20. Franceschi, R. T., DeLuca, H. F. 1981. The effect of inhibitors of protein and RNA synthesis on 1α,25-dihydroxyvitamin D_3-dependent calcium uptake

in cultured embryonic chick duodenum. *J. Biol. Chem.* 256:3848–52

21. Freedman, R. A., Weiser, M. M., Isselbacher, K. J. 1977. Calcium translocation by Golgi and lateral-basal vesicles from rat intestine: Decrease in vitamin D-deficient rats. *Proc. Natl. Acad. Sci. USA* 74:3612–16

22. Freund, T. S., Borzemsky, G. 1977. Vitamin D-dependent intestinal calcium-binding protein: A regulatory protein. In *Calcium-Binding Proteins and Calcium Function*, ed. R. H. Wasserman, R. A. Corradino, E. Carafoli, R. H. Kretsinger, D. H. MacLennan, F. L. Siegel, pp. 353–56. NY: Elsevier-North Holland

23. Fuchs, R., Peterlik, M. 1979. Vitamin D-induced transepithelial phosphate and calcium transport by chick jejunum. *FEBS Lett.* 100:357–59

24. Fullmer, C. S., Wasserman, R. H. 1981. The aminoacid sequence of bovine intestinal calcium binding protein. *J. Biol. Chem.* 256:5669–74

25. Ghijsen, W. E. J. M., DeJong, M. D., Van Os, C. H. 1980. Association between Ca²⁺-ATPase and alkaline phosphatase activities in plasma membranes of rat duodenum. *Biochem. Biophys. Acta* 599:538–51

26. Ghijen, W. E. J. M., Van Os, C. H. 1982. Regulation of Ca-ATPase and active Ca transport in basolateral plasmamembranes by 1,25(OH)₂D₃ in rat duodenum. *Proc. Fifth Workshop on Vitamin D, Williamsburg, VA, Feb. 14–19, 1982*, p. 106

27. Glenney, J. R. Jr., Bretscher, A., Weber, K. 1980. Calcium control of the intestinal microvillus cytoskeleton: Its implications for the regulation of microfilament organizations. *Proc. Natl. Acad. Sci. USA* 77:6458–62

28. Gmaj, P., Murer, H., Kinne, R. 1979. Calcium ion transport across plasma membranes isolated from rat kidney cortex. *Biochem. J.* 178:549–57

29. Gopinath, R. M., Vincenzi, F. F. 1977. Phosphodiesterase protein activator mimics red blood cell cytoplasmic activator of (Ca²⁺ + Mg²⁺)-ATPase. *Biochem. Biophys. Res. Commun.* 77:1203–9

30. Gregg, S., Wasserman, R. H. 1982. Unpublished data

31. Hamilton, J. W., Holdsworth, E. S. 1975. The role of calcium binding protein in the mechanism of action of cholecalciferol (vitamin D). *Austr. J. Exp. Biol. Med. Sci.* 53:469–78

32. Haussler, M. R., Brumbaugh, P. F. 1976. 1α,25-dihydroxyvitamin D₃ receptors in intestine. In *Hormone-Receptor Interaction: Molecular Aspects*, ed. G. S. Levey, pp. 301–32. NY: Marcel-Dekker

33. Haussler, M. R., Nagode, L. A., Rasmussen, H. 1970. Induction of intestinal brush border alkaline phosphatase by vitamin D and identity with CaATPase. *Nature* 228:1199–1201

33a. Hofman, T., Kawakami, M., Hitchman, A. J. W., Harrison, J. E., Dorrington, K. J. 1979. The amino acid sequence of porcine intestinal calcium-binding protein. *Can. J. Biochem.* 57:737–48

34. Holdsworth, E. S. 1970. The effect of vitamin D on enzyme activities in the mucosal cells of the chick small intestine. *J. Membr. Biology* 3:43–53

35. Howe, C. L., Keller, T. C. S. III, Mooseker, M. S., Wasserman, R. H. 1982. Analysis of cytoskeletal proteins and Ca²⁺-dependent regulation of structure in intestinal brush borders from rachitic chicks. *Proc. Natl. Acad. Sci. USA* 79:1134–38

36. Howe, C. L., Mooseker, M. S., Graves, T. A. 1980. Brush-border calmodulin. A major component of the isolated microvillus core. *J. Cell Biol.* 85:916–23

37. Jande, S. S., Brewer, L. M. 1974. Effects of vitamin D₃ on duodenal absorptive cells of chicks. An electron microscopic study. *Z. Anat. Entwicklungsgesch.* 144:249–65

38. Jande, S. S., Liskova-Kiar, M. 1981. Effects of cytocholasin B and dihydrocytochalasin B on calcium transport by intestinal absorptive cells. *Calcif. Tiss. Int.* 33:143–51

39. Jande, S. S., Tolnai, S., Lawson, D. E. M. 1981. Immunohistochemical localization of vitamin D-dependent calcium-binding protein in duodenum, kidney, uterus and cerebellum of chickens. *Histochemistry* 71:99–116

40. Jarrett, H. W., Penniston, J. T. 1977. Partial purification of the Ca²⁺-Mg²⁺ ATPase activator from human erythrocytes: Its similarity to the activator of 3′,5′-cyclic nucleotide phosphodiesterase. *Biochem. Biophys. Res. Commun.* 77:1210–12

41. Kempson, S. A., Kim, J. K., Northrup, T. E., Knox, F. G., Dousa, T. P. 1979. Alkaline phosphatase in adaptation to low dietary phosphate intake. *Am. J. Physiol.* 237:E465–73

42. Kendrick, N. C., Barr, C., DeLuca, H. F. 1981. Effect of vitamin D-deficiency

on *in vitro* labeling of chick intestinal proteins: analysis by two-dimensional electrophoresis. *Fed. Proc.* 40:1847

43. Kowarski, S., Schachter, D. 1980. Intestinal membrane calcium-binding protein. vitamin D-dependent membrane component of the intestinal calcium transport mechanism. *J. Biol. Chem.* 255:10834–40

44. Kretsinger, R. H. 1980. Structure and evolution of calcium-modulated proteins. In *Critical Reviews in Biochemistry*, ed. G. D. Fasman, pp. 119–74. Boca Raton, FL: CRC Press

45. Kretsinger, R. H., Mann, J. E., Simmonds, J. G. 1982. Model of enhanced diffusion of calcium by the intestinal calcium-binding protein. See Ref. 26, p. 89

46. Lane, S. M., Lawson, D. E. M. 1978. Differentiation of the changes in alkaline phosphatase from calcium ion-activated adenosine triphosphatase activities associated with increased calcium absorption in chick intestine. *Biochem. J.* 174:1067–70

47. Lawson, D. E. M., ed. 1978. In *Vitamin D*, p. 433. NY: Academic

48. MacLaughlin, J. A., Weiser, M. M., Freedman, R. H. 1980. Biophasic recovery of vitamin D-dependent Ca^{2+} uptake by rat intestinal Golgi membranes. *Gastroenterology* 78:325–32

49. Marche, P., Cassier, P., Mathieu, H. 1980. Intestinal calcium-binding protein. A protein indicator of enterocyte maturation associated with the terminal web. *Cell Tissue Res.* 212:63–72

50. Martin, D. L., DeLuca, H. F. 1969. Influence of sodium on calcium transport by the rat small intestine. *Am. J. Physiol.* 216:1351–59

51. Means, A. R., Tash, J. S., Chafouleas, J. G. 1982. Physiological implications of the presence, distribution and regulation of calmodulin in eukaryotic cells *Physiol. Rev.* 62:1–39

52. Melancon, M. J. Jr., DeLuca, H. F. 1970. Vitamin D stimulation of calcium-dependent ATPase in chick intestinal brush borders. *Biochemistry* 9:1658–64

53. Miller, A. III, Ueng, T.-H., Bronner, F. 1979. Isolation of a vitamin D-dependent calcium-binding protein from brush borders of rat duodenal mucosa. *FEBS Lett.* 103:319–22

54. Moriuchi, S., DeLuca, H. F. 1976. The effect of vitamin D$_3$ metabolites on membrane proteins of chick duodenal brush borders. *Arch. Biochem. Biophys.* 174:367–72

55. Murer, H., Haldemann, B. 1981. Transcellular transport of calcium and inorganic phosphate in the small intestinal epithelium. *Am. J. Physiol.* 240:G409–16

56. Narbsitz, R., Stumpf, W. E., Sar, M. 1981. The role of autoradiographic and immunocytochemical techniques in the clarification of sites of metabolism and action of vitamin D. *J. Histochem. Cytochem.* 29:91–100

57. Nellans, H. N., Popovitch, J. E. 1981. Calmodulin-regulated, ATP-driven calcium transport by basolateral membrane of rat intestine. *J. Biol. Chem.* 256:9932–36

58. Norman, A. W., ed. 1980. *Vitamin D: Molecular Biology and Clinical Nutrition.* NY: Marcel-Dekker. 800 pp.

59. Norman, A. W., Mircheff, A. K., Adams, T. H., Spielvogel, A. 1970. Vitamin D-mediated increase of intestinal brush border alkaline phosphatase activity. *Biochem. Biophys. Acta* 215:348–59

60. Norman, A. W., Putkey, J. A., Nemere I. 1982. Intestinal calcium transport: pleiotropic effects mediated by vitamin D. *Fed. Proc.* 41:78–83

61. O'Doherty, P. J. A. 1979. 1,25-Dihydroxyvitamin D$_3$ increases the activity of the intestinal phosphatidylcholine deacylation-reacylation cycle. *Lipids* 14:75–77

62. Oku, T., Wassrman, R. H. 1978. Properties of the vitamin D-stimulated calcium-dependent adenosinetriphosphatase and alkaline phosphatase in chick intestinal brush border. *Fed. Proc.* 37:408

63. Putkey, J. A., Saueheber, R. D., Norman, A. W. 1982. ESR analysis of intestinal epithelial cell membrane lipid structure: the effect of vitamin D. See Ref. 26, p. 108

64. Rasmussen, H., Fontaine, O., Max, E. E., Goodman, D. B. P. 1979. The effect of 1-hydroxyvitamin D$_3$-administration on calcium transport in chick intestine brush border membrane vesicles. *J. Biol. Chem.* 254:2993–99

65. Rasmussen, H., Matsumoto, T., Fontaine, O., Goodman, D. B. P. 1982. Role of changes in membrane lipid structure in the action of 1,25-dihydroxyvitamin D$_3$. *Fed. Proc.* 41:72–77

66. Rasmussen, H., Max, E. E., Goodman, D. B. P. 1977. The effect of 1α-OH-D$_3$ treatment on the structure and function of chick intestinal brush border membrane. In *Vitamin D: Biochemical, Chemical and Clinical Aspects Related to Calcium Metabolism,* ed. A. W. Nor-

man, K. Schaefer, J. W. Coburn, H. F. DeLuca, D. Fraser, H. G. Grigoleit, D. v. Herrath, pp. 913–25. Berlin/NY: de Gruyter
67. Roth, J., Thorens, B., Brown, D., Norman, A. W., Orci, L. 1982. Immunocytochemical localization of vitamin D-dependent calcium-binding protein (CaBP). See Ref. 26, p. 84
68. Russell, R. G. G., Monod, A., Bonjour, J.-P., Fleisch, H. 1972. Relation between alkaline phosphatase and Ca-ATPase in calcium transport. *Nature (New Biol.)* 240:126–27
69. Sadler, S. E., Maller, J. L. 1982. Identification of a steroid receptor on the surface of *Xenopus* oocytes by photoaffinity labeling. *J. Biol. Chem.* 257:355–61
70. Sanderman, H. Jr. 1978. Regulation of membrane enzymes by lipids. *Biochim. Biophys. Acta* 515:209–37
71. Schachter, D. 1969. Toward a molecular description of active transport. In *Biological Membranes*, ed. R. M. Dowben, pp. 157–76. Boston: Little, Brown
72. Schachter, D. 1962. Vitamin D and the active transport of calcium by the small intestine. In *The Transfer of Calcium and Strontium Across Biological Membranes*, ed. R. H. Wasserman, pp. 197–210. NY: Academic
73. Schiffle, H., Binswanger, U. 1980. Calcium ATPase and intestinal calcium transport in uremic rats. *Am. J. Physiol.* 238:G424–28
74. Shimura, F., Wasserman, R. H. 1982. Unpublished data
75. Szebenyi, D. M. E., Obendorf, S. K., Moffat, K. 1981. Structure of vitamin D-dependent calcium-binding protein from bovine intestine. *Nature* 294:327–32
76. Taylor, A. N. 1981. Immunocytochemical localization of the vitamin D-induced calcium-binding protein: Relocation of antigen during frozen section processing. *J. Histochem. Cytochem.* 29:65–73
77. Taylor, A. N. 1982. Time course of immunocytochemical distribution of intestinal vitamin D-induced calcium-binding protein following 1,25-dihydroxyvitamin D₃. See Ref. 26, p. 86
78. Thomasset, M., Molla, A., Parkes, O., DeMaille, J. G. 1981. Intestinal calmodulin and calcium-binding protein differ in their distribution and in the effect of vitamin D steroids on their concentration. *FEBS Lett.* 127:13–16
79. Van Os, C., Ghijsen, W., De Jonge, H. 1981. High affinity Ca-ATPase in baso-

lateral plasmamembranes of rat duodenum and kidney cortex. In *Calcium and Phosphate Transport Across Biomembranes*, ed. F. Bronner, M. Peterlik, pp. 159–62. NY: Academic
80. Warner, R. R., Coleman, J. R. 1975. Electron probe analysis of calcium transport by small intestine. *J. Cell Biol.* 64:54–74
81. Wasserman, R. H. 1980. Molecular aspects of the intestinal absorption of calcium and phosphorus. In *Pediatric Diseases Related to Calcium*, ed. H. F. DeLuca, C. S. Anast, pp. 107–32. NY: Elsevier
82. Wasserman, R. H., Brindak, M. E. 1979. The effect of cholecalciferol on the phosphorylation of intestinal membrane proteins. In *Vitamin D Basic Research and its Clinical Application*, ed. A. W. Norman, K. Schaefer, D. v. Herrath, H.-G. Grigoleit, J. W. Coburn, H. F. DeLuca, E. B. Mawer, T. Suda, pp. 703–10. Berlin/NY: De Gruyter
83. Wasserman, R. H., Brindak, M. E., Meyer, S. A., Fullmer, C. S. 1982. Calcium absorption and 1,25(OH)₂D₃: Studies with rachitic and partially vitamin D-repleted chicks. See Ref. 26, p. 102
84. Wasserman, R. H., Corradino, R. A. 1973. Vitamin D calcium and protein synthesis. *Vit. Horm.* 31:43–103
85. Wasserman, R. H., Corradino, R. A., Feher, J. J., Armbrecht, H. J. 1977. Temporal patterns of response of the intestinal calcium absorptive system and related parameters to 1,25-dihydroxycholecalciferol. See Ref. 66, pp. 331–40
86. Wasserman, R. H., Fullmer, C. S., Taylor, A. N. 1978. The vitamin D-dependent calcium-binding protein. See Ref. 47, pp. 133–66
87. Wasserman, R. H., Taylor, A. N. 1969. *Some Aspects of the Intestinal Absorption of Calcium, with Special Reference to Vitamin D*, ed. C. L. Comar, F. Bronner, pp. 321–403. NY: Academic
88. Webling, D. D.'A., Holdsworth, E. S. 1965. The effect of bile, bile acids and detergents on calcium absorption in the chick. *Biochem. J.* 97:408–21
89. Wehringer, E. J., Oldham, S. B., Bethune, J. E. 1978. A proposed cellular mechanism for calcium transport in the intestinal epithelial cell. *Calcif. Tiss. Res.* 26:71–79
90. Weiser, M. M., Bloor, J. H., Dosmohapatra, A., Freedman, R. A., MacLaughlin, J. A. 1981. Vitamin D-dependent rat intestinal Ca²⁺ trans-

port: Ca^{2+} uptake by Golgi membranes and early nuclear events. In *Calcium and Phosphate Transport Across Biomembranes*, ed. F. Bronner, M. Peterlik, pp. 269–73. NY: Academic

91. Wilson, P. W., Lawson, D. E. M. 1977. 1,25-Dihydoxyvitamin D stimulation of specific membrane proteins in chick intestine. *Biochem. Biophys. Acta* 497: 805–11

92. Wilson, P. W., Lawson, D. E. M. 1978. Incorporation of ^3H leucine into an actin-like protein in response to 1,25-dihydroxycholecalciferol in chick intestinal brush borders. *Biochem. J.* 173:627–31

93. Wilson, P. W., Lawson, D. E. M. 1981. Vitamin D-dependent phosphorylation of an intestinal protein. *Nature* 289: 600–2

RESPIRATORY PHYSIOLOGY

Introduction, Alfred P. Fishman, Section Editor

The papers that follow provide a sampler of current topics in the physiology of exercise, with particular reference to breathing. It will become clear in reading them not only that new and dramatic insights are currently being gained but also that large gulfs in understanding still persist.

The first two papers are devoted to the control of breathing during steady-state exercise. Whipp is concerned with the hyperpnea of moderate exercise and how the level of ventilation is set; his focus is on gas exchange in the lungs. Flenley & Warren are more concerned with the chemical drives to breathing, emphasizing throughout the interactions of the various control systems in achieving a level of ventilation in accord with the metabolic and hemodynamic needs of the body.

Sutton, Pugh & Jones examine the limits of human capabilities by drawing on the remarkable feat of Habeler and Messner, who succeeded in climbing Mount Everest in 1980 without supplementary oxygen. The description by Habeler and Messner of the last 48 meters to the summit can leave no doubt that they had reached the limit of human endurance. Bye, Farkas & Roussos then turn their attention to those elements of the respiratory system that could limit exercise capacity. After assessing gas exchange, respiratory mechanics, and energetics, they conclude that fatigue of the respiratory muscles is the critical element.

Labored breathing due to exercise-induced airway obstruction is considered in the fifth paper. The principal pathogenetic factor is identified as respiratory heat loss and the coincident cooling of the airways. The paper also indicates how much remains to be settled about the intermediary mechanisms that relate stimulus to response.

Finally, Killian & Campbell attack the sensation of dyspnea. They have little confidence that studies of the control of breathing are apt to shed light on the origins of this sensation. They favor explorations designed to uncover a psychophysical basis for unpleasant respiratory sensations in different circumstances, including exercise. They incline toward the idea that dyspnea at rest and during exercise is due to a quantitative disturbance in the perception of a respiratory load.

Clearly, these six papers deal with only a small fraction of exercise physiology. Much more could be examined about integrative mechanisms, metabolic-ventilatory interplay, hemodynamic changes, adaptation, neurohumoral mediators, etc. This sampler should suffice to direct the reader to the respiratory aspects of the problem without obscuring the larger framework within which they should be viewed.

Ann. Rev. Physiol. 1983. 45:393–413
Copyright © 1983 by Annual Reviews Inc. All rights reserved

VENTILATORY CONTROL DURING EXERCISE IN HUMANS

Brian J. Whipp

Division of Respiratory Physiology and Medicine, Department
of Medicine, Harbor-UCLA Medical Center, Torrance, California 90509
and Departments of Physiology and Medicine, UCLA School of Medicine,
Los Angeles, California 90024

Exercise entails an increased transformation rate of substrate free energy into the mechanical energy of muscle contraction, with ventilatory control functioning to regulate the composition of the fluid milieus of the force-generating cells. Analysis of ventilatory control during exercise therefore requires gas exchange as a crucial frame of reference. Although recent publications will be addressed primarily in this review, they will be considered within the context of prevailing control theories, even though these are based, in humans, almost entirely upon exercise performed under rigidly controlled, and arguably unnatural, laboratory conditions.

Ventilatory Response Characteristics

MODERATE EXERCISE Although an abrupt increase in ventilation ($\dot{V}_E$) occurring at the first respiratory cycle following the transition from rest to constant-load exercise was described by Krogh & Lindhard in 1913 (63), the pattern of the immediate ventilatory response and its determinants remain of considerable experimental interest. For example, Paulev (84), Whipp et al (120), and Jensen et al (54) have all demonstrated that the response, as evidenced by the start of a systematic change in the profile of respiratory airflow, begins in virtual synchrony with the onset of the work and can occur in either the inspiratory or expiratory phase of the respiratory cycle. This typically results in an increment of ventilation that is relatively constant, irrespective of the work rate (25, 53), and lasts for some 15–20 sec; if cued by a preparatory warning, the ventilatory changes may even precede the exercise (100). The dynamics of the early $\dot{V}_E$ response depends,

0066-4278/83/0315-0393 $02.00

393

however, upon whether the constant-load work is imposed from a background of rest or of mild exercise, a more slowly developing hyperpnea being evident for work-to-work transitions (13, 16, 69, 85, 124).

Recently, dynamic work-rate forcing techniques and computer analysis have detailed the response characteristics of this phase of the hyperpnea, which precedes altered mixed venous gas tensions (i.e. phase 1 or ϕ1). Thus Whipp et al (124) utilized multiple repetitions of constant-load exercise performed either from rest or from a background of mild work. Fujihara et al (37, 38) employed not only the square wave but also its integral and differential (i.e. the ramp and impulse functions respectively). Bennett et al (10) chose pseudorandom binary sequences of work rate, while Bakker et al (5) and Swanson (95) utilized sinusoidal forcing functions. The common feature of these studies [but not of the sinusoidal studies of Wigertz (125) and Casaburi et al (15)] is that a rapid $\dot{V}_E$ component was evident against a background of prior mild exercise. This component evidenced quite different kinetic characteristics from the subsequent nonsteady-state component of the response (i.e. phase 2 or ϕ2). Thus while both components are adequately described by the first-order transfer function:

$$A e^{-sT} 1/(1+s\tau) \qquad\qquad 1.$$

(where s is the Laplace transformation variable, A is the steady-state amplitude and τ and T are the time constant and delay parameters, respectively), the early response has a time constant of some 7 sec but that for the subsequent response is 40–50 sec. No statistical criteria were established to determine whether the ϕ1 response was, in fact, first-order.

Several groups have demonstrated that the ϕ1 hyperpnea is typically not associated with the increase in the gas exchange ratio (R) and end-tidal P_{O_2} and the decrease in end-tidal P_{CO_2} characteristic of hyperventilation (16, 54, 69, 75, 85, 109, 124). Others, however, have reported that hyperventilation is a consistent finding at exercise onset (2, 117). It has been suggested that such hyperventilation only results from more erratic breathing responses, often with evidence of $\dot{V}_E$ and airflow overshooting in ϕ1 (119).

Rather, there appear to be proportional increases in the ventilatory and cardiac output responses in ϕ1, at least as inferred from: (a) the constancy of alveolar gas tensions and R, and (b) $\dot{V}_{O_2}$ and $\dot{V}_{CO_2}$ both changing in concert with $\dot{V}_E$ during ϕ1, abruptly for rest-to-work transitions but markedly more slowly from a background of mild exercise (16, 69, 124). The latter, however, is complicated by functional residual capacity normally decreasing at the onset of constant-load exercise (69, 103), requiring correction for changes in the lung gas stores of O_2 and CO_2 (9, 96).

The onset of phase 2 is signalled by altered gas composition in the mixed venous blood entering the pulmonary capillaries, accelerating the rates of transfer of O_2 and CO_2 across the gas exchange interface. This results in an increase in $P_{ET}CO_2$ and a simultaneous decrease of $P_{ET}O_2$ and R (69, 75, 85, 109). However, the question of whether this secondary increase of ventilation actually occurs on the same breath as the increased rates of pulmonary gas exchange (i.e. suggesting intrapulmonary mediation) or whether the $\phi 2$ hyperpnea begins some two breaths or so later [i.e. reflecting the lung-to-carotid body transit delay (51, 86) and suggesting mediation by the conventional chemoreceptors] remains to be resolved.

Several investigators have applied a simple first-order or mono-exponential model (equation 1) to the $\dot{V}_E$ response to exercise instituted from prior mild exercise and estimate the time constant to be about 70 sec. More recently, however, more discriminating work-rate forcings and the application of systems-analytic techniques for model discrimination have resulted in the formulation of model structures more appropriate to the response characteristics of the exercise hyperpnea. The current consensus thus favors models that incorporate two compartments rather than one.

Fujihara et al (37, 38) used square-wave, ramp, and impulse forcings of work rate and concluded that the transient behavior of the exercise hyperpnea was best described by the additive interaction of two simple, first-order components operating in parallel, the response characteristics of the first being early and rapid and those of the second delayed and slow:

$$A e^{-sT}\, 1/(1+s\tau_1) + B e^{-sT}\, 1/(1+s\tau_2) \qquad\qquad 2.$$

where A and B are the steady-state amplitudes of the $\phi 1$ and $\phi 2$ response components, and τ_1, τ_2 and T_1, T_2 are the corresponding time constant and delay parameters. These authors elected to modify this model structure by including an additional time constant parameter (τ_3) in the slow $\phi 2$ compartment, whose action was to "filter" its response:

$$A e^{-sT_1}\, 1/(1+s\tau_1) + B e^{-sT_2}\, 1/(1+s\tau_2)(1+s\tau_3). \qquad\qquad 3.$$

And while it provided a statistically better fit to their data, these authors do not indicate whether this additional term is merely a mathematical expedient or has any physiological significance. Using pseudo-random binary sequences of work rate, Bennett et al (10) found that the modified model of Fujihara et al [(37, 38); equation 3] also provided a better description of their ventilatory data than did the simpler models (equations 1 & 2). Again, however, the physiological significance of the third time constant parameter was not discussed. Both Fujihara et al (37, 38) and Bennett et al (10) reported similar values for the $\phi 2$ delay parameter, T_2 (some 15–20 sec), and the two time constant parameters (some 40–60 sec and 16–19 sec, respectively).

Whipp et al (124), however, argued that the $\phi 2$ data resulting from multiple square-wave forcings of work rate were so well described by a mono-exponential that the incorporation of additional dynamic components appeared unwarranted. Furthermore, the $\phi 2$ time constant was not discernibly affected by whether the prior control condition was rest or mild exercise, a value of about 55 sec being obtained in both cases.

A fundamentally different model structure was used by Bakker et al (5). Based upon the results of sinusoidal and impulse work-rate forcings, a second-order model was selected in which the two simple, first-order components were placed in series rather than in parallel:

$$A_0 e^{-sT} \; 1/(1+s\tau_1)(1+s\tau_2) \qquad\qquad 4.$$

Although the authors do not detail the physiological basis of this model, it would be compatible with the ventilatory response dynamics reflecting the serial washout of two intervening compartments or, perhaps, the washout of a single compartment followed by a receptor mechanism responding with first-order kinetics. Furthermore, as the fit of the data to this model indicated the operation of a critically damped system (i.e. relative damping coefficient $\simeq 1$), these authors raised the possibility that the system might include feedback pathways in addition to the two components in the forward path.

Investigators have also attempted to relate the phase 2 $\dot{V}_E$ response dynamics to those of O_2 uptake and CO_2 output. Satisfactory descriptions of the $\phi 2$ gas exchange responses have been obtained from simple, first-order models (i.e. equation 1). The time constants of the $\dot{V}_{O_2}$ and $\dot{V}_{CO_2}$ responses, however, are appreciably different, that for $\dot{V}_{O_2}$ being some 35–40 sec and that for $\dot{V}_{CO_2}$ some 50–60 sec (69, 75, 124). The slower kinetics of $\dot{V}_{CO_2}$ relative to $\dot{V}_{O_2}$ reflects the considerable capacity for tissue storage of CO_2 (57, 109).

Clearly, the ventilatory response cannot "track" both $\dot{V}_{O_2}$ and $\dot{V}_{CO_2}$. It is with $\dot{V}_{CO_2}$ that $\dot{V}_E$ is most closely related during this nonsteady-state phase (15, 16, 75, 109, 118). Consequently, a transient fall in Pa_{O_2} should be evident, and the slightly slower time course of $\dot{V}_E$ than $\dot{V}_{CO_2}$ should also elicit a small transient rise in Pa_{CO_2}. Experimental evidence of such a transient arterial hypoxemia has been established (79, 123, 127). During sinusoidal work-rate forcing (6 min period; work rate below the anaerobic threshold), Whipp and associates (123) also demonstrated a significant sinusoidal variation of Pa_{CO_2} ($\sim \pm 1$ torr, mean to peak), the peak occurring when both $\dot{V}_E$ and $\dot{V}_{CO_2}$ were high, reflecting the small dynamic decoupling between these variables.

While the hyperpnea of moderate exercise appears to comprise elements whose characteristics are linear and first-order (or approximately so), few investigators have systematically addressed the question of linearity. For example, it is not known whether the time constant of the phase 2 $\dot{V}_E$ response is affected by the range of work rates over which the forcing function is applied. But since $\dot{V}_{O_2}$ exhibits static linearity (i.e. equal increments of power educe equal increments of $\dot{V}_{O_2}$ in the steady state) and also dynamic linearity (i.e. the same time constant obtains for different square-wave increments of power) and since the gas exchange ratio appears to have quite complex kinetics in $\phi 2$ (i.e. in response to a square-wave increment of power, it does not remain constant, change monotonically, or change instantaneously to a new value at the onset of $\phi 2$, but rather undershoots transiently), the presence of nonlinearities in the $\phi 2$ response of $\dot{V}_{CO_2}$ and, therefore, $\dot{V}_E$ should perhaps be expected. Indeed, Bakker et al (5) have reported the behavior of $\dot{V}_{O_2}$ to be linear, but that of $\dot{V}_{CO_2}$ and $\dot{V}_E$ to be quasi- or nonlinear. Further complicating the $\dot{V}_{CO_2}$ and $\dot{V}_E$ kinetics in this phase is the influence of the transient increase in blood lactate that occurs below the anaerobic threshold, this being especially prominent at the upper reaches of moderate-intensity exercise.

The steady-state or phase 3 ventilatory response is thought to represent the sum of the steady-state responses of the phase 1 and phase 2 components. It is generally conceded (19, 55, 107) that in the steady state both alveolar and minute ventilation increase as a linear function of $\dot{V}_{CO_2}$ (rather than $\dot{V}_{O_2}$) and, consequently, Pa_{CO_2} is regulated at or very close to its resting value. The linear $\dot{V}_A-\dot{V}_{CO_2}$ relationship passes through the origin:

$$\dot{V}_A = 863 \ \dot{V}_{CO_2}/Pa_{CO_2} \qquad\qquad 5.$$

but the $\dot{V}_E - \dot{V}_{CO_2}$ relationship has a positive intercept on the $\dot{V}_E$ axis of some 3–5 liters per min (25, 105):

$$\dot{V}_E = (863 \ \dot{V}_{CO_2}/Pa_{CO_2}) + \dot{V}_D \qquad\qquad 6.$$

or, alternatively:

$$\dot{V}_E = 863 \ \dot{V}_{CO_2}/Pa_{CO_2}(1-V_D/V_T) \qquad\qquad 7.$$

where $\dot{V}_D$ is the dead space ventilation and V_D/V_T is the physiological dead space fraction of the breath. Consequently, the ventilatory response to exercise is systematically greater when Pa_{CO_2} is caused to be low (58, 82) or $\dot{V}_D$ and V_D/V_T high (89, 105, 106).

Jones (56) has recently demonstrated that as $\dot{V}_{CO_2}$ was decreased in the steady state of moderate exercise by physical training (owing to a lowering of the R.Q.) $\dot{V}_E$ also decreased as a consequence and with an identical proportionality to that predicted by the $\dot{V}_E$–$\dot{V}_{CO_2}$ relationship originally induced by exercise prior to the training. Furthermore, both Jones et al (58) and Oren et al (82) have altered the regulated level of resting Pa_{CO_2} by means of sustained diet-induced metabolic acidosis and alkalosis. In these studies, $\dot{V}_E$ was changed during moderate exercise precisely as predicted for regulation of Pa_{CO_2} with an altered "set point" (i.e. equations 6 & 7).

Dempsey and his co-workers (29), however, have rightly cautioned that strict isocapnia during moderate exercise may be more a laboratory phenomenon than a manifestation of spontaneous exercise, the latter involving a much greater behavioral or supra-bulbar control of $\dot{V}_E$. To support their contention, these authors have actually measured a sustained respiratory alkalosis during prolonged, moderate running. Furthermore, in longer-term exercise (cycling for about 1 hr), Martin et al (73) found that $\dot{V}_E$ evidenced a continuous, slow drift that was not apparent in $\dot{V}_{CO_2}$. The estimated Pa_{CO_2}, however, remained constant, suggesting that the drift was a function of alterations in $\dot{V}_D$ of unknown origin. This was thought not to be related to the increased body temperature, although a good correlation was observed between the magnitude of the $\dot{V}_E$ increase and the plasma norepinephrine concentration.

HEAVY AND SEVERE EXERCISE   There has been less emphasis on analyzing $\dot{V}_E$ during heavy and severe exercise, owing largely to the nonlinearities in its response. These stem predominantly from the lactic acidosis that characterizes these work rates (72, 80, 111); but increased body temperature (29), catecholamines (73), and even, in some apparently normal but highly fit subjects, arterial hypoxemia (29) are also likely to contribute.

It has been shown recently that when an incremental exercise test is performed in which work rate is increased each minute or less, a range is observed above the anaerobic threshold within which $\dot{V}_E$ rises as a function of $\dot{V}_{CO_2}$ (109) in the same direct proportionality as below the threshold. This observation is supported by the results of studies in which sinusoidal fluctuations of work rate encroached above the anaerobic threshold by a small amount (16). This range of work rates has been termed the range of "isocapnic buffering," although direct support for arterial isocapnia, rather than mere $P_{ET_{CO_2}}$ constancy (109), remains to be established. Consequently, there appears to be no respiratory compensation for the metabolic acidosis in this range (i.e. lowering of Pa_{CO_2}). It is not clear at present why the ventilatory control system sensors do not "see" the decreased arterial pH in the phase of isocapnic buffering, while they do apparently respond if the work rate increment is prolonged to 4 min or more (108, 111); the carotid bodies, which are thought to mediate the compensatory hyperventilation (112, 122), have a time constant of response to exogenous H^+ of less than 1 sec [in the cat, at least (87)].

A further complication at very high work rates is that of mechanical limitation to air flow generation. While this is not a usual finding in normal subjects (66, 78), the extremely high work rates attainable by fit subjects render them more likely to encroach upon the mechanical limits for expiratory airflow during high-intensity, exhaustive exercise. Grimby et al (42) and Olaffson & Hyatt (78) have shown that highly fit subjects achieved expiratory airflows that reached their volume-specific maximum during high-intensity exercise. Furthermore, Follinsbee et al (35) demonstrated that such highly fit athletes reached a maximum exercise ventilation that was, on average, some 95% of their resting maximum voluntary ventilation, in contrast to the 60–70% normally attained in less fit subjects. Consequently, as athletes become more and more "fit," a greater requirement for optimum pulmonary mechanics is likely to be a determinant of successful performance.

Altered Control

PERIPHERAL NEUROGENIC DRIVE   Jaeger-Denavit et al (50) induced "passive movement of the knees" through 90° at a frequency of 1 Hz repeatedly in healthy subjects and in subjects with paraplegia resulting from clinically complete spinal-cord lesions at T12. The hyperpnea that normally occurred on the first "exercise" movement was absent in the paraplegic subjects. In a further group of paraplegics having only partial loss of sensation and movement in the knee region, the first-breath hyperpnea was significantly reduced compared to control. These authors concluded that afferents from the limbs play a determining role in the initial ventilatory response associated with movement. Unfortunately, the simultaneous gas exchange and alveolar gas tension responses were not reported in this study. Weissman et al (114) have demonstrated that if exercise is induced in normal subjects who constrain their $\dot{V}_E$ at the resting level, then alveolar gas tensions immediately change ($P_{ET}CO_2$ increasing and $P_{ET}O_2$ decreasing) to reflect the increased pulmonary blood flow without concomitant ventilatory response. Such measurements would have ruled out the possibility that the neurological deficit also altered cardiovascular reflexes.

Adams et al (1) have studied the $\dot{V}_E$ response to electrically induced limb movement in subjects with complete spinal transection at T3; but they also determined $\dot{V}CO_2$ and $P_{ET}CO_2$. They found that $\dot{V}_E$ increased on the first complete respiratory cycle following "exercise" onset similarly to normal subjects, $P_{ET}CO_2$ being unchanged in both cases. Subsequently, however, $\dot{V}_E$ rose more slowly to the steady state in the cord-transected subjects. But as $\dot{V}CO_2$ dynamics were similarly slowed, the authors concluded that the effect of spinal-cord transection on the early $\dot{V}_E$ response to the "exercise" was a consequence of the slower rate of CO_2 delivery to the lungs, rather than a direct effect of impaired neurogenesis per se. In addition, Asmussen et al (4) had previously demonstrated that the $\dot{V}_E$ and $P_{ET}CO_2$ responses to steady-state exercise were normal in a tabetic subject who evidenced complete loss of proprioceptive reflexes from the legs and lower trunk.

Jammes et al (52) administered high-frequency mechanical vibration unilaterally to the tendons of the biceps or triceps brachialis muscles in normal resting subjects, this technique having been shown to stimulate preferentially muscle spindle afferents both in animals and humans. These authors found that $\dot{V}_E$ increased on the first or second breath following the onset of the period of vibration and that $P_{ET}CO_2$ fell. No adaptation of the response was apparent. Since the hyperventilation occurred even though cardiac rhythm did not change, the authors concluded (contrary to other investigators) that actual contraction of the muscle is not a prerequisite for evoking the $\dot{V}_E$ effects induced by muscle afferent stimulation. However, unlike the initial hyperpnea of moderate dynamic exercise in humans, the responses to such high-frequency vibration resulted in hypocapnia. Furthermore, Hornbein et al (47) could not document significant effects on $\dot{V}_E$ in exercising humans of selectively blocking the γ-efferent system to the legs (without significant impairment to the α-fibers).

Tibes et al (99) correlated the nonsteady-state changes in $\dot{V}_E$ with those in the concentrations of various putative chemical mediators of the exercise hyperpnea in the venous effluent from the contracting leg muscles in spontaneously exercising subjects. Because $[K^+]$ correlated better with $\dot{V}_E$ than did femoral-venous P_{O_2}, P_{CO_2}, pH, lactate, or osmolarity, these authors concluded that $[K^+]$ in the interstitial fluid was likely to be stimulating the small-diameter type III and IV muscle afferents. In contrast, Comroe & Schmidt (17) were unable to induce hyperpnea when venous blood collected from the exercising limbs of dogs was infused into the arterial supply of limb muscle.

CENTROGENIC DRIVE

Corticogenic drive There is some evidence in humans suggestive of a cortical contribution to the exercise hyperpnea. Hyperventilation occurred in the the steady state of exercise in situations where the degree of conscious effort required to accomplish a specified motor task was greater than normal— e.g. following partial muscle paralysis by curarization (3, 77), by simultaneous activation of antagonist musculature (40), or by hypnotic suggestion (23, 76). Conversely, the use of hypnotic suggestion to abolish the perception of muscular effort during exercise led to a slight reduction in the magnitude of the exercise hyperpnea (23).

Hypothalamus   Eldridge et al (33) have recently demonstrated that electrical stimulation of the "hypothalamic motor area" in the cat induced rapid ventilatory and gas exchange responses. However, these results appear qualitatively unlike those obtained in studies of volitional exercise in humans, of "exercise" induced by stimulation of peripheral nerve or muscle in cat and dog (65, 115, 116), or even of "fictive locomotion" (33). That is, a profound and rapid hyperventilation ensued, possibly consequent to stimulation of extra-pyramidal pathways to the respiratory muscles. However, Eldridge's experiments provide a useful reminder to consider similarities between the role of the hypothalamus (and other limbic structures) in the integrative response to exercise as a "state," and its known and detailed role in the induction of rage, arousal, defence etc.

Central neural "reverberation"   Eldridge (32) has also suggested that central neural mechanisms may be important in determining the $\phi 2$ kinetics of the exercise hyperpnea. Specifically, he has demonstrated that the "respiratory centers" themselves have neural dynamics capable of sustaining an hyperpnea despite the removal of the causal stimulus. Rather than an immediate step-decrease in respiratory activity after abrupt removal of a carotid body or hindlimb stimulus, an early and abrupt fall was followed by a slower decline; the mechanism of this slower component was isolated to the brain stem (32). A similar phenomenon has also been described in resting humans following the abrupt cessation of a bout of isocapnic volitional hyperventilation (97, 98). These findings may be significant for the $\phi 2$ $\dot{V}_E$ kinetics of exercise, although the on-off symmetry of the $\phi 2$ time constant in humans is not as evident in the "reverberatory experiments" in the cat.

CAROTID BODY DRIVE   The peripheral chemoreceptors do not normally appear to influence significantly the magnitude of the $\phi 1$ hyperpnea in humans. Consequently, the abrupt $\phi 1$ hyperpnea did not differ appreciably from normal in a group of subjects who had undergone surgical resection of their carotid bodies (112). Neither was this response significantly affected in normal subjects by hypoxia, hyperoxia, or by sustained or acute hypercapnia (20, 27, 102). However, the parameters of the distribution of the $\phi 1$ $\dot{V}_E$ response and its reproducibility remain to be established, and so judgments regarding the normalcy of a particular response are often based upon less than rigorous criteria.

Several lines of evidence in humans, however, implicate the carotid bodies in $\phi 2$ ventilatory control. Cunningham et al (22) demonstrated that breathing pure O_2 to inactivate the carotid bodies markedly delayed the onset of the $\phi 2$ hyperpnea and appreciably slowed its kinetics, compared with the responses during hypoxia, a result supported by Linnarsson (69). Extending this approach, Griffiths et al (41) and Whipp & Wasserman (122) have demonstrated that the $\phi 2$ time constant was inversely proportional to carotid body responsiveness. Increased central chemoreceptor drive, however, does not appear to speed the $\phi 2$ kinetics (104).

Intriguingly, the $\phi 2$ hyperpnea appears to retain its exponentiality, regardless of the time constant of the response or the proportional role of the carotid bodies. It is difficult to envision how the ventilatory response of a simple additive control system can remain exponential as the carotid body component assumes progressively greater prominence. Consequently, the carotid body drive in $\phi 2$ may dictate the speed with which the fundamental process (likely within the brainstem respiratory centers) operates, while not disrupting its underlying exponentiality.

Furthermore, Oren et al (83) determined the influence on the $\phi 2$ $\dot{V}_E$ kinetics of metabolic acid-base changes induced by the ingestion of ammonium chloride (metabolic acidosis), sodium bicarbonate (metabolic alkalosis), and calcium carbonate (control), each for three days. The metabolic acidosis significantly reduced the $\phi 2$ time constant, whereas the metabolic alkalosis increased it. Because the carotid bodies in humans appear to be largely responsible for the $\dot{V}_E$ response to relatively acute metabolic acidosis, and because the $\phi 2$ time constant was lengthened in all three acid-base states to the same absolute value by hyperoxia, these investigators also believe that the carotid bodies in humans are important in establishing the $\dot{V}_E$ kinetics in $\phi 2$ of exercise.

Subjects who had undergone bilateral carotid body resection evidenced, on average, appreciably slower than normal kinetics for the $\phi 2$ response to moderate exercise, despite the magnitude of the $\phi 1$ and $\phi 2$ components being unaltered (112). As a consequence, an appreciable respiratory acidosis resulted during $\phi 2$. Although this is persuasive evidence, more precise quantification of the actual exponentiality (or the lack of it) of the $\phi 2$ ventilatory reponse and the influence of hyperoxia in such subjects would be most useful.

There is evidence, too, that the carotid bodies may also contribute to ventilatory control in $\phi 3$ of moderate exercise. Utilizing the abrupt and surreptitious substitution of O_2 for air, investigators found that the contribution of the carotid bodies to the $\phi 3$ hyperpnea appears to be somewhat greater than at rest (26, 93, 118). However, subjects who had previously undergone bilateral carotid body resection evidenced a $\phi 3$ response no different from normal with respect to $\dot{V}_E$ or arterial blood gas tensions (70, 112). One explanation for this is that other (presumably central chemoreceptor) mechanisms "take over" the normal carotid body component. It is not clear, however, what "takes over" the reduced carotid body drive in the carotid body resected subject, although the possibility that the resection removed a hyperventilatory component (which is commonly observed in subjects with bronchial asthma) may not be ruled out at present. Further complicating ready interpretation of the role of the carotid bodies is the fact that a group of Japanese who had undergone carotid body resection did evidence a reduction of the hyperpnea of moderate exercise (46), although they also showed evidence of significantly impaired pulmonary mechanics.

The carotid bodies have also been shown to mediate the respiratory compensation for the acute metabolic acidosis of heavy and severe exercise; subjects who had undergone bilateral carotid body resection evidenced no such compensation (112, 122). It would be interesting to know if subjects with little or no carotid-body sensitivity to hypoxemia, such as high-altitude natives (64), also have reduced responses to acute changes of [H$^+$] and, consequently, less complete respiratory compensation during heavy and severe exercise.

CENTRAL CHEMORECEPTOR DRIVE   The failure to discern a recognizable stimulus in the cerebrospinal fluid during $\phi 3$ of moderate exercise, at least in animals (12, 61, 67), has led to the belief that central chemoreceptor mechanisms are not involved in the ventilatory control process. However, there is a preliminary report that blocking Region "S" on the ventral medullary surface actually abolished the exercise hyperpnea in cats whose carotid sinus nerves had been sectioned (92). This observation suggests either that central chemoreceptor afferents (thought to course through Region "S") play a significant role in the exercise hyperpnea or that some other afferent or efferent excitatory activity can be inhibited by this regional block. Further consideration must, however, await detailed report of these experiments.

During heavy and severe exercise, the central chemoreceptors presumably exert a restraint upon the hyperpnea, from the supposed alkaline shift in the cerebrospinal fluid resulting from the arterial hypocapnia [demonstrated to date only in the pony, however (12)] and also possibly by suppressing carotid body afferent drive as has been demonstrated when the efferent activity in Hering's nerve is increased [as it has been shown to do in the cat when the cerebrospinal fluid becomes alkaline (71)]. Since no such evidence is available in humans, these considerations remain only plausible suppositions.

CARDIODYNAMIC DRIVE   Noting the stability of alveolar gas tensions characteristic of $\phi 1$, Wasserman and his associates (109, 110) questioned whether the implicit tight coupling of the pulmonary blood flow and $\dot{V}_E$ responses in this phase of the work might be causal rather than coincident. They therefore hypothesized that a primary change in cardiac output ($\dot{Q}$) might itself trigger the rapid hyperpnea. Any such increase that was not matched by an appropriate increase in $\dot{V}_A$ would necessarily result in a downstream error signal in pH, P_{CO_2}, and P_{O_2} that could be sensed by a "rapidly responding chemoreceptor," thereby providing a humoral stimulus to the early hyperpnea of exercise.

To test this hypothesis, these investigators (110) increased $\dot{Q}$ in awake and anesthestized dogs either by electrically "pacing" the right atrium or by small intravenous bolus injections of the β-stimulant isoproterenol. When $\dot{Q}$ rose (and not before), $\dot{V}_E$ increased consequently with little or no change in $P_{ET}CO_2$ or P_{aCO_2}. The term "cardiodynamic hyperpnea" was proposed for such a mechanism.

Mediation of the cardiodynamic component of the exercise hyperpnea, however, is not likely to require "downstream" chemoreception via the peripheral or central chemoreceptors directly, based upon their known transit delays from the lungs, the likely change in the error signal, and the chemoreflex gains. Furthermore, Wasserman et al showed that in humans the magnitude of the $\phi 1$ component of the exercise hyperpnea was not systematically different in subjects who had undergone bilateral carotid body resection and in control subjects (112).

Huszkczuk et al (48) recently proposed that the cardiodynamic hyperpnea may result from an afferent signal deriving from the heart itself. Under conditions in which right ventricular moving-average pressure ($P_{\overline{RV}}$)—a functional analog of RV work—was altered in the dog either by altered peripheral resistance and venous return or partial inflation of a balloon in the RV outflow tract, the ventilatory changes were highly correlated with both the magnitude and the time course of the changes in $P_{\overline{RV}}$.

However, changes in $\dot{Q}$ that are solely or predominatly induced by heart rate rather than by both rate and stroke volume do not appear to induce abrupt changes in $\dot{V}_E$. Thus work-to-work transitions in the upright position (13, 16, 124) or rest-to-work transitions in the supine position (60, 113) (i.e. with stroke volume already elevated to, or close to, its exercise level prior to the work) are not associated with a rapid $\phi 1$ hyperpnea. Furthermore, Jones et al (59) performed a more definitive study, inducing increases in heart rate in patients with permanent, demand-type pacemakers (placed for the management of atrioventricular block). When heart rate was abruptly increased from some 50 min^{-1} to 80 min^{-1}, there was no significant $\dot{V}_E$ response for approximately 20 sec on average, despite $P_{ET}CO_2$ having increased by a mean of 2.5 torr [and by some 4 torr in their subject example: Figure 1 in (59)], at which time $P_{ET}O_2$ had fallen by about 8 torr and the gas exchange ratio R by about 0.1. Because these changes were associated with increased $\dot{V}CO_2$ and $\dot{V}CO_2$, there was clear evidence of increased $\dot{Q}$ without hyperpnea. Subsequent increases in $\dot{V}_E$, beginning approximately 20 sec after the induced tachycardia, were observed and presumably resulted from humoral stimulation of the peripheral and central chemoreceptors by the altered arterial blood-gas composition.

Diversion of a portion of the normal venous return from the venae cavae into the aorta has been undertaken by several groups in the dog, (the returning blood being "arterialized" by a gas exchanger). Despite methodological differences, these studies had a strikingly similar result. Blood flow through the heart and lungs was reduced, either at rest (39, 88, 94) or in the steady state of exercise (49, 81), hypopnea developed, even inducing apnea with sufficient thoracic hypoperfusion.

Brown et al (14) examined the role of such a cardiodynamic mechanism in the steady state of moderate exercise in humans by infusing propranolol to block β-adrenergic receptors. A fall in $\dot{V}_E$ was observed consequent to the fall in $\dot{Q}$; the hypopnea only persisted, however, until mixed venous CO_2 content rose sufficiently to return the pulmonary CO_2 flux to normal (i.e. $\dot{V}CO_2$ was restored to its control exercise level). Consequently, a cardiodynamic mechanism for a component of the steady-state exercise hyperpnea appears likely, involving both feedforward and feedback control elements.

The Search for Humoral Stimuli

The question of whether the hyperpnea of moderate steady-state exercise, or some proportion of it, is attributable to some change in the chemical or physical characteristics of the blood or muscle or brainstem interstititial fluid, and operates through proportional control, remains a central issue.

Since chemoreceptors within the pulmonary artery, capillaries, and veins have been effectively ruled out, systemic arterial blood has received most attention in the search for humoral mediation. Although some have asserted that arterial P_{CO_2} or $[H^+]$ is increased systematically in $\phi 3$ of exercise, the experimental evidence overwhelmingly supports the contention that moderate exercise is isocapnic with respect to carefully established control values [see (118) for discussion]. Similarly, Pa_{O_2} does not change systematically during $\phi 3$ at these work rates.

Increased body temperature can induce hyperpnea, mediated especially via tachypnea (44); but for the increases of 1°C or less that are typical of moderate exercise, there appears to be little or no ventilatory stimulation out of proportion to metabolic rate (28, 43, 121). Furthermore, highly fit subjects with a wider range of work rates within the moderate intensity domain, and hence a higher core and muscle temperature at the extreme of the domain, do not hyperventilate. And unless the thermal stimulatory effects in such subjects are simply offsetting some reduced ventilatory drive from other sources, a case for a significant influence from body temperature at these work rates appears remote.

As neither cerebral blood flow, Pa_{CO_2} or pH_a, cerebral metabolic rate, nor bulk cerebrospinal fluid pH are thought to change with moderate exercise, it is supposed that no changes in local pH occur in the brainstem interstitial fluid composition at the sites of central chemoreception. Thus the search for a humoral mediator of the steady-state exercise hyperpnea has proven unsuccessful. Consequently, other CO_2-linked control mechanisms have been considered.

It has been suggested that the restriction of blood carbonic anhydrase to the interior of the erythrocyte (34, 36, 45) would delay the dehydration of carbonic acid in the arterial plasma to an extent that could provide a H^+ stimulus to the peripheral chemoreceptors. Such a stimulus would not be evident in equilibrated blood samples. Because the proposed pH stimulus to the carotid bodies would depend both on mixed venous P_{CO_2} and $\dot{Q}$, the "disequilibrium" theory for control of the exercise hyperpnea did meet the challenge of internal consistency.

Recently, however, the "disequilibrium" theory has undergone two irremediable setbacks. Firstly, the presence of carbonic anhydrase on the pulmonary capillary endothelial surface and its accessibility to the pulmonary capillary plasma have now been demonstrated (30, 62, 66). As a consequence, the dehydration of carbonic acid in plasma is accelerated, with little or no disequilibrium being discernible at the end of the pulmonary capillary bed. Secondly, Lewis & Hill (68) investigated the consequences on exercise $\dot{V}_E$ of introducing bovine carbonic anhydrase into the plasma of dogs (at a level designed to speed the dehydration of carbonic acid some 100-fold). However, the expected decrement of $\dot{V}_E$ that would result if the proposed disequilibrium were abolished did not occur.

Since the original suggestion by Yamamoto & Edwards (126), investigators have considered the possibility that the naturally occurring, respiratory-related oscillation of arterial pH and P_{CO_2} might contain information important to the control of the exercise hyperpnea [see (122) for discussion]. This is an attractive proposition because such a mechanism could provide the ventilatory control system with a CO_2-linked error signal that could operate in the absence of a change in mean arterial P_{CO_2} or pH. The presence of these oscillations has been determined from in-line pH measurements in humans (8) and experimental animals (6, 18); both their amplitude and rate of change can increase during exercise.

A correspondingly periodic pattern has been discerned in the afferent discharge from the carotid bodies (7, 11). However, because in humans the carotid bodies sense arterial oscillations at these frequencies and because subjects without carotid bodies can achieve the same $\phi 3$ $\dot{V}_E$ at moderate work rates as normal subjects, signals deriving from such intra-breath periodicities are presumably not obligatory determinants of a normal steady-state hyperpnea during exercise. But clearly the slow $\phi 2$ $\dot{V}_E$ kinetics in carotid body resected subjects (112) are compatible with a role for such oscillations in the normal $\phi 2$ response. The pH oscillation was virtually absent (16a) in subjects with chronic obstructive lung disease, suggesting that the slow ventilatory dynamics in such subjects may reflect the absence of these oscillations.

Saunders, however, has incorporated an ingenious modification of the "oscillations" theory into a model for the exercise hyperpnea. In simplest terms, it suggests that the carotid bodies sense not simply the shape but also the temporal density of the oscillations—i.e. they "count" the number of peaks per unit time (91). This novel approach would, of course, dispense with the necessity for a transit delay in the sensing of a cardiodynamically generated downstream error signal to provide humoral mediation in $\phi 1$ of exercise—i.e. increased blood flow itself would be sufficient. However, because it is by no means certain that carotid artery blood flow actually increases during exercise in humans, and because the magnitude of the ϕ 1 $\dot{V}_E$ increase is not discernibly different in carotid body resected subjects or when normal subjects breathe hyperoxic gas mixtures, this must be considered as a stimulating speculation.

It has also been suggested that the intra-breath arterial CO_2–H^+ oscillation may also influence $\dot{V}_E$ from its "phase-coupling" to the ongoing respiratory cycle (21, 101). This suggestion is based on the demonstration in the cat (31, 101) that bolus infusion of hypercapnic blood past the carotid bodies or electrical stimulation of the carotid sinus nerves could elicit ventilatory response, which was much more striking when applied during inspiration rather than expiration.

Petersen et al (86), however, have shown that the phase-coupling mechanism does not appear to influence $\phi 3$ $\dot{V}_E$ to any discernible extent through the spontaneously occurring oscillation; its significance in the $\phi 1$ and $\phi 2$ responses has not yet been investigated. On the other hand, Cross et al (18) have reported that the influence of the pH oscillation during exercise via such a phasing mechanism may account for some 17% of the steady-state ventilatory response to moderate exercise. In addition, Metias et al (74) recently demonstrated in humans that within-breath fluctuations of alveolar P_{CO_2} (created by an ingenious "plumbing" of the apparatus dead space) can affect the absolute level of $\dot{V}_E$, despite an apparently unaltered mean level.

Finally, Saunders (91) has shown that one can actually develop a simulation of the exercise hyperpnea using only components of the respiratory-related oscillatory humoral signal, the upstroke of the P_{CO_2} oscillation providing the important source of afferent information. Saunders's caveat to his own work (an undisguised reminder to "modelers" of the respiratory control system) deserves emphasis: "The fact that exercise and CO_2- breathing may be neatly stimulated using only components of the oscillating chemical signal does not imply that it is necessarily an actual source of information in real life, or, if actual, the only one."

In conclusion, a vast array of control mechanisms have been postulated to account for the exercise hyperpnea in humans, these being apparently confirmed in most instances by animal experiments. Were they all to operate in the proposed manner, the perplexity regarding the hyperpnea of moderate exercise would be not why ventilation actually increases but rather why it normally rises only to a level commensurate with the CO_2 output.

Literature Cited

1. Adams, L., Cross, A., Frankel, H., Furneaux, R., Garlick, J., Guz, A., Murphy, K., Semple, S. J. G. 1981. The dynamics of the ventilatory response to voluntary and electrically induced exercise in man: the influence of the spinal cord. *J. Physiol.* 306:67P
2. Asmussen, E. 1973. Ventilation at transition from rest to exercise. *Acta Physiol. Scand.* 89:68–78
3. Asmussen, E., Johansen, S. H., Jorgensen, M., Nielsen, M. 1965. On the nervous factors controlling respiration and circulation during exercise. *Acta Physiol. Scand.* 63:343–50
4. Asmussen, E., Nielsen, M., Wieth-Pedersen, G. 1943. Cortical or reflex control of respiration during muscular work? *Acta Physiol. Scand.* 6:168–75
5. Bakker, H. K., Struikenkamp, R. S., De Vries, G. A. 1980. Dynamics of ventilation, heart rate, and gas exchange: sinusoidal and impulse work loads in man. *J. Appl. Physiol.: Respir. Environ. Exer. Physiol.* 48:289–301
6. Band, D. M., Cameron, I. R., Semple, S. J. G. 1969. Oscillations in arterial pH with breathing in the cat. *J. Appl. Physiol.* 26:261–67
7. Band, D. M., Willshaw, P., Wolff, C. B. 1976. The speed of response of carotid body chemoreceptor. In *Morphology and Mechanisms of Chemoreceptors,* ed. A. S. Paintal, pp. 197–207. New Delhi: Navchetran Press
8. Band, D. M., Wolff, C. B., Ward, J., Cochrane, G. M., Prior, J. 1980. Respiratory oscillations in arterial carbon dioxide tension as a control signal in exercise. *Nature* 283:84–85
9. Beaver, W., Lamarra, N., Wasserman, K. 1981. Breath-by-breath measurement of true alveolar gas exchange. *J. Appl. Physiol.: Respir. Environ. Exer. Physiol.* 51:1662–75
10. Bennett, F. M., Reischl, P., Grodins, F. S., Yamashiro, S. M., Fordyce, W. E. 1981. Dynamics of ventilatory response to exercise in humans. *J. Appl. Physiol.* 51:194–203
11. Biscoe, T. J., Purves, M. J. 1967. Observations on the rhythmic variation in the cat carotid body chemoreceptor activity which has the same period as respiration. *J. Physiol.* 190:389–412
12. Bartoli, A., Cross, B. A., Guz, A., Jain, S. K., Noble, M. I. M., Trenchard, D. W. 1974. The effect of carbon dioxide in the airways and alveoli on ventilation; a vagal reflex studied in the dog. *J. Physiol.* 240:91–109
13. Broman, S., Wigertz, O. 1971. Transient dynamics of ventilation and heart rate with step changes in work load from different load levels. *Acta Physiol. Scand.* 81:54–74

14. Brown, H. V., Wasserman, K., Whipp, B. J. 1976. Effect of beta-adrenergic blockade during exercise on ventilation and gas exchange. *J. Appl. Physiol.* 41:886–92

15. Casaburi, R., Whipp, B. J., Wasserman, K., Beaver, W. L., Koyal, S. N. 1977. Ventilatory and gas exchange dynamics in response to sinusoidal work. *J. Appl. Physiol.: Respir. Environ. Exer. Physiol.* 42:300–11

16. Casaburi, R., Whipp, G. J., Wasserman, K., Stremel, R. W. 1978. Ventilatory control characteristics of the exercise hyperpnea as discerned from dynamic forcing techniques. *Chest* 73S: 280S–3S

16a. Cochrane, G. M., Prior, J. G., Wolff, C. B. 1981. Respiratory arterial pH and PCO_2 oscillations in patients with chronic obstructive pulmonary disease. *Clin. Sci.* 61:693–702

17. Comroe, J. H. Jr., Schmidt, C. F. 1943. Reflexes from the limbs as a factor in the hyperpnea of muscular exercise. *Am. J. Physiol.* 138:536–47

18. Cross, B. A., Grant, B. J. B., Guz, A., Jones, P. W., Semple, S. J. G., Stidwell, R. P. 1979. An assessment of the effect of the oscillatory component of arterial blood gas composition on pulmonary ventilation. In *Central Nervous Mechanisms in Breathing,* ed. C. von Euler, H. Lagercrantz, pp. 91–94. Oxford: Pergamon

19. Cunningham, D. J. C. 1974. Integrative aspects of the regulation of breathing; a personal view. In *MTP Int. Rev. Sci., Physiol., Ser. 1, Vol. 2, Respiration,* ed. J. G. Widdicombe, pp. 303–69. London: Butterworths

20. Cunningham, D. J. C. 1974. The control system regulating breathing in man. *Q. Rev. Biophys.* 6:433–83

21. Cunningham, D. J. C. 1975. A model illustrating the importance of timing in the regulation of breathing. *Nature* 253:440–42

22. Cunningham, D. J. C., Spurr, D., Lloyd, B. B. 1968. Ventilatory drive in hypoxic exercise. In *Arterial Chemoreceptors,* ed. R. W. Torrance, pp. 301–23. Oxford: Blackwell

23. Daly, W. J., Overley, T. 1966. Modification of ventilatory regulation by hypnosis. *J. Lab. Clin. Med.* 68:279–85

24. Davis, J. A., Whipp, B. J., Wasserman, K. 1978. Characteristics of physiological dead space ventilation during exercise in man. *Med. Sci. Sports* 10:44

25. Dejours, P. 1963. The regulation of breathing during muscular exercise in man. A neuro-humoral theory. In *The Regulation of Human Respiration,* ed. D. J. C. Cunningham, B. B. Lloyd, pp. 535–47. Oxford: Blackwell

26. Dejours, P. 1963. Control of respiration by arterial chemoreceptors. *Ann. N.Y. Acad. Sci.* 109:682–95

27. Dejours, P., Lefrançois, R., Flandrois, R., Teillac, A. 1960. Autonomie des stimulus ventilatoires oxygène, gaz carbonique et neurogenique de l'exercise musculaire. *J. Physiol. (Paris)* 52:63

28. Dejours, P., Teillac, A., Girard, F., Lacaisse, A. 1958. Etude du role de l'hyperthermie centrale moderee dans la regulation de la ventilation de l'exercise musculaire chez l'homme. *Rev. Franc. Etudes. Clin. Biol.* 3:755–61

29. Dempsey, J. A., Vidruk, E. H., Mastenbrook, S. M. 1980. Pulmonary control systems in exercise. *Fed. Proc.* 39:1498–1505

30. Effros, R. M., Chang, R. S. Y., Silverman, P. 1978. Carbonic anhydrase activity of the pulmonary vasculature. *Science* 199:427–29

31. Eldridge, F. L. 1972. The importance of timing on the respiratory effects of intermittent carotid body chemoreceptor stimulation. *J. Physiol.* 222:319–33

32. Eldridge, F. L. 1976. Central neural stimulation of respiration in anesthetized decerebrated cats. *J. Appl. Physiol.* 40:23–28

33. Eldridge, F. L., Millhorn, D. E., Waldrop, T. G. 1981. Exercise hyperpnea and locomotion: parallel activation from the hypothalamus. *Science* 211: 844–46

34. Filley, G. F., Heineken, F. G. 1976. A blood gas disequilibrium theory. *Br. J. Dis. Chest* 70:223–25

35. Folinsbee, L. J., Wallace, E. S., Bedi, J. A., Gliner, J. A., Horvath, S. M. 1982. Exercise respiratory pattern in elite athletes and sedentary subjects. *Am. Rev. Respir. Dis.* 125:240

36. Forster, R. E., Crandall, E. D. 1975. Time course of exchanges between red cells and extracellular fluid during CO_2 uptake. *J. Appl. Physiol.* 38:710–19

37. Fujihara, Y., Hildebrandt, J., Hildebrandt, J. R. 1973. Cardiorespiratory transients in exercising man. II. Linear models. *J. Appl. Physiol.* 35:68–76

38. Fujihara, Y., Hildebrandt, J., Hildebrandt, J. 1973. Cardiorespiratory transients in exercising man. I. Tests of superposition. *J. Appl. Physiol.* 35: 58–67

39. Galletti, P. M. 1961. Physiologic principles of partial extracorporeal circula-

tion for mechanical assistance to the failing heart. *Am. J. Cardiol.* 7:227–33

40. Goodwin, G. M., McCloskey, D. I., Mitchell, J. H. 1972. Cardiovascular and respiratory responses to changes in central command during isometric exercise at constant muscle tension. *J. Physiol.* 226:173–90

41. Griffiths, T. L., Henson, L. C., Huntsman, D., Wasserman, K., Whipp, B. J. 1980. The influence of inspired O_2 partial pressure on ventilatory and gas exchange kinetics during exercise. *J. Physiol.* 306:34P

42. Grimby, G., Saltin, B., Wilhelmsen, L. 1971. Pulmonary flow-volume and pressure-volume relationship during submaximal and maximal exercise in young well-trained men. *Bull. Physiopathol. Respir.* 7:157–68

43. Henry, J. D., Bainton, C. R. 1974. Human core temperature increase as a stimulus to breathing during moderate exercise. *Respir. Physiol.* 21:183–91

44. Hey, E. M., Lloyd, B. B., Cunningham, D. J. C., Jukes, M. G. M., Bolton, D. P. G. 1966. Effects of various respiratory stimuli on the depth and frequency of breathing in man. *Respir. Physiol.* 1:193–205

45. Hill, E. P., Power, G. G., Gilbert, R. D. 1977. Rate of pH changes in blood plasma in vitro and in vivo. *J. Appl. Physiol.: Respir. Environ. Exer. Physiol.* 42:928–34

46. Honda, Y., Watanabe, S., Hashizume, I., Satomura, Y., Hata, N., Sakakibara, Y., Severinghaus, J. W. 1979. Hypoxic chemosensitivity in asthmatic patients two decades after carotid body resection. *J. Appl. Physiol.* 46:632–38

47. Hornbein, T. F., Sorensen, S. C., Parks, C. R. 1969. Role of muscle spindles in lower extremities in breathing during bicycle exercise. *J. Appl. Physiol.* 27:476–79

48. Huszczuk, A., Jones, P. W., Wasserman, K. 1981. Pressure information from the right ventricle as a reflex coupler of ventilation and cardiac output. *Fed. Proc.* 40:568

49. Huszczuk, A., Oren, A., Nery, L. E., Shors, E., Whipp, B. J., Wasserman, K. 1982. Mechanisms of the isocapnic hypopnea resulting from partial cardiopulmonary bypass in the dog. *Fed. Proc.* 41:1102

50. Jaeger-Denavit, O., Lacert, P., Grossiord, A. 1973. Study of ventilatory response to passive movement of the legs in paraplegics. *Bull. Pathol. Physiol. Respir.* 9:709–10

51. Jain, S. K., Subramanian, S., Julka, D. B., Guz, A. 1972. Search for evidence of lung chemoreflexes in man: study of respiratory and circulatory effects of phenyldiguanide and lobeline. *Clin. Sci.* 42:163–77

52. Jammes, Y., Mathiot, M. J., Roll, J. P., Prefaut, C., Berthelin, F., Grimaud, C., Milic-Emili, J. 1981. Ventilatory responses to muscular vibrations in healthy humans. *J. Appl. Physiol.: Respir. Environ. Exer. Physiol.* 51:262–69

53. Jensen, J. I. 1972. Neural ventilatory drive during arm and leg exercise. *Scand. J. Clin. Lab. Invest.* 29:177–84

54. Jensen, J. I., Vejby-Christensen, H., Petersen, E. S. 1972. Ventilatory response to work initiated at various times during the respiratory cycle. *J. Appl. Physiol.* 33:744–50

55. Jones, N. L. 1976. Use of exercise in testing respiratory control mechanisms. *Chest* 70:169S–73S

56. Jones, N. L. 1975. Exercise testing in pulmonary evaluation: rationale, methods, and the normal respiratory response to exercise. *N. Engl. J. Med.* 293:541–44

57. Jones, N. L., Jurkowski, J. E. 1979. Body carbon dioxide storage capacity in exercise. *J. Appl. Physiol.: Respir. Environ. Exer. Physiol.* 46:811–15

58. Jones, N. L., Sutton, J. R., Taylor, R., Toews, J. 1977. Effect of pH on cardiorespiratory and metabolic responses to exercise. *J. Appl. Physiol.: Respir. Environ. Exer. Physiol.* 43:959–64

59. Jones, P. W., French, W., Weissman, M. L., Wasserman, K. 1981. Ventilatory responses to cardiac output changes in patients with pacemakers. *J. Appl. Physiol.: Respir. Environ. Exer. Physiol.* 51:1103–7

60. Karlsson, H., Lindborg, B., Linnarsson, D. 1975. Time courses of pulmonary gas exchange and heart rate changes in supine exercise. *Acta Physiol. Scand.* 95:329–40

61. Kao, F. F., Wang, C., Mei, S. S., Michel, C. C. 1965. The relationship of exercise hyperpnea to CSF pH. In *Cerebrospinal Fluid and the Regulation of Ventilation,* ed. C. Brooks, F. F. Kao, B. B. Lloyd, pp. 269–74. Oxford: Blackwell

62. Klocke, R. A. 1978. Catalysis of CO_2 reactions by lung carbonic anhydrase. *J. Appl. Physiol.* 44:882–88

63. Krogh, A., Lindhard, J. 1913. The regulation of respiration and circulation during the initial stages of muscular work. *J. Physiol.* 47:112–36

64. Lahiri, S. 1974. Physiological responses and adaptations to high altitude. In *MTP Int. Rev. Sci., Physiol., Ser. 1, Vol. 7, Environmental Physiology,* ed. D. Robertshaw, pp. 271–311. London: Butterworths
65. Lamb, T. W. 1968. Ventilatory responses to hind limb exercise in anesthetized cats and dogs. *Respir. Physiol.* 6:88–104
66. Leaver, D. G., Pride, N. B. 1971. Flow-volume curves and expiratory pressures during exercise in patients with chronic airways obstruction. *Scand. J. Respir. Dis.* 77:23–27
67. Leusen, I. 1965. Aspects of the acid-base balance between blood and cerebrospinal fluid. See Ref. 61, pp. 55–89
68. Lewis, S. M., Hill, E. P. 1980. Effect of plasma carbonic anhydrase on ventilation in exercising dogs. *J. Appl. Physiol.: Respir. Environ. Exer. Physiol.* 49:708–14
69. Linnarsson, D. 1974. Dynamics of pulmonary gas exchange and heart rate changes at start and end of exercise. *Acta Physiol. Scand. (Suppl.)* 415:1–68
70. Lugliani, R., Whipp, B. J., Seard, C., Wasserman, K. 1971. Effects of bilateral carotid body resection on ventilatory control at rest and during exercise in man. *N. Engl. J. Med.* 285:1105–11
71. Majcherczyk, S., Willshaw, P. 1973. Inhibition of peripheral chemoreceptor activity during superfusion with an alkaline c.s.f. of the ventral brainstem surface of the cat. *J. Physiol.* 231:26P
72. Margaria, R., Edwards, H. T., Dill, D. B. 1933. The possible mechanisms of contracting and paying the oxygen debt and the role of lactic acid in muscular contraction. *Am. J. Physiol.* 106:689–715
73. Martin, B. J., Morgan, E. J., Zwillich, C. W., Weil, J. V. 1979. Influence of exercise hyperthermia on exercise breathing pattern. *J. Appl. Physiol.: Respir. Environ. Exer. Physiol.* 47:1039–42
74. Metias, E. E., Petersen, E. S., Howson, M. G., Wolff, C. B., Cunningham, D. J. C. 1981. Reflex effects on human breathing of alternating the time profile of inspiratory PCO_2. *Pflügers Arch.* 389:243–50
75. Miyamoto, Y., Hiura, T., Tamura, T., Nakamura, T., Higuchi, J., Mikami, T. 1982. Dynamics of cardiac, respiratory, and metabolic function in men in response to step work load. *J. Appl. Physiol.: Respir. Environ. Exer. Physiol.* 52:1198–1208

76. Morgan, W. P., Raven, P. B., Drinkwater, B. L., Horvath, S. M. 1973. Perceptual and metabolic responsivity to standard bicycle ergometry following various hypnotic suggestions. *Int. J. Clin. Exp. Hypnosis* 21:86–101
77. Ochwadt, B., Bucherl, E., Kreuzer, H., Loeschcke, H. H. 1959. Beeinflussung der Atemsteigerung bei Muskel-arbeit durch partiellen neuro-muskulären Block (*Tubocurarin*). *Pflügers Arch.* 269:613–21
78. Olafsson, S., Hyatt, R. E. 1969. Ventilatory mechanics and expiratory flow limitation during exercise in normal subjects. *J. Clin. Invest.* 48:564–73
79. Oldenburg, F. A., McCormack, D. W., Morse, J. L. C., Jones, N. L. 1979. A comparison of exercise responses in stairclimbing and cycling. *J. Appl. Physiol.: Respir. Environ. Exer. Physiol.* 46:510–16
80. Owles, W. H. 1930. Alterations in the lactic acid content of the blood as a result of light exercise, and associated changes in the CO_2-combining power of the blood and in the alveolar CO_2 pressure. *J. Physiol.* 69:214–37
81. Oren, A., Huszczuk, A., Nery, L. E., Shors, E. C., Whipp, B. J., Wasserman, K. 1981. Isocapnic hypopnea resulting from partial cardiopulmonary bypass. *Physiologist* 23:101
82. Oren, A., Wasserman, K., Davis, J. A., Whipp, B. J. 1981. The effect of CO_2 set-point on the ventilatory response to exercise. *J. Appl. Physiol.* 51:185–89
83. Oren, A., Whipp, B. J., Wasserman, K. 1982. Effect of acid-base status on the kinetics of the ventilatory response to moderate exercise. *J. Appl. Physiol: Respir. Environ. Exer. Physiol.* 52:1013–17
84. Paulev, P. 1971. Respiratory and cardiac responses to exercise in man. *J. Appl. Physiol.* 30:165–72
85. Pearce, D. H., Milhorn, H. T. Jr. 1977. Dynamic and steady-state respiratory responses to bicycle ergometer exercise. *J. Appl. Physiol.* 42:959–67
86. Petersen, E. S., Whipp, B. J., Drysdale, D. B., Cunningham, D. J. C. 1978. The relation between arterial blood gas oscillations in the carotid region and the phase of the respiratory cycle during exercise in man: Testing a model. In *Regulation of Respiration during Sleep and Anesthesia,* ed. R. Fitzgerald, H. Gautier, S. Lahiri, pp. 335–42. NY: Plenum
87. Ponte, J., Purves, M. J. 1974. Frequency response of carotid body chemoreceptors in the cat to changes of

PaCO$_2$, PaO$_2$ and pH. *J. Appl. Physiol.* 37:635–47

88. Rawlings, C. A., Bisgard, G. E., Dufkek, J. H., Buss, D. D., Will, J. A., Birnbaum, M. L., Chopra, P. S., Kahn, D. R. 1975. Prolonged perfusion with a membrane oxygenator in awake ponies. *J. Thorac. Cardiovasc. Surg.* 69:539–51

89. Sackner, J. D., Nixon, A. J., Davis, B., Atkins, N., Sackner, M. A. 1980. Effects of breathing through external dead space on ventilation at rest and during exercise. *Am. Rev. Respir. Dis.* 122:933–40

90. Deleted in proof

91. Saunders, K. B. 1980. Oscillations of arterial CO$_2$ tension in a respiratory model: some implications for the control of breathing in exercise. *J. Theor. Biol.* 84:163–81

92. Spode, R., Schlaefke, M. E. 1975. Influence of muscular exercise on respiration after central and peripheral denervation. *Pflügers Arch. Suppl.* 359:R49

93. Stockley, R. A. 1978. The contribution of the reflex hypoxic drive to the hyperpnoea of exercise. *Respir. Physiol.* 35:79–87

94. Stremel, R. W., Whipp, B. J., Casaburi, R., Huntsman, D. J., Wasserman, K. 1979. Hypopnea consequent to diminished blood flow in the dog. *J. Appl. Physiol.* 46:1171–77

95. Swanson, G. D. 1978. Input stimulus design for model discrimination in human respiratory control. In *Modelling of a Biological Control System: The Regulation of Breathing,* ed. E. R. Carson, D. J. C. Cunningham, R. Herczynski, D. J. Murray-Smith, E. S. Petersen, p. 165. Oxford: Inst. Measurement and Control

96. Swanson, G. D. 1980. Breath-to-breath considerations for gas exchange kinetics. In *Exercise Bioenergetics and Gas Exchange,* ed. P. Ceretelli, B. J. Whipp, pp. 211–22. Elsevier: Amsterdam

97. Swanson, G. D., Ward, D. S., Bellville, J. W. 1976. Posthyperventilation isocapnic hyperpnea. *J. Appl. Physiol.* 40:592–96

98. Trawadrous, F. D., Eldridge, F. L. 1974. Posthyperventilation breathing patterns after active hyperventilation in man. *J. Appl. Physiol.* 37:353–56

99. Tibes, U., Hemmer, B., Boning, D. 1977. Heart rate and ventilation in relation venous K$^+$, osmolality, pH, PCO$_2$, PO$_2$, orthophosphate, and lactate at transition from rest to exercise in athletes and non-athletes. *Eur. J. Appl.*

Physiol. 36:127–49

100. Torelli, G., Brandi, G. 1961. Regulation of ventilation at the beginning of muscular exercise. *Int. Angew. Physiol.* 19:134–39

101. Torrance, R. W. 1974. Arterial chemoreceptors. See Ref. 19, pp. 247–71

102. Ward, S. A. 1979. The effects of sudden airway hypercapnia on the initiation of exercise hyperpnoea in man. *J. Physiol.* 296:203–14

103. Ward, S. A., Davis, J. A., Weissman, M. L., Wasserman, K., Whipp. B. J. 1979. Lung gas stores and the kinetics of gas exchange during exercise. *Physiologist* 22 (4):129

104. Ward, S. A., Russak, S., Blesovsky, L., Ashjian, A., Whipp, B. J. 1982. Chemoreflex modulation of ventilatory dynamics during exercise. *Fed. Proc.* 41:1102

105. Ward, S. A., Whipp, B. J. 1980. Ventilatory control during exercise with increased external dead space. *J. Appl. Physiol.* 48:225–31

106. Wasserman, K. 1978. Breathing during exercise. *N. Engl. J. Med.* 298:780–85

107. Wasserman, K., VanKessel, A. L., Burton, G. G. 1967. Interaction of physiological mechanisms during exercise. *J. Appl. Physiol.* 22:71–85

108. Wasserman, K., Whipp, B. J. 1975. Exercise physiology in health and disease. *Am. Rev. Respir. Dis.* 112:219–49

109. Wasserman, K., Whipp, B. J., Casaburi, R., Beaver, W. L., Brown, H. V. 1977. CO$_2$ flow to the lungs and ventilatory control. In *Muscular Exercise and the Lung,* ed. J. A. Dempsey, C. E. Reed, pp. 103–35. Madison: Univ. Wis. Press

110. Wasserman, K., Whipp, B. J., Castagna, J. 1974. Cardiodynamic hyperpnea: hyperpnea secondary to cardiac output increase. *J. Appl. Physiol.* 36:457–64

111. Wasserman, K., Whipp, B. J., Koyal, S. N., Beaver, W. L. 1973. Anerobic threshold and respiratory gas exchange during exercise. *J. Appl. Physiol.* 35:236–43

112. Wasserman, K., Whipp, B. J., Koyal, S. N., Cleary, M. G. 1975. Effect of carotid body resection on ventilatory and acid-base control during exercise. *J. Appl. Physiol.* 39:354–58

113. Weiler-Ravell, D., Cooper, D. M., Whipp, B. J., Wasserman, K. 1982. Effect of posture on the ventilatory response at the start of exercise. *Fed. Proc.* 41:1102

114. Weissman, M. L., Jones, P. W., Oren, A., Lamarra, N., Whipp, B. J., Wasserman, K. 1982. Cardiac output increase and gas exchange at start of exercise. *J. Appl. Physiol.: Respir. Environ. Exer. Physiol.* 52:236–44

115. Weissman, M. L., Wasserman, K., Huntsman, D. J., Whipp, B. J. 1979. Ventilation and gas exchange during phasic hindlimbs exercise in the dog. *J. Appl. Physiol.* 46:878–84

116. Weissman, M. L., Whipp, B. J., Huntsman, D., Wasserman, K. 1980. Role of neural afferents from working limbs in exercise hyperpnea. *J. Appl. Physiol.* 49:239–48

117. Wessel, H. U., Stout, R. L., Bastanier, C. K., Paul, M. H. 1979. Breath-by-breath variation of FRC: effect on V_{O_2} and V_{CO_2} measured at the mouth. *J. Appl. Physiol.: Respir. Environ. Exer. Physiol.* 46:1122–26

118. Whipp, B. J. 1981. The control of exercise hyperpnea. In *The Regulation of Breathing,* ed. T. Hornbein, pp. 1069–1139. NY: Dekker

119. Whipp, B. J., Mahler, M. 1980. Dynamics of pulmonary gas exchange during exercise. In *Pulmonary Gas Exchange,* ed. J. B. West, 2:33–96. NY: Academic

120. Whipp, B. J., Sylvester, J. T., Seard, C., Wasserman, K. 1971. Intrabreath respiratory responses following the onset of cycle ergometer exercise. In *Lung Function and Work Capacity,* ed. J. D.

Brooke, pp. 45–64. Salford, England: Univ. Salford

121. Whipp, B. J., Wasserman, K. 1970. Effect of body temperature on the ventilatory response to exercise. *Respir. Physiol.* 8:354–60

122. Whipp, B. J., Wasserman, K. 1980. Carotid bodies and ventilatory control dynamics in man. *Fed. Proc.* 39:2628–73

123. Whipp, B. J., Wasserman, K., Casaburi, R., Juratsch, C., Weissman, M. L., Stremel, R. W. 1978. Ventilatory control characteristics of conditions resulting in isocapnic hyperpnea. In *Control of Respiration During Sleep and Anesthesia,* ed. R. Fitzgerald, H. Gautier, L. Lahiri, pp. 355–66. NY: Plenum

124. Whipp, B. J., Wasserman, K., Davis, J. A., Lamarra, N., Ward, S. A. 1980. Determinants of O_2 and CO_2 kinetics during exercise in man. In *Exercise Bioenergetics and Gas Exchange,* ed. P. Ceretelli, B. J. Whipp, pp. 175–85. Amsterdam: Elsevier

125. Wigertz, O. 1970. Dynamics of ventilation and heart rate in response to sinusoidal work load in man. *J. Appl. Physiol.* 29:208–18

126. Yamamoto, W. S., Edwards, M. W. Jr. 1960. Homeostasis of carbon dioxide during intravenous infusion of carbon dioxide. *J. Appl. Physiol.* 15:807–18

127. Young, I. H., Woolcock, A. J. 1978. Changes in arterial blood gas tensions during unsteady-state exercise. *J. Appl. Physiol.* 44:93–96

Ann. Rev. Physiol. 1983. 45:415-26

VENTILATORY RESPONSES TO O_2 AND CO_2 DURING EXERCISE

D. C. Flenley and P. M. Warren

Department of Respiratory Medicine, University of Edinburgh,
Edinburgh, Scotland

Introduction

Mechanisms causing the hyperpnea of exercise remain undetermined (23, 88, 93, 99). Thus together with diving (83) and submarine exposures (81) to CO_2 during exercise, and exercise in altitude hypoxia (84a), the interaction of ventilatory stimulation by hypoxia or CO_2 breathing with that from exercise may aid in solving this problem. In this review we summarize recent results on hypoxic and CO_2 responses during exercise in humans. We discuss how these help us to understand exercise hyperpnea, concentrating first on studies in awake humans, then in awake animals, and finally in anesthetized or denervated animals.

The close correlation between ventilation ($\dot{V}_E$: liters BTPS min^{-1}) and CO_2 output ($\dot{V}CO_2$: liters STP min^{-1}) in steady-state aerobic human exercise (99) allows us to use the ratio $\dot{V}_E/\dot{V}CO_2$ to define normal exercise hyperpnea. Values above the 26 liters/liter (or less precisely $\dot{V}_E/\dot{V}O_2$ above 24 liters/liter) found with such exercise in normoxia indicate hyperventilation. We do not discuss partition of $\dot{V}_E$ between respiratory drive (V_T/T_i) and timing (T_i/T_{tot}) (37), both for lack of space, and because the mouthpiece used in most human studies may affect such measurements (4).

The Experimental Facts: Hypoxic and CO_2 Drives in Exercise

In humans the ventilation in steady-state exercise increases in acute hypoxia (7, 45). For example, in 10 subjects mean $\dot{V}_E/\dot{V}CO_2$ during walking rose from 23 liters/liter when breathing air to 29 liters/liter when breathing 13–14% oxygen (35). Because this lowers Pa_{CO_2}, $\dot{V}_E/\dot{V}CO_2$ is even greater if Pa_{CO_2} is kept at resting levels (59) during steady-state aerobic exercise—

415

0066-4278/83/0315-0415$02.00

e.g. by use of progressive isocapnic hypoxia (95). In 8 normal men aged 21–40 years (96), and in 16 male athletes aged 20–28 years (58), such hypoxic ventilatory response [recalculated as the negative slope of the linear relationship between $\dot{V}_E$ and Sao_2 ($\dot{V}_E/Sao_2$: liters $min^{-1}Sao_2\%^{-1}$, (74, 95)] increased as the intensity of the exercise ($\dot{V}o_2$) rose (Figure 1a). The steady-state ventilatory response to CO_2 breathing in humans can be expressed as $\dot{V}_E = S(Pco_2-B)$ (55). In three such recent studies (20, 64, 96) in normoxia or hyperoxia, in normal men aged 19–40 years, this slope (S:$\dot{V}_E/Pco_2$: liters $min^{-1}mm$ Hg^{-1}) rose as $\dot{V}o_2$ increased in steady-state exercise (Figure 1b), as in other studies not giving enough data to relate $\dot{V}_E/Pco_2$ to $\dot{V}o_2$ (42, 46). S did not usually rise in exercise when the Read rebreathing method (71) was used (14, 19, 58), possibly because the high $\dot{V}o_2$ shrinks the rebreathing bag too rapidly, so changing the linearity and rate of change of $Paco_2$ in rebreathing, and thus disturbing that unique brain tissue $Pco_2/Paco_2$ relationship that makes the Read method so precise (72). In very severe exercise $\dot{V}_E/Pco_2$ falls again as $\dot{V}_E$ approaches 150–170 liters min^{-1} (20), presumably as the load on respiratory muscles becomes unsustainable (14a).

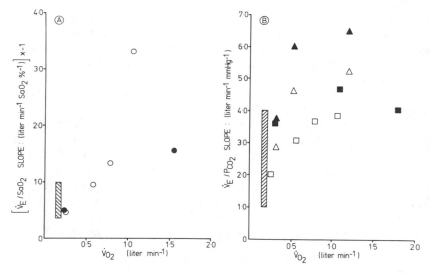

Figure 1 Relationship of: (A) sensitivity of the hypoxic drive to breathing ($\dot{V}_E/Sao_2$) with exercise intensity ($\dot{V}o_2$), in normal men (58 ●, 96 ○); and (B) ventilatory response to CO_2 ($\dot{V}_E/Pco_2$) with $\dot{V}o_2$ in normal men in normoxia (20 ■, 64 ▲) or hyperoxia (64 △, 96 □). $\dot{V}_E/Sao_2$ is the slope of the linear relationship between $\dot{V}_E$ and Sao_2 during progressive isocapnic hypoxia (95), normal values at rest ▨ being the mean ±1 SD in 44 men (43). $\dot{V}_E/Pco_2$ is value S in $\dot{V}_E = S(Pco_2-B)$, measured during steady state CO_2 responses in hyperoxia or normoxia, at rest and on exercise. Normal range ▨ includes 80% of the values in normal subjects at rest (73).

Relationship Between Ventilation and CO_2 Flow to the Lungs

The close correlation between $\dot{V}_E$ and $\dot{V}_{CO_2}$ in humans during aerobic bicycle [$\dot{V}_E$ = 24.6 $\dot{V}_{CO_2}$ + 3.19, r = 0.96, n = 142; (26)] and treadmill exercise [$\dot{V}_E$ = 23 $\dot{V}_{CO_2}$ + 1.69, r = 0.96, n = 458; (35)] in normoxia also extended in awake sheep to $\dot{V}_{CO_2}$ values below and above rest, when an extracorporeal membrane lung added or extracted CO_2 to (or from) venous blood (67, 68). Pa_{CO_2} then remained at resting levels, so resolving controversy about the effects of CO_2 given by either infusion or inhalation (69). In awake humans $\dot{V}_E/\dot{V}_{CO_2}$ also remained the same when cardiac pacing changed the CO_2 flow to the lungs (49). This close correlation between $\dot{V}_E$ and $\dot{V}_{CO_2}$ has suggested a causal linkage—the CO_2 flow hypothesis (92) —but this can be seen as the arithmetic consequence of the constant alveolar P_{CO_2} in human exercise (39), and of the correlation between dead space and $\dot{V}_{CO_2}$ on exercise (99), without identifying any mechanism. End tidal P_{CO_2} (PET_{CO_2}) is not kept at resting values in normoxic exercise in awake dogs, in which $\dot{V}_E/\dot{V}_{O_2}$ rose from 49 liters/liter in normoxic exercise (when PET_{CO_2} was 25 mm Hg) to 54 liters/liter in hypoxic exercise (34). This rise was abolished by sinocarotid chemodenervation, although $\dot{V}_E/\dot{V}_{O_2}$ still rose to 57 liters/liter in hypercapnic exercise (PET_{CO_2} 38 mm Hg). Hypercapnic potentiation of the exercise ventilatory drive thus depended little on carotid chemoreceptors, but these seem essential for hypoxic potentiation of exercise ventilation. However, the fall in PET_{CO_2} with normoxic exercise implies that ventilatory control may differ between dog and man—e.g. man does not pant.

Ventilatory Response to Transient Changes in P_{O_2} and P_{CO_2}

The subject's will can affect the size of the first breath of exercise, which may explain disagreements about the effect of workload, hypoxia, and hypercapnia on this response in both conscious dogs and humans (5, 8, 25, 84, 91). Pseudo-random variation of workload during bicycle exercise in humans (11) reveals that 10% of total $\dot{V}_E$ response is by a fast component, not previously shown by sinusoidal variation in workload (15). At rest the half times ($t_{1/2}$) of on and off responses of $\dot{V}_E$ to a step change in PET_{CO_2} in hyperoxia ("a central chemoreceptor stimulus") were 83 and 69 sec, but 11 and 6 sec for hypoxia in mild hypercapnia ("a peripheral chemoreceptor stimulus") in six healthy young adults (36). The time course in exercise is unknown. The importance of peripheral chemoreceptors for the hypoxic potentiation of $\dot{V}_E$ in human exercise (56), coupled with this fast response to P_{O_2} changes (36), has suggested a means to quantitate the sensitivity of peripheral chemoreceptors in humans, with minimal central ventilatory depression by hypoxia (97). The slope of the relationship between breath-by-breath $\dot{V}_E$ and PET_{O_2} ($\dot{V}_E/PET_{O_2}$), as PET_{O_2} was raised transiently from 60 to 130 mm Hg during steady-state hypoxic exercise, became steeper as exercise intensity ($\dot{V}_{O_2}$) increased in four healthy men (35). This slope was derived by an on-line computer method that allowed for delay in the $\dot{V}_E$ response. The method can also measure the transient ventilatory stimulation from three breaths of nitrogen during steady-state aerobic exercise when breathing air. This $\dot{V}_E/P_{ET_{O_2}}$ slope (the proposed measure of peripheral chemoreceptor sensitivity) varied up to 6-fold among 42 normal men (D. C. Flenley, unpublished data). Such variability in chemoreceptor sensitivity is similar to that shown by progressive isocapnic hypoxia in resting humans (73) and also by transient responses to hypoxia at rest (47, 48).

Oscillations Hypothesis

The idea that the oscillating Pa_{CO_2} (or pH) could drive exercise ventilation (101) has attracted recent experimental and theoretical support. Directly recorded intraarterial pH oscillations in conscious humans steepen rapidly at the start of exercise (9), suggesting that this could provide a control signal. In anesthetized dogs, electrically induced exercise increased the maximal rate of change in the downstroke of intraarterial pH oscillations (dpH/dt   max) (21), which will reflect Pa_{CO_2} changes inversely, by the acute in vivo $[H^+]/Pa_{CO_2}$ relationship (13). When small changes in PET_{CO_2} were produced within one breath in resting humans, $\dot{V}_E$ was affected, but only in hypoxia, although these effects did not increase in hypoxic exercise.

The mean ventilation perfusion ratio ($\dot{V}_A/Q$) increased in mild exercise, and wide $\dot{V}_A/Q$ distributions at rest then narrowed, so that A-aD_{O_2} fell (28). Such narrowing of $\dot{V}_A/Q$ distributions should increase dPa_{CO_2}/dt on exercise, but in harder exercise $\dot{V}_A/Q$ became less homogenous (38), which should reduce dPa_{CO_2}/dt! In hypoxic exercise pulmonary vasoconstriction may narrow $\dot{V}_A/Q$ distributions, but this is unproven. A recent computer model (79, 80) using as a controller the equation relating P_{CO_2} and P_{O_2} to $\dot{V}_E$ derived in humans at rest (55) predicts that the rate of change of the oscillating Pa_{CO_2} (dPa_{CO_2}/dt) will be independent of breathing pattern. The model predicts that dPa_{CO_2}/dt will be positively correlated with $\dot{V}_{CO_2}$ (as in exercise) but will fall slightly in CO_2 breathing at rest despite the rise in mean Pa_{CO_2}. Thus dPa_{CO_2}/dt could drive ventilation on exercise, as the measurements of arterial dpH/dt in dogs (21) and humans (9) suggest. Carotid chemoreceptors can respond rapidly enough for such a stimulus (31). The program (79, 80) has not been used to model CO_2 responses on exercise, but as dPa_{CO_2}/dt is then predicted to rise, yet to fall with CO_2 breathing at rest, the results of combining these stimuli would be of interest.

Although in normal humans hypoxia rapidly increased the $\dot{V}_E$ response to a sudden rise in Pa_{CO_2} at rest, this was much slower in subjects with bilateral carotid body resection (glomectomy) (10). Computer studies (79) predict that dPa_{CO_2}/dt will rise as cardiac output increases in exercise, so that in hypoxic exercise, where cardiac output is higher at the same $\dot{V}_{O_2}$ (35), the dPa_{CO_2}/dt stimulus to the carotid bodies will be even greater, and these may already be sensitized by hypoxia (61). Test of this hypothesis requires measurement of arterial dpH/dt max during hypoxic exercise in awake humans.

Muscle Afferents

The role of small-diameter group III and IV afferent nerve fibers from muscle (60) in control of $\dot{V}_E$ during exercise is controversial (57, 99) but highly relevant to hypoxic exercise. Both static (66) and dynamic (29) exercise reduce the P_{O_2} of venous effluent blood from exercising muscles, even in normoxia, so such receptors could be stimulated by the "local chemical change" in muscle on exercise, thus acting as a "multiplicative factor" to increase $\dot{V}_E$ in hypoxic exercise (27). This currently unfashionable proposal (23, 99) has recent experimental support.

In cats, tetanic leg muscle contraction from ventral spinal root stimulation increased $\dot{V}_E$, but not after the dorsal roots were cut. This implies a ventilatory stimulant role for muscle afferents via spinal pathways (63). However, phasic stimulation of ventral roots, so avoiding any ischemia (which may occur in tetany), also increased $\dot{V}_E$ in cats. This response persisted after cord transection (98), as did that from hamstring stimulation in dogs (22); but hyperventilation from phasic stimulation of the sciatic nerve in dogs was abolished by proximal cold block (85). Interpretation of these studies is difficult because Pa_{CO_2} was lower after cord transection (22, 98) and the anesthesia may play a role (22, 63, 85, 98). However, in awake humans steady-state $\dot{V}_E/\dot{V}_{CO_2}$ was also the same during mild electrically induced normoxic leg exercise in both normal and paraplegic subjects (1), although $\dot{V}_E$ rose more slowly after starting the exercise in the paraplegics (2).

Other evidence supports the notion that muscular afferents affecting ventilation are stimulated in hypoxic exercise by a factor related to "hard times in the muscles" [e.g. low P_{O_2}, lactic acid, potassium efflux (86)]. In exercise the mixed venous P_{O_2} ($P\bar{v}_{O_2}$) or $S\bar{v}_{O_2}$ is largely determined by the blood flow from exercising muscles. When this is restricted, as in ten patients with mitral stenosis, $\dot{V}_E/\dot{V}_{CO_2}$ was 36 liters/liter in modest exercise with $S\bar{v}_{O_2}$ 30%, but after mitral valvotomy when the cardiac output at the same $\dot{V}_{O_2}$ was higher, $S\bar{v}_{O_2}$ rose to 45% but $\dot{V}_E/\dot{V}_{CO_2}$ was then normal at 23 liters/liter, despite little other hemodynamic change (90). Acute experimental anemia in humans (Hb 66%) also reduced $P\bar{v}_{O_2}$ on exercise, with a raised $\dot{V}_E/\dot{V}_{O_2}$ (100), although in both mitral stenosis and anemia Pa_{O_2} [the unique determinant of hypoxic carotid body stimulation in humans (40, 53, 77)] is almost normal.

A high carboxyhemoglobin (COHb) concentration impairs O_2 transport despite a normal Pa_{O_2}. In 1941 this was shown to cause less hyperventilation on exercise than apparently similar reduction in arterial O_2 content from a low Pa_{O_2}, suggesting that muscle hypoxia did not cause exercise hyperventilation (6). In fact anaerobic metabolism was more evident in the exercise with low Pa_{O_2}, as lactate levels were then higher than in exercise with high COHb (6). However, in eight normal men an COHb of 20% on exercise gave a mean $\dot{V}_E/\dot{V}_{CO_2}$ of 32–34 liters/liter and $P\bar{v}_{O_2}$ 12–14 mm Hg, [calculated from measured $\dot{V}_{O_2}$, R, cardiac output, COHb, Pa_{O_2}, and pH; and measurements of the effect of COHb on the position and slope of the oxygen dissociation curve (75, 102)], whereas when COHb was <2% in exercise $\dot{V}_E/\dot{V}_{CO_2}$ was 30–31 liters/liter, and calculated $P\bar{v}_{O_2}$ 22–26 mm Hg (89). This again implies that hypoxia within the exercising muscles may contribute to hyperventilation in hypoxic exercise, for Pa_{O_2} was the same with and without the high COHb.

In humans, external cuffs occluding muscle circulation (27) kept $\dot{V}_E/\dot{V}_{O_2}$ high at 56 liters/liter following the isometric contraction of forearm muscles (30), as compared to only 40 liters/liter without such occlusion after the contraction. However, this high $\dot{V}_E/\dot{V}_{O_2}$ was associated with pain, and did not occur in two subjects with sensory loss who felt no pain. Nonetheless, similar occlusion of thigh muscles in five men during bicycle exercise was not painful, but still increased $\dot{V}_E/\dot{V}_{CO_2}$ from 29 liters/liter to 45 liters/ liter, with Pa_{CO_2} falling to 32 mm Hg, again suggesting stimulation of muscle afferents, either mechanically or from muscle hypoxia, as shown by the high blood lactate after the cuffs were released (78).

Catecholamines in Hypoxic Exercise

Plasma norepinephrine and epinephrine levels rise in exercise (17). Norepinephrine is more closely related to exercise hyperpnea (33), and soon rose to plateau at ten times the resting level in prolonged aerobic exercise in humans (3). Norepinephrine infusion potentiates the ventilatory response to hypoxia in humans at rest (24). Arterial plasma norepinephrine (which could thus act humorally on arterial chemoreceptors) was consistently higher in four normal men during steady-state aerobic exercise breathing 14% oxygen, than when they breathed air (18). When the breathing of 100% oxygen slightly lowered $\dot{V}_E/\dot{V}_{CO_2}$ on exercise, venous lactate fell and norepinephrine levels were halved (41). These results support the notion that norepinephrine may influence $\dot{V}_E/\dot{V}_{CO_2}$, probably through peripheral chemoreceptors.

Previous conflict over the action of beta-adrenergic blockade on human exercise hyperpnea (where some found a fall but others no change) has now been resolved, for the response depends upon the duration and severity of the exercise (87). Thus in the 5th minute of exercise at 70% $\dot{V}_{O_2}$max, both

$\dot{V}_E$ and venous lactate were higher during beta blockade than in control studies, possibly from more severe muscle hypoxia as a result of the lower cardiac output. The increase in $\dot{V}_E/\dot{V}_{CO_2}$ could then arise from hypoxic stimulation of type III and IV muscle afferents. A similar stimulus could also explain the high exercise $\dot{V}_E/\dot{V}_{CO_2}$ in a patient with myophosphorylase deficiency (70), in whom muscle glycogen could not fuel exercise.

Central Control Mechanisms

The old idea that nerve impulses from the higher centers driving muscular exercise also "irradiate" to the respiratory centers, so giving a proportional increase in ventilation (51), has now been tested experimentally. When unanesthetized decorticated cats, with vagi and carotid sinus nerves cut, walked either spontaneously or from electrical stimulation of sub-thalamic centers, phrenic motor discharge was proportional to the electrical activity in the exercising limb muscles (32). This relationship was preserved after muscular paralysis, so that afferent feedback from muscles or joints was not essential (32). This could be important in hypoxic hyperventilation in exercise. The conventional view (52) that acute hypoxia depresses central ventilatory drive is typical neither of awake animals (62) nor for modest hypoxia (65). Thus in awake resting goats CO breathing or reduction in cerebral blood flow, both of which lowered cerebral venous P_{O_2} from 33 to 22 mm Hg, increased ventilation despite a high Pa_{O_2} being used to prevent carotid body stimulation (16). Furthermore, in asthmatics with bilateral carotid glomectomy, Pa_{O_2} and Pa_{CO_2} were normal when breathing air at rest (44, 56) and $\dot{V}_E$ did not fall nor did Pa_{CO_2} rise when they breathed 12% O_2 at rest, despite a Pa_{O_2} of 42 mm Hg (56), although on exercise $\dot{V}_E/\dot{V}_{CO_2}$ was probably the same when breathing air as with 12% O_2. In Honda et al's studies (44) exercise hyperpnea was less in glomectomized asthmatics when breathing air than in asthmatics with intact carotid chemoreceptors who were matched for age and FEV_1. Hypoxic exercise hyperventilation in humans thus seems to require carotid chemoreceptors, as in awake dogs (33); but the evidence that hypoxia stimulates central ventilatory drive at rest in awake goats (77) seems stronger than that for hypoxic depression of ventilation in normal resting humans (97).

CO_2 inhalation raises Pa_{CO_2} and lowers CSF pH (12), thereby stimulating ventilation centrally through chemoreceptors on the ventro-lateral surface of the medulla (54), at least in rats, rabbits, cats, dogs (82), and presumably in humans. Days to weeks after coagulation of this medullary chemoreceptor area in awake cats the ventilatory response to CO_2 was abolished, yet some drive from hypoxia was preserved (82).

Hyperpnea on exercise when breathing air was either normal [probable $\dot{V}_E/\dot{V}_{CO_2}$ 22 liters/liter (56)] or slightly reduced [probable $\dot{V}_E/\dot{V}_{CO_2}$ 21 liters/liter (44)] in glomectomized asthmatics, although their Pa_{CO_2} rose from 43 at rest to 47 mm Hg on exercise in the latter study. In contrast, the CO_2 drive in exercise was normal in the glomectomized asthmatics of the earlier study, with a probable $\dot{V}_E/\dot{V}_{CO_2}$ value in exercise of 22 liters/liter at Pa_{CO_2} 36 mm Hg, rising to 43 liters/liter when Pa_{CO_2} in exercise was 47 mm Hg (56). However, $\dot{V}_E$ rose more slowly after starting exercise in glomectomized asthmatics (94). Although CO_2 drive at rest is mainly central in origin (82), it seems that on exercise peripheral chemoreceptors may also play a part in mediating this drive.

Summary and Synthesis

To synthesize these concepts, we suggest that ventilation increases during exercise in humans as a result of summation of many inputs to the respiratory centers, principally neural irradiation from cortico-spinal traffic to exercising muscles, in addition to a feedback from arterial chemoreceptors that probably depends upon the rate of change of the oscillating arterial P_{CO_2}.

In hypoxic exercise, potentiation of the ventilatory response comes about mainly from an increase in this arterial chemoreceptor input. The increase is due to a greater response of the glomus cells to the oscillating Pa_{CO_2} signal in hypoxia, with or without a contribution from the raised arterial norepinephrine level in hypoxic exercise. In addition, activity of type III and IV muscular afferent fibers increases, stimulated by some combination of the low P_{O_2} and the increased acidity, lactic acid, or potassium concentrations within the exercising muscles in hypoxia.

In hypercapnic exercise the high Pa_{CO_2} stimulates ventilation primarily through the central medullary $[H^+]$ receptor, probably with only minor contributions from arterial chemoreceptors, for the rate of change of the oscillating Pa_{CO_2} signal may well be reduced when compared to that in normocapnic exercise of similar severity.

The net effect of these interacting control systems is to provide sufficient flow of oxygen to the lung alveoli, for onward transport to the working muscles by the raised cardiac output, combined of course with elimination of CO_2. The evolutionary importance of this response, both for the hunt and the escape, seems to dictate the advantage of multiple control systems to preserve such a vital function.

Acknowledgment

We thank Professor S. J. G. Semple for comments and sight of papers in press, and Professor K. B. Saunders for comments. Dr. P. M. Warren is supported by the British MRC Programme Grant No. 978/988.

Literature Cited

1. Adams, L., Cross, B. A., Frankel, H., Furneaux, R., Garlick, J., Guz, A., Murphy, K., Semple, S. J. G. 1980. Effect of spinal cord transection on the steady-state ventilatory response to exercise in man. *J. Physiol.* 308:63P
2. Adams, L., Cross, B. A., Frankel, H., Furneaux, R., Garlick, J., Guz, A., Murphy, K., Semple, S. J. G. 1981. The dynamics of the ventilatory response to both voluntary and electrically induced exercise in man: the influence of the spinal cord. *J. Physiol.* 310:67P
3. Ahlborg, G., Felig, P. 1982. Lactate and glucose exchange across the forearm, legs, and splanchnic bed during and after prolonged leg exercise. *J. Clin. Invest.* 69:45–54
4. Askanazi, J., Milic-Emili, J., Broell, J. R., Hyman, A. I., Kinney, J. M. 1979. Influence of exercise and CO_2 on breathing pattern of normal man *J. Appl. Physiol.* 47:192–96
5. Asmussen, E. 1973. Ventilation at transition from rest to exercise. *Acta Physiol. Scand.* 89:68–78
6. Asmussen, E., Chiodi, H. 1941. The effect of hypoxemia on ventilation and circulation in man. *Am. J. Physiol.* 132:426–36
7. Asmussen, E., Neilsen, M. 1957. Ventilatory response to CO_2 during work at normal and at low oxygen tensions. *Acta Physiol. Scand.* 39:27–35
8. Bainton, C. R. 1972. Effect of speed vs. grade and shivering on ventilation in dogs during active exercise. *J. Appl. Physiol.* 33:778–87
9. Band, D. M., Wolff, C. B., Ward, J., Cochrane, G. M., Prior, J. 1980. Respiratory oscillations in arterial carbon dioxide tension as a control signal in exercise. *Nature* 283:84–85
10. Bellville, J. W., Whipp, B. J., Kaufman, R. D., Swanson, G. D., Aqleh, K. A., Wiberg, D. M. 1979. Central and peripheral chemoreceptor loop gain in normal and carotid body resected subjects. *J. Appl. Physiol.* 46:843–53
11. Bennett, F. M., Reischl, P., Grodins, F. S., Yamashiro, S. M., Fordyce, W. E. 1981. Dynamics of ventilatory response to exercise in humans. *J. Appl. Physiol.* 51:194–203
12. Bledsoe, S. W., Hornbein, T. F. 1981. Central chemosensors and the regulation of their chemical environment. In *Regulation of Breathing*, ed. T. F. Hornbein, Part 1, pp. 347–428. Basel: Marcel Dekker. 1436 pp.

13. Brackett, N. C., Cohen, J. J., Schwartz, W. B. 1965. Carbon dioxide titration curve of normal man: effect of increasing degrees of acute hypercapnia on acid-base equilibrium. *N. Engl. J. Med.* 272:6–12
14. Bradley, B. L., Mestas, J., Forman, J., Unger, K. M. 1980. The effect on respiratory drive of a prolonged physical conditioning program. *Am. Rev. Respir. Dis.* 122:741–46
14a. Bye, P. T. P., Farkas, G. A., Roussos, C. 1983. Respiratory factors limiting exercise. *Ann. Rev. Physiol.* 45: In press
15. Casaburi, R., Whipp, B. J., Wasserman, K., Beaver, W. L., Koyal, S. N. 1977. Ventilatory and gas exchange dynamics in response to sinusoidal work. *J. Appl. Physiol.* 42:300–11
16. Chapman, R. W., Santiago, T. V., Edelman, N. H. 1980. Brain hypoxia and control of breathing: neuromechanical control. *J. Appl. Physiol.* 49:497–505
17. Christensen, N. J., Galbo, H., Hansen, J. F., Hesse, B., Richter, E. A., Trap-Jensen, J. 1979. Catecholamines and exercise. *Diabetes* 28:(Suppl. 1) 58–62
18. Clancy, L. J., Critchley, J. A. J. H., Leitch, A. G., Kirby, B. J., Ungar, A., Flenley, D. C. 1975. Arterial catecholamines in hypoxic exercise in man. *Clin Sci. Mol. Med.* 49:503–6
19. Clark, T. J. H., Godfrey, S. 1969. The effect of CO_2 on ventilation and breath-holding during exercise and while breathing through an added resistance. *J. Physiol* 201:551–66
20. Clark, J. M., Sinclair, R. D., Lenox, J. B. 1980. Chemical and nonchemical components of ventilation during hypercapnic exercise in man. *J. Appl. Physiol.* 48:1065–76
21. Cross, B. A., Davey, A., Guz, A., Katona, P. G., MacLean, M., Murphy, K., Semple, S. J. G., Stidwill, R. 1982. The pH oscillations in arterial blood during exercise; a potential signal for the ventilatory response in the dog. *J. Physiol.* 329:57–73
22. Cross, B. A., Davey, A., Guz, A., Katona, P. G., MacLean, M., Murphy, K., Semple, S. J. G., Stidwill, R. 1982. The role of spinal cord transmission in the ventilatory response to electrically induced exercise in the anaesthetised dog. *J. Physiol.* 329:37–55
23. Cunningham, D. J. C. 1974. The control system regulating breathing in man. *Q. Rev. Biophys.* 6:433–83
24. Cunningham, D. J. C., Hey, E. N., Patrick, J. M., Lloyd, B. B. 1963. The effect

of noradrenaline infusion on the relation between pulmonary ventilation and the alveolar P_{O_2} and P_{CO_2} in man. *Ann. NY Acad. Sci.* 109:756–71

25. Cunningham, D. J. C., Lloyd, B. B., Spurr, D. 1966. The relationship between the increase in breathing during the first respiratory cycle in exercise and the prevailing background of chemical stimulation. *J. Physiol.* 185:73–75P

26. Davis, J. A., Whipp, B. J., Wasserman, K. 1980. The relation of ventilation to metabolic rate during moderate exercise in man. *Eur. J. Appl. Physiol.* 44:97–108

27. Dejours, P., Mithoefer, J. C., Labrousse, Y. 1957. Influence of local chemical change on ventilatory stimulus from the legs during exercise. *J. Appl. Physiol.* 10:372–75

28. Derks, C. M. 1980. Ventilation-perfusion distribution in young and old volunteers during mild exercise. *Bull. Eur. Physiopath. Respir.* 16:145–54

29. Donald, K. W., Wormald, P. N., Taylor, S. H., Bishop, J. M. 1957. Changes in the oxygen content of femoral venous blood and leg blood flow during leg exercise in relation to cardiac output response. *Clin. Sci.* 16:567–91

30. Duncan, G., Johnson, R. H., Lambie, D. G. 1981. Role of sensory nerves in the cardiovascular and respiratory changes with isometric forearm exercise in man. *Clin. Sci.* 60:145–55

31. Eldridge, F. L. 1972. The importance of timing on the respiratory effects of intermittent carotid sinus nerve stimulation. *J. Physiol.* 222:319–33

32. Eldridge, F. L., Millhorn, D. E., Waldrop, T. G. 1981. Exercise hyperpnea and locomotion: parallel activation from the hypothalamus. *Science* 211:844–46

33. Flandrois, R., Favier, R., Pequignot, J. M. 1977. Role of adrenaline in gas exchanges and respiratory control in the dog at rest and exercise. *Respir. Physiol.* 30:291–303

34. Flandrois, R., Lacour, J. R., Eclache, J. P. 1974. Control of respiration in exercising dog: interaction of chemical and physical humoral stimuli. *Respir. Physiol.* 21:169–81

35. Flenley, D. C., Brash, H., Clancy, L., Cooke, N. J., Leitch, A. G., Middleton, W., Wraith, P. K. 1979. Ventilatory response to steady-state exercise in hypoxia in humans *J. Appl. Physiol.* 46:438–46

36. Gardner, W. N. 1980. The pattern of breathing following step changes of alveolar partial pressures of carbon dioxide and oxygen in man. *J. Physiol.* 300:55–73

37. Gautier, H. 1980. Control of the pattern of breathing. *Clin. Sci.* 58:343–48

38. Gledhill, N., Froese, A. B., Dempsey, J. A. 1977. Ventilation to perfusion distribution during exercise in health. In *Muscular Exercise and the Lung*, ed. J. A. Dempsey, C. F. Reed, pp. 325–43. Madison: Univ. Wisc. Press

39. Haldane, J. S., Priestley, J. G. 1905. The regulation of the lung-ventilation. *J. Physiol.* 32:225–66

40. Hebbel, R. P., Kronenberg, R. S., Eaton, J. W. 1977. Hypoxic ventilatory response in subjects with normal and high oxygen affinity hemoglobins. *J. Clin. Invest.* 60:1211–15

41. Hesse, B., Kanstrup, I. L., Christensen, N. J., Ingemann-Hansen, T., Hansen, J. F., Halkjaer-Kristensen, J., Petersen, F. B. 1981. Reduced norepinephrine response to dynamic exercise in human subjects during O_2 breathing. *J. Appl. Physiol.* 51:176–78

42. Hickam, J. B., Pryor, W. W., Page, E. B., Atwell, R. J. 1951. Respiratory regulation during exercise in unconditioned subjects. *J. Clin. Invest.* 30:503–16

43. Hirshman, C. A., McCullough, R. E., Weil, J. V. 1975. Normal values for hypoxic and hypercapnic ventilatory drives in man. *J. Appl. Physiol.* 38:1095–98

44. Honda, Y., Myojo, S., Hasegawa, S., Hasegawa, T., Severinghaus, J. W. 1979. Decreased exercise hyperpnea in patients with bilateral carotid chemoreceptor resection. *J. Appl. Physiol.* 46:908–12

45. Hornbein, T. F., Roos, A. 1962. Effect of mild hypoxia on ventilation during exercise. *J. Appl. Physiol.* 17:239–42

46. Hulsbosch, M. A. M., Binkhorst, R. A., Folgering, H. T. 1981. Effects of positive and negative exercise on ventilatory CO_2 sensitivity. *Eur. J. Appl. Physiol.* 47:73–81

47. Jammes, Y., Fornaris, M., Guillot, C., Grimaud, C. 1979. Pattern of the ventilatory response to transient hypoxia in man: differences from transient hypercapnic test. *Arch. Int. Physiol. Biochim.* 87:229–43

48. Jennett, S., McKay, F. C., Moss, V. A. 1981. The human ventilatory response to stimulation by transient hypoxia *J. Physiol.* 315:339–51

49. Jones, P. W., French, W., Weissman, M. L., Wasserman, K. 1981. Ventilatory responses to cardiac output

changes in patients with pacemakers. *J. Appl. Physiol.* 51:1103–7

50. Deleted in proof

51. Krogh, A., Lindhard, J. 1913–1914. The regulation of respiration and circulation during the initial stages of muscular work. *J. Physiol.* 47:112–36

52. Lahiri, S., Gelfand, R. 1981. Mechanisms of acute ventilatory responses. See Ref. 12, Part II, pp. 773–843

53. Lahiri, S., Mulligan, E., Nishino, T., Mokashi, A., Davies, R. O. 1981. Relative responses of aortic body and carotid body chemoreceptors to carboxyhemoglobinemia. *J. Appl. Physiol.* 50:580–86

54. Loeschcke, H. H., Koepchen, H. P., Gertz, K. H. 1958. Über den Einfluss von Wasserstoffionenkonzentration und CO₂-Druck im Liquor cerebrospinalis auf die Atmung. *Pflügers Arch.* 266: 569–85

55. Lloyd, B. B., Jukes, M. G. M., Cunningham, D. J. C. 1958. The relation between alveolar oxygen pressure and the respiratory response to carbon dioxide in man. *Q. J. Exp. Physiol.* 43: 214–27

56. Lugliani, R., Whipp, B. J., Seard, C., Wasserman, K. 1971. Effect of bilateral carotid-body resection on ventilatory control at rest and during exercise in man. *N. Engl. J. Med.* 285:1105–11

57. Mahler, M. 1979. Neural and humoral signals for pulmonary ventilation arising in exercising muscle. *Med. Sci. Sports* 11:191–97

58. Martin, B. J., Weil, J. V., Sparks, K. E., McCullough, R. E., Grover, R. F. 1978. Exercise ventilation correlates positively with ventilatory chemoresponsiveness. *J. Appl. Physiol.* 45:557–64

59. Masson, R. G., Lahiri, S. 1974. Chemical control of ventilation during hypoxic exercise. *Respir. Physiol.* 22: 241–62

60. McCloskey, D. I., Mitchell, J. H. 1972. Reflex cardiovascular and respiratory responses originating in exercising muscle. *J. Physiol.* 224:173–86

61. Metias, E. F., Cunningham, D. J. C., Howson, M. G., Petersen, E. S., Wolff, C. B. 1981. Reflex effects on human breathing of breath-by-breath changes of the time profile of alveolar Pco₂ during steady hypoxia. *Pflügers Arch.* 389:243–50

62. Miller, M. J., Tenney, S. M. 1975. Hypoxia-induced tachypnea in carotid-deafferented cats. *Respir. Physiol.* 23: 31–39

63. Mitchell, J. H., Reardon, W. C., McCloskey, D. I. 1977. Reflex effects on

circulation and respiration from contracting skeletal muscle. *Am. J. Physiol.* 233:H374–78

64. Miyamura, M., Folgering, H. T., Binkhorst, R. A., Smolders, F. D. J., Kreuzer, F. 1976. Ventilatory response to CO₂ at rest and during positive and negative work in normoxia and hyperoxia. *Pflügers Arch.* 364:7–15

65. Morrill, C. G., Meyer, J. R., Weil, J. V. 1975. Hypoxic ventilatory depression in dogs. *J. Appl. Physiol.* 38:143–46

66. Myhre, K., Andersen, K. L. 1971. Respiratory responses to static muscular work. *Respir. Physiol.* 12:77–89

67. Phillipson, E. A., Bowes, G., Townsend, E. R., Duffin, J., Cooper, J. D. 1981. Role of metabolic CO₂ production in ventilatory response to steady-state exercise. *J. Clin. Invest.* 68:768–74

68. Phillipson, E. A., Duffin, J., Cooper, J. D. 1981. Critical dependence of respiratory rhythmicity on metabolic CO₂ load. *J. Appl. Physiol.* 50:45–54

69. Ponte, J., Purves, M. J. 1978. Carbon dioxide and venous return and their interaction as stimuli to ventilation in the cat. *J. Physiol.* 274:455–75

70. Porte, D., Crawford, D. W., Jennings, D. B., Aber, C., McIlroy, M. B. 1966. Cardiovascular and metabolic responses to exercise in a patient with McArdle's Syndrome. *N. Engl. J. Med.* 275:406–12

71. Read, D. J. C. 1967. A clinical method for assessing the ventilatory response to CO₂. *Aust. Ann. Med.* 16:20–32

72. Read, D. J. C., Leigh, J. 1967. Blood-brain tissue Pco₂ relationships and ventilation during rebreathing. *J. Appl. Physiol.* 23:53–70

73. Rebuck, A. S., Slutsky, A. S. 1981. Measurement of ventilatory responses to hypercapnia and hypoxia. See Ref. 12., Part II, pp. 745–72

74. Rebuck, A. S., Woodley, W. E. 1975. Ventilatory effects of hypoxia and their dependence on Pco₂. *J. Appl. Physiol.* 38:16–19

75. Roughton, F. J. W., Darling, R. C. 1944. The effect of carbon monoxide on the oxyhemoglobin dissociation curve. *Am. J. Physiol.* 141:17–31

76. Deleted in proof

77. Santiago, T. V., Edelman, N. H. 1976. Mechanism of the ventilatory response to carbon monoxide. *J. Clin. Invest.* 57:977–86

78. Sargeant, A. J., Rouleau, M. Y., Sutton, J. R., Jones, N. L. 1981. Ventilation in exercise studied with circulatory occlusion. *J. Appl. Physiol.* 50:718–23

79. Saunders, K. B. 1980. Oscillations of arterial CO_2 tension in a respiratory model: some implications for the control of breathing in exercise. *J. Theor. Biol.* 84:163–79

80. Saunders, K. B., Bali, H. N., Carson, E. R. 1980. A breathing model of the respiratory system: the controlled system. *J. Theor. Biol.* 84:135–61

81. Schaeffer, K. E. 1979. Physiological stresses related to hypercapnia during patrols on submarines. *Undersea Biomed. Res.* 6:(Suppl. S) 15–47

82. Schlaefke, M. E. 1981. Central chemosensitivity: a respiratory drive. *Rev. Physiol. Biochem. Pharmacol.* 90:171–244

83. Sinclair, R. D., Clark, J. M., Welch, B. E. 1971. Comparison of physiological responses of normal man to exercise in air and in acute and chronic hypercapnia. In *Underwater Physiology,* ed. C. J. Lambertsen, pp. 409–17. London: Academic. 575 pp.

83a. Sutton, J. R., Pugh, L. G. C. E., Jones, N. 1983. Exercise at altitude. *Ann. Rev. Physiol.* 45: In press

84. Szlyk, P. C., McDonald, B. W., Pendergast, D. R., Krasney, J. A. 1981. Control of ventilation during graded exercise in the dog. *Respir. Physiol.* 46: 345–65

85. Tibes, U. 1977. Reflex inputs to the cardiovascular and respiratory centers from dynamically working canine muscles. *Circ. Res.* 41:332–41

86. Tibes, U., Hemmer, B., Böning, D. 1977. Heart rate and ventilation in relation to venous [K^+], osmolality, pH, P_{CO_2}, P_{O_2}, [orthophosphate], and [lactate] at transition from rest to exercise in athletes and non-athletes. *Eur. J. Appl. Physiol.* 36:127–40

87. Twentyman, O. P., Disley, A., Gribbin, H. R., Alberti, K. G. M. M., Tattersfield, A. E. 1981. Effect of β-adrenergic blockade on respiratory and metabolic responses to exercise. *J. Appl. Physiol.* 51:788–93

88. Vidruk, E. H., Dempsey, J. A. 1980. Peripheral and central nervous system mechanisms controlling exercise-induced breathing patterns. *Exer. Sport Sci. Rev.* 8:129–47

89. Vogel, J. A., Gleser, M. A. 1972. Effect of carbon monoxide on oxygen transport during exercise. *J. Appl. Physiol.* 32:234–39

90. Wade, O. L., Bishop, J. M., Donald, K. W. 1954. The effect of mitral valvotomy on cardio-respiratory function. *Clin. Sci.* 13:511–33

91. Ward, S. A. 1979. The effects of sudden airway hypercapnia on the initiation of exercise hyperpnoea in man. *J. Physiol.* 296:203–14

92. Wasserman, K., Whipp, B. J., Casaburi, R., Beaver, W. L. 1977. Carbon dioxide flow and exercise hyperpnea: cause and effect. *Am. Rev. Respir. Dis.* 115:225–37 (Suppl.)

93. Wasserman, K., Whipp, B. J., Casaburi, R., Golden, M., Beaver, W. L. 1979. Ventilatory control during exercise in man. *Bull. Eur. Physiopath. Respir.* 15:27–47

94. Wasserman, K., Whipp, B. J., Koyal, S. N., Cleary, M. G. 1975. Effect of carotid body resection on ventilatory and acid-base control during exercise. *J. Appl. Physiol.* 39:354–58

95. Weil, J. V., Byrne-Quinn, E., Sodal, I. E., Friesen, W. O., Underhill, B., Filley, G. F., Grover, R. F. 1970. Hypoxic ventilatory drive in normal man. *J. Clin. Invest.* 49:1061–72

96. Weil, J. V., Byrne-Quinn, E., Sodal, I. E., Kline, J. S., McCullough, R. E., Filley, G. F. 1972. Augmentation of chemosensitivity during mild exercise in normal man. *J. Appl. Physiol.* 33:813–19

97. Weiskopf, R. B., Gabel, R. A. 1975. Depression of ventilation during hypoxia in man. *J. Appl. Physiol.* 39:911–15

98. Weissman, M. L., Whipp, B. J., Huntsman, D. J., Wasserman, K. 1980. Role of neural afferents from working limbs in exercise hyperpnea. *J. Appl. Physiol.* 49:239–48

99. Whipp, B. J. 1981. The control of exercise hyperpnea. See Ref. 12, Part II, pp. 1069–1139

100. Woodson, R. D., Wills, R. E., Lenfant, C. 1978. Effect of acute and established anemia on O_2 transport at rest, submaximal and maximal work. *J. Appl. Physiol.* 44:36–43

101. Yamamoto, W. S. 1960. Mathematical analysis of the time course of alveolar CO_2. *J. Appl. Physiol.* 15:215–19

102. Zhong, N. S., Morgan, A. C., Walker, J., Flenley, D. C. 1981. Effect of carbon monoxide on the oxygen dissociation curve and oxygen transport in patients with chronic bronchitis. *Clin. Sci.* 60:18–19P

Ann. Rev. Physiol. 1983. 45:427-37

EXERCISE AT ALTITUDE

John R. Sutton and Norman L. Jones

Department of Medicine, McMaster University, Hamilton, Ontario, Canada

L. Griffith C. E. Pugh

Department of Medicine, University College London Medical School, London, United Kingdom

INTRODUCTION

The outstanding recent event in high-altitude physiology was the "natural" experiment of Habeler and Messner, who climbed Everest without supplementary oxygen (15, 29). This feat has been repeated a number of times, the most remarkable being Messner's solo ascent in 1980. Here we examine exercise at extreme altitude through the Habeler/Messner achievement. We estimate the physiological demands and review the mechanisms that enabled the climbers to meet them. Although we concentrate on significant work published in the past 3–5 years, information obtained previously is reviewed in the light of other recent advances in respiratory physiology.

Many scientific observations have been made at high altitudes in recent years, including some on the summit of Mt. Everest (45, 55). The most comprehensive data on exercise at extreme altitude remain those obtained on Everest in 1953 (36, 37) and on Makalu during the "Silver Hut" expedition in 1960–61 (14, 39, 54).

A number of monographs (19, 21, 53), reviews (7, 10, 11, 24, 25), and symposium proceedings (4, 27, 50) deal comprehensively with the general topic of high-altitude physiology. Although exercise may be implicated in the pathogenesis of a number of high-altitude problems such as acute mountain sickness, pulmonary edema (48), and high-altitude retinal hemorrhage (28), the pathophysiology of altitude illness is not addressed here.

427

0066-4278/83/0315-0427$02.00

BAROMETRIC PRESSURE AND ALTITUDE

Barometric pressure measurements on high mountains in many parts of the world are higher than would be expected from the international altimeter calibration (IAC) formula (36). Extrapolation from measurements on Everest in 1953 at 7315 m and on Makalu in 1961 at 7830 m indicated a barometric pressure on the summit of Everest of approximately 250 mm Hg compared with the 236 mm Hg calculated by the IAC formulae used in decompression chamber experiments. A value of 250–253 mm Hg was confirmed in 1981 by Chris Pizzo on an American scientific expedition led by John West. This pressure is 14–17 mm Hg higher than that predicted from the IAC formulae, thus making the "physiological" altitude of Everest some 500 m lower than its surveyed altitude.

EXERCISE CAPACITY AT ALTITUDE

Exercise capacity becomes increasingly impaired as barometric pressure falls below 400 mm Hg (above 4500 m). Using data from the "Silver Hut" expedition West & Wagner (56) have predicted a $\dot{V}O_2$ max at Everest's summit of about 350–500 ml min^{-1} and certainly less than 700 ml min^{-1}. These predictions were for climbers with a sea level $\dot{V}O_2$max of 50 ml kg^{-1} min^{-1}, the average for Himalayan mountaineers of the 1950s and 1960s (38). They explain why such mountaineers were unable to climb Everest and return safely without supplementary oxygen. While no physiological measurements are available for Habeler and Messner, we know that in training Messner has climbed vertically 1000 m in 34 minutes. This rate of climbing represents a power output of about 1800 kpm min^{-1} or about 3.9 liters min^{-1} O_2 intake. Assuming that no more than 75–80% $\dot{V}O_2$max may be sustained for this length of time, these values imply a $\dot{V}O_2$max of 4.9–5.2 liters min^{-1} or 77–81 ml kg^{-1} min^{-1}. This is 40–50% greater than climbers on the "Silver Hut" expedition and about 25–30% higher than top Himalayan mountaineers of the 1980s (J. Milledge, personal communication).

If Habeler's and Messner's 50% increase in $\dot{V}O_2$max above that of average mountaineers at sea level was maintained at extreme altitude it would have resulted in a $\dot{V}O_2$max of 10.5 ml kg^{-1} min^{-1} on Everest's summit compared with 5–7 ml kg^{-1} min^{-1} estimated by Wagner & West (56) for the "Silver Hut" mountaineers. Such a value of about 10–12 ml O_2 kg^{-1} min^{-1}, or about 1 liter min^{-1}, can also be estimated from the detailed description of their climb (15, 28), making it possible for Messner and Habeler to climb Everest without supplementary oxygen.

While the measurements were not made at such extreme altitudes, a recent paper (12) provides longitudinal data on the remarkable high altitude scientist, D. B. Dill. At age 87 Dill exercised on White Mountain (P_B 485 mm Hg). His $\dot{V}O_2$max was 15 ml kg^{-1} min^{-1}, or 84% of the sea-level value. This altitude reduction was slightly smaller than that observed 43 years earlier when his altitude $\dot{V}O_2$max was 25 ml kg^{-1} min^{-1} and 74% of his sea-level maximum.

OXYGEN TRANSPORT

Control of Ventilation

This topic has been the subject of several recent and exhaustive reviews by Lahiri in 1977 (24) and Dempsey & Forster in 1982 (10). Although most authors claim that the high-altitude native has a blunted hypoxic ventilatory response and ventilates less with exercise (reviewed in 10, 24), two recent reports suggest that some Sherpas may differ from other high-altitude natives. Hackett et al (16) studied 24 Sherpas at 1377 m and 4243 m and found that resting ventilation was higher and $P_{a}CO_2$ lower than in 25 comparable Westerners. Schoene and co-workers (44) studied 10 high-altitude climbers who had been above 25,000 ft, including a Sherpa who has thrice reached Everest's summit, and found they all had normal hypoxic ventilatory responses.

Ventilation

Almost all reports of climbing at extreme altitudes mention marked breathlessness on effort. The smallest changes in gradient or in snow conditions bring the climber to an abrupt halt with breathlessness. This is explained by the increasing steepness of the $\dot{V}_E/\dot{V}O_2$ curve at extreme altitudes; an oxygen uptake of 1.5 liters min^{-1} is met by a $\dot{V}_E$ of 36 liters min^{-1} at sea level but a $\dot{V}_E$ of 122 liters min^{-1} at 7440 m (39).

Because air density decreases at altitude, the work of respiratory muscles against airflow resistance is minimized and is similar to that at sea level in spite of different levels of ventilation.

Ventilation at maximum exercise decreases above an altitude of 5800 m (7, 39). This may be due in part to the increasing hypoxia on exercise, which induces respiratory muscle fatigue. Jardim et al have shown a decreased endurance time and a shift in the power spectrum in the diaphragmatic EMG towards lower frequencies when normal subjects breathed 13% O_2 through a respiratory resistance at 80% of maximum mouth pressure (22).

Alveolar Gas Tensions

The most detailed information on alveolar gas tensions at extreme altitudes is that obtained on the "Silver Hut" expedition at altitudes of up to 7830 m P_B 288 mm Hg (14). Alveolar gas tensions predicted for the summit of Everest from these results were PAO_2 30–32 mm Hg; $P_{a}CO_2$ 10–12 mm Hg.

Applying these results to Habeler and Messner with a $\dot{V}_{O_2}$max 10.5 ml kg^{-1} min^{-1} and assuming an R of 1.0 and a 20% dead space, this implies a maximum exercise ventilation on the summit of Everest of 80–90 liters min^{-1} (BTPS).

Pulmonary Gas Exchange

Although barometric pressure is the most important variable, most authorities agree that diffusing capacity will limit oxygen transfer at extreme altitudes (35, 56). West & Wagner (56) estimate that at a P_B of 250 mm Hg even at rest there would be an alveolar–end capillary P_{O_2} difference of about 6 mm Hg caused by diffusion limitation. This would widen rapidly on exercise because of the accompanying falls in $S\bar{v}_{O_2}$ and decrease in capillary transit time. By increasing diffusing capacity from a normal of 40 ml min^{-1} mm Hg to 100 ml min^{-1} mm Hg, a value measured in Sherpa Dawa Tensing (39), the effective oxygen transfer would be almost doubled on the summit of Everest from 450 to 750 ml min^{-1} mm Hg. It seems likely that Habeler and Messner must have diffusing capacities of this order.

Oxyhemoglobin Dissociation Curve

Monge & Whittenburg (30) have reported a decreased P50 in many animals native to high altitude. In humans native to high altitude the position of the oxyhemoglobin dissociation curve has been reexamined by Winslow and colleagues, who plotted the entire dissociation curve in 46 Peruvians from Morococha P_B 432 mm Hg (57). They demonstrated considerable variability in P50 and found a P50 of 31.2 ± 1.9 mm Hg or 30.1 ± 2.2 mm Hg when corrected to the subjects' plasma pH, a figure not significantly different from sea-level controls of 29.2 ± 1.8 mm Hg. Thus in the physiological setting of their own environment, P50 is the same in native highlanders as in sea level dwellers.

Oxygen Transport, Hemoglobin, Hematocrit, and Cardiac Output

It has long been assumed that a Hb of 20–22 g 100 ml^{-1} in Peruvian highlanders and 18–20 g 100 ml^{-1} in acclimatized mountaineers at 5000–6000 m represented "optimal" adaptations. However, patients with polycythemia vera and chronic mountain sickness are improved by venesection. These observations from clinical medicine led mountaineers and physiologists to ask whether the advantages of the increased Hb and therefore increased oxygen carrying capacity of blood might be outweighed by the disadvantage of an increased viscosity arising from the increased Hct. It is interesting to note that some animals do not depend on this response; the altitude-adapted camelids, llama, alpaca, and vicuna have a Hb and Hct of

14g 100 ml^{-1} and 40%, respectively (43). Similarly, the altitude-acclimatized bar-headed goose has no increase in Hb compared to the sea-level-adapted Pekin duck when both are exposed to an altitude of 5640 m for 4 weeks (1). Thus is the increase in Hb and Hct seen in humans exposed to altitude an optimal response?

In vitro studies show that the viscosity of blood increases linearly with Hct up to 50–60% Hct, above which viscosity increases exponentially. However, Pappenheimer & Maes have shown in vivo that "apparent" viscosity is largely dependent on vasomotor tone (33). More recently Gaehtgens and co-workers (13), using a dog hind limb, showed no impairment of O_2 delivery to muscle with Hcts up to 70%. They suggested that the ideal hematocrit for O_2 delivery during exercise was 50–60%, in contrast to the generally accepted Hcts of 40–45% at rest.

In studies during exercise at altitude Cerretelli (6) measured $\dot{V}_{O_2}$max and estimated maximum O_2 flow ($= \dot{Q}$ max $\times$ Ca$_{O_2}$). He noted that the increase in $\dot{V}_{O_2}$max when subjects breathed 100% oxygen was less than would be expected from the increased Hb and concluded that there may be a peripheral impairment to O_2 uptake, perhaps due to the increased blood viscosity. On this basis it has been argued that bloodletting at altitude should improve performance. Horstman and colleagues (20) performed an experiment to test this idea. They removed 450 ml of blood from nine subjects after three weeks at 4300 m, decreasing Hct from 52.7% to 47.7% compared to a sea-level value of 46.4%. They observed a decrease in $\dot{V}_{O_2}$max in spite of an increase in $\dot{Q}$ max. Thus the effect of reducing oxygen carrying capacity outweighed any effect on peripheral perfusion. It seems unlikely to us that the normally acclimatized and hydrated climber will develop a Hct and blood viscosity that would impair O_2 delivery. It would, therefore, seem unsound to submit climbers to bloodletting even at extreme altitude.

Tissues

The final link in the oxygen transport chain is tissue O_2 transfer. Even after a short stay at altitude marked tissue adaptations are evident. Blanchero has shown that capillary density in dog skeletal muscle doubled in three weeks at P$_B$ 435 mm Hg (624–1262 cap mm^{-2}) (2). The increase in capillary density was even more dramatic in chronically altitude-adapted animals (as muscle fiber diameter was reduced) to 2016 cap mm^{-2}. Using the Krogh model, Blanchero (2) has calculated that these adaptations alone will increase P$_{O_2}$ in the "critical corner" from 16 to 31 mm Hg at P$_B$ of 435 mm Hg. Physiological evidence for an increase tissue capillarity has also been demonstrated by Tenney & Ou (51). Tissue myoglobin stores are well known to increase at altitude and to decrease on relocation to sea level (43).

The importance of myoglobin (58) and cytochrome oxidase and P450 (25) in facilitating O_2 diffusion has recently been stressed.

At the mitochondrial level Ou & Tenney (32) have shown a 40% increase in mitochondrial number, but no increase in mitochondrial size. Harris and co-workers (17) have demonstrated an increase in the activity of the mitochondrial enzyme succinic dehydrogenase in guinea-pig heart at altitude. Both these responses would facilitate aerobic metabolism at altitude.

METABOLISM

The supply of chemical energy for muscle contraction at altitude depends, as it does at sea level, on the continued supply of ATP. As muscle ATP stores are very small, ATP must be resynthesized continually from ADP in a variety of metabolic pathways, the most efficient being the mitochondrial oxidation of fat and carbohydrate. Mitochondrial oxidation of fat yields 131 moles of ATP per mole of fat and carbohydrate yields 37 moles of ATP per mole of glycogen, both being considerably greater than the 3 moles of ATP per mole of glycogen derived from anaerobic glycolysis.

The factors that govern the metabolic pathways for energy supply at altitude are likely to be identical to those operating at sea level and include the following:

Size of Fuel Stores

In a 70 kg man with 10% body fat, muscle triglycerides (11,000 K joules) and glycogen (6,000 K joules) provide readily available energy stores. The liver stores about 1,500 K joules of glycogen, which is available to muscle following glycogenolysis and transport via the bloodstream as glucose. Although by far the greatest energy store consists of adipose tissue triglycerides (560,000 K joules), this must first undergo lipolysis and be solubilized by combination with albumin before being transported to muscle as free fatty acids (FFA). Although there is a considerable store of protein in muscle (160,000 K joules), it does not normally contribute to muscle energy supply.

For mountaineers climbing 10–18 hr day^{-1} at altitude it seems clear that most of the energy is derived from fat, although glycogen is also available for short-term high-intensity exercise. However, after 18 days at a moderate altitude of 4300 m Young and co-workers (59) found that resting muscle glycogen was lower than at sea level. No data are available on liver and muscle glycogen at extreme altitudes, but with many consecutive days of strenuous work and an inadequate caloric intake it would not be surprising if glycogen resynthesis in liver and muscle was reduced. Thus Habeler and Messner would probably have depleted muscle glycogen stores and used fat as their major energy source during their final assault of Everest.

Mobilization of Fuels

The release of FFA from adipose tissue and of glucose from liver are hormonally controlled, principally by catecholamines, but also by glucagon and to a lesser extent glucocorticoids. Insulin inhibits both lipolysis and hepatic glycogenolysis while an elevated lactate inhibits lipolysis (3). Exercise on acute altitude exposure results in an increased plasma concentration of lactate (7), catecholamines (8), and cortisol (47) and a decrease in plasma insulin (47) when compared with the same exercise intensity at sea level. However, because elevations of FFA (23, 47), glycerol (23), and glucose (47) are also observed, it seems likely that the catecholamine effects on lipolysis and hepatic glycogenolysis override any depressive effect of lactate on FFA mobilization (45). As the time spent at altitude increases the net effect on exercise metabolism is that of hypoxia, which interacts with various adaptive processes, especially acid-base changes (31). In spite of increases in hemoglobin and myoglobin that would tend to increase buffering capacity, Cerretelli (7) has shown that there is a lowering of alkali reserve. Thus during exercise the increase in $[H^+]$ is about double that expected for the increased lactate concentration. Nevertheless, the increase in blood lactate with high-altitude exercise is much reduced during submaximal and maximal exercise, when compared to that at sea level (7). Fasting blood glucose (47, 49) and muscle glycogen are lower, and FFA concentrations increase (59). With heavy exercise FFA and glucose increase (49), glycerol shows a marked increase, while muscle glycogenolysis is reduced (59). These findings suggest that in sea-level humans exposed chronically to altitude, fat is the principle fuel for exercise and muscle glycogen resynthesis may be reduced. Whether the latter is an effect of altitude per se or is due to the low caloric intake of high-altitude expeditions is not yet clear.

Metabolic studies in high-altitude natives show changes similar to but more marked than those observed in sea-level humans exposed chronically to altitude. Fasting blood glucose is lower than in their sea-level counterparts (34, 40, 49) and also lower than in sea-level humans exposed chronically to altitude (49). Blood glucose increases with maximum exercise (49), and gluconeogenesis is normal (5). Blood lactate response to maximum exercise is reduced (7) while FFA levels increase (40), although the latter effect appears to be normally regulated as FFA levels are suppressed by a glucose load (49).

Although many of the studies reviewed above indicate the importance of fatty acid oxidation during exercise at altitude, maximum rates of FFA release from adipose tissue (18) are sufficient to support a $\dot{V}O_2$ of only 1.5 liters mm^{-1}, which would, however, be sufficient to meet the energy demands on Everest's summit of about 1 liter mm^{-1}. Nevertheless, for all but the lightest exercise a carbohydrate source is usually important, again stressing the value of adequate caloric dietary replacement during high-altitude climbing.

Activity of Rate-Limiting Enzymes

Rate-limiting enzymes regulate flux in metabolic pathways and so influence the relative use of different pathways. The main regulatory enzymes for carbohydrate metabolism are phosphorylase (glycogen to glucose-1-phosphate); hexokinase (glucose to glucose-6-phosphate); phospofructokinase (fructose-6-phosphate to fructose-1-6-bisphosphate); and pyruvate dehydrogenase (pyruvate to acetyl CoA). The regulatory enzymes for fat metabolism are less well understood but include triglyceride lipase and carnitine parmitoyl transferase (fatty acid transfer across mitochondrial membrane).

When seen in relation to lactate metabolism the importance of rate-limiting enzymes can be appreciated. Although increases in blood lactate concentration with exercise have been interpreted to indicate inadequate tissue oxygen supply, they may also represent an increase in pyruvate formation by glycolysis relative to pyruvate removal through the Krebs cycle. Because the lactate dehydrogenase reaction is always near equilibrium, the activity of pyruvate dehydrogenase (PDH) and the rate of pyruvate oxidation are the main determinants of lactate production in exercise. Recent work by Ward and co-workers (52) indicates that the activation of PDH in muscle is greatest during aerobic exercise and least with isometric exercise when muscle Po_2 is lowest.

The reduced glycogen depletion during exercise at altitude reported by Young and associates (59) also represents metabolic regulation by rate-limiting enzymes. These workers showed an enhanced fat metabolism, which Rennie & Holloszy in rats (41) and Costill et al (9) in humans have shown to spare muscle glycogen, probably by the citrate inhibition of phosphofructokinase and pyruvate dehydrogenase. Although recently refined concepts of metabolic regulation have yet to be applied directly to altitude physiology, they have clear relevance to the capacity to perform work under hypoxic conditions.

CONCLUSION

Most recent work on exercise at altitude has been conducted at moderate altitudes below 4500 m. Little new knowledge of exercise at extreme altitudes has been gained since the 1960s. The most notable exception has been the "experiment" of Habeler and Messner in climbing Everest without supplementary oxygen. This we have reviewed in some detail.

By any criteria Habeler and Messner are exceptional athletes. However, as they climbed the last 48 m to the summit of Everest even they were no doubt at their limits. "We can no longer keep on our feet to rest. . . . Every 10–15 steps we collapse into the snow to rest, then crawl on again." Habeler and Messner have proved that Everest can be climbed without supplementary oxygen—but only just, and with no margin for error.

ACKNOWLEDGMENTS

We wish to thank Uschi Demeter, Peter Habeler, and Reinhold Messner for their cooperation.

Literature Cited

1. Black, C. P., Tenney, S. M. 1980. Oxygen transport during progressive hypoxia in high altitude and sea level water fowl. *Respir. Physiol.* 39:217–39
2. Blanchero, N. 1975. Capillary density of skeletal muscle in dogs exposed to simulated altitude. *Proc. Soc. Exp. Biol. N.Y.* 148:435–439
3. Boyd, A. E., Giamber, S. R., Mager, M., Lebowitz, H. E. 1974. Lactate inhibition of lipolysis in exercising man. *Metabolism* 23:531–42
4. Brendel, W., Zink, R. A. 1982. *High Altitude Physiology and Medicine Symp., Murnau, 1979.* NY: Springer
5. Capderou, A., Polianski, J., Mensch-Dechene, J., Drouet, L., Antezana, G., Zelter, M., Lockhart, A. 1977. Splanchnic blood flow, O₂ consumption; removal of lactate and output of glucose in highlanders. *J. Appl. Physiol. Respir. Envir. Exer. Physiol.* 43:204–10
6. Cerretelli, P. 1976. Limiting factors to oxygen transport on Mt. Everest. *J. Appl. Physiol.* 76:658–67
7. Cerretelli, P. 1980. Gas exchange at high altitude. In *Pulmonary Gas Exchange,* ed. John B. West, 2:97–147. NY: Academic
8. Clancy, L. J., Critchley, J. A. J. H., Leitch, A. G., Kirby, B. J., Ungar, A., Flenley, D. C. 1975. Arterial catecholamines in hypoxic exercise in man. *Clin. Sci.* 49:503–6
9. Costill, D. L., Coyle, E., Dalsky, G., Evans, W., Fink, W., Hoopes, D. 1977. Effects of elevated plasma FFA and insulin on muscle glycogen usage during exercise. *J. Appl. Physiol.: Respir. Envir. Exer. Physiol.* 43:695–99
10. Dempsey, J. A., Forster, H. V. 1982. Mediation of ventilatory adaptations. *Physiol. Rev.* 62:262–346
11. Denison, D. M. 1981. High altitudes and hypoxia. In *Principles and Practice of Human Physiology,* ed. J. S. Weiner,

O. G. Edholm, pp. 241–307. London: Academic
12. Dill, D. B., Hillyard, S. D., Miller, J. 1980. Vital capacity, exercise performance and blood gases at altitude as related to age. *J. Appl. Physiol.: Respir. Envir. Exer. Physiol.* 48:6–9
13. Gaehtgens, P., Kreutz, F., Albrecht, K. H. 1979. Optimal hematocrit for canine skeletal muscle during rhythmic isotonic exercise. *Eur. J. Appl. Physiol.* 41:27–39
14. Gill, M. B., Milledge, J. S., Pugh, L. G. C. E., West, J. B. 1962. Alveolar gas composition at 21,000 and 25,700 ft. (6400–7830 m). *J. Physiol.* 163:373–77
15. Habeler, P. 1979. *Everest: Impossible Victory.* London: Arlington Books
16. Hackett, P. H., Reeves, J. T., Reeves, C. D., Grover, R. F., Rennie, D. 1980. Control of breathing in Sherpas at low and high altitude. *J. Appl. Physiol.: Respir. Envir. Exer. Physiol.* 49:374–79
17. Harris, P., Castillo, Y., Gibson, K., Heath, D., Arias Stella, J. 1970. Succinic and lactic dehydrogenase activity in myocardial homogenates from animals at high and low altitude. *J. Molec. Cell. Cardiol.* 1:189–93
18. Havel, R. J., Pernow, B., Jones, N. L. 1967. Uptake and release of free fatty acids and other metabolites in the legs of exercising men. *J. Appl. Physiol.* 23:90–96
19. Heath, D., Williams, D. R. 1981. *Man at High Altitude: The Pathophysiology of Acclimitization and Adaptation.* London: Churchill Livingstone
20. Horstman, D., Weiskopf, R., Jackson, R. E. 1980. Work capacity during 3 week sojourn at 4,300 m.: effects of relative polycythemia. *J. Appl. Physiol.: Respir. Envir. Exer. Physiol.* 49:311–18
21. Houston, C. S. 1980. *Going High* Burlington: C.S. Houston and American Alpine Club

22. Jardim, J., Farkas, G., Prefaut, C., Thomas, D., Macklem, P. T., Roussos, C. H. 1980. The failing inspiratory muscles under normoxic and hypoxic conditions. *Am. Rev. Respir. Dis.* 124:274–79

23. Jones, N. L., Robertson, D. G., Kane, J. W., Hart, R. A. 1972. Effect of hypoxia on free fatty acid metabolism during exercise. *J. Appl. Physiol.* 33:733–38

24. Lahiri, S. 1977. Physiological responses and adaptations to high altitude. *Int. Rev. Physiol.* 15:217–51

25. Lenfant, C., Sullivan, K. 1971. Adaptation to high altitude. *N. Engl. J. Med.* 284:1298–309

26. Longmuir, I. S., Pashko, L. 1977. The role of facilitated diffusion of oxygen in tissue hypoxia. *Int. J. Biometerol.* 21:179–87

27. Loeppky, J. A., Riedesel, M. L. 1982. *Oxygen Transport to Human Tissues.* NY: Elsevier Biomedical

28. McFadden, D. M., Houston, C. S., Sutton, J. R., Powles, A. C. P., Gray, G. W., Roberts, R. S. 1981. High altitude retinopathy. *J. Am. Med. Assoc.* 245:581–86

29. Messner, R. 1979. *Everest: Expedition to the Ultimate.* London: Kaye & Ward

30. Monge, C. C., Whittembury, J. 1974. Increased hemoglobin—oxygen affinity at extremely high altitude. *Science* 186:843–45

31. Newsholme, E. A., Jones, N. L. 1982. Hypoxia and acid base interaction on intermediary metabolism. See Ref. 50, pp. 29–37

32. Ou, L. C., Tenney, S. M. 1970. Properties of mitochondria from hearts of cattle acclimatized to high altitude. *Respir. Physiol.* 8:151–59

33. Pappenheimer, J. R., Maes, J. P. 1942. A quantitative measure of the vasomotor tone in the hindlimb muscles of the dog. *Am. J. Physiol.* 137:187–99

34. Picon-Reategui, E. 1963. Intravenous glucose tolerance test at sea level and at high altitudes. *J. Clin. Endocrinol. Metab.* 23:1256–61

35. Piiper, J., Scheid, P. 1981. Model for capillary-alveolar equilibrium with special reference to O_2 uptake in hypoxia. *Respir. Physiol.* 46:193–208

36. Pugh, L. G. C. E. 1957. Resting ventilation and alveolar air on Mount Everest; with remarks on the relationship of barometric pressure to altitude in mountains. *J. Physiol.* 135:590–610

37. Pugh, L. G. C. E. 1958. Muscular exercise on Mount Everest. *J. Physiol.* 141:233–61

38. Pugh, L. G. C. E. 1972. Maximal oxygen intake in Himalayan mountaineers. *Ergonomics* 15:133–37

39. Pugh, L. G. C. E., Gill, M. B., Lahiri, S., Milledge, J. S., Ward, M. P., West, J. B. 1964. Muscular exercise at great altitudes. *J. Appl. Physiol.* 19:431–40

40. Raynaud, J., Drouet, L., Martineaud, J. P., Bordachar, J., Coudert, J., Durand, J. Jr. 1981. Time course of plasma growth hormone during exercise in humans at altitude. *J. Appl. Physiol.: Respir. Envir. Exer. Physiol.* 50:229–33

41. Rennie, J. J., Holloszy, J. O. 1977. Inhibition of glucose uptake and glycogenolysis by availability of oleate in well oxygenated perfused skeletal muscle. *Biochem. J.* 168:161–70

42. Reynafarje, C. 1966. Physiological Patterns: hematological aspects. In *Life at High Altitude. Scientific Publications No. 140,* p. 32. Washington DC: Pan Am. Health Org.

43. Reynafarje, C., Faura, J., Villavicencio, D., Curaca, A., Reynafarje, B., Oyola, L., Contreras, L., Vallenas, E., Faura, A. 1975. Oxygen transport of hemoglobin in high altitude animals. (Camelidae) *J. Appl. Physiol.* 38:806–10

44. Schoene, R. B., Saxon, R., Pierson, D. J. 1981. Control of ventilation in climbers at extreme altitude. See Ref. 50, p. 195

45. Shi, Z. Y., Ning, X. H., Zhu, S. C., Zhao, D. M., Huang, P. G., Yang, S. Y., Wang, Y., Dong, D. S. 1980. Electrocardiogram made on ascending the Mount Qomolangma from 50 m a.s. 1. *Sci. Sin.* 23:1316–25

46. Stock, M. J., Chapman, C., Stirling, J. L., Campbell, I. J. 1978. Effects of exercise, altitude and food on blood hormone and metabolite levels. *J. Appl. Physiol.: Respir. Envir. Exer. Physiol.* 45:350–54

47. Sutton, J. R. 1977. Effect of acute hypoxia on the hormonal response to exercise. *J. Appl. Physiol.: Respir. Envir. Exer. Physiol.* 42:587–92

48. Sutton, J. R. 1983. High altitude pathophysiology. In *Seminars in Respiratory Medicine.* NY: Thieme Stratton

49. Sutton, J. R., Garmendia, F. 1982. Hormonal responses to exercise at altitude in sea level and mountain man. See Ref. 4, pp. 165–71

50. Sutton, J. R., Jones, N. L., Houston, C. S., eds. 1982. *Hypoxia: Man at Altitude.* NY: Thieme Stratton

51. Tenney, S. M., Ou, L. C. 1970. Physiological evidence for increased tissue

capillarity in rats acclimatized to high altitude. *Respir. Physiol.* 8:137–50
52. Ward, G. R., Sutton, J. R., Jones, N. L., Toews, C. J. 1982. Activation by exercise of human skeletal muscle pyruvate dehydrogenase in vivo. *Clin. Sci.* 63:87–92
53. Ward, M. 1975. *Mountain Medicine.* London: Crosby Lockwood, Staples
54. West, J. B., Lahiri, S., Gill, M. B., Milledge, J. S., Pugh, L.G.C.E., Ward, M. P. 1962. Arterial oxygen saturation during exercise at high altitude. *J. Appl. Physiol.* 17:617–21
55. West, J. B. 1982. Man at extreme altitude. *J. Appl. Physiol.: Respir. Envir. Exer. Physiol.* 52:1393–99
56. West, J. B., Wagner, P. D. 1980. Predicted gas exchange on the summit of

Mt. Everest. *Respir. Physiol.* 42:1–16
57. Winslow, R. M., Monge, C. C., Stratham, N. J., Gibson, C. G., Charache, S., Whittembury, J., Moran, O., Berger, R. L. 1981. Variability of oxygen affinity of blood—human subjects native to high altitude. *J. Appl. Physiol.: Respir. Envir. Exer. Physiol.* 51:1411–16
58. Wittenberg, J. B. 1970. Myoglobin-facilitated oxygen diffusion: role of myoglobin in oxygen entry in muscle. *Physiol. Rev.* 50:559–636
59. Young, A. J., Evans, W. J., Cymerman, A., Pandolf, K. B., Knapik, J. J., Maher, J. T. 1982. Sparing effect of chronic high altitude exposure on muscle glycogen utilization during exercise. *J. Appl. Physiol.: Respir. Envir. Exer. Physiol.* 52:857–62

Ann. Rev. Physiol. 1983. 45:439–51

RESPIRATORY FACTORS LIMITING EXERCISE

P. T. P. Bye, G. A. Farkas, and Ch. Roussos[1]

Meakins-Christie Laboratories, McGill University Clinic, Royal Victoria Hospital, Montreal, Quebec, Canada

INTRODUCTION

While in patients with lung disease the respiratory system may limit exercise capacity (26–28, 42, 53), traditionally the ventilatory system has not been thought to limit exercise in normal subjects. Much of the experimental evidence required to pronounce the respiratory system as guilty or innocent of imposing limits to exercise performance is not available. Thus this review must be in part theoretical.

A prime function of the respiratory system during exercise is to supply oxygen to the working muscles via the circulatory system. The respiratory system may fail directly or indirectly in this vital function and thus may limit exercise. Indirect failure would occur if any additional oxygen provided by an increase in ventilation were taken up by the ventilatory muscles, thus depriving the rest of the body of O_2. Direct failure would occur if the lung and chest wall were to fail to provide sufficient ventilation to oxygenate the blood adequately or if inefficiency of gas exchange were to lead to arterial hypoxemia. Lastly, although ventilation might be temporarily adequate, the onset of respiratory muscle fatigue could eventually cause ventilatory insufficiency and arterial hypoxemia.

PULMONARY GAS EXCHANGE

In normal subjects severe hypoxia is associated with a reduced maximum working capacity (23), reduced maximum oxygen consumption ($\dot{V}o_2max$) (9, 15, 23), and decreased endurance time (15). In terms of respiratory limitation to exercise performance, a fundamental question is whether or not efficient gas exchange occurs in the lung. Arterial hypoxemia and increased alveolar to arterial oxygen gradient ($AaDO_2$) can result from any

[1] Ch. Roussos is a Scholar of the Medical Research Council of Canada

439

combination of worsening ventilation-perfusion inequality, anatomical shunt and/or failure of complete transfer of O_2 by diffusion from the alveolus to the pulmonary capillary. During exercise, arterial hypoxemia has been demonstrated in normal humans at altitude (58), in some highly trained athletes (11–13, 19, 48), and in patients with a variety of lung diseases (25, 28). In fact, in patients with interstitial lung disease (ILD) arterial hypoxemia occurs despite exercise ventilations well above the normal range (28).

During hypoxia at simulated altitude it has been shown in dogs that diffusion within the normal lung is not adequate for complete equilibration of Pa_{O_2} between alveolar gas and end-capillary blood either at rest or during exercise (54). West & Wagner (59) predicted the constraints on gas exchange during exercise on the summit of Mount Everest. A striking feature of their analysis was the large alveolar end-capillary P_{O_2} difference during exercise, which was approximately 60% of the P_{O_2} difference between alveolar gas and mixed venous blood.

Wagner (56) studied gas exchange using the multiple inert gas elimination technique during moderate exercise in patients with chronic airflow limitation (CAL) and with ILD who developed arterial hypoxemia with steady-state exercise. In the group with ILD it was evident that not all of this hypoxemia during exercise could be attributed to the observed ventilation-perfusion mismatching. About 15% of the total AaD_{O_2} was thus presumably due to a failure of alveolar end-capillary diffusion equilibration for O_2 in well ventilated and well perfused gas exchange units. Similar findings in patients with ILD were observed independently in a separate study using the same technique (8). In contrast, patients with CAL had no demonstrable diffusion disequilibrium for O_2 during exercise. Thus, exercise in patients with ILD is the only situation in which there is clear evidence for diffusion disequilibrium at sea level (56).

None of the above studies was performed in normal subjects during high intensity exhaustive exercise such as may cause hypoxemia. Unfortunately the multiple inert gas elimination technique requires 5–10 minutes of steady-state conditions and thus could not be used to investigate the fall in arterial oxygen saturation (Sa_{O_2}) (48) and arterial hypoxemia (11–13, 19) that occurs when athletes perform short-duration high-intensity exercise. In the study of Rowell et al (48) the mean Sa_{O_2} percent at end exercise was 85%, while a reduction of 15–40 mm Hg in Pa_{O_2} occurred in some of the athletes studied by Dempsey et al (11–13). In the latter study the athletes who developed arterial hypoxemia showed minimal compensatory hyperventilation during exercise (Pa_{CO_2} was only 1–4 mm Hg below resting levels). In fact it appears that the level of hyperventilation and alveolar oxygen tension determined the degree of arterial hypoxemia since the subjects who hyperventilated least showed the greatest hypoxemia. Dempsey et al (11–13) suggested that the failure to increase ventilation adequately together with the very rapid transit time of some red blood cells through the pulmonary capillary bed could result in a failure of complete diffusion equilibration for oxygen. This explanation remains to be validated.

Irrespective of etiology it is important to note that the hypoxemia of these athletes was corrected when they breathed a mixture of (80%) helium and (20%) oxygen (HeO$_2$) (11–13). The result of breathing the low-density gas mixture was an increase in alveolar ventilation and Pao$_2$. Thus it appears that the respiratory system could have corrected the hypoxemia observed with air breathing if ventilation had increased. Why was there such a sluggish ventilatory response in some of these athletes? The ventilatory responses to CO$_2$ and hypoxia at rest, proposed (14, 33) as a key determinant of ventilation during exercise, were similar for all the athletes and were within the normal range. The contribution of other stimuli to ventilation (temperature, catecholamines, metabolic acidosis) cannot be excluded. However, the fact that the high exercise ventilations (12) of these athletes (range 139–216 liters min^{-1}) were increased with HeO$_2$ suggests that with air breathing, other factors—in particular the mechanics of the respiratory system and/or muscle fatigue or the energetics of respiratory muscle—may have set the ventilation at a lower level at the cost of arterial hypoxemia.

MECHANICS

In patients with CAL the exercise ventilation frequently attains the maximum breathing capacity (MBC) (10, 42). This is considered evidence of a ventilatory limitation to exercise performance. In normal subjects the exercise ventilation is usually less than the MBC, although Ouellet et al (40) have shown conflicting evidence at $\dot{V}o_2$max. However, the use of the MBC as a measure of ventilatory capacity against which to compare exercise ventilation can be questioned. In comparison with heavy exercise, normal subjects breathe at a higher lung volume during the MBC maneuver (36), and consequently a better expiratory flow is attained. An appraisal of the configuration of the tidal flow-volume ($\dot{V}$-V) loop during exercise may provide more appropriate information concerning possible ventilatory limitation. An important question therefore is whether in normals the characteristics of the $\dot{V}$-V curve do or do not constrain ventilation at the lung volume adopted during exercise.

When normal subjects perform moderate exercise there is no indication that the pulmonary characteristics might limit ventilation, since the tidal $\dot{V}$-V loop is situated well within the maximum $\dot{V}$-V curve (22, 26, 52). However, during heavy exercise the tidal loop approaches or attains the maximum $\dot{V}$-V curves at least towards end expiration (36). Furthermore, Grimby et al (22) have shown that athletes performing high-intensity exercise attain their maximum expiratory $\dot{V}$-V curves throughout most of expiration. Thus in these athletes there is a potential mechanical limitation to further increase in the expiratory flow and therefore to an increase in ventilation, unless the athletes increase their lung volume with the deleterious consequences of this strategy. With hyperinflation the inspiratory muscles are put at a mechanical disadvantage as they are shorter and the diaphragm flatter. The elastic work of breathing increases, the efficiency drops, and the vulnerability to fatigue increases (46).

The second alternative by which it would be possible to increase the exercise ventilation without changing lung volume would be to increase the inspiratory flow rates, thus shortening inspiratory time in order to allow sufficient time for expiration. However, studies at high intensities of exercise indicate that the inspiratory flow and pleural pressures are close to the maximum values normals can achieve (22, 36). There appears, therefore, to be a finite limit to which inspiratory flow can be increased. Agostoni & Fenn (1) have suggested that the velocity of airflow in maximal inspiratory efforts is limited by the metabolic force velocity requirements. It is known that muscles must liberate extra energy when they shorten and perform work. Such transformation of chemical energy into mechanical energy has a limiting rate; it follows that with a limited rate of energy available for work, less tension can be maintained at high velocities of contraction than at low velocities. This conclusion is supported by the observation that the alveolar pressure developed during maximal inspiratory efforts is an inverse function of the velocity of airflow. Therefore, the limiting factors to the rate of inspiration may be not only the airway resistance but also the force velocity characteristics of the inspiratory muscles.

If the $\dot{V}$-V curve does indeed provide a limitation to ventilation, it might be anticipated that exercise ventilation would be increased with HeO_2 breathing, and experimental evidence is consistent with this prediction (35, 39, 51, 57, 60). Thus although the energetics requirements of the respiratory muscles may have been improved with HeO_2 owing to a reduction in the resistive work of breathing, (35, 39, 57) it is equally possible that ventilation increases owing to enlargement of the maximum $\dot{V}$-V loop. An understanding of the improvement in ventilation in normal subjects with HeO_2 seems crucial to clarify the role of ventilation as a possible limit to exercise performance.

The studies of Dempsey et al (11–13) did not provide information about the maximum exercise tidal $\dot{V}$-V loops of the athletes. Nevertheless, the ventilation attained in this study was similar to that in the study of Grimby et at (22), in which the maximum $\dot{V}$-V curve was largely attained during exercise. Thus in the subjects studied by Dempsey et al (11–13) the relative hypoventilation can be explained by the following schema: When the maximum expiratory flow volume curves are attained, ventilation is set at relatively low levels with the occurrence of hypoxemia and a lessening of the respiratory alkalosis. This strategy is preferable to breathing at a higher lung volume, which from the point of view of the inspiratory muscles is mechanically disadvantageous and must predispose them to fatigue. Following the same schema it is predictable that on breathing HeO_2 exercise performance along with ventilation will improve. J. A. Dempsey (personal communication) has observed such an improvement, but there are conflicting reports concerning the effect of HeO_2 breathing on endurance performance in normal subjects (51, 60). As endurance performance is known to be determined by a large variety of factors, further clearly defined studies are needed to clarify this issue. In patients with CAL, ventilation tends to increase with HeO_2 compared to air breathing, yet endurance performance remains unchanged (5, 44). Presumably the patients continue to generate inspiratory forces at this higher ventilation that are still equivalent to those generated with air breathing. Thus even an improvement in arterial Po_2 with HeO_2 may not be sufficient either to offset the high energetic requirements for inspiration or to avoid respiratory muscle fatigue. This concept is discussed further in the following sections.

Sound evidence that airflow limitation can limit exercise ventilation and therefore exercise capacity is provided by studies in patients with CAL (10, 26, 42, 53) and in normal subjects breathing dense gases (61). In both groups exercise is terminated at levels of oxygen consumption and heart rate below the predicted maximum values. Both normal subjects during maximum exercise at 4–10 atmospheres and patients with CAL attain their static maximum expiratory flow rates and the exercise ventilation almost invariably equals the MBC. Thus even if other factors may contribute to exercise limitation (fatigue, high energy demands, dyspnea), the $\dot{V}$-V characteristics unquestionably can set a limit and are perhaps the most important determinant.

ENERGETICS

Evidence that oxygen transport limits maximum aerobic capacity is provided by the study of Buick et al (7), which shows a 5% mean increase in $\dot{V}o_2max$ and a 34% increase in running time to exhaustion following erythrocythemia induced after autologous reinfusion of freeze-preserved blood. If the proportion of the total oxygen consumption ($\dot{V}o_2$) going to the respiratory muscles during exercise is high, the amount of O_2 available to the exercising nonrespiratory muscles could be reduced. Therefore a stage could be reached when the $\dot{V}O_2$ during exercise is insufficient to meet the needs of both the respiratory muscles and the other exercising muscles. As a result either the exercising muscles or the respiratory muscles or both would go into oxygen debt and exercise tolerance would be limited.

The respiratory muscles consume little O_2 at low and moderate levels of ventilation (2) and have not been considered as utilizing a substantial fraction of the total energy consumed during exercise. However, at levels of ventilation ($\dot{V}_E$) above 100 liters min^{-1}, the oxygen consumption of the respiratory muscles ($\dot{V}O_2$resp) varies from 2 to 8 ml O_2 liter^{-1} $\dot{V}_E$ (2, 6, 29, 49). Accordingly, during strenuous exercise the $\dot{V}O_2$resp of breathing could vary from 0.5 to more than 1.0 liter min^{-1} (2, 6, 29). In patients with CAL, Levison & Cherniack (27) estimated the $\dot{V}O_2$resp during moderate exercise to be of the order of 9 ml O_2 liter^{-1} $\dot{V}_E$ or 35–40% of $\dot{V}O_2$.

In addition to the above estimates of $\dot{V}O_2$ resp via analysis of expired gas, blood flow experiments also confirm the high energy requirements of the respiratory muscles during both loaded breathing and exercise. Fixler et al (16) demonstrated in the dog that the greatest increase in organ perfusion during moderate exercise occurred in muscles involved with respiration, and reported a six-fold increase in blood flow to the diaphragm to a level of about 100 ml min^{-1} per 100 g muscle tissue. At high levels of exercise the percentage of the total blood flow to the respiratory muscles would be further increased as accessory muscles of respiration are recruited and require an increased blood flow. In experiments with increasing respiratory resistive loads, Robertson et al (45) measured the blood flow to the diaphragm at about 200 ml per 100 g muscle, and failed to demonstrate any plateau in blood flow with increasing loads. Furthermore, B. Buchler and Ch. Roussos (unpublished observations) found that in the dog blood flow to the diaphragm can be increased to 300–400 ml min^{-1} per 100 mg muscle tissue during the electrophrenic stimulation.

If Robertson et al's (45) value of diaphragmatic blood flow is considered in a theoretical calculation to be representative of the average blood flow to the entire respiratory muscle mass, which is about 4 kg in a 70 kg man, then 8 liters of blood might perfuse the respiratory muscles per minute during heavy exercise. Further, if the arteriovenous difference in O_2 content is presumed to be 15 vols %, then the $\dot{V}O_2$ resp would be 1.2 liters min^{-1} (or 1.6 liters min^{-1} for complete desaturation), which would represent at least 25% of $\dot{V}O_2$max in a young man. The conclusion that the respiratory muscles demand a substantial fraction of $\dot{V}O_2$ during heavy exercise seems reasonable.

In muscular exercise ventilation is usually found to bear an approximately linear relationship to $\dot{V}O_2$ (37) so that $\dot{V}O_2 = K\dot{V}_E$. Part of the O_2 consumption represents the requirement of the muscles of breathing, which can be estimated using the following formula of Otis (37) for calculating the power of breathing ($\dot{W}$) for high levels of ventilation when expiration is active: $\dot{W} = b\dot{V}_E^2 + c\dot{V}_E^3$, where b and c are constants representing nonelastic resistance involved in moving gas and displacing tissues. The amount of O_2 available for muscles other than those involved in breathing is thus given by $\dot{V}_{O_2} = K\dot{V}_E - b\dot{V}_E^2 - c\dot{V}_E^3$.

Otis argued that in theory a level of ventilation could be reached above which any further increase in $\dot{V}_{O_2}$ would be consumed entirely by the respiratory muscles. This so-called critical ventilation would occur when $d\dot{V}_{O_2}$ resp/$d\dot{V}_E = d\dot{V}_{O_2}/d\dot{V}_E$ (31, 37). Otis (37) estimated that critical ventilation to be 140 liters min^{-1} while Margaria et al (31) studied 2 subjects during exercise leading to exhaustion within 3–5 minutes and obtained values of 120–130 and 160–170 liters min^{-1}. These latter values, which were calculated using the above equations assuming a mechanical efficiency of 25%, were similar to the measured values for maximum ventilation in each of the subjects. Shephard (49) reported an efficiency of 7–8% in a similar study in which critical ventilation was calculated to be 120 liters min^{-1}. In fact, estimates of respiratory muscle efficiency are of the order of 3–10% (38). Using such values the critical ventilation in the two subjects described by Margaria et al (31) would occur at much lower levels.

It can be argued that at $\dot{V}_{O_2}$ max, the ratio $d\dot{V}_{O_2}/d\dot{V}_E = 0$ and therefore the point at which $d\dot{V}_{O_2}$ resp/$d\dot{V}_E = d\dot{V}_{O_2}/d\dot{V}_E$ must be reached prior to the attainment of $\dot{V}_{O_2}$max. Crucial to this proposition is that $\dot{V}_{O_2}$resp does not attain a maximal value and plateau prior to the $\dot{V}_{O_2}$max. Indeed Bradley & Leith (6) did not observe any plateau in $\dot{V}_{O_2}$resp during voluntary normocarbic hyperpnea up to 200 liters min^{-1}. Theoretically, therefore, it is conceivable that at high workloads the oxygen utilization by the ventilatory muscles may be so great that oxygen supply to the other tissues is compromised. Further increases in ventilation may result in anaerobic metabolism and eventual cessation of activity.

This concept of "energy stealing" (i.e. the respiratory muscles "steal" blood flow and energy potentially available for other working muscles) can also be applied to the findings of Dempsey et al (11–13) that some athletes do not increase their exercise ventilation sufficiently to avoid arterial hypoxemia. Advantages of not further increasing ventilation may be that extra flow-resistive work is avoided and that there is a reduction in $\dot{V}_{O_2}$resp. However, even if a critical ventilation is avoided, it must be stressed that $\dot{V}_{O_2}$resp at high ventilations remains a significant proportion of the $\dot{V}_{O_2}$. By implication, if the "energy stealing" effect can be avoided or minimized, performance will improve, perhaps in a manner similar to that observed in athletes following autologous reinfusion of blood (7).

FATIGUE OF RESPIRATORY MUSCLES

Respiratory muscle fatigue, defined as the inability of the respiratory muscles to continue generating a given pleural pressure, invariably occurs with extreme ventilatory tasks (46, 47). However, does fatigue of the ventilatory muscles occur during exercise? If it does, is it a coincidental phenomenon or does it actually set limits to exercise capacity that could be improved if the performance of the ventilatory muscles improved? No clear answer is available for either question, particularly for normal subjects.

Diaphragmatic fatigue occurs when the diaphragm develops pressure greater than 40% of maximum while fatigue of the inspiratory muscles results if the pleural pressure generated is greater than 50–70% of the maximum pressure (46, 47). Furthermore, fatigue occurs more rapidly at low inspired oxygen concentration (24, 47) or when subjects breathe at high lung volumes (46). Roussos et al (46) have shown that in a subject breathing at functional residual capacity plus half inspiratory capacity, fatigue occurs when pleural pressure exceeds 30% (or 25 cmH_2O) of the maximum static pressure that can be generated at that lung volume (about 80 cmH_2O).

However, is there evidence that the respiratory muscles generate forces leading to fatigue with exercise? From the exercise data of Olafsson & Hyatt (36) the maximum pleural pressure on inspiration in normal subjects (mean -30 cmH_2O) approaches the pressure developed during the MBC maneuver. It is also obvious from the pressure-volume curves shown in the latter study that the peak inspiratory pressures during exercise were generated at high lung volumes (approximately 80–90% TLC), at which the maximum static alveolar pressure predicted from the studies of Rahn et al (43) is about -50 cmH_2O. Similarly, Marshall et al (32) recorded negative pressure swings during inspiration at maximum exercise capacity of 50 cmH_2O in normal subjects and values only slightly less in patients with emphysema. Potter et al (42) reported values from -15 to -30 cmH_2O in patients with CAL during exhaustive exercise. Accordingly, if the values for critical inspiratory pressures reported as resulting in fatigue (46, 47) with resistance breathing can be applied to the exercise data, then the lowest inspiratory pressure swing in normal subjects above which fatigue would occur would be about 15 cmH_2O (perhaps lower for patients with CAL). The fact that the respiratory muscles have limited endurance in performing at high levels of activity has been confirmed by several investigators, who measured the endurance of respiratory muscles at different levels of MBC (17, 18, 55). It is clear from these studies that the respiratory muscles can sustain a ventilation above about 60% of MBC for only a finite period of time. This limited endurance time (t_{lim}) has an exponential relationship to MBC. Although it varies between subjects, the following equation has been proposed by Tenney & Reese (55) to describe the relationship: $t_{lim} = K'exp\,(-\%MBC/K'')$. Clearly, therefore, if large negative pleural pressures are developed during exercise or if the $\dot{V}_E$ is above 50–60% MBC, the respiratory system cannot be regarded as having considerable reserve.

If the above assumptions are valid two important conclusions emerge: (a) The ventilatory system has little if any reserve at very high work loads. (b) Even if the restriction imposed by the $\dot{V}$-V loop can be surmounted by hyperinflation and the "energy stealing" effect can be neglected, fatigue of the ventilatory muscles appears to constitute another possible limitation to exercise performance. Thus the schema previously proposed to explain the data of Dempsey et al (11–13) could be modified as follows: Exercise ventilation in athletes is reflexly set at a lower level owing to either $\dot{V}$-V limitations or high energy requirements at the expense of arterial hypoxemia. Alternatively, respiratory muscle fatigue occurs first and as a result ventilation decreases. We favor the first proposition. Only in those extreme situations when normal subjects or patients do not terminate exercise due to other factors (e.g. circulatory limitation, fatigue of peripheral muscles, dyspnea) might respiratory muscle fatigue provide a major limitation. We suggest that such an example may occur when motivated normal subjects breathe dense gas. It seems likely that these subjects drive their respiratory muscles to fatigue with resulting hypoventilation and the observed CO_2 retention (61).

What is the evidence that respiratory muscle fatigue may indeed occur with heavy exercise? Shephard (50) observed that the maximum voluntary ventilation performed after 20 min of exercise at a workload of 80% of $\dot{V}o_2max$ was significantly less than that after 5 min of exercise. This difference, however, disappeared after a period of exercise training, indicating that fatigue might have accounted for the findings before training. Further evidence consistent with respiratory muscle fatigue is found in the recent reports by Mahler & Loke (30) and Loke et al (27a) that there is a reduction in vital capacity and/or inspiratory and expiratory muscle strength after marathon running. In addition Martin et al (32a) observed that after ventilatory work in the form of prolonged hyperpnea short-term maximal running performance was reduced. Rats swimming for 5 hr were shown to have a marked reduction in the glycogen content of the respiratory muscles (20), and similar results were found during treadmill running to exhaustion (34). Glycogen depletion is well correlated with muscle fatigue of prolonged duration (4).

Using the EMG spectrum analysis, changes consistent with fatigue have been demonstrated in patients with CAL during exercise (21, 41). Furthermore, Pardy et al (41) and Belman & Mittman (3) have demonstrated improvement in the exercise performance of this group after specific training of the respiratory muscles, indicating that fatigue of the ventilatory muscles may have originally limited exercise performance.

Studies of respiratory muscle fatigue are in their infancy. Although the evidence cited is consistent with the occurrence of fatigue, much further work is necessary before we have a clear perception of the role of respiratory muscle fatigue as a factor limiting exercise.

SUMMARY

The question of respiratory factors limiting exercise has been examined in terms of possible limitations arising from the function of gas exchange, the respiratory mechanics, the energetics of the respiratory muscles, or the development of respiratory muscle fatigue. Exercise capacity is curtailed in the presence of marked hypoxia, and this is readily observed in patients with chronic airflow limitation and interstitial lung disease and in some athletes at high intensities of exercise. In patients with interstitial lung disease, gas exchange abnormality—partly the result of diffusion disequilibrium for oxygen transfer—occurs during exercise despite abnormally high ventilations. In contrast, in certain athletes arterial hypoxemia has been documented during heavy exercise, apparently as a result of relative hypoventilation. During strenuous exercise the maximum expiratory flow volume curves are attained both by patients with chronic airflow limitation and by normal subjects, in particular when they breathe dense gas, so that a mechanical constraint is imposed on further increases in ventilation. Similarly, the force velocity characteristics of the inspiratory muscles may also impose a constraint to further increases in inspiratory flows that affects the ability to increase ventilation. In addition, the oxygen cost of maintaining high ventilations is large. Analysis of results from blood flow experiments reveal a substantial increase in blood flow to the respiratory muscles during exercise, with the result that oxygen supply to the rest of the body may be lessened. Alternatively, high exercise ventilations may not be sustained indefinitely owing to the development of respiratory muscle fatigue that results in hypoventilation and reduced arterial oxygen tension.

ACKNOWLEDGMENTS

The authors are grateful to Drs. M. Becklake, J. Milic-Emili, and M. McGregor for their critical review of this work.

This work was supported by the Medical Research Council of Canada.

Literature Cited

1. Agostoni, E., Fenn, W. O. 1960. Velocity of muscle shortening as a limiting factor in respiratory airflow. *J. Appl. Physiol.* 15:349–53
2. Bartlett, R. G., Brubach, H. F., Specht, H. 1958. Oxygen cost of breathing. *J. Appl. Physiol.* 12:413–24
3. Belman, M. J., Mittman, C. 1980. Ventilatory muscle training improves exercise capacity in chronic obstructive pulmonary disease patients. *Am. Rev. Respir. Dis.* 121:273–80
4. Bergstrom, J., Hultman, E. 1972. Nutrition for maximal sports performance. *J. Am. Med. Assoc.* 221:999–1006
5. Bradley, B. L., Forman, J. W., Miller, W. C. 1980. Low-density gas breathing during exercise in chronic obstructive lung disease. *Respiration* 40:311–16
6. Bradley, M. E., Leith, D. E. 1978. Ventilatory muscle training and the oxygen cost of sustained hyperpnea. *J. Appl. Physiol: Respir. Envir. Exer. Physiol.* 45:885–92
7. Buick, F. J., Gledhill, N., Froese, A. B., Spriet, L., Meyers, E. C. 1980. Effect of induced erythrocythemia on aerobic work capacity. *J. Appl. Physiol: Respir. Envir. Exer. Physiol.* 48:636–42
8. Bye, P. T. P. 1981. *Studies of exercise and sleep in patients with interstitial lung disease.* PhD thesis. Univ. Sydney, Sydney, Australia. 314 pp.
9. Cerretelli, P. 1981. Maximal aerobic power at altitude: effects of oxygen breathing. In *Progress in Respiration Research: Gas Exchange Function of Normal and Diseased Lungs,* ed. J. Piiper, P. Scheid, 16:296–301. Basel: Karger. 318 pp.
10. Clark, T. J. H., Freedman, S., Campbell, E. J. M., Winn, R. R. 1969. The ventilatory capacity of patients with chronic airway obstruction. *Clin. Sci.* 36:307–16
11. Dempsey, J. A., Hanson, P. E., Mastenbrook, S. M. 1981. Arterial hypoxemia during exercise in highly trained runners. *Fed. Proc.* 40:396 (Abstr.)
12. Dempsey, J., Hanson, P., Pegelow, D., Claremont, A. 1982. *Limitations to exercise capacity and endurance: pulmonary system. Can. J. Appl. Sport Sci.* 7:4–13
13. Dempsey, J., Hanson, P., Pegelow, D., Fregosi, R. 1982. Mechanical vs. chemical determinants of hyperventilation in heavy exercise. *Med. Sci. Sports. Exer.* 14:131
14. Dempsey, J. A., Reddan, W., Rankin, J., Balke, B. 1966. Alveolar-arterial gas exchange during muscular work in obesity. *J. Appl. Physiol.* 21:1807–14
15. Faulkner, J. A., Kollias, J., Favour, C. B., Buskirk, E. R., Balke, B. 1968. Maximum aerobic capacity and running performance at altitude. *J. Appl. Physiol.* 24:685–91
16. Fixler, D. E., Atkins, J. M., Mitchell, J. H., Horwitz, L. D. 1976. Blood flow to respiratory, cardiac and limb muscles in dogs during graded exercise. *Am. J. Physiol.* 231:1515–19
17. Freedman, S. 1966. Prolonged maximum voluntary ventilation. *J. Physiol.* 184:42–44
18. Freedman, S. 1970. Sustained maximum voluntary ventilation. *Respir. Physiol.* 8:230–44
19. Gledhill, N., Spriet, L. L., Froese, A. B., Wilkes, D. L., Meyers, E. C. 1980. Acid-base status with induced erythrocythemia and its influence on arterial oxygenation during heavy exercise. *Med. Sci. Sports Exer.* 12:122 (Abstr.)
20. Gorski, J., Namiot, Z., Giedrojć, J. 1978. Effect of exercise on metabolism of glycogen and triglycerides in the respiratory muscles. *Pflügers Arch.* 377:251–54
21. Grassino, A., Gross, D., Macklem, P. T., Roussos, C., Zagelbaum, G. 1979. Inspiratory muscle fatigue as a factor limiting exercise. *Bull. Eur. Physiopath. Respir.* 15:105–11
22. Grimby, G., Saltin, B., Wilhelmsen, L. 1971. Pulmonary flow-volume and pressure-volume relationship during submaximal and maximal exercise in young well-trained men. *Bull. Physiopathol. Respir.* 7:157–68
23. Hughes, R. L., Clode, M., Edwards, R. H. T., Goodwin, T. J., Jones, N. L. 1968. Effect of inspired O_2 on cardiopulmonary and metabolic responses to exercise in man. *J. Appl. Physiol.* 24:336–47
24. Jardim, J., Farkas, G., Prefaut, C., Thomas, D., Macklem, P. T., Roussos, Ch. 1981. The failing inspiratory muscles under normoxic and hypoxic conditions. *Am. Rev. Respir. Dis.* 124:274–79
25. Jones, N. L. 1966. Pulmonary gas exchange during exercise in patients with chronic airway obstruction. *Clin. Sci.* 31:39–50
26. Leaver, D. G., Pride, N. B. 1971. Flow-volume curves and expiratory pressures during exercise in patients with chronic airways obstruction. *Scand. J. Respir. Dis.* Suppl. 77, pp. 23–27

27. Levison, H., Cherniack, R. M. 1968. Ventilatory cost of exercise in chronic obstructive pulmonary disease. *J. Appl. Physiol.* 25:21–27

27a. Loke, J., Mahler, D. A., Virgulto, J. A. 1982. Respiratory muscle fatigue after marathon running. *J. Appl. Physiol.: Environ. Exer. Physiol.* 52:821–24

28. Lourenço, R. V., Turino, G. M., Davidson, L. A. G., Fishman, A. P. 1965. The regulation of ventilation in diffuse pulmonary fibrosis. *Am. J. Med.* 38:199–216

29. McKerrow, C. B., Otis, A. B. 1956. Oxygen cost of hyperventilation. *J. Appl. Physiol.* 9:375–79

30. Mahler, D. A., Loke, J. 1981. Lung function after marathon running at warm and cold ambient temperatures. *Am. Rev. Respir. Dis.* 124:154–57

31. Margaria, R., Milic-Emili, G., Petit, J. M., Cavagna, G. 1960. Mechanical work of breathing during muscular exercise. *J. Appl. Physiol.* 15:354–58

32. Marshall, R., Stone, R. W., Christie, R. V. 1954. The relationship of dyspnea to respiratory effort in normal subjects, mitral stenosis and emphysema. *Clin. Sci.* 13:625–31

32a. Martin, B., Heintzelman, M., Chen, H. 1982. Exercise performance after ventilatory work. *J. Appl. Physiol.: Environ. Exer. Physiol.* 52:1581–85

33. Martin, B. J., Weil, J. V., Sparks, K. E., McCullough, R. E., Grover, R. F. 1978. Exercise ventilation correlates positively with ventilatory chemoresponsiveness. *J. Appl. Physiol.* 45:557–64

34. Moore, R. L., Gollnick, P. D. 1982. Response of ventilatory muscles of the rat to endurance training. *Pflüger's Arch.* 392:268–71

35. Nattie, E. E., Tenney, S. M. 1970. The ventilatory response to resistance unloading during muscular exercise. *Respir. Physiol.* 10:249–62

36. Olafsson, S., Hyatt, R. E. 1969. Ventilatory mechanics and expiratory flow limitation during exercise in normal subjects. *J. Clin. Invest.* 48:564–73

37. Otis, A. B. 1954. The work of breathing. *Physiol. Rev.* 34:449–58

38. Otis, A. B. 1964. The work of breathing. In *Handbook of Physiology, Section 3, Respiration*, Vol. 1, ed. W. O. Fenn, H. Rahn, 17:463–76. Baltimore: Waverly Press. 926 pp.

39. Otis, A. B., Bembower, W. C. 1949. Effect of gas density on resistance to respiratory gas flow in man. *J. Appl. Physiol.* 2:300–6

40. Ouellet, Y., Poh, S. C., Becklake, M. R. 1969. Circulatory factors limiting maximal aerobic exercise capacity. *J. Appl. Physiol.* 27:874–80

41. Pardy, R. L., Rivington, R. N., Despas, P. J., Macklem, P. T. 1981. The effects of inspiratory muscle training on exercise performance in chronic airflow limitation. *Am. Rev. Respir. Dis.* 123:426–33

42. Potter, W. A., Olafsson, S., Hyatt, R. E. 1971. Ventilatory mechanics and expiratory flow limitation during exercise in patients with obstructive lung disease. *J. Clin. Invest.* 50:910–19

43. Rahn, H., Otis, A. B., Chadwick, L. E., Fenn, W. O. 1946. The pressure-volume diagram of the thorax and lung. *Am. J. Physiol.* 146:161–78

44. Raimondi, A. C., Edwards, R. H. T., Denison, D. M., Leaver, D. G., Spencer, R. G., Siddorn, J. A. 1970. Exercise tolerance breathing a low density gas mixture, 35% oxygen and air in patients with chronic obstructive bronchitis. *Clin. Sci.* 39:675–85

45. Robertson, C. H. Jr., Foster, G. H., Johnson, R. L. Jr. 1977. The relationship of respiratory failure to the oxygen consumption of, lactate production by, and distribution of blood flow among respiratory muscles during increasing inspiratory resistance. *J. Clin. Invest.* 59:31–42

46. Roussos, C., Fixley, M., Gross, D., Macklem, P. T. 1979. Fatigue of inspiratory muscles and their synergic behaviour. *J. Appl. Physiol: Respir. Envir. Exer. Physiol.* 46:897–904

47. Roussos, C. S., Macklem, P. T. 1977. Diaphragmatic fatigue in man. *J. Appl. Physiol.* 43:189–97

48. Rowell, L. B., Taylor, H. L., Wang, Y., Carlson, W. S. 1964. Saturation of arterial blood with oxygen during maximal exercise. *J. Appl. Physiol.* 19:284–86

49. Shephard, R. J. 1966. The oxygen cost of breathing during vigorous exercise. *Q. J. Exp. Physiol.* 51:336–50

50. Shephard, R. J. 1967. The maximum sustained voluntary ventilation in exercise. *Clin. Sci.* 32:167–76

51. Spitler, D. L., Horvath, S. M., Kobayashi, K., Wagner, J. A. 1980. Work performance breathing normoxic nitrogen or helium gas mixtures. *Eur. J. Appl. Physiol.* 43:157–66

52. Stubbing, D. G., Pengelly, L. D., Morse, J. L. C., Jones, N. L. 1980. Pulmonary mechanics during exercise in

normal males. *J. Appl. Physiol.: Respir. Envir. Exer. Physiol.* 49:506–10
53. Stubbing, D. G., Pengelly, L. D., Morse, J. L. C., Jones, N. L. 1980. Pulmonary mechanics during exercise in subjects with chronic airflow obstruction. *J. Appl. Physiol.: Respir. Envir. Exer. Physiol.* 49:511–15
54. Sylvester, J. T., Cymerman, A., Gurtner, G., Hottenstein, O., Cote, M., Wolfe, D. 1981. Components of alveolar-arterial O_2 gradient during rest and exercise at sea level and high altitude. *J. Appl. Physiol.: Respir. Envir. Exer. Physiol.* 50:1129–39
55. Tenney, S. M., Reese, R. E. 1968. The ability to sustain great breathing efforts. *Respir. Physiol.* 5:187–201
56. Wagner, P. D. 1977. Ventilation-perfusion inequality & gas exchange during exercise in lung disease. In *Muscular Exercise and the Lung,* ed. J. A. Dempsey, C. E. Reed, pp. 345–356. Madison, WI: Univ. Wisconsin Press. 406 pp.

57. Ward, S. A., Poon, C., Whipp, B. J. 1980. Does turbulent airflow constrain compensatory hyperpnea during metabolic acidosis in exercise? *Med. Sci. Sports Exer.* 12:123 (Abstr.)
58. West, J. B., Lahiri, S., Gill, M. B., Milledge, J. S., Pugh, L. G. C. E., Ward, M. P. 1962. Arterial oxygen saturation during exercise at high altitude. *J. Appl. Physiol.* 17:617–21
59. West, J. B., Wagner, P. D. 1980. Predicted gas exchange on the summit of Mt. Everest. *Respir. Physiol.* 42:1–16
60. Wilson, G. D., Welch, H. G. 1980. Effects of varying concentrations of N_2/O_2 and He/O_2 on exercise tolerance in man. *Med. Sci. Sports Exer.* 12:380–84
61. Wood, L. D. H., Bryan, A. C. 1978. Exercise ventilatory mechanics at increased ambient pressure. *J. Appl. Physiol.: Respir. Envir. Exer. Physiol.* 44:231–37

Ann. Rev. Physiol. 1983. 45:453–63

EXERCISE-INDUCED AIRWAY OBSTRUCTION

E. R. McFadden, Jr., and R. H. Ingram, Jr.

Shipley Institute of Medicine and the Departments of Medicine
of the Brigham and Women's Hospital and Harvard Medical
School, Boston, Massachusetts 02115

INTRODUCTION

The tracheobronchial tree of the human is not a series of rigid tubes. Rather, the airways are dynamic structures capable of changing size in response to such factors as infectious agents and immunologic, chemical, pharmacologic, and physical stimuli. Many such stimuli have been studied extensively, yet their mechanisms of action (local versus reflex effects) are still the subject of controversy. In recent years, however, the phenomenon of exercise-induced airway obstruction (EIAO) has been under intense investigation. A wealth of new information has appeared. We review these new developments and explore their physiological implications.

DEFINITION AND DESCRIPTION

In exercise-induced airway obstruction strenuous physical exertion results in acute bronchoconstriction. This phenomenon is usually observed in asthmatics and has been called "exercise-induced asthma" or "exercise-induced bronchospasm" (27, 33, 35, 43). It has also been reported in other persons with hyper-reactive airways, such as first-degree relatives of asthmatics (27), and in some individuals with atopic histories but with no other stigmata of asthma (12, 27). Under certain circumstances, it can be made to develop in normal people (46).

The pattern of response to exercise is characteristic. Moderate bronchodilation occurs during the early part of exercise and gives way to bronchoconstriction after work ceases. The airway obstruction is progressive, generally reaching its peak 5–10 min after exercise has stopped. The obstruction then begins to abate. Spontaneous recovery is usual, tending to be complete within 30–90 min, depending upon the severity of the bronchospasm. Most authorities hold that EIAO in asthmatics is a nonspecific manifestation of heightened airway reactivity. A close relationship exists between the bronchial responsiveness to inhaled histamine or methacholine in a population of asthmatics and the severity of the obstruction induced by exercise (2, 36, 45). The magnitude of the response varies with the state of inflammation of the airways as the underlying disease process waxes and wanes (40)

HISTORICAL REVIEW

The association between strenuous exertion and the acute development of airway obstruction was first recorded by Aretaeus the Cappadocian in the 1st century A.D. (1). Thus exercise was one of the earliest stimuli to be recognized as a cause of respiratory impairment. Although some of the literature of the next millenium cautioned patients with lung disease against violent activity in the main, Aretaeus's observations lay dormant until 1698 when Sir John Floyer redescribed the phenomenon (25). Floyer pointed out that exercise tasks with the highest levels of ventilation produced the most severe symptoms. The significance of these observations went unappreciated for an additional three centuries.

In 1864, H. H. Salter recognized that the post-exertional obstructive response could be accentuated if the exercise was performed in a cold environment (51). He, too, suspected an effect of the degree of ventilation. He suggested that the "rapid passage of fresh and cold air over the bronchial mucous membrane" could stimulate the airways either directly or by producing irritability of the nervous system. The importance of these thoughts went unrecognized until recently. Eighty years after Salter's work, Herxheimer published the first account that included objective measures of lung function (33). He also thought that the hyperventilation of exercise was the key factor, but he reasoned that it brought about its effects through the constrictor action of airway hypocapnia, a view subsequently embraced by others (22, 24, 30). Many authors agreed that hyperventilation was important, but believed that stimulation of mechanoreceptors in the airways was the critical factor (8, 11, 49, 56, 58). Because of the close correlation between changes in hydrogen ion concentration and the magnitude of the post-exercise obstruction (8, 24, 49, 52, 55, 56, 60, 65), still others argued that humoral substances released by the exercising muscles (e.g. lactic acid) were the stimuli (65).

During the ensuing 36 years, controversy characterized these issues. Other postulates were put forth. Most lacked supporting evidence, and the majority view remained that the pathogenetic mechanism underlying EIAO was somehow related to increased airflow, hypocarbia, and/or the acid end-products of anaerobic metabolism. When it became possible to isolate from each other the effects of hypocapnia, hyperpnea, and acidosis, the relative importance of these 3 factors was finally determined. With the use of a partial rebreathing technique that permitted the independent evaluation of each variable (41), hypocapnic bronchoconstriction and the mechanical consequences of bulk airflow were excluded as stimuli. The possibility that acidemia or increased lactate levels in the blood served as major mediators was eliminated as well (60). Prevention of the acidemia of exercise by the infusion of bicarbonate did not influence the obstructive response, nor did the infusion of lactate.

CURRENT CONCEPTS OF PATHOGENESIS

Effects of Inspired Air Conditions

The reason for the previous confusion became clear when Strauss and associates (42) began their studies on the effects of inspired air conditions on the post-exercise response. Working first with cold air, these investigators objectively confirmed the qualitative observations of Salter that the combination of a frigid inspirate and exercise increased the obstruction. Subsequent experimentation in this (14, 16, 61) and other laboratories (4, 10) showed that the severity of the bronchoconstriction following exercise could be manipulated by changing the thermal characteristics of the inspired air. For a fixed ventilation, humidification of the inspirate reduces the severity of the response (4, 10, 14, 16, 61) while drying and cooling the air increases the response (12, 14, 16, 62). Inhaling air conditioned to body temperature and humidity during exercise prevents the obstruction from developing (14, 16, 61). For a given set of inspirate conditions, high levels of ventilation result in greater responses than do low levels (14).

The temperature and humidity of the inspired air are important interactive variables in addition to the absolute quantity of air being respired. Achieving and sustaining a certain level of ventilation is only part of the picture. The thermal environment of exercise is also critical. Thus activities such as ice hockey, skiing, or running outdoors produce more frequent and more severe episodes of obstruction in asthmatics than does swimming in an indoor heated pool (3, 14, 16, 27). In addition, since air temperature and humidity are not usually standardized, differing degrees of obstruction may result from seemingly controlled laboratory trials in the same subject at different times [e.g. free running outdoors versus running on a treadmill indoors (3)]. Variation in prevalence and severity would also be expected with the changes of seasons in the same locale, and from locale to locale where atmospheric conditions differ significantly (28). In addition to solving many previously perplexing problems, these studies suggest that the development of EIAO may be related to the conditioning of inspired air and thus to alterations in the thermal environment of the intrathoracic airways.

Airway Cooling and the Development of Obstruction

During inspiration, colder air is warmed to 37°C and dry air brought to full saturation by the time it reaches the alveoli. This is accomplished by the transfer of heat and water from the mucosa of the tracheobronchial tree. As the air is heated, its capacity to hold water increases and it is humidified by evaporation from the airway mucosa. Such evaporation accounts for most of the heat lost from the airway surface and cools the mucosa. On expiration, the process is reversed along thermal gradients; heat and water are recovered (15, 38, 47). If the airways were perfect heat exchangers, input would equal recovery, the temperature and water content of the expired air would equal those of the inspired air, and there would be no variation in airway temperature at any locus during the breathing cycle. This is not the case, however, and much heat escapes to the environment. The process of thermal exchange in the airway is quantifiable according to the following expression (16):

$$RHL = \dot{V}_E \left[HC \left(T_i - T_e \right) + HV \left(WC_i - WC_e \right) \right]$$

where RHL = respiratory heat loss in Kcal min^{-1}; $\dot{V}_E$ = minute ventilation in liters min^{-1} (BTPS); HC = heat capacity of the gas (specific heat·density) in Kcal liter^{-1} °C^{-1}; T_i = temperature of inspired gas in °C; T_e = temperature of expired gas in °C; HV = latent heat of vaporization of H_2O in Kcal g^{-1}; WC_i = water content of inspired gas in mg H_2O liter^{-1}; WC_e = water content of expired gas in mg H_2O liter^{-1}. The total quantity of heat lost varies directly with the level of ventilation and inversely with inspired air temperatures and water contents (14, 16).

Examination of the data from the aforementioned studies from the standpoint of respiratory heat exchange revealed a highly significant predictive positive relationship between the amount of heat lost during exercise and the magnitude of the post-exertional obstruction (16).

The above observations suggested a cause-and-effect relationship between RHL and post-exertional obstruction. If this were so, then equivalent thermal burdens would result in equivalent obstruction even without exercise. This possibility was tested by having asymptomatic asthmatic subjects simulate the hyperpnea of moderate and severe workloads by performing eucapnic hyperventilation while breathing air mixtures at several different temperatures and humidities (14). The airway consequences of voluntary hyperventilation exactly matched those seen with exercise when ventilation and inspired air conditions are matched. The severity of the obstruction is the same, the degree of airway cooling is the same, and the response to oxygen breathing and various drugs is identical (6, 7, 12–14, 32, 50). Thus exercise per se is not essential to the development of obstruction and there is no need to search for humoral substances released from the working muscles.

The hypotheses discussed above are predicated upon the assumption that incompletely warmed and humidified air penetrates to the intrathoracic airways. Is there evidence that this occurs? The answer is an unequivocal yes. Continuous recordings of the temperatures in the retrocardiac and retrotracheal esophagus and the rectum during exercise and/or eucapnic hyperventilation at different inspirate temperatures and humidities in normal and asthmatic subjects have shown that retrotracheal temperatures are systematically lower than, and can fall independently of, those in the other two sites (15). Direct recordings of the temperatures in the tracheobronchial tree have recently confirmed the earlier data. During hyperpnea, the temperatures of the intrathoracic airways beyond the intra-lobar bronchi fall substantially from the values recorded during quiet breathing (38). Therefore, whenever minute ventilation is increased, the temperature of the intrathoracic airways falls. If cooling becomes severe enough, bronchoconstriction develops. Individuals with reactive airways are affected much more readily than are normal people; however, if the stimulus is made large enough, even normal subjects respond (46). The severity of the obstruction is directly related to the degree of cooling (15); that, in turn, is related to the total heat lost from the airways (16).

POSSIBLE MECHANISMS WHEREBY AIRWAY COOLING LEADS TO OBSTRUCTION

Mediator Release

The mechanism whereby airway cooling leads to bronchial obstruction is not known. Of the mechanisms proposed, release of the mediators of immediate hypersensitivity from mast cells initially appeared most promising. The circumstantial evidence favoring this hypothesis comprises three lines of reasoning. (a) Physical cooling of the skin of patients with cold urticaria causes sensitized mast cells to discharge their contents (57). Since direct cooling of the airways occurs, and since many asthmatics have such mast cells on airways surfaces and in the submucosa, it is possible that an analogous situation occurs with EIAO. (b) Disodium cromoglycate, a drug once thought only to stabilize sensitized mast cells, blunts the obstruction that follows both exercise and isocapnic hyperpnea (6, 32). (c) Repetitive stints of exercise performed over short periods diminish the obstructive response

(18, 34, 43). This so-called "refractory period" has been speculatively attributed to the depletion of a stored mediator that needs time for regeneration (18, 34).

Several lines of evidence, also circumstantial, cast considerable doubt on the mediator-release hypothesis. (a) It has been extremely difficult to demonstrate an association between the presence of mast-cell-derived mediators and the development of EIAO (9, 17, 23, 40). In one study, when the same level of bronchoconstriction was produced by both antigen and airway cooling, only the former was associated with a measurable increase in the levels of mediators in the arterial blood (17). (b) Disodium cromoglycate has recently been shown to act independently of mediator release. For example, the obstructive response to inhaled sulfur dioxide, an irritant gas, is blunted by pretreatment with this agent in both normal and asthmatic subjects (31, 54). Further, the changes in mechanics that develop in normal people with airway cooling are also blocked by pretreatment with this drug (21). Thus the action of cromolyn solely as a specific stabilizer of sensitized mast cells is brought into question, and its effectiveness in EIAO becomes less compelling in support of the role of mediators. (c) In contrast to that produced by exercise, airway cooling produced by brief intervals of isocapnic hyperpnea exhibits no refractory period. This suggests that the neurohumoral compensations that occur with repetitive work may act as a form of auto-therapy (59). However, a direct assessment of this potential factor has yet to be made. (d) Normal subjects can be made to develop obstruction. Since they have no sensitized mast cells, it is difficult to invoke mediators to account for their response. Probably airway cooling, like pharmacological stimulation, merely identifies subjects with more responsive airways and hence represents another stimulus for nonspecific bronchial hyperresponsiveness rather than a mediator-specific response.

Reflex Effects

The role of reflexes in EIAO has been controversial. It has been hypothesized that there are thermally sensitive neural receptors in the posterior pharynx and airways that reflexly mediate the obstructive response induced by airway cooling (19, 42). This concept was derived from the observation that the application of a topical anesthetic to these areas before exercise diminished the subsequent bronchoconstriction. However, these studies were uncontrolled with respect to variables influencing heat exchange. A reanalysis of the problem using precisely controlled ventilations and inspired air conditions failed to confirm the original observations (20, 29).

The literature on the use of atropine and its congeners to block the development of obstruction in asthmatics suggests that these agents neither work in all patients (7, 13, 39, 48, 63) nor are equally effective at all inspired air conditions (7, 13). Some authors explain this behavior by postulating (*a*) a heterogeneous mechanism for the obstruction (39, 48, 63), and (*b*) that anticholinergics influence respiratory heat transfer (7). Others have suggested that the entire controversy emanates from the use of inadequate doses of parasympatholytics by previous investigators (53).

Recently a relationship has been observed between the intensity of the stimulus in EIAO and the degree of protection offered by drugs. Anticholinergics produce not an all-or-none effect but a parallel shift in the thermal stimulus-response curve (26). Thus as the stimulus for bronchoconstriction increases, the protection offered by the drug is overcome, and the airway obstruction returns. Consequently, an agent can have different effects at various times in the same individual, depending upon the thermal environment in which it is used and the severity of the challenge. Therefore it is impossible to use pharmacologic techniques to draw valid conclusions regarding the mechanisms for EIAO without analyzing how a given drug influences the overall thermal stimulus-response relationships.

EFFECTS OF COOLING ON SMOOTH MUSCLE

Virtually every effect of cooling on metabolic activity and on the responses of airway and vascular smooth muscle must be considered as a possible cause of bronchoconstriction after exercise. These effects have been described in nonhuman animal species and often in isolated tissues rather than intact organisms. Thus their applicability to the human situation remains speculative. Nonetheless, in view of the continuing controversies centering on mediators and vago-vagal reflexes, it is worthwhile to mention several of these effects as examples. They may serve as a focus for future studies aimed at understanding the link between airway cooling and post-exertional bronchial obstruction.

Cooling alone appears to have no measurable mechanical effect on smooth muscle (44). The response to neural, electrical, or pharmacologic stimulation, however, increases as the temperature is lowered to values near 28°C, a value close to that found by direct measurement in the intrathoracic airways of humans under moderate thermal stress (38). This increase in responsiveness is accompanied by a decrease in the resting membrane potential in vascular smooth muscle. Increased responsiveness appears to be related to improved electromechanical coupling rather than to any alteration in the contractile machinery (64).

Another potential thermal effect concerns the mutability of alpha and beta receptors. According to this interconversion hypothesis, lowering of the temperature of the tissue leads to conversion of beta receptors to an alpha configuration, which when stimulated would produce contraction

(37). The evidence for this hypothesis comes from submammalian species and has been challenged (5). It is worth mention, however, since it is potentially testable in the only species that develops exercise-induced asthma.

More recently, in vitro studies have focussed on the effects of cooling on the sodium-potassium ATPase pump of airway smooth muscle (44). Cooling to a realistic airway temperature apparently results in a diminution of the activity of the Na-K-ATPase pump accompanying the cold-induced enhancement of contraction (44). It is difficult to predict how, or whether, this observation will fit into the puzzle; but it opens the way to feasible experimental approaches in humans.

SUMMARY

Many previous discrepancies and conflicts concerning the pathophysiology of EIAO have been explained or reconciled by the observation that respiratory heat loss and concomitant airway cooling relate directly and probably causally to both the occurrence and magnitude of the airway obstruction that develops. Recent measurements have documented and quantitated observations made centuries ago.

Controversy continues concerning the role of mediator release and the relative contribution of vago-vagal reflexes to the response induced by airway cooling. Recent attempts to study the effects of cooling on both the responsiveness and metabolic processes of airway smooth muscle may well ascend the phylogenetic scale to the intact organism, eventually allowing the testing of hypotheses raised along the way. Meanwhile, we think it likely that airway cooling and the response to it will represent another example of nonspecific airway responsiveness, and that the links between this stimulus and the subsequent response will be multifactorial. The relative roles and interactive potentials of diverse processes will make the next step in understanding difficult, though not impossible.

Literature Cited

1. Adams, F. 1856. *The Extant Works of Aretaeus the Cappadocian,* p. 316. London: Syndenham Soc.
2. Anderson, S. D., Connolly, N. M., Godfrey, S. 1971. Comparison of bronchoconstriction induced by cycling and running. *Thorax* 26:396–401
3. Anderton, R. C., Cuff, M. T., Frith, P. A., Cockcroft, D. W., Morse, J. L. C., Jones, N. L., Hargreave, F. E. 1979. Bronchial responsiveness to inhaled histamine and exercise. *J. Allergy Clin. Immunol.* 63:315–20
4. Bar-Or, O., Neuman, I., Dotan, R. 1977. Effects of dry and humid climates on exercise-induced asthma in children and preadolescents. *J. Allergy Clin. Immunol.* 60:163–68
5. Benfey, B. G. 1980. The evidence against interconversion of α- and β-adrenoceptors. *Trends Pharmacol. Sci.* 1:193–94
6. Breslin, F. J., McFadden, E. R. Jr., Ingram, R. H. Jr. 1980. The effect of cromolyn sodium on the airway response to hyperpnea and cold air in

asthma. *Am. Rev. Respir. Dis.* 122: 11–16
7. Breslin, F. J., McFadden, E. R. Jr., Ingram, R. H. Jr., Deal, E. C. Jr. 1980. Effects of atropine on respiratory heat loss in asthma. *J. Appl. Physiol: Respir. Envir. Exer. Physiol.* 48:619–23
8. Chan-Yeung, M. M. W., Vyas, M. N., Gryzbowski, S. 1971. Exercise-induced asthma. *Am. Rev. Respir. Dis.* 104: 915–23
9. Charles, T. S., Hartley, J. P. R., Seaton, A., Taylor, W. J., Westwood, A. 1977. Arterial histamine in exercise-induced asthma. *Clin. Sci.* 56:8P (Abstr.)
10. Chen, W. Y., Horton, D. J. 1977. Heat and water loss from the airways and exercise-induced asthma. *Respiration* 34:305–13
11. Crompton, G. K. 1968. An unusual example of exercise-induced asthma. *Thorax* 23:165–67
12. Deal, E. C. Jr., McFadden, E. R. Jr., Ingram, R. H. Jr., Breslin, F. J., Jaeger, J. J. 1980. Airway responsiveness to cold air and hyperpnea in normal subjects and in those with hay fever and asthma. *Am. Rev. Respir. Dis.* 121: 621–28
13. Deal, E. C. Jr., McFadden, E. R. Jr., Ingram, R. H. Jr., Jaeger, J. J. 1978. Effects of atropine on potentiation of exercise-induced bronchospasm by cold air. *J. Appl. Physiol: Respir. Envir. Exer. Physiol.* 45:238–43
14. Deal, E. C., Jr., McFadden, E. R. Jr., Ingram, R. H. Jr., Jaeger, J. J. 1979. Hyperpnea and heat flux. The initial reaction sequence in exercise-induced asthma. *J. Appl. Physiol: Respir. Envir. Exer. Physiol.* 46:476–83
15. Deal, E. C. Jr., McFadden, E. R. Jr., Ingram, R. H. Jr., Jaeger, J. J. 1979. Esophageal temperature during exercise in asthmatic and non-asthmatic subjects. *J. Appl. Physiol: Respir. Envir. Exer. Physiol.* 46:484–90
16. Deal, E. C. Jr., McFadden, E. R. Jr., Ingram, R. H. Jr., Strauss, R. H., Jaeger, J. J. 1979. The role of respiratory heat exchange in the production of exercise-induced asthma. *J. Appl. Physiol.: Respir. Envir. Exer. Physiol.* 46:467–75
17. Deal, E. C. Jr., Wasserman, S. I., Soter, N. A., Ingram, R. H. Jr., McFadden, E. R. Jr. 1980. Evaluation of role played by mediators of immediate hypersensitivity in exercise-induced asthma. *J. Clin. Invest.* 65:659–65
18. Edmunds, A. T., Tooley, M., Godfrey, S. 1978. The refractory period after exercise-induced asthma: Its duration and relation to the severity of exercise. *Am. Rev. Respir. Dis.* 117:247–54
19. Enright, P. L., Souhrada, J. F. 1979. Effect of lidocaine anesthesia on the ventilatory response of asthmatics to exercise. *Am. Rev. Respir. Dis.* 122: 823–28
20. Fanta, C. H., Ingram, R. H. Jr., McFadden, E. R. Jr. 1980. A reassessment of the effects of oropharyngeal anesthesia in exercise-induced asthma. *Am. Rev. Respir. Dis.* 122:381–86
21. Fanta, C. H., McFadden, E. R. Jr., Ingram, R. H. Jr. 1981. Effects of cromolyn sodium on the response to respiratory heat loss in normal subjects. *Am. Rev. Respir. Dis.* 123:161–64
22. Ferguson, A., Addington, W., Gaensler, E. A. 1969. Dyspnea and bronchospasm from inappropriate postexercise hyperventilation. *Ann. Int. Med.* 71:1063–72
23. Ferris, L., Anderson, S. D., Temple, D. M. 1978. Histamine release in exercise-induced asthma. *Br. Med. J.* 1:1697–98
24. Fisher, H. K., Holton, P., Buxton, R. St. J., Nadel, J. A. 1970. Resistance to breathing during exercise-induced asthma attacks. *Am. Rev. Respir. Dis.* 101:885–96
25. Floyer, J. 1698. *A Treatise of the Asthma.* London: R. Wilkin
26. Fung, F., Griffin, M. P., Ingram, R. H. Jr., McFadden, E. R. Jr. 1982. Dose-response effects of atropine on the stimulus-response relationships to thermal stimuli in asthma. *Fed. Proc.* 41:(4) 1357 (Abstr.)
27. Godfrey, S. 1975. Exercise-induced asthma: clinical, physiological and therapeutic implications. *J. Allergy Clin. Immunol.* 56:1–17
28. Godfrey, S., Silverman, M., Anderson, S. D. 1973. Problems of interpreting exercise-induced asthma. *J. Allergy Clin. Immunol.* 52:199–209
29. Griffin, M. P., McFadden, E. R. Jr., Ingram, R. H. Jr., Pardee, S. 1982. A controlled analysis of the effects of inhaled lidocaine in exercise-induced asthma. *Thorax.* In press
30. Hafez, F. F., Crompton, G. K. 1968. The forced expiratory volume after hyperventilation in bronchitis and asthma. *Br. J. Dis. Chest* 62:41–45
31. Harries, M. G., Parkes, P. E. G., Lessof, M. H., Orr, T. S. C. 1981. Role of bronchial irritant receptors in asthma. *Lancet* 1:5–7
32. Haynes, R. L., Ingram, R. H. Jr., McFadden, E. R. Jr. 1976. An assessment of the pulmonary response to ex-

ercise in asthma and an analysis of the factors influencing it. *Am. Rev. Respir. Dis.* 114:739–52

33. Herxheimer, H. 1946. Hyperventilation asthma. *Lancet* 1:82–87

34. James, L., Faciane, J., Sly, R. M. 1976. Effect of treadmill exercise on asthmatic children. *J. Allergy Clin. Immunol.* 57:408–16

35. Jones, R. S., Buston, M. H., Wharton, M. J. 1962. The effect of exercise on ventilatory function in the child with asthma. *Brit. J. Dis. Chest* 56:78–86

36. Kiviloog, J. 1973. Bronchial reactivity to exercise and methacholine in bronchial asthma. *Scand. J. Respir. Dis.* 54:347–57

37. Kunos, G. 1980. Reciprocal changes in α- and β-adrenoceptor reactivity myth or reality? *Trends Pharmacol. Sci.* 1:282–84

38. McFadden, E. R. Jr., Denison, D. M., Waller, J. F., Assoufi, B., Peacock, A., Sopwith, T. 1982. Direct recordings of the temperatures in the tracheobronchial tree in normal man. *J. Clin. Invest.* 69:700–5

39. McFadden, E. R. Jr., Ingram, R. H. Jr., Haynes, R. L., Wellman, J. J. 1977. Predominant site of flow limitation and mechanisms of post-exertional asthma. *J. Appl. Physiol: Respir. Envir. Exer. Physiol.* 42:746–52

40. McFadden, E. R. Jr., Soter, N. A., Ingram, R. H. Jr. 1980. Magnitude and site of the airway response to exercise in asthmatics in relation to arterial histamine levels. *J. Allergy Clin. Immunol.* 66:472–77

41. McFadden, E. R. Jr., Stearns, D. R., Ingram, R. H. Jr., Leith, D. E. 1977. Relative contributions of hypocapnia and hyperpnea as mechanisms in post-exercise asthma. *J. Appl. Physiol: Respir. Envir. Exer. Physiol.* 42:22–27

42. McNally, J. F., Enright, P., Hirsch, J. E., Souhrada, J. F. 1979. The attenuation of exercise-induced bronchoconstriction by oropharyngeal anesthesia. *Am. Rev. Respir. Dis.* 119:247–52

43. McNeill, R. S., Nairn, J. R., Millar, J. S., Ingram, C. G. 1966. Exercise-induced asthma. *Q. J. Med.* 35:55–67

44. Myung, K. P., Hayashi, S., Wise, F. M., Robotham, J. L. 1982. Mechanisms of cooling-induced contraction of isolated smooth muscle. *Fed. Proc.* 41:(4) 1356 (Abstr.)

45. O'Byrne, P. M., Ryan, G., Morris, M., McCormack, D., Jones, N. L., Morse, J. L. C., Hargreave, F. E. 1982. Asthma induced by cold air and its relation to nonspecific bronchial responsiveness to methacholine. *Am. Rev. Respir. Dis.* 125:281–85

46. O'Cain, C. F., Dowling, N. B., Slutsky, A. S., Hensley, M. J., Strohl, K. P., McFadden, E. R. Jr., Ingram, R. H. Jr. 1980. Airway effects of respiratory heat loss in normal subjects. *J. Appl. Physiol: Respir. Envir. Exer. Physiol.* 49:875–80

47. Proctor, D. F., Swift, D. L. 1977. Temperature and water vapor adjustment. In *Respiratory Defense Mechanisms (Part 1), Lung Biology in Health and Disease*, ed. J. D. Braw, D. F. Procter, L. M. Reid, 5:95–125. NY: Marcel Dekker. 488 pp.

48. Rasmussen, F. V., Madsen, L., Bundgaard, A. 1979. Combined effect of an anticholinergic drug ipratropium bromide and disodium cromoglycate in exercise-induced asthma. *Scand. J. Respir. Dis. Suppl.* 103:159–63

49. Rebuck, A. S., Read, J. 1968. Exercise-induced asthma. *Lancet* 1:429–31

50. Resnick, A. D., Deal, E. C. Jr., Ingram, R. H. Jr., McFadden, E. R. Jr. 1979. A critical assessment of the mechanism by which hyperoxia attenuates exercise-induced asthma. *J. Clin. Invest.* 64:541–49

51. Salter, H. H. 1864. *On Asthma: Its Pathology and Treatment*, pp. 132–153. Philadelphia: Blanchard and Lea. 457 pp.

52. Seaton, A., Davies, G., Gaziano, D., Hughes, R. O. 1969. Exercise-induced asthma. *Br. Med. J.* 3:556–58

53. Sheppard, D., Epstein, J., Holtzman, M. J., Nadel, J. A., Boushey, H. A. 1981. Dose-dependent inhibition of cold-air-induced bronchoconstriction by atropine. *Physiologist* 24:28 (Abstr.)

54. Sheppard, D., Nadel, J. A., Boushey, H. A. 1981. Inhibition of sulfur dioxide-induced bronchoconstriction by disodium cromoglycate in asthmatic subjects. *Am. Rev. Respir. Dis.* 124:257–59

55. Silverman, M., Anderson, S. D., Walker, S. R. 1972. Metabolic changes preceding exercise-induced bronchoconstriction. *Br. Med. J.* 1:207–9

56. Simonsson, B. G., Skoogh, B. E., Ekstrom-Jodal, B. 1972. Exercise-induced airways constriction. *Thorax* 27:169–80

57. Soter, N. A., Austen, K. F. 1977. Urticaria, angioedema, and mediator release in humans in response to physical environment stimuli. *Fed. Proc.* 36:1736–40

58. Stanescu, D. C., Teculescu, D. B. 1970. Exercise and cough-induced asthma. *Respiration* 27:377–79

59. Stearns, D. R., McFadden, E. R. Jr., Breslin, F. J., Ingram, R. H. Jr. 1981. A reanalysis of the refractory period in exertional asthma. *J. Appl. Physiol: Respir. Envir. Exer. Physiol.* 50:503–8

60. Strauss, R. H., Ingram, R. H. Jr., McFadden, E. R. Jr. 1977. A critical assessment of the roles of circulating hydrogen ion and lactate in the production of exercise-induced asthma. *J. Clin. Invest.* 60:658–64

61. Strauss, R. H., McFadden, E. R. Jr., Ingram, R. H. Jr., Deal, E. C. Jr., Jaeger, J. J. 1978. Influence of heat and humidity on the airway obstruction induced by exercise in asthma. *J. Clin. Invest.* 61:433–40

62. Strauss, R. H., McFadden, E. R. Jr., Ingram, R. H. Jr., Jaeger, J. J. 1977. Enhancement of exercise-induced asthma by cold air breathing. *N. Engl. J. Med.* 297:743–47

63. Thomson, N. C., Patel, K. R., Kerr, J. W. 1978. Sodium cromoglycate and ipratropium bromide in exercise-induced asthma. *Thorax* 33:694–99

64. Van Houtte, P. M., Lorenz, R. R. 1970. Effect of temperature on reactivity of saphenous, mesenteric and femoral veins of the dog. *Am. J. Physiol.* 218:1746–50

65. Vassallo, C. L., Gee, J. B. L., Domm, B. M. 1972. Exercise-induced asthma: observations regarding hypocapnia and acidosis. *Am. Rev. Respir. Dis.* 105:42–49

Ann. Rev. Physiol. 1983. 45:465–79

DYSPNEA AND EXERCISE

K. J. Killian and E. J. M. Campbell

Department of Medicine, McMaster University, Hamilton, Ontario, Canada L8N 3Z5

INTRODUCTION

"Many physiologists and clinicians have written articles entitled 'Dyspnea' which were in fact articles on the regulation of respiration, the causes of hyperpnea or the causes of hyperventilation—which, in fact, had nothing to do with the sensation of dyspnea" (13). This remark was made by Julius Comroe in the opening statement of an international symposium on the topic of breathlessness in 1965. The remark remains true today. Although dyspnea occurs commonly during exercise, the role of exercise in the generation of respiratory distress is probably quantitative and there is nothing unique about exercise itself. Breathing is a particular motor act generating proprioceptive information of which we are not normally conscious. However, under certain circumstances this proprioceptive information gives rise to an unpleasant awareness of breathing and of respiratory distress.

This review falls into two main parts: (*a*) a detailed review of psychophysical work on the nature of the stimulus underlying respiratory sensation, and (*b*) a review of factors during exercise that are likely to modify these sensory stimuli.

Do Pulmonary Afferents Contribute directly to Dyspnea?

The possibility that afferents arising in the airways, lungs, or pulmonary circulation are sentient—i.e. are consciously perceived—and may contribute to dyspnea is implicit in much of the literature. No acceptable direct evidence enables a clear verdict on this question, but in our view the balance of evidence favors the view that these afferents contribute to dyspnea by altering the drives to the respiratory muscles and that the control and behavior of the respiratory muscles are the final common pathway to the respiratory sensation commonly meant by the term "dyspnea."

465

0066-4278/83/0315-0465$02.00

The Basic Sensations

The basic proprioceptive sensations are: position, which in the respiratory system is expressed as volume; displacement, which is expressed as change of volume or flow; and force, which is expressed most conveniently as pressure. Of perhaps greater importance are the compound sensations of load (elastance, resistance), which have the dimensions of both force and displacement. We review the basic and compound sensations after outlining the basic model and the methods used.

Basic Sensory Model

The model (Figure 1) we use is common to all sensory modalities but is perhaps most commonly used in relationship to the special senses. Neurophysiology comfortably encompasses the progression from sensory stimuli to the formation of sensory impression. However, we must not regard the formation of perception at the conscious level as merely the reconstruction of the primary sensory information. The sensory impression is interpreted in light of previous experience and learning and is thus modified by many physiological and psychological processes. These modifications fall most readily into the domain of behavioral psychology. Of course these subdivisions are artificial and the area of interest—the relationship between sensory stimuli and sensation—embraces both. Psychophysics is the quantitative study of the relationship between sensory stimuli and the evoked conscious response. This relationship is dependent on both neurophysiology and psychology and indeed on all the unit processes described. Were we narrowly to confine our interests to one or all of the unit processes in isolation we would fail to understand the integrated interaction of these processes in generating conscious sensation. Regrettably, the study of the integrated system is often neglected in favor of the in-depth study of the component parts.

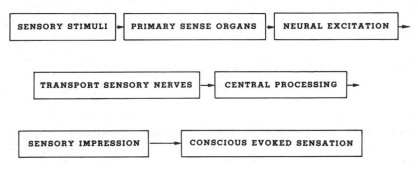

Figure 1   Basic sensory model

Psychophysics

Psychophysics looks at the quantitative relationship between the input parameters (i.e. the parameters of stimulation) and the output parameters (i.e. the evoked sensory response). Psychophysicists have confined their interest to well-defined domains, each of which asks specific questions about the psychophysical relationship: Is there something there (detection)? Is this different from that (discrimination)? What is it (recognition)? How big is it (scaling)? Each of these questions relates to the perception of a stimulus but always falls short of a total description (i.e. perception). Although all the domains are related, each question addresses a different aspect of the psychophysical relationship. The ability to discriminate stimuli is different from the ability to scale the magnitude of a stimulus or to recognize one sensory stimulus from another. Although this appears obvious, there has been much confusion between the different domains, especially between discrimination and scaling.

Detection and Discrimination

Detection and discrimination studies use essentially the same methods. The absolute and difference threshold may be determined using any of three classical methods: (a) The frequency method allows for the presentation of a range of stimuli around the expected threshold on a number of trials. The subject signals the detection or absence of a stimulus. The threshold is the stimulus magnitude at which the subject detects the stimulus with a 50% probability. (b) The method of limits allows for the presentation of a range of stimuli in ascending or descending order of magnitude. The subject signals detection or absence of a detectable stimulus as before. The trials are averaged and a detection threshold derived. (c) The method of constant stimuli or average error allows for the subject to reproduce a standard stimulus. The mean and standard deviation of the reproduced stimulus are calculated. The standard deviation essentially describes the discrimination threshold. Stimuli falling above this standard deviation are likely to be detected by the subject. This method gives results similar to those of the previous methods. The application of signal detection theory has shown that the detection threshold is the result of the neurophysiological sensitivity of the system and the response bias (selection criterion) adopted by the subject. In order to be rigorous both should be calculated; in practice this is very time consuming.

Scaling

The measurement of the perceived magnitude of a stimulus merely implies the matching of a number (length of line or handgrip, etc) to an object or event with arbitrarily selected preset rules. The rules are defined by the scaling method. Most of the scales used widely by psychologists are ordinal scales and are of little use in quantifying sensation. The interval scale is quantitative in the ordinary sense of the word. The subject attempts to maintain equality of differences. The zero point on an interval scale is a matter of convenience. The ratio scale requires the subject to maintain proportionality throughout.

If a subject is asked to select a number proportional to the intensity of a stimulus (e.g. the intensity of a light) the relationship between the number and the intensity of the stimulus has the attributes of a ratio scale. This technique is known as open magnitude scaling and using it S. S. Stevens (48) found that a wide range of sensory modalities obey a ratio scale. For a given increase in physical magnitude, there is a proportionate increase in sensory magnitude; this ratio remains constant through the whole range of stimulation. However, these ratios are not necessarily the same for different senses. If the perceived magnitude is plotted against the physical magnitude, doubling the length of a line increases its perceived length by 100%; doubling sound intensity increases perceived intensity by approximately 60%; doubling light intensity increases perceived intensity by 25%; and doubling a lifted weight increases perceived weight by 170%. To translate this into mathematical terms, the sensory magnitude (Ψ) is related to the physical magnitude (ϕ) by a power function, n, such that $\Psi = K\phi^n$ When the log Ψ is plotted against the log ϕ we get a straight line with a slope n and an intercept K:

$$\Psi = K\phi^n \quad \text{or} \quad \log \Psi = \log K + n \log \phi.$$

This simple proportionality, found across many sensory modalities, is not only intuitively appealing, but neural impulse frequency also increases as a power function of the physical magnitude of stimulation for many of the primary senses (3, 38, 49).

Basic Sensations

SENSE OF VOLUME AND DISPLACEMENT   There are several possible sources of volume and displacement information: vagally mediated stretch receptors, joint receptors, and muscle spindles. Recent work on limb muscles suggests that muscle receptors rather than joint receptors are the most likely source of kinesthetic sensation (16, 18, 21, 34). It is not unlikely that the sense of volume and displacement in the chest is also served by muscular receptors.

Bakers & Tenney (1) applied the psychophysical techniques of open magnitude scaling to the perception of volume changes in the chest. When they compared the physical and psychological magnitudes the data were well described by a power function. They did not address the question of the mechanism of volume perception. Using a variety of scaling and discrimination techniques, Halttunen (25) showed a consistent relationship between the subjective sensation and the volume changes induced by both inspiratory and expiratory muscle. Perception was different for inspiratory and expiratory efforts and there was a good correlation between the sensory magnitude and the total number of electromyograph (EMG) impulses. The number of EMG impulses and volume displacement might be expected to increase proportionately if the load or impedance to the respiratory system is constant. Salamon & von Euler (44) confirmed a power function relationship between sensation and volume changes in the chest. However, these relationships could not be defined by a single psychophysical power function. They suggested two power function relationships with different exponents—one applicable to volumes over functional residual capacity (FRC) and one operating below FRC. These exponents corresponded to the use of inspiratory muscle (above FRC) and expiratory muscle (below FRC). They concluded that sensory information from respiratory muscle is of dominant importance for the judgment of chest volume. Although receptors in the lungs and upper airways cannot be excluded, it appeared likely that these receptors were not a dominant source of information (44). The exponent found in this study was again greater than 1.0. Vagal firing frequency in response to changes in lung volume is known to follow a power function with an exponent of only 0.5 (12). In a subsidiary experiment the ability to reattain FRC was impaired following great efforts of the inspiratory muscle. These are known to alter normal sensory inputs from muscle spindles in the contracting muscle (23).

Using the psychophysical technique of volume matching, Wolkove et al (55) found that normal subjects can accurately match reference volumes. However, when the mechanical condition of the system altered between the control reference breath and the matching breath by the addition of any added resistance, the ability to match volumes deteriorated. Their results suggested that force or effort is an important input to the perception of volume changes in the respiratory system. However, as shown in the study of Salamon & von Euler (44), alterations in spindle activity can be expected with increased effort. Using similar techniques, Stubbing et al (50) found that both passive ventilation and chest vibration impaired the ability of subjects accurately to match volumes. They concluded that afferent information generated by receptors affected by respiratory muscle contraction was important in the perception of volume changes. Traditionally the joint receptors have been considered the most likely source of afferent information (34). However, their role is now questionable. They are most stimulated at the extremes of displacement, whereas the acuity of volume perception is stable throughout. In recent years primary and secondary endings from muscle spindles have been considered a more likely source of displacement information (for review see 34).

SENSE OF FORCE OR PRESSURE   Respiratory muscle and peripheral limb muscle are similar in many respects. Both make finely graded contractions. During the last decade, investigators have reassessed the means by which the sensorium perceives forces produced by muscle. Studies on the sensation of muscle force or apparent heaviness indicate that a mechanism proposed in the 19th century may operate. The centrally generated motor command delivered to the motor neurones can signal the perceived force during muscular contractions in the limbs—i.e. sense of effort (for review see 34; 19, 35, 43).

In addition to their study of the perception of volume, Bakers & Tenney (1) looked at the sensory magnitude of forces generated, predominately by expiratory muscles. As with volume, the sensory magnitude Ψ grew as a power function (n) of the physical magnitude ø, such that $\Psi = K\phi^n$. These workers had their subjects both estimate the sensory magnitude of a range of pressures and also reproduce pressure changes proportionate to a series of sensory estimates (magnitude estimation and magnitude production). The mean value of n was 1.6, close to that for the perceived magnitude of lifted weights or the force of contraction of limb muscle (46, 48). They also performed the experiment at both total lung capacity (TLC), when the expiratory muscles would be long, and at FRC, when they would be shortened. If the sense of effort were important, the sensory magnitude of an achieved pressure might be expected to increase at FRC compared to TLC. Unfortunately, the authors reported only the exponent n and did not report intercepts. There are no significant differences in exponents. With fatiguing contractions of peripheral limb muscle the sense of magnitude increases but the exponent remains the same (7). Gandevia et al (20) showed that with fatiguing static inspiratory muscle pressures the sensory magnitude of the achieved tension declines with fatigue. Simultaneously, the sense of effort increases continuously throughout the fatiguing contraction (20). In a recently completed study on the perceived magnitude of static inspiratory pressures, we also found that as the resting inspiratory muscle length shortened (increasing lung volume) the perception of achieved tension actually declined as the magnitude of effort increased (D. G. Stubbing, submitted for publication).

It would now appear that the sense of achieved force is independent of that of effort. However, as has been previously suggested, it is likely that the sense of effort is the dominant sensation. Although it appears likely that the sense of achieved force is related to information generated by muscular receptors such as the tendon organs, the mechanism subserving the sense of effort remains unclear. Although most studies support the contention that it is subserved by the awareness of an outgoing motor command, the evidence remains circumstantial.

SENSE OF LOAD   During the act of breathing, the inspiratory muscles generate force and the volume displacement achieved in the chest depends on the elastance and resistance of the respiratory system. The force of contraction of inspiratory muscle is carefully controlled to achieve physiological levels of ventilation. The intensity and duration of force are dependent not only on the metabolic requirements but also on the mechanical state of the chest wall and lungs. Chemoreceptors give an indirect indication of the resistance and elastance of the lungs, in that force requirements increase as the impedance of the respiratory system increases. There are, however, also afferent feedbacks from the lung, respiratory muscles, and chest wall. The sense of load is perhaps the most important of all of the sensory information generated in the chest.

In order to explore the psychophysical relationships of loading, calibrated elastic and resistive loads have been added to the breathing of normal subjects while the sensory response is measured. The early studies concentrated on the addition of very small loads, and just-noticeable differences in loads were studied. Campbell and his colleagues showed that normal subjects can reliably detect very small added resistances and elastances (2, 8). The detection threshold has subsequently been shown to depend on the background load and closely follows the general sensory law known as Weber's law (just noticeable change in stimulus ΔI bears a constant relationship to the background stimulus I such that $\Delta I/I = $ constant) (54). Extrapolating from their experience with load detection, Campbell & Howell (9) proposed that not only load detection but perhaps also dyspnea is dependent on the relationship between force and displacement. This general hypothesis became known as "length/tension inappropriateness." Many subsequent studies have provided evidence in accord with this general hypothesis (27, 28, 56).

The receptors and route of transfer of sensory afferents have received some attention. Guz et al (24) showed that load detection is not altered by vagal blockade. Therefore, visceral afferents arising within the lung and travelling via the vagus do not appear essential for load detection. Studies in subjects with spinal cord lesions or spinal anesthesia up to the cervical cord suggest that information from the chest wall is not necessary (15, 41, 57). Indeed, with complete transection of the spinal cord above C_3 load detection has been reported as normal (40). It would appear that any muscle, even an accessory muscle, can mediate the necessary information for load detection. Load detection in the presence of passive ventilation grossly deteriorates (29). Although upper airway receptors are undoubtedly sentient, they do not appear to mediate load detection for the following reasons. Load detection deteriorates in the presence of airflow obstruction when upper airway receptors would not be expected to function abnormally (6, 54). Anesthesia of the upper airway reduces the ability to detect loads but only in direct proportion to the increase in airway resistance consequent on anesthesia (11, 39). In an unpublished study, we found load detection was slightly reduced (0.6 cmH_2O $l^{-1}s^{-1}$ → 1.0 cmH_2O $l^{-1}s^{-1}$) when loads were added around the chest rather than at the mouth. This reduction can be accounted for by the increase in background elastance due to phase differences in pressure around the chest (45). When loads are added around the chest cage, many subjects localize the detection of load to the mouth. Hence subjective referral of proprioceptive information can be misleading.

Threshold detection has contributed to our understanding of loaded sensation, and small threshold loads may be of neurophysiological interest; but subjective symptoms of distress are generally associated with much larger loads.

More recently, scaling procedures have been used to assess the sensory responses to much larger loads. Using open magnitude scaling, Gottfried et al (22) found that the sensory magnitude of a range of added resistive loads increased as a power function of the added load. The exponent describing the rate of increase was significantly smaller in the presence of chronic airflow obstruction. Killian et al (30) found that in normal subjects the sensory magnitude of both resistive and elastic loads followed this same power function. In subjects with a high exponent for resistance they also found a high exponent for elastance. There was a wide range of exponents in both normal subjects and patients with airflow obstruction. This wide range of perceptual responses may explain the variability of dyspnea in the presence of comparable degrees of mechanical impedance. Pursuing this variability further, Killian et al found that the sensory magnitude of an added load is in part dependent on the pattern of breathing (31). With added resistive loads, the perceived magnitude increased as the load increased but also as the flow rate increased. Similarly, with added elastic loads the magnitude increased as the load increased but also as the tidal volume increased. In both cases, the sensory magnitude increased as mouth pressure increased ($\dot{V} \times \Delta R = Pm$ or $Vt \times \Delta E = Pm$) and also as the inspiratory duration increased. When expressed as a function of both mouth pressure (Pm) and inspiratory duration (t_i), the sensory magnitude (ψ) grows as a power function: $\psi = K_o Pm^{1.3} t_i^{0.56}$. This relationship is quite similar to the perceived magnitude of the force of contraction of peripheral muscle (47).

Although the sensory magnitude appeared related to mouth pressure, which might suggest that airway receptors were important, we had subjects inspire with various patterns of breathing (rib cage, abdomen-diaphragm, or their freely selected combination) to see if the sensory magnitude for the same mouth pressure varied with the pattern. Sensory magnitude did indeed vary as might be expected if the force generated by the inspiratory muscle rather than the airway was the source of primary sensation (K. J. Killian, submitted for publication). We also found that the perceived magnitude of static inspiratory pressures of constant duration varied with different patterns of breathing in the same manner (D. G. Stubbing, submitted for publication).

The sensory magnitude of a given force is also uniquely related to the pattern of force expenditure. For the same total force expended over time, the perceived magnitude increases to a much greater degree with peak force. The sensory magnitude of a small peak force maintained over a long time is much less than that resulting from a high peak force maintained over a short time. Rather than operating (as Mead suggested) to minimize force expenditure, the pattern of breathing may favor lower peak forces even if this entails longer breaths (37).

Because the drive to breathe ultimately controls the intensity and duration of inspiratory force, drive may be an important parameter in the perceived magnitude of added loads. Burdon et al found that the perceived magnitude of added resistive loads increases with hypoxia, hypercapnia, and exercise. The increase in sensation was closely related to inspiratory pressure (4).

Although the perceptual response to added resistive or elastic loads to breathing may well be explained by the sensory magnitude of achieved force or the effort necessary to generate this force, the relevance of these findings to dyspnea remains speculative. Perhaps the major reservation about their applicability to dyspnea is due to clinical experience. There appears to be wide variability in respiratory distress for comparable mechanical impedances. Were the perception of force or effort of central importance then some degree of variability might be expected due to factors such as length/tension, force/velocity, distortion, pattern of breathing, and the presence or absence of fatigue. However, of greater potential importance is the state of adaptation. It is a general sensory principle that following prolonged periods of stimulation the perceptual magnitude of a stimulus declines (temporal adaptation). There is little doubt that adaptation plays a major role in respiratory sensation. Patients with chronic airflow obstruction are frequently asymptomatic whereas patients with asthma who suddenly develop comparable mechanical impedances are much distressed. It is difficult to establish the time course of adaptation and the factors that influence it. In the special senses of sight, hearing, etc, the time course is short and can be empirically ascertained. The general form follows a simple exponential relationship where the sensory magnitude ψ declines with the time constant r and a reduction in sensory magnitude j such that $\psi = K_0 e^{-t/r} + j$. Although the correspondence is not perfect, there is a possibility that the rate and reduction of sensory magnitude are in part dependent on the magnitude of the stimulus. For high stimulus magnitude the rate of decline and the absolute reduction in sensation are greater (33).

The empirical study of temporal adaptation is greatly facilitated by the presence of two eyes, ears, etc (the adapted eye can be compared with the unadapted eye). In the respiratory system it is considerably more difficult and methodology is a major limiting factor. Owing to time constraints only short-term adaptation can be studied. Using a technique of category scaling, McCloskey (36) found that after as little as twenty breaths there was a significant reduction in the perceived magnitude of added resistive loads. Time and memory limit the continuation of stimulation until either a plateau is reached or sensation is completely adapted.

Discrimination decreases as the magnitude of background stimuli increases, which suggests that sensory magnitude might follow a similar relationship. Studying the effects of short-term adaptation on the perceived magnitude of added resistive loads, Burdon et al found that this was not the case (5). Although discrimination deteriorates with increasing background loads, there is not a comparable decrease in the sensory magnitude of added loads. The study of adaptation in the respiratory system is in its infancy. Many factors (e.g. ventilatory capacity) may well prove to account for major differences in sensory responses as a function of temporal adaptation.

FACTORS IN EXERCISE THAT MAY MODIFY SENSORY STIMULI

The role of exercise in the genesis of dyspnea is, in our opinion, quantitative. There is little unique about exercise itself. Many factors, such as exercise, mechanical impedance to breathing, hyperpnea, muscle weakness, etc, contribute to dyspnea; but the central unifying feature is the force generated by the inspiratory muscle. We have already presented some preliminary data to suggest that not the force itself but the effort necessary to generate this force is of primary importance. Although the evidence is circumstantial, a conscious awareness of the outgoing motor command may be dominant in our appreciation not only of muscular effort but also of respiratory distress. The demands made on inspiratory muscle, force, or effort are considerably increased during exercise.

Impedance of the Respiratory System

During exercise, patients with airflow obstruction or fibrotic conditions of the lung are considerably more dyspneic than normal subjects for comparable levels of ventilation. In fact, in patients with respiratory disease, breathlessness is usually the limiting factor to exercise (26). Most patients with respiratory disability reach close to a limiting ventilation predicted from their spirometry (26). The mechanical determinants of maximum ventilation are the maximum force the subject can maintain (without fatigue) and the impedance of the respiratory system (17). In physiological circumstances normal subjects do not approach maximum inspiratory forces and experience only mild to moderate respiratory distress. On the other hand, patients with respiratory disability reach maximum forces or close to maximum force at maximum exercise capacity and are usually breathless. For a given level of ventilation the force generated by the inspiratory muscles is directly related to the impedance of the respiratory system. Impedance is thus a major factor in the determination of respiratory distress with exercise.

With progressive airflow obstruction, the resting end-expiratory lung volumes increase, resulting in a shortening of the inspiratory muscle length. For a given inspiratory muscle working against a given impedance, both the motor neural output and the sense of effort would be expected to increase (D. G. Stubbing, submitted for publication). Similarly, with muscle weakness resulting either from primary myopathies or secondary to peripheral neuropathies the motor neural output might also be expected to increase in view of the reduced muscle mass. The consequent increase in sense of effort may well account for the respiratory distress that occurs with muscle weakness (10).

Alveolar Ventilation

The increased cellular requirements for oxygen uptake and CO_2 excretion during exercise must be accompanied by an appropriate increase in ventilation in order to prevent cellular dysfunction due to tissue anoxia and respiratory acidosis. Ventilation with exercise is remarkably attuned to the rate of oxygen consumption and carbon dioxide output. This places increased demand on the inspiratory muscles since the forces generated depend on the level of metabolic demand and the impedance of the respiratory system. At low intensities of exercise, alveolar ventilation increases linearly with oxygen uptake and CO_2 output. At more strenuous levels of exercise, ventilation increases at a greater rate, and this is accompanied by an increase in lactic acid accumulation. The point at which ventilation increases more than oxygen uptake is known as the anaerobic threshold. Excessive increase in ventilation places an additional demand on the inspiratory muscles. In normal subjects the anaerobic threshold occurs at approximately 50% of the maximum oxygen uptake ($\dot{V}_{O_2}$max). However, patients with impaired cardiac output increase their blood lactate at low workloads, leading to excessive ventilatory demands and increasing breathlessness. The threshold is also related to work capacity and fitness and is delayed in those who are well-conditioned to exercise (conditioning reduces both ventilatory demands and the necessity for excessive force development by inspiratory muscles) (14, 42, 51, 52, 53). This excessive increase in ventilation is compounded by the excessive forces due to added impedance such as airflow obstruction or pulmonary congestion.

Total Ventilation

As the total ventilation is the sum of the alveolar ventilation and the deadspace ventilation, any increase in anatomic or physiological deadspace results in an increased requirement for inspiratory muscle force development. High $\dot{V}/\dot{Q}$ areas in the lung result in an ineffectiveness of gas exchange and an increase in the level of ventilation for a given oxygen transfer. This results in an increase in force required of the inspiratory muscles. When tidal volume is constrained by increased loads to breathing, such as airflow obstruction or fibrotic conditions of the lung, ventilation is increased predominately by an increase in frequency with small tidal volumes. This results in an inappropriate increase in total ventilation due to excessive deadspace ventilation. Again, the cost is borne by the respiratory muscles and the result is breathlessness. Pulmonary arterial obstruction due to pulmonary emboli also results in an increase in deadspace ventilation and excessive breathlessness. Stimulation of the receptors in the pulmonary circulation, particularly J receptors, may also contribute to breathlessness.

Distortion

There is no single elastance or resistance to the respiratory system. It has now become popular to describe the respiratory system in terms of two major degrees of freedom, each involving its own elastance. The minimum cost to inspiratory muscle is along the passive relaxation characteristic. However, in some cases distortion may occur, resulting in excessive force costs (32); in normal subjects this effect may not be great. In the presence of chest wall weakness due to spinal cord lesions the diaphragm must also bear the brunt of the failure of the rib cage muscles to expand the chest. This results in an indrawing of the chest and an increase in force cost for ventilation.

Fatigue

The perception of inspiratory effort increases in the presence of fatigue (20). Respiratory muscle fatigue is likely to occur when the force generated by respiratory muscles is excessive. This might occur when the added impedance to breathing is very high or the ventilatory demands of the respiratory system are considerably increased. Although not extensively studied, inspiratory muscle fatigue may well contribute to increasing breathlessness.

In Summary

Recent work promises to show that dyspnea at rest and exercise is largely explicable in terms of a quantitative disturbance of the sense of respiratory load. Of all acts involving muscles, breathing is the most compelling and unavoidable. As Dr. Comroe perceived, studies of such topics as the control of breathing, although important to filling out the picture, will not elucidate the sensation itself.

ACKNOWLEDGMENTS

The authors wish to thank Dr. N. L. Jones and associates for helpful suggestions and critical reading of this manuscript.

This work was supported by grants from the Medical Research Council of Canada and the Canadian Lung Association.

Dr. K. J. Killian was supported by a Rose Levy Rosenstadt Scholar Award.

Literature Cited

1. Bakers, J. H. C. M., Tenney, S. M. 1970. The perception of some sensations associated with breathing. *Respir. Physiol.* 10:85–92
2. Bennett, E. D., Jayson, M. I. V., Rubenstein, D., Campbell, E. J. M. 1962. The ability of man to detect added non-elastic loads to breathing. *Clin. Sci.* 23:155–62
3. Borg, G., Diamant, H., Ström, L., Zotterman, Y. 1967. The relation between neural and perceptual intensity. A comparative study of the neural and psychophysical response to taste stimuli. *J. Physiol.* 192:13–20
4. Burdon, J. G. W., Killian, K. J., Campbell, E. J. M. 1982. The effect of ventilatory drive on the perceived magnitude of added loads to breathing. *J. Appl. Physiol.* In press
5. Burdon, J. G. W., Killian, K. J., Stubbing, D. G., Campbell, E. J. M. 1982. The effect of background loads on the perception of added loads to breathing. *J. Appl. Physiol.* In press
6. Burki, N. K., Mitchell, K., Chaudhary, B. A., Zechman, F. W. 1978. The ability of asthmatics to detect added resistive loads. *Am. Rev. Respir. Dis.* 117:71–75
7. Cain, W. S., Stevens, J. C. 1971. Effort in sustained and phasic handgrip contractions. *Am. J. Psychol.* 34:52–65
8. Campbell, E. J. M., Freedman, S., Smith, P. S., Taylor, M. E. 1951. The ability of man to detect added elastic loads to breathing. *Clin. Sci.* 20:223–31
9. Campbell, E. J. M., Howell, J. B. L. 1963. The sensation of breathlessness. *Br. Med. Bull.* 19:36–40
10. Campbell, E. J. M., Gandevia, S. C., Killian, K. J., Mahutte, C. K., Rigg, J. R. A. 1980. Changes in the perception of inspiratory resistive loads during partial curarization. *J. Physiol.* 309:93–100
11. Chaudhary, B. A., Burki, N. K. 1978. Effects of airway anaesthesia on the

ability to detect added inspiratory resistive loads. *Clin. Sci.* 54:621–26
12. Clark, F. J., von Euler, C. 1972. On the regulation of depth and rate of breathing. *J. Physiol.* 222:267–95
13. Comroe, J. H. 1965. Some theories of the mechanism of dyspnoea in breathlessness. In *Breathlessness,* ed. J. B. L. Howell, E. J. M. Campbell, pp. 1–7. Oxford: Blackwell Scientific
14. Davis, J. A., Frank, M. W., Whipp, B. J., Wasserman, K. 1972. Anaerobic threshold alterations caused by endurance training in middle-aged men. *J. Appl. Physiol.* 46:1039–46
15. Eisele, J., Trenchard, D., Burki, N., Guz, A. 1968. The effect of chest wall block on respiratory sensation and control in man. *Clin. Sci.* 35:23–33
16. Eklund, G. 1972. Position sense and state of contraction; the effects of vibration. *J. Neurol. Neurosurg., Psychiatry* 35:606–11
17. Freedman, S. 1970. Sustained maximum voluntary ventilation. *Respir. Physiol.* 8:230–44
18. Gandevia, S. C., McCloskey, D. I. 1976. Joint sense, muscle sense, and their combination as position sense, measured at the distal interphalangeal joint of the middle finger. *J. Appl. Physiol.* 260:387–407
19. Gandevia, S. C., McCloskey, D. I. 1977. Sensation of heaviness. *Brain* 100:345–54
20. Gandevia, S. C., Killian, K. J., Campbell, E. J. M. 1981. The effect of respiratory muscle fatigue on respiratory sensations. *Clin. Sci.* 60:463–66
21. Goodwin, G. M., McCloskey, D. I., Matthews, P. B. C. 1972. The contribution of muscle afferents to kinaesthesia shown by vibration induced illusions of movement and by the effects of paralysing joint afferents. *Brain* 95:705–48
22. Gottfried, S. B., Altose, M. D., Kelson, S. G., Fogarty, C. M., Cherniack, N. S. 1978. The perception of changes in airflow resistance in normal subjects and patients with chronic airways obstruction. *Chest* 73:286–88
23. Granit, R. 1972. Constant errors in the execution and appreciation of movement. *Brain* 95:649–60
24. Guz, A., Noble, M. I. M., Widdicombe, J. G., Trenchard, D., Mushin, W. W., Makey, A. R. 1966. The role of vagal and glossopharyngeal afferent nerves in respiratory sensation control of breathing and arterial pressure regulation in conscious man. *Clin. Sci.* 30:161–70

25. Halttunen, P. K. 1974. The voluntary control in human breathing. *Acta Physiol. Scand.* Suppl. 419. 47 pp.
26. Jones, N. L., Campbell, E. J. M. 1982. *Clinical Exercise Testing.* Philadelphia: Saunders. 268 pp. 2nd ed.
27. Killian, K. J., Campbell, E. J. M., Howell, J. B. L. 1979. The effect of increased ventilation on resistive load discrimination. *Am. Rev. Respir. Dis.* 120:1233–38
28. Killian, K. J., Mahutte, C. K., Howell, J. B. L., Campbell, E. J. M. 1980. Effect of timing, flow, lung volume, and threshold pressures on resistive load detection. *J. Appl. Physiol.* 49(6):958–63
29. Killian, K. J., Mahutte, C. K., Campbell, E. J. M. 1980. Resistive load detection during passive ventilation. *Clin. Sci.* 59:493–95
30. Killian, K. J., Mahutte, C. K., Campbell, E. J. M. 1981. Magnitude scaling of externally added loads to breathing. *Am. Rev. Respir. Dis.* 123:12–15
31. Killian, K. J., Bucens, D. D., Campbell, E. J. M. 1981. The effect of patterns of breathing on the perceived magnitude of added loads to breathing. *J. Appl. Physiol.* In press
32. Konno, K., Mead, J. 1968. Static volume pressure characteristics of rib cage and abdomen. *J. Appl. Physiol.* 24:544–48
33. Marks, L. E. 1974. *Sensory Processes, the New Psychophysics.* NY: Academic. 334 pp.
34. McCloskey, D. I. 1978. Kinesthetic sensibility. *Physiol. Rev.* 58:768–820
35. McCloskey, D. I., Ebeling, P., Goodwin, G. M. 1974. Estimation of weights and tensions and apparent involvement of a 'sense of effort'. *Exp. Neurol.* 42:220–32
36. McCloskey, D. I. 1973. The effects of pre-existing loads upon detection of externally applied resistances to breathing in man. *Clin. Sci.* 45:561–64
37. Mead, K. 1960. Control of respiratory frequency. *J. Appl. Physiol.* 15:325–36
38. Mountcastle, V. B., Poggio, G. F., Werner, G. 1963. The relation of thalamic cell response to peripheral stimuli varied over an intensive continuum. *J. Neurophysiol.* 26:807–34
39. Newsom Davis, J. 1967. Contribution of somatic receptors in the chest wall to detection of added inspiratory airway resistance. *Clin. Sci.* 33:249–60
40. Noble, M. I. M., Frankel, H. L., Else, W., Guz, A. 1971. The ability of man to detect added resistive loads to breathing. *Clin. Sci.* 41:285–87

41. Noble, M. I. M., Frankel, H. L., Else, W., Guz, A. 1972. The sensation produced by threshold resistive loads to breathing. *Eur. J. Clin. Invest.* 2:72–77

42. Owles, W. H. 1930. Alternations in the lactic acid content of the blood as a result of light exercise, and associated changes in the CO_2-combining power of the blood and in the alveolar CO_2 pressure. *J. Physiol.* 69:214–37

43. Roland, P. E., Ladegaard-Pederson, H. 1977. A quantitative analysis of sensations of tension and kinaesthesia in man. Evidence for peripherally originating muscular sense and for a sense of effort. *Brain* 100:671–92

44. Salamon, M., von Euler, C., Franzen, O. 1975. *Perception of mechanical factors in breathing.* Presented at the Int. 'Physical Work and Effort', Wenner-Gren Center, Stockholm

45. Shahid, S. U., Goddard, B. A., Howell, J. B. L. 1981. Detection and interaction of elastic and flow-resistive respiratory loads in man. *Clin. Sci.* 61:339–43

46. Stevens, J. C., Macu, J. D. 1959. Scales of apparent force. *J. Exp. Psychol.* 58:405–13

47. Stevens, J. C., Cain, W. S. 1970. Effort in muscular contractions related to force level and duration. *Percept. Psychophys.* 8:240–44

48. Stevens, S. S. 1957. On the psychophysical law. *Psychol. Rev.* 64:153–81

49. Stevens, S. S. 1970. Neural events and the psychophysical law. *Science* 170:1043–50

50. Stubbing, D. G., Killian, K. J., Campbell, E. J. M. 1981. The quantification of respiratory sensations by normal subjects. *Respir. Physiol.* 44:251–50

51. Taylor, R., Jones, N. L. 1979. The reduction by training of CO_2 output during exercise. *Eur. J. Cardiol.* 9:53–62

52. Wasserman, K. 1981. Physiology of gas exchange and exertional dyspnoea. *Clin. Sci.* 61:7–13

53. Wasserman, K., Whipp, B. J., Koyal, S. N., Beaver, W. L. 1973. Anaerobic threshold and respiratory gas exchange during exercise. *J. Appl. Physiol.* 35:236–43

54. Wiley, R. L., Zechman, F. W. Jr., 1966–1967. Perception of added airflow resistance in humans. *Respir. Physiol.* 2:73–87

55. Wolkove, N., Altose, M. D., Kelsen, S. G., Kondapalli, P. G., Cherniak, N. S. 1981. Perception of changes in breathing in normal human subjects. *J. Appl. Physiol.* 50(1):78–83

56. Zechman, F. W., Davenport, P. W. 1978. Temporal differences in the detection of resistive and elastic loads to breathing. *Respir. Physiol.* 34:267–77

57. Zechman, F. W., O'Neill, R., Shannon, R. 1967. Effect of low cervical spinal cord lesions on detection of increased airflow resistance in man. *Physiologist* 10:356

RENAL AND ELECTROLYTE PHYSIOLOGY

Introduction, Thomas E. Andreoli, *Section Editor*

This year's section on Renal Physiology marks the fifth in a new format, in which one aspect of renal physiology is analyzed in detail by different experts. The four preceding topics treated arguments that were generally related to topography, whole organ function, hemodynamics, or segmental analysis of transport processes in various nephron segments. However, after explosive growth in the field of renal physiology, modern studies focus in large part on evaluating some of the cardinal canons of renal physiology from a subcellular point of view. The articles in this year's section have as their general theme "Recent Advances in Tubular Physiology" and draw heavily on the measurement of a variety of intracellular parameters as indexes to the validity of a variety of long-standing models.

In the first article, Walter Boron and Henry Sackin survey the methodologies available for determining intracellular ionic composition in renal tubular cells. These workers have summarized the available data on the intracellular ionic composition for Na^+, K^+, Cl^-, H^+, HCO_3^- and Ca^{2+}; and they consider the implication of these data with particular regard to current models for transepithelial ionic transport in renal tubular cells.

In the second article, B. M. Koeppen, B. A. Biagi, and Gerhard Giebisch review the electrophysiology of the mammalian nephron, with a particular emphasis on the information obtained using intracellular voltage recording techniques and ion-sensitive microelectrodes. It is obvious that a precise understanding of transport processes in renal tubular epithelia will require explicit information about transport processes across apical and basal membranes. But the information summarized by Koeppen et al provides a first approximation to the relative roles of apical and basal membranes in regulating transport processes in the nephron.

In the third article of this series, E. E. Windhager and Ann Taylor explore the crucial role of intracellular calcium ions in regulating sodium transport in renal tubular epithelia. The Windhager & Taylor review provides an elegant summary of the relations between alterations in intracellular calcium activity, the ways in which perturbations in intracellular calcium activity modify transepithelial sodium transport in the mammalian nephron, and the relations of these processes to those observed in other epithelia, notably amphibian epithelia.

In the last article of this series, Maurice Burg and David Good explore the details of coupled transport processes, with particular emphasis on the role of Na^+/Cl^- coupled transport events as alternate modalities to classical electrogenic sodium transport. The Burg & Good paper thus evaluates in some detail not only the plausible mechanisms for coupling of ion transport processes, but also the evidence for the occurrence of these kinds of coupled processes in various segments of the nephron.

Ann. Rev. Physiol. 1983. 45:483–96

MEASUREMENT OF INTRACELLULAR IONIC COMPOSITION AND ACTIVITIES IN RENAL TUBULES

Walter F. Boron

Department of Physiology, Yale University School of Medicine, New Haven, Connecticut 06510

Henry Sackin

Department of Physiology, Cornell University Medical College, New York, New York 10021

INTRODUCTION

The transport of solutes through renal-tubule cells is a two-step process involving the independent movement of solute across both luminal and basolateral cell membranes. An understanding of transcellular solute transport thus necessitates a separate analysis of transport at opposite surfaces of the epithelial cell, as well as a determination of solute composition within that cell. In this brief review we (*a*) survey the methodologies available for determining intracellular ion composition in renal-tubule cells; (*b*) summarize the data on intracellular ion composition for Na^+, K^+, Cl^-, H^+, HCO_3^-, and Ca^{2+}; and (*c*) consider the implications of these data with regard to the mechanisms of ion transport in renal-tubule cells.

TECHNIQUES FOR MEASURING INTRACELLULAR IONIC COMPOSITION

Classical Chemical Analysis

Classical analytical techniques measure the average intracellular concentration of a solute throughout all the cells of a tissue sample but cannot directly detect binding or compartmentalization. The tissue sample is equilibrated

0066-4278/83/0315-0483$02.00

with an extracellular space (ECS) marker, such as radioactively labelled inulin. Total sample H_2O content (w in g H_2O g^{-1} tissue wet weight) is determined from wet and dry tissue weights, or by employing tritiated water. The extracellular portion of sample water (v in g H_2O g^{-1} wet weight) is the ratio of the ECS-marker concentration in the tissue sample's water to its concentration in the bulk extracellular water. The solute's intracellular concentration, $[X]_i$, is:

$$[X]_i = ([X]_t - v[X]_o)/(w-v),$$

where the solute's concentration in the tissue sample is $[X]_t$ (in mole kg^{-1} wet weight) and that in the bulk extracellular fluid is $[X]_o$ (in mole/kg^{-1} H_2O).

Advantages of this technique are its ease and its accuracy when employed with large samples. A major disadvantage is the inaccuracy of the ECS determination. The consistently higher values of $[Na^+]_i$ and lower values of $[K^+]_i$, compared to electron microprobe analysis (see below), are likely due to an underestimation of ECS (3). Another disadvantage is that tissue heterogeneity precludes an analysis of a particular cell type.

Electron Microprobe Analysis (EMA)

When atoms are excited by irradiation with an electron beam, they subsequently relax by emitting X-rays that fall into two classes: "characteristic" and "continuum" X-rays. The former appear as a single sharp peak whose location is unique for each element and whose area corresponds to the amount of the element present. The latter produce a diffuse signal, whose intensity, in thin sections of biological material, is proportional to total sample mass (20). Standard energy-dispersive X-ray detectors can analyze elements of atomic number greater than 11 (i.e. Na). Unique advantages of EMA are its ability to measure several elemental concentrations simultaneously and, in biological sections, to do so for particular cells or extracellular compartments, provided these can be recognized in the electron microscope. Inherent limitations, shared with classical analyses, are that elemental concentrations and not ion activities are measured, and that a tissue sample cannot be continuously monitored during an experiment.

Three aspects of sample preparation are currently of special concern: freezing and sectioning temperature, section thickness, and state of hydration. Samples are quick frozen by immersion in a liquid such as Freon at $\sim -160°C$ (12) and then sectioned in a cryomicrotome. Since the crystalline structure of ice changes at $\sim -75°$, sectioning should be done at $-80°C$ or less (55) so that diffusion of solutes is minimized. Although sectioning at $\sim -30°C$ improves morphological detail, control studies (52) have failed to demonstrate that ion gradients can be preserved at the resolution of a renal cell.

Epithelial section thicknesses are currently 0.1–1 μm. Thicker sections produce increased signal but reduced morphologic detail and spatial resolution. An example of the last is the study of Beck et al (3) on 1 μm thick sections of rat renal cortex. $[Na^+]_i$ and $[K^+]_i$ values near the center of the proximal-tubule cell were reasonable, but those near the apical and basal regions were consistent with a 20–30% extracellular contamination.

Sections can be prepared fully hydrated or freeze-dried. Since fully hydrated sections can be analyzed before and after dehydration on the microprobe's stage, elemental concentrations can be accurately expressed in mmole per kg water (19). In addition, extracellular spaces, such as the tubule lumen, remain filled and can be analyzed; this is impossible in freeze-dried sections. However, fully hydrated samples must be manipulated carefully to avoid condensation or sublimation of water, and their poor contrast greatly reduces morphological detail. Freeze-dried sections offer ease of preparation and greatly improved morphology. Unfortunately, elemental concentration can be related only indirectly to cell water.

Ion-Selective Microelectrodes

In theory the voltage (E) across an ion-selective sensor, such as a liquid ion exchanger (LIX) or a selective glass membrane, is Nernstian. In practice, however, the electrode's slope (S) is determined empirically by

$$E = E_o + S \log a,$$

where E_o is the standard electrode voltage, and a is the ion activity in a test solution. If, in addition to its sensitivity to ion i, the sensor also responds to a second ion, j, of the same valence, then:

$$E = E_o + S \log (a_i + k_{ij} a_j),$$

where $1/k_{ij}$ is the ratio of the electrode's sensitivity to ions i and j.

Intracellular ion activity (a_i) measurements require that both ion-sensitive and indifferent electrodes be miniaturized and placed within cells, preferably in the same cell. The latter insures that no voltage drop occurs between microelectrode tips. Although it is difficult to impale one cell with two separate microelectrodes, impalement with a single double-barreled electrode is feasible (27). However, the miniaturization of a glass or LIX ion-sensitive electrode degrades the latter's selectivity and/or time response. Thus for a given performance level, the double-barreled is larger than the single-barreled electrode and more likely to damage cells upon impalement. Alternatively, two nearby cells may be impaled with two single-barreled electrodes, an approach validated on the salamander proximal tubule (7), which is of a single cell type.

A major advantage of ion-sensitive electrodes is their nondistructive nature, which permits continuous recording of a_i. In addition, the activity measurements can be made in a specific cell type. The major limitation of electrodes is their potential sensitivity to more than one ion. Although negligible for pH- or Na-sensitive glass, this problem can be more serious with LIX sensors, for which increased sharpness generally is associated with decreased slope and selectivity. Cl-sensitive electrodes (1 μm tip size) made of Corning's #477315 LIX resin have a selectivity of Cl⁻ over HCO_3^- of only about 10:1, and K^+ electrodes made of Corning's #477317 resin have a K^+/Na^+ selectivity of only about 50:1. Fortunately, intracellular levels of HCO_3^- and Na^+ are considerably lower than those of Cl⁻ and K^+ so that major errors in activity measurements are unlikely to occur unless $[Cl^-]_i$ or $[K^+]_i$ are very low. Although the Na^+/K^+ selectivity of Na^+ LIX electrodes has in the past been especially poor, newer electroneutral carriers (54) promise much better performance. A second limitation of ion-sensitive electrodes arises when transient changes of a_i are employed as an index of ion transport. Since ion transport is really related to changes of intracellular ion *content,* rather than to *concentration* per se, changes in cell volume can independently alter a_i and thus mask or exaggerate true changes in ion content.

Dyes

Dyes are available for measuring pH, Ca^{2+} and Mg^{2+}. The pH-sensitive dye neutral red has been used to measure qualitative changes in external pH on suspensions of rabbit tubules (37). In the approach pioneered by Thomas et al (59), cells are exposed to a colorless and permeable acetate derivative of a pH-sensitive dye. When the derivative enters the cell, native esterases cleave the acetate, releasing the impermeable dye. This approach has been used to study pH_i transients in salamander proximal tubules (9). Similar derivatives of Ca-sensitive dyes have also been prepared (60).

Nuclear Magnetic Resonance (NMR) Spectroscopy

Certain atomic nuclei (e.g. ¹H, ¹³C, and ³¹P) possess a quantum mechanical property called spin, which generates a magnetic moment along the spin's axis. ³¹P NMR spectroscopy can measure pH_i because the ³¹P peak for $H_2PO_4^-$ is shifted with respect to that for HPO_4^{2-}. Since the interconversion $H_2PO_4^- \rightleftharpoons HPO_4^{2-} + H^+$ (pK $\cong$ 6.8) occurs rapidly, there is a single inorganic phosphate peak whose position depends on $[H_2PO_4^-]/[HPO_4^{2-}]$, and thus on pH. Because ³¹P NMR can quantitate other ³¹P-containing compounds, it is also useful for studying metabolism in vivo. The technique is noninvasive, capable of continuous monitoring, measures only the unbound portion of the substance, and can detect compartmentalization. NMR's major disadvantage, aside from its great expense, is its relative insensitivity: millimolar concentrations are required. ^{31}P NMR has been used in intact rat kidneys (47,53) and in suspensions of rabbit renal tubules (2). Na^+, K^+, Cl^-, and Ca^{2+} could be examined by the NMR technique as well. For reviews, see (2) and (48).

APPLICATIONS

Thermodynamic Driving Force

Knowledge of an ion's intracellular activity is essential for determining net thermodynamic driving force $V_m - E$, where V_m is the membrane potential and E is the equilibrium potential. The former is measured with a Ling-Gerard microelectrode. The latter is defined by:

$$E = \frac{RT}{zF} \ln \frac{a_o}{a_i},$$

where a_o and a_i are the ion's extra- and intracellular activities, respectively; z is valence; and F, R, and T have their usual meanings. Note that E may be different at the luminal and basolateral membranes. If V_m equals E, there can be no net passive movement of the ion, whereas if V_m deviates from E, there is a *tendency* for the ion to either passively enter or leave the cell. Although the presence of a gradient implies that at least one primary or secondary active transport system (see 1) acts on the ion, by itself it does not indicate whether the required transport process is located at the luminal and/or basolateral membrane. If other experiments localize a net flux to either the luminal or basolateral membrane, the relation between V_m and E determines whether the flux requires active transport, or whether it *could* be explained by simple diffusion. Even in the latter case, a contribution by an active transport process cannot be ruled out.

Ion Permeability Ratios

If V_m is completely described by the Goldman-Hodgkin-Katz equation, then V_m is a function only of intra- and extracellular ion activities, as well as the membrane's permeability to those ions. In practice, however, V_m is affected by nondiffusive processes that produce current flow across the membrane (e.g. electrogenic transport processes and the shunt current in leaky epithelia). An accurate determination of ion permeability ratios thus requires a systematic study of changes in (a) transepithelial voltage, (b) membrane voltage, and (c) intracellular ion activities during luminal and basolateral substitutions of the ion under consideration.

Calculation of Net Fluxes

An ion's net influx (J) is proportional to the rate of change of intracellular content of that ion. Assuming no binding, the amount of the ion inside the cell is simply $a_i U/\gamma$, where a_i is the activity, U is the volume of cell water, and γ is the ionic activity coefficient. Thus

$$J = \frac{1}{A} \frac{d}{dt} (\frac{a_i U}{\gamma}),$$

where A is the membrane surface area. Assuming that γ is constant, and that both a_i and U change with time,

$$J = \frac{1}{A\gamma} (U \frac{da_i}{dt} + a_i \frac{dU}{dt}).$$

Although in theory both a_i and U must be monitored to determine net flux, in practice measurements of a_i alone may provide qualitative information, provided changes in U are relatively small. Even if the net flux of an ion is accurately measured, it remains to be determined how much of that flux occurs across the luminal as opposed to the basolateral membrane. This problem may be approached by blocking transport of the ion selectively across one of the membranes, or by removing the ion from either the luminal and basolateral solution.

Thermodynamics of Coupled Transport.

The net driving force for a carrier that mediates the transport of more than one ion is readily calculated from a_i data, provided that the direction of net transport is determined solely by the sum of gradients for each of the transported ions, and not by metabolic processes. For example, the direction of net transport by an electroneutral NaCl cotransporter will be inward, provided $a_o^{Na} \cdot a_o^{Cl} > a_i^{Na} \cdot a_i^{Cl}$.

IONIC COMPOSITION OF RENAL-TUBULE CELLS

Sodium

PROXIMAL TUBULE   Early estimates of a_i^{Na} (see Table 1) in *Necturus* tubules (21, 29) were obtained using LIX electrodes with a very poor Na^+/K^+ selectivity. the most recent a_i^{Na} estimates, derived from experiments with either glass or LIX Na-sensitive electrodes having a Na^+/K^+ selectivity greater than 40:1, indicate that a_i^{Na} is in the range of 11 to 15 mM in *Necturus* (10, 36), and about 24 mM in *Ambystoma* (49). The higher values in *Ambystoma* vs *Necturus* may reflect a species difference since, in a few cases, the same microelectrode was used in the two preparations. The 22 mM estimate for a_i^{Na} in the bullfrog (15) was obtained with a double-barreled LIX electrode having a Na^+/K^+ selectivity of 7:1. The only estimate of Na^+ composition in a mammalian proximal tubule is the electron microprobe value of 33 mM (3), consistent with an a^{Na}_i in the range reported for amphibian tubules.

There is general agreement that a^{Na}_i is substantially below the value predicted for electrochemical equilibrium of Na^+ across either luminal or basolateral membranes. Assuming an a^{Na} of 75 mM in both the luminal (a^{Na}_l) and basolateral (a^{Na}_{bl}) solutions, and an a^{Na}_i of 15 mM, the calculated E_{Na} is +41 mV across both membranes. Given reasonable values for V_l and V_{bl} (e.g. $\sim$–60 mV), a substantial driving force exists favoring the passive influx of Na^+ across both membranes. The relatively low value of a^{Na}_i thus implies the existence of an Na-extruding pump, such as a basolateral Na-K ATPase.

Measurements of a^{Na}_i can also be used to study processes in which the transport of Na^+ is coupled to that of other solutes. For example, in *Necturus* proximal tubule, adding 10 mM glucose to the lumen increases a^{Na}_i by $\sim$50% (21), consistent with luminal Na-glucose cotransport. In the same preparation, replacement of luminal Cl^- by isethionate or cyclamate produces a 33–56% decrease of a^{Na}_i, consistent with luminal NaCl cotransport (21, 29). Note, however, that a portion of the a^{Na}_i decline may be produced by the accompanying luminal-membrane depolarization, which should reduce passive luminal Na^+ entry. A third example of Na-coupled transport is the basolateral Na-K pump; a^{Na}_i reversibly increases following removal of basolateral K^+ (authors' unpublished data). Other Na^+-coupled transport systems identified in the proximal tubule are Na-H exchange and Na^+/HCO_3^- cotransport (see the section on pH, below), as well as Na-Ca exchange (see the section on Ca, below).

DISTAL TUBULE   As for the proximal tubule, the distal tubule's a^{Na}_i is consistently below its equilibrium value for both luminal and basolateral membranes, arguing for an active, Na-extruding mechanism in these cells. The only studies to date of coupled Na^+ transport in the distal tubule are by Oberleithner et al (45) on the diluting segment of *Amphiuma*. Their suggestion that Na^+, K^+, and Cl^- enter the cell tightly coupled to one another is supported by the observation that a^{Na}_i falls markedly when furosemide (50 μM) is added to or when either Cl^- or K^+ is removed from the lumen. Voltage measurements during luminal removal of Na^+, K^+, and Cl^- are also consistent with luminal cotransport of Na^+, K^+, and Cl^- in the diluting segment of *Ambystoma* (51) and thick ascending limb of rabbit (16). Corroborating evidence from a^{Cl}_i measurements is discussed in the section on chloride, below.

Potassium

PROXIMAL TUBULE   The data of Table 1 indicate that a^K_i in amphibian proximal-tubule cells is in the range of 55 to 72 mM. Although the earliest

Table 1 Ionic composition of renal-tubule cells[a]

Ion	Segment	Species	Preparation	Concentration	Activity	Reference
Sodium						
	Proximal	*Necturus*	In vivo	42 (Ch)	20.0	21
	Proximal	*Necturus*	Doubly perfused		29.7	29
	Proximal	*Necturus*	Doubly perfused		10.5	10
	Proximal	*Necturus*	Isolated perfused		15.1	36
	Proximal	*Ambystoma*	Isolated perfused		23.7	49
	Proximal	Bullfrog	Doubly perfused		21.6	15
	Proximal	Rat		33.4 (EM)		3
	Distal	*Amphiuma*	In vivo	36 (Ch)	16.3	21
	Distal	*Amphiuma*	Doubly perfused		10.1	45
	Distal	Rat	In vivo		16.4	21
	Distal	Rat	In vivo	17.3 (EM)		3
Potassium						
	Proximal	*Necturus*	In vivo	103 (Ch)	58.7	28
	Proximal	*Necturus*	Doubly perfused	133 (Ch)	59.6	32
	Proximal	*Ambystoma*	Isolated perfused		54.7	50
	Proximal	Bullfrog	Doubly perfused		67.4	15
	Proximal	Rat	In vivo	136 (Ch)	54.4	22
	Proximal	Rat	In vivo	113 (Ch)	82	14
	Proximal	Rat	In vivo		65.9	11
	Proximal	Rat	In vivo	203 (EM)		3
	Proximal	Rabbit	Isolated perfused		48.6	4
	Proximal	Guinea pig	In vivo	156 (Ch)		61
	Distal	*Amphiuma*	In vivo		47	21
	Distal	*Amphiuma*	Doubly perfused		73	44
	Distal	Rat	In vivo	142 (Ch)[†]		41
	Distal	Rat	In vivo		46.5	26
	Distal	Rat	In vivo	197 (EM)		3
Chloride						
	Proximal	*Necturus*	In vivo	32.1	18.7	24
	Proximal	*Necturus*	Doubly perfused		24.5	56
	Proximal	*Necturus*	Doubly perfused		14.6	13
	Proximal	*Necturus*	Doubly perfused		13.2	17
	Proximal	*Ambystoma*	Isolated, perfused		16.8	7
	Proximal	Bullfrog	Doubly perfused		9.9	15
	Proximal	Rat	In vivo	49.4 (EM)		3
	Distal	*Amphiuma*	Doubly perfused		11.5	43
	Distal	Rat	In vivo		42.3	23
	Distal	Rat	In vivo	27.1 (EM)		3
pH/Bicarbonate						
	Proximal	*Necturus*	In vivo	HCO$_3^-$ LIX (DB)	7.33	25
	Proximal	Bullfrog	In vivo	Sb elec. (DB)	7.49	40
	Proximal	Bullfrog	In vivo	H$^+$ LIX (DB)	7.36	39
	Proximal	*Ambystoma*	Isolated perfused	Glass elec.	7.30	7
	Proximal	*Ambystoma*	Single tubule	Dye	7.35	9
	Proximal	*Necturus*	Doubly perfused	Glass elec.	7.15	46
	Proximal	Dog	Cortical suspension	DMO	7.32	58
	Proximal	Rabbit	Cortical suspension	DMO	7.4	31
	Proximal	Rabbit	Cortical suspension	DMO	7.51 (28°)	5

Table 1 *(Continued)*

Ion	Segment	Species	Preparation	Concentration	Activity	Reference
pH/Bicarbonate						
(continued)	Proximal	Rabbit	Cortical suspension	^{31}P NMR	7.25	2
—		Rabbit	Medullary suspension	^{31}P NMR	7.1	2
—		Rabbit	Papillary suspension	^{31}P NMR	7.2	2
	Whole kidney	Rat	Isolated, perfused kidney	^{31}P NMR	7.2	53

[a] "In vivo" = kidney is blood perfused; "doubly perfused" = both tubule and capillaries are perfused with Ringer. Ch = chemical analysis; EM = electron microprobe analysis; DB = double-barreled electrode; DMO = distribution of 5,5-dimethyl-2,4-oxazolidinedione. All concentrations expressed as millimoles kg $\cdot$ H_2O^{-1} except that indicated by †, which is given in millimoles kg^{-1} wet weight.

study with K^+ LIX electrodes suggested that K^+ might be in electrochemical equilibrium across both luminal and basolateral membranes (28), more recent work has consistently indicated that the K^+ gradient favors the net passive efflux of K^+ across the basolateral (15, 32, 33, 50) and luminal membranes (15). For example, in experiments on bullfrog proximal tubules, Fujimoto et al (15) found that a^K_i was 67 mM when mean basolateral and luminal K^+ activities were 2.6 mM and 2.9 mM, respectively. The calculated basolateral E_K of −82 was substantially more negative than the V_{bl} of −68 mV. Similarly, the calculated luminal E_K of −79 was more negative than the V_l of −60 mV.

Reported values of a^K_i in mammalian proximal tubules range from 49 to 82 mM. The consensus of recent studies (4, 10 14) is that, as in amphibian proximal tubules, a^K_i is too high for K^+ to be in equilibrium across either the luminal or basolateral membranes. Thus an active transport mechanism is responsible for the net uptake of K^+ across either or both membranes. One likely candidate is a basolateral Na-K pump, inasmuch as the basolateral application of ouabain causes a fall of a^K_i (4). Another is an active, luminal K^+ uptake system, which is necessary for normal proximal-tubule K^+ reabsorption.

DISTAL TUBULE   Bulk chemical analyses of the renal cortex, which consists mostly of proximal tubules, provide little information on distal-tubule composition. In an early microelectrode study, Khuri (21, 26) estimated a^K_i to be ~47 mM in both the *Amphiuma* and the rat distal tubule, consistent with an equilibrium distribution for K^+ across the basolateral membrane. More recently, Oberleithner et al (42, 44) found a substantially higher a^K_i, about 73 mM, in *Amphiuma*. Given identical a^K_l and a^K_{bl} values of 2.2 mM, the E_K across both membranes is −90 mV, considerably more negative than the mean V_{bl} of -70 or the mean V_l of -75 mV. Thus the electrochemical gradients favor K^+ efflux across both luminal and basolateral membranes. A basolateral K^+ uptake system, such as a Na-K pump, could not only maintain the high a_i^K, but also account for the normal, net transcellular K^+ secretion.

Chloride

PROXIMAL TUBULE   There is general agreement that a_i^{Cl} in amphibian tubules is higher than predicted if Cl^- were in equilibrium across either the luminal or basolateral membrane. Given a typical V_{bl} of -60 mV and an a_{bl}^{Cl} of 70 mM, a_i^{Cl} would be ~6 mM if Cl^- were in equilibrium across the basolateral membrane. Even though the limited selectivity of the Cl^- LIX electrode means that a portion of the apparent a_i^{Cl} (e.g. 3–5 mM) may represent other anions, only the 10 mM a_i^{Cl} value in bullfrog (15) could correspond to an equilibrium distribution for Cl^-. The other a_i^{Cl} measurements are substantially higher than the equilibrium value, indicating that one or more active processes move Cl^- into the cell. One possibility, a luminal NaCl cotransporter driven by the inward Na^+ gradient, is supported by the experiments of Spring & Kimura (56). After a_i^{Cl} was reduced by exposing cells to a Cl-free, SO_4^{2-} Ringer at both luminal and basolateral surfaces, subsequent perfusion of the lumen with the Cl^- salts of K^+, Li^+, and tetramethylammonium produced no significant increase of a_i^{Cl}, whereas perfusion with 100 mM NaCl produced a dramatic rise. In addition, both doubly perfused Necturus (18) and isolated perfused Ambystoma (8) proximal tubules, exhibit a reversible fall in a_i^{Cl} upon removal of luminal Na^+. At the basolateral membrane of the proximal-tubule, Cl^- may exit the cell in exchange for Na^+ and HCO_3^- (18).

DISTAL TUBULE   The published a_i^{Cl} values (see Table 1) in the distal tubule are both too high for Cl^- to be in equilibrium across either the luminal or basolateral membrane. The unusually high value for a_i^{Cl} in the rat proximal tubule may be the result of the unstable and very short-lived impalements, characteristic of intracellular recordings on mammalian distal tubules. An a_i^{Cl} value above equilibrium implies active transport of Cl^- into the cell at the luminal and/or basolateral membranes. With regard to Cl^- cotransport processes, experiments by Oberleithner et al (43) on the diluting segment of Amphiuma have shown that the luminal application of furosemide (50 μM) or the luminal removal of either Na^+ or Cl^- causes a marked fall of a_i^{Cl}. This suggests that luminal Cl^- transport is tightly coupled to Na^+.

pH and HCO_3^-

Several techniques have been used to measure pH_i in renal-tubule cells, including pH-sensitive microelectrodes and dyes, the distribution of the weak acid DMO, and ^{31}P NMR (see Table 1). Most renal determinations of pH_i have been made on proximal tubules, and only this nephron segment is discussed below.

Proximal-tubule pH_i is generally estimated to be 7.25–7.50. Assuming a pH_i of 7.3 and a pH_{bl} of 7.4, E_H is $\sim$ –6 mV at the basolateral membrane. Inasmuch as reported basolateral membrane potentials are in the range –50 to –70 mV, there is a substantial gradient favoring H^+ influx or HCO_3^- efflux across this surface. Similar arguments apply to the luminal membrane as well. Thus, if pH_i is to be maintained at its normal value, an active transport system at the luminal and/or basolateral membranes must extrude acid from the cell. Luminal acid extrusion, which is necessary for renal acid secretion, probably occurs by an exchange of external Na^+ for internal H^+. Na-H exchangers have been identified in vesicles derived primarily from proximal-tubule brush-border membranes of rat (41a) and rabbit (30). In addition, studies with pH- and Na-sensitive microelectrodes in isolated perfused salamander proximal tubules (7) have provided evidence for Na-H exchange by demonstrating reciprocal changes in a^H_i and a^{Na}_i. Interestingly, the exchangers appeared to be localized in the basolateral as well as the luminal membranes. Further support for Na-H exchange are the observations by Bichara et al (5) and Blumenthal & Kleinman (6) in rabbit tubule suspensions that an inward Na^+ gradient raises the DMO-derived pH_i, whereas an outward Na^+ gradient has the opposite effect. Finally, sensitivity of Na-H exchange to amiloride has been shown in vesicles (30) and intact cells (7).

In addition to luminal Na-H exchange, proximal-tubule acid secretion also requires, at the basolateral membrane, either the influx of acid or efflux of base. Evidence for basolateral HCO_3^- exit is the observation (31) that either anion-flux inhibitor SITS or the carbonic-anhydrase inhibitor acetazolamide raises pH_i in rabbit tubule suspensions. This probably reflects continued luminal Na-H exchange in the face of reduced basolateral HCO_3^- efflux. Experiments on the salamander indicate that HCO_3^- may cross the basolateral membrane coupled to Na^+ (8). When either $[HCO_3^-]_{bl}$ or $[Na^+]_{bl}$ is reduced, both pH_i and a^{Na}_i fall and the basolateral membrane transiently depolarizes; all changes are reversible and blocked by SITS. The voltage changes suggest that HCO_3^- and Na^+ leave the cell carrying net negative charge. Thus the stoichiometry may be one Na^+ for two HCO_3^- (or an equivalent species).

Ca^{2+}

The availability of a high-quality, Ca-sensitive LIX resin (54) has permitted the measurement a^{Ca}_i in the relatively large cells of the *Necturus* proximal tubule. In doubly perfused tubules, Lee et al (34) obtained a mean a^{Ca}_i of 116 nM under normal conditions, of the same order of magnitude as the

66 nM obtained by Lorenzen et al (35) on isolated perfused tubules. Employing an extracellular Ca-sensitive dye, Mandel & Murphy (38) measured the net uptake or release of Ca by rabbit proximal-tubule cells in suspension. At an a_o^{Ca} of 450nM, no net uptake or release of Ca^{2+} was observed when the cell membranes were disrupted by digitonin. At this null point, a_o^{Ca} is presumably the same as a_i^{Ca}.

These a_i^{Ca} values, taken together with reasonable values for a_o^{Ca} (e.g. 0.5 mM) and V_l and V_{bl} (e.g. –60 mV), indicate that there is a steep gradient favoring the passive influx of Ca^{2+} across both luminal and basolateral membranes. The Ca^{2+}-extruding mechanism required for maintaining a_i^{Ca} at such low values may be a basolateral Na-Ca exchanger since a 90% reduction of $[Na^+]_{bl}$ causes a 2.2-fold net increase of a_i^{Ca} in Necturus proximal tubules (34). Increases in a_i^{Ca} are also observed in these tubules following application of ouabain, which raises a_i^{Na} (35). Conversely, application of ouabain in a suspension of rabbit proximal tubules causes a decrease of a_o^{Ca}, presumably a reflection of a net Ca^{2+} uptake by the tubule cells (37). Thus maneuvers that diminish the inward-directed, basolateral Na^+ gradient appear to reduce Na-Ca exchange at this membrane, causing an increase in cytosolic calcium.

ACKNOWLEDGMENTS

This work was supported by NIH grants RO1-AM30344 (WFB) and RO1-AM29775 and KO4-AM00969 (HS).

Literature Cited

1. Aronson, P. S. 1981. Identifying secondary active solute transport in epithelia. Am. J. Physiol. 240:F1–11
2. Balaban, R. S. 1982. Nuclear magnetic resonance studies of epithelial metabolism and function. Fed. Proc. 41:42–47
3. Beck, F., Bauer, R., Bauer, U., Mason, J., Dörge, A., Rick, R., Thurau, K. 1980. Electron microprobe analysis of intracellular elements in the rat kidney. Kidney Int. 17:756–63
4. Biagi, B., Sohtell, M., Giebisch, G. 1981. Intracellular potassium activity in the rabbit proximal straight tubule. Am. J. Physiol. 241:F677–86
5. Bichara, M., Paillard, M., Leviel, F., Gardin, J.-P. 1980. Hydrogen transport in rabbit kidney proximal tubules—Na:H exchange. Am. J. Physiol. 238:F445–51
6. Blumenthal, S., Kleinman, J. 1982. Passive Na^+-H^+ exchange in renal tubule cells. Kidney Int. 21:233

7. Boron, W. F., Boulpaep, E. L. 1983. Intracellular pH regulation in the renal proximal tubule of the salamander: Na-H exchange. J. Gen. Physiol. 81: In press
8. Boron, W. F., Boulpaep, E. L., 1983. Intracellular pH regulation in the renal proximal tubule of the salamander: Basolateral HCO_3^- transport. J. Gen. Physiol. 81: In press
9. Boron, W. F. 1982. Optical measurement of intracellular pH in isolated, perfused renal proximal tubules of the salamander. Fed. Proc. 41:1011
10. Cemerikic, D., Giebisch, G. 1981. Intracellular Na activity measurements in Necturus kidney proximal tubule. Abstr. 8th Int. Congr. Nephrol. Athens, p. 71
11. Cemerikic, D., Wilcox, C. S., Giebisch, G. 1982. Intracellular potential and K^+ activity in rat kidney proximal tubular cells in acidosis and K^+ depletion. J. Membr. Biol. 69:159–65

12. Dörge, A., Rick, R., Gehring, K., Thurau, K. 1978. Preparation of freeze-dried cryosection for quantitative X-ray microanalysis of electrolytes in biological soft tissues. *Pflügers Arch.* 373: 85–97

13. Edelman, A., Bouthier, M., Anagnostopoulos, T. 1979. Proximal tubule cell chloride activity during changes of peritubular (PT) or luminal (LM) fluid composition. *Kidney Int.* 16:812

14. Edelman, A., Curci, S., Samarzija, I., Frömter, E. 1978. Determination of intracellular K+ activity in rat kidney proximal tubular cells. *Pflügers Arch.* 378:37–45

15. Fujimoto, M., Naito, K., Kubota, T. 1980. Electrochemical profile for ion transport across the membrane of proximal tubular cells. *Membr. Biochem.* 3:67–97

16. Greger, R., Schlatter, E. 1981. Presence of luminal K+, a prerequisite for active NaCl transport in the cortical thick ascending limb of Henle's loop of rabbit kidney. *Pflügers Arch.* 392:92–94

17. Guggino, W. B., Boulpaep, E. L., Giebisch, G. 1982. Electrical properties of chloride transport across the *Necturus* proximal tubule. *J. Membr. Biol.* 65: 185–96

18. Guggino, W., London, R., Boulpaep, E. L., Giebisch, G. 1983. Chloride transport across the basolateral membrane of the *Necturus* proximal tubule: Dependence on bicarbonate and sodium *J. Membr. Biol.* In press

19. Gupta, B. L. 1979. The electron microprobe X-ray analysis of frozen hydrated section with new information on fluid transporting epithelia. In *Microbeam Analysis in Biology,* ed. C. P. Lechene, R. R. Warner, pp. 375–408

20. Hall, T. A. 1979. Problems of the continuum normalization method for the quantitative analysis of sections of soft tissue. See Ref. 19, 185–208

21. Khuri, R. N. 1979. Electrochemistry of the nephron. In *Membrane Transport in Biology,* ed. G. Giebisch, D. C. Tosteson, H. H. Ussing, IV A, pp. 47–95. NY; Springer

22. Khuri, R. N., Agulian, S. K., Bogharian, K. 1974. Electrochemical potentials of potassium in proximal renal tubule of rat. *Pflügers Arch.* 346:310–26

23. Khuri, R. N., Agulian, S. K., Bogharian, K. 1974. Electrochemical potentials of chloride in distal renal tubule of the rat. *Am. J. Physiol.* 227:1352–55

24. Khuri, R. N., Agulian, S. K., Bogharian, K., Aklajian, D. 1975. Electro-chemical potentials of chloride in proximal renal tubule of *Necturus maculosus.* *Comp. Biochem. Physiol. A* 50:695–700

25. Khuri, R. N., Agulian, S. K., Bogharian, K., Nassar, R., Wise, W. M. 1974. Intracellular bicarbonate in single cells of *Necturus* kidney proximal tubule. *Pflügers Arch.* 349:295–99

26. Khuri, R. N., Agulian, S. K., Kalloghlian, A. 1972. Intracellular potassium in cells of the distal tubule. *Pflügers Arch.* 335:297–308

27. Khuri, R. N., Hajjar, J. J., Agulian, S. K. 1972. Measurement of intracellular potassium with liquid ion-exchange microelectrodes. *J. Appl. Physiol.* 32: 419–22

28. Khuri, R. N., Hajjar, J. J., Agulian, S., Bogharian, K., Kallaghlian, A., Bizni, H. 1972. Intracellular potassium in cells of the proximal tubule of *Necturus maculosus.* *Pflügers Arch.* 388:73–80

29. Kimura, G., Spring, K. R. 1979. Luminal Na+ entry into *Necturus* proximal tubule cells. *Am. J. Physiol.* 236:F295–301

30. Kinsella, J. L., Aronson, P. S. 1980. Properties of the Na+-H+ exchanger in renal microvillus membrane vesicles. *Am. J. Physiol.* 238:F461–69

31. Kleinman, J. G., Brown, W. W., Ware, R. A., Schwartz, J. H. 1980. Cell pH and acid transport in renal cortical tissue. *Am. J. Physiol.* 239:F440–44

32. Kubota, T., Biagi, B., Giebisch, G. 1980. Intracellular K+ activity measurements in single proximal tubules of *Necturus* kidney. *Curr. Top. Membr. Trans.* 13:63–72

33. Kubota, T., Biagi, B., Giebisch, G. 1983. Intracellular potassium activity measurements in single proximal tubules of *Necturus* kidney. *Am. J. Physiol.* Submitted

34. Lee, C. O., Taylor, A., Windhager, E. E. 1980. Cytosolic calcium ion activity in epithelial cells of *Necturus* kidney. *Nature* 287:859–61

35. Lorenzen, M., Lee, C. O., Windhager, E. E. 1982. Effect of quinidine and ouabain on intracellular calcium and sodium ion activities of isolated perfused proximal tubules of *Necturus* kidney. *Kidney Int.* 21:281

36. Lorenzen, M., Sackin, H., Lee, C. O., Windhager, E. E. 1981. Intracellular Na+ activity, basolateral membrane potential and transepithelial voltage in isolated perfused proximal tubules of *Necturus* kidney. *Fed. Proc.* 40:394

37. Mandel, L. J. 1982. Use of noninvasive fluorometry and spectrophotometry to

study epithelial metabolism and transport. *Fed. Proc.* 41:36–41

38. Mandel, L. J., Murphy, E. 1982. Cytosolic free Ca^{2+} in rabbit proximal tubules. *Kidney Int.* 21:282

39. Matsumura, Y., Aoki, S., Kajino, K., Fujimoto, M. 1980. The double-barrelled microelectrode for the measurement of intracellular pH, using liquid ion-exchanger, and its biological application. *Proc. Int. Congr. Physiol. Sci., 28th, Budapest* 14:572

40. Matsumura, Y., Kajino, K., Fujimoto, M. 1980. Measurement of intracellular pH of bullfrog skeletal muscle and renal tubular cells with double-barreled antimony microelectrodes. *Membr. Biochem.* 3:99–129

41. Maude, D. L. 1969. Effects of K and ouabain on fluid transport and cell Na in proximal tubule in vitro. *Am. J. Physiol.* 216:1199–1206

41a. Murer, H., Hopfer, U., Kinne, R. 1976. Sodium/proton antiport in brush-border-membrane vesicles isolated from rat small intestine and kidney. *Biochem. J.* 154:597–604

42. Oberleithner, H., Giebisch, G. 1981. Mechanism of potassium transport across distal tubular epithelium of *Amphiuma*. In *Epithelial Ion and Water Transport*, ed. D. Macknight, J. Leader, pp. 97–105

43. Oberleithner, H., Guggino, W. B., Giebisch, G. 1982. Mechanism of distal tubular chloride transport in *Amphiuma* kidney. *Am. J. Physiol.* 242:F331–39

44. Oberleithner, H., Kubota, T., Giebisch, G. 1980. Potassium transport and intracellular K^+ activity in distal tubules of *Amphiuma*. *Fed. Proc.* 39:1079

45. Oberleithner, H., Lang, F., Wenhiu, W., Giebisch, G. 1983. Effects of inhibition of chloride transport on intracellular sodium activity in distal amphibian nephron. *Pflügers Arch.* 394:55–60

46. O'Regan, M. G., Malnic, G., Giebisch, G. 1982. Cell pH and luminal acidification in *Necturus* proximal tubule. *J. Membr. Biol.* 69:99–106

47. Radda, G. K., Ackermann, J. J. H., Bore, P., Sehr, P., Wong, G. G., Ross, B. D., Green, Y., Bartlett, S., Lowry, M. 1980. ^{31}P NMR studies on kidney intracellular pH in acute renal acidosis. *Int. J. Biochem.* 12:277–82

48. Roos, A., Boron, W. F. 1981. Intracellular pH. *Physiol. Rev.* 61:296–434

49. Sackin, H., Boron, W. F., Boulpaep, E. L. 1981. Intracellular sodium activity in *Ambystoma* renal proximal tubule. *Kidney Int.* 19:255 (Abstr.)

50. Sackin, H., Boulpaep, E. L. 1981. Isolated perfused salamander proximal tubule. II. Monovalent ion replacement and rheogenic transport. *Am. J. Physiol.* 241:F540–55

51. Sackin, H., Morgunov, N., Boulpaep, E. L. 1982. Electrical potentials and luminal membrane ion transport in the amphibian renal diluting segment. *Fed. Proc.* 41:1495

52. Sauberman, A. J., Beeuwkes, R. III, Peters, P. D. 1981. Application of scanning electron microscopy to X-ray analysis of frozen-hydrated sections. II. Analysis of standard solutions and artificial electrolyte gradients. *J. Cell. Biol.* 88:268–73

53. Sehr, P. A., Bore, P. J., Papatheofanis, J., Radda, G. K. 1979. Non-destructive measurement of metabolites and tissue pH in the kidney by ^{31}P NMR. *Br. J. Exp. Pathol.* 60:632–39

54. Simon, W., Ammann, D., Oehme, M., Morf, W. E. 1978. Calcium-selective electrodes. *Ann. NY Acad. Sci.* 307:52–70

55. Somlyo, A. V., Shuman, H., Somlyo, A. P. 1977. Elemental distribution in striated muscle and the effects of hypertonicity. Electron probe analysis of cryosections. *J. Cell Biol.* 74:828–57

56. Spring, K. R., Kimura, G. 1978. Chloride reabsorption by renal proximal tubules of *Necturus. J. Membr. Biol.* 3:233–54

57. Spring, K. R., Kimura, G. 1979. Intracellular ion activities in *Necturus* proximal tubule. *Fed. Proc.* 38:2729–32

58. Struyvenberg, A., Morrison, R. B., Relman, A. S. 1968. Acid-base behavior of separated canine renal tubule cells. *Am. J. Physiol.* 214:1155–62

59. Thomas, J. A., Buchsbaum, R. N., Zimniak, A., Racker, E. 1979. Intracellular pH measurements in Ehrlich ascites tumor cells utilizing spectroscopic probes generated *in situ. Biochemistry* 18:2210–18

60. Tsien, R. Y. 1981. A non-disruptive technique for loading calcium buffers and indicators into cells. *Nature* 290:527–28

61. Whittembury, G. 1965. Sodium extrusion and potassium uptake in guinea pig kidney cortex slices. *J. Gen. Physiol.* 48:699–717

Ann. Rev. Physiol. 1983. 45:497–517

ELECTROPHYSIOLOGY OF MAMMALIAN RENAL TUBULES:
Inferences from Intracellular Microelectrode Studies

Bruce M. Koeppen, and Gerhard Giebisch

Yale University School of Medicine, Department of Physiology, New Haven, Connecticut 06510

Bruce A. Biagi

Ohio State Medical School, Department of Physiology, Columbus, Ohio 43210

INTRODUCTION

With the development and refinement of the techniques of in vivo micropuncture and in vitro microperfusion of individual renal tubules, it has been possible to define the transepithelial electrophysiological properties of all regions of the mammalian nephron (for reviews see 6, 9–11, 29, 66, 103, 104). Although these techniques have provided valuable insight into the mechanisms of ion transport, they are limited in that the cellular compartment is treated as a "black box." In order to understand more precisely the cellular mechanisms of ion transport, it is necessary to obtain measurements of the driving forces and membrane conductances for ion movement across both the luminal and peritubular membranes of the cell. In this regard intracellular potentials and ion activities have been measured with routine success in several nonmammalian tissues, owing in part to the fact that the individual tubule cells are large and relatively easy to impale with microelectrodes (see the chapter by Boron & Sackin in this section). In addition, it has been possible to obtain intracellular recordings in several mammalian nephron segments (see Table 1).

In this chapter we review the electrophysiology of the mammalian nephron, with emphasis on information obtained with intracellular voltage

Table 1 Transepithelial and cellular electrical properties of mammalian nephron segments

Species	Preparation	Transepithelial potential (mV)	References	Transepithelial resistance (Ωcm^2)	References	Intracellular potential (mV)	References
Proximal convoluted tubule							
Rat	in vivo	+0.2 to +1.0	28, 29	5	28, 29	−65 to −76	9, 15, 21, 25, 29
Dog	in vivo	−2.0	9, 13	5.6	9, 13	−51	7
Rabbit	in vitro	−2.2 to −5.8	6, 9, 66, 103, 104	7	81		
	in vitro nonperfused					−27 to −49	119
Guinea pig	in vitro slices					−53	94
Proximal straight tubule							
Rabbit	in vitro perfused	−2.0	6, 9, 60, 103, 104	8.6	81	−38 to −61	5, 7, 8
	in vitro nonperfused					−17	118
Medullary thick ascending limb of Henle							
Rabbit	in vitro	+2.5 to +6.7	64, 99, 111				
Rat	in vitro	+5.9	65, 102				
Mouse	in vitro	+4.7 to +50	51, 57–59, 64, 102	11.0	57		
Cortical thick ascending limb of Henle							
Rabbit	in vitro	+2.6 to +7.0	17, 18, 40–48	24.6–34.0	18, 41	−69	40, 44, 45
Mouse	in vitro	+6.7 to +7.4	26, 27				

Distal convoluted tubule							
Rabbit	in vitro, DCT$_a$	+7.2 to −40.4	49, 50, 106				
Rat	in vivo, DCT$_b$	+8.0 to −19.3	1, 2, 9, 55, 56, 66			−57 to −65	9, 73, 126
Rabbit	in vitro, DCT$_b$	−28.7 to −40.4	49, 50, 106	8.13–382.2	9, 22, 23, 83, 125		
Rabbit	in vitro, DCT$_g$	−13.8 to −27.0	65, 106				
Rat	in vivo, DCT$_l$ & random	−18.0 to −46.9	1, 2, 9, 35, 38, 55, 56, 66, 120	40.0–250.8	9, 22, 23, 83, 125	−65 to −75	9, 35, 37, 83, 122, 123, 126
Dog	in vivo, random	−42.7	9	600	9		
Cortical collecting duct							
Rabbit	in vitro	−5.5 to −45.4	10, 53, 74–77, 88–92, 110, 112, 113	118–867	10, 62, 63, 75, 91, 92, 115	−84	74–76
Human	in vitro	+6.8	67				
Medullary collecting duct							
Rabbit	in vitro, outer	−4.2 to −27.6	112–114				
Rabbit	in vitro, inner	+10.6 to +15.0	112–114				
Papillary collecting duct							
Hamster	in vivo	−14 to −34	9, 79, 96, 124	1000–2000	9, 97		
Rat	in vivo	−12 to +1	9, 54, 100				
Rabbit	in vitro	+1	98			−15, +25	118

recording and ion-sensitive microelectrodes. For a presentation of the methodology, limitations, and pitfalls of the techniques used in most of the studies discussed here see the review by Boulpaep & Giebisch (12).

PROXIMAL TUBULE

Transepithelial Potential Differences

The transepithelial potential of the proximal tubule has been the subject of extensive investigation in recent years. The major areas of interest have centered upon the heterogeneity of nephron function with regard to both axial differences along the length of the nephron and differences between the superficial and juxtamedullary nephron populations (6, 66). Within the context of such nephron heterogeneity, emphasis has also been placed upon the relative permeabilities of the paracellular pathway for Na^+, Cl^- and HCO_3^-. The implications of such differences for active and passive mechanisms of NaCl absorption along the proximal nephron have been discussed (29, 103, 104).

Intracellular Potential Measurements

Because of the small size and complex geometry of mammalian proximal tubular cells, intracellular potential measurements have been difficult to obtain. It has been possible, however, to evaluate both the intracellular electrical potential and the ion activity gradients for potassium and chloride across the cell borders of the rat proximal convoluted tubule in vivo (15, 16, 29, 33, 34, 70, 101). Electrical and chemical gradients for Na^+, K^+ and Cl^- in kidney cortex slices from the guinea pig have also been examined (94). The most recent studies have extended cellular measurements to the proximal tubule segments of the rabbit in vitro (5, 7, 8, 118, 119) and to the further use of ion sensitive microelectrodes to examine in vivo proximal tubules of the rat (20, 21, 25). As a consequence, comparisons of absolute values of cell potentials and ion gradients between species, nephron segments, and experimental preparations are both necessary and inevitable.

Intracellular potentials in the rat proximal convoluted tubule (PCT) range between −65 and −76 mV (15, 20, 21, 25, 29) and are higher than the −51 mV value observed in the perfused rabbit proximal convoluted tubule (7) and the rabbit proximal straight tubule (PST), where reported values range between −43 and −61 mV (5, 7, 8). In nonperfused rabbit tubules, values for cell potentials in S_1, S_2, and S_3 segments have been reported to be −46, −27, and −17 mV, respectively (118). In this preparation, differences between potentials in cells along the collapsed portion of PCT (−29 mV) and potentials measured at the everted ends of the same tubules (−49 mV) suggest the influence of the luminal membrane and/or luminal solution composition on the measured potential.

Basolateral Membrane Permeability

The characteristics of the basolateral membrane have been examined with regard to passive permeabilities, factors that appear to influence the permeability to potassium, and the electrical properties of the Na^+-K^+ pump. The permeability sequence of the basolateral membrane obtained from ion substitution experiments in the rat PCT is (28): $P_{HCO_3} > P_K \gg P_{Na}, P_{Cl}$. A high potassium permeability and low sodium and chloride permeabilities have also been demonstrated in the rabbit proximal straight tubule (5), but systematic studies in rabbit PCT are not yet available. An increase in bath $[K^+]$ has also been shown to depolarize nonperfused PCT (119) and perfused PST (7, 8). Peritubular Ba^{2+} depolarizes the cell potential; it has been used as an effective blocker of basolateral potassium permeability in the rat proximal convoluted tubule (16) and in the rabbit proximal straight tubule (5, 7, 8). The large depolarization associated with Ba^{2+} is not accompanied by a change in intracellular potassium activity (8). This observation further supports a decrease in potassium permeability as the principal effect of Ba^{2+} on the basolateral membrane.

The high apparent bicarbonate permeability in the basolateral membrane of the rat proximal tubule is well-established (15, 16, 29, 34). Estimates of bicarbonate transference as high as 0.62 (29) are derived from the large $[HCO_3^-]$-dependent depolarization of the cell potential when the $[HCO_3^-]$ is reduced at constant pH. This initial depolarization is transient, lasting approximately 5 sec [see (15), Figure 1] and is inhibited by blockers of carbonic anhydrase (34). Similar spike transients are observed when bicarbonate buffer is replaced with glycodiazine and the glycodiazine concentration is rapidly reduced (16). This latter observation has led to the conclusion that buffer permeation through the basolateral membrane is in the form of OH^- and CO_2.

Reducing the bath $[HCO_3^-]$ at constant pH in the rabbit proximal straight tubule has led to divergent results (5, 7, 8). In contrast to rat PCT, spike depolarizations are not observed and therefore do not support a significant HCO_3^- (OH^-) permeability in this species (5, 7, 8). However, the bath exchange in vitro may not be sufficiently fast to observe an initial rapid spike. Therefore, a finite HCO_3^- permeability cannot be ruled out. Reducing bath bicarbonate at constant pH did lead to steady-state depolarization (after several minutes) of approximately 22 mV in one series of experiments (5). This effect was decreased in the presence of bath Ba^{2+}, suggesting that a fall in intracellular $[HCO_3^-]$, perhaps via a change in intracellular pH, reduces basolateral potassium conductance.

Changes in external pH (at constant $[HCO_3^-]$) also influence basolateral potassium permeability in both the rat PCT (15, 16) and the rabbit PST (7, 8). Reducing pH decreases P_K and results in a depolarization of the cell potential. The magnitude of this effect, however, is smaller in the rat (5.4 mV/pH unit) than in the rabbit (42 mV/pH unit). In the rabbit PST, the depolarization resulting from a reduction in the bath pH is inhibited by Ba^{2+} and is not accompanied by a change in intracellular potassium activity (7, 8). The striking differences obtained when pH and/or $[HCO_3^-]$ are changed in the rat PCT and rabbit PST remain to be resolved. Species and/or segmental differences are the obvious choices; however, the possibilities of methodological factors or unstirred layer effects have also been suggested (5, 15, 16). Further experiments will clearly be required to resolve these questions.

Electrical Properties of the Basolateral Na^+-K^+ Pump

Several lines of evidence have been used to establish the electrogenic character of the basolateral Na^+-K^+ pump. In the rat PCT, ouabain results in a rapid (a half time less than 2 sec) cellular depolarization (29, 33). In guinea-pig slices, measurements of the intracellular potential during recovery from cellular Na^+ loading and K^+ depletion have shown that the cell potential hyperpolarizes to values about 30 mV more negative than the K^+ equilibrium potential (94). Similar results have been found in rabbit proximal tubules following low K^+ (0.1 mM) bath inhibition of the pump. In these studies increasing the bath $[K^+]$ to control levels resulted in a rapid hyperpolarization of ~ 14 mV in both PCT and PST, which was inhibited by ouabain (7, 8). In PST, it was possible to demonstrate by measuring intracellular potassium activity that the basolateral potential could be more negative than the K^+ equilibrium potential during this transient phase of recovery (8). Thus the evidence suggests an electrogenic pump mechanism in PCT of rat, rabbit, and guinea pig, as well as in the PST of the rabbit particularly under the conditions of enhanced Na^+ extrusion following cellular sodium loading.

Characteristics of the Luminal Membrane

The permeability sequence of the luminal membrane determined from ion substitution experiments is $P_K \gg P_{Na}$, P_{Cl}, P_{HCO}, in the rat proximal convoluted tubule (28, 29). Similar experiments have not been performed in rabbit proximal tubules, but luminal perfusion of PST with a solution resembling late proximal tubular fluid (no organics, low $[HCO_3^-]$ and high $[Cl^-]$, pH = 6.7) results in only a small hyperpolarization (~ 4 mV) of the cell potential (7).

The most extensively studied aspects of luminal membrane function are the electrical characteristics of sodium-coupled organic substrate transport. The results from the rat proximal convoluted tubule are the most complete and have been recently summarized by Frömter (31). In the rat, addition of luminal glucose (or amino acids) results in a depolarization of the cell potential and a hyperpolarization of the transepithelial potential. Similar effects are seen in rabbit proximal tubule (7). The response in the rabbit PCT is about four times larger than in the PST (7), a finding in good agreement with the well-known effects of glucose on the transepithelial voltage in these segments. Based upon the observations that the cellular depolarization is extremely rapid (100–200 msec) and is dependent upon substrate concentration, Na^+ concentration, and intracellular potential, Frömter has concluded that glucose and amino acid transport systems within the brush border of the rat proximal tubule are rheogenic (31). In addition, individual membrane resistances have been evaluated using glucose-induced current and the voltage changes across the cell membranes and paracellular shunt path (28, 29, 31). This analysis yields a ratio of the apical membrane resistance/ basolateral membrane resistance between 2.1 and 2.8 and, in combination with the low transepithelial resistance of 5 Ω · cm^2, a calculated luminal membrane resistance of 200–260 Ω · cm^2, and a basolateral membrane resistance of 90–120 Ω · cm^2. Finally, the coupling ratio of Na^+ to glucose is probably close to 1.0 (31). A variety of similar transport systems, which include luminal and peritubular amino acid systems and luminal anion absorption systems, have been detected in rat PCT using microelectrode techniques but await a more complete description (29, 30, 101). However the number of systems that depend upon the sodium electrochemical gradient across the cell membranes clearly suggests the basis for the interactions between measured solute and ion fluxes in proximal tubules (24).

Intracellular Ion Activity Measurements

Ion-selective microelectrodes have now been used to describe the intracellular activities of K^+, Cl^-, and HCO_3^- in the rat PCT (20, 21, 25, 70, 71, 107) and of K^+ in the rabbit PST (8).

Values of intracellular potassium activity in the rat PCT have been reported to be 54.4 mM (70, 71), 82 mM (25), and 66 mM (21). In contrast to the initial conclusion that potassium was distributed at electrochemical equilibrium (70, 71), more recent reports have demonstrated that K^+ is clearly above electrochemical equilibrium across both the luminal and basolateral membranes (21, 25). Cemerikic et al (21), have also shown that cellular potassium activity is significantly reduced (48 mM) under conditions of metabolic acidosis and K^+ depletion (58 mM). However, the simultaneously measured intracellular potential was reduced to -48 mV in metabolic acidosis from a control value of -66 mV, but increased to -75 mV in K^+ depletion. Respiratory acidosis also depolarized the cell potential to -46 mV, but cellular K^+ activity was unchanged from control. Under all conditions K^+ was distributed above electrochemical equilibrium, suggesting that peritubular $[HCO_3^-]$ is an important factor in maintaining normal cellular K^+ distribution. Cellular $[HCO_3^-]$ and pH have been reported to be 25 mM and 7.43 under control conditions in rat PCT (70, 71). It would be extremely interesting to have these studies extended to similar conditions of acid-base imbalance.

In rabbit PST, an intracellular potassium activity of 48 mM has been reported, and this value is also above electrochemical equilibrium. Inhibition of the basolateral Na^+-K^+ pump with either a low bath $[K^+]$ (0.1 mM) or bath ouabain (10^{-5}M) reversibly reduced cell K^+ activity and the cell potential. These results support the conclusion that the activity of the Na^+-K^+ ATPase in the basolateral membrane is the active mechanism that maintains cell K^+ activity above equilibrium, but additional luminal membrane systems have not been ruled out (8).

Intracellular Cl^- activity has also been measured in rat PCT and the question of equilibrium distribution addressed. Initial reports of a cellular Cl^- activity equal to 8.5 mM when cell potential was -72 mV suggested that Cl^- could be at equilibrium across the basolateral membrane (107). A more recent report, however, gives values for chloride activity of 11 mM when the cell potential is -73 mV, suggesting that intracellular Cl^- activity does not conform to an equilibrium distribution (20). This apparent discrepancy remains to be resolved.

THICK ASCENDING LIMB OF HENLE'S LOOP

Recent studies have shed new light on the mechanism of NaCl transport by the thick ascending limb of Henle's loop (TALH). It is now clear that the reabsorption of NaCl occurs by a coupled mechanism located at the luminal cell membrane [(121); and see the chapter by Burg & Good in this section]. However, the precise relationship between the transport of NaCl and the transepithelial electrical properties of this nephron segment remains largely unknown.

The cortical (cTALH) and/or the medullary (mTALH) portions of this segment have been isolated from kidneys of the rabbit, rat, and mouse, and studied in vitro (17, 18, 26, 27, 40–48, 51, 57–60, 64, 99, 102, 111). Regardless of the species the transepithelial potential of both the cTALH and the mTALH is oriented lumen-positive (2 to 10 mV). Furthermore, the transepithelial potential and the net reabsorption of NaCl are inhibited by "loop diuretics" and ouabain (17, 18, 26, 27, 40, 42, 43, 51, 57, 64), suggesting that both portions share a similar mechanism for NaCl reabsorption. However, important species and internephron differences have been reported. For example, vasopressin increases the transepithelial potential and net NaCl reabsorption by the rat and mouse mTALH approximately two-fold (51, 57–60, 102) but has no effect on the mTALH of the rabbit (102). In addition, vasopressin does not alter the electrical or transport properties of the cTALH (57, 102). The species and internephron specificities of this response to vasopressin correspond to the distribution of vasopressin-stimulated adenylate cyclase activity both between species and between the cortical and medullary portions of the nephron segment (86).

An additional important difference between the cTALH and the mTALH, at least in the mouse, has recently been described (26, 27, 57). In the mouse cTALH approximately 50% of the net NaCl reabsorption and a comparable fraction of the lumen-positive potential is dependent upon the presence of HCO_3^- and CO_2 (26, 27). No such dependency has been found in the mouse mTALH (57) or in the cTALH of the rabbit (R. Greger, personal communication). The nature of this $HCO_3^- + Co_2$ dependency remains to be elucidated, but it appears that two distinct mechanisms for NaCl transport may exist in the mouse cTALH.

Microelectrode Measurements

Intracellular recordings have only been reported for the rabbit cTALH. The voltage across the basolateral cell membrane averages -69 mV (40, 44, 45), and the ratio of apical to basolateral membrane resistance ranges from 1.9–2.6 (40, 45, 47, 48).

The conductive properties of the luminal and peritubular membranes have been assessed by single ion substitutions. Step increases in the $[K^+]$ of either the luminal or peritubular solution causes rapid and reversible depolarizations of the intracellular potential (40, 47). Ba^{2+}, a potent inhibitor of conductive K^+ movement, produces similar effects on the intracellular potential but has quite different effects on the transepithelial and membrane resistances (46–48). Luminal Ba^{2+} causes an eight-fold increase in the transepithelial resistance (46, 48) and abolishes current flow across the luminal cell membrane (R. Greger, personal communication). In contrast, peritubular Ba^{2+} has no effect on either the transepithelial resistance or the membrane resistance ratio (47, 48). This differential effect of Ba^{2+} has been interpreted as evidence for conductive movement of K^+ across the luminal cell membrane and electroneutral movement across the basolateral membrane (40, 47, 48). The observed depolarization of the intracellular potential with increases in the peritubular $[K^+]$ has been attributed to the existence of a Ba^{2+} inhibitable KCl cotransport system in parallel with a conductive pathway for Cl^- (47, 48). In support of this, a reduction of the peritubular $[Cl^-]$ causes a depolarization of this membrane (46), as would be expected if Cl^- moved by a conductive mechanism across this membrane.

The nature of the luminal entry step for NaCl has been examined by determining the effect of furosemide on the intracellular potential. Furosemide consistently hyperpolarizes the intracellular potential by approximately 15 mV (40, 44, 45). Such a hyperpolarization could result from the inhibition of a positively charged carrier for Na^+ and Cl^-, or from changes in intracellular ion activities. At present it is not possible to distinguish between these possibilities.

From the dependency of the transepithelial potential and the transepithelial resistance on luminal $[Na^+]$ and $[Cl^-]$, a stoichiometry of 1 Na^+ and 2 Cl^- has been postulated for the luminal carrier (43, 44). Such a stoichiometry would not be consistent with the observed hyperpolarization of the intracellular potential seen with furosemide. Because of this, and in view of the dependency of the transepithelial potential on luminal K^+ (46, 60), a stoichiometry of 1 Na^+, 2 Cl^-, 1 K^+ has been proposed (46). Inhibition of this electroneutral transporter by furosemide would not be expected to alter the membrane potential or the resistance of the tubule directly. However hyperpolarization of the intracellular potential could result from changes in the equivalent EMFs for K^+ and Cl^- at the luminal and basolateral cell membranes, respectively, and the membrane and transepithelial resistance could change secondarily. In this regard, furosemide increases the transepithelial resistance by 27% (43), although the precise mechanism of this resistance change is not known.

From the above information a tentative model for NaCl transport by both the cTALH and the mTALH can be formulated [see also (121) and the chapter by Burg & Good in this section]. Na^+, Cl^+, and K^+ would enter the cell across the luminal cell membrane by a furosemide-inhibitable cotransport system. The precise stoichiometry of this entry step is not known but may be 1 Na^+, 2 Cl^-, 1 K^+. Na^+ and Cl^- would then exit the cell across the basolateral membrane: Na^+ via the Na^+-K^+-ATPase, and Cl^- either conductively or coupled to K^+. The K^+ that enters the cell across the luminal membrane (coupled to Na^+ and Cl^-) or across the basolateral membrane (Na^+-K^+-ATPase) would recycle across the luminal cell membrane and, as noted above, exit across the basolateral cell membrane coupled to Cl^-. As noted above, an additional mechanism for NaCl transport, possibly related to intracellular pH and working in parallel with the Na^+, K^+, Cl^- cotransport system, may be present in the mouse cTALH.

Within the context of the above models the lumen-positive transepithelial potential could result by several mechanisms. First, the cotransport system for Na^+ and Cl^- at the luminal cell membrane could be electrogenic (43, 44). Second, the existence of conductive pathways for K^+ at the luminal membrane and Cl^- at the basolateral membrane could result in the development of a lumen-positive potential by virtue of different equivalent EMFs (ϵ_K and ϵ_{Cl}) at each membrane (40, 47, 48). Third, the existence of a cation-selective paracellular pathway could lead to the development of a lumen-positive potential if solute (NaCl) accumulated to a significant degree within the lateral intercellular space and then Na^+ diffused across the cation-selective junctional complex back into the tubule lumen (58). Further studies, particularly with intracellular microelectrodes, will be needed to test these models.

DISTAL CONVOLUTED TUBULE

The distal convoluted tubule, as defined in early micropuncture studies, extends from the macula densa to the first branch with another tubule. It is now apparent that considerable functional and structural heterogeneity exists within this segment (69, 87, 108).

The first segment (DCT_a) begins at the macula densa and in general does not reach the surface of the kidney (69, 87, 108). Consequently, it is not accessible to study by the techniques of in vivo micropuncture. The transepithelial potential of single rabbit distal convoluted tubules perfused at the macula densa, and therefore containing the DCT_a, ranges from $+7$ to -40 mV (49, 50, 106). The reason for the wide range in measured potential is not known. It is possible that the lumen-negative segments were slightly more distal in origin (see below), or that functional heterogeneity between superficial and deep cortical tubules exists, since in the study where lumen-positive potentials were observed (106), tubules were obtained from the deep cortex.

The second portion of the distal convoluted tubule (DCT_b) extends to the surface of the kidney and is termed the early distal tubule in micropuncture studies. In the rat, the transepithelial potential ranges from $+7$ mV (1–4) to -20 mV (22, 37, 55, 56, 73, 83, 117, 125), with the measured value being dependent upon the type of electrode and the technique used to record the voltage.

The connecting tubule (DCT_g) comprises the third portion of the distal convoluted tubule. In superficial nephrons it usually lies beneath the capsule and is therefore not accessible to study in vivo. In deep nephrons the connecting tubule forms long branching arcades (65, 69). Studies of rabbit connecting tubules have shown that the transepithelial potential is lumen-negative and ranges from -13 to -30 mV (65, 106).

The last segment of the distal convoluted tubule (DCT_l) represents the initial portion of the collecting tubule. It is the last portion of the distal convoluted tubule accessible to study by micropuncture, where it is frequently termed the late distal tubule. The transepithelial potential of this segment in the rat ranges from -20 to -50 mV (1–4, 22, 35, 37, 38, 55, 56, 72, 73, 83, 85, 120, 123, 125, 126) and, in contrast to the earlier portions, its magnitude is dependent upon mineralocorticoids (2, 122, 123, 126).

Na^+ and Cl^- are reabsorbed along the length of the distal tubule, while

K^+ secretion takes place only in the late portion (84, 85, 95). Acidification of the luminal fluid also occurs, with lower pH values being found in the late segments (78, 82). The lumen-negative potential, particularly in the DCT_1, provides a favorable electrical gradient for K^+ and H^+ secretion and Cl^- reabsorption. However, under some conditions the transport of K^+, H^+, and Cl^- occurs against a transepithelial electrochemical potential difference and hence is presumably active (35, 68, 83, 95).

Microelectrode Studies

Numerous studies have reported intracellular potentials in rat distal tubules (35, 37, 70–73, 83, 122, 123, 126). However, in most cases the reported values represent transient "spike" potentials observed during attempts to introduce voltage recording Ling-Gerard electrodes into the tubule lumen, and as such interpretation of many of the data is difficult.

In random impalements primarily localized to the late distal tubule (DCT_1), mean values of the basolateral membrane potential range from -65 to -75 mV (35, 37, 83, 122, 123, 126), with single values as high as -90 mV observed on occasion (125). In cells of the early distal tubule (DCT_b), the membrane voltage is somewhat lower and averages -55 to -65 mV (73, 126). In adrenalectomized rats, the basolateral membrane potential of the DCT_1 is depolarized from -68 to -49 mV (122, 123). Similarly, systemic acidosis, but not alkalosis, depolarizes the cell potential from -69 to -49 mV (73).

The ratio of luminal to basolateral cell membrane resistance has been measured in late segments of the rat distal convoluted tubule (DCT_1); it averages 9.75 (35). Because of the reported transient nature of the measured potential this value probably represents an overestimate of the true ratio.

Intracellular activities of Na^+, K^+, and Cl^- have been measured with double-barreled liquid ion-exchange microelectrodes. Intracellular Na^+ and K^+ activities are the same in both early (DCT_b) and late convolutions (DCT_1) and average 16.4 mM (71) and 47 mM (73), respectively. Intracellular K^+ activity is decreased with restriction of dietary K^+ (73), adrenalectomy (122), and systemic acidosis (73). Conversely, intracellular K^+ activity is increased in K^+-loaded rats and during systemic alkalosis (73). In the DCT_1 intracellular Cl^- activity averages 42.3 mM (72). Since many of the impalements made with the double-barreled electrodes are transient [see (73), Figure 2], the reported activities of Na^+ and Cl^- are likely overestimates, whereas the K^+ activity is an underestimate.

The mechanism for Na^+ reabsorption and K^+ secretion by the DCT_1 appears to be similar to that proposed for the rabbit cortical collecting tubule [(36), and see below]. Since under some conditions net K^+ reabsorption is observed, a luminal K^+ reabsorptive mechanism seems likely (36). Recent evidence suggests that this K^+ reabsorptive mechanism is coupled to Cl⁻ (120) and may occur in cells distinct from those involved in K^+ secretion (109).

COLLECTING DUCT

The mammalian collecting duct system is divided morphologically into three portions: the cortical collecting duct, the outer medullary collecting duct, and the inner medullary or papillary collecting duct (69). Functionally, the collecting duct can be subdivided further, since electrophysiologic differences exist between segments of the medullary collecting duct obtained from the outer and inner stripe (112, 113). Microelectrode measurements have thus far been reported only for the isolated cortical (74–76) and papillary (119) collecting ducts of the rabbit, although transient "spike" potentials in studies of the rat papillary collecting duct have been reported (96, 124).

Cortical Collecting Duct

The transepithelial potential of the rabbit cortical collecting duct varies widely, ranging from +10 mV to greater than –100 mV (52, 53, 62, 63, 74–77, 88–93, 105, 110, 112–116). The magnitude and polarity of the potential reflect the mineralocorticoid status of the animal.

The lumen-negative potential is dependent upon Na^+ transport. Removal of luminal Na^+ (53, 77, 116), addition of amiloride to the luminal fluid (53, 63, 75, 88, 91–93, 115, 116), or addition of ouabain to the peritubular solution (19, 39, 53, 77) all abolish the lumen-negative potential and in most instances cause the potential to reverse polarity.

The origin of the lumen-positive transepithelial potential is less certain. In the rabbit, the lumen-positive potential seen after inhibition of Na^+ transport (luminal Na^+ removal, amiloride, or ouabain) appears to reflect electrogenic acid transport (77, 116). The potential is increased by treatment of the animal with mineralocorticoids (77), is not affected by furosemide or ouabain (53, 77), but is inhibited by acetazolamide and SITS (77). A dependency of this potential on Cl⁻ has been reported (53) but not confirmed in other studies (77, 116). The dependency of the transepithelial potential on Cl⁻ has been interpreted by some investigators as evidence for electrogenic Cl⁻ reabsorption (53).

The reabsorption of Na^+ and the secretion of K^+ and H^+ occur against electrochemical potential differences (39, 77, 116). In contrast, Cl⁻ appears to be passively distributed across the tubular epithelium (52, 63, 93, 116), although some evidence for active Cl⁻ reabsorption in mineralocorticoid treated tubules has been reported (53).

Microelectrode Studies

The basolateral membrane potential of the rabbit cortical collecting tubule averages approximately -85 mV (74–76). The potential is hyperpolarized by pretreatment of the rabbit with mineralocorticoids (61, 75), while addition of ouabain to the peritubular solution results in a depolarization of the cell potential (61, 75). A step increase in the $[K^+]$ of the luminal and/or peritubular solutions results in a rapid and reversible depolarization of the cell potential (75), consistent with the presence of conductive K^+ pathways at these membranes.

The luminal to basolateral membrane resistance ratio is low, averaging 0.84 (75). The luminal cell membrane contains conductive pathways for Na^+ and K^+, which are blocked by amiloride and Ba^{2+}, respectively (75, 76, 88–92). Amiloride causes a 2–3-fold increase in the membrane resistance ratio, while Ba^{2+} produces a 10–20-fold increase [(75); R. G. O'Neil, personal communication]. Thus the conductive properties of the luminal membrane reflect predominantly the properties of the K^+ pathway. Since in many tubules the combined addition of amiloride and Ba^{2+} to the luminal fluid increases the membrane resistance ratio to values greater than 30:1, Na^+ and K^+ appear to be the major conductive ion species across this membrane (75, 76). The conductive properties of the basolateral cell membrane are less well-defined. A variable K^+ conductance does exist (39, 74, 75, 91, 92), and there is some evidence for conductive movement of Cl^- (92). The mechanism of luminal fluid acidification has not yet been studied with intracellular microelectrode techniques.

From the results of both transepithelial and microelectrode studies the following model for Na^+ and K^+ transport by the cortical collecting duct has been proposed (75, 99, 110). Both Na^+ reabsorption and K^+ secretion is driven by the Na^+-K^+-ATPase located at the basolateral cell membrane. Na^+ enters and K^+ exits the cell down their respective electrochemical gradients via separate conductive pathways at the luminal membrane. Amiloride inhibits the Na^+ entry step, while the K^+ secretory step is blocked by Ba^{2+}. Since under most conditions the transepithelial potential of the cortical collecting duct is lumen-negative, cellular exit of K^+ across the luminal membrane is favored, and net K^+ secretion results.

This model provides some insight into the mechanisms by which mineralocorticoids, amiloride, ouabain, and lumen acidification effect net Na^+ and K^+ transport by the cortical collecting tubule. Both Na^+ reabsorption and K^+ secretion are increased in mineralocorticoid pretreated tubules (93, 105). The electrical consequences of such treatment are a hyperpolarization of both the transepithelial (49, 50, 52, 65, 75, 77, 93, 105, 110, 113) and basolateral membrane potentials (61, 75) and a depolarization of the luminal membrane potential (75). The net result is that the electrochemical driving forces for K^+ are poised in such a way that the cell can more efficiently secrete K^+ into the tubule lumen. Since the membrane resistance ratio falls with mineralocorticoid treatment (75), presumably reflecting increases in both the Na^+ and K^+ conductive properties of the tissue (63, 93), K^+ secretion would be further augmented, as would net Na^+ reabsorption. Both ouabain and amiloride inhibit net Na^+ reabsorption and net K^+ secretion (39, 63, 93, 116). The primary effect of ouabain would be to abolish the electrochemical gradients for Na^+ and K^+. Amiloride would inhibit Na^+ reabsorption by blocking the Na^+ entry step at the luminal cell membrane. Since amiloride has no direct effect on the luminal K^+ pathway (75, 76, 88, 91, 92), its effect on net K^+ secretion appears to reflect a change in the electrochemical driving force for K^+ movement across the luminal cell membrane (75, 76). Acidification of the luminal fluid decreases net K^+ secretion and has little effect on net Na^+ reabsorption (14). The recently reported reduction of luminal K^+ conductance by low luminal fluid pH would provide a mechanism for this response (90). The measurement of intracellular ion activities will be important in validating this model and the effects of various physiological and pharmacological manipulations.

Outer Medullary Collecting Duct

Recent studies have shown that functionally the outer medullary collecting duct can be subdivided into two distinct segments, reflecting their location within the outer and inner stripe (113).

Segments obtained from the outer stripe ($OMCD_o$) develop a transepithelial potential of -4 to -35 mV, while segments from the inner stripe ($OMCD_i$) maintain lumen-positive potentials of $+9$ to $+15$ mV (112–114). Pretreatment of rabbits with mineralocorticoids does not alter the transepithelial potential in either segment (113). The lumen-positive potential of the $OMCD_i$ is not affected by ouabain (112) and probably reflects electrogenic acid transport (80).

Microelectrode studies of either segment have not yet been reported. Such studies, particularly in the $OMCD_i$, would be most interesting in that they could provide insight into the cellular mechanism of H^+ transport.

Papillary Collecting Duct

Reported values of the transepithelial potential in the papillary collecting duct vary widely. This may reflect not only species differences but also technical differences in measurement of the potential. Under free flow conditions, and using microelectrodes with tip diameters of 0.5–5.0 μm, the transepithelial potential in the hamster ranges from -4 to -20 mV (79, 96, 124). Values in the rat are near zero, and range from -12 to $+1$ mV (54, 100). In general, larger lumen-negative potentials have been obtained with microelectrodes having tip diameters less than 1 μm. It should also be noted that in some studies values near zero millivolts have not been summarized on the assumption that these values reflect "leaky impalements" (96, 100). The open papillary tip can produce shunting of the measured potential. In the hamster, insulating the duct opening with oil increases the measured potential from −15 to −34 mV (96). The transepithelial potential of the rabbit papillary collecting duct perfused in vitro is approximately +1 mV (98).

Microelectrode Studies

Transtubular impalements with Ling-Gerard microelectrodes on occasion result in the recording of large negative "spike" potentials (−40 to −70 mV), which have been attributed to intracellular localization of the microelectrode tip (96, 124).

Recently, intracellular measurements have been made in nonperfused rabbit papillary collecting ducts (119). Of interest is the finding of two electrically distinct cell populations. Approximately 40% of the cells have negative intracellular potentials. These potentials are frequently transient and rapidly decay toward zero. The mean value of the peak or spike potential is −15 mV, but values as large as −42 mV are observed. These potentials appear to correspond to the transient negative potentials reported in micropuncture studies of this segment (96, 124).

The remaining cells of the papillary collecting duct have intracellular potentials that are positive with respect to the extracellular fluid. In contrast to the transient nature of the negative potentials, the positive intracellular potentials are stable for long periods and have a mean value of +25 mV. The potential of these cells depolarizes when the extracellular [K$^+$] is raised but is not affected by ouabain.

The two populations of intracellular potentials do not appear to reflect the properties of morphologically distinct cell types (69) but probably reflect different functional states of the cells. Further work is necessary before the role of these cells in electrolyte transport by the papillary collecting duct is understood.

ACKNOWLEDGMENT

The authors would like to thank individuals who kindly submitted reprints, manuscripts, and abstracts of their work. We regret that, owing to space limitations, all work could not be included.

Work done by the authors and cited here was supported by NIH grants AM17433 and AM27051 and by a fellowship from the Connecticut Affiliate of the American Heart Association.

Literature Cited

1. Allen, G. G., Barratt, L. J. 1981. Electrophysiology of the early distal tubule: Further observations on electrode techniques. *Kidney Int.* 19:24–35
2. Allen, G. G., Barratt, L. J. 1981. Effect of aldosterone on the transepithelial potential difference of the rat distal tubule. *Kidney Int.* 19:678–86
3. Barratt, L. J. 1976. The effect of amiloride on the transepithelial potential difference of the distal tubule of the rat kidney. *Pflügers Arch.* 361:251–54
4. Barratt, L. J., Rector, F. C. Jr., Kokko, J. P., Tisher, C. C., Seldin, D. W. 1975. Transepithelial potential difference profile of the distal tubule of the rat kidney. *Kidney Int.* 8:368–75
5. Bello-Reuss, E. 1982. Electrical properties of the basolateral membrane of the straight portion of the rabbit proximal renal tubule. *J. Physiol.* 326:49–64
6. Berry, C. A. 1982. Heterogeneity of tubular transport processes in the nephron. *Ann. Rev. Physiol.* 44:181–201
7. Biagi, B., Kubota, T., Sohtell, M., Giebisch, G. 1981. Intracellular potentials in rabbit proximal tubules perfused in vitro. *Am. J. Physiol.* 240:F200–10
8. Biagi, B., Sohtell, M., Giebisch, G. 1981. Intracellular potassium activity in the rabbit proximal straight tubule. *Am. J. Physiol.* 241:F677–86
9. Boulpaep, E. L. 1979. Electrophysiology of the kidney. In *Membrane Transport in Biology, Vol. IVA, Transport Organs*, ed. G. Giebisch, D. C. Tosteson, H. H. Ussing, pp. 97–144. NY: Springer
10. Boulpaep, E. L. 1976. Recent advances in electrophysiology of the nephron. *Ann. Rev. Physiol.* 38:20–36
11. Boulpaep, E. L. 1976. Electrical phenomena in the nephron. *Kidney Int.* 9:88–102
12. Boulpaep, E. L., Giebisch, G. 1978. Electrophysiological measurements on the renal tubule. In *Methods of Pharmacology, Vol. 4B, Renal Pharmacology*, ed. M. Martinez-Maldonado, pp. 165–93. NY: Plenum
13. Boulpaep, E. L., Seely, J. F. 1971. Electrophysiology of proximal and distal tubules in the autoperfused dog kidney. *Am. J. Physiol.* 221:1084–96
14. Boudry, J., Stoner, L., Burg, M. 1976. The effect of lumen pH on potassium transport in renal cortical collecting tubules. *Am. J. Physiol.* 230:239–44
15. Burckhart, B. C., Frömter, E. 1980. Bicarbonate transport across the peritubular membrane of rat kidney proximal tubule. In *Hydrogen Ion Transport in Epithelia*, ed I. Schulz, G. Sachs, J. G. Forte, K. J. Ullrich, pp. 277–85. NY: Elsevier/North-Holland
16. Burckhart, B. C., Frömter, E. 1981. Bicarbonate and hydroxyl ion permeability of the peritubular cell membrane of rat renal proximal tubular cells *Pflügers Arch.* 389:R40 (Abstr.)
17. Burg, M. B., Bourdeau, J. E. 1978. Function of the thick ascending limb of Henle's loop. In *New Aspects of Renal Function*, ed. H. G. Vogel, K. J. Ullrich, pp. 91–102. Amsterdam: Excerpta Medica
18. Burg, M. B., Green, N. 1973. Function of the thick ascending limb of Henle's loop. *Am. J. Physiol.* 224:659–68
19. Burg, M. B., Issacson, L., Grantham, J., Orloff, J. 1968. Electrical properties of isolated perfused rabbit renal tubules. *Am. J. Physiol.* 215:788–94
20. Cassola, A. C., Gebler, B., Frömter, E. 1981. Measurements of intracellular Cl$^-$ activity in proximal convolution of rat kidney. *Pflügers Arch.* 391:R17 (Abstr.)
21. Cemerikíc, D., Wilcox, C. S., Giebisch, G. 1982. Intracellular potential and K$^+$ activity in rat kidney proximal tubular cells in acidosis and K$^+$ depletion. *J. Membr. Biol.* 69:159–65
22. deBurmudez, L., Windhager, E. E. 1975. Osmotically induced changes in electrical resistance of distal tubules of rat kidney. *Am. J. Physiol.* 229:1536–46
23. DeMello, G. B., Lopes, A. G., Malnic, G. 1976. Conductances, diffusion and streaming potentials in the rat proximal tubule. *J. Physiol.* 260:553–69
24. Dennis, V. W., Brazy, P. C. 1978. Sodium, phosphate, glucose, bicarbonate, and alanine interactions in the isolated convoluted tubule of the rabbit kidney. *J. Clin. Invest.* 62:387–97
25. Edelman, A., Curci, S., Samarzija, I., Frömter, E. 1978. Determination of intracellular K$^+$ activity in rat kidney proximal tubular cells. *Pflügers Arch.* 378:37–45
26. Friedman, P. A., Andreoli, T. E. 1981. Bicarbonate stimulated transepithelial voltage and NaCl transport in the mouse renal cortical thick ascending limb. *Clin. Res.* 29:462A (Abstr.)
27. Friedman, P. A., Hebert, S. C., Andreoli, T. E. 1981. Bicarbonate-dependent NaCl transport and transepithelial voltage in the cortical thick ascending limb of the mouse. *Proc. 8th Int. Congr. Nephrol., Athens, Greece*, p. 41 (Abstr.)

28. Frömter, E. 1977. Magnitude and significance of the paracellular shunt path in rat kidney proximal tubule. In *Intestinal Permeation,* ed. M. Kramer, F. Lauterbach, pp. 166–78. Amsterdam: Excerpta Medica

29. Frömter, E. 1979. Solute transport across epithelia: What can we learn from micropuncture studies on kidney tubules? *J. Physiol.* 288:1–31

30. Frömter, E. 1980. Introductory remarks to electrophysiology and epithelial transport: The use of fast concentration step experiments in the electrical analysis of transport across renal tubules. *Proc. 27th Int. Congr. Physiol., Budapest, Hungary,* pp. 118–19 (Abstr.)

31. Frömter, E. 1981. Electrical aspects of tubular transport of organic substances. In *Organic Transport of Organic Substances,* ed. R. Greger, F. Lang, S. Selbernagh, pp. 30–44, NY: Springer

32. Frömter, E., Gessner, K. 1974. Active transport potentials, membrane diffusion potentials, membrane diffusion potentials and streaming potentials across rat kidney proximal tubule. *Pflügers Arch.* 351:85–98

33. Frömter, E., Gessner, K. 1975. Effect of inhibitors and diuretics on electrical potential differences in rat kidney proximal tubule. *Pflügers Arch.* 357:209–24

34. Frömter, E., Sato, K. 1976. Electrical events in active H^+/HCO_3^- transport across rat kidney proximal tubular epithelium. In *Gastric Hydrogen Ion Secretion,* ed. D. K. Kasbekar, G. Sachs, W. S. Rehm, pp. 382–403. NY: Dekkar

35. Garcia-Filho, E., Malnic, G., Giebisch, G. 1980. Effects of changes in electrical potential difference on tubular potassium transport. *Am. J. Physiol.* 238:F235–46

36. Giebisch, G. 1981. Problems of epithelial potassium transport: special consideration of the nephron. *Fed. Proc.* 40:2395–97

37. Giebisch, G., Malnic, G., Klose, R. M., Windhager, E. E. 1966. Effect of ionic substitutions on distal potential differences in rat kidney. *Am. J. Physiol.* 211:560–68

38. Good, D. W., Wright, F. S. 1980. Luminal influence on potassium secretion: Transepithelial voltage. *Am. J. Physiol.* 239:F289–98

39. Grantham, J. J., Burg, M. B., Orloff, J. 1970. The nature of transtubular Na and K transport in isolated rabbit renal collecting tubules. *J. Clin. Invest.* 49:1815–26

40. Greger, R. 1981. Coupled transport of Na^+ and Cl^- in the thick ascending limb of Henle's loop of rabbit nephron. *Scand. J. Audiol.* 14:1–15 (Suppl.)

41. Greger, R. 1981. Cation selectivity of the isolated perfused cortical thick ascending limb of Henle's loop of rabbit kidney. *Pflügers Arch.* 390:30–37

42. Greger, R. 1981. Chloride reabsorption in the rabbit cortical thick ascending limb of the loop of Henle. A sodium dependent process. *Pflügers Arch.* 390:38–43

43. Greger, R., Frömter, E. 1981. Time course of ouabain and furosemide effects on transepithelial potential difference in cortical thick ascending limbs of rabbit nephrons. In *Advances in Physiological Science, Vol. 11, Kidney and Body Fluids,* ed. L. Takáca, pp. 375–79. Budapest: Pergamon

44. Greger, R., Frömter, E., Schlatter, E. 1981. Electrophysiological studies on the NaCl reabsorption in the cortical thick ascending limb of Henle's loop (cTAL) of rabbit kidney. See Ref. 27, p. 71

45. Greger, R., Frömter, E., Schlatter, E. 1981. Intracellular measurements of the electrical potential difference in the isolated perfused cortical thick ascending limb of rabbit nephrons. *Pflügers Arch.* 389:R40 (Abstr.)

46. Greger, R., Schlatter, E. 1981. Presence of luminal K^+, a prerequisite for active NaCl transport in the cortical thick ascending limb of Henle's loop of rabbit kidney. *Pflügers Arch.* 392:92–94

47. Greger, R., Schlatter, E. 1981. Evidence for conductive and electroneutral chloride exit across the basolateral membrane of rabbit cortical thick ascending limb of Henle's loop (cTAL). *Fed. Proc.* 41:1695 (Abstr.)

48. Greger, R., Schlatter, E. 1982. Evidence for electroneutral KCl exit across the basolateral membrane of rabbit cortical thick ascending limb of Henle's loop (cTAL). *Pflügers Arch.* (Abstr.) 392:R15

49. Gross, J. B., Imai, M., Kokko, J. P. 1975. A functional comparison of the cortical collecting tubule and the distal convoluted tubule. *J. Clin. Invest.* 55:1284–94

50. Gross, J. B., Kokko, J. P. 1977. Effects of aldosterone and potassium-sparing diuretics on electrical potential differences across the distal nephron. *J. Clin. Invest.* 59:82–89

51. Hall, D. A., Varney, D. M. 1980. Effect of vasopressin on electrical potential

difference and chloride transport in mouse medullary thick ascending limb of Henle's loop. *J. Clin. Invest.* 66:792–802

52. Hanley, M. J., Kokko, J. P. 1978. Study of chloride transport across the rabbit cortical collecting tubule. *J. Clin. Invest.* 62:39–44

53. Hanley, M. J., Kokko, J. P., Gross, J. B., Jacobson, H. R. 1980. Electrophysiologic study of the cortical collecting tubule of the rabbit. *Kidney Int.* 17:74–81

54. Hayslett, J. P., Backman, K. A., Schon, D. A. 1980. Electrical properties of the medullary collecting duct in the rat. *Am. J. Physiol.* 239:F258–64

55. Hayslett, J. P., Boulpaep, E. L., Giebisch, G. H. 1978. Factors influencing transepithelial potential difference in mammalian distal tubule. *Am. J. Physiol.* 234:F182–91

56. Hayslett, J. P., Boulpaep, E. L., Kashgarian, M., Giebisch, G. H. 1977. Electrical characteristics of the mammalian distal tubule: Comparison of Ling-Gerard and macroelectrodes. *Kidney Int.* 12:324–31

57. Hebert, S. C., Culpepper, R. M., Andreoli, T. E. 1981. NaCl transport in mouse medullary thick ascending limbs. I. Functional nephron heterogeneity and ADH-stimulated NaCl cotransport. *Am. J. Physiol.* 241:F412–31

58. Hebert, S. C., Culpepper, R. M., Andreoli, T. E. 1981. NaCl transport in mouse medullary thick ascending limbs. II. ADH enhancement of transcellular NaCl cotransport; origin of transepithelial voltage. *Am. J. Physiol.* 241:F432–42

59. Hebert, S. C., Culpepper, R. M., Andreoli, T. E. 1981. NaCl transport in mouse medullary thick ascending limbs. III. Modulation of the ADH effect by peritubular osmolality. *Am. J. Physiol.* 241:F443–51

60. Hebert, S. C., Friedman, P. A., Andreoli, T. E. 1982. Cellular conductive properties of mouse medullary thick ascending limbs (mTALH). *Clin. Res.* (Abstr.) 30:449A

61. Helman, S. I. 1973. Microelectrode studies of isolated cortical collecting tubules. *Am. Soc. Nephrol., 6th Ann. Meet., Washington DC*, p. 49 (Abstr.)

62. Helman, S. I., Grantham, J. J., Burg, M. B. 1971. Effect of vasopressin on electrical resistance of renal cortical collecting tubules. *Am. J. Physiol.* 220:1825–32

63. Helman, S. I., O'Neil, R. G. 1977. Model of active transepithelial Na and K transport of renal collecting tubules. *Am. J. Physiol.* 233:F559–71

64. Imai, M. 1977. Effect of bumetanide and furosemide on the thick ascending limb of Henle's loop of rabbits and rats perfused in vitro. *Eur. J. Pharmacol.* 41:409–16

65. Imai, M. 1979. The connecting tubule: A functional subdivision of the rabbit distal nephron segments. *Kidney Int.* 15:346–56

66. Jacobson, H. R. 1981. Functional segmentation of the mammalian nephron. *Am. J. Physiol.* 241:F203–18

67. Jacobson, H. R., Gross, J. B., Kawamura, S., Waters, J. D., Kokko, J. P. 1976. Electrophysiological study of isolated perfused human collecting ducts. Ion dependency of the transepithelial potential difference. *J. Clin Invest.* 58:1233–39

68. Jones, S. M., Hayslett, J. P. 1982. Demonstration of active potassium secretion in late distal tubule. *Fed. Proc.* 41:1007 (Abstr.)

69. Kaissling, B., Kriz, W. 1979. Structural analysis of the rabbit kidney. *Adv. Anat. Embryol. Cell Biol.* 56:1–123

70. Khuri, R. N. 1979. Intracellular ion activity measurements in kidney tubules. *Curr. Top. Membr. Transp.* 13:73–92

71. Khuri, R. N. 1979. Electrochemistry of the nephron. See Ref. 9, pp. 47–95

72. Khuri, R. N., Agulian, S. K., Bogharian, K. 1974. Electrochemical potentials of chloride in distal renal tubule of the rat. *Am. J. Physiol.* 227:1352–55

73. Khuri, R. N., Agulian, S. K., Kalloghlian, K. 1972. Intracellular potassium in cells of the distal tubule. *Pflügers Arch.* 335:297–308

74. Koeppen, B., Biagi, B., Giebisch, G. 1981. Intracellular potentials of rabbit cortical collecting tubules perfused in vitro. *Fed. Proc.* 40:356 (Abstr.)

75. Koeppen, B. M., Biagi, B. A., Giebisch, G. H. 1983. Microelectrode characterization of the rabbit cortical collecting duct. *Am. J. Physiol.* In press

76. Koeppen, B., Giebisch, G. 1982. Microelectrode study of rabbit cortical collecting tubules: Properties of the apical membrane. *Kidney Int.* 21:280 (Abstr.)

77. Koeppen, B. M., Helman, S. I. 1982. Acidification of luminal fluid by the rabbit cortical collecting tubule perfused in vitro. *Am. J. Physiol.* 242:F521–31

78. Lacaz-Vieira, F., Malnic, G. 1968. Hydrogen ion secretion by rat renal cortical tubules as studied by an antimony

microelectrode. *Am. J. Physiol.* 214: 710–18

79. Laurence, R., March, D. J. 1971. Effect of diuretic states on hamster collecting duct electrical potential differences. *Am. J. Physiol.* 220:1610–16

80. Lombard, W. E., Jacobson, H. R., Kokko, J. P. 1980. Effect of in vivo and in vitro acid-base manipulations on collecting duct bicarbonate transport. *Clin. Res.* 28:535A (Abstr.)

81. Lutz, M., Cardinal, J., Burg, M. B. 1973. Electrical resistance of renal proximal tubule perfused in vitro. *Am. J. Physiol.* 225:729–34

82. Malnic, G., DeMello-Aires, M., Giebisch, G. 1972. Micropuncture study of renal tubular hydrogen ion transport in the rat. *Am. J. Physiol.* 222:147–58

83. Malnic, G., Giebisch, G. 1972. Some electrical properties of distal tubular epithelium in the rat. *Am. J. Physiol.* 223:797–808

84. Malnic, G., Klose, R. M., Giebisch, G. 1966. Micropuncture study of distal tubular potassium and sodium transport in rat nephron. *Am. J. Physiol.* 211:529–47

85. Malnic, G., Klose, R. M., Giebisch, G. 1966. Microperfusion study of distal tubular potassium and sodium transfer in rat kidney. *Am. J. Physiol.* 211: 548–59

86. Morel, F. 1981. Sites of hormone action in the mammalian nephron. *Am. J. Physiol.* 240:F159–64

87. Morel, F., Chabardes, D., Imbert, M. 1976. Functional segmentation of the rabbit distal tubule by microdetermination of hormone-dependent adenylate cyclase activity. *Kidney Int.* 9:264–77

88. O'Neil, R. G. 1981. Potassium secretion by the cortical collecting tubule. *Fed. Proc.* 40:2403–7

89. O'Neil, R. G. 1982. Apical cell membrane K conductance properties of the cortical collecting tubule: Influence of Ba and Cs. *Kidney Int.* 21:283 (Abstr.)

90. O'Neil, R. G. 1982. Effect of luminal H⁺ and Ba⁺⁺ on the apical cell membrane K⁺ conductance of the cortical collecting tubule (CCT). *Fed. Proc.* 41:1006 (Abstr.)

91. O'Neil, R. G., Boulpaep, E. L. 1979. Effect of amiloride on the apical cell membrane cation channels of a sodium-absorbing, potassium-secreting renal epithelium. *J. Memb. Biol.* 50:365–87

92. O'Neil, R. G., Boulpaep, E. L. 1982. Ionic conductive properties and the electrophysiology of rabbit cortical collecting tubule. *Am. J. Physiol.* 243:F81–95

93. O'Neil, R. G., Helman, S. I. 1977. Transport characteristics of renal collecting tubules: Influences of DOCA and diet. *Am. J. Physiol.* 233:F544–58

94. Proverbio, F., Whittembury, G. 1975. Cell electrical potentials during enhanced sodium extrusion in guinea-pig kidney cortex slices. *J. Physiol.* 250: 559–78

95. Rector, F. C. Jr., Clapp, J. R. 1962. Evidence for active chloride reabsorption in the distal renal tubule of the rat. *J. Clin. Invest.* 41:101–7

96. Rau, W. S., Frömter, E. 1974. Electrical properties of the medullary collecting ducts of the golden hamster kidney. I. The transepithelial potential difference. *Pflügers Arch.* 351:99–111

97. Rau, W. S., Frömter, E. 1974. Electrical properties of the medullary collecting ducts of the golden hamster kidney. II. The transepithelial resistance. *Pflügers Arch.* 351:113–31

98. Rocha, A. S., Kudo, L. H. 1978. Sodium chloride transport and electrical gradients across the isolated perfused papillary collecting duct. *Proc. 7th Int. Congr. Nephrol., Montreal, Canada,* p. C-5., (Abstr.)

99. Rocha, A. S., Kokko, J. P. 1973. Sodium chloride and water transport in the medullary thick ascending limb of Henle. Evidence for active chloride transport. *J. Clin. Invest.* 52:612–23

100. Sakai, F., Jamison, A. L., Berliner, R. W. 1965. A method for exposing the rat renal medulla in vivo: micropuncture of the collecting duct. *Am. J. Physiol.* 209:663–68

101. Samarzija, I., Molnar, V., Frömter, E. 1980. Mechanism of Na⁺-coupled anion absorption across the brush-border membrane of rat renal proximal tubule. *Proc. 27th Int. Congr. Physiol., Budapest, Hungary,* p. 678, (Abstr.)

102. Sasaki, S., Imai, M. 1980. Effects of vasopressin on water and NaCl transport across the in vitro perfused medullary thick ascending limb of Henle's loop of mouse, rat, and rabbit kidneys. *Pflügers Arch.* 383:215–21

103. Schaffer, J. A., Andreoli, T. E. 1979. Rheogenic and passive Na⁺ absorption by the proximal nephron. *Ann. Rev. Physiol.* 41:211–25

104. Schaffer, J. A., Andreoli, T. E. 1979. See Ref. 9, pp. 473–538

105. Schwartz, G. J., Burg, M. B. 1978. Mineralocorticoid effects on cation transport by cortical collecting tubules

in vitro. *Am. J. Physiol.* 235:F576–F85
106. Shareghi, G. R., Stoner, L. C. 1978. Calcium transport across segments of the rabbit distal nephron in vitro. *Am. J. Physiol.* 235:F367–75
107. Sohtell, M. 1978. Studies on chloride and bicarbonate ion reabsorption in the proximal tubules of the rat kidney. *Acta. Univ. Upsal.* 293:1–16
108. Stanton, B. A., Biemesderfer, D., Wade, J. B., Giebisch, G. 1981. Structural and functional study of the rat distal nephron: Effects of potassium adaptation and depletion. *Kidney Int.* 19:36–48
109. Stetson, D. L., Wade, J. B., Giebisch, G. 1980. Morphologic alterations in the rat medullary collecting duct following potassium depletion. *Kidney Int.* 17:45–56
110. Stokes, J. B. 1981. Potassium secretion by cortical collecting tubule: relation to sodium absorption, luminal sodium concentration, and transepithelial voltage. *Am. J. Physiol.* 241:F395–402
111. Stokes, J. B. 1979. Effect of prostaglandin E_2 on chloride transport across the rabbit thick ascending limb of Henle. *J. Clin. Invest.* 64:495–502
112. Stokes, J. B. 1982. Sodium and potassium transport across the cortical and outer medullary collecting tubule of the rabbit: Evidence for diffusion across the outer medullary portion. *Am. J. Physiol.* 242:F514–20
113. Stokes, J. B., Ingram, M. J., Williams, A. D., Ingram, D. 1981. Heterogeneity of the rabbit collecting tubule: Localization of mineralocorticoid hormone action to the cortical portion. *Kidney Int.* 20:340–47
114. Stokes, J. B., Tisher, C. C., Kokko, J. P. 1978. Structural-functional heterogeneity along the rabbit collecting tubule. *Kidney Int.* 14:585–93
115. Stoner, L. C. 1979. Studies with amiloride on isolated distal nephron segments. In *Amiloride and Epithelial Sodium Transport,* ed. A. W. Cuthbert,

G. M. Fanelli, Jr., A. Scriabine, pp. 51–60. NY: Urban & Schwartz
116. Stoner, L. C., Burg, M. B., Orloff, J. 1974. Ion transport in cortical collecting tubule; effect of amiloride. *Am. J. Physiol.* 227:453–59
117. Temple-Smith, P., Costanzo, L., Windhager, E. E. 1977. Re-examination of transepithelial potential difference in distal convoluted tubules of the rat. In *Electrophysiology of the Nephron,* pp. 115–24. Paris: Inserm
118. Terreros, D. A., Grantham, J. A., Tarr, M. 1981. Axial heterogeneity of transmembrane electrical potential in isolated proximal renal tubules. *Kidney Int.* 19:259 (Abstr.)
119. Terreros, D. A., Tarr, M., Grantham, J. J. 1981. Transmembrane electrical potential differences in cells of isolated renal tubules. *Am. J. Physiol.* 241:F61–68
120. Velázquez, H., Wright, F. S., Good, D. W. 1982. Luminal influences on potassium secretion: Chloride replacement with sulfate. *Am. J. Physiol.* 242:F46–55
121. Warnock, D. G., Eveloff, J. 1982. NaCl entry mechanisms in the luminal membrane of the renal tubule. *Am. J. Physiol.* 242:F561–74
122. Wiederholt, M., Agulian, S. K., Khuri, R. N. 1974. Intracellular potassium in the distal tubule of the adrenalectomized and aldosterone treated rat. *Pflügers Arch.* 347:117–23
123. Wiederholt, M., Schoormans, W., Hansen, L., Behn, C. 1974. Sodium conductance changes by aldosterone in the rat kidney. *Pflügers Arch.* 348:155–65
124. Windhager, E. E. 1964. Electrophysiological study of renal papilla of golden hamsters. *Am. J. Physiol.* 206:694–700
125. Wright, F. S. 1971. Increasing magnitude of electrical potential along the renal distal tubule. *Am. J. Physiol.* 220:624–38
126. Wright, F. S., Strieder, N., Fowler, N. B., Giebisch, G. 1971. Potassium secretion by distal tubule after potassium adaptation. *Am. J. Physiol.* 221:437–48

Ann. Rev. Physiol. 1983. 45:519–32

REGULATORY ROLE OF INTRACELLULAR CALCIUM IONS IN EPITHELIAL NA TRANSPORT

Erich E. Windhager

Department of Physiology, Cornell University Medical College, New York, NY 10021

Ann Taylor

Laboratory of Physiology, Oxford University, Oxford OX1-3PT, England

INTRODUCTION

Whereas several early studies indicated that extracellular calcium levels can influence the rate of sodium movement across amphibian epithelia (15, 16), only during the last decade has it become apparent that cytosolic calcium ions are potentially important regulators of transepithelial ion and water transport. The first suggestive evidence that intracellular calcium ions play such a role was obtained in studies with quinidine in the urinary bladder of the toad (46). Quinidine, an agent presumed to increase the level of cytosolic free calcium ions (4, 29, 10, 22), was found to inhibit vasopressin-dependent water permeability and net sodium transport across the isolated toad bladder (46, 50). Subsequently, Erlij & Grinstein (18, 25) reported that a reduction in the sodium concentration of the medium bathing the inner surface of the isolated frog skin inhibits the rate of active transepithelial sodium transport in a calcium-dependent manner. Their interpretation of this finding was based on the concept that a Na-Ca exchange mechanism operates across the basolateral border of epithelial cells, as in excitable cells, as originally proposed by Blaustein (7). Wiesmann et al (56) employed the ionophore A23187 to explore the regulatory role of intracellular calcium in the toad bladder; these investigations first described and characterized the

519

inhibitory effect of this agent on net sodium transport. These studies were followed by reports that exposure to low peritubular sodium, quinidine, and calcium ionophores result in inhibition of sodium absorption by proximal convoluted and collecting tubules of rabbit kidneys (20, 21). Some of the conjectures regarding experimentally induced changes in cytosolic calcium have been at least partially substantiated by direct measurements of cytosolic calcium ion activity using calcium-selective microelectrodes in proximal tubular epithelium from *Necturus* kidneys (32, 36, 57). Moreover, the hypothesis (25, 49) that elevated intracellular free calcium levels reduce transport of sodium ions across epithelium by diminishing the sodium permeability of the apical membrane has recently been confirmed in studies on isolated toad bladders and on isolated membrane vesicles prepared from apical membranes of toad bladder epithelium (12, 13).

MAINTENANCE OF LOW LEVELS OF CYTOSOLIC CALCIUM ION ACTIVITY

Using Ca ion selective microelectrodes Lee et al (32) found that in proximal tubular cells of the perfused *Necturus* kidney the cytosolic Ca^{2+} activity (a_{Ca}^i) averages about 116 nM. Somewhat lower values (about 60 nM) have recently been observed on isolated perfused proximal tubules of the *Necturus* kidney (57). Estimates of intracellular concentration of free calcium in cultured isolated monkey kidney cells with aequorin (8) gave similar values (mean: 57 nM). Lee (33) has given an account of the preparation and characteristics of the electrodes used in *Necturus* (32, 36, 57, 58). Although highly selective for calcium ions, their voltage response to changes in a_{Ca}^i is less than Nernstian in the activity range below 10^{-6} M Ca^{2+}. Attention must be paid to the EGTA-Ca stability constant used in preparing standards for calibrating such electrodes with solutions containing calcium ions at activities lower than 10^- M. Selectivity coefficients were: k_{CaK} 10^{-6} to 10^{-5}; k_{CaMg} 10^{-7} to 10^{-6}; k_{CaNa} 10^{-5} to 10^{-4} (33). Because of the high viscosity of the neutral Ca ligand used in preparing the Ca-selective microelectrodes, only glass pipettes with outside tip diameters barely less than 1 μm can be used. These microelectrodes are therefore too large to be applied for intracellular measurements in toad bladder or mammalian tubular epithelium. Stable measurements of Ca^{2+} activity can, however, be obtained in the relatively large (20 μm) cells of proximal tubular epithelium of *Necturus* kidneys.

The mechanisms responsible for maintaining the low levels of a_{Ca}^i include ATP-driven Ca pumps (23, 30) and a Na-Ca exchange mechanism (20). Such processes have been localized in the contraluminal cell membrane of toad bladder (12) and renal tubular epithelium (23, 30), either directly in vesicles (12, 23, 30) prepared from peritubular membranes or indirectly by evaluating epithelial responses to changes in driving forces acting upon Na-Ca exchange at the contraluminal cells membrane (7, 11, 14, 20, 21, 25, 32, 47–51, 54). We do not know the relative importance of primary ATP-driven active transport of calcium versus secondary active Ca extrusion energized by the electrochemical potential gradient for sodium ions across the contraluminal cell membrane, in the maintenance of physiological levels $(10^{-7}$ M) of a_{Ca}^{i}. Gmaj et al (23) found that the ATP-driven Ca^{2+} uptake by basolateral membrane vesicles is saturable by increasing Ca^{2+} concentrations. The double-reciprocal analysis of these results (Ca^{2+} uptake in the presence of ATP minus Ca^{2+} uptake in the absence of ATP) at 10 min of vesicle incubation yielded an apparent K_m of 0.5 μM and a V_{max} of 10.4 nmol. per 10 min per mg of protein. This K_m value is given in units of free calcium ion concentration. Assuming an activity coefficient of 0.32 (33) the K_m value calculated is $\sim$ 1.5–2.7 times higher than the levels of cytosolic Ca ion activity measured in proximal tubule cells of *Necturus*. Kinetic data on Na-Ca exchange have only been obtained in vesicles prepared from basolateral plasma membranes of toad bladder epithelium. These studies (12) suggest that the stoichiometry is 3 Na : 1 Ca, in agreement with measured cytosolic Ca and Na ion activities and membrane voltages in proximal tubules of *Necturus* (57). In the absence of ATP, K_m values of 251–272 μM (Ca) were obtained at external Na concentrations between 1.7 and 155.0 mM while the internal Na concentration was always 155.0 mM (12). Such K_m values are much higher than those reported for Na-Ca exchange processes in other tissues (9) and exceed the directly measured levels of a_{Ca}^{i} (32) by three orders of magnitude. It is however, conceivable that the lack of ATP in the preparation used may account for the very low affinity of the Na-Ca exchanger for calcium ions. Thus in excitable tissue, addition of ATP reduced the concentration of internal ionized Ca^{2+} needed to provide a half-maximal rate of Na-dependent Ca^{2+} efflux from a level of 10–20 μM to 0.2–0.3 μM (9). Therefore, a similar reduction in affinity may have been, at least in part, responsible for the high K_m values obtained by Chase & Al-Awqati (12).

Evidence for the view that Na-Ca exchange plays a role in cellular calcium homeostasis under physiological conditions is the observation of Ullrich et al (54) that removal of sodium ions from or addition of ouabain to the peritubular fluid inhibits active Ca^{2+} transport by proximal tubules of rat or hamster kidneys. In both experimental conditions, a reduction in the electrochemical potential gradient for Na ions across the contraluminal cell membrane results in diminished Ca transport across the epithelium, and by implication, across the peritubular plasma membrane. Thus secondary active transport due to Na-Ca exchange is apparently the dominant mechanism for Ca reabsorption in renal tubules.

Direct proof that alterations in the magnitude of the electrochemical potential gradient for sodium ions across the peritubular cell membrane affect the intracellular Ca^{2+} level has been obtained by Lee et al (32). Lowering the Na concentration from 100 to 10 mM (by choline substitution) led to an increase in a_{Ca}^i from a control level of 106 to 37ΰ nM. At least in proximal tubules of *Necturus,* the apparent decrease in secondary active Ca extrusion out of the cell via the Na-Ca exchange mechanism could not be fully compensated by the activity of the ATP-driven Ca pump within the plasma membrane nor by buffering of calcium ions by intracellular organelles.

Murphy & Mandel (39) have argued that intracellular storage sites, in particular mitochondria, act as important regulators of the intracellular concentration of free calcium ions in isolated nonperfused mammalian tubules prepared as a tubular suspension. This conclusion was reached from estimates of intracellular Ca^{2+} concentrations by means of a null-point method using Arsenazo III after disruption of the plasma membrane. Control values for intracellular free calcium ion concentrations averaged 450 nM ($\sim$ 144 nM calcium ion activity)—i.e. 2.3 times higher than the values measured with Ca-selective microelectrodes in isolated *Necturus* proximal tubules. Murphy & Mandel (39) further observed that addition of the calcium ionophore A23187 increased cytosolic calcium ion concentration eight-fold. Total mitochondrial Ca content was estimated by measuring the quantity of Ca released after addition of 4 μM FCCP (fluorocyanocarbonyl-phenylhydrazine). The presence of this compound, known to uncouple mitochondrial oxydative phospholylation, led to the release of 80% of total Ca, suggesting that the mitochondria play indeed a major role in calcium homeostasis in these tubules. However, the Ca content of mitochondria cannot be measured in vivo, and the high values obtained in isolated mitochondria or in vitro tissue may be due to damage occurring during the preparation of the specimens (45). Thus using rapid freezing techniques and electron probe analysis of freeze-dried cryosections of vascular smooth, cardiac, and skeletal muscle, Somlyo and his collaborators (45) found the in situ Ca content of mitochondria to be negligibly small; they could not detect increases in Ca content of mitochondria during a 30 min contracture of vascular smooth muscle—i.e. under conditions when cytosolic calcium ion activity presumably increases significantly. A high Ca content of mitochondria was observed only in damaged cells (44). These investigators therefore concluded that mitochondria do not play a significant role in the physiological regulation of cytosolic Ca ion activity. It would be desirable to extend this in situ approach to transporting epithelia, including renal tubules.

EVIDENCE THAT CYTOSOLIC CALCIUM ION LEVELS INFLUENCE NA-TRANSPORT

Effect of Quinidine and of Ca-ionophores

The first indication that intracellular Ca^{2+} may influence the rate of trans-epithelial sodium movement was obtained by the use of chemical compounds believed to increase a_{Ca}^i. Quinidine was used initially because of its known influence on muscle contractility, an effect attributed to its ability to increase sarcoplasmic Ca^{2+} levels (29). Quinidine has also been found to reduce calcium uptake by isolated muscle mitochondria (4) and sarcoplasmic reticulum vesicles (3, 4, 10) and may induce the release of calcium from these intracellular organelles (3, 4, 10, 29). Studies on turtle bladder epithelial cells by Arruda & Sabatini (1) support the notion that the drug increases the cytosolic Ca^{2+} concentration by causing the release of calcium from intracellular stores since ^{45}Ca efflux from cells preloaded with the isotope was enhanced by quinidine. The most direct evidence for the view that levels of intracellular Ca^{2+} are raised by quinidine was obtained by the use of Ca ion selective microelectrodes (57, 58). In isolated perfused proximal tubules of *Necturus* kidney, addition of 10^{-4} M quinidine increased a_{Ca}^i from a control value of 62 nM to 648 nM, an effect that was at least partially reversible in all instances.

The effect of quinidine on sodium transport was first studied on the urinary bladder of the toad (46, 50). When added to the serosal solution at a concentration of 4×10^{-4} M, the drug induced a progressive fall in short-circuit current to 43% of the paired controls 45 min after addition of quinidine. This inhibition of the net transport of sodium ions was associated with a somewhat smaller drop in transepithelial voltage, indicating that the transepithelial resistance was increased by 34%. Addition of vasopressin to the quinidine-treated hemibladders produced an increase in short-circuit current to levels observed in the paired controls. This result argues against the notion that quinidine inhibits sodium transport by a grossly toxic effect on cellular metabolism.

Quinidine was also shown to inhibit net sodium transport by urinary bladders of freshwater turtles (1). This inhibitory effect was dose-dependent, independent of extracellular calcium concentration, and not readily reversible after removal of quinidine from the bathing medium. As in toad bladders (46, 50), the reduction in short-circuit current was accompanied by a proportionally smaller decrease in transepithelial voltage, indicating that the electrical resistance of the epithelium was increased.

Quinidine also inhibits renal tubular Na transport. In studies on isolated perfused proximal tubules of the rabbit Friedman et al (20) found that addition of 10^{-4} M quinidine to the bathing solution resulted in a consistent fall in fluid reabsorption—an index of sodium net reabsorption—from a control value of 1.05 to 0.66 nl min^{-1} mm^{-1}. Associated with this reduction in water reabsorption was a fall in the unidirectional sodium permeability from 10.4 to 7.5 X 10^{-5} cm sec^{-1}.

Calcium ionophores have been employed to increase intracellular Ca^{2+} concentration in transporting renal and urinary bladder epithelium, and their action on sodium transport has been evaluated. The calcium ionophores A-23187 and X-537A more or less specifically promote the movement of divalent, and in the case of X-537A, monovalent cations across cell membranes (reviewed in 41, 42). Wiesmann et al (56) first studied the effect of A-23187 on sodium transport by toad bladders. They found that serosal addition of the ionophore to yield a final concentration of 1 μM caused a progressive inhibition of the short-circuit current, which was dependent upon the calcium concentration of the serosal bath. When isolated toad bladder epithelial cells were exposed to A-23187 their ^{45}Ca uptake increased. Ludens (37) confirmed the conclusion that A-23187 inhibits sodium transport in toad bladders. He demonstrated that the inhibition of the short-circuit current is associated with a decrease in the unidirectional mucosal-to-serosal flux of ^{22}Na without any change in the serosal-to-mucosal flux. Thus the reduction in net transport of sodium is brought about by inhibition at a site along the transcellular active transport route for sodium and not by increased passive backflux of sodium ions. Both groups of investigators (37, 56) assumed that the inhibitory effect of A-23187 is caused by an increase in calcium levels within the cytosol, brought about by the ionophore-induced increase in calcium influx across the plasma membrane. Taylor et al (47, 50) also found that calcium ionophores inhibit the net transport of sodium ions in toad bladders. The degree of inhibition by A-23187 was dependent upon the external calcium concentration. Bathing hemibladders in 0.89 mM calcium A-23187 at a final concentration of 10 μM caused a fall in short-circuit current by 57%. In paired controls bathed in 0.1 mM calcium, short-circuit current fell by only 28%. As in the quinidine studies, vasopressin reversed the drug-induced inhibition of sodium transport. Essentially similar results were obtained with X-537A. At a concentration of 5 μM, X-537A induced a fall in short-circuit current in toad bladders to 52% of the control values after 60 min. However, in contrast to the observations with A-23187, the degree of inhibition by X-537A was not found to vary with the extracellular calcium concentration nor did vasopressin fully reverse the inhibition of sodium transport.

The action of A-23187 was also examined in perfusion studies on isolated proximal tubules of rabbit kidneys (20). After addition of 5 × 10⁻⁶ M A-23187 to the bathing solution fluid reabsorption by the tubules was reduced by 40% of the control values. Unidirectional sodium efflux from the lumen declined from 17.3 to 14.6 × 10⁻⁹ eq cm⁻² sec⁻¹ upon addition of the ionophore to the bath, again suggesting that the transcellular route of sodium reabsorption was affected, either at the site of passive, luminal entry into or the active, contraluminal exit of sodium ions from the epithelial cells. An increase in a_{Ca}^i is a common denominator for the effect of quinidine (57, 58) and the calcium ionophores (23), strengthening the view that the inhibition of net transport of sodium by these compounds is brought about by an increase in intracellular Ca^{2+} concentration (49, 50). Taylor (50, 51) further proposed that since vasopressin could overcome the effect of the assumed increase in a_{Ca}^i induced by quinidine, the observed stimulation of sodium transport by this hormone may have been mediated by a decrease in intracellular calcium ion activity.

Studies with calcium ionophores on the frog skin have led to different conclusions. Balaban & Mandel (2) found that addition of A-23187 to the inside solution of the frog skin resulted in an approximately 40% transient stimulation of the short-circuit current and ionic conductance, which decayed after 1–2 hr. Similar results had previously been reported by Nielsen (40). Balaban & Mandel (2) attributed their findings to an ionophore-induced increase in a_{Ca}^i, which supposedly stimulates Na transport by increasing the apical membrane permeability to this ion. They further proposed that the natriferic response of the frog skin to vasopressin is mediated by an increase in intracellular Ca^{2+} concentration. However, Nielsen (40) interpreted the ionophore-induced increase in short-circuit current as being due to an increase in K permeability of the contraluminal cell membrane caused by the high a_{Ca}^i. Responses similar to those found in toad bladders have been observed on isolated frog skin epithelium by Grinstein et al (26). Furthermore, Erlij et al (19) have found evidence that A-23187 and the calcium ionophore ionomycin increase the prostaglandin E_1 release from frog skins into the inside bathing solution and that the ionophore-induced stimulation of Na transport in frog skin could be reduced by prior addition of indomethacin (10⁻⁶ M) or acetylsalicylic acid (10⁻³ M) to the inside solution. They concluded that stimulation of Na transport caused by Ca ionophores in the frog skin is secondary to the release of prostaglandin E_1. Ionophore studies on frog skin may also be complicated by the presence of subepithelial glands that can transport Na^+ inward and also secrete Cl^- (55). Since chloride secretion is known to be stimulated by A-23187 in other epithelia (6) it is conceivable that the ionophore-induced increase in short-circuit current is at least partly related to movement of Cl^-.

Effect of Changes in the Electrochemical Potential Gradient for Sodium Ions at the Contraluminal Cell Membrane

The presence of a Na-Ca exchange mechanism at the contraluminal cell membrane of toad bladder (12, 47, 49, 50, 51), frog skin (18, 25), and renal tubular epithelium (20, 23, 30, 32, 54, 57) provides a means of altering the level of cytosolic Ca^{2+} by changing the driving force for sodium backflux into the cell across this cell boundary. Specifically, lowering of the sodium concentration in the contraluminal fluid compartment should reduce the rate of sodium entry into the cell, thereby diminish the coupled calcium extrusion rate out of the cell, and utimately increase a_{Ca}^i. As mentioned, increased intracellular calcium ion levels have indeed been measured in proximal tubular cells of *Necturus* kidney when the sodium concentration in peritubular fluid was reduced (32). Changes in net transport of sodium associated with lowering of the contraluminal sodium concentration may thus be attributable to increased a_{Ca}^i (12, 20, 25, 32, 49, 50, 51, 57).

Several reports in the older literature (5, 31, 38) attest to the marked influence of the removal of sodium from the contraluminal fluid compartment on net transport of sodium. Inhibition of short-circuit current was observed in toad bladder (5, 31) and frog skin (38) when sodium was absent in the serosal or inner bathing medium. These observations remained unexplained, until Grinstein & Erlij (25) reported that in frog skins this inhibition was prevented when Ca^{2+} ions had been removed from the inner bath. They concluded that the inhibition of sodium transport by removal of sodium from contraluminal fluid is due to an increase in a_{Ca}^i that in turn causes a decrease in sodium permeability of the luminal cell membrane. Similar conclusions have been reached in toad bladder studies (12, 13, 47, 48, 49, 50). Lowering of serosal Na to 2 mM reduced the short-circuit current to about 50% of control values 15 min after the low sodium concentration was applied to the contraluminal surface of the epithelial preparation. The inhibition of net transport could be reversed by vasopressin, suggesting that cellular metabolism was functioning. The degree of inhibition was a function of extracellular calcium concentrations. Inhibition was least at low extracellular calcium levels and was reduced in the presence of lanthanum (48). Previous studies by Leaf (31) had shown that the fall in short-circuit current induced by low serosal sodium in toad bladder preparations is associated with a parallel decline in mucosal-to-serosal ^{24}Na flux.

Similar experiments have been performed in isolated perfused proximal tubules of rabbit kidneys (20). In these experiments, the tubular lumen was perfused with solutions containing 145 mEq liter^{-1} sodium at all times. The same sodium concentration was used in the peritubular bath during control and recovery periods. However, during experimental periods, peritubular sodium was reduced to 40 mEq liter^{-1} by substitution of lithium for sodium. Fluid absorption (J_v) was estimated using ^{125}I-iothalamate. Under control conditions, J_v averaged 1.13 nl min^{-1} mm^{-1} length; during the experimental periods when peritubular sodium had been reduced, fluid reabsorption amounted to only 0.44 nl min^{-1} mm^{-1} length—i.e. some 40% of the control values. Fluid reabsorption recovered to values not different from controls when sodium concentrations were restored to their physiological level in the contraluminal bathing fluid. Measurements of bidirectional fluxes of sodium isotopes were also carried out to test whether sodium efflux from tubular lumen to bath or backflux into the lumen was responsible for the observed reduction in fluid movement. During experimental periods, when NaCl was partially replaced by LiCl in the peritubular fluid, ^{22}Na-efflux fell significantly to 72% of the control value. This reduction in efflux accounts for some 50% of the simultaneously observed drop in fluid reabsorption. Lithium backflux accounted for the remaining 50% reduction in fluid transport but not for the inhibition of unidirectional sodium efflux. The reduction in sodium efflux also occurred when sodium was replaced by choline or tetraethylammonium and was dependent upon the extracellular calcium concentration.

Recent experiments on isolated perfused collecting tubules of rabbit indicate that a Na-Ca exchange mechanism may exist in the peritubular membrane and that increased cytosolic Ca^{2+} levels may inhibit sodium reabsorption in this nephron segment (21). Isotopic Na efflux was reduced by lowering the sodium concentration in the peritubular bath. A small but significant increase in unidirectional sodium efflux occurred when pitressin was added during the low-Na periods.

Cytosolic calcium ion levels can also be raised by inhibition of the Na pump, thereby increasing the intracellular sodium ion concentration and thus decreasing the driving force for sodium entry across the contraluminal cell membrane. Studies with ion-selective microelectrodes on proximal tubules of *Necturus* have indeed demonstrated that 10^{-4} M ouabain leads to a marked increase in both intracellular sodium (58) and calcium ion activity (36) (and reduction in peritubular membrane potential).

MECHANISM OF INHIBITION OF SODIUM TRANSPORT BY ELEVATED LEVELS OF CYTOSOLIC CALCIUM ION CONCENTRATION

The decrease in transcellular sodium efflux produced by quinidine, Ca ionophores, or low peritubular sodium concentrations may result from an inhibitory effect of high a_{Ca}^i on one or more of the several steps that determine the overall rate of transepithelial sodium transport: (a) intrinsic activity of the Na pump, (b) energy supply to the Na pump, (c) permeability of the luminal (apical) membrane to sodium ions, or (d) permeability of the tight junction. Among these factors, the latter has been ruled out as contributing to the observed inhibition of transport in proximal tubules, a leaky epithelium in which tight junction permeability is of quantitative significance. The apparent permeability for the backflux of Na, a relative index of the permeability of tight junction to Na, was not altered significantly by lowering the peritubular sodium concentration (20).

Regarding an effect of calcium on the activity of the sodium pump, or on its energy supply, it is known that high levels of Ca may inhibit Na^+-K^+-ATPase (17, 52), interfere with mitochondrial metabolism, and hence affect the energy supply to the sodium pump (34). In fact, Humes & Weinberg (28) found A-23187 reduced oxydative phosphorylation in isolated toad bladder epithelial cells. However, several arguments (49, 51) make it unlikely that the inhibition of transepithelial sodium transport observed in the various experimental conditions in which cytosolic Ca^{2+} levels are elevated can be attributed entirely to such a mechanism. Thus inhibition of the Na^+-K^+-ATPase activity is half-maximal at calcium concentrations of about 5×10^{-4} M (52) and minimal inhibition requires at least 10^{-5} M Ca^{2+} (24). Calcium uptake by mitochondria, which may interfere with ATP synthesis (34), has a relatively low affinity, with a K_m of about 10^{-5} M (Ca^{2+}) in the presence of nearly physiological levels of magnesium (9). Recent measurements in proximal tubular cells of Necturus kidney using Ca^{2+}-selective microelectrodes indicate that the calcium ion activity is increased to some 380 nM by lowering peritubular [Na] (32), to 638 nM during quinidine administration (57) and to approximately 660 nM in ouabain treated tubules (36). These measurements indicate that cytosolic calcium ion activity is still below that required to inhibit significantly Na^+-K^+-ATPase or mitochondrial metabolism in vitro. Evidence that maneuvers leading to an increase in intracellular calcium ion concentration do not limit the energy supply to the Na pump derives from the observations in toad bladder that vasopressin completely reverses the inhibitory effect of low serosal sodium concentrations, quinidine, or A-23187 on short-circuit current. In fact, the short-circuit current in these experiments was as high as or higher than in toad bladders treated with vasopressin alone (46, 51). On the other hand, there are as yet no direct data on changes in a_{Ca}^i in transporting mammalian proximal or distal nephron segments during experimental maneuvers that inhibit Na transport. Yingst & Hoffman (60) reported that 10^{-6} M (Ca^{2+})$_i$ causes a 40% inhibition of the Na pump in resealed human erythrocyte ghosts; therefore it cannot be ruled out that the inhibition of Na efflux in mammalian tubules exposed to low peritubular [Na], quinidine, or A-23187 is due, in part, to an inhibitory effect of intracellular Ca^{2+} on the activity of the Na pump.

The third possibility—that changes in cytosolic Ca^{2+} primarily influence the sodium permeability of the apical cell membrane—is supported by several recent studies on toad bladder (12, 13) and renal tubules (57, 58). Inhibition of Na permeability by intracellular Ca^{2+} is not unprecedented in other tissues (27, 59). Chase & Al-Awqati (11, 12) have demonstrated that ^{22}Na-influx across the apical membrane of toad bladder epithelium is reduced in the presence of A-23187 or at a low serosal sodium concentration or in K^+-free solutions and that the degree of reduction in influx is equivalent to the simultaneous decrease in short-circuit current. Subsequently, Chase & Al-Awqati (13) found that the sodium permeability of apical membrane vesicles prepared from toad bladder epithelium decreases when the Ca^{2+} concentration is increased within the submicromolar range. Additional evidence has been derived from studies with ion-selective microelectrodes on isolated perfused proximal tubules of *Necturus* kidney (57, 58). Quinidine (10^{-4} M) at normal levels of external calcium but not when external calcium was deleted (M. Lorenzen, C. O. Lee, unpublished observations) was found to increase cytosolic Ca^{2+} but to reduce the intracellular activity of sodium ions (a^i_{Na}). These results are not compatible with a primary inhibition of the sodium pump. In fact, when ouabain, a direct inhibitor of the Na^+-K^+-ATPase, was administered a^i_{Na} within the cells rose markedly, simultaneously with a rise in a^i_{Ca} (36).

Calcium-induced changes in Na permeability of the apical membrane have been incorporated into a model of feedback control of epithelial sodium transport (43, 49, 51, 53). According to this hypothesis, a primary reduction in Na pump activity would lead to an increase in intracellular Na^+ concentration that would reduce the rate of Na-Ca exchange in the contraluminal cell membrane and hence increase a^i_{Ca}. The latter is presumed to decrease luminal Na permeability and thus prevent overloading of the cell with sodium. Schultz (43) has added the view that increased cytosolic Ca^{2+} may also enhance the K^+ permeability of the contraluminal cell membrane in accord with the well-known "Gardos effect" (reviewed in 35) in other tissues. Unfortunately, there is at present no direct information regarding the relationship between changes in a^i_{Ca} and K^+ permeability of the cell membranes of transporting epithelia.

CONCLUSIONS

There is strong evidence that changes in cytosolic Ca^{2+} concentration can influence sodium transport in toad bladder, frog skin, and renal tubular epithelium. Intracellular Ca^{2+} affects the Na permeability of the apical membrane. Cytosolic Ca^{2+} levels are regulated in part by a Na-Ca exchange process within the contraluminal cell membrane (in addition to an ATP-driven Ca pump) that may provide a link in the feedback process between Na pump and apical entry of sodium. The molecular mechanisms by which calcium ions influence Na permeability are presently unknown.

Literature Cited

1. Arruda, J. A. L., Sabatini, S. 1980. Effect of quinidine on Na$^+$, H$^+$, and water transport by the turtle and toad bladders. *J. Membr. Biol.* 55:141–47
2. Balaban, R. S., Mandel, L. J. 1979. Comparison of the effects of increased intracellular calcium and antidiuretic hormone on active sodium transport in frog skin. *Biochim. Biophys. Acta.* 555:1–12
3. Balzer, H. 1972. The effect of quinidine and drugs with quinidine-like actions (propranolol, verapamil and tetracaine) on the calcium transport system in isolated sarcoplasmic reticulum vesicles of rabbit skeletal muscle. *Naunyn-Schmiedebergs Arch. Pharmakol.* 274:256–72
4. Batra, S. 1974. The effects of drugs on calcium uptake and calcium release by mitochondria and sarcoplasmic reticulum of frog skeletal muscle. *Biochem. Pharmacol.* 23:89–101
5. Bentley, P. J. 1960. The effects of vasopressin on the short-circuit current across the wall of the isolated bladder of the toad, *Bufo marinus*. *J. Endocrinol.* 21:161–70
6. Berridge, M. J. 1980. The role of cyclic nucleotides and calcium in the regulation of chloride transport. *Ann. NY Acad. Sci.* 341:156–71
7. Blaustein, M. P. 1974. The interrelationship between sodium and calcium fluxes across cell membranes. *Rev. Physiol. Biochem. Pharmacol.* 70:33–82
8. Borle, A. B., Snowdowne, K. W. 1982. Measurements of intracellular free calcium in monkey kidney cells with aequorin. *Science* 217:252–54
9. Carafoli, E., Crompton, M. 1978. The regulation of intracellular calcium. In *Current Topics in Membrane and Transport*, ed. F. Bronner, A. Kleinzeller, 10:151–216. NY: Academic
10. Carvalho, A. P. 1968. Calcium-binding properties of sarcoplasmic reticulum as influenced by ATP, caffeine, quinine, and local anaesthetics. *J. Gen. Physiol.* 52:622–41
11. Chase, H. S., Al-Awqati, Q. 1979. Removal of ambient K$^+$ inhibits net Na$^+$

transport in toad bladder by reducing Na$^+$ permeability of the luminal border. *Nature* 28:494–95
12. Chase, H. S., Al-Awqati, Q. 1981. Regulation of the sodium permeability of the luminal border of toad bladder by intracellular sodium and calcium. *J. Gen. Physiol.* 77:693–712
13. Chase, H. Jr., Al-Awqati, Q. 1981. Submicromolar calcium regulates Na permeability of luminal membrane vesicles from toad bladder as measured by fast reaction methods. *Kidney Int.* 21:270
14. Costanzo, L., Windhager, E. E., Taylor, A. 1978. Sodium-calcium interaction in the distal tubule. In *New Aspects of Renal Function*, ed. H. G. Vogel, K. J. Ullrich, pp. 147–52. Amsterdam/Oxford: Excerpta Medica
15. Curran, P. F., Gill, J. R. 1962. The effect of calcium on sodium transport by frog skin. *J. Gen. Physiol.* 45:625–41
16. Curran, P. F., Herrera, F. C., Flanigan, W. J. 1963. The effect of Ca and antidiuretic hormone on Na transport across frog skin. *J. Gen. Physiol.* 46:1011–27
17. Epstein, F. H., Whittam, R. 1966. The mode of inhibitors by calcium of cell-membrane adenosine-triphosphatase activity. *Biochem. J.* 99:232–38
18. Erlij, D., Grinstein, S. 1977. Intracellular calcium regulates transepithelial sodium transport in the frog skin. *Biophysical J.* 17:23a
19. Erlij, D., Gersten, L., Sterba, G. 1981. Calcium, prostaglandin and transepithelial sodium transport. *J. Physiol.* 320:136
20. Friedman, P. A., Figueiredo, J. F., Maack, T., Windhager, E. E. 1981. Sodium-calcium interactions in the renal proximal convoluted tubule of the rabbit. *Am. J. Physiol.* 240:F558–68
21. Frindt, G., Windhager, E. E. 1982. Inhibition of Na^{22} efflux by low bath (Na)$_b$ in isolated perfused rabbit collecting tubules. *Fed. Proc.* 41:1695
22. Fuchs, F., Gertz, E. W., Briggs, F. N. 1968. The effects of quinidine on calcium accumulation by isolated sarcoplasmic reticulum of skeletal and car-

diac muscle. *J. Gen. Physiol.* 52:955–68
23. Gmaj, P., Murer, H., Kinne, R. 1979. Calcium ion transport across plasma membranes isolated from rat kidney cortex. *Biochem. J.* 178:549–57
24. Godfraind, T., De Pover, A., Verbeke, N. 1977. Influence of pH and sodium on the inhibition of guinea-pig heart (Na⁺ – K⁺)-ATPase by calcium. *Biochim. Biophys. Acta* 481:202–11
25. Grinstein, S., Erlij, F. 1978. Intracellular calcium and the regulation of sodium transport in the frog skin. *Proc. R. Soc. London (Biol. Ser.)* 202:353–60
26. Grinstein, S., Candia, O., Erlij, D. 1978. Nonhormonal mechanisms for the regulation of transepithelial sodium transport: The roles of surface potential and cell calcium. *J. Membr. Biol.* 40:261–80
27. Hagins, W. A., Yoshikami, S. 1974. The role for Ca^{2+} in excitation of retinal rods and cones. *Exp. Eye Res.* 18:299–305
28. Humes, H. D., Weinberg, J. M. 1980. Ionophore A 23 187 induced reduction in toad urinary bladder epithelial cell oxydative phosphorylation and viability. *Pflügers Arch.* 388:217–20
29. Isaacson, A., Sandow, A. 1967. Quinine and caffeine effects on ⁴⁵Ca movements in frog sartorius muscle. *J. Gen. Physiol.* 50:2109–28
30. Kinne-Saffran, E., Kinne, R. 1974. Localization of a calcium-stimulated ATPase in the basal-lateral plasma membranes of the proximal tubule of rat kidney cortex. *J. Membr. Biol.* 17:263–74
31. Leaf, A. 1965. Transepithelial transport and its hormonal control in toad bladder. *Ergeb. Physiol. Biol. Chem. Exp. Pharmakol.* 56:215–63
32. Lee, C. O., Taylor, A., Windhager, E. E. 1980. Cytosolic calcium ion activity in epithelial cells of *Necturus* kidney. *Nature* 287:859–61
33. Lee, C. O. 1981. Ionic activities in cardiac muscle cells and application of ion-selective microelectrodes. *Am. J. Physiol.* 241:H459–78
34. Lehninger, A. L. 1970. *Biochemistry.* NY: Worth. p. 395–416
35. Lew, V. L., Beauge, L. 1979. Passive cation fluxes in red cell membranes. In *Membrane Transport in Biology. Transport Across Single Biological Membranes,* ed. D. C. Tosteson, 2:81–155. Berlin: Springer
36. Lorenzen, M., Lee, C. O., Windhager, E. E. 1982. Effect of quinidine and ouabain on intracellular calcium (a^i_{Ca}) and sodium (a^i_{Na}) ion activities in isolated

perfused proximal tubules of *Necturus* kidney. *Kidney Int.* 21:281
37. Ludens, J. H. 1978. Studies on the inhibition of Na⁺ transport in toad bladder by the ionophore A-23187. *J. Pharmacol. Exp. Ther.* 206:414–22
38. Mandel, L. J., Curran, P. F. 1973. Response of the frog skin to steady-state voltage clamping. II. The active pathway. *J. Gen. Physiol.* 62:1–24
39. Murphy, E., Mandel, L. J. 1982. Cytosolic free calcium levels in rabbit proximal kidney tubules. *Am. J. Physiol.* 242:C124–28
40. Nielsen, R. 1978. Effect of the polyene antibiotic filipin and the calcium ionophore A23187 on sodium transport in isolated frog skin (*Rana temporaria*). *J. Membr. Biol.* 40:331–46
41. Pfeiffer, D. R., Taylor, R. W., Lardy, H. A. 1978. Ionophore A23187: cation binding and transport properties. *Ann. NY Acad. Sci.* 307:402–23
42. Pressman, B. C. 1976. Biological application of ionophores. *Ann. Rev. Biochem.* 45:501–30
43. Schultz, S. G. 1981. Homocellular regulatory mechanisms in sodium-transporting epithelia: avoidance of extinction by "flush-through". *Am. J. Physiol.* 241:F579–90
44. Somlyo, A. P., Somlyo, A. V., Shuman, H. 1979. Electron probe analysis of vascular smooth muscle composition of mitochondria, nuclei and cytoplasm. *J. Cell Biol.* 81:316–55
45. Somlyo, A. P., Somlyo, A. V., Shuman, H., Scarpa, A., Endo, M., Inesi, G. 1981. Mitochondria do not accumulate significant Ca concentrations in normal cells. In *Calcium and Phosphate Transport Across Biomembranes,* ed. F. Bronner, M. Teterlik, pp. 87–93. NY: Academic
46. Taylor, A. 1975. Effect of quinidine on the action of vasopressin. *Fed. Proc.* 34:385
47. Taylor, A., Eich, E., Pearl, M. 1977. Cytosolic calcium and action of vasopressin in toad bladder. *Proc. Int. Congr. Physiol. Sci., 27th, Paris,* p. 745
48. Taylor, A., Eich, E. 1978. Evidence for Na-Ca exchange in toad urinary bladder (Abstract). *Proc. Int. Congr. Nephrol., 7th, Montreal,* p. C-8
49. Taylor, A., Windhager, E. E. 1979. Possible role of cytosolic calcium and Na-Ca exchange in regulation of transepithelial sodium transport. *Am. J. Physiol.* 236:F505–12
50. Taylor, A., Eich, E., Pearl, M., Brem, A. 1979. Role of cytosolic calcium and

Na-Ca exchange in the action of vasopressin. In *Hormonal Control of Epithelial Transport,* ed. J. Bourguet, J. Chevalier, M. Parisi, P. Ripoche, pp. 167–74. Paris: Inserm

51. Taylor, A. 1981. Role of cytosolic calcium and sodium-calcium exchange in regulation of transepithelial sodium and water absorption. In *Ion Transport by Epithelia,* ed. S. G. Schultz, pp. 233–59. NY: Raven

52. Tobin, T., Akera, T., Baskin, S. I., Brody, T. M. 1973. Calcium ion and sodium- and potassium-dependent adenosine triphosphatase: its mechanism of inhibition and identification of the E_1-P intermediate. *Mol. Pharmacol.* 9:336–49

53. Turnheim, K., Frizzel, R. A., Schultz, S. G. 1978. Interaction between cell sodium and the amiloride-sensitive sodium entry step in rabbit colon. *J. Membr. Biol.* 39:233–56

54. Ullrich, K. J., Rumrich, G., Klöss, S. 1976. Active Ca^{2+} reabsorption in the proximal tubule of rat kidney. *Pflügers Arch.* 364:223–28

55. Ussing, H. H. 1960. The alkali metal ions in isolated systems and tissues. In *The Alkali Metal Ions in Biology,* ed. O.

Eichler, A. Farah, pp. 1–195. Berlin: Springer

56. Wiesmann, W., Sinha, S., Klahr, S. 1977. Effects of ionophore A23187 on base-line and vasopressin-stimulated sodium transport in the toad bladder. *J. Clin. Invest.* 59:418–25

57. Windhager, E. E., Taylor, A., Maack, T., Lee, C. O., Lorenzen, M. 1982. Studies on renal function. In *Functional Regulation at the Cellular and Molecular Level,* ed. R. A. Corradino, pp. 299–316. NY/Amsterdam-Oxford: Elsevier North-Holland

58. Windhager, E. E. 1981. Interaktionen zwischen Natrium- und Calciumresorption In *Diuretika II - II. Diuretika Symposium Paris 1981,* ed. F. Krück, A. Schrey, pp. 171–78. Munich: Universitätsdruckerei C. Wolf und Sohn

59. Yau, K. W., McNaughton, P. A., Hodgkin, A. L. 1981. Effect of ions on the light-sensitive current in retinal rods. *Nature* 292:502–5

60. Yingst, D. R., Hoffman, J. F. 1981. Effect of intracellular Ca on inhibiting the Na-K pump and stimulating Ca-induced transport in resealed human red cell ghosts. *Fed. Proc.* 40:543

Ann. Rev. Physiol. 1983. 45:533–47

SODIUM CHLORIDE COUPLED TRANSPORT IN MAMMALIAN NEPHRONS

Maurice Burg and David Good

National Heart Lung and Blood Institute, Bethesda, Maryland, 20205

INTRODUCTION

Mammalian nephrons filter large amounts of sodium chloride. Under normal conditions they reabsorb virtually all of it, and only a fraction of a percent appears in the urine. The parallel reabsorption of sodium and chloride is one of the principal functions of the nephron. Although there is convincing evidence that primary active sodium transport couples cellular energy to transport of sodium chloride and other substances in renal tubules, there is no evidence of any primary active chloride transport. Therefore, the coupling of sodium transport to that of chloride reduces to a question of how the primary active sodium transport results in parallel transepithelial transport of sodium and chloride.

We review the coupling of sodium chloride transport in several parts of the mammalian renal tubule. We emphasize the thick ascending limb of Henle's loop since it has recently been intensively scrutinized.

MECHANISMS OF COUPLING OF SODIUM TO CHLORIDE TRANSPORT

A variety of possible mechanisms for coupling sodium and chloride transport have been proposed for mammalian nephrons, several in fact for each segment that has been thoroughly studied.

Electro-Diffusive Coupling

The counter-ion may traverse pores or channels in the cell membranes or between the cells, driven by its electrochemical potential. Depending on the

533

0066-4278/83/0315-0533$02.00

channels' sizes and other characteristics, there may be specificity for the counter-ion, and its transport may be more or less constrained. In contrast to a carrier, a channel does not alter its orientation in the membrane or its configuration to vary access cyclically through its two ends.

Carrier-Mediated Coupling

A carrier may contain one or more sites that interact with transported substrates and are cyclically exposed to the two sides of the barrier it traverses. The cycles result in transport across the barrier. Sodium and chloride can be combined on a single carrier or can be on two independent carriers in parallel, one transporting sodium and the other, chloride.

COMBINED SODIUM CHLORIDE CARRIER   A single carrier may simultaneously transport both sodium and chloride, directly coupling their transport. Depending on the stoichiometry of sodium versus chloride (and any other ions that are also carried) the carrier can be rheogenic or electrically neutral.

INDEPENDENT CARRIERS FOR SODIUM AND FOR CHLORIDE Sodium and chloride may be transported on independent carriers operating in parallel. They can be electrically coupled if one or both carriers are rheogenic. Alternatively, other solutes may be transported simultaneously on the carriers and can provide coupling. For example, parallel sodium-proton and chloride-hydroxyl exchange carriers can be coupled via intracellular pH.

Solvent Drag

Osmotic absorption of water will result in coupled sodium chloride absorption by solvent drag, provided the sodium chloride reflection coefficient is less than one.

SODIUM CHLORIDE COUPLING IN INDIVIDUAL NEPHRON SEGMENTS

Proximal Tubule

Virtually all the coupling mechanisms outlined above have been postulated to contribute to sodium chloride reabsorption in mammalian proximal tubules. The primary active transport is of sodium, mediated by sodium and potassium activated adenosine triphosphatase (Na-K-ATPase) in basolateral cell membranes. Sodium transport is coupled in a complex fashion to the accompanying absorption of chloride and other components of glomerular filtrate (3, 12, 96).

In the initial 1–2 mm of the proximal convoluted tubule only about 10–20% of sodium absorption is coupled to that of chloride (3). The major counter-ion is bicarbonate (11, 29, 65, 94). The small amount of chloride absorption that occurs results from solvent drag (26) and from electro-diffusion driven by the lumen-negative voltage created by cotransport of sodium with neutral organic solutes (2, 17, 25, 57).

Rapid absorption of bicarbonate along the first millimeter of proximal convoluted tubule decreases its concentration in the lumen to a low steady value, following which its absorption rate is greatly reduced in the remainder of the proximal tubule. Sodium absorption continues, however, coupled increasingly to chloride as bicarbonate absorption decreases.

Sodium chloride absorption in the late proximal tubule involves both active and passive transport. The driving force for the passive transport follows from the preferential absorption of bicarbonate earlier in the tubule (2, 65). As bicarbonate concentration in the lumen decreases below plasma levels, there is a reciprocal increase in chloride concentration (29, 32, 50, 65, 78). Sodium concentration and osmolality do not change (3, 12). Once established, these anion gradients drive passive absorption of sodium and chloride, as follows (3, 11, 65). Chloride is absorbed passively down its concentration gradient. Since permeability to chloride exceeds that to bicarbonate, at least in proximal tubules of superficial nephrons (4, 6, 26, 46), a chloride-bicarbonate bi-ionic potential develops, oriented lumen-positive (2, 4, 6, 25, 57, 78). This positive voltage drives absorption of sodium. The passive sodium chloride absorption presumably proceeds through the lateral intercellular spaces which are a lower resistance pathway than through the cells (5, 78). Although the opposing transepithelial gradients of chloride and bicarbonate are essentially equal, the reflection coefficient of bicarbonate exceeds that of chloride, providing an effective transepithelial osmotic pressure that drives fluid absorption (26, 65, 77). Since the NaCl reflection coefficient is less than one (26, 58), coupled sodium chloride absorption results by solvent drag (1, 26).

In proximal tubules of superficial nephrons in rats (21, 31–33) and rabbits (77, 79) approximately one third of the NaCl and fluid absorbed along mid and late proximal tubules can be accounted for by these passive driving forces. In deep nephrons where the chloride permeability is relatively low [at least in rabbits (4, 46, 50)] this passive transport mechanism is presumably less important.

The remaining two thirds of sodium absorption in late proximal tubule occurs by active transport (32, 50, 76). "Simple" electrogenic sodium transport was found in rabbit proximal straight tubules perfused in the absence of anion gradients and organic solutes (76). Under those conditions transepithelial voltage was oriented lumen-negative and salt and fluid absorption were due to active sodium transport coupled via the voltage to electro-diffusive chloride absorption. This process may be important in the late proximal tubule of juxtamedullary nephrons, which, based on in vitro results, may have lumen-negative voltage in vivo. In the late proximal tubules of superficial nephrons electrogenic sodium transport decreases the magnitude of the positive voltage, as evidenced by an increase in the positive voltage when ouabain was added (20).

Carrier-mediated sodium chloride coupling has been identified in the lumen membrane of *Necturus* proximal tubule (82), but it is questionable whether the same mechanism also exists in mammalian proximal tubule. In *Necturus* proximal tubules carrier-coupled sodium chloride cotransport is driven by the gradient for sodium whose concentration is lower in the cell than in the lumen. Thus the downhill movement of sodium into the cells across the lumen membrane is coupled to uphill entry of chloride. As a result, the electrochemical potential of chloride is higher in the cells than in the extracellular fluids (40, 82). Since impalements of rat proximal tubule cells with chloride-sensing microelectrodes failed to show elevated chloride electrochemical potential (81) similar to that in *Necturus,* there is no evidence for carrier-mediated coupling of sodium chloride transport in mammalian proximal tubules. If carrier-mediated coupling occurs in mammalian proximal tubules, it could be via parallel sodium/proton and chloride/hydroxyl carriers or their equivalent. There is considerable evidence for carrier-mediated sodium/proton countertransport in the lumen membranes of proximal tubules (55, 64). The existence of a significant luminal anion exchange mechanism is less firmly established. Anion exchange was suggested because SITS and furosemide, inhibitors of anion exchange in red blood cells, blocked sodium and fluid absorption when added to the lumen of rat proximal tubule (60), and appropriately oriented pH gradients increased chloride uptake in brush-border vesicles (95). Ullrich et al (90) found that SITS affected proximal absorption in rats only when applied from the peritubular side, however, implying an effect on basolateral transport processes. Also, chloride/hydroxyl exchange was not found in all vesicle studies (19), leaving a question about the significance of luminal anion exchange. Further studies will be required to characterize and to establish the importance of carrier-mediated coupling of NaCl transport in mammalian proximal tubule.

Thick Ascending Limb of Henle's Loop

This part of the nephron is conventionally divided into two parts, medullary and cortical (53). The basic mechanisms of coupling sodium to chloride transport, however, appear to be the same in both.

Sodium chloride absorption by thick ascending limbs causes its concentration to decrease in the tubule fluid because osmotic water permeability is low. Water permeability ranged from 28 μm sec^{-1} down to values indistinguishable from zero in various studies (15, 41, 45, 47, 74, 75). Considering the very low rate of fluid absorption, solvent drag presumably does not contribute significantly to the coupling of NaCl transport.

In thick ascending limbs both the rate of sodium chloride absorption and its permeability are high. With equal concentration in the tubular and peritubular fluids, the rate of absorption of sodium chloride greatly exceeds that of other ions. In medullary thick ascending limbs the rate was 40 peq cm·sec^{-1} in rabbit (74) and 14–22 in mice (41, 44). In cortical thick ascending limbs it was 13 in rabbits (15) and 25 in mice (24). Sodium chloride absorption decreases as its concentration falls in the lumen (13, 44) to a limiting value or "static head." The static head in vivo can be estimated from the NaCl concentration of 30–60 mM measured by micropuncture in the earliest accessible part of the distal tubule (28). In vitro the static head was 65 mM in isolated perfused rabbit cortical thick ascending limbs (15, 47) and 117 mM in the medullary portion (74). The transepithelial sodium and chloride permeabilities, estimated from radioisotope fluxes, are high— i.e. 0.10–0.63 μm sec^{-1} (15, 45, 74). The transepithelial electrical resistance is correspondingly low—i.e. 11–34 Ωcm^2 (15, 35, 36, 45).

The transepithelial voltage normally is lumen-positive in thick ascending limbs (10). Therefore, transepithelial chloride transport is active since it proceeds against both concentration and electrical gradients. Sodium transport, on the other hand, cannot be so simply characterized; it proceeds against its chemical gradient but along its electrical gradient. The mean transepithelial voltage is between 3 and 10 mV lumen-positive in both the medullary and cortical portion in the different species at high flow rates (7, 15, 18, 23, 24, 35, 36, 38, 41, 45, 49, 74, 75, 80, 85, 88, 89). The voltage increases when flow is slowed, because a NaCl "dilution potential" occurs that adds to the transport voltage as NaCl transport lowers its concentration in the tubule fluid. The permeability to sodium measured with radioisotopes is two to six times that to chloride (15, 45, 74). The relatively high sodium permeability accounts for the dilution potential. The dilution potential can be measured directly by perfusing rapidly with NaCl concentrations different from the bath. It is symmetrical—i.e. the same regardless of the direction of the imposed concentration gradient (15, 36, 45)—and from its magnitude a Na/Cl conductance ratio can be calculated (15, 36, 45). The ratio is in reasonable agreement with the ratio of Na to Cl permeability measured with radioisotopes. When perfusion stops completely, the transepithelial voltage rises to a mean steady value of 10 (74) to 25 mV (15, 41).

This is the voltage at static head. The intracellular voltage is negative in both mammalian thick ascending limbs (38) and in the analogous segment of *Amphiuma,* which is its early distal tubule or diluting segment (69, 70, 83).

Most investigators now believe that the active transepithelial chloride transport present in thick ascending limbs is secondary active, coupled to the primary active transport of sodium. This is illustrated in Figure 1. Primary active sodium transport out of the epithelial cells via the Na-K-ATPase, g, lowers cell sodium activity. The resultant sodium concentration difference across the lumen membrane drives coupled NaCl transport into the cell. This secondary active chloride transport increases the cell chloride concentration. There is no consensus on the exact nature of the coupling, however, or on the origin of the transepithelial potential. Some possibilities are illustrated by alternatives b–f in Figure 1. We first summarize the evidence for primary active sodium transport, and then consider the other parts of the model.

Primary active sodium transport is driven by the Na-K-ATPase. This enzymatic cation pump is present in large amounts in thick ascending limbs (27, 54). In fact, if the results for rabbit tubules (27) are considered, there is sufficient Na-K-ATPase activity to transport sodium at a stoichiometry of only two sodiums per ATP, similar to the ratio in tissues known to transport sodium actively. Thus there is sufficient Na-K-ATPase to energize

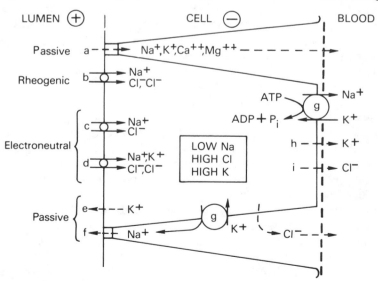

Figure 1   Model illustrating sodium chloride coupling in thick ascending limbs (10). A number of alternative possibilities are shown for some of the steps.

directly the observed sodium transport. In contrast, there is no evidence of a Cl-ATPase to drive primary active chloride transport. Ouabain, which is a specific inhibitor of Na-K-ATPase, inhibits NaCl absorption (and the accompanying positive voltage) in thick ascending limbs and diluting segments (15, 36, 45, 48, 49, 66, 73, 74, 86). Removal of potassium from the bath (which inhibits the Na-K-ATPase) also inhibits NaCl absorption and the positive voltage (13). Thus Na-K-ATPase activity is both sufficient and necessary for the NaCl absorption, supporting the theory that active sodium transport is primary.

The transport of sodium out of the cells by the Na-K-ATPase results in a low intracellular sodium concentration. This was demonstrated in *Amphiuma* diluting segments by use of sodium-selective microelectrodes (71) but has not been reported in mammalian thick ascending limbs. Because the cell sodium is lower than that in the lumen there is a driving force for sodium entry across the apical cell border. Chloride entry into the cell is believed to be coupled to that of sodium on a combined sodium chloride carrier. Such coupling is consistent with observations that sodium chloride transport and the transepithelial voltage are inhibited if either sodium (35, 66) or chloride (7, 13, 15, 35, 66, 74, 86) is completely eliminated from the bathing solutions, but the exact nature of the coupled entry step is uncertain, and a number of theories have been proposed. Some of the proposals are illustrated in Figure 1b, c, and d. The various proposals have in common that the coupling results in secondary active chloride transport that maintains the cell chloride electrochemical potential higher than in either the lumen or blood. The high cell chloride activity was demonstrated directly by the use of chloride-specific microelectrodes in *Amphiuma* (70). The high cell chloride electrochemical potential provides a driving force for conductive chloride flux out of the cells at their base (Figure 1i), but there is no direct evidence that this is the actual mechanism.

At this point it is useful to digress and consider the action of various diuretics that inhibit the active chloride transport, since they have been used extensively in studying it. The most widely studied inhibitor is furosemide. Its action was first studied in rabbit cortical thick ascending limbs (18). When placed in the lumen it rapidly inhibited the transepithelial voltage and sodium chloride reabsorption. The effects in cortical thick ascending limbs were subsequently confirmed (37), and the same result was found in medullary thick ascending limbs (41, 45, 88). The effect of furosemide became a hallmark of the active chloride transport system, since no comparable effect of the drug was reported in other nephron segments (18). Bumetanide, a related compound, has the same effect and is somewhat more potent than furosemide in rabbit thick ascending limbs (49). Mersalyl (16), MK-196 (88), and ethacrynic acid (or more precisely its cysteine adduct)

(14) also inhibit the active chloride transport system. Furosemide acts from the lumen [as do the other diuretics (14, 16)] and not from the serosal side (18, 45, 66). The action of furosemide is rapid, requiring less than one second to inhibit the voltage (37). Since it acts so quickly and only in the lumen it presumably inhibits an active chloride transporter at that site, such as shown in Figure 1b, c, or d. Other effects of the diuretics are small compared to the virtually complete inhibition of chloride transport. They increase transepithelial electrical resistance slightly (14, 16, 18, 37) but do not alter the ratio of sodium to chloride conductance (14, 16, 18, 45). Since furosemide specifically inhibits the active chloride transport at the lumen membrane, it has been useful in analyzing that system. Furosemide caused cell sodium (71) and chloride (70) concentrations to fall in *Amphiuma*. Also, elimination of lumen sodium caused cell chloride to fall (70) and vice versa (71) in *Amphiuma*. All of these findings are consistent with the various cotransport schemes shown in Figure 1.

Accepting that cotransport of sodium and chloride across the lumen membrane drives secondary active chloride transport, questions remain about the origin of the transepithelial voltage and its role in sodium chloride coupling. Greger proposed that the stoichiometry was one sodium per two chlorides, which is directly electrogenic (Figure 1b). He considered that the extremely rapid effect of furosemide could not be otherwise explained (37). The involvement of two chlorides is also suggested by the sigmoid shape of the curve relating short-circuit current to chloride concentration in rabbit cortical thick ascending limbs (34) and sodium uptake to chloride concentration in luminal membrane vesicles prepared from the cells of rabbit medullary thick ascending limbs (56). The voltage across the lumen membrane was not affected by furosemide in thick ascending limbs (34) or in *Amphiuma* diluting segments (69–71), however, and there are other possible explanations for the voltage besides directly rheogenic transport. Hebert et al (44) have theorized that even with an electroneutral coupling of one chloride per sodium (Figure 1c) the voltage could be produced by back diffusion of transported sodium through sodium-selective tight junctions (Figure 1f). Most recently, the role of potassium has been emphasized. The transepithelial voltage is inhibited when potassium is eliminated from the perfusate (38, 69) or barium (a potassium conductance blocker) is added (38). Perhaps two chlorides are cotransported with one sodium and one potassium (Figure 1d) (38, 69). This is electroneutral by itself, but a conductive potassium leak back across the lumen membrane (Figure 1e) through the high potassium conductance measured there (38, 69, 83) would generate the observed voltage.

The lumen-positive transepithelial voltage probably couples electro-diffusive sodium transport to the secondary active chloride transport. The existence of passive electro-diffusive sodium absorption across thick ascending limbs and diluting segments is supported by considerable indirect evidence, which has been extensively summarized (13, 15, 34, 38, 74). In brief, the transepithelial sodium conductance is so high that the observed transepithelial voltage should drive sodium transport at a rate that is a large fraction of that observed. Further, at static head the observed voltage equals or exceeds that required for equilibrium with the observed sodium concentration ratio. Finally, the short-circuit current (calculated from the open circuit voltage and the transepithelial electrical conductance) approximates the rate of net sodium chloride transport (measured with an open circuit) (36). Since the large sodium conductance is probably through the tight junctions and paracellular spaces (9), the passive sodium transport probably follows that route (Figure 1a). The passive flux in effect amplifies active sodium transport. For example, if the stoichiometry of the lumen transporter is two chlorides per sodium, then the primary active transport of one sodium could result in the transepithelial transport of a total of up to two chlorides and two sodiums. One of the sodiums is directly transported by the Na-K-ATPase (Figure 1g) and the other is transported passively through the paracellular pathway (Figure 1a).

There may be a different form of sodium chloride coupled transport in mouse cortical thick ascending limbs. Friedman & Andreoli (24) found that sodium chloride reabsorption by mouse cortical thick ascending limbs was greatly inhibited when bicarbonate and carbon dioxide were eliminated from external solutions without altering the pH. They did not, however, observe any transepithelial net bicarbonate transport. The bicarbonate and carbon dioxide stimulated sodium chloride transport was inhibited by the carbonic anhydrase inhibitor ethoxolamide, and both bicarbonate and carbon dioxide dependent and independent sodium chloride transport were completely inhibited by furosemide. This system is apparently not present in medullary thick ascending limbs of mice, nor cortical thick ascending limbs of rabbits in which removing bicarbonate and carbon dioxide did not inhibit the voltage. The authors suggested that there are parallel sodium/-proton and chloride/hydroxyl exchangers or their equivalent in the lumen membrane. If so, at least part of the sodium chloride coupling in mouse cortical thick ascending limbs involves independent carriers for sodium and chloride in the lumen membrane, coupled by the cell pH.

Distal Tubule

Most information on sodium chloride transport by distal tubules has come from micropuncture studies of superficial nephrons of rats (96). The distal tubule, defined conventionally as the region between the macula densa and the confluence of tubules to form collecting ducts, is morphologically and functionally heterogeneous. It is composed of at least four distinct parts: (a) a short post-macula densa portion of thick ascending limb. (b) distal convoluted tubule, (c) connecting tubule, and (d) initial collecting duct (22, 53). Since micropuncture studies have not generally distinguished between the different divisions of the distal tubule, there is little direct information on the mechanism of Na-Cl coupling in individual parts of the distal tubule. We consider the results of the micropuncture studies without trying to make this distinction.

Sodium concentration in the fluid entering distal tubules from thick ascending limbs is below that in plasma (63). The transepithelial voltage increases along the distal tubule from near zero at the beginning to 40–50 mV, lumen-negative, over the last half (97). Thus sodium absorption proceeds against an electrochemical potential gradient and is by definition active. It is presumably driven by Na-K-activated ATPase located in the basolateral cell membrane, as in the other segments. The chloride conductance is sufficient to couple at least part of the observed chloride absorption (61, 93) to sodium transport by electro-diffusion driven by the negative transepithelial voltage (61, 62). Under some conditions, however, lumen chloride concentration is lower (72) or chloride absorption is faster (62) than can be be accounted for by the transepithelial chloride electrochemical potential, suggesting a component of active chloride transport. In recent studies there was evidence of carrier-mediated NaCl cotransport, which is consistent with active chloride transport (91). Rat distal tubules were perfused in vivo. Progressive reduction of perfusate sodium concentration at constant lumen chloride concentration caused chloride absorption to decrease, whereas reducing lumen chloride at constant sodium concentration caused sodium absorption to decrease. The relations were hyperbolic with half-maximal rates at concentrations of about 8 mM. Removal of chloride from the perfusate (93) or addition of furosemide (92) inhibited sodium chloride absorption with little effect on transepithelial voltage, implying that the coupling is electroneutral. Together these observations are consistent with existence in the luminal membrane of a furosemide-sensitive NaCl cotransport system (93). How it compares to that in the thick ascending limb remains unknown.

Collecting Ducts

Cortical collecting ducts absorb sodium at a relatively slow rate but are capable of generating steep transepithelial concentration gradients (30, 87). Active sodium absorption generates a lumen-negative transepithelial voltage. Sodium absorption and voltage are reduced by ouabain (30) or amiloride (67, 87) but not by furosemide (18). The chloride conductance of cortical collecting ducts is sufficiently great so that most of their observed chloride absorption could be electro-diffusive, driven by the lumen-negative voltage (87). Chloride absorption was observed to be higher in cortical collecting ducts taken from rabbits treated with DOCA (42, 84). This could be logically attributed to the increase in voltage following DOCA (39, 42, 68, 84), but that may not be the complete explanation since chloride conductance decreased following DOCA administration (68). Also, lumen-to-bath chloride flux was unaffected by changes in transepithelial voltage (42). Thus chloride transport mechanisms other than electro-diffusion are suggested. Along this line, chloride was recently observed to be transported against its electrochemical potential in this segment (43). The possibility of carrier-mediated chloride transport in cortical collecting tubule is further suggested by studies of radioactive chloride fluxes that demonstrate a large component of chloride exchange diffusion (42, 87). Also there is a complex interaction of chloride with bicarbonate. Replacement of lumen chloride with sulfate inhibits bicarbonate secretion into ducts from bicarbonate-loaded rabbits (8), and net bicarbonate absorption is converted to net secretion if 50 mM of bath chloride is replaced with cyclamate (59). The exact nature of these chloride-bicarbonate interactions, and whether carrier-mediated chloride transport contributes to overall transepithelial sodium chloride transport, are still uncertain.

Although sodium chloride absorption has been measured in outer (23, 84) and inner (52) medullary collecting ducts, there is little information about sodium chloride coupling in these segments.

Water permeability of collecting ducts is low and is increased by antidiuretic hormone (51). There is no evidence that the sodium chloride reflection coefficient is low in collecting ducts (51), however, and thus no indication that solvent drag contributes appreciably to coupling of sodium chloride absorption.

SUMMARY

A number of possible modes of coupling of sodium chloride transport have been considered, and their roles in the various parts of the renal tubule have been reviewed. Many modes of coupling have been found in various combinations in one or another of the segments. Of special interest are the observations of carrier coupling of sodium to chloride transport in some of the segments, such as the thick ascending limbs of Henle's loop.

Literature Cited

1. Andreoli, T. E., Schafer, J. A., Troutman, S. L., Watkins, M. L. 1979. Solvent drag component of Cl flux in superficial proximal straight tubules: evidence for a paracellular component of isotonic fluid absorption. *Am. J. Physiol.* 237(6) (*Renal Fluid Electrol. Physiol.* 6):F455–62

2. Barratt, L. J., Rector, F. C. Jr., Kokko, J. P., Seldin, D. W. 1974. Factors governing the transepithelial potential difference across the proximal tubule of the rat kidney. *J. Clin. Invest.* 53:454–64

3. Berry, C. A., Rector, F. C. Jr. 1980. Active and passive sodium transport in the proximal tubule. *Min. Electrol. Metab.* 4:149–60

4. Berry, C. A., Warnock, D. G., Rector, F. C. Jr. 1978. Ion selectivity and proximal salt reabsorption. *Am. J. Physiol.* 235:F234–45

5. Boulpaep, E. L. 1976. Recent advances in electrophysiology of the nephron. *Ann. Rev. Physiol.* 38:20–36

6. Boulpaep, E. L., Seely, J. F. 1971. Electrophysiology of proximal and distal tubules in the autoperfused dog kidney. *Am. J. Physiol.* 221:1084–96

7. Bourdeau, J. E., Burg, M. B. 1979. Voltage dependence of calcium transport in the thick ascending limb of Henle's loop. *Am. J. Physiol.* 236:F357–64

8. Boyer, J., Burg, M. 1980. Bicarbonate secretion by isolated perfused rabbit cortical collecting ducts. *Kidney Int.* 19:233 (Abstr.)

9. Burg, M. 1982. Renal tubular paracellular transport. In *The Paracellular Pathway,* ed. S. E. Bradley, E. F. Purcell, pp. 117–31. NY: Macy Fnd.

10. Burg, M. 1983. Thick ascending limb of Henle's loop. *Kidney Int.* In press

11. Burg, M. 1982. Chloride transport in the renal tubule. In *Chloride Transport in Biological Membranes,* ed. J. A. Zadunaisky, pp. 111–22. NY: Academic

12. Burg, M. 1981. Renal handling of sodium, chloride, water, amino acids and glucose. In *The Kidney,* ed. B. Brenner, F. C. Rector, Jr., pp. 328–70. Philadelphia: Saunders

13. Burg, M., Bourdeau, J. E. 1978. Function of the thick ascending limb of Henle's loop. In *New Aspects of Renal Function,* ed. H. G. Vogel, K. J. Ullrich, pp. 91–102. Amsterdam/Oxford: Exerpta Medica

14. Burg, M., Green, N. 1973. Effect of ethacrinic acid on the thick ascending limb of Henle's loop. *Kidney Int.* 4:301–8

15. Burg, M., Green, N. 1973. Function of the thick ascending limb of Henle's loop. *Am. J. Physiol.* 224:659–68

16. Burg, M., Green, N. 1973. Effect of mersalyl on the thick ascending limb of Henle's loop. *Kidney Int.* 4:245–51

17. Burg, M., Patlak, C., Green, N., Villey, D. 1976. The role of organic solutes in fluid absorption by renal proximal convoluted tubules. *Am. J. Physiol.* 231:627–37

18. Burg, M., Stoner, L., Cardinal, J., Green, N. 1973. Furosemide effect on isolated perfused tubules. *Am. J. Physiol.* 225:119–24

19. Burnham, C., Muenzesheimer, T., Rabon, E., Sachs, G. 1981. The Na:H antiporter of renal brush border vesicles. *Fed. Proc.* 40:462 (Abstr.)

20. Cardinal, J., Lutz, M. D., Burg, M. B., Orloff, J. 1975. Lack of relationship of potential difference to fluid absorption in the proximal renal tubule. *Kidney Int.* 7:94–102

21. Chantrelle, B., Rector, F. C. Jr. 1980. Active and passive components of volume reabsorption in rat superficial proximal convoluted tubule. *Clin. Res.* 28:441A (Abstr.)

22. Crayen, M. L., Thoenes, W. 1978. Architecture and cell structure in the distal nephron of the rat kidney. *Cytobiologie* 17:197–211

23. Fine, L. G., Trizna, W. 1977. Influence of prostaglandins on sodium transport of isolated medullary nephron segments. *Am. J. Physiol.* 232:F383–90

24. Friedman, P. A., Andreoli, T. E. 1981. Bicarbonate-stimulated transepithelial voltage and NaCl transport in the mouse renal cortical thick ascending limb. *Clin. Res.* 29:462 (Abstr.)

25. Frömter, E., Gessner, K. 1974. Active transport potentials, membrane diffusion potentials and streaming potentials across rat kidney proximal tubule. *Pflügers Arch.* 351:85–98

26. Frömter, E., Rumrich, G., Ullrich, K. J. 1973. Phenomenologic description of Na, Cl, and bicarbonate absorption from proximal tubules of the rat kidney. *Pflügers Arch.* 343:189–220

27. Garg, L. C., Knepper, M. A., Burg, M. B. 1981. Mineralocorticoid effects on Na-K-ATPase in individual nephron segments. *Am. J. Physiol.* 240:F536–44

28. Giebisch, G., Windhager, E. 1973. Electrolyte transport across renal tubular membranes. In *Handbook of Physi-*

ology, Sect. 8, Renal Physiology. Washington DC: Am. Physiol. Soc. pp. 315–76

29. Gottschalk, C. W., Lassiter, W. E., Mylle, M. 1960. Localization of urine acidification in the mammalian kidney. Am. J. Physiol. 198:581–85

30. Grantham, J. J., Burg, M. B., Orloff, J. 1970. The nature of transtubular Na and K transport in isolated rabbit renal collecting tubules. J. Clin. Invest. 49:1815–26

31. Green, R., Bishop, J. V. H., Giebisch, G. 1979. Ionic requirements of proximal tubular sodium transport. III. Selective luminal anion substitution. Am. J. Physiol. 236:F268–77

32. Green, R., Giebisch, G. 1975. Ionic requirements of proximal tubular sodium transport. I. Bicarbonate and chloride. Am. J. Physiol. 229:1205–15

33. Green, R., Moriarty, R. J., Giebisch, G. 1981. Ionic requirements of proximal tubular fluid reabsorption: Flow dependence of fluid transport. Kidney Int. 20:580–57

34. Greger, R. 1981. Coupled transport of Na⁺ and Cl⁻ in the thick ascending limb of Henle's loop of rabbit nephron. In Ototoxic Effects of Diuretics, ed. R. Klinke, W. Lahn, H. Querfurth, J. Scholtholt. Scand. Audiol. Suppl. 14: 1–15

35. Greger, R. 1981. Chloride reabsorption in the rabbit cortical thick ascending limb of the loop of Henle. Pflügers Arch. 390:38–43

36. Greger, R. 1981. Cation selectivity of the isolated perfused cortical thick asc. limb of Henle's loop in the rabbit kidney. Pflügers Arch. 390:30–37

37. Greger, R., Frömter, E. 1980. Time course of ouabain and furosemide effects on transepithelial potential differences in cortical thick ascending limbs of rabbit nephrons. Proc. Int. Congr. Physiol. Sci., 28th, Budapest, p. 445 (Abstr.)

38. Greger, R., Schlatter, E. 1981. Presence of luminal K⁺, a prerequisite for active NaCl transport in cortical thick ascending limb of Henle's loop of rabbit kidney. Pflügers Arch. 392:92–94

39. Gross, J. B., Imai, M., Kokko, J. P. 1975. A functional comparison of the cortical collecting tubule and the distal convoluted tubule. J. Clin. Invest. 55:1284–94

40. Guggino, W. B., London, R. D., Boulpaep, E. L., Giebisch, G. 1981. Regulation of intracellular chloride in the Nec-

turus proximal tubule. Fed. Proc. 40:356 (Abstr.)

41. Hall, D. A., Varney, D. M. 1980. Effect of vasopressin on electrical potential difference and chloride transport in mouse medullary thick ascending limb of Henle. J. Clin. Invest. 66:792–802

42. Hanley, M. J., Kokko, J. P. 1978. Study of chloride transport across the rabbit cortical collecting tubule. J. Clin. Invest. 62:39–44

43. Hanley, M. J., Kokko, J. P., Gross, J. B., Jacobson, H. R. 1980. Electrophysiologic study of the cortical collecting tubule of the rabbit. Kidney Int. 17:74–81

44. Herbert, S. C., Culpepper, R. M., Andreoli, T. E. 1981. NaCl transport in mouse medullary thick ascending limbs. II. ADH enhancement of transcellular NaCl contransport; origin of the transepithelial voltage. Am. J. Physiol. 241:F432–42

45. Herbert, S. C., Culpepper, R. M., Andreoli, T. E. 1981. NaCl transport in mouse medullary thick ascending limbs. I. Functional nephron heterogeneity and ADH-stimulated NaCl cotransport. Am. J. Physiol. 241:F412–31

46. Holmberg, C., Kokko, J. P., Jacobson, H. R. 1981. Determination of chloride and bicarbonate permeabilities in proximal convoluted tubules. Am. J. Physiol. 241 (Renal Fluid Electrol. Physiol. 10):F386–94

47. Horster, M. 1978. Loop of Henle functional differentiation in vitro perfusion of the isolated thick ascending segment. Pflügers Arch. 378:15–24

48. Imai, M. 1978. Calcium transport across the rabbit thick ascending limb of Henle's loop perfused in vitro. Pflügers Arch. 374:255–63

49. Imai, M. 1977. Effect of bumetanide and furosemide on the thick ascending limb of Henle's loop of rabbits and rats perfused in vitro. Eur. J. Pharmacol. 41:409–16

50. Jacobson, H. R. 1979. Characteristics of volume reabsorption in rabbit superficial and juxtamedullary proximal convoluted tubules. J. Clin. Invest. 63:410–18

51. Jamison, R. L. 1981. Urine concentration and dilution: The roles of antidiuretic hormone and urea. See Ref. 12, pp. 495–550

52. Jamison, R. L., Sonnenberg, H., Stein, J. H. 1979. Questions and replies: role of the collecting tubule in fluid, sodium and potassium balance. Am. J. Physiol.

237 (*Renal Fluid Electrol Physiol.* 6) (4):F247–61

53. Kaissling, B., Kriz, W. 1978. Structural analysis of the rabbit kidney. In *Advances in Anatomy, Embryology and Cell Biology*, ed. A. Brodal, W. Wild, J. van Limborgh, R. Ortmann, T. H. Schiebler, G. Tondury, E. Wolff, 56:1–123. Berlin/Heidelberg/NY: Springer

54. Katz, A. I., Doucet, A., Morel, F. 1979. Na-K-ATPase activity along the rabbit, rat, and mouse nephron. *Am. J. Physiol.* 237:F114–20

55. Kinsella, J. L., Aronson, P. S. 1980. Properties of the Na^+-H^+ exchanger in renal microvillus membrane vesicles. *Am. J. Physiol.* 238 (*Renal Fluid Electrol Physiol.* 7) (6):F461–69

56. Koenig, B., Kinne, R. 1982. Sodium transport by plasma membranes isolated from cells of the thick ascending limb of Henle's loop. *Fed. Proc.* 41:1007 (Abstr.)

57. Kokko, J. P. 1973. Proximal tubule potential difference: dependence on glucose, bicarbonate and amino acids. *J. Clin. Invest.* 52:1362–67

58. Kokko, J. P., Burg, M. B., Orloff, J. 1971. Characteristics of NaCl and water transport in the renal proximal tubule. *J. Clin. Invest.* 50:69–76

59. Laski, M. E., Warnock, D. G., Rector, F. C. Jr. 1981. Chloride gradients affect total carbon dioxide flux in cortical collecting tubules. *Kidney Int.* 21:236 (Abstr.)

60. Lucci, M. S., Warnock, D. G. 1979. Effects of anion-transport inhibitors on NaCl reabsorption in the rat superficial proximal convoluted tubule. *J. Clin. Invest.* 64:570–79

61. Malnic, G., DeMello Aires, M., Vieira, F. 1970. Chloride excretion in nephrons of rat kidney during alterations of acid-base equilibrium. *Am. J. Physiol.* 218:20–26

62. Malnic, G., Giebisch, G. 1972. Some electrical properties of distal tubular epithelium in the rat. *Am. J. Physiol.* 223:797–808

63. Malnic, G., Klose, R. M., Giebisch, G. 1966. Micropuncture study of distal tubular potassium and sodium transport in rat nephron. *Am. J. Physiol.* 211:529–47

64. Murer, H., Hopfer, U., Kinne, R. 1976. Sodium/proton antiport in brush-border membrane vesicles isolated from rat small intestine and kidney. *Biochem. J.* 154:597–604

65. Neumann, K. H., Rector, F. C. Jr. 1976. Mechanism of NaCl and water

reabsorption in the proximal convoluted tubule of rat kidney. Role of chloride concentration gradients. *J. Clin. Invest.* 58:1110–18

66. Nishimura, H., Imai, M., Ogawa, M. 1982. Sodium chloride and water transport in the renal distal tubule of rainbow trout. *Am. J. Physiol.* In press

67. O'Neil, R. G., Boulpaep, E. L. 1979. Amiloride effects on the apical cell membrane cation channels in a sodium absorbing, potassium secreting renal epithelium. *J. Membr. Biol.* 50:365–87

68. O'Neil, R. G., Helman, S. I. 1977. Transport characteristics of renal collecting tubules: influences of DOCA and diet. *Am. J. Physiol.* 233(6):F544–58

69. Oberleithner, H., Guggino, W., Giebisch, G., Lang, F., Wenhui, W. 1983. Cellular mechanism of the furosemide sensitive transport system in the kidney. *Klin. Wochenschr.* In press

70. Oberleithner, H., Guggino, W., Giebisch, G. 1982. Mechanism of distal tubular chloride transport in Amphiuma kidney. *Am. J. Physiol.* (*Renal Fluid Electrol. Physiol.*): F331–39

71. Oberleithner, H., Lang, F., Wenhui, W., Giebisch, G. 1982. Effects of inhibition of chloride transport on intracellular sodium activity in distal *Amphiuma* nephron. *Pflügers Arch.* In press

72. Rector, F. C. Jr., Clapp, J. R. 1962. Evidence for active chloride reabsorption in the distal renal tubule of the rat. *J. Clin. Invest.* 41:101–7

73. Rocha, A., Magaldi, J. B., Kokko, J. P. 1977. Calcium and phosphate transport in isolated segments of rabbit Henle's loop. *J. Clin. Invest.* 59:975–83

74. Rocha, A. S., Kokko, J. P. 1973. Sodium chloride and water transport in the medullary thick ascending limb of Henle. *J. Clin. Invest.* 52:612–24

75. Sasaki, S., Imai, M. 1980. Effects of vasopressin on water and NaCl transport across the thick ascending limb of Henle's loop of mouse, rat, and rabbit kidneys. *Pflügers Arch.* 383:215–21

76. Schafer, J. A., Andreoli, T. E. 1979. Rheogenic and passive Na^+ absorption by the proximal nephron. *Ann. Rev. Physiol.* 41:211–27

77. Schafer, J. A., Patlak, C. S., Andreoli, T. E. 1975. A component of fluid absorption linked to passive ion flows in the superficial pars recta. *J. Gen. Physiol.* 66:445–71

78. Schafer, J. A., Troutman, S. L., Andreoli, T. E. 1974. Volume reabsorption, transepithelial potential differ-

ences, and ionic permeability properties in mammalian superficial proximal straight tubules. *J. Gen Physiol.* 64:582–607

79. Schafer, J. A., Troutman, S. L., Watkins, M. L., Andreoli, T. E. 1981. Flow dependence of fluid transport in the isolated superficial pars recta: Evidence that osmotic disequilibrium between external solutions drives isotonic fluid absorption. *Kidney Int.* 20:588–97

80. Shareghi, G. R., Agus, Z. S. 1982. Magnesium transport in the cortical thick ascending limb of Henle's loop of the rabbit. *J. Clin. Invest.* 69:759–69

81. Sohtell, M. 1978. Electrochemical forces for chloride transport in the proximal tubules of the rat kidney. *Acta Physiol. Scand.* 103:363–69

82. Spring, K. R., Kimura, G. 1978. Chloride reabsorption by renal proximal tubules of *Necturus. J. Membr. Biol.* 38:233–54

83. Stanton, B., Guggino, W., Giebisch, G. 1982. Electrophysiology of isolated and perfused distal tubules of *Amphiuma. Kidney Int.* 21:289 (Abstr.)

84. Stokes, J. B., Ingram, M. J., Williams, A. D., Ingram, D. 1981. Heterogeneity of the rabbit collecting tubule: Localization of mineralocorticoid hormone action to the cortical portion. *Kidney Int.* 20:340–47

85. Stokes, J. B. 1979. Effect of prostaglandin E2 on chloride transport across the rabbit thick ascending limb of Henle. *J. Clin. Invest.* 64:495–502

86. Stoner, L. C. 1977. Isolated, perfused amphibian renal tubules: the diluting segment. *Am. J. Physiol.* 233:F438–44

87. Stoner, L. C., Burg, M., Orloff, J. 1974. Ion transport in cortical collecting tubule; effect of amiloride. *Am. J. Physiol.* 227:453–59

88. Stoner, L. C., Trimble, M. E. 1982. Effects of MK-196 and furosemide on in

vitro rat medullary thick ascending limb of Henle. *J. Pharmacol. Exp. Therap.* In press

89. Suki, W. N., Rouse, D., Ng, R. C. K., Kokko, J. P. 1980. Calcium transport in the thick ascending limb of Henle. Heterogeneity of function in the medullary and cortical segments. *J. Clin. Invest.* 66:1004–9

90. Ullrich, K. J., Capasso, G., Rumrich, F., Papavassiliou, F., Kloss, S. 1977. Coupling between proximal tubular transport processes. Studies with ouabain, SITS, and bicarbonate-free solutions. *Pflügers Arch.* 368:245–52

91. Velazquez, H., Good, D. W., Wright, F. S. 1981. Mutual dependence of sodium and chloride absorption by renal distal tubule. *Fed. Proc.* 40:395 (Abstr.)

92. Velazquez, H., Wright, F. S. 1982. Distal potassium secretion is enhanced by low lumen chloride despite adverse voltage change, and is not increased by luminal furosemide. *Kidney Int.* 21:290 (Abstr.)

93. Velazquez, H., Wright, F. S., Good, D. W. 1982. Luminal influences on potassium secretion: chloride replacement with sulfate. *Am. J. Physiol.* 242 (*Renal Fluid Electrol Physiol.* 11):F46–55

94. Warnock, D. G., Rector, F. C. Jr. 1981. Renal acidification mechanisms. See Ref. 12, pp. 440–94

95. Warnock, D. G., Yee, V. J. 1981. Chloride uptake by brush border membrane vesicles isolated from rabbit renal cortex. *J. Clin. Invest.* 67:103–15

96. Windhager, E. E. 1978. Sodium chloride transport. In *Membrane Transport in Biology,* ed. G. G. Giebisch, D. C. Tosteson, H. H. Ussing, 4A:145–213. Berlin/Heidelberg/NY: Springer

97. Wright, F. S. 1971. Increasing magnitude of electrical potential along the renal distal tubule. *Am. J. Physiol.* 220:624–38

SPECIAL TOPIC: THE DEVELOPMENT OF SYNAPSES

Introduction, Paul H. Patterson, *Section Editor*

The establishment of specific synaptic connections between neurons and their target cells is the basis for the function of the nervous system. It is also one of the most profound examples of cellular interaction and recognition in biology. Neurons can send out axons over considerable distances, and these growing processes follow tortuous routes to their appropriate target regions. Once there, the growth cones often seek out among thousands of candidates a cell or class of cells to synapse with, and do so only on a restricted region of the target cell's surface. Just prior to, or coincident with, the onset of synaptic transmission, changes begin to occur in both the presynaptic nerve terminal and the postsynaptic membrane of the target cell. Such local specializations at the site of contact include clustering of transmitter receptors in the postsynaptic membrane, concentration of enzymes for transmitter breakdown and of particular antigens in the extracellular matrix, and localization of numerous synaptic vesicles in the nerve terminal. Other changes may include the frequency and amount of transmitter released, the amount and even the types of enzymes responsible for transmitter synthesis, aggregation of several filamentous proteins near the pre- and postsynaptic membranes, the turnover rate and molecular properties of receptors, and the clustering of calcium channels and amino acid uptake sites in the nerve terminal. Each of these changes in the synaptic partners can occur with a very different time course and can be driven by a different mechanism. For example, changes in the acetylcholine receptor distribution in muscle cells begin within hours after contact by motor neurons, and synaptic transmission is not required for this receptor clustering to occur. In contrast, acetylcholinesterase clusters at the same sites, but this takes longer and is often the consequence of activity induced in the muscle by the nerve.

As these multitudinous changes start to occur, a second aspect of synaptogenesis has also begun: The number of axons in the target area is being drastically reduced. This quantitative reduction in available inputs occurs in two phases. First, the number of neurons sending axons to the region drops, typically by half. Thus there was an initial overproduction of neurons and many of these die in a subsequent competitive struggle. Second, the surviving neurons then reduce the number of axon branches they have grown, thereby losing synaptic contact with many target cells. This rearrangement of synapses leaves each neuron with stronger control over fewer target cells. The construction of the final synaptic array therefore involves not only the formation but also the removal of synapses. Moreover, this sculpting can continue in adults, even on the same large scale seen during development. For instance, hormonal cycles—seasonal in birds, menstrual in mammals—can cause sharp changes in the number and size of neurons in particular areas of the peripheral and central nervous systems involved in reproductive activities. Some of these synaptic rearrangements have been implicated in the learning of new behaviors.

Obviously, the development of even a single type of synapse encompasses an extremely broad range of phenomena. The recurring themes are recognition, differentiation, and competition. A few aspects of this field are treated in this Special Topics Section. Dale Purves and Jeff Lichtman review the issues of specificity in neuron–neuron synapse formation. What is meant by the term specificity, how rigid are the rules, and what factors govern connectivity? Story Landis discusses neuronal growth cones: their morphological and biochemical properties, the mechanism of movement, the roles of diffusible vs. surface-bound molecules in governing the direction of growth, and the problem of how new surface membrane is added. Josh Sanes reviews the burst of recent progress in the role of the extracellular matrix in synaptogenesis. Matrix molecules have been implicated as directional signals for the migration of neural crest cells, for the regeneration of motor neurons back to their original synaptic sites, and for the localization of specializations on the pre- and postsynaptic membranes. Finally, most explanations of the phenomena of neuronal cell death and synaptic rearrangement involve trophic molecules secreted by target cells. Yves-Alain Barde, David Edgar, and Hans Thoenen review the numerous recent studies of such putative trophic factors and compare them to the well-characterized progenitor of the field, Nerve Growth Factor.

Since the reviews in this Section can cover only a few aspects of synaptogenesis, readers desiring further information should consult the list below.

551

Recent Reviews of Interest

Cotman, C. W., Nieto-Sampedro, M., Harris, E. W. 1981. Synapse replacement in the nervous system of adult vertebrates. *Physiol. Rev.* 61:684–784

Dennis, M. J. 1981. Development of the neuromuscular junction: inductive interactions between cells. *Ann. Rev. Neurosci.* 4:43–68

Gottlieb, D. I., Glaser, L. 1980. Cellular recognition during neural development. *Ann. Rev. Neurosci.* 3:303–18

Harris, W. A. 1981. Neural activity and development. *Ann. Rev. Physiol.* 43:689–710

Landmesser, L. 1980. the generation of neuromuscular specificity. *Ann. Rev. Neurosci.* 3:279–302

Le Douarin, N. M., Smith, J., Le Lievre, C. S. 1981. From neural crest to the ganglia of the peripheral nervous system. *Ann. Rev. Physiol.* 43:653–71

Oppenheim, R. W. 1981. Neuronal cell death and some related regressive phenomena during neurogenesis: A historical review and a progress report. In *Studies in Developmental Neurobiology: Essays in Honor of Victor Hamburger,* ed. W. M. Cowan, pp. 74–133. NY: Oxford Univ. Press

Patterson, P. H. 1980. On studying the molecular determinants of synapse formation. In *Ontogenesis and Functional Mechanisms of Peripheral Synapses,* ed. J. Taxi, pp. 3–13. NY: Elsevier/North Holland Biomedial Press

Patterson, P. H., Purves, D. 1982. *Readings in Developmental Neurobiology.* NY: Cold Spring Harbor Laboratory. 700 pp.

Solesz, E., Sreter, F. A. 1981. Development, innervation and activity-pattern induced changes in skeletal muscle. *Ann. Rev. Physiol.* 43:531–52

Ann. Rev. Physiol. 1983. 45:553-65

SPECIFIC CONNECTIONS BETWEEN NERVE CELLS

Dale Purves and Jeff W. Lichtman

Department of Physiology and Biophysics, Washington University School of Medicine, St. Louis, Missouri 63110

INTRODUCTION

In general, neurobiologists use the term neuronal specificity to refer to the highly stereotyped patterns of connections between nerve cells that characterize the mature nervous system. These patterns are the culmination of a variety of developmental events including neuronal proliferation and death, neuronal migration and differentiation, axonal outgrowth, trophic interactions, and synapse formation. In this article we focus on the final pattern of synaptic connections in vertebrates. We have limited the discussion to three parts of the nervous system where connections between nerve cells have been intensively studied: the retinal innervation of the optic tectum, the sensory innervation of spinal motor neurons, and the spinal innervation of autonomic ganglion cells. Specificity in these three neuronal systems has several features in common that may help define the rules that underlie patterned connections generally.

QUALITATIVE AND QUANTITATIVE ASPECTS OF SPECIFIC INNERVATION

The pattern of connections between nerve cells can be viewed in two ways. The first is qualitative and concerns the way nerve cells come to innervate appropriate postsynaptic partners. The second perspective is quantitative and concerns the degree of convergence and divergence in the connections formed between neurons. Although recognition of appropriate postsynaptic cells is a topic that has been debated for 40 years, the quantitative features of neural connectivity have not been given much attention until quite recently.

553

0066-4278/83/0315-0553$02.00

Qualitatively Appropriate Synaptic Connections

THE RETINO-TECTAL SYSTEM   Historically, the most influential work on neuronal specificity has centered on the projection of retinal ganglion cells to the optic tectum in lower vertebrates. When a portion of the retina is stimulated while recording from the surface of the exposed tectum, the retinal projection is found to form a continuous map. Thus the experimental hallmark of specific connectivity in this part of the nervous system is an orderly map of the visual world on the tectum.

In 1925, R. Matthey showed that a newt can see normally again a few weeks after optic nerve section (45). The importance of this observation, however, was not appreciated until the 1940s when R. W. Sperry and others adopted this system for work on neural specificity (69–72; see also 73, 74). At that time the prevailing view, promulgated by P. Weiss, was that stereotyped neural connections arose from initially disordered axonal outgrowth with subsequent selection through neural activity (76). This idea was called the resonance hypothesis. Sperry questioned this explanation because he had found that inappropriate neuromuscular connections failed to induce the sort of compensatory changes that Weiss's ideas predicted (68).

To investigate the merits of the resonance hypothesis, Sperry cut the optic nerve in newts and rotated the eye 180° in an experiment now considered the classic observation in this field (70; see also 73). As a result of this manipulation, animals with rotated eyes behaved as if their visual world had been inverted and shifted left for right. This showed that retinal ganglion cells grew back to approximately the same tectal cells they had originally contacted, even though these connections were now maladaptive. Furthermore, no amount of practice could reverse the deficit: animals that viewed the world through a rotated eye continued to strike inappropriately at a lure for as long as the experimenter had the patience to continue the "training" (69).

Attardi & Sperry (1) provided additional evidence that axons from particular regions of the retina regenerate preferentially to appropriate regions of the tectum (see also 24). After removing most of the retina in goldfish, they found that axons from the remaining retinal piece reached the tectum by running in the appropriate division of the optic tract. Moreover, these fractional projections evidently ignored large areas of the denervated target to contact the part of the tectum in which they had originally terminated. Clearly these results favored recognition rather than resonance.

Sperry's experiments left several issues unsettled, however. Is the point to point projection that defines specificity in the retino-tectal system a result of axon guidance, or is the retinal projection also (or even primarily) accounted for by cell recognition during synapse formation? There is, on the one hand, some evidence for order among axons en route to tectum—indeed the original experiments of Attardi & Sperry (1) showed that retinal axons from different regions occupy different parts of the optic tract. More recent experiments have argued explicitly for a detailed ordering of axons in the optic nerve and tract (e.g. 14, 64, 65). On the other hand, retention of neighbor relationships between axons is not an adequate explanation for retino-tectal specificity. When optic nerve axons reach the tectum their arrangement is evidently reorganized (64, 65); indeed, they can find their way even after intentional disordering (72). Moreover, in mammals, retinal axons arising from the same region of the retina stray rather widely among other axons in the optic nerve (20). Even in lower vertebrates the final pattern of connectivity in the tectum is apparently attained by means of a certain amount of local trial and error (12, 13).

An additional complication in interpreting Sperry's work is that retino-tectal preferences appear to be flexible. For example, if half of the tectum is removed from adult goldfish, then the remaining half will accept regenerating axons from the entire retina (16, 78; see also 63). During development as well, the retino-tectal connections initially formed are apparently not permanent but represent a continually shifting set, as might be expected from the changing size and relationship of the retina and the tectum (5, 15).

In spite of these uncertainties, the evidence for specific retino-tectal connections has led a number of workers to seek a molecular basis for this phenomenon (see 17). One intriguing biochemical finding in this field is that the chick retina contains a molecule that is distributed in a gradient across the retina (75). Such a topographical gradient, identified by a monoclonal antibody, is consistent with the idea that systematic differences in the surface properties of neurons are important in retino-tectal preferences. Indeed a number of studies have demonstrated preferential adhesivity of retinal and tectal cells taken from corresponding positions (17).

To summarize, Sperry's studies of retino-tectal reinnervation have given rise to the notion that qualitative specificity in the central nervous system depends on highly ordered chemoaffinities between sets of pre- and post-synaptic neurons. Although the chemoaffinity hypothesis is now generally accepted, experiments in the retino-tectal system fail to provide conclusive evidence for this idea. One reason for this is that most of these observations do not distinguish between axon guidance and recognition of target cells at the level of synapse formation. Another is the practical and conceptual difficulty presented by the apparent flexibility of retino-tectal connections. A third reason is the possibility that regeneration and normal development are not equivalent. As a result, retino-tectal experiments done after Sperry's pioneering work have generated considerable contention.

THE VERTEBRATE SPINAL CORD   Although not often considered in accounts of neuronal specificity, the organization of the spinal cord bears importantly on this issue. This is because studies of the spinal cord (unlike those of the retino-tectal system) have emphasized the innervation of individual neurons, in particular the innervation of spinal motor neurons.

Spinal motor neurons are the final common path for the motor output to the trunk and limbs of vertebrates. These cells are divided into groups (motor neuron pools) that innervate particular muscles. Although a pool is usually spread over one or a few segments in the spinal cord, each group has a characteristic position in both the rostro-caudal and tranverse planes. Thus motor neuron pools can be recognized by their location. Segregation is not very strict, however, since different motor neuron pools often overlap (see 3, 18, 19, 27).

The pattern of innervation to motor neurons is difficult to analyze because many different classes of axons impinge upon these cells. Moreover, the vast majority of the several thousand synapses on each motor neuron derive from interneurons, a type of cell that is particularly difficult to study. However, one class of input to motor neurons has proved tractable: the innervation provided by stretch-sensitive afferents arising from muscle spindles. In fact, these connections are probably more thoroughly understood than any other synapses in the vertebrate central nervous system.

In the 1940s and 1950s D. P. C. Lloyd and J. C. Eccles showed that the connections between muscle afferents and motor neuron pools are specific in the sense that the afferents from a particular muscle end preferentially on the motor neurons that subserve that muscle (6, 43). These connections are the central limb of the myotatic or stretch reflex (42). More recently, connections between individual stretch-sensitive afferents and motor neurons have been studied using the technique of spike-triggered averaging (47, 48, 66). In accord with earlier results, each sensory axon from a particular muscle in the cat makes stronger synaptic connections with the motor neurons that innervate that muscle (homonymous connections) than with motor neurons that innervate synergist muscles (heteronymous connections); antagonist motor neurons are usually not innervated at all. For example, each of the approximately 60 primary afferent fibers from the medial gastrocnemius elicits a measurable synaptic response in nearly every medial gastrocnemius motor neuron (over 300 cells) (47). On the other hand, each afferent axon projects to only about 60% of the motor neurons in a synergist pool (lateral gastrocnemius) (47, 66). Similar experiments in frogs have shown that the projection frequency and synaptic influence of individual sensory afferents are greater on homonymous than on heteronymous motor neurons (37).

The relative affinity between afferents and particular motor neurons can be assessed by determining the number of synaptic contacts between related pairs. Surprisingly, only a few synapses are found between an individual afferent and a homonymous motor neuron (2, 4, 23, 37, 61). In the bullfrog, for example, the smallest synaptic potential elicited in a motor neuron by stimulating a sensory axon is about 40 μV and presumably represents the effect of a single synaptic bouton; since the average synaptic potential elicited by a stretch-sensitive afferent in a homonymous motor neuron is only about 200 μV, there are apparently about 5 synaptic contacts between connected cells (37). Indeed, in both the cat and the frog intracellular staining of individual afferents with horseradish peroxidase consistently shows fewer than 10 contacts between homonymous pairs (2, 4, 23, 37, 61). This is all the more remarkable as there is no obvious segregation of connected and unconnected sensory-motor sets in the spinal cord; all of the relevant sensory axons and motor neuron dendrites ramify in the same general region [(10); J. W. Lichtman, S. Jhaveri, E. Frank, unpublished observations].

In summary, afferents growing into the spinal cord generally innervate appropriate motor neurons and eschew motor neurons supplying other unrelated muscles, even though the number of synapses formed between an appropriate pair is minuscule. In contrast to the retinal innervation of the tectum, it is difficult to imagine how axon guidance or neighbor relations between axons could give this pattern of connectivity in the spinal cord. The afferent axons evidently recognize different classes of motor neurons and form a precise number of contacts with them; this occurs even though the target cells are scattered among other neurons that are inappropriate.

Unlike the axons of retinal ganglion cells in lower vertebrates, the central projections of sensory axons do not usually regenerate following injury; therefore it is not possible to investigate the reinnervation of motor neurons. However, some studies have explored recognition during development. In tadpoles, for instance, extirpation of the dorsal root ganglion that supplies all the sensory innervation to the forearm causes an adjacent ganglion to send novel sensory processes into the arm. Remarkably, these axons establish appropriate synaptic connections in the sense that novel afferents from a particular arm muscle innervate the motor neurons to that muscle more strongly than other motor neurons (10, 11). This suggests that neuronal connections in the developing spinal cord (as those in the retinotectal system) are malleable [but see (7)].

THE PERIPHERAL AUTONOMIC SYSTEM   Perhaps the simplest region of the vertebrate nervous system that has been studied in order to understand specific connectivity between nerve cells is the peripheral autonomic system. In a variety of mammals the superior cervical ganglion, the most rostral of the segmental chain of sympathetic ganglia, receives innervation from preganglionic neurons in 5–8 different thoracic spinal cord segments (29, 50, 62). However, activation of the preganglionic axons from each segmental level elicits a largely distinctive constellation of end-organ responses. For example, stimulating an upper thoracic segment (T1) causes pupillary dilation but has little effect on blood vessels in the ear or on piloerection; conversely, stimulating a lower thoracic segment (T4) has marked effects on the ear and on hairs, but little effect on the eye (29, 40, 50).

A number of experiments have examined the cellular basis of these observations (56). Intracellular recordings from individual superior cervical ganglion cells during stimulation of the preganglionic axons arising from various segments show that each ganglion cell is innervated in a highly stereotyped manner. Although each target neuron is contacted by many axons arising from several different spinal levels, an individual ganglion cell is invariably innervated by axons from a contiguous subset of the spinal cord segments that contribute to the ganglion as a whole. Moreover, the strength of each segment's contribution to a cell falls off as a function of distance from a dominant segment that innervates the neuron most strongly (50; see also 41).

This matching of different classes of ganglion cells and preganglionic axons appears to be related to the positional qualities of the synaptic partners. Although the sympathetic innervation of the smooth muscle associated with blood vessels and hairs extends throughout the entire territory served by the superior cervical ganglion, vessels and hairs in different locations are activated by preganglionic axons arising from different spinal segments (40). Thus the rule seems to be that ganglion cells that send their axons to different positions in the postganglionic periphery are innervated in turn by preganglionic axons that reside at different rostro-caudal levels of the spinal cord.

The positional attributes of the synaptic partners are probably not the only criteria that determine the qualitative pattern of synaptic connections in autonomic ganglia. Indeed, there is considerable evidence that the functional modality of ganglion cells also plays a role. For instance, autonomic neurons are sometimes innervated in a systematic way by preganglionic axons that have particular conduction velocities (44, 49, 77), a parameter that presumably reflects a functional quality of the synaptic partners.

The matching of ganglion cells and preganglionic innervation could arise in a number of ways. For example, particular classes of pre- and postsynaptic cells might be the only ones available at a crucial point in development; in this case apparently selective connections could have formed because of limited choice. However, studies of the reinnervation of adult ganglia argue against this possibility. Following interruption of the axons to the superior cervical ganglion, the preganglionic fibers readily regenerate. In general, the end-organ responses to segmental stimulation regain their original quality after ganglion cell reinnervation (30, 31, 51, 52; see also 9, 28). The contiguity and segmental dominance that characterize the innervation of individual ganglion cells are also restored (51), even from the first contacts made upon ganglion cells by regenerating axons (52).

It seems unlikely that successful reinnervation can be attributed to axon guidance since there is no obvious topographical arrangement of target cells within a ganglion (40, 60). Rather, preganglionic axons and ganglion cells seem able to bias synapse formation by virtue of some intrinsic and more or less permanent property. This idea is further supported by the finding that the same set of preganglionic axons is able to distinguish between ganglion cells transplanted from different segmental levels (59; see also 43a, 58).

An important implication of the innervation of sympathetic ganglion cells (and their appropriate reinnervation) is that the normal pattern of connections represents a competitive balance that depends on the availability of different classes of preganglionic axons. A number of experiments provide direct evidence for this idea. If one class of axons is removed (by cutting a portion of the input to the superior cervical ganglion, for example) the remaining axons make connections with otherwise inappropriate ganglion cells (47a). On the other hand, when the interrupted axons return, the normal balance of connectivity is restored [(17a); J. Maehlen, A. Nja, personal communication].

Taken together, these observations on sympathetic ganglia argue for mutual recognition of individual ganglion cells and preganglionic axons at the level of synapse formation during development and throughout life (see also 9, 28). However, recognition between autonomic neurons does not have the quality of a lock and key, but rather a bias that promotes synaptic connectivity between preferred classes without strict prohibitions. Thus to a large degree the final pattern of connectivity must represent a competitive balance.

Quantitatively Appropriate Synaptic Connections

In addition to establishing qualitatively correct connections, nerve cells must also establish connections that are quantitatively accurate. Thus each innervating axon must contact the correct number of target cells with an appropriate number of synapses, and each target neuron must be innervated by a number of synapses and axons appropriate to its integrative function.

Some indication of how the quantitative regulation of connections between neurons occurs has been provided by recent studies in several parts of the developing nervous system. Autonomic ganglion cells, for example, are innervated by several times as many axons at birth as at maturity (25, 35, 36, 38). This transition takes place during the first few weeks of postnatal life and shares several features with the postnatal rearrangement of synaptic connections that has been observed at the developing neuromuscular junction, in the visual system, and in the cerebellum (see 2a, 57).

The number of innervating axons and target cells in the one autonomic ganglion that has been studied in this regard remains constant during postnatal life (25); therefore the number of these ganglion cells innervated by each preganglionic axon must decrease. The number of ganglionic synapses, however, actually increases postnatally (25, 35, 67); indeed, a gradual accumulation of synapses postnatally appears to be characteristic of many parts of the nervous system (e.g. see 57). The common denominator of postnatal synaptic rearrangement appears to be a reduction in the number of axons innervating each target neuron, rather than simply an elimination of some synaptic connections.

An obvious question is why some ganglion cells (or neurons in general) are ultimately innervated by one or a few axons whereas others are innervated by many. A major difference between neurons that are singly innervated and those that remain innervated by a number of different axons in maturity is their geometry (57). The apparent correlation between geometry and degree of innervation has been explored directly in the ciliary ganglion of the rabbit (55). An advantage of this preparation is that a more or less homogeneous population of neurons differs strikingly in geometry. Some cells lack dendrites altogether, whereas others have a substantial number of processes (25, 55). The relation between degree of innervation and geometry was tested by staining individual neurons after electrophysiological determination of the number of inputs they received. Most ciliary ganglion cells innervated in maturity by a single axon lack dendrites altogether, whereas cells innervated by more than one axon have one or more dendritic processes. Moreover, dendritic complexity increases in proportion to the number of innervating axons. Since the full adult range of geometries is present at birth when virtually all these neurons are multiply innervated (25), the loss of some inputs is presumably influenced by ganglion cell shape (21). Although the mechanism of this process is not understood, the presence of dendrites may mitigate competition between inputs that would otherwise interact and be eliminated (22, 39).

Although these aspects of specificity have not yet been explored in either the spinal cord or the retino-tectal system, recent studies of retinal axon segregation in the tectum (8, 33) suggest that the competitive establishment of quantitatively appropriate connectivity is also characteristic of these more complex parts of the nervous system.

FEATURES OF SPECIFICITY SHARED BY THESE SYSTEMS

Each region of the nervous system that we have considered consists of a broadly similar population of presynaptic cells (retinal ganglion cells, muscle afferents, or preganglionic neurons) that innervate a relatively uniform population of postsynaptic cells (tectal neurons, motor neurons, or autonomic ganglion cells). Neurons within these broadly defined pre- and postsynaptic populations can be further categorized according to both functional and positional criteria. Although relatively little is known about functional division within the several neuronal populations we have considered, such classes clearly exist. Thus various retinal ganglion cells have distinct functions (e.g. see 34), sympathetic neurons subserve different modalities (piloerection and vasoconstriction, for example), and different classes of muscle afferents convey different sorts of sensory information. In each of these systems, cells within both the pre- and postsynaptic populations also differ from one another in a positional sense. These differences are obvious in the retino-tectal system, where the overall arrangement is topographical. In the sensory-motor system as well, sensory afferents are distinguished by the muscle they arise from and motor neurons are grouped according to the muscles they innervate. Although less obvious, positional organization is also apparent in the autonomic nervous system. Thus sympathetic ganglion cells innervate different postganglionic territories, and preganglionic axons differ according to their segment of origin.

During development, the division of neuronal populations according to position and function evidently gives rise to preferential connections between pre- and postsynaptic cells from corresponding groups: Axons from a particular part of the retina prefer to innervate a corresponding tectal region, afferents from a particular muscle prefer the homonymous motor neuron pool, and preganglionic neurons from a particular spinal segment prefer ganglion cells that innervate a particular region of the postganglionic periphery. In each of these cases, however, smaller numbers of synapses are also established with other target cells. For instance, afferents from a given muscle form weak connections with motor neurons to synergist muscles, and preganglionic axons from spinal segments remote from the dominant segment to a particular sympathetic ganglion cell make weak connections with it.

Finally, these systems show a stereotyped pattern of convergence and divergence. Thus every spinal motor neuron is innervated by only a few synaptic boutons from each homonymous afferent, and each autonomic ganglion cell receives innervation from a number of different axons that is closely tied to its geometry. These observations imply precise regulation of these quantitative aspects of neural connectivity.

Based on these considerations one can list some requirements of an explanation of specific connectivity:

1. An adequate explanation must account for connectivity that is normally limited to connections between corresponding populations of pre- and postsynaptic cells, even though synaptic connections can be induced to form across normal population boundaries. For example, motor neurons can be

made to innervate autonomic ganglion cells (32, 46), preganglionic neurons can be made to innervate skeletal muscle (26), and so on. The absence of such bizarre connections in normal animals is presumably the result of lack of opportunity during development.

2. An adequate explanation must take account of the fact that normal recognition during synapse formation is relative: Recognition provides a bias rather than absolute certainty. The basis of recognition appears to depend in part on positional qualities of the neurons involved, but not necessarily their anatomical position. This is most striking in sympathetic ganglia where positionally matched ganglion cells and preganglionic axons are not topographically arranged (40, 60).

3. An adequate explanation must account for the precise regulation of convergence and divergence. This aspect of specific connectivity is only tangentially related to recognition of qualitatively appropriate synaptic partners. We have argued elsewhere that quantitative regulation involves competition for trophic feedback molecules produced and secreted by target neurons (53, 54, 56, 67) and that acquisition of such factors is somehow tied to patterns of neural activity and neuronal geometry (39, 57).

In the light of these requirements, the conventional view that neural specificity will be explained by recognition molecules on neuronal surfaces is inadequate. The final pattern of connections formed between neurons in any part of the nervous system is evidently the result of opportunity, recognition, and competition. Thus an explanation of specific connectivity will have to encompass the basis of these several processes and the manner of their interaction.

Literature Cited

1. Attardi, D. G., Sperry, R. W. 1963. Preferential selection of central pathways by regenerating optic fibers. *Exp. Neurol.* 7:46–64
2. Brown, A. G., Fyffe, R. E. W. 1981. Direct observation on the contacts made between Ia afferent fibres and α-motoneurones in the cat's lumbosacral spinal cord. *J. Physiol.* 313:121–40
2a. Brown, M. C., Holland, R. L., Hopkins, W. G. 1981. Excess neuronal inputs during development. In *Development in the Nervous System*, ed. D. R. Garrod, J. D. Feldman, pp. 245–62. Cambridge: Cambridge Univ. Press
3. Burke, R. E., Strick, P. L., Kanda, K., Kim, C. C., Walmsley, B. 1977. Anatomy of medial gastrocnemius and soleus motor nuclei in cat spinal cord. *J. Neurophysiol.* 40:667–80
4. Burke, R. E., Walmsley, B., Hodgson, J. A. 1979. HRP anatomy of group Ia

afferent contacts on α motoneurons. *Brain Res.* 160:347–52
5. Chung, S. H., Keating, M. J., Bliss, T. V. P. 1974. Functional synaptic relations during the development of the retino-tectal projection in amphibians. *Proc. R. Soc. London Ser. B* 187:449–59
6. Eccles, J. C., Eccles, R. M., Lundberg, A. 1957. The convergence of monosynaptic excitatory afferents on to many different species of alpha motoneurons. *J. Physiol.* 137:22–50
7. Eide, A. L., Jansen, J. K. S., Ribschester, R. R. 1982. The effect of lesions in the neural crest on the formation of synaptic connexions in the embryonic chick spinal cord. *J. Physiol.* 324:453–78
8. Fawcett, J. W., Willshaw, D. J. 1982. Compound eyes project stripes on the optic tectum in *Xenopus. Nature* 296:350–52

9. Feldman, D. H. 1979. Specificity of reinnervation of frog sympathetic ganglia. *Soc. Neurosci. Abstr.* 5:625

10. Frank, E., Westerfield, M. 1982. Synaptic organization of sensory and motor neurones innervating triceps brachii muscles in the bullfrog. *J. Physiol.* 324:479–94

11. Frank, E., Westerfield, M. 1982. The formation of appropriate control and peripheral connexions by foreign sensory neurones of the bullfrog. *J. Physiol.* 324:495–505

12. Fujisawa, H. 1981. Retinotopic analysis of fiber pathways in the regenerating retinotectal system of the adult newt *Cynops pyrrhogaster. Brain Res.* 206: 27–37

13. Fujisawa, H., Tani, N., Watanabe, K., Ibata, Y. 1982. Branching of regenerating retinal axons and preferential selection of appropriate branches for specific neuronal connection in the newt. *Devel. Biol.* 90:43–57

14. Fujisawa, H., Watanabe, K., Tani, N., Ibata, Y. 1981. Retinotopic analysis of fiber pathways in amphibians. II. The frog *Rana nigromaculata. Brain Res.* 206:21–26

15. Gaze, R. M., Keating, M. J., Ostberg, A., Chung., S.-H. 1979. The relationship between retinal and tectal growth in larval *Xenopus:* implications for the development of the retino-tectal projection. *J. Embryol. Exp. Morphol.* 53: 103–43

16. Gaze, R. M., Sharma, S. C. 1970. Axial differences in the reinnervation of goldfish optic tectum by regenerating optic nerve fibres. *Exp. Brain Res.* 10:171–81

17. Gottlieb, D. I., Glaser, L. 1980. Cellular recognition during neural development. *Ann. Rev. Neurosci.* 3:303–18

17a. Guth, L., Bernstein, J. J. 1961. Selectivity in the reestablishment of synapses in the superior cervical sympathetic ganglion of the cat. *Exp. Neurol.* 4:59–69

18. Hollyday, M. 1980. Motoneuron histogenesis and the development of limb innervation. *Curr. Top. Devel. Biol.* 16: 181–215

19. Hollyday, M. 1980. Organization of motor pools in the chick lumbar lateral motor column. *J. Comp. Neurol.* 194: 143–70

20. Horton, J. C., Greenwood, M. M., Hubel, D. H. 1980. Non-retinotopic arrangement of fibres in the cat optic nerve. *Nature* 282:720–22

21. Hume, R. I., Purves, D. 1981. Geometry of neonatal neurones and the regulation of synapse elimination. *Nature* 293:469–71

22. Hume, R. I., Purves, D. 1982. Apportionment of innervation to mammalian neurons. *Soc. Neurosci. Abstr.* 8:709

23. Iles, J. F. 1976. Central terminations of muscle afferents on motoneurones in the cat spinal cord. *J. Physiol.* 262:91–117

24. Jacobson, M., Gaze, R. M. 1965. Selection of appropriate tectal connections by regenerating optic nerve fibers in adult goldfish. *Exp. Neurol.* 13: 418–30

25. Johnson, D. A., Purves, D. 1981. Postnatal reduction of neural unit size in the rabbit ciliary ganglion. *J. Physiol.* 318:143–59

26. Landmesser, L. 1971. Contractile and electrical responses of vagus-innervated frog sartorius muscle. *J. Physiol.* 213:707–25

27. Landmesser, L. 1978. The distribution of motoneurones supplying chick hind limb muscles. *J. Physiol.* 284:371–89

28. Landmesser, L., Pilar, G. 1970. Selective re-innervation of two cell populations in the adult pigeon ciliary ganglion. *J. Physiol.* 211:203–16

29. Langley, J. N. 1892. On the origin from the spinal cord of the cervical and upper thoracic sympathetic fibres, with some observations on white and grey rami communicantes. *Philos. Trans. R. Soc. Lond.* 183:85–124

30. Langley, J. N. 1895. Note on regeneration of pre-ganglionic fibres of the sympathetic. *J. Physiol.* 18:280–84

31. Langley, J. N. 1897. On the regeneration of pre-ganglionic and post-ganglionic visceral nerve fibres. *J. Physiol.* 22:215–30

32. Langley, J. N., Anderson, H. K. 1904. On the union of the fifth cervical nerve with the superior cervical ganglion. *J. Physiol.* 30:439–42

33. Law, M. I., Constantine-Paton, M. 1981. Anatomy and physiology of experimentally produced striped tecta. *J. Neurosci.* 1:741–59

34. Lettvin, J. Y., Maturana, H. R., McCulloch, W. S., Pitts, W. H. 1959. What the frog's eye tells the frog's brain. *Proc. IRE* 47:1940–51

35. Lichtman, J. W. 1977. The reorganization of synaptic connexions in the rat submandibular ganglion during postnatal development. *J. Physiol.* 273: 155–77

564   PURVES & LICHTMAN

36. Lichtman, J. W. 1980. On the predominantly single innervation of submandibular ganglion cells in the rat. *J. Physiol.* 302:121–30
37. Lichtman, J. W., Frank, E. 1981. Projections of individual muscle sensory fibers to homonymous and heteronymous motoneurons in the bullfrog. *Soc. Neurosci. Abstr.* 7:362
38. Lichtman, J. W., Purves, D. 1980. The elimination of redundant preganglionic innervation to hamster sympathetic ganglion cells in early post-natal life. *J. Physiol.* 301:213–28
39. Lichtman, J. W., Purves, D. 1981. Regulation of the number of axons that innervate target cells. In *Development in the Nervous System,* ed. D. R. Garrod, J. D. Feldman, pp. 233–243. Cambridge: Cambridge Univ. Press
40. Lichtman, J. W., Purves, D., Yip, J. W. 1979. On the purpose of selective innervation of guinea-pig superior cervical ganglion cells. *J. Physiol.* 292:69–84
41. Lichtman, J. W., Purves, D., Yip, J. W. 1980. Innervation of sympathetic neurones in the guinea-pig thoracic chain. *J. Physiol.* 298:285–99
42. Liddell, E. G. T., Sherrington, C. 1924. Reflexes in response to stretch (myotatic reflexes). *Proc. R. Soc. London (Biol.)* 96:212–42
43. Lloyd, D. P. C. 1943. Reflex action in relation to pattern and peripheral source of afferent stimulation. *J. Neurophysiol.* 6:111–20
43a. Maehlen, J., Nja, A. 1981. Selective synapse formation during sprouting and after partial denervation of the guinea-pig superior cervical ganglion. *J. Physiol.* 319:555–67
44. Marwitt, R., Pilar, G., Weakly, J. N. 1971. Characterization of two ganglion cell populations in avian ciliary ganglia. *Brain Res.* 25:317–34
45. Matthey, R. 1925. Recuperation de la vue apres resection des nerfs optiques chez le triton. *C. R. Séance. Soc. Biol.* 93:904–6
46. McLachlan, E. 1974. The formation of synapses in mammalian sympathetic ganglia re-innervated with preganglionic or somatic nerves. *J. Physiol.* 237:217–42
47. Mendell, L. M., Henneman, E. 1971. Terminals of single Ia fibers: location, density, and distribution within a pool of 300 homonymous motoneurons. *J. Neurophysiol.* 34:171–87
47a. Murray, J. G., Thompson, J. W. 1957. The occurrence and function of collateral sprouting in the sympathetic nervous system of the cat. *J. Physiol.* 135:133–62
48. Nelson, S. G., Mendell, L. M. 1978. Projection of single knee flexor Ia fibers to homonymous and heteronymous motoneurons. *J. Neurophysiol.* 41:778–87
49. Nishi, S., Soeda, H., Koketsu, K. 1965. Studies on sympathetic B and C neurons and patterns of preganglionic innervation. *J. Cell. Comp. Physiol.* 66:19–32
50. Nja, A., Purves, D. 1977. Specific innervation of guinea-pig superior cervical ganglion cells by preganglionic fibres arising from different levels of the spinal cord. *J. Physiol.* 264:565–83
51. Nja, A., Purves, D. 1977. Re-innervation of guinea-pig superior cervical ganglion cells by preganglionic fibres arising from different levels of the spinal cord. *J. Physiol.* 272:633–51
52. Nja, A., Purves, D. 1978. Specificity of initial synaptic contacts made on guinea-pig superior cervical ganglion cells during regeneration of the cervical sympathetic trunk. *J. Physiol.* 281:45–62
53. Purves, D. 1977. The formation and maintenance of synaptic connections. In *Function and Formation of Neural Systems,* ed. G. S. Stent, pp. 21–49. Berlin: Dahlem Konferenzen
54. Purves, D. 1981. Selective formation of synapses in the peripheral nervous system and the chemoaffinity hypothesis of neural specificity. In *Studies in Developmental Neurobiology. Essays in Honor of Viktor Hamburger,* ed. W. M. Cowan, pp. 231–42. NY: Oxford Univ. Press
55. Purves, D., Hume, R. I. 1981. The relation of postsynaptic geometry to the number of presynaptic axons that innervate autonomic ganglion cells. *J. Neurosci.* 1:441–52
56. Purves, D., Lichtman, J. W. 1978. Formation and maintenance of synaptic connections in autonomic ganglia. *Physiol. Rev.* 58:821–62
57. Purves, D., Lichtman, J. W. 1980. Elimination of synapses in the developing nervous system. *Science* 210:153–57
58. Purves, D., Thompson, W. 1979. The effects of post-ganglionic axotomy on selective synaptic connexions in the superior cervical ganglion of the guinea-pig. *J. Physiol.* 297:95–110
59. Purves, D., Thompson, W., Yip, J. W. 1981. Re-innervation of ganglia transplanted to the neck from different levels of the guinea-pig sympathetic chain. *J. Physiol.* 313:49–63

60. Purves, D., Wigston, D. J. 1983. Neural units in the superior cervical ganglion of the guinea-pig. *J. Physiol.* In press
61. Redman, S., Walmsey, B. 1981. The synaptic basis of the monosynaptic stretch reflex. *Trends Neurosci.* 4:248–51
62. Rubin, E., Purves, D. 1980. Segmental organization of sympathetic preganglionic neurons in the mammalian spinal cord. *J. Comp. Neurol.* 192:163–74
63. Schmidt, J. T., Cicerone, C. M., Easter, S. S. 1978. Expansion of the half retinal projection to the tectum in goldfish: an electrophysiological and anatomical study. *J. Comp. Neurol.* 177:257–78
64. Scholes, J. H. 1979. Nerve fibre topography in the retinal projection to the tectum. *Nature* 278:620–24
65. Scholes, J. 1981. Ribbon optic nerves and axonal growth patterns in the retinal projection to the tectum. In *Development in the Nervous System*, ed. D. R. Garrod, J. D. Feldman, pp. 181–214. Cambridge: Cambridge Univ. Press
66. Scott, J. G., Mendell, L. M. 1976. Individual EPSPs produced by single triceps surae Ia afferent fibers in homonymous and heteronymous motoneurons. *J. Neurophysiol.* 39:679–92
67. Smolen, A. J., Raisman, G. 1980. Synapse formation in the rat superior cervical ganglion during normal development and after neonatal deafferentation. *Brain Res.* 181:315–23
68. Sperry, R. W. 1941. The effect of crossing nerves to antagonistic muscles in the hind-limb of the rat. *J. Comp. Neurol.* 75:1–19
69. Sperry, R. W. 1943. Effect of 180 degree rotation of the retinal field on visuomotor coordination. *J. Exp. Zool.* 92:263–79
70. Sperry, R. W. 1943. Visuomotor coordination in the newt (*Triturus viridescens*) after regeneration of the optic nerve. *J. Comp. Neurol.* 79:33–55
71. Sperry, R. W. 1944. Optic nerve regeneration with return of vision in anurans. *J. Neurophysiol.* 7:57–69
72. Sperry, R. W. 1963. Chemoaffinity in the orderly growth of nerve fiber patterns and connections. *Proc. Natl. Acad. Sci. USA* 50:703–10
73. Stone, L. S. 1944. Functional polarization in the retinal development and its re-establishment in regenerating retinae of rotated grafted eyes. *Proc. Soc. Exp. Biol. Med.* 57:13–14
74. Stone, L. S., Zaur, I. S. 1940. Reimplantation and transplantation of adult eyes in the salamander (*Triturus viridescens*) with return of vision. *J. Exp. Zool.* 85:243–69
75. Trisler, G. D., Schneider, M. D., Nirenberg, M. 1981. A topographic gradient of molecules in retina can be used to identify neuron position. *Proc. Natl. Acad. Sci. USA* 78:2145–49
76. Weiss, P. 1936. Selectivity controlling the central-peripheral relations in the nervous system. *Biol. Rev.* 11:494–531
77. Wigston, D. J. 1983. Innervation of individual guinea-pig superior cervical ganglion cells by axons with similar conduction velocities. *J. Physiol.* In press
78. Yoon, M. 1971. Reorganization of retinotectal projection following surgical operations on the optic tectum in goldfish. *Exp. Neurol.* 33:395–411

Ann. Rev. Physiol. 1983. 45:567–80

NEURONAL GROWTH CONES

S. C. Landis

Department of Neurobiology, Harvard Medical School, Boston, Massachusetts 02115

The growing tip of the axon, the growth cone, plays a critical role in the formation of appropriate neuronal connections since it is the part of the neuron that seeks out and contacts potential target cells during development. Any attempt to explain axon growth and guidance and specific synapse formation must take into account the properties actually displayed by axonal growth cones. The growing tip of the axon is motile, it actively explores its surround, and it is able to respond to a variety of environmental cues. These properties were ascribed to the growth cone by Ramon y Cajal (76) who first recognized the expanded tip of the growing axon as a specialized region in Golgi preparations in 1890 and named it "cone d'accroissement" or growth cone. He later described its activities: "From the functional point of view, the growth cone may be regarded as a sort of club or battering ram, endowed with exquisite chemical sensitivity, with rapid ameboid movements and with certain impulsive force, thanks to which it is able to proceed forward and overcome obstacles met in its way, forcing cellular interstices until it arrives at its destination" (76). Twenty years later, Harrison (36) was able to see living growth cones extending from explant cultures of frog nervous tissue. It was clear from these early tissue culture observations that the growing tips corresponded to the growth cones described by Ramon y Cajal in fixed material and that they possessed the properties he had predicted.

Recent studies of axonal growth cone structure and function have focused on the issues of motility, growth, and guidance [see (14, 19, 45) for other recent reviews]. Most have been carried out in culture because there the growth cones can be easily identified, their past history can be charted, and they are accessible to a variety of manipulations that would be far more difficult in living animals. It will be important, however, to determine that

567

the properties displayed by growth cones in culture mirror the properties displayed in vivo, particularly since in many cases the axons produced in culture represent regeneration rather than primary outgrowth. Insofar as comparisons have been made, the observations made in culture are consistent with those made in vivo. The growing tips of peripheral axons in culture morphologically resemble the growth cones of the developing sensory innervation of skin and somites observed with the scanning electron microscope (47, 79). The mode of movement and response to the environment exhibited by growth cones that Speidel observed in the intact tadpole tail fin expansion (89) closely resemble these behaviors detailed in culture studies (36, 65, 75, 97). Further comparisons are being facilitated by the recent development of new techniques for labeling entire young neurons in vivo with intracellular tracers and cell-surface markers (e.g. 3, 40, 43, 49).

STRUCTURE

The growth cone consists of a protoplasmic enlargement, the varicosity or cone, that contains most of the organelles, and of thin peripheral regions that are motile (Figure 1). The peripheral extensions may take the form of filopodia, which are long, thin finger-like projections (approximately 0.15 μm in diameter and tens of μm long), or of lamellipodia, which are thin, sheet- or veil-like projections. Differences have been reported in the morphological appearance of the peripheral extensions of growth cones from different classes of neurons growing in culture (75). However, individual growth cones may possess both filopodia and lamellipodia (60), and no systematic study of the effect of neuronal source or substrate on growth cone structure has yet been reported.

Numerous morphological studies of growth cones in vivo and in vitro [e.g. (1, 12, 13, 46, 51, 60, 66, 77, 90, 93, 101, 102) and Figure 2] have revealed a relatively consistent complement of membranous organelles. The varicosity usually contains agranular reticulum which may form interconnecting channels, clear vesicles and vacuoles, coated vesicles, large dense-core vesicles, mitochondria, and lysosomal structures. The filopodia and lamellipodia possess only occasional elements of smooth endoplasmic reticulum. In general, growth cones of cultured neurons and of peripheral neurons in vivo tend to be more complex in form and organelle-rich while those from the central nervous system of intact animals tend to be simpler in form and organelle-poor. Growing dendrites also possess growth cones that morphologically and functionally resemble those of axons.

The several membranous organelles are likely to serve a number of functions since the membrane dynamics of the growth cone appear to be complex, involving both retrieval and insertion (4, 7, 13, 17, 75, 98). The

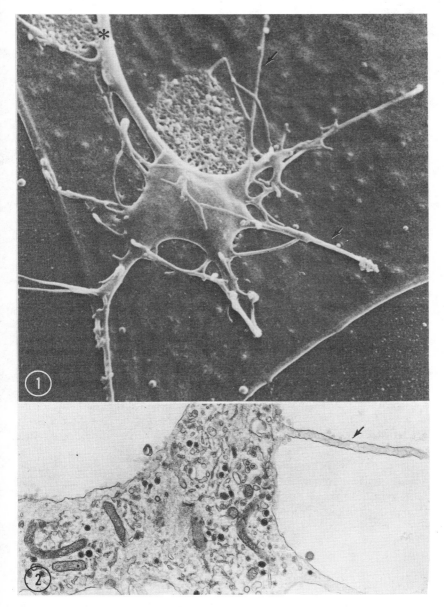

Figure 1 Scanning electron micrograph of a growth cone of a sympathetic neuron in culture. The axon (asterisk upper left) expands into a bulbous enlargement, the varicosity of the growth cone, on the surface of a nonneuronal cell. Numerous fine filopodia (arrows) extend from the varicosity. (X 9,000)

Figure 2 Transmission electron micrograph of the central portion of a cultured sympathetic neuron growth cone. Most of the organelles are concentrated in the central region while the filopodia (arrow) contain primarily microfilaments. (X 17,000)

vacuoles, clear and coated vesicles, and lysosomal structures can function in the internalization of membrane and sequestration of macromolecules. This has been demonstrated for electron-dense markers such as ferritin and horseradish peroxidase [HRP (4, 13, 95, 98)]. Also, binding of lectins to cell-surface receptors can cause rapid clearing of the complexes from the growth cone filopodia and varicosity, internalization, and retrograde transport (17, 57). Presumably, these mechanisms for uptake and sequestration exist for biologically important molecules like Nerve Growth Factor (NGF). The agranular reticulum, clear vesicles, and vacuoles also represent possible sources of membrane to be incorporated into the plasmalemma (see below). Further dissection of the roles of these several classes of organelles will require morphological probes that reflect function. In addition, there are variable numbers of small synaptic-size vesicles, approximately 50 nm in diameter. In the growth cones of sympathetic neurons, many of these small vesicles contain neurotransmitter; a granular precipitate is present in the vesicles after permanganate fixation, a morphological assay for the presence of vesicular stores of norepinephrine (51). In fact, the presence of neurotransmitter may be a general property of growing axons. The growth cones of catecholamine neurons in the central nervous system have endogenous catecholamine histofluorescence (91) and tyrosine hydroxylase immunoreactivity (87, 88). Not only is neurotransmitter present, but calcium action potentials have been recorded from growth cones of neuroblastoma cells using optical techniques (33), and physiological examination of forming nerve-muscle contacts suggests that growth cones release neurotransmitter (22, 31). The release of neurotransmitters or other substances from the growth cone could mediate some of the early interactions between a growing axon and its target cells during synapse formation.

The cytoskeletal elements of the growth cone, the microtubules, neurofilaments, and microfilaments, were initially identified and their distribution mapped in thin-section studies [(12, 90, 101, 102); see also (9, 32) for recent reviews of cytoskeletal proteins and their function]. These descriptions have been verified recently in immunofluorescence studies using antisera generated against several cytoskeletal proteins (41, 42, 44, 48, 61, 62) and by examination of whole mount and cytoskeletal preparations (42, 48, 56, 59). Microtubules appear bundled together in the neurite, but when they extend into the growth cone varicosity they splay out to form a fan; they do not, however, extend to the plasmalemma or into the filopodia (9, 41, 44, 61, 102). Intermediate or 10 nm neurofilaments have not been mapped as extensively as microtubules, but the distributions appear to be similar. Actin microfilaments form a complex polygonal meshwork directly beneath the entire plasma membrane of the growth cone and are virtually the only constituent of the filopodia and lamellipodia (12, 101, 102). Some of the membrane-associated filaments appear to insert into the plasmalemma (60,

78). In addition, some of the actin present in the growth cone is organized into filament bundles that course through the varicosity and into the filopodia where they form a filamentous core (41, 48, 58, 61). In immunofluorescence studies and in whole mounts of growth cones examined with the electron microscope, these bundles present a palmate appearance like bones in the hand. Myosin immunoreactivity appears to co-localize with that of actin (48, 58, 86). It is of interest that both microtubules in axons (15, 38) and actin filaments in filopodia (42) appear to be polarized so that growth or the addition of new monomers occurs distally.

MOTILITY

The working assumption is that cytoskeletal components are responsible for the extension, contraction, and motility of the filopodia and lamellipodia, as well as the forward movement of the entire growth cone. In fact, treatment of growing axons with cytochalasin, which disrupts microfilament function, causes microspikes to retract, growth cones to round up, and the axon to stop elongating (18, 101–103). This effect is reversible. After removal of the drug, microspikes reappear, the growth cone regains its normal morphology, and the axon elongates. In contrast, treatment with mitotic inhibitors such as colchicine, which disrupt microtubular function, have no early effects on the shape or activity of the growth cone or its filopodia (26, 101). Axons initially continue to elongate, but then after a brief lag retraction begins. Thus the microtubular system appears to be responsible for structural support of the axon and transport of cytoplasmic materials essential for elongation while the network of actin microfilaments is reponsible for locomotory function. As in other systems, the cellular and molecular mechanisms responsible for motility and elongation are incompletely understood. It is clear from a number of studies that regions of the growth cone varicosity and the veil and the tips of the filopodia can adhere strongly to appropriate substrata (53, 56, 64, 65, 97) and that as a result, individual filopodia and the growth cone as a whole can exert tension on the axon (8). Presumably the adhesive contacts stabilize particular regions of the growth cone, influence the organization of the microfilamentous network within the cone, and promote directional expansion of the surface. The interplay between surface attachment and directed motility is demonstrated by the ability to induce branch points and steer neurites with microneedles (8, 99) and to direct elongation through manipulation of the substratum (see below). However, the molecular mechanisms that underlie these growth cone activities remain to be elucidated.

Motility and substrate adhesion appear to be restricted to the growth cone. In fact, the process of axon initiation appears to involve the restriction of motility to one or a few areas on the cell body (23, 96). Shortly after plating, microspikes and ruffling membranes extend from the entire neuronal surface, but gradually most of the surface becomes quiescent as activity is limited to one or several areas from which the axons will extend. Although motility is normally restricted to the growing tip, the entire axon has the potential to flatten and become motile. When a growing axon is severed, the distal end rounds up, reorganizes, and then forms new growth cones (84). Similarly, the proximal stump can form a new growth cone (10, 96). The presence of microtubules in the neurite may be responsible for the normal suppression of growth cone properties along the axon since treatment with low concentrations of antimitotic drugs that interfere with microtubular function causes the appearance of growth cone-like areas at nonterminal regions (10).

GROWTH AND MEMBRANE PROPERTIES

Axon elongation requires the expansion of the plasma membrane. An axon 0.5 μm in diameter that is growing at the rate of 0.5-1 mm per day will require the addition of 0.5-1 μm^2 of plasma membrane per minute (72). Attention has focused on where and how this membrane is added to the surface of developing neurons. Harrison (36) and Speidel (89), among others, pointed out that axonal branch points remained fixed with respect to the cell body and their immediate environment. This observation suggested that significant membrane addition occurs close to or at the growing tip. Further evidence for growth at the tip was obtained by Bray (5, 6). He examined dissociated neurons in culture and found that branch points and added carmine marker particles remained a constant distance from the cell body and each other while the distance to the growth cone gradually increased.

Membrane addition has been examined further through the use of markers for particular surface membrane components. A prerequisite for these studies has been a partial characterization of the membrane properties of developing neurons and their growth cones. Such characterization is important since developmental cell-cell interactions such as axon guidance and target recognition are likely to be mediated in part by cell-surface molecules. Cultured neurons possess numerous lectin receptors on their cell surfaces several days after plating (17, 27, 57, 72, 73, 83). Light-microscopic and preliminary ultrastructural analyses suggested that the receptors for many lectins were distributed uniformly over cell body, axon, and growth cone regions (17, 57, 72). However, regional differences do exist in the amount of binding of certain lectins (27, 83), and the lectin-binding profile of growth cones is different from that of perikarya and axon shafts (73). Another difference between growth cone and perikaryonal membrane appears to be the density of intramembranous particles revealed by freeze-fracture that are thought to represent integral membrane proteins: Growth cone membrane is relatively particle-poor while cell body membrane is particle-rich. However, this difference involves comparison of spinal cord growth cones with sympathetic neuron cell bodies (70). Evidence for a differential particle distribution on the same class of neuron comes from the observation that particle densities are greater in proximal than distal regions of growing spinal cord (70) and regenerating olfactory axons (85). Not only do the cell surface properties of the growth cone and perikarya differ within a class of neuron but the growth cones of different classes of neurons exhibit different carbohydrate specificities (72, 73). For example, growth cones of neurons derived from the neural tube possess many more terminal sialic acid residues than neurons from the neural crest. Although the demonstration of the differential distributions of lectin receptor and intramembranous particles is interesting, the developmental significance of these properties is unclear. It will be important to develop additional probes for membrane components that are relevant to the biological processes of interest and whose function we know or can elucidate in experimental studies. Two such probes currently exist. One is NGF (see the review by Thoenen & Barde in this section), which can determine the direction of axonal growth by acting locally on the growing tip (16, 34, 35, 55). High-affinity NGF binding sites appear to be five times more numerous on neuritic shafts and growth cones than on cell bodies (20). A second molecule of interest is the neuronal aggregation molecule [N-CAM (92)]. N-CAM appears to be distributed over the entire neuritic surface of several classes of neurons and to mediate the side-to-side adhesion between neurites to form fascicles (80–82). The characterization of the growth cone membrane will be greatly facilitated by the recent development of a cell-fractionation technique that yields a fetal rat brain fraction significantly enriched for growth cones (71). Biochemical and immunological analysis of the plasma membrane of this fraction is currently in progress. One dimensional gel electrophoresis reveals only 12 major proteins.

The sites and mechanisms of membrane incorporation have been studied using several of the membrane markers discussed above. If axons from retinal explants are examined 24 hr after labelling briefly with concanavalin A (ConA) immobilized by anti-ConA, the new lengths of axon are free of the previously applied label but can be labelled with additional ConA (30). Ferritin conjugates of ricin I and wheat germ agglutinin have been used to study membrane incorporation at the ultrastructural level. Initially, the lectin binding sites are uniformly distributed over the cell surface of sympathetic neurons. After a short time (3–20 min), relatively label-free regions appear in the peripheral regions of the growth cone, in particular on filopodia and over clusters of large clear vesicles. Label-free regions contain lectin binding sites since relabelling with the same lectin yields a uniform density of ferritin binding. These experiments, like the earlier ones, suggest that plasmalemmal expansion occurs by means of bulk addition of membrane at the growing tip, although interpretation may be complicated by the observation that with longer incubation times lectin binding can cause receptor clearing from growth cones (17, 57). Interest has focused on particular regions of the growth cone, the subplasmalemmal vesicle clusters, as a possible internal membrane pool for addition to the plasmalemma (70–72, 74, 100). These regions appear as mounds on the growth cone and in sections they contain numerous large, clear vesicles that lack a surrounding ground substance. In freeze-fracture replicas, mounds and the vesicle clusters beneath are particle-free. Since the growth cone region is relatively particle-poor in comparison to the perikaryon, Pfenninger has proposed that subplasmalemmal vesicles fuse with the plasma membrane to form mounds that represent new membrane. However, in growth cones as well as in other systems, the presence of mounds, subplasmalemmal vesicles clusters, and particle-free membrane have not been observed in rapidly frozen preparations and appear to result from primary aldehyde fixation (21, 37, 51, 67, 78). Furthermore, at least some of the subplasmalemmal vesicles appear to have pinched off from the surface since many mound vesicles can be labelled when markers such as HRP or ferritin are present before or during fixation (13, 14). Thus while it seems likely that an internal pool of recently synthesized membrane exists in the growth cone, the subplasmalemmal vesicle clusters are not the morphological representation of this pool [but see (70, 74)]. Not all membrane constituents appear to be incorporated into the plasmalemma at the growth cone. Based on the differential distribution of intramembranous particles and of lectin-binding sites, Pfenninger has suggested that these membrane components are inserted at the cell body and then diffuse in the plane of the membrane to the growing tips (72–74). In contrast, alpha-bungarotoxin binding sites appear to be incorporated into the plasma membrane along the entire surface (18).

DIRECTIONAL GUIDANCE

One of the most important functions of the growth cone is to guide the growing axon to the appropriate target. That some form of guidance occurs during development has been indicated by a number of recent studies in systems such as chick limb, which demonstrate that when axons first grow out they do not form random, diffuse, or inappropriate projection patterns under normal conditions (e.g. 49, 50, 52). It is important to point out as did Harrison (36) that the distance the first neurons must navigate to find their targets early in development is relatively short. In several insect systems, many sensory axons grow in from the periphery along preestablished pathways laid down by early pioneer neurons (2). How is the pioneer pathway itself established? The pioneer growth cones are very large and appear to search for and recognize a nearby neuroblast; having reached this signpost, they then search for the next neuroblast and so on. Thus the original pathway appears to be the result of random filopodial outgrowth and peripheral adhesion to appropriately placed neuroblasts (3, 40).

Several general mechanisms have been proposed for axonal guidance in vivo: The growth cone could respond to (a) weak electrical fields, (b) presence of a gradient of a diffusible substance, (c) mechanical guides, or (d) substrate-associated chemical cues. Examination of the properties of growth cones in culture have shown that all four classes of environmental cues can, in fact, guide their growth. More neurons sprout neurites in a weak electric field, and these neurites are preferentially directed toward the cathode (39, 68). Recent experiments have provided direct evidence for a role for the diffusible protein, NGF, in orienting axon extension. Sympathetic neurites will grow into culture chambers that contain NGF, but not into chambers that lack it (16); and after intracerebral injections of NGF, they will grow into the parenchyma of the central nervous system, which they normally never enter (63). Neurites from explants of NGF-sensitive cells will also grow towards capillary tubes containing NGF and producing a steep but transient gradient of NGF (29, 80). It is likely that such a gradient would affect only the first axons to grow out; experiments with antisera raised against CAM suggest that the extensive asymmetric outgrowth is due, in part, to neurite fasciculation (80). At least some dissociated sensory axons will also orient up an NGF gradient established in agar (55). Perhaps the most striking example of NGF-mediated guidance has been reported by Gundersen & Barrett (34, 35). All of the sensory neurons they tested turned toward an NGF-containing micropipette within 20 min of positioning it in the culture dish. In fact, in some cases they could reverse the initial direction of growth by sequentially repositioning the NGF source. It seems clear from these studies that the growth cones of NGF-sensitive neurons can respond to NGF gradients by directed growth. Whether or not gradients of NGF and other NGF-like factors exist during development and are functionally important for axon guidance remains to be determined.

The growth of neurons in culture can also be guided by environmental cues provided by the substrate. Purely mechanical factors such as an aligned collagen matrix can channel the growth of neurites to some extent (28, 94). However, much more intriguing effects on axonal growth have been obtained through manipulation of the adhesivity of the substrate. Letourneau determined the relative adhesivity of growth cones to various substrata (53) and then examined the behavior of growth cones on surfaces patterned with more or less adhesive regions (54). He found that although the filopodia sampled widely, the growth cones always elongated on the more adhesive surface. The surfaces used in these studies were artificial, but similar growth guidance has recently been achieved by coating portions of the culture dish with an attachment factor derived from heart conditioned medium (23–25). It seems likely that the fasciculation and the preferential growth on nonneuronal cells displayed by axons of cultured neurons also result from differential adhesivity of the several surfaces available for growth (11, 64, 97).

During development, the axonal growth cone grows to the correct target and forms appropriate synaptic connections. Despite the important role of growth cones, knowledge of their properties is incomplete. The organelles of the growth cone have been cataloged but the exact roles of the individual constituents are unclear. The cytoskeletal elements have been mapped but the mechanisms of motility remain to be elucidated. Plasmalemmal expansion occurs at the growing tip but how and where particular membrane components are inserted is unknown. In fact, little is known about the membrane composition of growth cones. Finally, although axon growth can be guided by several environmental cues in culture the relevance of these cues to guidance in vivo remains to be demonstrated.

ACKNOWLEDGMENTS

I thank Shirley Wilson for excellent help with the manuscript, numerous friends for their advice, several authors for sending unpublished manuscripts, and the American Heart Association and the NINCDS for support.

Literature Cited

1. Al-qhaith, L. K., Lewis, J. H. 1982. Pioneer growth cones in virgin mesenchyme: an electron-microscope study in the developing chick wing. *J. Embryol. Exp. Morphol.* 68:149–60
2. Bate, C. M. 1976. Pioneer neurones in an insect embryo. *Nature* 260:54–55
3. Bentley, D. R., Keshishian, H. 1982. Pioneer neurons and pathways in insect appendages. *Trends Neurosci.* 5:354–358
4. Birks, R. J., Mackey, M. C., Weldon, P. R. 1972. Organelle formation from pinocytotic elements in neurites of cultured sympathetic ganglia. *J. Neurocytol.* 1:311–40
5. Bray, D. 1970. Surface movements during the growth of single explanted neurons. *Proc. Natl. Acad. Sci. USA* 65:905–10
6. Bray, D. 1973. Branching patterns of individual sympathetic neurons in culture. *J. Cell Biol.* 56:702–12
7. Bray, D. 1973. Model for membrane movements in the neural growth cone. *Nature* 244:93–96
8. Bray, D. 1979. Mechanical tension produced by nerve cells in tissue culture. *J. Cell Sci.* 37:391–410
9. Bray, D., Gilbert, D. 1981. Cytoskeletal elements in neurons. *Ann. Rev. Neurosci.* 4:505–23
10. Bray, D., Thomas, C., Shaw, G. 1978. Growth cone formation in cultures of sensory neurons. *Proc. Natl. Acad. Sci. USA* 75:5226–29
11. Bray, D., Wood, P., Bunge, R. P. 1980. Selective fasciculation of nerve fibers in culture. *Exp. Cell Res.* 130:241–50

12. Bunge, M. B. 1973. Fine structure of nerve fibers and growth cones of isolated sympathetic neurons in culture. *J. Cell Biol.* 56:713–35

13. Bunge, M. B. 1977. Initial endocytosis of peroxidase or ferritin by growth cones of cultured nerve cells. *J. Neurocytol.* 6:407–39

14. Bunge, M. B., Johnson, M. I., Agiro, V. J. 1982. Studies of regenerating nerve fibers and growth cones. In *Proceedings of the 1st International Symposium on Spinal Cord Reconstruction,* ed. C. Kao, R. Bunge. NY: Raven Press. In press

15. Burton, P. R., Paige, J. L. 1981. Polarity of axoplasmic microtubules in the olfactory nerve of the frog. *Proc. Natl. Acad. Sci. USA* 78:3269–73

16. Campenot, R. B. 1977. Local control of neurite development by nerve growth factor. *Proc. Natl. Acad. Sci. USA* 74:4516–19

17. Carbonetto, S., Argon, Y. 1980. Lectins induce the redistribution and internalization of receptors on the surface of cultured neurons. *Devel. Biol.* 80:364–78

18. Carbonetto, S., Fambrough, D. M. 1979. Synthesis, insertion into the plasma membrane, and turnover of α-bungarotoxin receptors in chick sympathetic neurons. *J. Cell Biol.* 81:555–69

19. Carbonetto, S., Muller, K. J. 1982. Nerve fiber growth and the cellular response to axotomy. *Curr. Top. Devel. Biol.* 17. In press

20. Carbonetto, S., Stach, R. W. 1982. Localization of nerve fiber growth factor bound to neurons growing nerve fibers in culture. *Devel. Brain Res.* 3:463–73

21. Chandler, D. E., Heuser, J. E. 1980. Arrest of membrane fusion events in mast cells by quick freezing. *J. Cell Biol.* 86:666–74

22. Cohen, S. A. 1980. Early nerve-muscle synapses *in vitro* release transmitter over postsynaptic membrane having low acetylcholine sensitivity. *Proc. Natl. Acad. Sci. USA* 77:644–48

23. Collins, F. 1978. Axon initiation by ciliary neurons in culture. *Devel. Biol.* 65:50–57

24. Collins, F., Garrett, J. E. 1980. Elongating nerve fibers are guided by a pathway of material released from embryonic nonneuronal cells. *Proc. Natl. Acad. Sci. USA* 77:6226–28

25. Collins, F. 1980. Neurite outgrowth induced by the substrate associated material from nonneuronal cells. *Devel. Biol.* 79:247–52

26. Daniels, M. P. 1972. Colchicine inhibition of nerve fiber formation *in vitro. J. Cell Biol.* 53:164–76

27. Denis-Donini, S., Estenoz, M., Augusti-Tocco, G. 1978. Cell surface modifications in neuronal maturation. *Cell Diff.* 7:193–201

28. Ebendal, T. 1976. The relative roles of contact inhibition and contact guidance in orientation of axons extending on aligned collagen fibrils *in vitro. Exp. Cell Res.* 98:159–69

29. Ebendal, T., Jacobson, C.-O. 1977. Tissue explants affecting extension and orientation of axons in cultured chick embryo ganglia. *Exp. Cell Res.* 105:379–87

30. Feldman, E. L., Axelrod, D., Schwartz, M., Heacock, A. M., Agranoff, B. W. 1981. Studies on the localization of newly added membrane in growing neurites. *J. Neurobiol.* 12:591–98

31. Frank, E., Fischbach, G. D. 1979. Early events in neuromuscular junction formation *in vitro. J. Cell Biol.* 83:143–58

32. Goldman, R. D., Milsted, A., Schloss, J. A., Starger, J., Yerna, M.-J. 1979. Cytoplasmic fibers in mammalian cells. *Ann. Rev. Physiol.* 41:703–22

33. Grinvald, A., Farber, I. 1981. Optical recording of calcium action potentials from growth cones of cultured neurons with a laser microbeam. *Science* 212:1164–67

34. Gundersen, R. W., Barrett, J. N. 1979. Neuronal chemotaxis; chick dorsal root axons turn toward high concentrations of Nerve Growth Factor. *Science* 206:1079–80

35. Gundersen, R. W., Barrett, J. N. 1980. Characterization of the turning response of dorsal root neurites toward Nerve Growth Factor. *J. Cell Biol.* 87:546–54

36. Harrison, R. G. 1910. The outgrowth of the nerve fiber as a mode of protoplasmic movement. *J. Exp. Zool.* 9:787–846

37. Hasty, D. L., Hay, E. D. 1978. Freeze-fracture studies of the developing cell surface. II. Particle free membrane blisters on glutaraldehyde fixed corneal fibroblasts are artifacts. *J. Cell Biol.* 78:756–68

38. Heidemann, S. R., Landers, J. M., Hamborg, M. A. 1981. Polarity orientation of axonal microtubules. *J. Cell Biol.* 91:661–65

39. Hinkle, L., McCaig, C. D., Robinson, K. R. 1981. The direction of growth of differentiating neurones and myoblasts from frog embryos in an applied electric field. *J. Physiol.* 314:121–35

40. Ho, R. K., Goodman, C. S. 1982. Peripheral pathways are pioneered by an array of central and peripheral neurones in grasshopper embryos. *Nature* 297:404–6

41. Isenberg, G., Rieske, E., Kreutzberg, G. W. 1977. Distribution of actin and tubulin in neuroblastoma cells. *Cytobiologie* 15:382–89

42. Isenberg, G., Small, J. V. 1978. Filamentious actin, 100 Å filaments and microtubules in neuroblastoma cells. *Cytobiologie* 16:326–44

43. Jan, L. Y., Jan, Y. N. 1982. Antibodies to horseradish peroxidase as specific neuronal markers in *Drosophila* and in grasshopper embryos. *Proc. Natl. Acad. Sci. USA* 79:2700–4

44. Jockusch, H., Jockusch, B. N. 1981. Structural proteins in the growth cone of cultured spinal cord neurons. *Exp. Cell Res.* 131:345–52

45. Johnston, R. N., Wessells, N. K. 1980. Regulation of the elongating nerve fiber. *Curr. Top. Devel. Biol.* 16:165–206

46. Kawana, E., Sandri, C., Akert, K. 1971. Ultrastructure of growth cones in the cerebellar cortex of the neonatal rat and cat. *Z. Zellforsch. Mikrosk. Anat.* 115:284–98

47. Kordykuski, L. 1978. Scanning electron microscopic observations of the development of the somites and their innervation in anuran larvae. *J. Embryol. Exp. Morphol.* 45:215–27

48. Kuczmarski, E. R., Rosenbaum, J. L. 1979. Studies on the organization and localization of actin and myocin in neurons. *J. Cell Biol.* 80:356–71

49. Lance-Jones, C., Landmesser, L. 1981. Pathway selection by chick lumbosacral motoneurons during normal development. *Proc. R. Soc. London Ser. B* 214:1–18

50. Lamb, A. H. 1976. The projection patterns of the ventral horn to the hind limb during development. *Devel. Biol.* 54:82–99

51. Landis, S. C. 1978. Growth cones of cultured sympathetic neurons contain adrenergic vesicles. *J. Cell Biol.* 78: R8–14

52. Landmesser, L., Morris, D. G. 1975. The development of functional innervation in the hind limb of the chick embryo. *J. Physiol.* 249:301–26

53. Letourneau, P. C. 1975. Possible roles for cell-to-substratum adhesion in neuronal morphogenesis. *Devel. Biol.* 44: 77–91

54. Letourneau, P. C. 1975. Cell-to-substratum adhesion and guidance of axonal elongation. *Devel. Biol.* 44:92–101

55. Letourneau, P. C. 1978. Chemotactic response of nerve fiber elongation to nerve growth factor. *Devel. Biol.* 66:183–96

56. Letourneau, P. C. 1978. Cell-substratum adhesion of neurite growth cones and its role in neurite elongation. *Exp. Cell Res.* 124:127–38

57. Letourneau, P. C. 1979. Inhibition of cellular adhesion by Concanavalin A is associated with Concanavalin A-mediated redistribution of surface receptors. *J. Cell Biol.* 80:128–40

58. Letourneau, P. C. 1981. Immunocytochemical evidence for colocalization in neurite growth cones of actin and myosin and their relationship to cell-substratum adhesions. *Devel. Biol.* 85:113–22

59. Letourneau, P. C. 1982. Analysis of microtubule number and length in cytoskeletons of cultured chick sensory neurons. *J. Neurosci.* 2:806–14

60. Ludueña, M. A., Wessells, N. K. 1973. Cell locomotion, nerve elongation and microfilaments. *Devel. Biol.* 30:427–40

61. Marchisio, P. C., Osborn, M., Weber, K. 1978. The intracellular organization of actin and tubulin in cultured C-1300 neuroblastoma cells (clone NB41A3). *J. Neurocytol.* 7:571–82

62. Marchisio, P. C., Osborn, M., Weber, K. 1978. Changes in intracellular organization of tubulin and actin in N-18 neuroblastoma cells during the process of axon extension induced by serum deprivation. *Brain Res.* 155:229–37

63. Menesini-Chen, M. G., Chen, J. S., Levi-Montalcini, R. 1978. Sympathetic nerve fibers ingrowth in the central nervous system of neonatal rodent upon intracerebral NGF injections. *Arch. Ital. Biol.* 116:53–84

64. Nakai, J. 1960. Studies on the mechanism determining the course of nerve fibers in tissue culture. II. The mechanism of fasciculation. *Z. Zellforsch. Mikrosk. Anat.* 52:427–49

65. Nakai, J., Kawasaki, Y. 1959. Studies on the mechanism determining the course of nerve fibers in tissue culture. I. The reactions of the growth cone to various obstructions. *Z. Zellforsch. Mikrosk. Anat.* 51:108–22

66. Nordlander, R. H., Singer, M. 1982. Morphology and position of growth cones in the developing *Xenopus* spinal cord. *Devel. Brain Res.* 4:181–93

67. Nuttall, R. P., Wessells, N. K. 1979. Veils, mounds, and vesicle aggregates in

neurons elongating *in vitro. Exp. Cell Res.* 119:163–74

68. Patel, N., Poo, N. M. 1982. Orientation of neurite growth by extracellular electric fields. *J. Neurosci.* 2:483–96

69. Pfenninger, K. H. 1979. Subplasmalemmal vesicle clusters: real or artifact? In *Freeze-Fracture: Methods, Artifacts and Interpretations,* ed. J. E. Rash, C. S. Hudson, pp. 71–80. NY: Raven Press

70. Pfenninger, K. H., Bunge, R. P. 1974. Freeze-fracturing of nerve growth cones and young fibers. A study of developing plasma membrane. *J. Cell Biol.* 63: 180–96

71. Pfenninger, K. H., Ellis, L., Friedman, L. B., Johnson, M. P., Somlo, S. 1982. Nerve growth cones isolated by subcellular fractionation from fetal rat brain. *J. Cell Biol.* 95:95a

72. Pfenninger, K. H., Maylié-Pfenninger, M. F. 1980. Properties and dynamics of plasmalemmal glycoconjugates in growing neurites. *Prog. Brain Res.* 51: 83–94

73. Pfenninger, K. H., Maylié-Pfenninger, M. F. 1981. Lectin labeling of sprouting neurons. I. Regional distribution of surface glycoconjugates. *J. Cell Biol.* 89:536–46

74. Pfenninger, K. H., Maylié-Pfenninger, M. F. 1981. Lectin labeling of sprouting neurons. II. Relative movement and appearance of glycoconjugates during plasmalemmal expansion. *J. Cell Biol.* 89:547–59

75. Pomerat, C. M., Hendelman, W. J., Raiburn, C. W., Massey, J. F. 1967. Dynamic activities of nervous tissue in vitro. In *The Neuron,* ed. H. Hyden, pp. 119–78. NY: Elsevier

76. Ramon y Cajal, S. 1904. *Histologie du Systeme Nerveux de L'Homme et des Vertebres Vol. I.* Madrid: Consejo Superior de Investigaciones Cientificas. pp. 597–98; 603, 604, 609

77. Rees, R., Bunge, M. B., Bunge, R. P. 1976. Morphological changes in the neurite growth cone and target neuron during synaptic junction development in culture. *J. Cell Biol.* 68:240–63.

78. Rees, R. P., Reese, T. S. 1981. New structural features of freeze-substituted neuritic growth cones. *Neuroscience* 6:247–54

79. Roberts, A. 1976. Neuronal growth cones in an amphibian embryo. *Brain Res.* 118:526–630

80. Rutishauser, U., Edelman, G. M. 1980. Effects of fasciculation on the outgrowth of neurites from spinal ganglia in culture. *J. Cell Biol.* 87:370–78

81. Rutishauser, U., Gall, W. E., Edelman, G. M. 1978. Adhesion among neural cells of the chick embryo. IV. Role of the cell surface molecule CAM in the formation of neurite bundles in cultures of spinal ganglia. *J. Cell Biol.* 79:382–93

82. Rutishauser, U., Thiery, J.-P., Brackenbury, R., Edelman, G. M. 1978. Adhesion among neural cells of the chick embyo. III. Relationship of the surface molecule CAM to cell adhesion and the development of histotypic patterns. *J. Cell Biol.* 79:371–81

83. Schwab, M., Landis, S. 1981. Membrane properties of cultured rat sympathetic neurons: morphological studies of adrenergic and cholinergic differentiation. *Devel. Biol.* 84:67–78

84. Shaw, G., Bray, D. 1977. Movement and extension of isolated growth cones. *Exp. Cell Res.* 104:55–62

85. Small, R., Strichartz, R., Pfenninger, K. H. 1979. Membrane properties of the growing axon: intramembranous particles and saxitoxin binding sites. *J. Cell Biol.* 83:279a

86. Sotelo, J., Toh, B. H., Yildiz, A., Osung, O., Holbrow, E. J. 1979. Immunofluorescence demonstrates the distribution of actin, myosin and intermediate filaments in cultured neuroblastoma cells. *Neuropathol. Appl. Neurobiol.* 5:499–505

87. Specht, L. A., Pickel, V. M., Joh, T., Reis, D. J. 1981. Fine structure of the nigrostriatal anlage in fetal rat brain by immunocytochemical localization of tyrosine hydroxylase. *Brain Res.* 218: 49–65

88. Specht, L. A., Pickel, V. M., Joh, T., Reis, D. J. 1981. Light microscopic immunocytochemical localization of tyrosine hydroxylase in prenatal rat brain. I. Early ontogeny. *J. Comp. Neurol.* 199: 233–53

89. Speidel, C. C. 1933. Studies of living nerves. II. Activities of ameboid growth cones, sheath cells, and myelin segments, as revealed by prolonged observation of individual nerve fibers in frog tadpoles. *Am. J. Anat.* 52:1–75

90. Tennyson, V. M. 1970. The fine structure of the axon and growth cone of the dorsal root neuroblast of the rabbit embryo. *J. Cell Biol.* 44:62–79

91. Tennyson, V. M., Barrett, R. E., Cohen, G., Coté, L., Heikila, R., Mytilineou, C. 1972. The developing neostriatum of the rabbit: correlation of fluorescence histochemistry, electron microscopy, endogenous dopamine levels and

[³H]dopamine uptake. *Brain Res.* 46:251–85

92. Thiery, J.-P., Brackenbury, R., Rutishauser, U., Edelman, G. M. 1977. Adhesion among neural cells of the chick embryo. II. Purification and characterization of a cell adhesion molecule from neural retina. *J. Biol. Chem.* 252:6841–45

93. Vaughn, J. E., Henrikson, C. K., Wood, J. G. 1976. Surface specializations of neurites in embryonic mouse spinal cord. *Brain Res.* 110:431–45

94. Weiss, P. 1934. In vitro experiments on the factors determining the course of the outgrowing nerve fiber. *J. Exp. Zool.* 68:393–448

95. Weldon, P. R. 1975. Pinocytotic uptake and intracellular distribution of colloidal thorium dioxide by cultured sensory neurites. *J. Neurocytol.* 4:341–56

96. Wessels, N. K., Johnson, S. R., Nuttall, R. P. 1978. Axon initiation and growth cone regeneration in cultured motor neurons. *Exp. Cell Res.* 117:335–45

97. Wessells, N. K., Letourneau, P. C., Nuttall, R. P., Lalueña-Anderson, M., Geiduschek, J. M. 1980. Responses to cell contacts between growth cones, neurites and ganglionic non-neuronal cells. *J. Neurocytol.* 9:647–64

98. Wessells, N. K., Ludueña, M. A., Letourneau, P. C., Wrenn, J. T., Spooner, B. S. 1974. Thorotrast uptake and transit in embryonic glia, heart fibroblasts and neurons *in vitro. Tiss. Cell* 6:757–76

99. Wessells, N. K., Nuttall, R. P. 1978. Normal branching, induced branching and steering of cultured parasympathetic motor neurons. *Exp. Cell Res.* 115:111–22

100. Wessells, N. K., Nuttall, R. P., Wrenn, J. T., Johnson, S. 1976. Differential labeling of the cell surface of single ciliary ganglion neurons *in vitro. Proc. Natl. Acad. Sci. USA* 73:4100–4

101. Yamada, K. M., Spooner, B. S., Wessells, N. K. 1970. Axon growth: roles of microfilaments and microtubules. *Proc. Natl. Acad. Sci.* 66:1206–12

102. Yamada, K. M., Spooner, B. S., Wessells, N. K. 1971. Ultrastructure and function of growth cones and axons of cultured nerve cells. *J. Cell Biol.* 49:614–35

103. Yamada, K. M., Wessells, N. K. 1973. Cytochalasin B: Effects on membrane ruffling, growth cone and microspike activity and microfilament structure not due to altered glucose transport. *Dev. Biol.* 31:413–20

Ann. Rev. Physiol. 1983. 45:581–600

ROLES OF EXTRACELLULAR MATRIX IN NEURAL DEVELOPMENT

Joshua R. Sanes

Department of Physiology and Biophysics, Washington University School of Medicine, St. Louis, Missouri 63110

Among the most important steps in the development of the nervous system are: (*a*) migration of cells and growth of processes to appropriate locations, (*b*) acquisition of distinctive phenotypes by neurons and glia, and (*c*) formation of synapses between neurons and their targets. In none of these steps do developing cells act autonomously; all require communication among cells and with the environment. Until recently, the search for mechanisms that underly these interactions focused on two classes of molecules: soluble factors (e.g. hormones and "trophic" agents) and constituents of the plasma membrane (e.g. transmitter or hormone receptors and "adhesion" molecules). During the past several years, however, increasing attention has been paid to the components of a third compartment, the extracellular matrix (ECM).

ECM is the material that occupies and maintains spaces between cells. During the past decade, remarkable progress has been made in isolating components of the ECM, studying its metabolism, and elucidating some roles it plays in the development of nonneural cells (33, 52, 53, 56, 62, 68). These advances have begun to inspire studies on the involvement of ECM in neural development. Here I summarize this recent work. A brief overview of the structure of the ECM is followed by descriptions of three aspects of neural development in which ECM has been implicated: the migration of neural crest cells, the ensheathment of peripheral axons by Schwann cells, and the formation of neuromuscular junctions. Finally, I consider other roles that ECM might play in the developing nervous system.

581

0066-4278/83/0315-0581$02.00

THE EXTRACELLULAR MATRIX

Figure 1 diagrams several structural components of the ECM. The *glycoca-lyx* coats the plasma membrane and includes the external domains of integral membrane proteins as well as molecules more loosely adherent to the cell surface (79). Most nonmigratory cells bear a felt-like *basal lamina* (BL) along surfaces that do not abut other cells (56, 62). The more electron-dense layer of the BL (the lamina densa) is usually about 10 nm thick and separated from the cell membrane by a relatively electron-lucent layer (the lamina rara) of about 2–5 nm. The BL is considerably thicker in kidney glomerulus and lens; these heartier BLs have been preferred sources for biochemical analyses. Beyond the BL is the *ground substance,* which contains striated and nonstriated fibrils embedded in an amorphous matrix (51, 52, 78). In some tissues, the fibrils are concentrated in a layer adjacent to BL, called the *reticular lamina* (56). BL and reticular lamina together form the *basement membrane* that was seen as a single layer and defined by light microscopists.

These structures are built of protein and carbohydrate molecules. All the protein is glycosylated, and nearly all of the carbohydrate is attached to

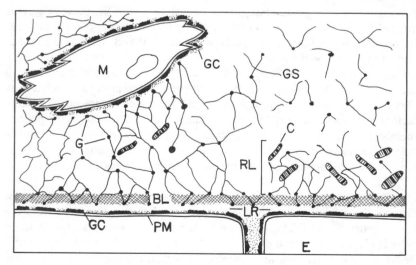

Figure 1   Some elements of the ECM. The glycocalyx (GC) follows the contours of the outer leaflet of the plasma membrane (PM). Epithelial cells (E) bear a basal lamina (BL), the dense center (lamina densa) of which is separated from PM by a narrow lamina rara (LR). Collagen (C) and other fibers are embedded in an amorphous ground substance (GS). Fibrillar elements are sometimes concentrated in a layer called reticular lamina (RL) that abuts BL. Granules (G) rich in GAGs coat fibrils and some BLs. Migrating or mesenchymal cells (M) do not bear a BL, but are connected to other elements of ECM. [Modified from (51, 110)]

protein. The three most prevalent classes of molecules in the ECM are collagenous and noncollagenous glycoproteins, and glycosaminoglycans (GAGs) (33, 52, 56).

Several features set the *collagens* apart from other glycoproteins (15, 33, 53, 127). Each collagen molecule contains a triple helical segment and is rich in glycine, proline, and hydroxyproline. The helical segment resists proteolysis by enzymes such as pepsin that are otherwise fairly indiscriminate, but is degraded by bacterial collagenase, which spares most proteins. The collagens form a set of genetically distinct, although closely related molecules. Five members of the family (Types I–V) have been characterized in detail, and others are still being discovered.

The best studied *noncollagenous glycoprotein* of the ECM is fibronectin (96, 136). The fibronectin molecule is elongated and bears an array of binding sites for collagen, GAGs, and components of cell membranes. This arrangement suggests that fibronectin could mediate the attachment of cells to components of the ECM, and many studies in vitro support this idea (68). Two other glycoproteins that also promote attachment of cells to collagen in vitro are laminin, which is found in many BLs and mediates adhesion of epithelial cells to collagen IV (68, 120, 136), and chondronectin, which is found in cartilage and mediates adhesion of chondrocytes to collagen II (57). Very recent reports suggest that fibronectin, laminin, and chondronectin may be members of a large family of "-nectin" or connecting glycoproteins (25, 35).

GAGs are long, unbranched polymers of disaccharide units (49). Each GAG is defined by its sugar unit; examples are hyaluronic acid, chondroitin sulfate, and heparan sulfate. All GAG in tissue, with the possible exception of hyaluronic acid, is covalently linked to protein; the complex is called a *proteoglycan*. Proteoglycans are distinguished from glycoproteins not only by the nature of their carbohydrate moieties but also by the ratio of sugar to protein mass in the macromolecule, which is ≥ 1 for most proteoglycans and substantially < 1 for most glycoproteins.

Localization of ECM molecules

The most successful strategy for localization of molecules within the ECM has been to purify components from tissue extracts or culture fluids and prepare antibodies for use as immunocytochemical stains. Collagens (127), noncollagenous glycoproteins (e.g. 83, 105), and the protein portion of proteoglycans (e.g. 50) have all been successfully localized in tissue and in cultures by immunocytochemical methods. GAGs are nonimmunogenic [but see (29)], but are preferentially stained by some cationic dyes such as Alcian Blue and Ruthenium Red (79). To determine which GAGs are present, samples can be treated with purified GAG-degrading enzymes such as hyaluronidase or chondroitinase before staining (36).

A combination of immunocytochemical, histochemical, and biochemical analyses has begun to reveal where, within the ECM, its various components are located. Most BLs contain collagen IV, laminin, and a heparan sulfate proteoglycan (41, 62, 105). Collagen IV is a major component of the lamina densa, while laminin and proteoglycan are concentrated in the lamina rara. Some BLs also contain chondroitin sulfate, hyaluronate, fibronectin, and possibly collagen V (41, 44, 49, 83). Large striated fibers are made of Type I collagen, while smaller fibrils may contain Type II, III, or V collagens, depending on the tissue (52, 127). Both striated and nonstriated fibrils are coated with other molecules, including proteoglycans (51) and fibronectin (83). GAGs, particularly hyaluronic acid, are also distributed throughout the ground substance in amorphous forms that are not readily visible by electron microscopy.

Increasingly sophisticated studies on ECM are revealing complex relationships between microscopic structures and molecular species. For example, fibronectin is present in some fibrils, reticular laminae, and BLs, in the glycocalyx of some cells that do not assemble a BL, and in serum (96, 136). Serum and cell-associated fibronections differ subtly, but soluble and bound forms of this molecule may be in equilibrium (55, 93). Acetylcholinesterase also exists in soluble, BL-associated, and membrane-bound forms; insoluble forms may have soluble precursors (82). Furthermore, apparent borders between microscopic structures are influenced by the method of specimen preparation. BL can appear clearly separated from or nearly continuous with plasma membrane, depending on the stain used (44, 83; see also 67). GAGs that extend between fibrils collapse and appear as granules after fixation and dehydration (49, 52). Thus although classifications of the sort made in Figure 1 are useful, they do not reflect the complexity of the network of macromolecules in the ECM.

ROLES IN DEVELOPMENT

Migration: The Neural Crest

The neural crest is a transitory aggregate of cells that forms on the dorsal rim of the neural tube as the tube separates from the overlying ectoderm (Figure 2). Cells leave the neural crest and migrate along defined pathways to target sites throughout the embryo, where they form a variety of cell types including autonomic and sensory neurons, Schwann cells, and melanocytes (92, 133). Evidence that the migration of neural crest cells is guided by components of the migratory environment comes from transplantation experiments. When a piece of the neural crest is excised and replaced

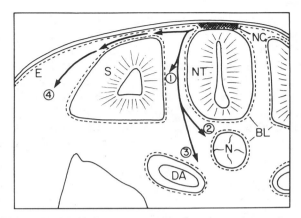

Figure 2 Cross-section through an embryo in the trunk region at the time of neural crest migration. The crest (NC) forms as the neural tube (NT) separates from the overlying ectoderm (E). Cells leave the crest and migrate dorso-laterally or ventro-medially through BL-bounded cell-free space. Some cells stop near NT ① to form dorsal root ganglia. Other pass somite(s) and notochord (N) and stop near the dorsal aorta (DA) to form sympathetic ganglia ② and adrenal medulla ③ . Many cells that follow the dorsal pathway ④ enter dermis and become melanocytes. [Modified from (16)]

with crest from a different region of the embryo (91) or stage of development (134), many cells that leave the graft migrate along pathways and to sites that are characteristic of the implantation site but not of the donor. Neural crest derivatives (ganglion cells and melanocytes), some noncrest cells (retinal pigment epithelium and tumor cells), and even latex beads can also migrate along crest pathways to crest target sites when appropriately implanted (16–18, 39, 71). Thus, information about the migratory pathway is not an intrinsic part of the crest cell's program, but must be derived from the environment.

Anatomical studies of the migratory pathway reveal that ECM must be involved in guiding the movements of crest cells (7, 38, 51, 75, 88, 124, 125, 135). The terrain through which crest cells begin to migrate is, except for the crest cells themselves, a cell-free space (Figure 2). BLs bound the space and separate it from surrounding tissues. Within the space, the ECM is organized into a network of fibrils and granules. Crest cells move through the space not as a tissue, with abundant intercellular contacts, but as small clumps of cells, surrounded by ECM. Recent studies have begun to explore the roles that particular structures and molecules in the ECM play in guiding crest migration.

BASAL LAMINA   BLs may regulate neural crest migration in two ways. First, BLs that surround the cell-free space through which crest cells move define the migratory pathway and may hold cells within it (37, 85, 90, 121). Second, dissolution of the narrow strip of BL that covers the premigratory crest (Figure 2) may be involved in triggering migration. Just before migration, BL covers the lateral margin of the neural crest as well as nearby ectoderm and neural tube. As migration begins, BL is lost from over crest, while nearby neural tube and ectoderm BLs remain intact (7, 87, 88, 124, 125). BL could thus constrain the young crest and its loss could "open the gates" to allow migration to begin. The ultimate control of the formation and loss of BL lies with the cells that make and degrade it, but these have yet to be identified.

HYALURONIC ACID   Based on studies of developing limb, cartilage, and cornea, Toole (122–123) proposed that hyaluronic acid plays important roles in the initial migration and subsequent differentiation of mesenchymal cells. In each case, increases in hyaluronic acid concentration are correlated with the appearance of cell-free space and the onset of migration. As a highly hydrated molecule that occupies a large domain relative to its mass, hyaluronate provides an attractive migratory environment. Subsequently, compaction of the cell-free space, condensation of the mesenchyme, and the onset of differentiation are correlated with appearance of hyaluronidase and loss of hyaluronic acid. Hyaluronate can also inhibit differentiation of some cultured cells. Thus, without acting as a specific inducer, hyaluronic acid could regulate the timing and course of cell migration.

This scheme seems to apply to the neural crest. Just before migration, the cell-free space of the ventral pathway becomes rich in hyaluronic acid (14, 36, 98, 99). Autoradiographic studies following administration of labeled precursor show high synthetic activity along the pathway (42). Both crest cells and surrounding structures (e.g. neural tube and surface ectoderm) make hyaluronic acid and other GAGs in vitro (49, 54, 98, 119). Injection of hyaluronidase into chick embryos at about this stage causes cell-free spaces to collapse (42) and cell migrations to cease (100; but see 3). Later, as the migration proceeds and ends, the concentration of hyaluronic acid decreases and the ratio of sulfated GAG to hyaluronate increases (14, 36, 45, 98, 135). Levels of hyaluronic acid are markedly reduced at some sites, such as where crest cells condense to form dorsal root ganglia (36). Cells from this region, when explanted, make less and degrade more GAG than migratory crest cells or younger ganglionic rudiments (66). Changes in the levels of GAGs might thus be involved not only in facilitating migration but also in terminating migration and triggering ganglion formation.

FIBRONECTIN   Since fibronectin may mediate adhesion of cells to ECM, its involvement in crest-ECM interactions has recently been studied. Immunocytochemistry shows that fibronectin is a prominent component of the migratory pathway and of BLs that line the pathway (37, 83, 88, 121). Levels of fibronectin increase in the cell-free space of the pathway just before crest migration begins, and decline as migration ends; little fibronectin is seen at sites where ganglia form. Thus fibronectin, although by no means confined to the migratory pathway, is appropriately distributed both spatially and temporally to play a role in neural crest migration.

The responsiveness of crest cells to fibronectin has been demonstrated in vitro. Attachment of crest cells to collagenous substrata is fibronectin-dependent (46). Fibronectin also enhances migration of crest cells (89), acting as both a chemokinetic (cells are more active in the presence than in the absence of fibronectin) and a chemotactic (cells move from regions of low to high fibronectin concentration) agent (46). Interestingly, while many cell types can synthesize fibronectin, few crest cells seem to produce this molecule (9, 88, 115, 133). In fibroblasts, the ability of some cell lines to respond to exogenous fibronectin is thought to depend on their inability to produce fibronectin. It has therefore been suggested that the neural crest is susceptible to guidance by fibronectin in its pathway precisely because it makes none of its own (17, 39). Two results lend support to this idea. First, tumor cells that lack fibronectin on their surface migrate along the ventral crest pathway when injected near the neural tube, while heart or limb fibroblasts, which make fibronectin, remain near the injection site (39). Second, uncoated or albumin-coated latex beads injected into somites are transported to appropriate target sites, while fibronectin-coated beads remain with the somite (17).

INTERSTITIAL BODIES   Granules of 0.1–1 μm diameter, called *interstitial bodies,* are present in the ECM of the migratory pathway (75, 78, 83, 87, 89, 123, 125). These structures have attracted attention because their appearance is highly correlated with the spatial and temporal pattern of crest cell migration. They are present shortly before the onset of migration, increase in number about the time migration begins, and disappear as migration ends. Interstitial bodies contain several common ECM components, such as fibronectin, collagen, and GAG. However, they delineate the migratory pathway more precisely than any molecular species so far studied (125) and are accused of "guilt by association" in the guidance of crest migration (83) since they disappear rapidly as migration ends. Thus the interstitial bodies might be the form in which ECM molecules aggregate to guide migration.

SUMMARY   Morphological studies have identified molecules (fibronectin and GAG) and structures (BL and interstitial bodies) that may well be involved in guiding neural crest migration. Two questions that remain are how the pathways form and how crest cells move along them in the appropriate direction. Fibrils are oriented in the direction of migration in amphibian embryos (75) but not in the chick (125). No components of ECM have been found to be present in any obvious gradient that could play a directive role. Interactions among crest cells that impart a "contact inhibition of movement" similar to that seen in fibroblasts have been postulated to render the migration unidirectional (92, 121, 133). However, the observation that implanted latex beads are transported unidirectionally along the crest pathways (17) suggests (if it can be ruled out that the beads are "catching a ride" on endogenous crest cells) that contact inhibition cannot provide a full answer. One possibility is that migratory spaces are narrow and short-lived and thus define transient pathways of ECM that ensure correct directionality (37, 121). By modifying the ECM as they traverse it, crest cells could take part in keeping the migration directional (133). If these ideas are correct, it will be especially important to find out how the pathways are formed, maintained, and finally obliterated.

Differentiation: Schwann Cells

Schwann cells are the glia of the peripheral nervous system. Derivatives of the neural crest, they envelop neuronal cell bodies in autonomic and sensory ganglia, ensheath axons in peripheral nerve, and myelinate the larger axons they encounter. The Schwann cell assembles a BL that covers the circumference of the Schwann cell–axon unit. In culture, Schwann cells form a BL when they are in contact with axons but not when they are grown alone (5, 21, 22). Fibroblasts, which are also present in peripheral nerve, are not necessary for myelination or for production of BL, but they do contribute to the ECM (22).

A relationship between ECM and Schwann cell function was first suggested by observations of dorsal root ganglia in culture (19). When ganglia are explanted onto a collagen substrate, axons grow out from the ganglion and ganglionic Schwann cells migrate along axons, ensheathing the smaller axons and myelinating the larger ones. In some cases, proximal portions of axons detach from the substratum but remain tethered between the ganglion and the still-adherent distal segment. In these suspended regions, Schwann cells fail to multiply, invade axon bundles, ensheath axons, or form myelin. However, when a narrow, collagen-coated strip of plastic or a collagen clot is placed in contact with the suspended fascicle, Schwann cells divide and ensheath and myelinate axons. Thus like a variety of other cells (68), Schwann cells depend on contact with ECM for normal proliferation and differentiation.

A second link between ECM and ensheathment comes from studies of a genetically dystrophic strain (dy) of mouse. Although first studied as a model of muscular dystrophy, the dy mouse also has peripheral nerve defects that are not obviously related to the muscular lesion. In distal portions of motor and sensory nerves, Schwann cells myelinate axons abnormally and their BL is discontinuous (59, 80). Cultures of dorsal root ganglia from dy mice, which contain neurons, Schwann cells, and fibroblasts, exhibit patchy BL and aberrant myelination (94). Experiments in which normal and dy neurons and Schwann cells were separated, freed of fibroblasts, and recombined showed that Schwann cells but not axons are responsible for the defects (20, 31). However, when dy neurons and Schwann cells were recombined with normal skin (20) or nerve (31) fibroblasts, the BL defect was corrected. Unfortunately, the effect of normal fibroblasts on dy ensheathment is more difficult to assess and has not yet been reported. The interpretation offered, however, is that dy Schwann cells are deficient in some component or enzyme associated with ECM that is also required for proper ensheathment; normal but not dy fibroblasts can compensate for this defect.

Three other observations are consistent with a relationship between ECM and ensheathment. First, Schwann cells grown on sensory axons in a defined, serum-free medium proliferate, but neither form BL nor ensheath the axons; ensheathment occurs and BL forms if supplements are restored (86). Second, treatment of Schwann cell–axon cultures with cis-hydroxyproline, an inhibitor of collagen assembly (68), inhibits both BL formation and ensheathment (30). Finally, fibronectin promotes Schwann cell motility in culture (9). Since motility may be required for establishment of appropriate axon-glia relationships (13) this response to fibronectin could explain some effects of ECM on ensheathment.

Synaptogenesis: The Neuromuscular Junction

REINNERVATION OF ADULT MUSCLE   Axons reinnervating denervated skeletal muscle show a remarkable preference for original synaptic sites [for references and exceptions see (11)]. In frog muscle, for example, synaptic sites occupy only about 0.1% of the muscle fiber surface. Following denervation, however, over 95% of the contacts between regenerated axons and muscle fibers occur at original synaptic sites and over 95% of original synaptic membrane is reinnervated (72, 110).

Experiments on damaged muscle implicate the ECM in this case of topographic specificity. Each muscle fiber is ensheathed by a layer of basement membrane, comprising both BL and reticular lamina (105). When muscle is damaged, the myotubes degenerate and are phagocytized, but their sheaths of basement membrane survive (Figure 3). Satellite cells

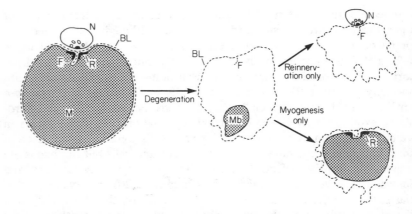

Figure 3 Nerve terminals (N) and muscle (M) (sketched here in cross-section) degenerate when they are injured, but the muscle fiber's sheath of BL persists. Myotubes regenerate from myoblastic satellite cells (Mb) within the BL but can be prevented from doing so by X-irradiation (top right). Axons regenerate to contact BL unless nerves are severely or repeatedly damaged (bottom right). In normal muscle, active zones (peri-membranous density and accumulation of synaptic vesicles) in nerve terminals occur opposite mouths of junctional folds (F) in the muscle fiber surface. Acetylcholine receptors (R) cluster at the tops and sides of folds. Axons that regenerate in the absence of muscle fibers contact synaptic BL and form active zones opposite struts of BL that mark the sites where mouths of junctional folds once were. When myotubes regenerate but axons do not, acetylcholine receptors accumulate in regions where myotube membrane contacts synaptic BL. Schwann cell processes that cap nerve terminal are not shown.

within the sheath survive, divide, fuse, and differentiate to form new myotubes. X-irradiation blocks muscle regeneration; but reinnervation, which does not require cell divisions, is immune to the anti-mitotic effects of X-rays. To explore the requirements for reinnervation of original synaptic sites, frog muscles were damaged, denervated and X-irradiated in situ; the regeneration of axons to the "empty" basement membrane sheaths was followed by electron microscopy (81, 110). Over 95% of the axonal process that contacted the BL did so at original synaptic sites, and nearly half of the original sites were reinnervated. Thus reinnervation is as topographically precise, although not as complete, in the absence of muscle fibers as in their presence. Therefore, the postsynaptic cell itself need not be present for axons to recognize appropriate synaptic sites. Axons often regenerate through tubes of perineural connective tissue, but similar results were obtained when axons were displaced from their original pathways and had to cross expanses of extrasynaptic surface to reach synaptic sites (110). Schwann cells at synaptic sites may also guide axons, but reinnervation of undamaged muscle is topographically precise even when it is delayed long enough for Schwann cells to migrate away (72). What is left, then, is the

ECM. Axons might recognize molecules in the synaptic BL, be guided by the Schwann cell BL that overlies the synaptic site, or be repelled by molecules in extrasynaptic BL.

The transformation of regenerating axons into nerve terminals is also guided by components of BL. Portions of axons that contact synaptic sites on the BL sheaths acquire active zones, synaptic vesicles, a nerve terminal–specific antigen, and the capability for stimulation-dependent uptake of electron-dense tracers into vesicles (i.e. vesicle recycling); thus they are morphologically, chemically, and functionally specialized (43, 110). Notably the new active zones form precisely in register with the struts of BL that mark sites where junctional folds once were (Figure 3). This precise correspondence between active zones and fold BL, which reconstitutes the normal geometry of the synapse, provides strong evidence that components of synaptic BL regulate the differentiation of the nerve terminal.

FORMATION OF POSTSYNAPTIC SPECIALIZATIONS   In normal, adult muscle, acetylcholine receptors are found almost exclusively in the post-synaptic membrane, where they form a nearly crystalline array of protein at the crests of junctional folds. Further experiments on damaged muscle showed that components of BL can induce or maintain accumulations of acetylcholine receptors at synaptic sites (6, 23). Muscles were damaged and denervated but not irradiated such that myotubes would regenerate but axons would not (Figure 3). New myotubes formed within the basement membrane sheaths and synthesized acetylcholine receptors that could be detected by the use of α-bungarotoxin, a snake toxin that binds to acetylcholine receptors. Some receptors were present throughout the myotube membrane, as expected for denervated muscle, but high-density clusters of receptors formed only where myotube membrane contacted synaptic BL. The plasma membrane was thickened and folded in these regions of apposition, as is characteristic of normal muscle (23). Thus components of synaptic BL can guide the differentiation of post- as well as presynaptic membranes when neuromuscular junctions regenerate following injury.

Another molecule concentrated in the synaptic fraction of the muscle fiber surface is acetylcholinesterase, the enzyme that hydrolyzes acetylcholine released from nerve terminals. While there is no direct evidence that components of BL direct the localization of this enzyme, a sizeable fraction of the acetylcholinesterase at the neuromuscular junction is actually connected to the BL (12, 48, 84), probably through a collagenous subunit that the BL-associated form of the enzyme bears (82, 102). In some cases, muscles can deposit new acetylcholinesterase at denervated synaptic sites (47, 76, 129), suggesting that the nerve leaves a "trace" on the muscle fiber surface that directs the localization of newly synthesized enzyme. This "trace" might be associated with BL.

COMPOSITION OF MUSCLE FIBER BASEMENT MEMBRANE   The demonstration that the BL of the synaptic cleft regulates synapse formation provoked interest in comparing synaptic and extrasynaptic portions of the basement membrane sheath. Because no methods are yet available for separating the small synaptic regions from the broader extrasynaptic expanses to which they are attached, this comparison has relied largely on immunocytochemical assays. Several antibodies define antigens that are concentrated in synaptic BL. One is acetylcholinesterase; others, still-uncharacterized, are recognized by monoclonal and polyclonal antibodies to connective tissue or collagen-rich extracts (26, 40, 108). In contrast, collagen IV, fibronectin, and laminin are present in both synaptic and extrasynaptic portions of muscle fiber BL (105, 127). Collagen V and another collagen (perhaps related to "50K" collagen) are closely associated with extrasynaptic BL but are excluded from synaptic sites (105). Together, these immunochemical results (a) demonstrate molecular differences between synaptic and extrasynaptic portions of the ECM, (b) define three classes of antigens in the muscle basement membrane—synaptic, extrasynaptic, and shared—and (c) provide tools for further studies of ECM.

DEVELOPMENT   The involvement of BL in synaptogenesis has been demonstrated in experiments on adults. Does BL play any role in the initial development of neuromuscular junctions? This question is intriguing, since the relationship of nerve and muscle to ECM in the embryo is fundamentally different from that in the adult. During regeneration, axons and myotubes contact and are influenced by sheaths of BL that have already been segregated into distinct synaptic and extrasynaptic regions. During development, in contrast, cells must assemble an ECM de novo. Thus neuromuscular interactions in the embryo might both regulate and be regulated by BL.

Neuromuscular junctions form nearly as soon as myotubes are generated and before they have acquired a continuous coat of BL (63, 69). However, tufts of BL appear on very young myotubes, and BL-like material is present in the cleft of newly formed synapses before a full BL forms. A synapse-specific BL antigen becomes concentrated at, and an extrasynaptic antigen is excluded from, synaptic sites soon after acetylcholine receptors begin to accumulate but well before synaptic differentiation is complete (26; see also 130). Thus components of BL could, in principle, be involved in synapse formation and maturation.

Factors that regulate the metabolism and distribution of BL can profitably be studied in vitro. Cultured myotubes assemble a BL and a network of extracellular fibrils, (74, 111, 128, 131, 132). BL antigens that are "shared" in vivo are present throughout the myotube BL (34, 109), while "synaptic" BL antigens are concentrated in small patches, many of which coincide with regions of high acetylcholine receptor density (58, 109, 116).

Thus in the absence of nerve, muscle can accumulate synaptic antigens and arrange components of ECM in a way that reflects their distribution in vivo. Nonetheless, it seems likely that neurons are important in regulating the distribution of BL components. Two ways in which nerve can influence muscle are by evoking muscle activity and by releasing soluble factors (101, 106). The role of activity can be studied in vitro by comparing spontaneously active with anesthetic-paralyzed myotubes, while soluble factors can be studied by supplementing the medium with neural extracts. Results of such experiments show that both activity and soluble factors stimulate accumulation of BL, with activity having a selective effect on shared antigens and brain extract enhancing accumulation of synaptic antigens (107, 109). These results suggest that nerve may regulate BL by both activity-dependent and -independent mechanisms, a prediction that can now be tested in nerve-muscle coculture (4) or in vivo.

Cultured muscle is also being used to study the involvement of BL in the clustering of acetylcholine receptors. Patches of BL (4, 24, 34, 104) rich in synaptic BL antigens (109, 116) are preferentially associated with regions of high receptor density in aneural cultures. Fragments of ECM from the synapse-rich *Torpedo* electric organ, or high-salt extracts of this ECM, can induce receptor aggregation on chick myotubes (103); similar preparations from muscle (in which only a small fraction of the BL is synaptic) are only slightly active. Soluble neural extracts can also induce acetylcholine receptors to cluster (27, 60, 104), a result taken as evidence that the receptor aggregation that occurs during synaptogenesis in embryos is triggered by molecules released from nerve terminals. Are BL- and extract-induced clustering related? Neural extracts that aggregate receptors also enhance processing of collagen (61) and accumulation of BL (104, 107). New receptor clusters that nerves or extracts induce are associated with BL (4, 34, 131) that contains synaptic antigens (107). Collagenase prevents (61) and laminin enhances (126) the induction of receptor aggregation by an embryonic brain extract. Perhaps some receptor-clustering factors act by enhancing accumulation of BL components which, in turn, interact with receptors. Alternatively, some neural extracts might contain, in soluble form, factors that can also be associated with ECM. Precedents are acetylcholinesterase and fibronectin, both of which occur in both soluble and BL-bound forms (see above).

PROSPECTS AND CONCLUSION

The evidence summarized in this review implicates components of ECM in the migration of autonomic and sensory neuroblasts, the differentiation of Schwann cells, and the formation of neuromuscular junctions. Are these isolated cases or might ECM regulate other aspects of neural development?

One possibility is that some growing axons, like migrating neuroblasts, are guided to their targets by components of ECM. In grasshopper embryos, for example, axons grow out in predictable patterns along an ectodermal BL and may follow pathways encoded in ECM (10). Motor axons in chick embryos are apparently guided to appropriate muscles by short-range interactions along their paths (70). These axons contact ECM as they grow (38) and might use extracellular markers as cues. Several observations made in vitro are consistent with the notion that ECM could guide growing axons. Neurons and their targets secrete collagens, glycoproteins, and GAGs, and can form an ECM (e.g. 2, 32); neurons adhere to components of ECM (112); and patterns of axonal outgrowth are influenced by components of the substratum (1, 73), including extracellular materials released from potential target cells (28, 70a).

Another possibility is that ECM regulates the differentiation of neurons. Components of ECM (77, 114), including fibronectin (77, 115), affect the adrenergic differentiation of neural crest cells in vitro; in vivo, changes in ECM accompany gangliogenesis (see above). Thus ECM could interact with other factors (95) that "epigenetically" determine neuronal phenotype.

It is more difficult to imagine developmental roles for ECM in the central nervous system. Central nervous tissue is notably lacking in ECM, and the only BLs within the brain are those of blood vessels and ventricular spaces. However, the synaptic cleft of many interneuronal synapses is widened and contains an amorphous material rich in protein and carbohydrate (64, 97). Conceivably, this cleft material contains components similar to those present and attached to BL at the neuromuscular junction. In both fish (65) and leech (113), identified axons have been shown to terminate at appropriate synaptic sites after their normal target neurons have been destroyed, a phenomenon similar to that described above for neuromuscular junctions. Furthermore, ECM surrounds the entire central nervous system, and at least one observation raises the possibility that this material could bear developmentally significant information: In an assay in which cells from half retinae bound preferentially to the retinotopically appropriate half tectum, the cells adhered to ECM on the tectal surface (8). Finally, in development and regeneration, it has been proposed that axonal growth is guided (or constrained) by oriented extracellular channels (117, 118); ECM presumably fills, and may well induce or maintain these channels.

In conclusion, there is now strong evidence that ECM plays important roles in the development of a variety of cells and tissues, and ECM has been implicated in the control of several aspects of neural development. This work motivates consideration of ECM in searches for molecules and structures that regulate other developmentally interesting phenomena in the nervous system. Whatever the outcome of this work, however, the roles of

ECM that have already been documented clearly show that the extracellular environment is not an empty space through which cells move and soluble molecules diffuse. Rather, it is a repository of important information that cells both contribute to and use as they develop.

ACKNOWLEDGMENTS

I thank Drs. A. Chiu, J. Lichtman, J. McDonald, D. Purves, and K. Tosney for comments.

Literature Cited

1. Akers, R. M., Mosher, D. F., Lilien, J. E. 1981. Promotion of retinal neurite outgrowth by substratum-bound fibronectin. *Devel. Biol.* 86:179–88
2. Alitalo, K., Kurkinen, M., Vaheri, A., Virtanen, I., Ronde, H., Timpl, R. 1980. Basal lamina glycoproteins are produced by neuroblastoma cells. *Nature* 287:465–67
3. Anderson, C. B., Meier, S. 1982. Effects of hyaluronidase treatment on the distribution of cranial neural crest cells in the chick embryo. *J. Exp. Zool.* 221:329–35
4. Anderson, M. J., Fambrough, D. M. 1981. Nerve-induced deposition of basal lamina during the development of an amphibian neuromuscular junction in cell culture. *Neurosci. Abstr.* 7:670
5. Armati-Gulsan, P. 1980. Schwann cells, basement lamina and collagen in developing rat dorsal root ganglia *in vitro. Devel. Biol.* 77:213–17
6. Bader, D. 1981. Density and distribution of α-bungarotoxin-binding sites in postsynaptic structures of regenerated rat skeletal muscle. *J. Cell Biol.* 88:338–45
7. Bancroft, M., Bellairs, R. 1976. The neural crest cells of the trunk region of the chick embryo studied by SEM and TEM. *Zoon* 4:73–85
8. Barbera, A. J. 1975. Adhesive recognition between developing retinal cells and the optic tecta of the chick embryo. *Devel. Biol.* 46:167–91
9. Baron-Van Evercooven, A., Kleinman, H. K., Seppa, H. E. J., Rentier, B., Dubois-Dalcq, M. 1982. Fibronectin promotes rat Schwann cell growth and motility. *J. Cell Biol.* 93:211–16
10. Bate, C. M., Grunewald, E. B. 1980. Embryogenesis of an insect nervous system. II. A second class of neuron precursor cells and the origin of the intersegmental connectives. *J. Embryol. Exp. Morphol.* 61:317–30

11. Bennett, M. R., Pettigrew, A. G. 1976. The formation of neuromuscular synapses. *Cold Spring Harbor Symp. Quant. Biol.* 40:409–24
12. Betz, W., Sakmann, B. 1973. Effects of proteolytic enzymes on function and structure of frog neuromuscular junctions. *J. Physiol.* 230:673–88
13. Billings-Gagliardi, S., Webster, H. DeF., O'Connell, M. F. 1974. In vivo and electron microscopic observations on Schwann cells in developing tadpole nerve fibers. *Am. J. Anat.* 141:375–92
14. Bolender, D. L., Seliger, W. G., Markwald, R. R. 1980. A histochemical analysis of polyanionic compounds found in the extracellular matrix encountered by migrating cephalic neural crest cells. *Anat. Rec.* 196:401–12
15. Bornstein, P., Sage, H. 1980. Structurally distinct collagen types. *Ann. Rev. Biochem.* 49:957–1003
16. Bronner, M. E., Cohen, A. M. 1979. Migratory patterns of cloned neural crest melanocytes injected into host chicken embryos. *Proc. Natl. Acad. Sci. USA* 76:1843–47
17. Bronner-Fraser, M. 1982. Distribution of latex beads and retinal pigment epithelium cells along the ventral neural crest pathway. *Devel. Biol.* 91:50–63
18. Bronner-Fraser, M., Cohen, A. M. 1980. Analysis of the neural crest ventral pathway using injected tracer cells. *Devel. Biol.* 77:130–41
19. Bunge, R. P., Bunge, M. B. 1978. Evidence that contact with connective tissue matrix is required for normal interaction between Schwann cells and nerve fibers. *J. Cell Biol.* 78:943–50
20. Bunge, R. P., Bunge, M. B., Williams, A. K., Wartels, L. K. 1982. Does the dystrophic mouse nerve lesion result from an extracellular matrix abnormality? In *Disorders of the Motor Unit,* ed. D. L. Schotland, Ch. 2. NY: John Wiley

21. Bunge, M. B., Williams, A. K., Wood, P. M. 1982. Neuron-Schwann cell interaction in basal lamina formation. *Devel. Biol.* 92:449–60

22. Bunge, M. B., Williams, A. K., Wood, P. M., Uitto, J., Jeffrey, J. J. 1980. Comparison of nerve cell and nerve cell plus Schwann cell cultures with particular emphasis on basal lamina and collagen formation. *J. Cell Biol.* 84:184–202

23. Burden, S. J., Sargent, P. B., McMahan, U. J. 1979. Acetylcholine receptors in regenerating muscle accumulate at original synaptic sites in the absence of the nerve. *J. Cell Biol.* 82:412–25

24. Burrage, T. G., Lentz, T. L. 1981. Ultrastructural characterization of surface specializations containing high-density acetylcholine receptors on embryonic chick myotubes *in vivo* and *in vitro*. *Devel. Biol.* 85:267–86

25. Carlin, B., Jaffe, R., Bender, B. L., Chung, A. E. 1981. Entactin, a novel basal lamina-associated sulfated glycoprotein. *J. Biol. Chem.* 256:5209–14

26. Chiu, A. Y., Sanes, J. R. 1982. Differentiation of basal lamina is an early event in the development of neuromuscular junctions *in vivo*. *Neurosci. Abstr.* 8:128

27. Christian, C. N., Daniels, M. P., Sugiyama, H., Vogel, Z., Jacques, L., Nelson, P. G. 1978. A factor from neurons increases the number of acetylcholine receptor aggregates on cultured muscle cells. *Proc. Natl. Acad. Sci. USA* 75:4011–15

28. Collins, F., Garrett, J. E. Jr. 1980. Elongating nerve fibers are guided by a pathway of material released from embryonic nonneuronal cells. *Proc. Natl. Acad. Sci. USA* 77:6226–28

29. Conrad, G. W., Ager-Johnson, P., Woo, M.-L. 1982. Antibodies against the predominant glycosaminoglycan of the mammalian cornea, keratan sulfate-I. *J. Biol. Chem.* 257:464–71

30. Copio, D. S., Bunge, M. B. 1980. Use of a proline analog to disrupt collagen synthesis prevents normal Schwann cell differentiation. *J. Cell Biol.* 87:114a

31. Cornbrooks, C. J., Mithen, F., Cochran, J. M., Bunge, R. P. 1982. Factors affecting Schwann cell basal lamina formation in cultures of dorsal root ganglia from mice with muscular dystrophy. *Devel. Brain Res.* In press

32. Culp, L. A., Ansbacher, R., Domen, C. 1980. Adhesion sites of neural tumor cells: biochemical composition. *Biochemistry* 19:5899–907

33. Cunningham, L. W., Frederiksen, D. W., eds. 1982. *Methods in Enzymology,*

Vol. 82. *Structural and Contractile Proteins, Part A, Extracellular Matrix.* NY: Academic

34. Daniels, M. P., Vigny, M., Bauer, H., Sonderegger, P., Vogel, Z. 1981. Laminin and other basement membrane proteins codistribute with acetylcholine receptors on the surface of cultured myotubes. *Neurosci. Abstr.* 7:143

35. Delpech, B., Halavent, C. 1981. Characterization and purification from human brain of a hyaluronic acid-binding glycoprotein, hyaluronectin. *J. Neurochem.* 36:855–59

36. Derby, M. A. 1978. Analysis of glycosaminoglycans within the extracellular environments encountered by migrating neural crest cells. *Devel. Biol.* 66:321–36

37. Duband, J. L., Thiery, J. P. 1982. Distribution of fibronectin in the early phase of avian cephalic crest cell migration. *Devel. Biol.* In press

38. Ebendahl, T. 1977. Extracellular matrix fibrils and cell contacts in the chick embryo. Possible roles in orientation of cell migration and axon extension. *Cell Tissue Res.* 175:439–58

39. Erickson, C. A., Tosney, K. W., Weston, J. A. 1980. Analysis of migratory behavior of neural crest and fibroblastic cells in embryonic tissues. *Devel. Biol.* 77:142–56

40. Fambrough, D. M., Rotundo, R., Gardner, J. M., Bayne, E. K., Wakshull, E., Anderson, M. J. 1982. Cell surface and secretory proteins of skeletal muscle. See Ref. 20, pp. 197–210

41. Farquhar, M. G. 1980. The glomerular basement membrane: A selective macromolecular filter. See 53, pp. 335–78

42. Fisher, M., Solursh, M. 1977. Glycosaminoglycan localization and role in maintenance of tissue spaces in the early chick embryo. *J. Embryol. Exp. Morphol.* 42:195–207

43. Glicksman, M., Sanes, J. R. 1982. Functional and biochemical differentiation of motor nerve terminals formed in the absence of muscle fibers. *Neurosci. Abstr.* 8:128

44. Gordon, J. R., Bernfield, M. R. 1980. The basal lamina of the postnatal mammary epithelium contains glycosaminoglycans in a precise ultrastructural organization. *Devel. Biol.* 74:118–35

45. Greenberg, J. H., Pratt, R. M. 1977. Glycosaminoglycan and glycoprotein synthesis by cranial neural crest cells *in vitro*. *Cell Differ.* 6:119–32

46. Greenberg, J. H., Seppa, S., Seppa, H., Hewitt, A. T. 1981. Role of collagen

and fibronectin in neural crest adhesion and migration. *Devel. Biol.* 87:259–66

47. Guth, L., Zalewski, A., Brown, W. C. 1966. Quantitative changes in cholinesterase activity of denervated sole plates following implantation of nerve into muscle. *Exp. Neurol.* 16:136–47

48. Hall, Z. W., Kelly, R. B. 1971. Enzymatic detachment of endplate acetylcholinesterase from muscle. *Nature New Biol.* 232:62

49. Hascall, V. C., Hascall, G. K. 1981. Proteoglycans. See Ref. 53, pp. 39–64.

50. Hassell, J. R., Robey, P. G., Barrach, H. J., Wilczek, J., Rennard, S. L., Martin, G. R. 1980. Isolation of a heparan sulfate-containing proteoglycan from basement membrane. *Proc. Natl. Acad. Sci. USA* 77:4494–98

51. Hay, E. D. 1978. Fine structure of embryonic matrices and their relation to the cell surface in ruthenium red-fixed tissue. *Growth* 42:399–423

52. Hay, E. D. 1981. Extracellular matrix. *J. Cell Biol.* 91:205–23s

53. Hay, E. D., ed. 1981. *Cell Biology of Extracellular Matrix.* NY: Plenum

54. Hay, E. D., Meier, S. 1974. Glycosaminoglycan synthesis by embryonic inductors: neural tube, notochord and lens. *J. Cell Biol.* 62:889–98

55. Hayman, E. G., Rouslahti, E. 1979. Distribution of fetal bovine serum fibronectin and endogenous rat cell fibronectin in extracellular matrix. *J. Cell Biol.* 83:255–59

56. Heathcote, J. G., Grant, M. E. 1981. The molecular organization of basement membranes. *Int. Rev. Connect. Tissue Res.* 9:191–264

57. Hewitt, A. T., Kleinman, H. K., Pennypacker, J. P., Martin, G. R. Identification of an adhesion factor for chondrocytes. *Proc. Natl. Acad. Sci. USA* 77:385–88

58. Inestrosa, N. C., Silberstein, L., Hall, Z. W. 1982. Association of the synaptic form of acetylcholinesterase with extracellular matrix in cultured muscle cells. *Cell* 29:71–79

59. Jaros, E., Bradley, W. G. 1979. Atypical axon-Schwann cell relationships in the common peroneal nerve of the dystrophic mouse: an ultrastructural study. *Neuropathol. Appl. Neurobiol.* 5:133–47

60. Jessell, T. M., Siegel, R. E., Fischbach, G. D. 1979. Induction of acetylcholine receptors on cultured skeletal muscle by a factor extracted from brain and spinal cord. *Proc. Natl. Acad. Sci. USA* 76:5397–401

61. Kalcheim, C., Vogel, Z., Duksin, D. 1982. Embryonic brain extract induces collagen biosynthesis in cultured muscle cells: involvement in acetylcholine receptor aggregation. *Proc. Natl. Acad. Sci. USA* 79:3077–81

62. Kefalides, N. A., Alper, R., Clark, C. C. 1979. Biochemistry and metabolism of basement membranes. *Int. Rev. Cytol.* 61:167–228

63. Kelly, A. M., Zacks, S. I. 1969. The fine structure of motor endplate morphogenesis. *J. Cell. Biol.* 42:154–69

64. Kelly, P., Cotman, C. W., Gentry, C., Nicolson, G. L. 1976. Distribution and mobility of lectin receptors on synaptic membranes of identified neurons in the central nervous system. *J. Cell Biol.* 71:487–96

65. Kimmel, C. B., Sessions, S. K., Kimmel, R. J. 1979. Target recognition in neurogenesis: formation of the Mauthner axon cap. *Proc. Natl. Acad. Sci. USA* 76:4691–94

66. Kinsella, M., Weston, J. 1978. Modification of extracellular glycosaminoglycans during gangliogenesis in the avian embryo. *Am. Zool.* 18:643

67. Kjellen, L., Pettersson, I., Hook, M. 1981. Cell-curface heparan sulfate: An intercalated membrane proteoglycan. *Proc. Natl. Acad. Sci. USA* 78:5371–75

68. Kleinman, H. K., Klebe, R. J., Martin, G. R. 1981. Role of collagenous matrices in the adhesion and growth of cells. *J. Cell Biol.* 88:473–85

69. Kullberg, R. W., Lentz, T. L., Cohen, M. W. 1977. Development of the myotomal neuromuscular junction in *Xenopus laevis:* an electrophysiological and fine structural study. *Devel. Biol.* 60:101–29

70. Lance-Jones, C., Landmesser, L. 1981. Pathway selection by embryonic chick motoneurons in an experimentally altered environment. *Proc. R. Soc. London Ser. B* 214:19–52

70a. Lander, A. D., Fujii, D. K., Gospodarowicz, D., Reichardt, L. F. 1982. Characterization of a factor that promotes neurite outgrowth: Evidence linking activity to heparan sulfate proteoglycan. *J. Cell. Biol.* In press

71. LeLievre, C. S., Schweizer, G. G., Ziller, C. M., LeDouarin, N. M. 1980. Restrictions of developmental capacities in neural crest cell derivatives as tested by *in vivo* transplantation experiments. *Devel. Biol.* 77:362–78

72. Letinsky, M. S., Fischbeck, K. H., McMahan, U. J. 1976. Precision of reinnervation of original postsynaptic sites

598   SANES

in frog muscle after a nerve crush. *J. Neurocytol.* 5:691–718

73. Letourneau, P. C. 1975. Cell-to-substratum adhesion and guidance of axonal elongation. *Devel. Biol.* 44:92–101

74. Lipton, B. H. 1977. Collagen synthesis by normal and bromodeoxyuridine-modulated cells in myogenic culture. *Devel. Biol.* 61:153–65

75. Löfberg, J., Ahlfors, K., Fällström, C. 1980. Neural crest cell migration in relation to extracellular matrix organization in the embryonic axolotl trunk. *Devel. Biol.* 75:148–67

76. Lømo, T., Slater, C. R. 1980. Control of junctional acetylcholinesterase by neural and muscular influences in the rat. *J. Physiol.* 303:191–202

77. Loring, J., Glimelius, B., Weston, J. A. 1982. Extracellular matrix materials influence quail neural crest cell differentiation *in vitro. Devel. Biol.* 90:165–74

78. Low, F. N. 1970. Interstitial bodies in the early chick embryo. *Am. J. Anat.* 128:45–56

79. Luft, J. H. 1976. The structure and properties of the cell surface coat. *Int. Rev. Cytol.* 45:291–382

80. Madrid, R. E., Jaros, E., Cullen, M. J., Bradley, W. G. 1975. Genetically determined defect of Schwann cell basement membrane in dystrophic mice. *Nature* 257:319–21

81. Marshall, L. M., Sanes, J. R., McMahan, U. J. 1977. Reinnervation of original synaptic sites on muscle fiber basement membrane after disruption of the muscle cell. *Proc. Natl. Acad. Sci. USA* 74:3073–77

82. Massoulie, J., Bon, S. 1982. The molecular forms of cholinesterase and acetylcholinesterase in vertebrates. *Ann. Rev. Neurosci.* 5:57–106

83. Mayer, B. W., Hay, E. D., Hynes, R. O. 1981. Immunocytochemical localization of fibronectin in embryonic chick trunk and area vasculosa. *Devel. Biol.* 82:267–86

84. McMahan, U. J., Sanes, J. R., Marshall, L. M. 1978. Cholinesterase is associated with the basal lamina at the neuromuscular junction. *Nature* 271:172–74

85. Mead, P. A., Norr, S. C. 1977. The onset of neural crest cell migration: the basal laminae. *J. Cell Biol.* 75:48a

86. Moya, F., Bunge, M. B., Bunge, R. P. 1980. Schwann cells proliferate but fail to differentiate in defined medium. *Proc. Natl. Acad. Sci. USA* 77:6902–6

87. Newgreen, D., Gibbins, I. 1982. Factors controlling the time of onset of the mi-

gration of neural crest cells in the fowl embryo. *Cell Tissue Res.* 224:145–60

88. Newgreen, D., Thiery, J.-P. 1980. Fibronectin in early avian embryos: synthesis and distribution along the migration pathways of neural crest cells. *Cell Tissue Res.* 211:269–91

89. Newgreen, D. F., Gibbins, I. L., Sauter, J., Wallenfels, B., Wutz, R. 1982. Ultrastructural and tissue-culture studies on the role of fibronectin, collagen and glycosaminoglycans in the migration of neural crest cells in the fowl embryo. *Cell Tissue Res.* 221:521–49

90. Nichols, D. H. 1981. Neural crest formation in the head of the mouse embryo as observed using a new histological technique. *J. Embryol. Exp. Morphol.* 64:105–20

91. Noden, D. M. 1975. An analysis of the migratory behavior of avian cephalic neural crest cells. *Devel. Biol.* 42:106–30

92. Noden, D. M. 1978. Interactions directing the migration and cytodifferentiation of avian neural crest cells. In *Receptors and Recognition, B4, Specificity of Embryological Interactions,* ed. D. R. Garrod, pp. 3–50. London: Chapman & Hall

93. Oh, E., Pierschbacher, M., Rouslahti, E. 1981. Deposition of plasma fibronectin in tissues. *Proc. Natl. Acad. Sci. USA* 78:3218–21

94. Okada, E., Bunge, R. P., Bunge, M. B. 1980. Abnormalities expressed in long-term cultures of dorsal root ganglia from the dystrophic mouse. *Brain Res.* 194:455–70

95. Patterson, P. H. 1978. Environmental determination of autonomic neurotransmitter functions. *Ann. Rev. Neurosci.* 1:1–17

96. Pearlstein, E., Gold, L. I., Garcia-Pando, A. 1980. Fibronectin: a review of its structure and biological activity. *Mol. Cell Biochem.* 29:103–28

97. Pfenninger, K. H. 1978. Organization of neuronal membranes. *Ann. Rev. Neurosci.* 1:445–71

98. Pintar, J. E. 1978. Distribution and synthesis of glycosaminoglycans during quail neural crest morphogenesis. *Devel. Biol.* 67:444–64

99. Pratt, R. M., Larsen, M. A., Johnston, M. C. 1975. Migration of cranial neural crest cells in a cell-free hyaluronate-rich matrix. *Devel. Biol.* 44:298–305

100. Pratt, R., Morriss, G., Johnston, M. 1976. The source, distribution and possible role of hyaluronate in the migra-

tion of chick cranial neural crest cells. *J. Gen. Physiol.* 68:15a–16a

101. Purves, D. 1976. Long term regulation in the vertebrate peripheral nervous system. *Int. Rev. Physiol. Neurophysiol.* 2:125–77

102. Rosenberry, T. L., Barnett, P., Mays, C. 1982. Acetylcholinesterase. See Ref. 33, pp. 325–39

103. Rubin, L. L., McMahan, U. J. 1982. Regeneration of the neuromuscular junction: Steps toward defining the molecular basis of the interaction between nerve and muscle. See Ref. 20, pp. 187–96

104. Salpeter, M. M., Spanton, S., Holley, K., Podleski, T. R. 1982. Brain extract causes acetylcholine receptor redistribution which mimics some early events at developing neuromuscular junctions. *J. Cell Biol.* 93:417–25

105. Sanes, J. R. 1982. Laminin, fibronectin, and collagen in synaptic and extrasynaptic portions of muscle fiber basement membrane. *J. Cell Biol.* 93:442–51

106. Sanes, J. R. 1982. Regeneration of synapses. In *Repair and Regeneration of the Nervous System,* ed. J. G. Nicholls, pp. 127–54. Berlin: Springer

107. Sanes, J. R., Feldman, D. H., Lawrence, J. C. Jr. 1982. Activity and neural extract regulate accumulation of basal lamina by cultured myotubes. *Neurosci. Abstr.* 8:129

108. Sanes, J. R., Hall, Z. W. 1979. Antibodies that bind specifically to synaptic sites on muscle fiber basal lamina. *J. Cell Biol.* 83:357–70

109. Sanes, J. R., Lawrence, J. C. Jr. 1983. Activity-dependent accumulation of basal lamina by cultured rat myotubes. *Devel. Biol.* In press

110. Sanes, J. R., Marshall, L. M., McMahan, U. J. 1978. Reinnervation of muscle fiber basal lamina after removal of myofibers. Differentiation of regenerating axons at original synaptic sites. *J. Cell Biol.* 78:176–98

111. Sasse, J., von der Mark, H., Kühl, U., Dessau, W., von der Mark, K. 1981. Origin of collagen types I, III, and V in cultures of avian skeletal muscle. *Devel. Biol.* 83:79–89

112. Schubert, D., LaCorbiere, M. 1982. The specificity of extracellular glycoprotein complexes in mediating cellular adhesion. *J. Neurosci.* 2:82–89

113. Scott, S. A., Muller, K. J. 1980. Synapse regeneration and signals for directed axonal growth in the central nervous system of the leech. *Devel. Biol.* 80:345–63

114. Sieber-Blum, M., Cohen, A. M. 1980. Clonal analysis of quail neural crest cells: they are pluripotent and differentiate *in vitro* in the absence of noncrest cells. *Devel. Biol.* 80:96–106

115. Sieber-Blum, M., Sieber, F., Yamada, K. M. 1981. Cellular fibronectin promotes adrenergic differentiation of quail neural crest cells *in vitro. Exp. Cell Res.* 133:285–95

116. Silberstein, L., Inestrosa, N., Hall, Z. W. 1982. Aneural muscle cell cultures make synaptic basal lamina components. *Nature* 295:143–45

117. Silver, J., Sidman, R. L. 1980. A mechanism for the guidance and topographic patterning of retinal ganglion cell axons. *J. Comp. Neurol.* 189:101–11

118. Singer, M., Nordlander, R. H., Egar, M. 1979. Axonal guidance during embryongenesis and regeneration in the spinal cord of the newt: the blueprint hypothesis of neuronal pathway patterning. *J. Comp. Neurol.* 185:1–22

119. Solursh, M., Fisher, M., Singley, C. T. 1979. The synthesis of hyaluronic acid by ectoderm during early organogenesis in the chick embryo. *Differentiation* 14:77–85

120. Terranova, V. P., Rohrbach, D. H., Martin, G. R. 1980. Role of laminin in the attachment of PAM 212 (epithelial) cells to basement membrane collagen. *Cell* 22:719–26

121. Thiery, J. P., Duband, J. L., Delouvee, A. 1982. Pathways and mechanisms of avain trunk neural crest cell migration and localization. *Devel. Biol.* In press

122. Toole, B. P. 1981. Glycosaminoglycans in morphogenesis. See Ref. 53, pp. 259–94

123. Toole, B. P., Trelstad, R. L. 1971. Hyaluronate production and removal during corneal development in the chick. *Devel. Biol.* 26:28–35

124. Tosney, K. W. 1978. The early migration of neural crest cells in the trunk region of the avian embryo: an electron microscopic study. *Devel. Biol.* 62:317–33

125. Tosney, K. W. 1982. The segregation and early migration of cranial neural crest cells in the avian embryo. *Devel. Biol.* 89:13–24

126. Vogel, Z., Daniels, M. P., Vigny, M., Bauer, H. C., Sonderegger, P., Christian, C. N. 1981. The effect of laminin, a basement membrane protein on the cell surface aggregation of acetylcholine receptors of cultured myotubes. *Neurosci. Abstr.* 7:143

600   SANES

127. von der Mark, K. 1981. Localization of collagen types in tissues. *Int. Rev. Connect. Tissue Res.* 9:265–324

128. Walsh, F. S., Moore, S. E., Dhut, S. 1981. Monoclonal antibody to human fibronectin: production and characterization using human muscle cultures. *Devel. Biol.* 84:121–32

129. Weinberg, C. B., Hall, Z. W. 1979. Junctional form of acetylcholinesterase restored at nerve-free endplates. *Devel. Biol.* 68:631–35

130. Weinberg, C. B., Sanes, J. R., Hall, Z. W. 1981. Formation of neuromuscular junctions in adult rats: accumulation of acetylcholine receptors, acetylcholinesterase, and components of synaptic basal lamina. *Devel. Biol.* 84:255–66

131. Weldon, P. R., Cohen, M. W. 1979. Development of synaptic ultrastructure at neuromuscular contacts in an amphibian cell culture system. *J. Neurocy-tol.* 8:239–59

132. Weldon, P. R., Moody-Corbett, F., Cohen, M. W. 1981. Ultrastructure of sites of cholinesterase activity on amphibian embryonic muscle cells cultured without nerve. *Devel. Biol.* 84:341–50

133. Weston, J. A. 1982. Motile and social behavior of neural crest cells. In *Cell Behavior*, ed. R. Bellairs, A. Curtis, G. Donn, pp. 429–70. London: Cambridge Univ. Press

134. Weston, J. A., Butler, S. L. 1966. Temporal factors affecting localization of neural crest cells in the chicken embryo. *Devel. Biol.* 14:246–66

135. Weston, J. A., Derby, M. A., Pintar, J. E. 1978. Changes in the extracellular environment of neural crest cells during their early migration. *Zoon* 6:103–13

136. Yamada, K. M. 1981. Fibronectin and other structural proteins. See Ref. 53, pp. 95–114

Ann. Rev. Physiol. 1983. 45:601–12

NEW NEUROTROPHIC FACTORS

Y.-A. Barde, D. Edgar and H. Thoenen

Max Planck Institute for Psychiatry, D 8033 Martinsried, German Federal Republic

INTRODUCTION

The death of young neurons occurs as a normal part of the development of the vertebrate nervous system (26). Early cell proliferation gives rise to an excess of neurons, and the subsequent death of many of these is believed to adapt neuronal numbers to the size of the field to which they project. Experimental manipulation of the size of innervation fields can dramatically influence the number of surviving afferent neurons, indicating that survival is regulated by epigenetic factors. This conclusion is supported by experiments performed with nerve growth factor (NGF), a protein proposed to be a retrograde trophic messenger (29, 48). Neutralization of endogenous NGF by antibodies or isolation of the neuronal perikarya from their peripheral source of NGF by axotomy leads to the death of NGF target neurons during development (and impairment of their differentiated properties in the adult). Conversely, administration of NGF inhibits this experimentally induced neuronal death and can also rescue neurons that would otherwise die during normal development.

NGF is the only neurotrophic factor with an established physiological role because it was possible to characterize and raise antibodies to NGF purified from an extremely rich source, the submandibular gland of the male mouse (14). Considerable evidence (partly reviewed here) indicates that NGF is probably only one of a spectrum of neurotrophic factors. In the peripheral nervous system the action of NGF is restricted to sympathetic and sensory neurons (29, 48), whereas the trophic influence of the periphery on its afferent neurons is common to many neuronal types of both the peripheral and central nervous systems (26).

In this review we discuss the assay systems used to characterize new neurotrophic factors and the criteria necessary to distinguish them from

601

0066-4278/83/0315-0601$02.00

NGF. The sources of these factors are then described, together with the attempts and strategies to purify them. Factors that can determine the pathway of differentiation [specifying or instructive factors; see (43)] are not discussed, the review being limited to factors that, like NGF, support neuronal survival and may also regulate properties of their differentiated target neurons.

TECHNIQUES TO ASSAY NEUROTROPHIC ACTIVITY

Culture experiments provide convenient assays of trophic factor activity, which are necessary if the molecule responsible is to be characterized and purified. The development of the bioassay for NGF by Levi-Montalcini (30) was essential for its purification and characterization by Cohen (14), and this explant bioassay remains the definitive test for NGF activity (48). Tissue culture systems lend themselves to investigation of trophic factors in general because they are simpler than whole-animal experiments and so allow a more definitive interpretation of results. Furthermore, because the neurons are isolated when cultured, addition to the culture of extracts of tissues that normally surround the neurons or their projections is a direct way to assay any activity present that supports neuronal survival or development.

Cultured Explants

Explants of nervous system tissue have been an extremely useful tool for the determination of NGF and other as yet undefined factors produced by a variety of co-cultured explants or present in tissue extracts and conditioned culture media[1] (50). However, the use of cultured explants is limited owing to the difficulty in interpreting the observations made. Typically, neurite outgrowth or enzymic activities of the explant are measured in response to a given factor (see e.g. 24), whereby it is not always clear if these parameters represent a change in (a) neuronal survival, (b) the biochemical or morphological maturation of neurons which would survive anyway, or (c) the program of differentiation of the neurons. Furthermore, because explants contain different types of neuronal and nonneuronal cells, it is not possible to determine whether the putative factor tested has a direct effect on the neurons or acts to affect the neurons via an intermediate cell type (19).

---

[1]The term "conditioned media" means media that have previously been used to culture cells or tissue explants.

Cultured Isolated Neurons

In order to circumvent the ambiguities inherent in explant cultures it is necessary to use cultures of neurons dissociated from nervous tissue (6). If very numerous, the nonneuronal cells must be effectively removed not only to obviate the possibility of indirect effects, but also because these cells themselves support neuronal survival (12) and so could mask the effect of any added trophic factors. The survival of the neurons in response to an added factor can then be readily quantitated and used as a measure of the amount of trophic activity present. However, to assess the ability of a factor to support the survival of the neurons present in the whole neuronal population of a given tissue the techniques for tissue dissociation must be such that a high yield of neurons can be brought into culture, representative of the tissue as a whole. This is most easily achieved using embryonic ganglia from the peripheral nervous system, which offer the additional advantage of having fairly homogenous neuronal populations. With the 8-day embryonic chick ciliary ganglia, for example, neuron yields of at least 90% are common (40, 52). Practical ways to resolve the problems mentioned here have recently been reviewed and described in detail (6).

DETERMINATION OF SPECIFIC NEURONAL TYPES   Dissociates from most regions of the central nervous system can be expected to contain different types of neurons whose responses to neurotrophic factors may differ. In addition, it is often difficult to distinguish between neurons and nonneuronal cells by simply looking at cell morphology. To define the action of a factor it is therefore necessary to isolate specific populations of neurons or to define a particular population by using cell markers. Recently it was demonstrated that motorneurons can be isolated from dissociates of embryonic chick or rat spinal cord, enriched cultures then being used to investigate the requirements for survival of motor neurons (46). Adopting the alternative approach, Bennett et al specifically labelled subpopulations of central neurons by retrograde axonal transport of horseradish peroxidase from their terminal fields. Using this elegant technique, the survival factor requirements of embryonic spinal motor neurons and chick retinal ganglion cells could be demonstrated (10, 42).

SOURCES AND CHARACTERIZATION OF NEUROTROPHIC FACTORS

Numerous workers have described the effects of various tissue extracts and conditioned media on cultured neurons. This work has been extensively reviewed recently (50). Table 1 lists examples where agents other than NGF

Table 1 Sources of factors and their responsive neurons[a]

Neuron type		Source of factor	References
Parasympathetic ganglia			
Chick ciliary	CM:[b]	Heart cells	3, 15, 22
		Skeletal muscle	9
	Extract:	Whole embryo	1, 49
		Heart	11
		Skeletal muscle	37
		Eye	1, 25
Mouse submandibular	CM:	Heart cells	17
Sympathetic ganglia			
Chick paravertebral	CM:	Heart cells	18, 21, 53
		Schwann cells	53
		Schwannoma cells	53
		Glioma cells	18
	Extract:	Eye	35
Mouse superior cervical	CM:	Heart cells	17
Sensory ganglia			
Chick spinal	CM:	Heart cells	21
		Astrocytes	31
		Glioma cells	5, 8
	Extract:	Brain	5, 32
		Peripheral nerve	44, 45
		Heart	32
		Liver	32
		Gut	45
Mouse spinal	CM:	Heart cells	53
		Schwannoma cells	53
	Extract:	Eye	35
Chick and rat nodose	CM:	Astrocytes	31
Mouse nodose	CM:	Heart cells	17
Chick and rabbit trigeminal	CM:	Corneal epithelial cells	13
Central nervous system			
Chick spinal motoneurons	CM:	Skeletal muscle	10, 46
Chick retinal ganglion cells	CM:	Tectal cells	42
Rat hippocampus	CM:	Astroglial cells	4
Rat hypothalamus		Contact with nonneuronal cells from hypothalamus	54

[a] Only those examples are given where the survival of isolated neurons is shown to be supported by a factor other than NGF.
[b] CM: Conditioned medium.

have been shown to be responsible for the survival of isolated neurons in vitro.

Early experiments showed that tissue extracts from the chick affected the survival of cultured neurons and provided evidence that the effect was not due to NGF. The survival of cultured spinal sensory neurons was increased when both NGF and saturating concentrations of tissue extract were present (47).

The action of NGF in the peripheral nervous system is limited to sympathetic and spinal sensory neurons (29), so that trophic factors other than NGF can most easily be identified by selecting neurons which do not respond to NGF. Thus Coughlin showed that parasympathetic neurons of the mouse pelvic and submandibular ganglia responded to a humoral factor released from salivary epithelium, while NGF had no effect (16). Because anti–mouse NGF antiserum did not inhibit the effect it was concluded that the factor responsible was also antigenically distinct from mouse NGF (16). These criteria of neuronal and antigenic specificity have subsequently been used by many workers to identify new neurotrophic factors (Table 1).

Factors in Conditioned Media

Media conditioned by many cell types have been shown to support neuronal survival in vitro [Table 1; see also (50, 53)]. Helfand et al (22) showed that medium conditioned by chick embryo heart cells contained a macromolecular factor(s) that supported not only the survival of cultured parasympathetic neurons but also that of sensory and sympathetic neurons (21). Although the latter two neuronal types also respond to NGF, the activity of the conditioned medium was shown to be different (a) because anti-NGF antiserum did not inhibit the effect, (b) it had a chemical stability different from that of NGF, and (c) the conditioned medium did not inhibit the binding of NGF to its receptors on sensory neurons, consistent with the two factors having different receptors. Working on the central nervous system, Banker (4) showed that astrocytes conditioned their culture medium to support the survival of neurons dissociated from rat hippocampus in cultures containing few nonneuronal cells. At this stage of development essentially only pyramidal neurons are present. The astrocytic factor was not NGF, since the latter had no effect. This well-defined study demonstrates that cells of the central nervous system exhibit trophic phenomena similar to those commonly observed using peripheral nervous tissue.

Conditioned media are complex mixtures of compounds shed or possibly secreted by cells in culture and may well contain more than one factor. Lindsay has shown, for example, that cultured astrocytes produce both

NGF and a factor that supports the survival of NGF-insensitive neurons of the nodose ganglion (31).

In addition to multiple survival factors, conditioned media contain other activities affecting neurons. Collins (15) demonstrated that heart conditioned medium contains a factor that binds to culture substrates to promote neurite outgrowth, although it does not support neuronal survival. Conversely, a trophic factor(s) of the heart conditioned medium does not bind to the substrate and does not stimulate neurite outgrowth from parasympathetic neurons although it supports their survival (3). As for the neurotrophic activity, neurite-promoting activity is found in many conditioned media (36, 50) (although apparently not in tissue extracts; see below) and is probably a glycoprotein (2). It may well be related to those activities present on cell surfaces (20) or in microexudates from cultured corneal cells. The latter was shown to be associated with a sulfated proteoglycan (28). Although such substrate-attached factors do not themselves support neuronal survival, they can act to modulate the survival of neurons in response to a neurotrophic factor. Thus while NGF can only maintain part of the total population of chick sympathetic neurons alive in culture (18), essentially all the neurons will survive in response to NGF if the substrate has previously been coated with material from heart conditioned medium (18a, 33).

Fiber outgrowth activity (without effect on survival) has also been detected in medium conditioned by C6-glioma cells using NB2A neuroblastoma cells as a test system (39). Using anion exchange followed by Affi-blue and carboxymethylsepharose chromatography, Monard et al (38) identified a basic molecule of 32,000–33,000 daltons that was active at concentrations of less than 1 ng ml^{-1}. This activity was achieved after a purification factor of more than 1,000-fold. The physiological function of this molecule remains to be determined.

Factors in Tissue Extracts

The production of neurotrophic factors by cultured cells is no guarantee that factors are produced in vivo. For example, many cells only begin to produce detectable quantities of NGF when they are cultured (48). Surprisingly, the ease of detection of new trophic factors is in complete contrast to the problems encountered when looking for endogenous NGF (48). Many tissue extracts can be shown to possess neurotrophic activities that may be distinguished from NGF because they act on different neuronal types and/or are not blocked by anti-NGF antibodies [Table 1; see also (50)]. While the physiological relevance of such a wide-spread distribution of putative neurotrophic factors is still open to question, it is interesting that in some cases there seems to be a specific localization. For example, eye tissues are a rich source of factor(s) that supports the survival of cultured chick parasympathetic neurons from the ciliary ganglion that innervates the eye (1). This, coupled with the observation that the amount of trophic activity of the eye increases as the naturally occurring neuronal death in the ciliary ganglion decreases (27), suggests there may be a physiological function for ocular trophic activity. (Given enough trophic support even those ciliary neurons that would have died in vivo can be kept alive in culture; see 40). As with conditioned media, tissue extracts may contain more than one compound capable of affecting neuronal survival and maturation (41), which may complicate the analysis of their actions.

Interactions of Neurotrophic Factors

Both in vivo experiments and explant culture systems have shown that embryonic chick sympathetic and spinal sensory neurons display an age-dependent response to NGF (29). Quantitative measurements on neuronal survival in culture demonstrated that NGF was able to support the survival of these neuronal types only during specific periods of their development (5, 18). Application of this technique to other putative factors showed that C6 glioma conditioned medium or brain extracts act to support the survival of older spinal sensory neurons than those responding maximally to NGF, the age-dependent action of these factors providing a basis for their classification. Furthermore, a substantial proportion of young sensory neurons required the presence of two factors, NGF plus either glioma conditioned medium or brain extract, in order to survive in culture (5). Thus the chick sensory neurons have multiple and changing requirements for neural survival factors during their development.

PURIFICATION OF NEW NEUROTROPHIC FACTORS

The previous section illustrated that there are many potential sources of neurotrophic factors distinct from NGF. However, in the absence of any obvious rich source analogous to that provided by the male mouse submandibular gland for NGF, progress in the purification of new neurotrophic factors has been slow. The many descriptions of protease-sensitive macromolecular factors indicate that in principle these molecules can be isolated using the extensive repertoire of protein purification methods available, and their purity assessed by biochemical techniques. The examples chosen below illustrate the sorts of strategies used and the difficulties encountered during attempts at purification. The work described is grouped according to the neuronal assay system used by different laboratories, and the unit (U) of biological activity is defined as the concentration of material (in μg or ng ml^{-1}) required to maintain half of the maximum number of neurons that would survive in response to a saturating amount of any one factor. However, the figures obtained by different groups cannot be directly compared because the experimental conditions used (substrate, time at which survival is evaluated, etc) are often quite different.

Ciliary Parasympathetic Neurons

Parasympathetic neurons from chick embryos (usually 8 days old) can readily be isolated from the ciliary ganglia. Numerous groups have shown that these neurons die rapidly in culture (within 48 hr or less; e.g. see 22) unless the medium is supplemented with conditioned medium or tissue extracts, NGF having no effect.

Varon and colleagues have chosen as starting material the normal target structures of the ciliary ganglion—i.e. the choroid, iris, and ciliary body from the eyes of 15-day-old chick embryos (34). Although necessarily limited in amounts (about 0.4 mg protein is obtained per embryo), these structures have the advantage of a very high starting specific activity (about 65 ng ml^{-1} U^{-1}, when the effect on short-term neuronal survival of 24 hr was measured). Gel filtration studies revealed a main peak of activity of 35,000–40,000 daltons, and an isoelectric point of about 5.0 was determined by isoelectric focusing. Some increase in specific activity (about four-fold) was then obtained by fractionation on DEAE-cellulose followed by concentration over an Amicon PM-10 filter. The activity of the material thus obtained was destroyed by trypsin treatment and exposure to 56°C for 60 min.

In addition to promoting the survival of chick ciliary neurons, this preparation also enhanced the survival of embryonic chick sympathetic neurons and neonatal mouse dorsal root ganglia (35). Although the latter neuronal types also respond to NGF by increased survival, NGF had no additive effect when added to the cultures together with material isolated from the chick eye, indicating that NGF and the partially purified extract act on the same sympathetic and sensory neurons. However, the effect of the eye material was not blocked by antibodies to mouse or cobra NGF. Because the factor was not pure, it is not known if the molecule acting on the sympathetic and sensory neurons is the same as that affecting parasympathetic neurons.

Hendry and colleagues have used the same assay system but a different source of neurotrophic activity, the ox heart (11). In this case the obvious advantage is the abundance of the starting material, although it has a much lower specific activity (about 300 μ ml^{-1} U^{-1}) than the eye structures used by Varon et al. Gel filtration studies performed at low ionic strength (20 mM Tris HCl buffer, pH 7.4) indicated a molecular weight of about 50,000.

However, this material dissociated at high ionic strength (0.1 M Tris-HCl plus 0.5 M NaCl, pH 7.4) to give an active compound of about 19,000 daltons. The isoelectric point of this smaller entity was about 5.0. Recently (23), by using gel filtration at low- then high-ionic strength, and chromatography on hydroxylapatite, these authors have reached a purification factor of about 1,000-fold. This material, when iodinated and injected into the anterior chamber of the eye was transported retrogradely to the cell bodies of the ciliary ganglion, where it accumulated. It was not demonstrated, however, that this transport was specific and saturable as for NGF in its target neurons, or that the accumulation of activity reflected nonspecific retrograde transport of material.

Sympathetic Neurons

Coughlin et al (17) used as an assay system the survival of dissociated sympathetic ganglia (superior cervical) from the mouse embryo. The source of trophic activity was medium conditioned by dissociated mouse embryo heart cells in the presence of 10% fetal calf serum. The conditioned medium was first concentrated on a DEAE Biogel agarose column. The NGF activity contained in the conditioned medium migrated through the column. The biological activity different from NGF was then eluted with 0.4 M NaCl. The activity was concentrated over Millipore filters with a molecular weight exclusion limit of 100,000 to give a specific activity of 1.6 μg ml^{-1} U^{-1} (which was 700-fold higher than that of the starting material) with a yield of about 30%. This material was found also to enhance the survival of neurons isolated from the mouse (parasympathetic) submandibular ganglion, but not that of neurons from mouse dorsal root ganglion. The activity could be destroyed by incubation with trypsin or boiling (but not by heating for 30 min at 60°C). It was, however, not destroyed by incubation with collagenase, hyaluronidase, or neuraminidase.

Sensory Neurons

We used as an assay system the survival of sensory neurons dissociated from the 10-day-old chick embryo (7). The starting material was pig brain, which, like heart extract for ciliary neurons, has a low specific activity (about 500 μg ml^{-1} U^{-1}). However, the easy access to large amounts of material made it possible to purify a molecule of 12,300 daltons with an isoelectric point of $\geqslant$ 10.1, the calculated purification factor being over one million and the specific activity of the purified factor estimated to be 0.4 ng ml^{-1} U^{-1}, very close to the specific activity of NGF in this system. The material, which migrates as one band on gel electrophoresis in the presence of sodium dodecylsulfate, was purified using a scheme adapted for extractions of basic proteins: acidification of the brain homogenate, ammonium sulphate precipitation, adsorption and elution from CM-cellulose and hydroxylapatite. A purification factor of 5,000-fold was achieved by this stage. Proteins were then separated by 2-dimensional gel electrophoresis. The purified factor has several characteristics of the starting brain homogenate: (*a*) It supports the survival of about 30% of the cultured sensory neurons, (*b*) its effect is additive to that of NGF (so that the combination gives about 65% survival), and (*c*) the effect is not blocked by antiserum to NGF. Unlike the initial homogenate, however, it did not support the survival of chick embryo sympathetic neurons, indicating the presence of more than one neurotrophic activity in extracts of pig brain (7). The physiological role of this factor is not yet known.

CONCLUSION

Tissue culture techniques have been used to identify new putative neurotrophic factors that support the survival of neurons in vitro and that may be distinguished from NGF by antigenic and functional criteria. However, these techniques are only a means to the end of purifying factors with neurotrophic activity whose physiological role must ultimately be confirmed by experiments in vivo. The fact that the same approach was adopted for NGF, the only factor shown to have a physiological role, indicates that it may indeed be used with sucesss to establish the significance of the new factors.

Literature Cited

1. Adler, R., Landa, K. B., Manthorpe, M., Varon, S. 1979. Cholinergic neuronotrophic factors: intraocular distribution of trophic activity for ciliary neurons. *Science* 204:1434–36
2. Adler, R., Manthorpe, M., Varon, S. 1981. Substratum-bound neurite promoting factors. *J. Cell Biol.* 91:193a
3. Adler, R., Varon, S. 1980. Cholinergic neuronotrophic factors: V Segregation of survival—and neurite—promoting activities in heart conditioned media. *Brain Res.* 188:437–48
4. Banker, G. A. 1980. Trophic interactions between astroglial cells and hippocampal neurons in culture. *Science* 209:809–10
5. Barde, Y.-A., Edgar, D., Thoenen, H. 1980. Sensory neurons in culture: changing requirements for survival factors during embryonic development. *Proc. Natl. Acad. Sci. USA* 77:1199–1203
6. Barde, Y.-A., Edgar, D., Thoenen, H. 1982. Molecules involved in the regula-

tion of neuron survival during development. In *Neuroscience Approached Through Cell Culture,* ed. S. Pfeiffer, 1:69–86. Boca Raton: CRC Press
7. Barde, Y.-A., Edgar, D., Thoenen, H. 1982. Purification of a new neurotrophic factor from mammalian brain. *EMBO J.* 1:549–53
8. Barde, Y.-A., Lindsay, R. M., Monard, D., Thoenen, H. 1978. New growth factor released by glioma cells supporting survival and growth of sensory neurones. *Nature* 274:818
9. Bennett, M. R., Nurcombe, V. 1979. The survival and development of cholinergic neurons in skeletal conditioned media. *Brain Res.* 173:543–48
10. Bennett, M. R., Nurcombe, V. 1980. Identification of embryonic motoneurons in vitro: their survival is dependent on skeletal muscle. *Brain Res.* 190:537–42
11. Bonyhady, R. E., Hendry, I. A., Hill, C. E., McLennan, I. S. 1980. Characterization of a cardiac muscle factor required

for the survival of cultured parasympathetic neurons. *Neurosci. Lett.* 18:197–201

12. Burnham, P., Raiborn, C., Varon, S. 1972. Replacement of nerve growth factor by ganglionic nonneuronal cells for the survival in vitro of dissociated ganglionic neurons. *Proc. Natl. Acad. Sci. USA* 69:3556–60

13. Chan, K. Y., Haschke, R. H. 1981. Action of a trophic factor(s) from rabbit corneal epithelial culture on dissociated trigeminal neurons. *J. Neurosci.* 1:1155–62

14. Cohen, S. 1960. Purification of a nerve-growth promoting protein from the mouse salivary gland and its neurocytotoxic antiserum. *Proc. Natl. Acad. Sci. USA* 46:302–11

15. Collins, F. 1978. Induction of neurite outgrowth by a conditioned-medium factor bound to the culture substratum. *Proc. Natl. Acad. Sci. USA* 75:5210–13

16. Coughlin, M. D. 1975. Target organ stimulation of parasympathetic nerve growth in the developing mouse submandibular gland. *Dev. Biol.* 43:140–58

17. Coughlin, M. D., Bloom, E. M., Black, I. B. 1981. Characterization of a neuronal growth factor from mouse heart-cell-conditioned medium. *Dev. Biol.* 82:52–68

18. Edgar, D., Barde, Y.-A., Thoenen, H. 1981. Subpopulations of cultured chick sympathetic neurones differ in their requirements for survival factors. *Nature* 289:294–95

18a. Edgar, D., Thoenen, H. 1982. Modulation of NGF-induced survival of chick sympathetic neurons. *Dev. Brain Res.* 5:89–92

19. Fukada, K. 1980. Hormonal control of neurotransmitter choice in sympathetic neurone cultures. *Nature* 287:553–55

20. Hawrot, E. 1980. Cultured sympathetic neurons: effects of cell-derived and synthetic substrate on survival and development. *Dev. Biol.* 74:136–51

21. Helfand, S. L., Riopelle, R. J., Wessells, N. K. 1978. Non-equivalence of conditioned medium and nerve growth factor for sympathetic, parasympathetic and sensory neurons. *Exp. Cell Res.* 113:39–45

22. Helfand, S. L., Smith, G. A., Wessells, N. K. 1976. Survival and development in culture of dissociated parasympathetic neurons from ciliary ganglia. *Dev. Biol.* 50:541–47

23. Hendry, I. A., Bonyhady, R. E., Hill, C. E. 1981. The role of target tissues in development and regeneration—retro-

phins. Presented at Int. Symp. Nervous System Regeneration, Catania, Italy

24. Hill, C. E., Hendry, I. A. 1976. Differences in sensitivity to nerve growth factor of axon formation and tyrosine hydroxylase activity in mouse superior cervical ganglion. *Neuroscience* 1:489–96

25. Hill, C. E., Hendry, I. A., Bonyhady, R. E. 1981. Avian parasympathetic neurotrophic factors: age-related increases and lack of regional specificity. *Dev. Biol.* 85:258–61

26. Jacobson, M. 1978. Cellular interactions and interdependence during development of the nervous system. In *Developmental Neurobiology*, pp. 253–307. NY/London: Plenum. 562 pp. 2nd ed.

27. Landa, K. B., Adler, R., Manthorpe, M., Varon, S. 1980. Cholinergic neuronotrophic factors. III. Developmental increase of trophic activity for chick embryo ciliary ganglion neurons in their intraocular target tissues. *Dev. Biol.* 74:401–8

28. Lander, A. D., Fujii, D. K., Gospodarowicz, D., Reichardt, L. F. 1981. A heparan sulfate glycoprotein induces rapid-neurite outgrowth in vitro. *Soc. Neurosci. Abstr.* 7:348

29. Levi-Montalcini, R., Angeletti, P. U. 1968. Nerve growth factor. *Physiol. Rev.* 48:534–69

30. Levi-Montalcini, R., Meyer, H., Hamburger, V. 1954. In vitro experiments as the effects of mouse sarcomas 180 and 37 on the spinal and sympathetic ganglia of the chick embryo. *Cancer Res.* 14:49–57

31. Lindsay, R. M. 1979. Adult rat brain astrocytes support survival of both NGF-dependent and NGF-insensitive neurones. *Nature* 282:80–82

32. Lindsay, R. M., Tarbit, J. 1979. Developmentally regulated induction of neurite outgrowth from immature chick sensory neurons (DRG) by homogenates of avian or mammalian heart, liver and brain. *Neurosci. Lett.* 12:195–200

33. Longo, F. M., Manthorpe, M., Varon, S. 1982. Spinal cord neuronotrophic factors: I. Bioassay of Schwannoma and other conditioned media. *Dev. Brain Res.* 3:277–94

34. Manthorpe, M., Skaper, S., Adler, R., Landa, K., Varon, S. 1980. Cholinergic neurotrophic factors: fractionation properties of an extract from selected chick embryonic eye tissues. *J. Neurochem.* 34:69–75

35. Manthorpe, M., Skaper, S. D., Barbin, G., Varon, S. 1982. Cholinergic neuro-

notrophic factors. Concurrent activities on certain nerve growth factor—responsive neurons. *J. Neurochem.* 38: 415–21

36. Manthorpe, M., Varon, S., Adler, R. 1981. Neurite-promoting factor in conditioned medium from RN22 Schwannoma cultures: bioassay, fractionation and properties. *J. Neurochem.* 37: 759–67

37. McLennan, I. S., Hendry, I. A. 1978. Parasympathetic neuronal survival induced by factors from muscle. *Neurosci. Lett.* 10:269–73

38. Monard, D., Niday, E., Limat, A., Solomon, F. 1982. Inhibition of protease activity can lead to neurite extension in neuroblastoma cells. *Prog. Brain Res.* In press

39. Monard, D., Solomon, F., Rentsch, M., Gysin, R. 1973. Glia-induced morphological differentiation in neuroblastoma cells. *Proc. Natl. Acad. Sci. USA* 70:1894–97

40. Nishi, R., Berg, D. K. 1977. Dissociated ciliary ganglion neurons in vitro: survival and synapse formation. *Proc. Natl. Acad. Sci. USA* 74:5174–75

41. Nishi, R., Berg, D. K. 1981. Two components from eye tissue that differentially stimulate the growth development of ciliary ganglion neurons in cell culture. *J. Neurosci.* 1:505–13

42. Nurcombe, V., Bennett, M. R. 1981. Embryonic chick retinal ganglion cells identified "in vitro". *Exp. Brain Res.* 44:249–58

43. Patterson, P. H. 1978. Environmental determination of autonomic neurotransmitter functions. *Ann. Rev. Neurosci.* 1:1–17

44. Riopelle, R. J., Boegman, R. J., Cameron, D. A. 1981. Peripheral nerve contains heterogeneous growth factors that support sensory neurons in vitro. *Neurosci. Lett.* 25:311–16

45. Riopelle, R. J., Cameron, D. A. 1981. Neurite outgrowth promoting factors

on embryonic chick ontogeny, regional distribution and characteristics. *J. Neurobiol.* 12:175–86

46. Schnaar, R. L., Schaffner, A. E. 1981. Separation of cell types from embryonic chick and rat spinal cord: characterization of motoneuron-enriched fractions. *J. Neurosci.* 1:204–17

47. Sensenbrenner, M., Lodin, Z., Treska, J., Jacob, M., Kage, M. P., Mandel, P. 1969. The cultivation of isolated neurons from spinal ganglia of chick embryo. *Z. Zellforsch.* 98:538–49

48. Thoenen, H., Barde, Y.-A. 1980. Physiology of nerve growth factor. *Physiol. Rev.* 60:1284–335

49. Tuttle, J. B., Suszkiw, J. B., Ard, M. 1980. Long-term survival and development of dissociated parasympathetic neurons in culture. *Brain Res.* 183: 161–80

50. Varon, S., Adler, R. 1981. Trophic and specifying factors directed to neuronal cells. In *Advances in Cellular Neurobiology*, ed. S. Fedoroff, L. Herz, 2:115–63. NY: Academic. 450 pp.

51. Varon, S. S., Bunge, R. P. 1978. Trophic mechanisms in the peripheral nervous system. *Ann. Rev. Neurosci.* 1:327–61

52. Varon, S., Manthorpe, M., Adler, R. 1979. Cholinergic neuronotrophic factors: I. Survival, neurite outgrowth and choline acetyltransferase activity in monolayer cultures from chick embryo ciliary ganglia. *Brain Res.* 173:29–45

53. Varon, S., Skaper, S. D., Manthorpe, M. 1981. Trophic activities for dorsal root and sympathetic ganglionic neurons in media conditioned by Schwann and other peripheral cells. *Dev. Brain Res.* 1:73–87

54. Whatley, S. A., Hall, C., Lim, L. 1981. Hypothalamic neurons in dissociated cell culture: the mechanism of increased survival times in the presence of nonneuronal cells. *J. Neurochem.* 36: 2052–56

GASTROINTESTINAL PHYSIOLOGY

Introduction, Trudy M. Forte, *Section Organizer*

This series of articles attempts to place into perspective recent studies on lipid (both exogenous and endogenous) and apolipoprotein metabolism in the enterohepatic circulation. The intestinal tract is the main regulator of metabolism of exogenous lipids while the liver is responsible for secretion of endogenous lipids and bile acids. Both sites secrete apolipoproteins important in the transport and catabolism of lipids.

The report by Carey, Small & Bliss summarizes changes in physical and chemical properties of lipids during their progress along the intestinal tract. This includes data on lingual lipases and colon lipid metabolism not usually covered in reviews on intestinal absorption. A new concept of small intestine formation of 400–600 Å unilamellar liposomes is also presented; these structures may have important pathophysiological consequences in humans.

Lipids absorbed by intestinal cells are resynthesized as lipoprotein particles, particularly chylomicrons and intestinal high-density lipoproteins. Recent developments in the synthesis, composition, and metabolic fate of lipoproteins and apolipoproteins secreted by enterocytes are discussed by Bisgaier and Glickman. Our limited understanding of regulation of apolipoprotein synthesis in the enterocyte becomes apparent in this review.

Apolipoprotein B (apo B) associated with lower-density lipoproteins has long been considered a single protein of large molecular weight. Until recently, studies with this protein have been confounded by its insolubility in aqueous medium upon delipidation. Recent approaches have shown that apo B has more than one molecular species; one protein (B48) appears to be secreted solely by the small intestine and the other (B100) by the liver. The origin and physiological significance of the various apo B species in both humans and rats are reviewed in the chapter by Kane. This chapter attempts to unify the diverse nomenclature thus far applied to apo B variants from humans and rats by various investigators and hence makes cross-comparisons easier.

The section by Bisgaier and Glickman suggests that synthesis of some or all the apolipoproteins in the small intestine may be regulated by diet, although other factors cannot be excluded. Studies with the liver, however, have provided convincing evidence that physiological control of apolipoprotein synthesis can be effected by hormones. The most well-defined system for such studies is estrogen regulation of apolipoproteins in cockerel livers. This topic is reviewed by Chan, who draws together evidence that estrogen in the cockerel stimulates apo VLDL-II production by increasing the total amount of mRNA in hepatocytes. The structure of the gene involved in sequencing apo VLDL-II is also discussed.

Formation of bile acids and the pathophysiology related to dysfunctions in bile acid secretion are reviewed by Salen & Shefer. Formation of bile acids plays a key role in cholesterol and lipoprotein metabolism in the enterohepatic system. As this review points out, however, regulation and modulation of key enzyme steps in bile acid synthesis are not well understood.

Ann. Rev. Physiol. 1983. 45:615–23

HORMONAL CONTROL OF APOLIPOPROTEIN SYNTHESIS

Lawrence Chan

Departments of Cell Biology and Medicine, Baylor College of Medicine, Houston, Texas 77030

The role of plasma lipoproteins in lipid transport has been under investigation for many years. In this chapter, I review the mechanism of apolipoprotein synthesis and its regulation by hormones, an area that has received much attention only within the last decade.

Mechanism of Apolipoprotein Synthesis

BIOCHEMICAL STUDIES The simplest and most thoroughly studied model of apolipoprotein synthesis to date comes from an avian apoprotein. ApoVLDL-II is a major apolipoprotein in VLDL of the laying hen (13). It is an 82-amino acid peptide, the sequence of which is shown in Figure 1 (14, 15, 20). It exists in blood as a dimer, the two monomers being connected by a disulfide bond at residue 75.

Under the influence of estrogen, apoVLDL-II becomes a very major protein synthesized by the liver (see below). The protein is thus relatively easy to isolate in large quantities, and antisera can be readily generated against it. These facts aided tremendously in the initial studies on the biosynthesis of apoVLDL-II.

When apoVLDL-II is translated in vitro (from either total liver mRNA or from liver polysomal RNA), the initial translation product has an apparent molecular weight of approximately 11,000 whereas that of apoVLDL-II is approximately 9,500 (13). Further analysis of the product (10, 12, 13, 16), together with subsequent data from DNA sequencing (see below), indicates that the initial product has an N-terminal peptide extension of 24 amino acids. The sequence of this signal peptide is shown in Figure 1 (10, 16). The main features in this sequence are very similar to those reported by others for various secreted proteins (3, 4). There is an abundance of hydrophobic amino acids in general, and these are clustered in the interior segment of the peptide. The few charged and hydroxyl-containing residues are located near the ends. Use of Chou-Fasman rules (14) for conformation prediction indicates that the peptide has a high potential for β-structure from residues −5 to −21 and the presence of a β-turn at residues −2 to +2 (10). The production of the mature protein by enzymatic cleavage would then occur at the β-turn region. It is interesting to note that β-turn regions are also predicted to occur at the cleavage site of a number of preproteins (7, 10).

It is thus evident that apoVLDL-II is initially synthesized as a preapolipoprotein. This fact is intriguing since apolipoproteins bind lipid spontaneously. Thus the translocation of preapoVLDL-II represents a unique case of vectorial migration of a protein through the membrane of

```
                     -20
Met   Val   Gln   Tyr   Arg   Ala   Leu   Val   Ile   Ala   Val   Ile   Leu
                      ( +     +     +     +     +     +     +     +     +     +     +     +

      -10                                                                   1
Leu   Leu   Ser   Thr   Thr   Val   Pro   Glu   Val   His   Ser   Lys   Ser
 +  +   +     +     +     +     +     +     +     +   ) ( §     §     §     §     § )

                                                      11
Ile   Ile   Asp   Arg   Glu   Arg   Arg   Asp   Trp   Leu   Val   Ile   Pro
                                              ( +     +     +     +     +     +     +     + )

                            21
Asp   Ala   Ala   Ala   Ala   Tyr   Ile   Tyr   Glu   Ala   Val   Asn   Lys
 ( *   *     *     *     *     *  *   *     *     *     *     *   ) (+     +     +     +     +     +

            31                                                              41
Val   Ser   Pro   Arg   Ala   Gly   Gln   Phe   Leu   Leu   Asp   Val   Ser
 +  +)  ( §     §     §     §     §   ) (+     +     +     +     +     +     +     +     +     +

                                                51
Gln   Thr   Thr   Val   Val   Ser   Gly   Ile   Arg   Asn   Phe   Leu   Ile
 +     +     +   + +   +     +     +     +     +     +     +     +     +     +     +

                              61
Asn   Glu   Thr   Ala   Arg   Leu   Thr   Lys   Leu   Ala   Glu   Gln   Leu
 +     +     +     +     +     +   + +   ) ( *     *     *     *     *     *     *     *     *   *

                  71
Met   Glu   Lys   Ile   Lys   Asn   Leu   Cys   Tyr   Thr   Lys   Val   Leu
 *   *     *     *   *     *     *     *     *     *     *     *   ) ( +     +     +     +     +     +     +

81
Gly   Tyr
 +     +   + )
```

Figure 1   Amino acid sequence and schematic structure of the predicted secondary structure of preapoVLDL-II. The secreted protein sequence starts with amino acid 1, lysine. The assignment of each stretch of amino acids to a specific conformation is based on calculations using Chou-Fasman rules (14). +++++ β-structure; §§§§§, β-turn; *****, α-structure. The stretch of α-structure from residues 59 to 75 forms an amphipathic helix and constitutes the phospholipid binding region of the molecule.

the rough endoplasmic reticulum. The function of apoVLDL-II is the transport of neutral lipids (triacylglycerol) in the form of VLDL in the plasma. This protein binds to phospholipid and forms an outer polar shell surrounding the water-insoluble lipid core. It can do this because a region of the molecule (residues 59–75 in Figure 1) folds into an amphipathic helix (7, 10, 33) in which one face is polar and interacts with the aqueous environment while the opposite face is nonpolar and interacts with the lipid. In the case of preapoVLDL-II, the protein must be transported through the rough endoplasmic reticulum membrane for final assembly into VLDL. The same protein, however, has a structural component that would normally bind spontaneously to a phospholipid matrix such as the rough endoplasmic reticulum outer membrane. Translocation of this phospholipid-binding protein requires some mechanism to prevent interaction of the amphipathic region with the outer membrane surface. The mechanism for such control is presently unknown.

The situation is not peculiar to apoVLDL-II. A number of apolipoproteins have since been found to have signal peptides–e.g. avian apoA-I (9, 19), rat apoA-I (17, 26), and apoE (25). In the case of rat intestinal preapoA-I, Gordon et al (17) showed that cleavage of the 18-amino acid signal peptide still left a pro-segment of 6 amino acids. The latter was cleaved post-translationally, producing the mature plasma protein. In the case of rat liver apoE, Lin-Lee et al (25) demonstrated that exogenous microsomal membrane fractions not only cleaved the signal peptide, but also effected the simultaneous core glycosylation of the nascent peptide.

MORPHOLOGICAL STUDIES   Apolipoproteins are secretory proteins and as such are expected to be synthesized mainly on the membrane-bound ribosomes (30). Morphological confirmation of such a premise was provided initially by Alexander et al (1). Using antisera specific against apoB, they localized immunoreactive apoB in the rat liver by electron microscopy. Fab fragments of the antisera were conjugated to horseradish peroxidase. Specific reaction product was identified in the cisternae on the ribosomes of the rough endoplasmic reticulum, in the vesicles located between the rough endoplasmic reticulum and the Golgi apparatus, and inside secretory vesicles. The tubules and vesicles of typical hepatocyte smooth endoplasmic reticulum did not contain reaction product. Hence, the authors first demonstrated the presence of apoB in its presumed site of synthesis (on ribosomes attached to the rough endoplasmic reticulum). They also detailed the subsequent pathway by which the apoprotein picked up its associated lipids and ended up in secretory vesicles before it was secreted as lipoprotein particles by fusion of the vesicular membrane with the plasma membrane of the hepatocyte.

While there is no biochemical correlation to the morphological studies on rat apoB synthesis, the general pathway is probably valid for most, if not all, apolipoproteins since similar observations were made on a well-studied apolipoprotein, apoVLDL-II (24). The immunoelectron microscopic localization of apoVLDL-II was also carried out by the direct Fab immunoperoxidase technique. Again, immunoreactive apoVLDL-II was demonstrated in the cisternae of the nuclear envelope and the rough endoplasmic reticulum. It was also present on the surface of lipid particles in the Golgi apparatus and secretory vesicles. Some secretory vesicles containing immunoreactive apoVLDL-II were seen during the process of fusion with the plasma membrane. Such fusion took place against the plasma membrane lining the space of Disse as well as the intercellular spaces. Immunoreactive apoVLDL-II was not detected in the smooth endoplasmic reticulum.

These morphological studies coupled with the biochemical observations indicate that apolipoproteins are similar to many other secretory proteins in the pattern of their synthesis. They are synthesized on bound ribosomes, initially with an N-terminal signal peptide. The nascent peptide chains are vectorially discharged into the cisternae of the rough endoplasmic reticulum, the signal peptide being removed during the process by a specific peptidase. In the case of some glycosylated apolipoproteins [e.g. rat apoE (25)], core glycosylation also takes place at the membrane of the endoplasmic reticulum. While the smooth endoplasmic reticulum is probably involved in the synthesis of lipids, the newly synthesized apolipoprotein does not traverse this organelle. Instead, it seems to pick up lipids in the cisternae of the Golgi apparatus where, in the case of glycosylated apolipoproteins, there is probably also modification of the carbohydrate on the protein. The fully assembled lipoprotein particles are enclosed in secretory vesicles and are secreted when the vesicles fuse with the plasma membrane.

Hormonal Regulation of Apolipoprotein Synthesis

It is well known that the plasma concentration of lipoproteins is regulated by various hormones (2, 29, 32, 41). However, the effects of these hormones on the biosynthesis of individual apolipoproteins are generally not known. One animal in which the influence of a hormone has been studied in detail is the cockerel (18). In this animal, estrogen increases the concentration of plasma VLDL. It thus serves as a model for the hypertriacylglycerolemia that is observed clinically in some women on birth-control pills (29, 41).

EFFECTS OF ESTROGEN ON apoVLDL-II SYNTHESIS   The VLDL of estrogen-treated cockerel contain multiple apoproteins. Two of these make up over 95% of the protein content of VLDL. They are apoB and apoVLDL-II. Both apoproteins are stimulated by estrogen (6, 13). The basal levels of the two proteins are quite different: about 26 μg ml^{-1} for apoB and about 1–40 ng ml^{-1} for apoVLDL-II (5). Following a single dose of estrogen, there is a rapid accumulation of both apoVLDL-II and apoB in plasma. While there is evidence for increased synthesis of both apoproteins, the studies on apoVLDL-II synthesis are much more extensive and are reviewed below.

Basal VLDL concentrations are very low in the 4-week-old cockerel. A single injection of an estrogen (estradiol or diethylstilbestrol) resulted in an initial drop in VLDL that lasted about an hour or more; both the magnitude and duration of this initial fall in VLDL varied directly with the dose of hormone administered (12, 13). The mechanism of this transient decrease in plasma VLDL is unknown, but might be related to an increase in the hepatic uptake of the lipoproteins secondary to an estrogen-induced increase in hepatic receptors for such proteins [such a mechanism had been demonstrated in rats (38)]. This fall is immediately followed by a rapid increase in the concentration of VLDL.

It is known from the studies of Luskey et al (27) that the avian liver synthesized VLDL apoproteins and that the rate of synthesis was markedly stimulated by estrogen. Lin & Chan (22, 23) studied the accumulation of apoVLDL-II in the liver of untreated and estrogen-treated cockerels. They found by immunocytochemical staining that apoVLDL-II was present in a small proportion of the hepatocytes (about 1–2%) in 4-week-old cockerels. Following a single injection of estrogen (diethylstilbestrol 2.5 mg), the number of cells containing apoVLDL-II increased to 20–25% in 24 hr. With chronic estrogen treatment (diethylstilbestrol 2.5 mg daily for 14 days), over 90% of the hepatocytes contained apoVLDL-II. Furthermore, the intensity of the peroxidase staining for apoVLDL-II immunoreactivity was also markedly increased. The most straightforward interpretation of the morphological observations is that the hepatic response to estrogen consists of both an increase in the biosynthetic rate of apoVLDL-II in cells previously committed to its production, and a recruitment of the majority of the hepatocytes previously uninvolved in its production. It is noteworthy that even under intense estrogen stimulation about 5–10% of the hepatocytes still failed to produce any detectable apoVLDL-II. In the same series of studies, Lin & Chan (22, 23) did not observe any significant change in the number of cells harboring immunoreactive albumin. Interestingly, the proportion of hepatocytes containing the major HDL apoprotein, apoA-I (19), did not change following a single injection of estrogen but increased from less than 1% to 10–15% following chronic estrogen treatment.

The accumulation of intracellular apoVLDL-II suggests that the hepatocytes synthesize increased amounts of the protein. Direct proof that such was the case came from radiolabeling and immunochemical studies (13). Liver slices from cockerels treated with a single injection of estrogen were incubated in culture medium in the presence of [³H]lysine. Immunoprecipitable radioactivity in apoVLDL-II increased within 2 hr from low baseline levels and reached a peak at 24 hr when it comprised about 11% of the total soluble protein synthesized. When actinomycin D was administered simultaneously with estrogen, the induction of apoVLDL-II synthesis was totally inhibited. This observation suggested that the estrogenic stimulation of apoVLDL-II synthesis was mediated at a transcriptional level.

EFFECTS OF ESTROGEN ON apoVLDL-II mRNA ACCUMULATION AND TRANSLATION   The radiolabeling experiments reviewed above indicate that in response to estrogen the hepatocytes synthesize apoVLDL-II at a markedly increased rate. This increase could be caused by the cytoplasmic translation of increased numbers of apoVLDL-II mRNA, an increase in the efficiency of apoVLDL-II mRNA translation, or both. When total cytoplasmic mRNA was isolated from cockerel liver and translated in a heterologous system in vitro, the concentration of translatable apoVLDL-II mRNA was found to increase from a low baseline level (<1%) to a high level (~ 12%) within 24 hr after estrogen treatment (9, 13). Hence, estrogen appears to stimulate apoVLDL-II synthesis mainly at a pretranslational level.

There are also features of cockerel liver mRNA conformation that are responsive to estrogen. For example, the hormone stimulated the aggregation of polyribosomes in this organ (9). There are also features peculiar to specific mRNAs that are not regulated by estrogen. For instance, the ribosome density per number of nucleotides is high for apoVLDL-II mRNA compared to the density for albumin mRNA or vitellogenin (a yolk protein) mRNA (37). The ribosome density is a reflection of ribosome binding avidity and translational initiation efficiency. It seems to be an inherent property of apoVLDL-II mRNA and is not regulated by estrogen.

Thus estrogen affects mainly the accumulation of apoVLDL-II mRNA. Studies with cloned cDNA as a hybridization probe have confirmed that apoVLDL-II specific sequences accumulate rapidly under the influence of estrogen (11, 39). Within 3 hr of hormone treatment, apoVLDL-II mRNA concentration increased over 100 fold (W. Palmer, L. Chan, unpublished observation). Such a rapid rate of accumulation strongly suggests that the rate of transcription of the apoVLDL-II gene is stimulated by the hormone. It also indicates that the effect of estrogen on apoVLDL-II transcription precedes any detectable changes in lipid synthesis.

apoVLDL-II mRNA AND GENE STRUCTURE   ApoVLDL-II is the first apolipoprotein structural gene purified by molecular cloning (8, 11, 36, 39). The double-stranded complementary DNA for apoVLDL-II mRNA was inserted into the Pst I site of the plasmid pBR322 by the dGdG tailing techniques. The sequences were amplified in *E. coli* host. Sequence determination indicated that the cloned DNA was closely related to apoVLDL-II. However, identity of the clones was not initially established since the derived amino acid sequence from the DNA sequence did not completely match two previously reported amino acid sequences for apoVLDL-II (15, 16, 20, 35). This observation brought out the possibility that apoVLDL-II might exhibit sequence heterogeneity and that only selected DNA sequences were amplified and sequenced. This premise was important since sequence heterogeneity was thought to be present in some mammalian apolipoproteins such as apoE (34). This hypothesis was proved wrong when DNA sequence analysis was coupled with careful reexamination of the amino acid sequence. There was no difference between the amino acid sequence predicted from the DNA sequence and that determined directly from the protein (16). The previous amino acid sequences proved erroneous.

Genomic DNA sequences containing the apoVLDL-II gene have been isolated from bacteriophage libraries of native avian DNA. Preliminary studies indicate the presence of three introns in the genomic DNA. The detailed structure of the native gene is currently under investigation (28, 40).

ACKNOWLEDGMENTS

The author's work described in this review was supported by National Institutes of Health grant HL-16512. I thank Mr. M. Scheib for typing the chapter.

Literature Cited

1. Alexander, C. A., Hamilton, R. L., Havel, R. J. 1976. Subcellular localization of B apoprotein of plasma lipoproteins in rat liver. *J. Cell Biol.* 69: 241–63
2. Allen, J. K., Frazer, I. S. 1981. Cholesterol, high density lipoprotein and Danazol. *Endocrinology* 53:149–52
3. Austen, B. M. 1979. Predicting secondary structure of the amino-terminal extension sequence of secreted protein. *FEBS Lett.* 103:308–13
4. Blobel, G. 1980. Intracellular protein topogenesis. *Proc. Natl. Acad. Sci. USA* 77:1496–1500
5. Blue, M.-L., Williams, D. L. 1981. Induction of avian serum apolipoprotein II and vitellogenin by Tamoxifen. *Biochem. Biophys. Res. Commun.* 98: 795–91
6. Capony, F., Williams, D. L. 1981. Antiestrogen action in avian liver: The interactions of estrogens and antiestro-

gens in the regulation of apolipoprotein B synthesis. *Endocrinology* 108: 1862–68
7. Chan, L., Bradley, W. A. 1982. Signal peptides: Properties and interactions. In *Cellular Regulation of Secretion and Release,* ed. P. M. Conn, pp. 301–21. NY: Academic
8. Chan, L., Bradley, W. A., Dugaiczyk, A., Means, A. R. 1980. Lipoprotein biosynthesis: The avian model. *Ann. NY Acad. Sci.* 348:427–28
9. Chan, L., Bradley, W. A., Jackson, R. L., Means, A. R. 1980. Lipoprotein synthesis in the cockerel liver: Effects of estrogen on hepatic polysomal messenger ribonucleic acid activities for the major apoproteins in very low and high density lipoproteins and for albumin and evidence for precursors to these secretory proteins. *Endocrinology* 106: 275–83

10. Chan, L., Bradley, W. A., Means, A. R. 1980. Amino acid sequence of the signal peptide of apoVLDL-II, a major apoprotein in avian very low density lipoproteins. *J. Biol. Chem.* 255:10060–63

11. Chan, L., Dugaiczyk, A., Means, A. R. 1980. Molecular cloning of the gene sequences of a major apoprotein in avian very low density lipoproteins. *Biochemistry* 19:5631–37

12. Chan, L., Jackson, R. L., Means, A. R. 1978. Regulation of lipoprotein synthesis: Studies on the molecular mechanisms of lipoprotein synthesis and their regulation by estrogen in the cockerel. *Circ. Res.* 43:209–17

13. Chan, L., Jackson, R. L., O'Malley, B. W., Means, A. R. 1976. Synthesis of very low density lipoproteins in the cockerel: Effects of estrogen. *J. Clin. Invest.* 58:368–79

14. Chou, P. Y., Fasman, G. D. 1978. Emperical predictions of protein conformation. *Ann. Rev. Biochem.* 47:251–76

15. Dopheide, T. A. A., Inglis, A. S. 1976. Primary structure of apo vitellenin I from hen egg yolk and its comparison with emu apovitellenin I. *Aust. J. Biol. Sci.* 29:175–80

16. Dugaiczyk, A., Inglis, A. S., Strike, P. M., Burley, R. W., Beattie, W. G., Chan, L. 1981. Comparison of the nucleotide sequence of cloned DNA coding for an apolipoprotein (apoVLDL-II) from avian blood and the amino acid sequence of an egg-yolk protein (apovitellenin I): Equivalence of the two sequences. *Gene* 14:175–82

17. Gordon, J. I., Smith, D. P., Andy, R., Alpers, D. H., Schonfeld, G., Strauss, A. W. 1982. The primary translation product of rat intestinal apolipoprotein A-I mRNA is an unusual preprotein. *J. Biol. Chem.* 257:971–78

18. Hillyard, L. A., Entenman, C., Charkoff, I. L. 1956. Concentration and composition of serum lipoproteins of cholesterol-fed and stilbestrol-injected birds. *J. Biol. Chem.* 223:359–68

19. Jackson, R., Lin, H.-Y. U., Chan, L., Means, A. R. 1976. Isolation and characterization of the major apolipoprotein from chicken high density lipoproteins. *Biochim. Biophys. Acta* 420:342–49

20. Jackson, R. L., Lin, H.-Y., Chan, L., Means, A. R. 1977. Amino acid sequence of a major apoprotein from hen plasma very low density lipoproteins. *J. Biol. Chem.* 252:250–53

21. Kudzma, D. J., Hegstad, P. M., Stoll, R. E. 1973. The chick as a laboratory model for the study of estrogen-induced hyperlipidemia. *Metab. Clin. Exp.* 22:423–34

22. Lin, C. T., Chan, L. 1980. Effects of estrogen on specific protein synthesis in the cockerel liver: An immunocytochemical study on major apoproteins in very low and high density lipoproteins and albumin. *Endocrinology* 107:70–75

23. Lin, C. T., Chan, L. 1981. Estrogen regulation of yolk and non-yolk protein synthesis in the avian liver: An immunocytochemical study. *Differentiation* 18:105–14

24. Lin, C. T., Chan, L. 1982. Localization of apoVLDL-II, a major apoprotein in very low density lipoproteins in the estrogen-treated cockerel liver by immunoelectron microscopy. *Histochemistry*. In press

25. Lin-Lee, Y.-C., Bradley, W. A., Chan, L. 1981. mRNA-dependent synthesis of rat apolipoprotein E *in vitro*: Cotranslational processing and identification of an endoglycosidase H-sensitive glycopeptide intermediate. *Biochem. Biophys. Res. Commun.* 99:654–61

26. Lin-Su, M.-H., Lin-Lee, Y.-C., Bradley, W. A., Chan, L. 1981. Characterization, cell-free synthesis, and processing of apolipoprotein A-I of rat high density lipoproteins. *Biochemistry* 20:2470–75

27. Luskey, K. L., Brown, M. S., Goldstein, J. L. 1974. Stimulation of the synthesis of very low density lipoproteins in rooster liver by estradiol. *J. Biol. Chem.* 249:5939–47

28. Meijlink, F. C. P. W., van het Schip, A. F., Arnberg, A. C., Wieringa, B., AB, G., Bruber, M. 1981. Structure of the chicken apo very low density lipoprotein II gene. *J. Biol. Chem.* 256:9668–71

29. Molitch, M. E., Oill, P., Odell, W. D. 1974. Massive hyperlipemia during estrogen therapy. *J. Am. Med. Assoc.* 227:522–25

30. Palade, G. E. 1975. Intracellular aspects of the process of protein synthesis. *Science* 189:347–58

31. Deleted in proof

32. Patsch, W., Kim, K., Wiest, W., Schonfeld, G. 1980. Effects of sex hormone on rat lipoproteins. *Endocrinology* 107:1085–94

33. Segrest, J. P., Jackson, R. L., Morrisett, J. D., Gotto, A. M. 1974. A molecular theory of lipid-protein interactions in the plasma lipoproteins. *FEBS Lett.* 38:247–53

34. Weisgraber, K. H., Rall, S. C. Jr., Mahley, R. W. 1981. Human E apoprotein heterogeneity: Cysteine-arginine inter-

changes in the amino acid sequence of the apoE isoforms. *J. Biol. Chem.* 256:9077–83

35. Wieringa, B., AB, G., Gruber, M. 1981. The nucleotide sequence of the very low density lipoprotein II mRNA from chicken. *Nucl. Acids Res.* 9:489–501

36. Wieringa, B., Roskam, W., Arnberg, A., vander Zwaag-Gerritsen, J., AB, G., Bruber, M. 1979. Purification of the mRNA for chicken very low density lipoprotein II and molecular cloning of its full-length double-stranded cDNA. *Nucl. Acids Res.* 7:2147–63

37. Wieringa, B., van der Zwaag-Gerritsen, J., Mulder, J., AB, G., Gruber, M. 1981. Translation *in vivo* and *in vitro* of mRNAs coding for vitellogenin, serum albumin and very low density lipoprotein II from chicken liver: A difference in translational efficiency. *Eur. J. Biochem.* 114:635–41

38. Windler, E. E. T., Kovanen, P. T., Chao, Y.-S., Brown, M. S., Havel, R. J., Goldstein, J. L. 1980. The estradiol-stimulated lipoprotein receptor of rat liver. A binding site that mediates the uptake of rat lipoproteins containing apoproteins B and E. *J. Biol. Chem.* 255:10464–71

39. Wiskocil, R., Bensky, P., Dower, W., Goldberger, R. F., Gordon, J. I., Deeley, R. G. 1980. Coordinate regulation of two estrogen-dependent genes in avian liver. *Proc. Natl. Acad. Sci. USA* 77:4474–78

40. Wiskocil, R., Goldman, R., Deeley, R. G. 1981. Cloning and structural characterization of an estrogen-dependent apolipoprotein gene. *J. Biol. Chem.* 256:9662–67

41. Wynn, V., Doar, J. W. H., Mills, G. L., Stokes, T. 1969. Fasting serum triglycerides, cholesterol, and lipoprotein levels during oral contraceptive therapy. *Lancet* 2:756–60

Ann. Rev. Physiol. 1983. 45:625–36

INTESTINAL SYNTHESIS, SECRETION, AND TRANSPORT OF LIPOPROTEINS

Charles L. Bisgaier and Robert M. Glickman

Department of Medicine, Gastrointestinal Unit, Columbia University College of Physicians and Surgeons, New York, New York 10032

INTRODUCTION

A large portion of the Western diet (100 g day^{-1}) consists of lipids, largely triglycerides. These and the lipids of the enterohepatic circulation are efficiently absorbed (95%) into the enterocyte where they are resynthesized into lipoproteins and secreted into mesenteric lymph. New information has been obtained concerning aspects of intestinal lipoprotein formation and metabolism.

Here we review the more recent developments in our understanding of the composition and synthesis of intestinal lipoproteins. General reviews of this topic are available (9, 22, 55, 56).

LYMPH CHYLOMICRON COMPOSITION

Chylomicrons are spherical triglyceride-rich particles (750–6000 Å) formed within the intestine during triglyceride absorption. Particle size is largely determined by the flux of triglyceride through the intestinal cell; large chylomicrons are formed during the peak of lipid absorption (49), perhaps reflecting a conservation of surface constituents (apoproteins, phospholipids) that require active synthesis by the enterocyte. The particles are composed mainly of triglyceride (86–92%) and cholesteryl ester (0.8–1.4%), free cholesterol (0.8–1.6%), phospholipids (6–8%), and protein (1–2%). Triglyceride composition largely reflects dietary fatty acids while phospholipid and cholesteryl ester fatty acids bear little relationship to dietary tryglyceride.

625

0066-4278/83/0315-0625$02.00

Structurally the particles consist of a core of apolar lipids (triglyceride, cholesteryl ester) surrounded by a polar surface coating of phospholipid, protein, and free cholesterol. Chylomicrons contain sufficient phospholipid to cover almost the entire surface (> 80%). Protein covers approximately 20% of the chylomicron surface (71). As discussed below, chylomicron surface components are metabolically redistributed to plasma high density lipoproteins (HDL) during chylomicron metabolism.

There is conflicting evidence about whether two classes of triglyceride-rich lipoproteins are present in mesenteric lymph. During fasting periods, triglyceride particles the size of very low density lipoproteins (VLDL, 200–800 Å) are present in mesenteric lymph. These carry 50% of lymph cholesterol and triglyceride in the fasting state. These particles represent the absorptive route for endogenous intestinal and biliary lipids (41). While the particles are the size of plasma VLDL, their apoproteins are quite different and resemble lymph chylomicrons (24), as do their lipids. As intestinal VLDL resemble chylomicrons more closely than plasma VLDL, they have been regarded as small chylomicrons. During higher rates of lipid absorption, particle size increases to accommodate the increased lipid flux across the intestinal mucosa, and chylomicrons become the predominant triglyceride-rich lipoprotein in lymph. Mahley et al (38) have suggested that rat intestinal chylomicrons and VLDL-sized particles are distinct by demonstrating limited mixing of these particles in individual Golgi vesicles. Recent studies suggest that low temperatures normally used in the isolation of lipoproteins may result in crystallization of core triglyceride (especially saturated triglyceride), which may increase particle density (7). The original suggestion (42) that saturated fatty acid feeding results in a smaller chylomicron (VLDL-sized) particle must be reexamined in this light.

Despite the fact that chylomicron apoproteins comprise only 1–2% of the mass of chylomicrons, the large flux of lipid passing across the intestine each day results in the synthesis of substantial amounts of individual apoproteins. Figure 1 indicates the similar apoproteins of rat and human chylomicrons derived from intestinal lymph. As shown, the major chylomicron apoproteins from both sources comprise apo B (10%), apo A-IV (10%), apo E (5%), apo A-I (15–35%), and the group of C apoproteins (45–50%). Apo A-II, a minor apoprotein in the rat, is present on human chylomicrons. It has become clear that not all of the apoproteins associated with lymph chylomicrons are synthesized by the intestine. It is known that upon exposure to plasma, both in vivo and in vitro, triglyceride-rich lipoproteins acquire apo E and apo C (24, 29). While the apoprotein pattern of chylomicrons when isolated from lymph appears relatively constant, it is probable that apoprotein transfer has already occurred in lymph. Evi-

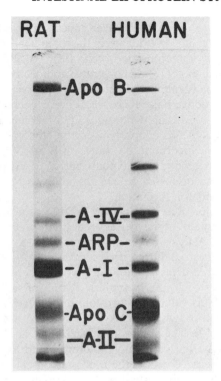

Figure 1 SDS polyacrylamide gels (5.6%) of apoproteins of rat mesenteric lymph chylomi-crons and human chylous urine chylomicrons (24). ARP = apo E. An ink marker is apparent at the bottom of each gel.

dence exists in both the rats and humans that the intestine actively synthe-sizes apoproteins B, A-I, A-IV, and small amounts of apo C-II; in humans it also synthesizes apo A-II.

Apo B is a high-molecular-weight, hydrophobic apoprotein found on the triglyceride-rich lipoproteins of all species studied. Recent data have de-scribed a heterogeneity of apo B in rats and humans with distinctive forms present in plasma and intestinal triglyceride-rich lipoproteins. In both rats (37) and humans (32) chylomicron apo B is a smaller protein than plasma apo B found in low density lipoprotein (LDL). In rats, chylomicron apo B has a mol wt of 240,000 vs 353,000 in plasma LDL. In humans, chylomi-cron apo B has a mol wt of 264,000 vs 549,000 for the major species of plasma LDL apo B. In humans, the data strongly suggest that these forms of apo B, while sharing some immunologic cross-reactivity, are organ spe-cific (32, 39). In the rat, while intestinal chylomicrons contain only the lower-molecular-weight apo B, the liver appears to synthesize both forms of apo B (10). Several lines of evidence in the rat indicate that apo B is newly synthesized as a chylomicron apoprotein during triglyceride absorption. Studies of Glickman et al (15) demonstrated radioactive amino acid incorporation into apo B of lymph chylomicrons during triglyceride absorption. After a single radioactive pulse there was a linear decrease in chylomicron apo B specific activity during continuous lipid infusion suggesting continued active synthesis of this apoprotein during chylomicron formation. In addition, the isotopic incorporation studies of Wu & Windmueller (68, 69) demonstrate an increased intestinal contribution to the plasma apo B pool with fat feeding. As discussed below, the ability to synthesize apo B is essential for chylomicron formation.

Apo A-I, the major protein of plasma HDL, has a mol wt of 28,000 in both rats and humans. Triglyceride-rich lipoproteins from mesenteric lymph contain apo A-I as a major apoprotein (12, 16, 24, 29, 36, 57). Apo A-I is actively synthesized during triglyceride absorption. Studies in the rat by several laboratories demonstrate that approximately 130–140 mg hr^{-1} of apo A-I is transported in the mesenteric lymph of saline- or glucose-fed animals (30, 51). This value rises two-fold during triglyceride absorption; a greater proportion of lymph apo A-I is associated with the d < 1.006 g ml^{-1} lipoproteins (12). The studies of Imaizumi et al (30) show that only 3–5% of the apo A-I on lymph chylomicrons could have originated from the plasma. As discussed below, the mucosal content of apo A-I is small compared to the lymphatic output and is probably maintained by a high rate of intestinal mucosal apo A-I synthesis. Isotopic incorporation studies by Wu & Windmueller indicate that the intestine contributes 56% of the total daily synthesis of apo A-I (69).

Studies in humans are more limited, but a similar picture emerges. Apo A-I has been identified as a major apoprotein of d < 1.006 g ml^{-1} lipoproteins from thoracic duct lymph (36, 57) and from chyluric patients (24). It comprises 15% of chylomicron protein. This is probably an underestimate since in vitro studies show a transfer of apo A-I from chylomicrons when HDL are present in the incubation medium, a situation naturally occuring in lymph or plasma. Studies in chyluric patients (24) or patients with thoracic duct drainage (2) indicate that 30–40% of the daily body synthesis of apo A-I is carried on intestinal triglyceride-rich lipoproteins, a figure similar to estimates in the rat. After fat feeding, plasma levels of apo A-I are increased (14).

Recently, isoforms of apo A-I have been described in both rats (29) and humans (70) with chylomicrons enriched in certain isoforms. It is probable that these isoforms represent post-translational modification of a single gene product as suggested by the studies of Gordon et al (20).

Recently it has been suggested that in Tangier disease there may be an impairment in the conversion of chylomicron isoforms to those normally found on plasma HDL (33). Further information is required to clarify the physiological role of apo A-I isoforms and their role in states of altered lipoprotein metabolism.

Swaney et al (62) first described *apo A-IV* as a 46,000 mol wt component of rat plasma HDL. The presence of this protein was soon noted in rat, human, and canine chylomicrons (23, 64, 66).

Fat feeding results in increased lymphatic secretion of apo A-IV. In chyluric humans the secretion of apo A-IV (23) and the content of apo A-IV in intestinal cells (25) were markedly stimulated by fat feeding. Fat feeding in normal humans raises plasma levels of the apoprotein (23). Estimates in the rat indicate that the intestine may contribute up to 60% of the daily synthesis of this apoprotein (69).

While in both rats and humans apo A-IV appears to enter the plasma in association with triglyceride-rich lipoproteins, the metabolic fate of apo A-IV may differ in these two species. In the rat, apo A-IV appears to transfer to the HDL fraction of plasma during the catabolism of chylomicrons (63). In humans, chylomicron apo A-IV also leaves the chylomicron surface but is found mainly in the d $>$ 1.21 g ml^{-1} fraction of plasma. When human plasma is fractionated by agarose gel chromatography rather than ultracentrifugation, as much as 23% of apo A-IV is associated with lipoproteins of d $<$1.21 g ml^{-1}, suggesting that apo A-IV may also be an HDL apoprotein (23). It is not clear at which stage apo A-IV becomes associated with the HDL fraction and in what form apo A-IV exists in the d $>$1.21 g ml^{-1} fraction of plasma.

Studies in abetalipoproteinemia, a disease characterized by the absence of chylomicron or VLDL secretion, indicate that apo A-IV levels are reduced approximately 50% (23). This suggests that chylomicron secretion is not obligatory for apo A-IV secretion, and that this apoprotein may enter the plasma by an alternative mechanism. The metabolic functions of apo A-IV are unknown at this time.

There is litter evidence that the intestine actively synthesizes *apo E* in significant amounts, if at all (30, 51). Both in vivo and in vitro studies suggest apo E appears to associate with chylomicrons after secretion (29).

The group of *C apoproteins* are low-molecular-weight components of the chylomicrons in rats and humans. Estimates of synthesis by the intestine of the C apoproteins are low ($<$10%) (69). The liver is thought to be the major synthetic source. After secretion from the enterocyte, triglyceride-rich lipoproteins gain apo C from HDL (29). This acquisition is important for chylomicron catabolism since apo C-II is an activator of lipoprotein lipase and the C apoproteins inhibit hepatic uptake of chylomicrons. This enables peripheral catabolism to occur before hepatic uptake of the remnant particles.

INTESTINAL MUCOSAL ASPECTS
OF CHYLOMICRON APOPROTEIN AND LIPID
SYNTHESIS

Newly absorbed fatty acid crosses the microvillus membrane by passive diffusion and is first visible morphologically as triglyceride droplets within profiles of the smooth endoplasmic reticulum (SER). Subsequently, lipid droplets appear in profiles of the ER and accumulate in the Golgi apparatus in the supranuclear portion of cell. Migration of elements of the Golgi complex occurs toward the basolateral aspect of the cell. Fusion of Golgi membranes with the lateral cell membrane occurs with lipoproteins discharged into the intercellular space by reverse pinocytosis. It is not known whether intracellular membrane receptors mandate specific sites of membrane fusion. Microtubules have also been implicated in the directed intracellular movement of triglyceride through the enterocyte (19, 48). Morphologically, the process of chylomicron formation and secretion is rapid as are the various synthetic events in chylomicron formation (31).

The products of luminal triglyceride lipolysis, monoglyceride and fatty acid, are resynthesized to triglyceride within the enterocyte. Cytosolic transport of fatty acids is facilitated by an intracellular fatty acid binding protein (FABP). This protein is thought is facilitate long-chain transport of fatty acids to the SER (43, 44). The predominant pathway within the SER synthesizes triglyceride directly from 2-monoglyceride by the addition of two molecules of fatty acid (34). An alternate pathway of triglyceride synthesis, the α-glycerophosphate pathway, adds 3 molecules of fatty acid to glycerol-3-phosphate yielding triglyceride. The synthesis of phospholipid for the chylomicron surface preferentially utilizes readily available biliary phospholipid. Biliary lysolecithin, generated in the lumen by the action of pancreatic phospholipase (40), is absorbed and reacylated. When luminal phospholipid is not readily available, lecithin, can also be synthesized de novo by the enterocyte. Cholesterol, another chylomicron component, is added to the core of chylomicrons as cholesteryl ester. Cholesteryl ester can be formed either through the action of cholesteryl esterase (5) or acyl-CoA-cholesterol acyltransferase (ACAT) (27). Which pathway is predominant remains to be determined.

Active synthesis of *intestinal apoproteins* is necessary for normal chylomicron formation. Studies with protein synthesis inhibitors produce an accumulation of triglyceride droplets within the intestinal cell and lead to decreased lymphatic secretion of chylomicrons (17, 54). Chylomicrons secreted during protein synthesis inhibition are larger and contain reduced amounts of apo A-I. Of interest is the preservation of apo A-IV and apo B on these particles, suggesting their potential requirement in chylomicron formation (16).

During chylomicron formation the active synthesis of rat intestinal *apo B* has been demonstrated by amino acid incorporation into immunoprecipitable apo B prepared from in vitro tissue slices (4) and microsomes (35). After fat feeding the content of apo B in rat intestine increases 2–3-fold by 2 hr (58). There is reason to believe, however, that this response is more rapid since studies using fluorescent antibodies (both in rats and humans) suggest an increase of cellular apo B as early as 10 min after lipid exposure (13, 18). The most recent studies from our laboratory indicate that the cellular content of apo B in rat intestine (measured by radioimmunoassay) increases as early as 15 min and shows no evidence of depletion despite continued lipid stimulation (A. Samuelson, R. M. Glickman, unpublished observations). These results differ from studies on human intestinal biopsies (45), where after lipid feeding a marked decrease in apo B content was found, suggesting that the rate of chylomicron apo B secretion exceeded the rate of synthesis. The explanation for these seemingly contradictory results in rats and humans must await further studies on the time course of apo B synthesis in humans in response to lipid feeding.

Additional findings suggest that there may be a pool of apo B within the intestinal epithelium that may not be totally mobilized by the process of triglyceride transport. Administration of protein synthesis inhibitors to rats not absorbing exogenous lipid produces a modest decrease in the apo B content of intestinal cells (20% reduction). Biliary diversion known to deplete the intestinal mucosa of triglyceride also produces a modest reduction in cellular apo B content. In addition, protein synthesis inhibitors administered to rats actively absorbing triglyceride, can deplete the intestinal mucosal apo B content by approximately 50% but no further, suggesting a limit beyond which cellular apo B cannot be decreased (A. Samuelson, R. M. Glickman, unpublished observations).

Ultrastructurally apo B is localized within the intestine in the RER and on the triglyceride droplets in profiles of the SER, suggesting an addition of apo B early in chylomicron formation (52). Similar studies in rat liver suggest apo B addition to triglyceride in the SER (1).

The most graphic example of the central role of apo B in triglyceride transport is the disease abetalipoproteinemia. This disease is characterized by the inability to form lipoproteins containing apo B, with resulting accumulation of triglyceride droplets in liver and intestine. Immunochemical localization studies have failed to demonstrate apo B in enterocytes from patients with abetalipoproteinemia, supporting the inability to synthesize apo B in this disorder (13, 59). As discussed in greater detail elsewhere in this volume, the recent finding of discrete forms of apo B arising from liver and intestine (10, 32, 37, 39, 65) and the description of a patient with the inability to secrete hepatic apo B while preserving chylomicron secretion are of great interest (39). It is probable that patients will be discovered with an isolated defect of intestinal apo B synthesis and secretion and a preservation of hepatic VLDL secretion. Such patients will have normal levels of VLDL and LDL (hepatic apo B) but will have intestinal biopsies engorged with triglyceride; postprandial lipemia will be absent.

Direct demonstration of *apo A-I* in rat (15) and human (14, 47) enterocytes has been achieved by immunochemical localization and isotope incorporation studies (46). The content of apo A-I in rat intestinal epithelial cells is 80–150 ng mg^{-1} protein (58). In humans, recent studies show a similar content of apo A-I in the duodenum (200 ng mg^{-1} protein) (25). As discussed earlier there is excellent evidence that fat feeding results in an increased secretion of apo A-I from the intestine into lymph. Despite this evidence it has been difficult to determine the dynamics of apo A-I synthesis within the intestinal epithelium. Immunofluorescence antibody studies in rats and humans suggest an increase in the content of apo A-I with lipid feeding (14, 16). It has been difficult, however, to document an increase in the apo A-I content of rat enterocytes after lipid feeding, suggesting that synthesis and export are rapid. Recent studies from our laboratory show a doubling of the apo A-I content of duodenal enterocytes in humans after fat feeding, supporting earlier immunofluorescence studies (25).

Significant new information has been provided by the studies of Gordon et al (20), which demonstrate that the primary translation product of rat intestinal apo A-I mRNA is a higher mol wt preproprotein. It is not clear how these findings relate to the organ culture studies of Zannis et al (70), who described multiple immunoprecipitable intracellular isoforms of apo A-I, two of these isoforms having higher mol wt components. A surprising finding was that fat feeding in the rat did not result in an increase in enterocyte apo A-I mRNA. Thus it is not clear at what level apo A-I synthesis is regulated and at what point fat feeding affects the process. In the rat, the total apo A-I content of the entire mucosa can be estimated at approximately 2 μg. Yet during fat feeding, lymphatic secretion of apo A-I on chylomicrons is 20–50 times this amount. It therefore seems that a rapid apo A-I synthesis and secretion is critical. These important questions relating to the control of apo A-I synthesis remain to be resolved.

It has also become clear that the synthesis of apo A-I can proceed independent of triglyceride absorption. Studies of Windmueller & Wu show significant apo A-I secretion in glucose-infused rats (68). Studies from our laboratory (3) demonstrate that secretion of apo A-I into rat mesenteric lymph is maintained in bile fistula animals, largely occurring in lymph HDL (see below). Mucosal apo A-I levels in bile-diverted animals are not decreased despite the elimination of triglyceride flux. Thus apo A-I secretion appears to be maintained by additional factors that require further definition.

In recent studies we have demonstrated that the ileal mucosa of both rats and humans (25) contain amounts of apo A-I and apo B comparable to those in proximal intestinal mucosa and that under non–fat fed conditions these apoproteins are secreted into ileal lymph (R. M. Glickman, unpublished observations). Thus the distal bowel may also be an important source of apoproteins/lipoproteins.

In humans, fasting mucosal *apo A-IV* is 12 μg mg^{-1} protein, rising to 46 μg mg^{-1} protein after lipid feeding (25). Thus apo A-IV is present within the enterocyte in substantially greater amounts than other apoproteins. Gordon et al (21) have recently determined that the amount of rat intestinal apo A-IV mRNA is markedly increased after lipid feeding. The exact role of apo A-IV in chylomicron formation is unknown.

OTHER LYMPH LIPOPROTEINS

Only small amounts of lipid have been isolated in the 1.006–1.063 g ml^{-1} density range of rat mesenteric lymph; these probably represent filtered plasma LDL. Chronic cholesterol feeding in rats, however, results in an increased proportion of lymph cholesterol carried in the LDL density fraction. These particles were triglyceride and cholesteryl ester rich and contained apo B and apo A-I, suggesting that they were derived from the intestine (51). Human thoracic duct lymph also contains LDL, but their origin is uncertain.

There is increasing evidence that the rat intestine secretes characteristic forms of HDL into mesenteric lymph. Studies from our laboratory described a heterogeneous population of HDL particles in mesenteric lymph consisting of spherical as well as discoidal particles (26). The entire HDL fraction was enriched in phospholipid, poor in cholesteryl ester, and had as its major apoprotein apo A-I with little apo E. These compositional and morphological characteristics suggested that these particles were not derived from plasma. In a subsequent study (3) bile diversion, which depletes intestinal epithelial cells and mesenteric lymph of triglyceride-rich lipoproteins, resulted in a sustained mesenteric apo A-I and discoidal HDL output. It was estimated that 70% of the apo A-I in the HDL fraction of lymph originated in the intestine. The HDL fraction of lymph was not derived from lymph triglyceride-rich lipoproteins, and a large proportion of the apo A-I in lymph HDL was not filtered. Most recently, using density gradient centrifugation and gradient gel electrophoresis, we have resolved mesenteric lymph HDL into discrete fractions including a discoidal fraction, a spherical HDL fraction similar in size to plasma HDL, and a small spherical particle fraction not present in plasma. Duodenal infusion of ^{3}H-cholesterol resulted in an increase in cholesteryl ester specific activity in lymph spherical HDL (especially the small spherical particles) when compared with plasma HDL. Fatty acids of cholesteryl ester from the spherical lymph HDL were more saturated than those from plasma HDL suggesting an intestinal origin (11). These studies strongly reinforce the concept that both surface and core components of lymph HDL may originate in the intestine.

Human thoracic duct lymph contains particles similar to plasma HDL. However, these particles are enriched in triglyceride and phospholipid resembling HDL_{2A} (2). No studies are available that determine the origin of this HDL. A small spherical particle found in the plasma of patients with abetalipoproteinemia is similar to the small spherical particle found in rat lymph. The origin of this particle is not known. It may be of intestinal origin (8).

METABOLIC FATE OF INTESTINAL LIPOPROTEINS

It is beyond the scope of this brief review to discuss in detail the metabolic fate of intestinal lipoproteins except to stress that they are an important source of plasma lipoprotein constituents, especially plasma HDL. Chylomicron metabolism proceeds in two stages. Initially, core triglyceride is removed via lipoprotein lipase. Surface constituents such as phospholipid and apoproteins such as apo A-I and apo A-II are rapidly distrubuted to the HDL fraction of plasma (28, 50, 57, 63). The chylomicron remnant is then rapidly cleared via receptor-mediated uptake by the liver, which recognizes apo E and perhaps intestinal apo B (60, 67). Intestinal triglyceride-rich lipoproteins do not appear to be a source of plasma LDL in the rat or human (65). The mechanisms by which chylomicron surface constituents are converted into plasma HDL are not fully understood but appear to involve the action of LCAT on nascent or discoidal particles. From a quantitative standpoint, chylomicron phospholipid and apoproteins represent a major source of these constituents for plasma HDL.

Our studies in the rat suggest an additional source of plasma HDL is secreted directly by the intestine, but we lack supporting data in humans.

CONCLUSION

Thus the intestine has been shown to be a major synthetic site of several apoproteins and an important metabolic source of plasma lipoproteins such as HDL. Future work is required to determine factors within the intestinal epithelium that regulate the synthesis of these apoproteins and influence their subsequent metabolism. Present data support the important role of the intestine in lipoprotein metabolism.

Literature Cited

1. Alexander, C. A., Hamilton, R. L., Havel, R. J. 1976. *J. Cell. Biol.* 69: 241–63
2. Anderson, D. W., Schaefer, E. J., Bronzert, T. J., Lindgren, F. T., Forte, T., Starzl, T. E., Niblack, G. D., Zech, L. A., Brewer, H. B. Jr. 1981. *J. Clin. Invest.* 67:857–66
3. Bearnot, H. R., Glickman, R. M., Weinberg, L., Green, P. H. R. 1982. *J. Clin. Invest.* 69:210–17
4. Blue, M. -L., Protter, A. A., Williams, D. L. 1980. *J. Biol. Chem.* 225: 10048–51
5. Borja, C. R., Vahouny, G. V., Treadwell, C. R. 1963. *Am. J. Physiol.* 206:223–28
6. Cardell, R. R. Jr., Badenhaussen, S., Porter, K. R. 1967. *J. Cell Biol.* 34: 123–55
7. Clark, S. B., Atkinson, D., Hamilton, J. A., Forte, T., Russell, B., Feldman, E., Small, D. M. 1982. *J. Lipid. Res.* 23: 28–40
8. Deckelbaum, R., Eisenberg, S., Oschry, Y., Blum, C. 1981. *Arteriosclerosis* 1:392a (Abstr.)
9. Dietschy, J. M., Gotto, A. M. Jr., Ontko, J. A., eds. 1978. *Disturbances in Lipid and Lipoprotein Metabolism.* Bethesda, MD: Am. Physiol. Soc. 295 pp.
10. Eloyson, J., Huang, Y.O., Baker, N., Kannan R. 1981. *Proc. Natl. Acad. Sci. USA* 78:157–61
11. Forester, G. P., Tall, A. R., Bisgaier, C. L., Glickman, R. M. 1982 *Gastroenterology* 82:1059 (Abstr.)
12. Glickman, R. M., Green, P. H. R. 1977. *Proc. Natl. Acad. Sci. USA* 74:2569–73
13. Glickman, R. M., Green, P. H. R., Lees, R. S., Lux, S. E., Kilgore, A. 1979. *Gastroenterology* 76:288–92
14. Glickman, R. M., Green, P. H. R., Lees, R. S., Tall, A. R. 1978. *N. Engl. J. Med.* 299:1421–27
15. Glickman, R. M., Kilgore, A., Khorana, J. 1978. *J. Lipid Res.* 19: 260–68
16. Glickman, R. M., Kirsch, K. 1973. *J. Clin. Invest.* 52:2910–20
17. Glickman, R. M., Kirsch, K., Isselbacher, K. J. 1972. *Clin. Invest.* 51: 356–63
18. Glickman, R. M., Khorana, I., Kilgore, A. 1976. *Science* 193:1254–55
19. Glickman, R. M., Perrotto, J., Kirsch, K. 1976. *Gastroenterology* 70:347–52
20. Gordon, J. I., Smith, D. P., Andy, R., Alpers, D. H., Schonfeld, G., Strauss, A. W. 1982. *J. Biol. Chem* 257:971–78
21. Gordon, J. I., Strauss, A. W., Smith, D. P., Ockner, R., Alpers, D. H. 1982. *Gastroenterology* 82:1071 (Abstr.)
22. Green, P. H. R., Glickman, R. M. 1981. *J. Lipid Res.* 22:1153–73
23. Green, P. H. R., Glickman, R. M., Riley, J. W., Quinet, E. 1980. *J. Clin. Invest.* 65:911–19
24. Green, P. H. R., Glickman, R. M., Saudek, C. D., Blum, C. B., Tall, A. R. 1979. *J. Clin. Invest.* 64:233–42
25. Green, P. H. R., Lefkowitch, J. H., Glickman, R. M., Riley, J. W., Quinet, E., Blum, C. B. 1982. *Gastroenterology* 83:1223–30
26. Green, P. H. R., Tall, A. R., Glickman, R. M. 1978. *J. Clin. Invest.* 61:528–34
27. Haugen, R., Norum, K. R. 1976. *Scand. J. Gastroenterol.* 11:615–21
28. Havel, R. J. 1957. *J. Clin. Invest.* 36: 848–54
29. Imaizumi, K., Fainaru, M., Havel, R. J. 1978. *J. Lipid Res.* 19:712–22
30. Imaizumi, K., Havel, R. J., Fainaru, M., Vigne, J-L. 1978. *J. Lipid Res.* 19:1038–46
31. Jersild, A. R. Jr. 1966. *Am. J. Anat.* 118:135–41
32. Kane, J. P., Hardman, D. A., Paulus, H. E. 1980. *Proc. Natl. Acad. Sci. USA* 77:2465–69
33. Kay, L. L., Ronan, R., Schaefer, E. J., Brewer, H. B. Jr. 1982. *Proc. Natl. Acad. Sci. USA* 79:2485–89
34. Kayden, J. J., Senior, J. R., Mattson, F. H. 1967. *J. Clin. Invest.* 46:1695–1703
35. Kessler, J. E., Stein, J., Dannacker, D., Narcesseri, P. 1970. *J. Biol. Chem.* 245:5281–88
36. Kostner, G., Holasek, G. 1972. *Biochemistry* 11:1217–23
37. Krishnaiah, K. V., Walker, L. F., Boresztajn, J., Schonfeld, G., Getz, G. S. 1980. *Proc. Natl. Acad. Sci. USA* 77:3806–10
38. Mahley, R. W., Bennett, B. D., Morré, D. J., Gray, M. E., Thistlethwaite, W., LeQuire, V. S. 1971. *Lab. Invest.* 25:435
39. Malloy, M. J., Kane, J. P., Hardman, D. A., Hamilton, R. L., Dalal, K. B. 1981. *J. Clin. Invest.* 67:1441–50
40. Mansbach, C. M. II. 1977. *J. Clin. Invest.* 60:411–20
41. Ockner, R. K., Hughes, F. B., Isselbacher, K. J. 1969. *J. Clin. Invest.* 48:2079–88
42. Ockner, R. K., Hughes, F. B., Isselbacher, K. J. 1969. *J. Clin. Invest.* 48:2367–73
43. Ockner, R. K., Manning, J. M. 1974. *J. Clin. Invest.* 54:326–88

44. Ockner, R. K., Manning, J. M. 1976. *J. Clin. Invest.* 58:632–41
45. Rachmilewitz, D., Albers, J. J., Saunders, D. R. 1976. *J. Clin. Invest.* 57: 530–33
46. Rachmilewitz, D., Albers, J. J., Saunders, D. R., Fainaru, M. 1978. *Gastroenterology* 75:667–82
47. Rachmilewitz, D., Fainaru, M. 1979. *Metabolism* 28:739–43
48. Reaven, E. P., Reaven, G. M. 1977. *J. Cell Biol.* 75:559–72
49. Redgrave, T. G., Dunne, K. B. 1975. *Atherosclerosis* 22:389–400
50. Redgrave, T. G., Small, D. M. 1979. *J. Clin. Invest.* 64:162–71
51. Riley, J. W., Glickman, R. M., Green, P. H. R., Tall, A. R. 1980. *J. Lipid Res.* 21:942–52
52. Rubin, E. C., Perkins, W. D., Surawicz, C. M., McDonald, G. B., Albers, J. J. 1980. *Gastroenterology* 78:1248
53. Sabesin, S. M., Frase, S. 1977. *J. Lipid Res.* 18:496–511
54. Sabesin, S. M., Isselbacher, K. J. 1965. *Science* 147:1149–51
55. Scanu, A. M., Landsberger, F. R. 1980. *Ann. Acad. Sci.* 348:1–436
56. Schaefer, E. J., Eisenberg, S., Levy, R. I. 1978. *J. Lipid Res.* 19:667–86
57. Schaefer, E. J., Jenkins, L. L., Brewer, H. B. Jr. 1978. *Biochem. Biophys. Res. Commun.* 80:405–12
58. Schonfeld, G., Bell, E., Alpers, D. H. 1978. *J. Clin. Invest.* 61:1539–50
59. Schwartz, D. E., Liotta, L., Schaefer, E., Brewer, H. B. Jr. 1978. *Circulation* 50:II–90 (Abstr.)
60. Shelburne, F., Hanks, J., Meyers, W., Quarfordt, S. 1980. *J. Clin. Invest.* 65:652–58
61. Strauss, E. S. 1966. *J. Lipid Res.* 7: 307–23
62. Swaney, J. B., Reese, H., Eder, H. A. 1974. *Biochem. Biophys. Res. Commun.* 59:513–18
63. Tall, A. R., Green, P. H. R., Glickman, R. M., Riley, J. W. 1979. *J. Clin. Invest.* 64:977–89
64. Utermann, G., Beisiegel, U. 1979. *Eur. J. Biochem.* 99:333–43
65. Van't Hooft, F. M., Hardman, D. A., Kane, J. P., Havel, R. J. 1982. *Proc. Natl. Acad. Sci. USA* 79:179–82
66. Weisgraber, K. H., Bersot, T. P., Mahley, R. W. 1978. *Biochem. Biophys. Res. Commun.* 85:287–92
67. Windler, E., Chao, Y., Havel, R. J. 1980. *J. Biol. Chem.* 255:5475–80
68. Windmueller, M. G., Wu, A-L. 1981. *J. Biol. Chem.* 256:3012–16
69. Wu, A.-L., Windmueller, H. G. 1979. *J. Biol. Chem.* 254:7316–22
70. Zannis, V., Breslow, J. L., Katz, A. J. 1980. *J. Biol. Chem.* 255:8612–17
71. Zilversmit, D. G. 1965. *J. Clin. Invest.* 44:1610–22

Ann. Rev. Physiol. 1983. 45:637–50

APOLIPOPROTEIN B: STRUCTURAL AND METABOLIC HETEROGENEITY

John P. Kane

Cardiovascular Research Institute, University of California School of Medicine, San Francisco, California 94143

INTRODUCTION

The large number of protein species present in the lipoprotein complexes in blood suggests a number of biochemical roles of proteins in lipoprotein metabolism and perhaps also in nontransport functions. One group of apolipoproteins, the B proteins, clearly participates in organizing the structure of lipoprotein complexes. At least one of these proteins (B-100) also interacts with high-affinity receptors that function in the endocytosis of lipoproteins (6, 16). Unlike many of the smaller apolipoproteins, there is no measureable concentration of soluble B protein in the aqueous medium in equilibrium with B protein bound to lipoproteins. Also, the B proteins do not appear to transfer between particles but maintain organized lipoprotein complexes throughout successive stages of metabolism until the end products are removed from plasma. In all, their behavior resembles that of the intrinsic proteins of cell membranes. Because of transfer and exchange of lipids and non-B apolipoproteins, the B proteins may be the only constituents that remain fixed throughout the metabolism of a given particle. All the B proteins share the property of insolubility in water after delipidation by organic solvents and are rapidly precipitated by 4.2 M tetramethylurea, a solvent that solubilizes the smaller apolipoproteins (23).

In humans there appear to be two original species of apo B and two principal pathways of metabolism. The species with the larger molecular weight is secreted by liver into the space of Disse in nascent particles of very low density lipoproteins (VLDL). Metabolism of these particles mediated by the lipoprotein lipase system yields a succession of smaller particles poorer in triglycerides. The end products of this process, VLDL remnants,

637

are somehow transformed, with the participation of the liver, to low density lipoproteins (LDL). The B protein is conserved in LDL, but some of it appears to be subjected to scission, yielding two complementary proteins. In contrast, remnant particles formed from chylomicrons, which contain a different species of apo B, are removed from circulation without forming LDL. The circumstances appear to be much more complex in the only other animal species studied in detail, the rat, which has several species of apo B of hepatic origin.

Secretion of VLDL and chylomicrons is totally dependent upon the B proteins. In humans with recessive abetalipoproteinemia and homozygous hypobetalipoproteinemia, in whom neither primary species of apo B is secreted, neither VLDL nor chylomicrons are produced. The absence of LDL in these disorders appears to be a consequence of the inability of liver to secrete its precursor, VLDL. Observations on a newly discovered disorder, in which chylomicrons containing the species of lower molecular weight are secreted but no VLDL or LDL, and non of the hepatic B proteins are present, suggest that the primary species of apo B are under separate genetic control (35).

STRUCTURE OF B APOPROTEINS

Species of Apo B

Whereas the presence of small subunits in B proteins remains unsettled, these proteins have functional elements of high molecular weight that are now being characterized as to structure and sites of origin and catabolism. Because absolute estimates of molecular weights (mol wt) of these elements differ substantially among laboratories, and because their apparent molecular weights (mol wt_{app} would be expected to bear a consistent relationship to one another within a given analytical system, my colleagues and I have proposed a nomenclature based on relative apparent molecular weights to facilitate comparison of results (22). In this system, the large component that predominates in LDL and VLDL is arbitrarily designated B-100 and the relative mobilities of all other elements are expressed on a centile scale. This system has the advantage of providing numerical assignments for the minor components found in many specimens. Because different nomenclature has been applied to rat apo B by four groups of investigators and because of the value of comparison with the human B proteins, the centile system is used for rat proteins in this review.

Apo B in Humans

Investigations in our laboratory using analytical SDS gel electrophoresis showed four major species of apo B in human lipoproteins (22). A band of mol wt_{app} 5.4×10^5, virtually the sole form in normal VLDL, is the principal species in LDL. Many specimens of LDL also contain two species with mol wt_{app} 0.74 and 0.26 times that of the major constituent, which are denoted B-74 and B-26. The B protein of human thoracic duct lymph chylomicrons shows a small amount of a component of B-100 mobility, but the predominant B protein has a relative mobility of 0.48 (B-48). B-100 is the sole B protein in Lp(a) lipoproteins (J. P. Kane, D. A. Hardman, unpublished observations). The four species of B protein were isolated by a new technique of preparative electrophoresis (18). The amino acid compositions of the B-100 protein of VLDL, LDL, and of the d ≤ 1.006 g/ml fraction of thoracic duct lymph are indistinguishable, but the B-74 and B-26 proteins are clearly different from one another and from the B-100 protein. Because the sum of their apparent molecular weights equals that of the B-100 protein, the weighted sum of their amino acid compositions was compared to that of B-100 to determine whether they might be fragments of it. The summed composition of B-74 and B-26 was indistinguishable from that of B-100. Also, the aminoacyl mass of each in several samples of apo LDL showed a precise 1 : 1 molar stoichiometry. Collectively, these data support the hypothesis that the B-74 and B-26 proteins are complementary fragments of the B-100 protein. B-74 and B-26 are more abundant in the denser subfractions of LDL from both adult human serum and umbilical cord blood (J. P. Kane, D. A. Hardman, T. Forte, P. A. Davis, unpublished observations). The amino acid composition of the B-48 protein of lymph or plasma chylomicrons differs significantly from that of the other B species, indicating that it is a distinct protein and cannot be merely the monomeric form of a dimeric B-100.

In our laboratory, a protein with the same apparent molecular weight as the B-48 protein has been isolated as a minor component from human LDL (22). However, its amino acid composition clearly differs from that of B-48. Thus the presence of a protein band with the appropriate mobility for the B-48 species does not establish the presence of B-48 protein of chylomicron origin in a lipoprotein preparation. Further evidence, such as amino acid analysis or other chemical characterization, is required for definite identification. Very small amounts of other large proteins resembling apo B are observed in SDS gel electrophoretograms of apo LDL and of the TMU insoluble protein of chylomicrons.

Apo B in the Rat

A component analogous to the B-48 protein of human chylomicrons has been described in the lipoproteins of rat plasma (13, 26, 64, 67). Its mobility on SDS gels is identical to that of human B-48 protein. It is essentially the sole B protein in mesenteric lymph chylomicrons (26, 64, 67) and it is abundant in the d ≤ 1.006 g/ml lipoproteins of plasma from fed rats. It persists in the plasma of animals given orotic acid, a compound that inhibits hepatic secretion of lipoproteins (26). The situation is complicated in the rat by the presence of a B protein of identical apparent molecular weight in liver perfusates (64, 67) and Golgi preparations (13). Persistence of both higher molecular weight apo B species and a B-48 component in rat plasma, despite complete drainage of mesenteric lymph, indicates that the larger, and at least a portion of the smaller, components are produced in the liver (67). Though it has been assumed that hepatic B-48 protein is identical to B-48 of mesenteric lymph, no immunochemical data nor chemical characterizations of these proteins have been reported that would support this supposition. A protein of similar mobility to the B-48 of chylomicrons and VLDL has been reported in rat LDL (13, 26). The predominant B apoproteins of rat VLDL and LDL show bands in SDS gels that are designated B-100 and B-95 in the centile system used for human apo B. The structural relationships of these proteins to each other and to the B-48 protein(s) are not yet established. Krishnaiah et al. (26) have reported a comparison of the amino acid compositions of B-48 protein from mesenteric lymph with that of the apo B of LDL, which contains B-100, B-95, and B-48 protein. They considered the compositions indistinguishable; however, differences of 8–12% were evident in the contents of certain amino acids. Sparks & Marsh observed two peaks when B protein from rat plasma was separated by gel filtration in SDS (57). The first must contain both the B-95 and B-100 proteins. The amino acid compositions of a single preparation of each fraction showed differences of 8–12% in certain amino acids. Further, the compositions reported from the two laboratories disagreed appreciably. Thus the relationship of these components remains unknown. The finding that the chymotryptic maps of rat B-100 protein appear to contain some peptides not seen in maps of B-48 protein suggests that the two species are related but structurally distinct (13).

Several questions about the species of rat apo B remain unanswered. These include the structural relationship of B-100 to the B-95 component, for which no amino acid composition has been reported; the question of whether common peptide sequences or subunits are shared by B-48 and the species of higher molecular weight; and the possibility that the B-48 proteins of hepatic and intestinal origin may be structurally distinct.

Studies Seeking the Monomeric Molecular Weights of B Apoproteins

Severe technical obstacles have impeded the identification of the monomeric units of the B proteins. One of these is extreme self association upon removal of lipids. The B proteins are completely insoluble in aqueous buffers after extraction with organic solvents. Even when solubilized with guanidine hydrochloride, urea, or detergents, they may show some stable aggregates with particle weights of 1×10^6 or more. Apo B from LDL interacts anomalously with SDS (19). There is cooperativity in binding of SDS above the critical micellar concentration, accompanied by an increase in helicity (60). Steele & Reynolds have reported a stable dimer of apo B from LDL in SDS (60, 61). Apo B from LDL is also dimeric with n-dodecyl octaethyleneglycol monoether (65), forming a linear complex with 5–6 equivalent micelles of the amphiphile (68).

Apo B is highly susceptible to cleavage by proteases. Of potential importance is scission by plasmin (59). Proteolysis by plasmin during preparation of LDL cannot explain the presence of the B-74 and B-26 proteins, however, because plasmin inhibitors have no effect on the content of these B proteins (8). Plasmin might cause scission of B-100 into those fragments in vivo, however. A common cause of cleavage of apo B during preparation appears to be bacterial protease activity. The resulting fragments of apo B that appear in SDS gel electrophoresis resemble those reported by several laboratories as putative subunits of apo B from LDL. When ultracentrifuge tube caps, glassware, and solutions are sterilized and antimicrobial agents are added to solutions, these numerous fragments of apo B are no longer observed (8). The cleavage of B protein by azide is inhibited by EDTA (51). Apolipoproteins are also altered by products of lipid peroxidation, possibly both by scission and cross linking. These reactions are also inhibited by EDTA. These and perhaps other reactions in which molecular oxygen takes part may modify apo B significantly during preparation by methods commonly in use. Lee et al have reported improved solubility of apo B when prepared with antioxidants and in the absence of oxygen (32).

A further problem in identifying apo B subunits is the presence of other apolipoproteins that predominate in VLDL and chylomicrons (30, 31). Even near the modal density of LDL, other proteins (chiefly C apoproteins) may account for 2–3% of the protein mass. The Lp(a) specific protein (20) might also be mistaken for a subunit species because Lp(a) lipoproteins occur within the LDL density range.

The physical state of B apoproteins appears to be dependent upon their handling. If they are allowed to dry even partially during removal of organic solvents, aggregation usually becomes irreversible. Thus the history of preparation is critical to the interpretation of data on apparent molecular weights.

The apo B of LDL is a glycoprotein in which the carbohydrate content is 8–10% of the protein mass (37). It contains galactose, mannose, glucosamine, and neuraminic acid (33, 63). Both high mannose and complex chains are present (63). The carbohydrate may account for some of the discordance between estimates of molecular weight from SDS gel electrophoresis and from ultracentrifugation of apo B.

Shore & Shore, using sedimentation equilibrium in 8 M urea and SDS, reported a value of 64 X 10³ daltons for LDL apo B (49). Others have reported components of 80 X 10³ (11) daltons by gel permeation in SDS, and 80–100 X 10³ by ultracentrifugation (41). Groups using SDS (34) or sodium deoxycholate (9, 10) reported a series of proteins, some as small as 9.5 X 10³ daltons. The patterns on SDS gel electrophoresis resemble those associated with digestion by microbial endopeptidases and could not be confirmed when repeated under strict antimicrobial conditions [(8); D. A. Hardman, J. P. Kane, unpublished observations]. Krishnaiah & Wiegandt later attributed this phenomenon to protease activity associated with LDL (27).

Acylation of apo B has been employed to increase interchain or intrachain electrostatic repulsion. Scanu et al. (45) found heterogeneous particles with a minimum mol wt of 37 X 10³ for succinylated apo LDL. Later, this group reported a minimum value of 27 X 10³ daltons in urea at high pH (41). Interfacial extraction of maleyl LDL in guanidine by organic solvents yielded soluble apo B. Its major component had a mol wt$_{app}$ of ≥ 200 X 10³, but that of another component with a different amino acid composition was 2.6 X 10³ (24). These results were confirmed by Shore & Shore (50). These authors (50) and Pinon et al (40), using ion exchange chromatography, have separated three fractions from maleyl apo B that differ in amino acid composition.

Socorro & Camejo have sought to prevent self-aggregation of apo B by delipidation of LDL with non-ionic detergents while it is bound to an ion exchange resin (55). Delipidation appears to be complete, yielding soluble protein that retains reactivity with antisera to apo B. SDS gel electrophoresis of this material shows considerable heterogeneity of particle size. These authors conclude that the array of polypeptides obtained is compatible with mixed oligomers of two subunits with mol wt 8 X 10³ and 22 X 10³. Olofsson et al (38) solubilized apo LDL in acetic acid after delipidation with organic solvents. They purified one component with an apparent mol wt of 72–76 X 10³ on electrophoresis in SDS.

Further inference favoring the presence of multiple subunits in apo B of LDL is drawn from study of fragments obtained with cyanogen bromide (5, 12). These polypeptides are aggregated; however, ten bands can be resolved on SDS gel electrophoresis. The finding of no more than six free N-terminal amino acids is compatible with a monomeric mol wt of only 20–30 X 10³. However, if the B-100 protein were to contain repeating sequences, such data would also be obtained.

Others have reported much larger apparent molecular weights for apo B of LDL on the basis of hydrodynamic behavior in denaturing solvents. Smith et al (54) solubilized apo B in guanidine or SDS following extraction with organic solvents. Sedimentation equilibrium in 7.6M guanidine yielded a mol wt_{app} of 250 X 10^3. Gel permeation in 6 M guanidine gave an elution volume compatible with a mol wt of 275 X 10^3. They also reported a mol wt^{app} of 255 X 10^3 by SDS gel electrophoresis. Steele & Reynolds (61) reported instead that apo B of LDL is dimeric in SDS. A mol wt_{app} of 250 X 10^3 for apo B from LDL was obtained using sedimentation equilibrium in guanidine after delipidation with SDS. Because the mol wt_{app} of the protein was not affected by reduction of disulfide bonds, it appears that the major functional elements of apo B are not dimeric in LDL. The small effect on Stokes radius resulting from reduction suggests that disulfide bridging is local in B-100 protein. Recently Jacobs et al (J. C. Jacobs, V. N. Schumaker, J. Elovson, R. C. LeBoeuf, unpublished observations) have studied the B-100 species from human LDL and the B-48 species from the rat. The rat B-48 appears to have a mol wt of 200 X 10^3 from sedimentation and diffusion data. The observation that its mol wt_{app} on SDS gel electrophoresis is 210 X 10^3 indicates that it is monomeric in SDS. However, B-100 was found to have a mol wt_{app} of 350 X 10^3 on the basis of sedimentation and diffusion, and by sedimentation and gel permeation in 6 M guanidine. The total mass of apo B protein measured independently in LDL, 645 X 10^3 a.m.u., is compatible with two moles of B-100 per particle, allowing for the carbohydrate moiety. The mass of protein in small rat chylomicrons suggests a content of two copies of the B-48 protein (3). Thus even using rigorous hydrodynamic techniques there is appreciable variation in the estimates of mol wt of the large elements of apo B. It is possible that B-100 and B-48 are composed of smaller subunits that aggregate despite the presence of denaturing solvents, or that small subunits are linked covalently (28, 48). If the cross linking occurs at the ends of subunits, the resulting polymers could show hydrodynamic behavior compatible with that described above.

Immunochemical Studies of Apo B

Krishnaiah et al (26) reported recognition of rat mesenteric lymph chylomicrons by antiserum to rat LDL and reaction of rat LDL with antiserum to the apo B of mesenteric lymph chylomicrons. However, the presence of B-48 protein in rat LDL limits the interpretation of both observations. Displacement curves for rat lymph VLDL and LDL in a radioimmunoassay were markedly different from those of plasma LDL, using an antibody to plasma LDL (26), suggesting only partial immunochemical identity. However, it is probable that important differences in conformation exist for a given species of apo B at different stages of metabolism of VLDL and chylomicrons, which could account for this observation. In fact, Schonfeld et al have demonstrated appreciable changes in immunoreactivity of VLDL-B attendant to lipolysis in vitro (47).

In our laboratory, a number of polyclonal antibodies raised against purified human B-48 protein reacted with human VLDL or LDL. One antiserum to B-48, which could detect B-48 in chylomicrons, was unreactive with LDL, however, suggesting that at least some portion of the B-48 molecule is dissimilar to the LDL B-100 protein in structure, subunit composition, or conformation. Antisera against B-26 and B-74 each reacted with LDL and VLDL, and each reacted with B-100 in SDS. However, antisera raised against B-26 protein reacted well with B-26 and B-100 protein in SDS and not with B-74; antiserum to B-74 reacted with B-100 and B-74 and not with B-26 in SDS, suggesting that few epitopes are common to the B-74 and B-26 proteins.

Studies with monoclonal antibodies are beginning to refine the mapping of B proteins. L. Curtiss and T. Edgington (personal communication) found seven epitopes common to LDL B-100 and B-26 in SDS, with but one shared with B-74. Four of the same epitopes were evident in B-48 from plasma chylomicrons. None of the monoclonal antibodies reacted with apo E, a finding of interest because apo B-100 and apo E share the ability to interact with certain high-affinity receptors on cell membranes. This is suggestive but not conclusive evidence that apo E is not a subunit of B proteins. With B. P. Tsao, these authors detected one group of antibodies that react equally well in displacement assay with VLDL, IDL, and LDL. Other groups react preferentially with VLDL and IDL, or with IDL and LDL, suggesting that apo B undergoes appreciable conformational change in the transformation of VLDL to LDL.

Another group (Y. L. Marcel, M. Hogue, R. Theolis, Jr., and R. W. Milne, personal communication) have prepared five monoclonal antibodies that react with human B-100 and B-74 proteins in SDS but not with B-26, whereas one antibody to B-100 reacted with B-26 but not B-74, supporting the view that these complementary fragments contain little or no common sequence. Two monoclonal antibodies were reactive with both B-100 and B-48 proteins, one also with B-26 and the other with B-74. All the antibodies that affected binding of LDL to the B-100 : E receptor failed to react with B-48 in SDS, suggesting that the B-48 moiety is not a ligand for that receptor.

Summary

In spite of extensive efforts using classical techniques of protein chemistry to determine the subunit proteins that comprise the apo B species, it is unknown whether the B proteins are single polypeptide chains or are composed of multiple subunits. Several conclusions can be drawn at this point, however. If they are single polypeptide chains, immunochemical evidence indicates that at least a portion of the B-48 protein of human chylomicrons corresponds to a segment of the human B-100 chain. The observation that

B-48 protein can be secreted normally in humans when the B-100 protein is absent indicates that these two proteins could be products of separate structural genes, possibly resulting from gene duplication. Production of B-48 by incomplete transcription or transcription from a B-100 structural gene in the intestine is also possible. Another compatible model is that of multiple subunits. In such cases, the B-100 and B-48 proteins would probably contain a common subunit, but B-100, would contain at least one additional, organ-specific subunit species. The hydrodynamic data on apo B would be compatible with this model only if subunits were arranged in a linear sequence. The extreme resistance of the B proteins to techniques that readily dissociate subunits of many complex proteins suggests that if multiple subunits are present they may be united by covalent cross links.

METABOLISM OF APO B

Biosynthesis

Studies on the biosynthesis of apo B are beginning to yield detailed information on the elaboration of the protein, its glycosylation, and its assembly into lipoprotein complexes. Such studies hold promise of determining the molecular weights of the monomeric units of B proteins. In mammals, the secretion of B proteins appears to be limited to the liver and intestine (44, 66), but in the the chicken, the kidney also synthesizes a protein with properties of apo B (4).

Immunocytochemical methods have established the presence of apo B determinants in the rough endoplasmic reticulum (ER) and in nascent particles in the cisternae adjacent to the rough ER of hepatocytes (1). Bell-Quint, Forte & Graham (2) have demonstrated the synthesis of two species of apo B consistent with B-100 and B-48 by cultured rat hepatocytes. The B-48 protein is the only species separated from the medium in the HDL density interval. Isotopic evidence adduced by Wu & Windmueller (67) and Sparks et al (56) supports the production of both B-100 and B-48 proteins by liver. R. J. Padley, L. L. Swift, and G. S. Getz have found that B-100 and B-48 isolated from rat liver Golgi apparatus show different rates of synthesis (unpublished observations). They report that B-100 protein labeling peaks at 15 min, whereas peak activity in B-48 occurs at 30 min after a pulse of [³H] amino acids. Production of apo B by cultured human hepatoma cells has recently been demonstrated (43). The varied differential incorporation of amino acid label into the B-48 and B-100 proteins of rat liver (67) has suggested that the relative production rates of different types of VLDL may be under metabolic control. Recent studies in cultured hepatocytes by Roger Davis (unpublished observations) show time courses of synthesis for the large and small mol wt forms of apo B that are not compatible with a precursor : product relationship. Synthesis of total apo B is increased in hepatocytes from rats fed sucrose, with a preponderance of the smaller mol wt species, whereas fasting reduces the production of the small apo B.

Using an immunoprecipitation technique, Siuta-Mangano et al have studied the synthesis of apo B in estrogen-induced chicken liver cells in culture (53). Maximum synthesis of apo B occurred 10 min after a pulse of [^{3}H] leucine, whereas the smaller apolipoproteins were labeled much more rapidly. This finding is compatible with synthesis of a single chain with a mol wt of 350×10^3 at a translation rate of 7 amino acid residues per second. A further 20 min were required for appearance of apo B in the medium. Nascent apo B associated with polysomes ranged in mol wt_{app} from $30-350 \times 10^3$ in SDS gels. Core glycosylation appeared to occur in two stages, at mol wt of 120×10^3 and 280×10^3. Normally, apo B accounts for about 2% of protein synthesis in the liver of nonstimulated roosters. This synthesis is unaffected by the estrogen antagonist tamofixen. The 6–7-fold increase induced by estrogen can be blocked completely by tamofixen (7), suggesting that it is based on increases in apolipoprotein m-RNA, resembling established mechanisms of steroid action in other systems. The lack of effect of tunicamycin indicates that glycosylation is not required for secretion of lipoprotein complexes containing B protein (62).

To date, all studies of the immunocytochemistry of apo B in the intestine have utilized antisera to LDL-apo B. Synthesis of immunoreactive material by a rat intestinal microsome fraction has been demonstrated (25). Schonfeld et al demonstrated increases in apo B in rat intestinal mucosa after administration of fat (46). Incorporation of apo B into mesenteric lymph chylomicrons is demonstrable within 30 min of fat administration (15, 17), though basal apo B synthesis occurs in the absence of fat absorption. Synthesis of B protein has also been demonstrated in cultured human intestinal mucosa (42). Wu & Windmueller (67) have shown that 95% of apo B radioactivity in the mesenteric lymph of lymph-diverted rats, after intraintestinal administration of labeled amino acids, is in the B-48 band on SDS gels. Their finding that 5% of the label was on a band corresponding to B-100 mobility, even after both lymph and blood were diverted from an isolated jejunal segment, suggests that limited synthesis of B-100 might take place in the gut. Because the small amount of putative B-100 protein in this case might have been B-48 dimer, the conclusion that the B-100 protein can be synthesized in the intestine must await more definitive identification of the protein.

Metabolism of Circulating Apo B

HUMAN   In the human it is probable that little if any B-48 apoprotein is secreted by the liver. Because this protein is essentially absent from the plasma of normal fasted humans (22), kinetic studies carried out on the apo B of normal subjects probably remain valid. These data show conversion of 70–100% of the apo B of VLDL to LDL and the exclusive origin of LDL apo B from VLDL (29, 39, 52). Studies on individuals with hyperlipemia, however, have shown that a portion of the apo B label may disappear from the d ≤ 1.006 g/ml lipoproteins without formation of LDL apo B. The d ≤ 1.006 g/ml lipoprotein fraction of many fasted individuals who have hypertriglyceridemia contains appreciable amounts of B-48 protein (J. P. Kane, M. J. Malloy, D. A. Hardman, unpublished results). Also, the "beta VLDL" of fasted individuals with familial dysbetalipoproteinemia include a considerable quantity of remnant lipoproteins containing the B-48 protein, which are presumably derived from chylomicrons (21). Thus it is probable that the diminished conversion of apo B from what was thought to be VLDL to LDL in hypertriglyceridemic patients is due in some instances to the presence of B-48 protein that is not a precursor of LDL apo B. Reassessment of the origin of LDL in these states will depend upon differentiation of B protein species. A reinfusion study using radiolabeled chylomicrons showed a plasma half-time of 50 min for B-48 protein, with no conversion to LDL (36).

RAT   Studies on the fate of the total apo B of VLDL show that only about 5% is converted to LDL apo B, largely accounting for the low levels of LDL in the rat (14). Elovson et al (13) showed that the B-48 component of the d ≤ 1.006 g/ml lipoproteins of plasma decayed with a half-life of 8 min in contrast with the half-life of 13 min for the B-100/B-95 proteins. Similarly, they found faster decay of the B-48 protein in IDL and LDL. These kinetic relationships are compatible with separate species of VLDL containing either B-100/B-95 or B-48 protein, rather than the presence of heterodimers. Relatively more rapid removal of B-48-containing particles from the d ≤ 1.006 g/ml lipoproteins of plasma has been confirmed by others (56, 58, 67). However, the VLDL in the studies of Elovson et al might have included particles of enteric origin that would influence the apparent kinetics of the B-48 protein of plasma. Van't Hooft et al studied the metabolism of the B-48 protein of reinfused mesenteric lymph chylomicrons (64). They found essentially no conversion to LDL. Extremely small amounts of label in IDL decayed rapidly. Thus it is clear that the B-48-containing VLDL of the rat are converted to a subspecies of LDL (albeit one that is removed rapidly) whereas the remnants of chylomicrons are removed from blood without formation of LDL.

Literature Cited

1. Alexander, C. A., Hamilton, R. L., Havel, R. J. 1976. Subcellular localization of B apoprotein of plasma lipoproteins in rat liver. *J. Cell. Biol.* 69:241–63
2. Bell-Quint, J., Forte, T., Graham, P. 1981. Synthesis of two forms of apolipoprotein B by cultured rat hepatocytes. *Biochem. Biophys. Res. Commun.* 99:700–6
3. Bhattacharya, S., Redgrave, T. G. 1981. The content of apolipoprotein B in chylomicron particles. *J. Lipid Res.* 22:820–28
4. Blue, M.-L., Protter, A. A., Williams, D. L. 1980. Biosynthesis of apolipoprotein B in rooster kidney, intestine, and liver. *J. Biol. Chem.* 255:10048–51
5. Bradley, W. A., Rohde, M. F., Gotto, A. M. Jr., Jackson, R. L. 1978. The cyanogen bromide peptides of the apoprotein of low density lipoprotein (apo B): Its molecular weight from a chemical view. *Biochem. Biophys. Res. Commun.* 81:928–35
6. Brown, M. S., Goldstein, J. L. 1975. Regulation of the activity of the low density lipoprotein receptor in human fibroblasts. *Cell* 6:307–16
7. Capony, F., Williams, D. L. 1980. Apolipoprotein B of avian very low density lipoprotein: characteristics of its regulation in nonstimulated and estrogen-stimulated rooster. *Biochemistry* 19:2219–26
8. Chapman, M. J., Kane, J. P. 1975. Stability of the apolipoprotein of human serum low density lipoprotein: absence of endogenous endopeptidase activity. *Biochem. Biophys. Res. Commun.* 66:1030–36
9. Chen, C. H., Aladjem, F. 1978. Further studies on the subunit structure of human serum low density lipoprotein. *Biochem. Med.* 19:178–87
10. Chen, C. H., Aladjem, F. 1974. Subunit structure of the apoprotein of human serum low density lipoproteins. *Biochem. Biophys. Res. Commun.* 60:549–54
11. Day, C. E., Levy, R. S. 1968. Determination of the molecular weight of apoprotein subunits from low density lipoprotein by gel filtration. *J. Lipid Res.* 9:789–93
12. Deutsch, D. G., Heinrikson, R. L., Foreman, J., Scanu, A. M. 1978. Studies of the cyanogen bromide fragments of the apoprotein of human serum low density lipoproteins. *Biochim. Biophys. Acta* 529:342–50

13. Elovson, J., Huang, Y. O., Baker, N., Kannan, R. 1981. Apolipoprotein B is structurally and metabolically heterogenous in the rat. *Proc. Natl. Acad. Sci. USA* 78:157–61
14. Faergeman, O., Sata, T., Kane, J. P., Havel, R. J. 1975. Metabolism of apoprotein B of plasma very low density lipoproteins in the rat. *J. Clin. Invest.* 56:1396–1403
15. Glickman, R. M., Kirsch, K. 1973. Lymph chylomicron formation during the inhibition of protein synthesis. Studies of chylomicron apoproteins. *J. Clin. Invest.* 52:2910–20
16. Goldstein, J. L., Brown, M. S. 1977. The low density lipoprotein pathway and its relation to atherosclerosis. *Ann. Rev. Biochem.* 897–930
17. Green, P. H. R., Glickman, R. M. 1981. Intestinal lipoprotein metabolism. *J. Lipid Res.* 22:1153–73
18. Hardman, D. A., Kane, J. P. 1980. Improved separation of high molecular weight proteins by preparative SDS gel electrophoresis: application to apolipoprotein B. *Anal. Biochem.* 105:174–80
19. Helenius, A., Simons, K. 1971. Removal of lipids from human plasma and low-density lipoprotein by detergents. *Biochemistry* 10:2542–47
20. Jurgens, G., Kostner, G. M. 1971. Studies on the structure of the Lp(a)-specific antigen. *Immunogenetics* 1:560–69
21. Kane, J. P., Chen, G. C., Malloy, M. J., Hardman, D. A., Hamilton, R. L., Havel, R. J. 1983. Remnants of lipoproteins of hepatic and intestinal origin in the plasma of patients with familial dysbeta-lipoproteinemia (type III hyperliperlipoproteinemia). *Arteriosclerosis.* In press
22. Kane, J. P., Hardman, D. A., Paulus, H. E. 1980. Heterogeneity of apolipoprotein B: isolation of a new species from human chylomicrons. *Proc. Natl. Acad. Sci. USA* 77:2465–69
23. Kane, J. P. 1973. A rapid electrophoretic technique for identification of apoprotein species in serum lipoproteins. *Anal. Biochem.* 53:350–64
24. Kane, J. P., Richards, E. G., Havel, R. J. 1970. Subunit heterogeneity in serum beta lipoprotein. *Proc. Natl. Acad. Sci. USA* 66:1075–82
25. Kessler, J. E., Narcesseri, P., Maudlin, D. P. 1970. Biosynthesis of low density lipoprotein by cell-free preparations of rat intestinal mucosa. *J. Biol. Chem.* 245:5281–88

26. Krishnaiah, K. V., Walker, L. F., Borensztajn, J., Schonfeld, G., Getz, G. S. 1980. Apolipoprotein B variant derived from rat intestine. *Proc. Natl. Acad. Sci. USA* 77:3806–10

27. Krishnaiah, K. V., Wiegandt, O. H. 1974. Demonstration of a protease-like activity in human serum low density lipoprotein. *FEBS Lett.* 40:265–68

28. Kuehl, D. S., Ramm, L. E., Langdon, R. G. 1977. Chemical evidence for subunit structure of low density lipoprotein. *Fed. Proc.* 36:828

29. Langer, T., Strober, W., Levy, R. I. 1972. The metabolism of low density lipoprotein in familial type II hyperlipoproteinemia. *J. Clin. Invest.* 51:1528–36

30. Lee, D. M., Alaupovic, P. 1974. Composition and concentration of apolipoproteins in very low and low density lipoproteins of normal human plasma. *Atherosclerosis* 19:501–20

31. Lee, D. M., Alaupovic, P. 1974. Physiochemical properties of low density lipoproteins of normal human plasma. Evidence for the occurrence of lipoprotein B in associated and free form. *Biochem. J.* 137:155–67

32. Lee, D. M., Valente, A. J., Kuo, W. H., Maeda, H. 1981. Properties of apolipoprotein B in urea and in aqueous buffers: the use of glutathione and nitrogen in its solubilization. *Biochim. Biophys. Acta* 666:133–46

33. Lee, P., Breckenridge, W. C. 1976. Isolation and carbohydrate composition of glycopeptides of human apo low density lipoprotein from normal and type II hyperlipoproteinemic subjects. *Can. J. Biochem.* 54:829–32

34. Lipp, K., Weigandt, H. 1973. Studies on the B-protein of human serum betalipoprotein using SDS-polyacrylamide gel electrophoresis. *Hoppe-Seyler's Z. Physiol. Chem.* 354:262–66

35. Malloy, M. J., Kane, J. P., Hardman, D. A., Hamilton, R. L., Dalal, K. 1981. Normotriglyceridemic abetalipoproteinemia. Absence of the B-100 apolipoprotein. *J. Clin. Invest.* 67:1441–50

36. Malloy, M. J., Kane, J. P. 1981. Normotriglyceridemic abetalipoproteinemia: fate of apolipoprotein B of chylomicrons. *Ped. Res.* 15(2):635

37. Margolis, S., Langdon, R. G. 1966. Studies on human serum B_1-lipoprotein. *J. Biol. Chem.* 241:469–76

38. Olofsson, S.-O., Bostrom, K., Svanberg, U., Bondjers, G. 1980. Isolation and partial characterization of a polypeptide belonging to apolipoprotein B from low-density lipoproteins of human plasma. *Biochemistry* 19:1059–64

39. Packard, C. J., Third, J. L. H. C., Shepherd, J., Lorimer, A. R., Morgan, H. G., Lawrie, T. D. V. 1976. Low density lipoprotein metabolism in a family of familial hypercholesterolemic patients. *Metabolism* 25:995–1006

40. Pinon, J. C., Kane, J. P., Havel, R. J., Laudat, P. 1973. Heterogeneity in the protein moiety of human serum low density lipoprotein. *Conf. Lipoproteins Graz* B2, 44 (Abstr.)

41. Pollard, H., Scanu, A. M., Taylor, E. W. 1969. On the geometrical arrangement of the protein subunits of human serum low-density lipoprotein: evidence for a dodecahedral model. *Proc. Natl. Acad. Sci. USA* 64:304–10

42. Rachmilowitz, D., Sharon, P., Eisenberg, S. 1980. Lipoprotein synthesis and secretion by cultured intestinal mucosa. *Eur. J. Clin. Invest.* 10:125–31

43. Rash, J. M., Rothblat, G. M., Sparks, C. E. 1981. Lipoprotein apolipoprotein synthesis by human hepatoma cells in culture. *Biochim. Biophys. Acta* 666: 294–98

44. Roheim, P. S., Gidez, L. I., Eder, H. A. 1966. Extrahepatic synthesis of lipoprotein of plasma and chyle: role of the intestine. *J. Clin. Invest.* 45:297–300

45. Scanu, A., Pollard, H., Reader, W. 1968. Properties of human serum low density lipoproteins after modification by succinic anhydride. *J. Lipid Res.* 9:342–49

46. Schonfeld, G., Bell, E., Alpers, D. M. 1978. Intestinal apoprotein during fat absorption. *J. Clin. Invest.* 61:1539–50

47. Schonfeld, G., Patsch, W., Pfleger, B., Witztum, J. L., Weidman, S. W. 1979. Lipolysis produces changes in the immunoreactivity and cell reactivity of very low density lipoproteins. *J. Clin. Invest.* 64:1288–97

48. Shore, B., Shore, V. 1976. Gamma glutamyl epsilon lysine in human low density lipoproteins. *Abstr. 30th Ann. Meet. Counc. Atherosclerosis, Am. Heart Assoc.* 38

49. Shore, B., Shore, V. 1967. The protein moiety of human serum beta lipoproteins. *Biochem. Biophys. Res. Commun.* 28:1003–7

50. Shore, V., Shore, B. 1972. The apolipoproteins: their structure and functional roles in human serum lipoproteins. In *Blood Lipids and Lipoproteins: Quantitation, Composition, and Metabolism*, ed. G. J. Nelson, pp. 789–824. NY: Wiley-Interscience

51. Shuh, J., Fairclough, G. F. Jr., Haschemeyer, R. M. 1978. Oxygen-mediated heterogeneity of apo-low-density lipoprotein. *Proc. Natl. Acad. Sci. USA* 75:3173–77

52. Sigurdsson, G., Nicoll, A., Lewis, B. 1975. Conversion of very low density lipoprotein to low density lipoprotein: A metabolic study of apolipoprotein B kinetics in human subjects. *J. Clin. Invest.* 56:1481–90

53. Siuta-Mangano, P., Howard, S. C., Lennars, W. J., Lane, M.D. 1982. Synthesis, processing, and secretion of apolipoprotein B by the chick liver cell. *J. Biol. Chem.* 257:4292–300

54. Smith, R., Dawson, J. R., Tanford, C. 1972. The size and number of polypeptide chains in human serum low density lipoprotein. *J. Biol. Chem.* 247:3376–81

55. Socorro, L., Camejo, G. 1979. Preparation and properties of soluble immunoreactive apo LDL. *J. Lipid Res.* 20:631–38

56. Sparks, C. E., Huatink, O., Marsh, J. B. 1981. Hepatic and intestinal contribution of two forms of apolipoprotein B to plasma lipoprotein fractions in the rat. *Can. J. Biochem.* 59:693–99

57. Sparks, C. E., Marsh, J. B. 1981. Analysis of lipoprotein proteins by SDS gel filtration column chromatography. *J. Lipid Res.* 22:514–18

58. Sparks, C. E., Marsh, J. B. 1981. Metabolic heterogeneity of apolipoprotein B in the rat. *J. Lipid Res.* 22:519–27

59. Steele, J. C. H. Jr. 1979. The effect of plasmin on human plasma low density lipoprotein. *Thromb. Res.* 15:573–79

60. Steele, J. C. H. Jr., Reynolds, J. A. 1979. Characterization of the apolipoprotein B polypeptide of human plasma low density lipoprotein in detergent and denaturant solutions. *J. Biol. Chem.* 254:1633–38

61. Steele, J. C. H. Jr., Reynolds, J. A. 1979. Molecular weight and hydrodynamic properties of apolipoprotein B in guanidine hydrochloride and sodium dodecyl sulfate solutions. *J. Biol. Chem.* 254:1639–43

62. Struck, D. K., Sinta, P. B., Lane, M. D., Lennarz, W. J. 1978. Effect of tunicamycin on the secretion of serum proteins by primary cultures of rat and chick hepatocytes. *J. Biol. Chem.* 253:5332–37

63. Swaminathan, N., Aladjem, F. 1976. The monosaccharide composition and sequence of the carbohydrate moiety of human serum low density lipoproteins. *Biochemistry* 15:1516–22

64. Van't Hooft, F. M., Hardman, D. A., Kane, J. P., Havel, R. J. 1982. Apolipoprotein B (B-48) of rat chylomicrons is not a precursor of the apolipoprotein of low density lipoproteins. *Proc. Natl. Acad. Sci. USA* 79:179–82

65. Watt, R. M., Reynolds, J. A. 1980. Solubilization and characterization of apolipoprotein B from human serum low density lipoprotein in n-dodecyl octaethyleneglycol monoether. *Biochemistry* 19:1593–98

66. Wu, A.-L., Windmueller, H. G. 1979. Relative contributions by liver and intestine to individual plasma lipoproteins in the rat. *J. Biol. Chem.* 254:7316–22

67. Wu, A.-L., Windmueller, H. G. 1981. Variant forms of plasma apolipoprotein B. *J. Biol. Chem.* 256:3615–18

68. Zampighi, G., Reynolds, J. A., Watt, R. J. 1980. Characterization of apolipoprotein B from human serum low density lipoprotein in n-dodecyl octaethyleneglycol monoether: an electron microscope study. *J. Cell. Biology* 87:55–61

Ann. Rev. Physiol. 1983. 45:651–77

LIPID DIGESTION AND ABSORPTION

Martin C. Carey

Department of Medicine, Harvard Medical School, Division of
Gastroenterology, Brigham and Women's Hospital, Boston, Massachusetts
02115

Donald M. Small

Biophysics Institute and Departments of Medicine and Biochemistry, School of
Medicine, Boston University Medical Center, Boston, Massachusetts 02118

Charles M. Bliss

Department of Medicine, Boston University School of Medicine, Section of
Gastroenterology, Boston City Hospital, Boston, Massachusetts 02118

INTRODUCTION

Gastrointestinal lipid digestion consists of three sequential steps: (*a*) the
dispersion of bulk fat globules into finely divided emulsion particles, (*b*) the
enzymatic hydrolysis of fatty acid esters at the emulsion-water interface,
and (*c*) the desorption and dispersion of insoluble lipid products into an
absorbable form. Here we emphasize several newer aspects of the biochemistry and biophysics of lipid digestion and absorption. We review the physical-chemical behavior of dietary lipids in model systems and correlate this
information with their physiological behavior throughout the alimentary
canal.

Dietary Phospholipids, Triglycerides, and Cholesterol
In both animals and plants long-chain triglycerides constitute the major
biological form of storage lipids. These stores occur intracellularly as liquid
oil droplets stabilized by a layer of phospholipid and protein (1). Cells also
contain a variety of membranes whose lipids are largely phospholipids. The
average western adult consumes about 150 g of triglyceride and 4–8 g of

651

0066-4278/83/0315-651$02.00

phospholipids (predominantly lecithin) each day, of which two thirds is of animal origin (2). Quantitatively more important is endogenous phospholipid (essentially pure lecithin) of hepatic origin (7–22 g/day) which is secreted into the intestinal lumen via the bile (3–6).

In the solid crystalline state, a triglyceride molecule (Figure 1) adopts a tuning-fork conformation (7–9) with the sn-2 fatty acids pointing in the opposite direction to the sn-1 and sn-3 fatty acids. Solid triglycerides are polymorphic; and by means of X-ray diffraction, three distinct chain crystallization patterns (β, β' and α) have been identified (10). In the liquid state, atoms rotate around all single-bonded aliphatic chain carbons. However, the individual molecules are probably not oriented randomly in space (Figure 1); Larsson's (10) X-ray scattering studies suggest short-range order in liquid triglyceride with close-packed swarms of molecules, and Callahan's ^{13}C spin-relaxation NMR measurements (11) suggest nearest neighbor interactions of up to $\cong 200$Å in liquid tristearin. Pure synthetic triglyceride mixtures exhibit complex composition- and temperature-dependent physical-chemical behavior (12, 13).

Because natural fats are complex blends of triglycerides, melting occurs over a wide temperature range. Human fat melts a few degrees below the ambient temperature: ~ 30–$35°$C for visceral fat, and 0–$10°$C for peripheral subcutaneous fat (14). Lard and tallow do not melt completely until $\cong 50$–$60°$C (9) and hence are either a mixture of liquid and solid fats or supercooled melts at $37°$C. A variety of triglyceride-rich lipoproteins are, in fact, metastable emulsions at $37°$C in which the triglyceride core is undercooled several degrees below its true melting point (15–18).

Long-chain triglycerides and lecithins are essentially insoluble in water, (molecular solubility is $< 10^{-20}$ and $< 10^{-10}$ M, respectively). A useful classification based on bulk and surface aqueous behavior is that long-chain triglycerides are insoluble nonswelling amphiphiles; lecithins are insoluble swelling amphiphiles (19). Both molecules spread to form stable monomolecular surface films.

The interfacial orientation of triglycerides is shown in Figure 1. Medium-chain triglycerides form more expanded surface films ($\cong 100$Å^2/molecule) than long-chain saturated triglycerides which form condensed or solid monomolecular films ($\cong 60$Å^2/molecule) (20). In both (Figure 1), the chains of the three fatty acids project in parallel toward the hydrophobic side of the interface (20, 21). Synthetic short-chain triglycerides (triacetin and tripropionin) give the smallest interfacial areas ($\cong 40$–50Å^2/molecule) (21) and adopt a tuning-fork arrangement at interfaces with one fatty acid chain projecting into the aqueous phase. Triglycerides such as butter fat that contain one short chain and two long chains probably are oriented with the

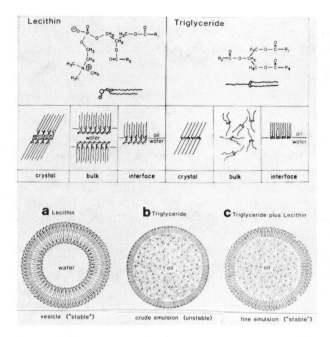

Figure 1   Above: Chemical structures, short-hand representations, and physical states of a typical long-chain lecithin (3-sn-phosphatidylcholine) and triglyceride (triacylglycerol) molecules. The two (R_1, R_2) long-chain fatty acids of lecithin (wriggly lines) are esterified to the sn-1 and sn-2 hydroxyl groups of glycerol (sausage-shaped symbol); the sn-3 group of glycerol is esterified to the zwitterionic phosphoryl choline (head) group. In all physical states, the glycerol moiety lies in line with the sn-1 fatty acid and both are perpendicular to the interface. Natural triglyceride has three (often different) (R_1, R_2, R_3) fatty acids esterified to the hydroxyl groups of the glycerol molecule.

Below: Dispersed states of the major dietary lipids in water. (*a*) Lecithin, showing configuration of the molecules in a typical unilamellar vesicle (or liposome). The molecules form a complete and continuous bilayer enclosing a water core. The phosphorylcholine head-groups, the glycerol moieties, and the ester linkages of the sn-2 fatty acids are all hydrated and have the configuration shown above. (*b*) Triglyceride forming an unstable emulsion particle in water. All 3 fatty acid chains of the surface monolayer of molecules are directed toward the core in a configuration typical of triglyceride at an oil-water interface (above). The glycerol moiety lies normal to the interface and is hydrated. The triglyceride molecules in the core adopt a tuning-fork arrangement typical of that in the crystal or isotropic melt (above). (*c*) Triglyceride droplet emulsified with a monomolecular layer of lecithin molecules: The core triglyceride molecules are identical in configuration to that described under (*b*), and the surface layer of lecithin molecules is equivalent to that in the outer monolayer of a vesicle. The surface monolayer of lecithin contains a few triglyceride molecules ($\cong$ 3%) that are available for direct hydrolysis by lipases (38).

short chains projecting into the aqueous side of the interface (D. Kodali, T. Redgrave, J. Hamilton, D. Small, unpublished observations).

In the solid state, lecithins form bilayer lamellae, tilted with respect to the interface to allow close packing between their two long fatty acid chains. A number of polymorphic forms of crystalline and lamellar liquid crystalline lecithins have been described (22–28). The average orientation of the phosphorylcholine head-group in crystals, gels, liquid crystals and monolayers of natural and synthetic lecithins (29–31) is approximately *in* the bilayer plane, i.e. parallel to the interface (Figure 1). Cholesterol can be incorporated in equimolar ratios into lamellar liquid crystals (32) and forces the hydrocarbon chains to adopt an "intermediate fluid" nature; *trans* conformations are increased in the proximal parts of the chains, and *gauche* conformations at the terminal ends; however, the head-group conformation is unaltered (33–35). Saturated lecithin monolayers when fully expanded occupy an interfacial area of 60–70$Å^2$/molecule, condensed films $\cong$ 46–50 $Å^2$/molecule, and solid films $\cong$ 40$Å^2$/molecule, or about two thirds of the corresponding areas for long-chain triglyceride molecules (20, 31, 36). Lecithins with unsaturated chains don't form solid films above 0°C, and their areas at an interface are several $Å^2$ larger than saturated lecithins (36). Liquid crystalline bilayers (60–70$Å^2$/ molecule) are the predominant physical state of natural lecithins (22) and natural mixed phospholipids in aqueous systems and in vivo at 37°C.

When shaken in excess water, triglyceride forms crude unstable emulsion droplets and lecithins disperse to form relatively stable concentric lamellar structures called myelin figures or liposomes. Liposomes can be further dispersed as unilamellar liposomes by ultrasonication (Figure 1). When these molecules physically interact in their dietary proportions (50:1 → 20:1) they form stable emulsions with the phospholipid acting as the emulsifier by forming a stable monolayer enveloping the triglyceride droplets (Figure 1). Emulsification with phospholipids increases the oil-water interfacial area (i.e. surface-volume ratio) by the dispersion of large oil masses into fine oil/water emulsion particles. The interfacial tension between pure triglyceride and water is $\cong$ 15–20mN m^{-1} whereas that between phospholipids and water is $\cong$ 1–5mN m^{-1}. Therefore, phospholipids lessen the energy requirements for emulsification by significantly lowering the lipid-water interfacial tension. They also stablize the emulsion droplet; they prevent coalescence and breakage of the emulsion by forming close-packed monolayers. By this means the interfacial "concentration" of molecules is increased, thus promoting hydrolysis of both phospholipid and triglyceride by various lipases (37).

Recent studies using phase equilbra techniques (38) and ^{13}C NMR spectroscopy (39) define the phase diagram of egg lecithin, triolein, cholesterol, and water (Figure 2). The surface monolayer of lecithin on an emulsion particle was found to contain about 3% triglyceride by weight. As free cholesterol was increased in the emulsions, it entered both the surface and core of the emulsion and slightly decreased the amount of triglyceride in the surface to approximately 2% at maximum saturation and equilibrium of the surface; that is, one molecule of cholesterol for one molecule of lecithin. The conformation of triglyceride in the interface indicates that all three chains lie parallel to the chains of the lecithin molecules, and the glycerol end of the molecule is directed toward the water (Figure 1). The ^{13}C NMR studies indicated that the sn-1 and sn-3 positions were more highly hydrated than the sn-2 positions; further, the sn-1 and 3 positions appear to lie slightly below the level of the sn-2 carbonyl of the lecithin. Finally, the rate of exchange between the core and surface was estimated to be rapid, and therefore the interfacially oriented triolein could be a substrate for lipases. First, it is surface oriented where the water molecules and enzyme could reach it easily. Second, the 1 and 3 positions are more conveniently located for hydrolysis than the 2 position. And finally, rapid movement of molecules from core to surface should occur, thus replenishing the surface concentration.

More complex systems containing small proportions of fatty acids, cholesterol esters, and partial glycerides as well as triglyceride, phospholipid, and cholesterol do not greatly change the surface composition relative to triglyceride (K. Miller, D. M. Small, unpublished observations) (Figure 2). Similar surface compositions appear to be present in triglyceride-rich lipoproteins and presumably in emulsion droplets occurring in the intestinal lumen during fat absorption. Studies on short-chain lecithins and triglycerides show a similar picture with perhaps somewhat more triglyceride located in the surface (40). The low concentrations of triglyceride in the surface layer may be related to the lag phase and low hydrolytic rates noted when pure pancreatic lipase is added to phospholipid emulsified triglycerides (37, 41, 42).

ROLE OF THE STOMACH AS A DIGESTIVE ORGAN

Muscle contractions of the stomach—particularly peristalsis against a closed pylorus and the squirting of fat through a partially opened pyloric canal—produce the shear forces sufficient for emulsification. Potential emulsifiers that can function in the acid milieu of the stomach include peptic digests of dietary proteins, complex polysaccharides, and membrane-derived phospholipids. Enzymatic hydrolysis of triglycerides also begins in the stomach (43–45), and since triglyceride is stored for 2–4 hours, 30% of the total dietary triglyceride may be digested. However, quantitative hy-

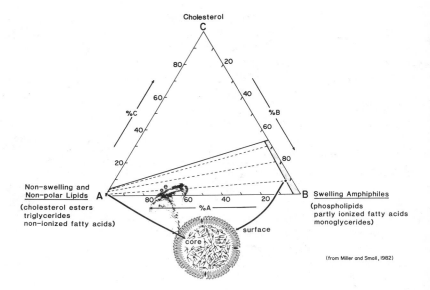

Figure 2   Phase equilibrium of emulsified lipid systems: The system involves cholesterol (C); swelling amphiphilic molecules (B), principally phospholipids, partly ionized fatty acids and monoglycerides; and nonswelling and nonpolar lipids (A), principally cholesterol esters, triglycerides, and non-ionized fatty acids. This system roughly approximates a 4-component (A, B, C, and H_2O) system. It is represented here as a 3-component system (A, B, and C) with water held constant at 80% (by weight). At equilibrium, this 3-component system divides into 4 regions. A 1-phase region on the right, rich in phospholipid, contains up to 33% free cholesterol and small amounts (3–5% by weight) of nonswelling and nonpolar lipids; a 1-phase region on the left, a narrow zone extending up from A to the phase boundary at about 4% (by weight) cholesterol. This phase is an oil composed of nonswelling and nonpolar lipids with a small amount of free cholesterol dissolved in the oil. Between these is a 2-phase region bounded between the oily phase region and the phospholipid-rich phase region. Above the traverse solid line is a 3-phase region. An emulsion having a composition at point *e* is a 2-phase system consisting of surface and core. By drawing the tie-line through point *e* to the surface composition on the right and the core composition on the left, the compositions of core and surface can be determined (38). For instance, the emulsion *e* having a composition of 70% A, 27% B, and 3% C, has a core composition of 99.1% A, 0% B and 0.9% C; whereas the surface composition is 3% A, 89% B, and 8% C. For a system containing triglycerides, phospholipids, and cholesterol, A would be equivalent to the triglyceride concentration, B the phospholipid concentration, and C the cholesterol concentration. Thus in emulsions, small amounts of core components such as triglycerides are contained in the surface and are available for enzyme hydrolysis; small amounts of free cholesterol are contained in the core. As emulsion particles decrease in size, this free cholesterol distributes back into the surface monolayer [adapted from (38)].

drolysis and absorption, especially of the long-chain fatty acids, require less acidic conditions, appropriate lipases and detergents (bile salts), and specialized absorptive cells. This environment is provided by the lumen and mucosa of the upper small intestine.

Lingual Lipase Hydrolysis

The major source of gastric lipolytic activity originates in a group of serous glands (von Ebner) beneath the circumvallate papillae of the tongue (46). The acini of the glands drain through short ducts into troughs that surround the papillae. The fine structure of these lingual glands is reminiscent of pancreatic acinar cells. Basal secretion apparently occurs continuously but can be stimulated by neural (sympathetic agonists), dietary (high fat), and mechanical (suckling and deglutition) factors (47). Although unrecognized as such, the calf, kid goat, and lamb lipases are important components of rennet paste and have been used by Mediterranean cheesemakers for centuries to curdle milk (48). Thus lingual lipases (usually called pre-gastric esterases or pharyngeal or salivary lipases) have received much attention in the dairy and veterinary literature (49). Despite their discovery in 1924 (49), no lingual lipase has yet been purified to homogeneity. The partially purified rat enzyme (50) is a sparingly soluble hydrophobic glycoprotein ($M_r \cong$ 50,000) specific for triglycerides. It is neither inhibited by, nor demonstrates a lag response with, lecithin-coated emulsions or short-chain lecithin-triglyceride mixed micelles. It is inhibited $\cong$ 20% by bile salts above their critical micellar concentration (in contrast to 100% for the pancreatic enzyme). With tributyrin and triolein, the pH optimum is 4–4.5, but activity begins at pH 2 and is still detectable at pH 7.5.

Both lingual and pancreatic lipases are true lipases (in contrast to esterases) and by definition act only on insoluble aggregated substrates. They are specific for the primary (sn-1 and sn-3) ester bonds of triglycerides; and fatty acid ester linkages of 2-monoglycerides, phospholipids, and cholesterol esters are resistant (5). Both enzymes are much more active on triglycerides with short-chain than on those with long-chain fatty acids (50–53). However, in contrast to pancreatic lipase, lingual lipase cleaves the fatty acid at the sn-3 ester linkage in preference to the sn-1 position (52–54). This appears to be a stereo-specific preference independent of the sn-3 fatty acid chain length (53, 54). In addition, product inhibition apparently occurs since the major products in vitro and in vivo are diglycerides and fatty acids (51–53, 55). In contrast, sn-2 monoglycerides and fatty acids are the final products of pancreatic lipase hydrolysis.

Physical State and Fate of Hydrolytic Products

In milk triglycerides short- and medium-chain fatty acids are esterified principally at the sn-3 position (51), whereas long-chain fatty acids occupy all three ester positions of common animal and vegetable triglycerides (49). With the former, lingual lipase hydrolysis produces short- or medium-chain free fatty acids and sn-1,2 diacylglycerols containing the long-chain fatty acids. Short- and medium-chain fatty acids in water exhibit pK'a values in the vicinity of 4.8 (56), but because they are hydrophilic they are fairly soluble in both ionized and un-ionized states. As indicated in Figure 3, these fatty acids leave the surface of the fat droplets and are absorbed passively by the stomach mucosa, to be transported to the liver bound to albumin in the portal vein (52, 53, 57). The aqueous pK'a values of long-chain fatty acids released by lingual lipase hydrolysis of common triglycerides are at or above neutrality (58–60); thus they will be predominantly protonated at stomach pH values and form liquid fatty acid oils. In micelles, oleic acid is 50% ionized at pH 7, in phospholipid bilayers at pH 8, and in triolein emulsions at pH 9 (D. P. Cistola, J. A. Hamilton, D. M. Small, unpublished observations). In both their crystalline structures (61) and in the liquid state, protonated fatty acids are extensively hydrogen bonded intermolecularly via their carboxyl groups (58, 60). Because they are hydrophobic, their solubility in triglyceride/diglyceride droplets is high (62), and in the stomach at low pH they probably partition mainly within the core of fat droplets with only a small fraction in the interface (Figure 3).

DIGESTION IN THE UPPER SMALL INTESTINE

Lingual lipase hydrolysis of dietary fat in the stomach facilitates duodenal-jejunal hydrolysis in a number of ways. (a) Long-chain fatty acids dissolved with the fat droplets become partly ionized and promote fine emulsification in the duodenum (63–66). (b) Small amounts of partially ionized long-chain fatty acids increase the binding of colipase (an essential cofactor for pancreatic lipase action) to the emulsion interface (67). (c) As a result of b the binding of lipase to colipase (67-69) is promoted. (d) Diglycerides being more surface active may be preferentially located at the emulsion-water interface; they are hydrolyzed faster by pancreatic lipase (70). (e) Absorption of long-chain fatty acids (and not triglyceride) in the duodenum initiates the release of CCK, which induces gallbladder contraction, relaxation of Oddi's sphincter, and pancreatic enzyme secretion (71, 72). (f) Being unaffected by luminal amphiphiles, including bile salts (50), lingual lipase continues to hydrolyze tri- and diglycerides in the upper small intestine at pH 5–7 (73).

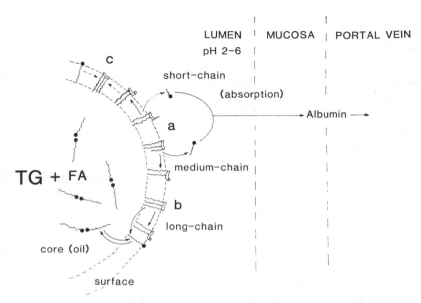

Figure 3 Hypothetical depiction of the physical states and fate of fatty acids released by lingual lipase hydrolysis of triglyceride molecules in the stomach. Only the substrate and product molecules are shown. Most of the surface is actually covered by phospholipid. The sn-3 fatty acid ester linkage is preferentially hydrolyzed, releasing medium- and short-chain fatty acids in the case of milk fat (a), and long-chain fatty acids in the case of common dietary fats (b). Fatty acids (FA), irrespective of chain length, are predominantly undissociated (i.e. un-ionized) at the low stomach pH. In this state, the short- and medium-chain species have appreciable aqueous solubility (a); thus they leave the emulsion and diffuse as monomers to the mucosa, where they are absorbed by passive diffusion mechanisms to enter tributaries of the portal vein. From here they are transported to the liver, bound to albumin, and provide an immediate source of metabolizable energy (ruminants obtain the majority of their energy sources from the production and absorption of volatile FA in the rumen). Protonated long-chain fatty acids (b) are hydrogen bonded crystals or oils at 37°C and are mainly solubilized within the core of the triglyceride (+ diglyceride) droplets, although some partition into the surface coat. Lingual lipase also catalyzes resynthesis of some triglycerides from these long-chain fatty acids and diglycerides (c) [from data in (51–55, 57)].

Fine Emulsification

The emulsion particles in the upper small intestine are generally less than 0.5 μm in diameter and are extremely stable (74–76). When stomach chyme is propelled through the small opening of the pyloric canal into the duodenum, the strong shear forces (analogous to those produced in a commercial "colloid mill") tear the liquid interfaces apart (77, 78). The oil solubilized and protonated long-chain fatty acids diffuse from the bulk to the surface of the triglyceride droplets and become partially ionized. Here they mix with dietary phospholipids and amphiphilic peptic digests of dietary proteins (79). Fatty acids induce a minimum interfacial tension and maximal emulsion stability only when they are partially ionized to form 1:1 "acid soaps." However, in pure systems the bulk pH at which pure long chain-fatty acids are 50% ionized is > pH 7 (58–60, 80–82). Using hydrocarbons emulsified with laurate, Saleeb and colleagues (80) found that maximal emulsion stability occurred at a bulk pH of 8.0. Thus "acid soap" formation would be only partly effective at emulsification at the usual duodenal pH (~ 6.5). Nevertheless, several other amphiphiles and ions may lower the bulk pH at which long-chain fatty acids are 50% ionized. Thus bile salts (83–85), bile salts and monoacylglycerol (86), calcium (87), and perhaps other amphiphiles increase the ionization of the interface and apparently facilitate emulsification at the prevailing pH values of the post-prandial upper small intestine (Figure 4).

In the duodenum, peristaltic and segmental contractions continue to supply mechanical energy (shearing/compression forces) that increases the interfacial area of fat droplets and as a consequence reduces the size of the particles (74). Further, *internal* physical-chemical processes occur near the interface that lead to a breakup of the bulk oil phase in the presence of low interfacial tensions (often loosely termed "spontaneous emulsification"). These arise principally from the non-uniform distribution of the amphiphile

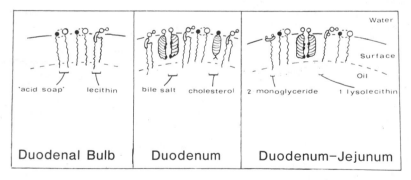

Figure 4 Molecular arrangements of potential physiological emulsifiers of triglyceride at an oil-water interface in regions of the small intestine. Fine emulsification is promoted continually as fat droplets progress through the duodenum. In the stomach, phospholipids and peptic digests of dietary protein align at the interface (see Figure 3). At the pH of the duodenal bulb (pH 5–6), partially ionized fatty acids ("acid soaps") are adsorbed to the interface from the bulk oil. In the mid-duodenum, biliary lipids (bile salts, lecithin, and cholesterol) mix with the emulsifier layer. Once hydrolysis is initiated, the digestive products ("acid soaps," monoglycerides, and lysophosphatides) are added and act as potent emulsifiers.

molecules at the interface, which induces surface shearing forces, turbulence, and interfacial agitation (78).

As bile enters the duodenum it mixes with these particles. While pure bile salts are extremely poor emulsifiers of fat (64, 65, 88), bile salts in dilute combinations with triglyceride digestive products and biliary lipids aid in fat emulsification (Figure 4). Recent work on the phase equilibria and structure of biliary mixed micelles (89, 90) and upper intestinal contents after a fatty meal (91; R. J. Stafford, M. C. Carey, unpublished observations) suggests that the biliary micellar phase becomes saturated with lecithin when diluted within the intestinal lumen. Similarly, the micellar phase during established fatty digestion is saturated with the products of lipolysis (91; R. J. Stafford, M. C. Carey, unpublished observations). Figure 4 displays how the emulsion droplets within the upper small intestine could be enveloped with a monolayer of biliary lipids mixed with the products of hydrolysis. Lairon et al (92) demonstrated that the composition of an adsorbed monomolecular film of porcine biliary lipids around siliconized glass beads was 1 cholesterol : 2 phospholipid : 3 bile salt molecules; Nalbone et al (93) found most of the biliary phospholipid associated with the emulsion particles during fat digestion in the rat. Other studies (64, 65) indicate that binary or ternary combinations of bile salts, lecithin, "acid-soap," and monoglycerides in appropriate physiologic ratios and concentrations produce triglyceride emulsion particles that are extremely small and stable at pH 6.5 and require low shear forces or even emulsify "spontaneously" (Figure 4).

Pancreatic Lipase-Colipase and Phospholipase A_2 Hydrolysis

In humans and most animals there appear(s) to be one (or at the most two) form(s) of the classic pancreatic lipase, and the enzyme(s) is(are) secreted in an active form. Both pancreatic colipase and phospholipase A_2 are secreted in a procoenzyme and proenzyme form, respectively, and require activation by tryptic hydrolysis of an Arg-Gly and Arg-Ala bond in their N-terminal chains, respectively (94, 95). Pancreatic phospholipase A_2 catalyzes the hydrolysis of fatty acids esterified at the sn-2 position of a variety of phosphoglycerides (phosphatidylcholine, phosphatidylethanolamine, phosphatidylglycerol, phosphatidylserine, phosphatidylinositol, cardiolipin) but is without effect on sphingolipids (sphingomyelin, cerebrosides, and gangliosides) (96). The enzyme has an absolute requirement for Ca^{2+} ions which bind in a 1 : 1 stoichiometry to substrate and enzyme (97). It has been suggested that this ensures fixation and stabilization of the enzyme-substrate complex. Aggregation of the substrate is necessary, and this appears to facilitate the nonequivalent interaction of the sn-2 fatty acid ester with the catalytic site of the enzyme (98). Hydrolytic rates also depend on the type of aggregation (liposomes, mixed micelles, emulsions), and the presence of other lipids which presumably influences the packing of the fatty acid chains and head-group area (99).

In the absence of bile salts and phospholipids, lipase can readily bind by hydrophobic interactions to the triglyceride-water interface; the enzyme then becomes highly active. In model systems, bile salts, like other detergents, induce desorption of water-soluble proteins (including pancreatic lipase) from triglyceride-water interfaces (100). Colipase binds a bile salt–covered triglyceride-water interface and provides a high-affinity "anchor" site for lipase. With physiological triglyceride emulsions carrying an envelope of dietary phospholipids, biliary bile salts, lecithin and cholesterol, and partially ionized fatty acids from lingual lipase hydrolysis (Figure 4), the interactions of pancreatic lipase, phospholipase A_2, colipase, and bile salts are highly complex (Figure 5). The "physico-chemical" interpretation

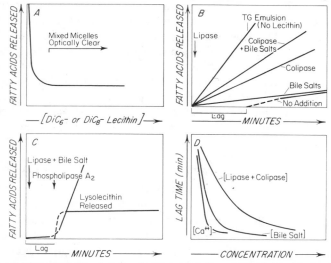

Figure 5   A: The extent of hydrolysis of tributyrin, a short-chain triglyceride, by pancreatic lipase is sharply decreased by the addition of a short-chain lecithin. *B:* The rates of hydrolysis of emulsified long-chain triglycerides by pancreatic lipase. The highest rate occurs with triglycerides emulsified with gum arabic (no lecithin). All the other curves represent hydrolysis rates of triglycerides emulsified with long-chain lecithin. There is a long lag period and then a slight hydrolysis in the absence of additives. With added bile salts, the lag period is abolished, but the hydrolysis rates are still low. Both colipase and colipase plus bile salts accelerate the hydrolytic rates [from (37, 41)]. *C:* Phospholipase A_2 hydrolysis of part of the phospholipid emulsifier (as indicated by lysolecithin release) interrupts the lag phase and allows triglyceride hydrolysis by pancreatic lipase to proceed rapidly [from (37, 41, 42)]. *D:* Increases in the lipase and colipase concentration, bile salt concentration, and Ca^{2+} concentration reduce the length of the lag phase during pancreatic lipase hydrolysis of triglyceride emulsified with lecithin [from (37)].

of these data is that pancreatic lipase alone (in contrast to lingual lipase) is inhibited by emulsifying amphiphiles, presumably because the interface is not recognized, since only 2–3% of triglyceride is solubilized without the emulsifying monolayer at any time. Thus, depending on the physical form of the substrates, fatty acids are released slowly from mixed micelles (Figure 5A) or demonstrate a "lag inhibition" from emulsions (Figure 5B) (37, 41, 42, 101). The "lag-inhibition" (Figure 5) can be counteracted by colipase (Figure 5B, D) (37, 41, 42), which is known to penetrate and perturb lecithin bilayers (102). The cofactor attaches to the ester bond region of triglyceride by hydrogen bonding and possibly electrostatic interactions; lipase tightly anchors to colipase by electrostatic bonding and is then in a suitable configuration to hydrolyze the substrate (103). Bile salts may enhance (a) the binding of colipase (Figure 5B, D) by forming colipase–bile salt aggregates (104), and (b) the binding of phospholipase A_2. Phospholipase A_2 hydrolysis of the emulsifier (Figure 5C) may be a mechanism for facilitating triglyceride hydrolysis in vivo (37, 41, 42). Phospholipase A_2 prepared according to standard procedures contains 0.1–0.2% colipase; it has been shown that pure phospholipase A_2–treated milk fat globules require colipase to be hydrolyzed by lipase in the presence of bile salts (105). In addition to promoting phospholipase A_2 hydrolysis, calcium ions (Figure 5D) may facilitate the desorption of the lipolytic products from the interfaces (106). Thus pancreatic lipase, colipase, phospholipase A_2, calcium, and bile salts all act synergistically in the lipid hydrolytic reactions of the upper small intestine.

Pancreatic Nonspecific Lipase, Cholesterol Esterase, and Human Milk Lipase Hydrolysis

Pancreatic nonspecific lipase (carboxylic esterase), a "minor" lipase of pancreatic juice, and pancreatic cholesterol esterase are apparently the same enzyme (5). The rat enzyme (107) is secreted in an inactive monomeric form ($M_r \cong 65,000$) and only becomes active when polymerized by trihydroxy bile salts to a higher molecular weight form ($M_r \cong 400,000$). The human enzyme has also been purified and characterized (108–111) and has been shown to be a glycoprotein with a broad substrate specificity. It catalyzes the hydrolysis of water-soluble carboxyl esters (triacetin, tripropionin, methylbutyrate, lysolecithin) and insoluble esters (of cholesterol and lipovitamins A, D, and E) dispersed in bile salt micelles (110). Emulsified substrates appear to be hydrolyzed poorly. The monomeric form of the enzyme ($M_r \cong 100,000$) dimerizes to the active form in the presence of 3α, 7α-hydroxylated primary bile salts (cholate, chenodeoxycholate, and their conjugates) in concentrations well below their critical micellar concentrations. As with lingual lipase, the interfacial adsorption of the active dimeric enzyme is not affected by micellar concentrations of bile salts (111).

While the milk of all mammals contains a lipoprotein lipase derived from serum, only the milks of humans (112) and gorillas (113) are known to contain in addition a nonspecific true lipase that is activated by bile salts. There is now biochemical and immunological evidence that this lipase may be identical to the pancreatic nonspecific lipase-cholesterol esterase just described. The enzyme has been purified to homogeneity (114) and characterized (115–117). It is a glycoprotein ($M_r \cong 125,000$) that is stable at pH 3.5 for 1 hr at 37°C; it requires activation by primary bile salts in concentrations below their CMC values. The enzyme hydrolyzes dispersed water-insoluble substrates (triglycerides, lipovitamin-, and cholesterol esters) and water-soluble substrates (short- and medium-chain mono-glycerides, etc). Activation by taurocholate is due to enhancement of the binding of the enzyme to its substrate with enhanced product formation (115). However, bile salt–induced dimerization has not yet been investigated. In view of its similar properties to those of pancreatic nonspecific lipase (cholesteryl esterase), and since it is immunologically identical with a pancreatic enzyme (118), its origin in the pancreas is virtually certain. It is possible that lipase moves from blood to human milk via a receptor-mediated transfer in the lactating mammary gland. The enzyme may play an important role in intestinal digestion of milk triglycerides and others esters in the neonate (119–122), at a time when exocrine pancreatic function and bile salt secretion are suboptimal (119–22).

Chemical Concentrations of Substrates and Enzymes

The physical-chemical environment during lipid digestion and absorption is remarkably constant. Between 1 and 1.5 hr after the ingestion of a meal, the mean pH of the upper intestinal contents falls from a pH $\cong$ 6.8 to about pH 5.3 (123, 124) as stomach acid briefly overwhelms the bufferering capacity of the duodenum. Owing to the buffering capacity of food, the pH of which is $\cong$ 6.0, this pH value is typical of that in the human stomach about 30 min after the ingestion of a meal (123). While osmolality of stomach contents generally reflects that of the diet ($>$ 600 mOsm/kg), osmotic equilibration occurs in the duodenum (but not in the stomach) and lowers the osmolality of gastric chyme to 300–350 mOsm/kg (123). This value is only slightly higher than that of plasma. Due to continuous duodenal secretion of hepatic bile, fasting bile salt levels are in the range of 3–7 mM (125). Postprandial gallbladder emptying causes a transient elevation in total bile acid concentration to 13–46 mM (125). During established lipid digestion (i.e. $>$ 30 min after a meal), the bile salt concentration decreases to 2.5–10 mM and remains constant despite 2–3 enterohepatic cycles of the bile salt pool (4, 125). The triglyceride concentration is also fairly constant, $\cong$ 10–40 mM (37, 126), but the total phospholipid concentration (127–131) is somewhat more variable (0.3–5.5 mM). Owing to biliary lecithin secretion, the molar ratio of lecithin to triglyceride in duodenal contents is about $\cong$ 1 : 10, in contrast to $\cong$ 1 : 40 in the diet. Calcium concentrations vary from 5 to 15 mM (129); sodium and potassium concentrations are $\cong$ 100mM and $\cong$ 25mM (129), respectively. Lipase and colipase are secreted in equimolar proportions, giving duodenal concentrations of $\sim 1 \rightarrow 2 \times 10^{-7}$ M (132). These concentrations can release 150–300 μmoles of sn-1 and sn-3 long-chain fatty acids/min/ml of intestinal fluid (5) (Figure 6). The corresponding activity of intestinal phospholipase A_2 is much lower, releasing 0.5–1.5 μmoles of sn-2 long-chain fatty acids/min/ml of intestinal fluid (127) (Figure 6). The fatty acids become partially ionized and immediately form "acid soaps" within the surface coat. Together with 2-monoglycerides and 1-lysophospholipids, they greatly expand the surface, reduce the size of and stabilize the emulsions, and eventually desorb from the surface with bile salts into dispersed physical states (Figure 7). Pancreatic lipase has a remarkably high turnover number: 250,000 to 500,000 long-chain triglyceride molecules/min. Its activity in intestinal content is 100–1000-fold in excess of that needed for complete hydrolysis of triglycerides in the upper small intestine. Phospholipase A_2 hydrolysis is less efficient, and dietary and

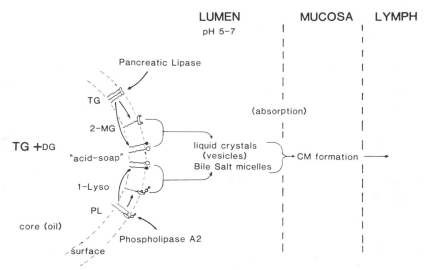

Figure 6 Hydrolytic products of pancreatic lipase and phospholipase A_2 in the duodenum. Fatty acids, 2-monoglycerides (MG), and 1-lysolecithin (1-Lyso) are dispersed in liquid crystalline liposomes or bile salt micelles for absorption by enterocytes. Within the mucosal cell, chylomicrons (CM) containing a triglyceride core and a phospholipid and apoprotein surface are synthesized, secreted into lymph, and transported into blood via the thoracic duct.

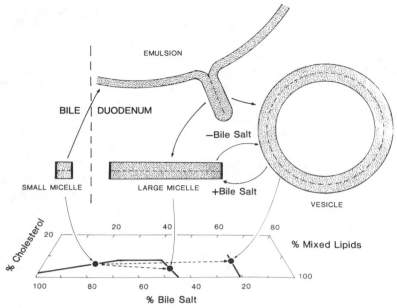

Figure 7   Composite and simplified phase diagram and physical states of gallbladder bile and intestinal aqueous contents after a fatty meal in a healthy person. The mixed lipids are treated as a single component such as lecithin in the case of gallbladder bile. This component includes partially ionized fatty acid, monoglycerides, lecithin, and traces of diglycerides in the case of aqueous duodenal content. The water content is assumed to be 98% and the pH 6.5. The boundaries vary with pH, temperature, and composition (R. J. Stafford, M.C. Carey, unpublished observations). In bile, the relative composition of the mixed micelles (particle diameter ~ 60Å) is ~ 50% saturated with lecithin and 100% saturated with cholesterol. In postprandial duodenal content in addition to the emulsion particles at least two other dispersed phases are present: a phase of large micelles saturated with both mixed lipids and cholesterol (hydrodynamic radii ~ 200Å), and unilamellar vesicles (liposomes) of mixed lipids saturated with bile salts. The hydrodynamic radii of the liposomes are ~ 400–600Å [from (91, 147); R. J. Stafford, M. C. Carey, unpublished observations].

endogenous phospholipids undergo continued hydrolysis in the jejunum and possibly in the ileum (127).

PHYSICAL-CHEMICAL STATE OF LIPIDS DURING DIGESTION

Hofmann & Borgström's work (133, 134) and subsequent studies (128–131, 135–145) concluded that the postprandial human intestine contained a "two-phase" lipid system composed of oil and aqueous micellar phases. To isolate the phases these authors relied on either prolonged ultracentrifugation (130, 131, 133–145) after lipase inactivation at 70°C, or multiple ul-trafiltrations after mild centrifugation (128, 129). Heat treatment, filtration, and centrifugation induced demulsification (38, 78). Further, by initially stimulating lipase activity, heating increases fatty acid production, alters phospholipid composition (128) and perturbs phase boundaries (89). Several workers (128, 129, 146) have suggested that the Hofmann-Borgström hypothesis may be an oversimplification. Ultracentrifugation produces a marked aqueous bile salt–fatty acid gradient and only a small portion of duodenal fluid becomes optically clear (128). Other authors have noted that an insoluble pellet phase is invariably present (146) and that ultrafiltration generally results in a slightly turbid aqueous filtrate (128, 129).

Patton & Carey (126) examined the digestion of stomach emulsions and purified olive oil by light microscopy in vitro and observed the sequential appearance of a birefringent calcium soap phase and a nontriglyceride 1 : 1 monoglyceride–fatty acid phase (viscous isotropic phase). The remaining oil phase was largely triglyceride and diglyceride. In an attempt to reconcile these findings with the Hofmann-Borgström hypothesis, Stafford & Carey [(91, 147), and unpublished observations] defined the phase equilibria of simplified model systems of the aqueous intestinal lipids for typical physiologic conditions (Figure 7) and also elucidated the compositions of the aqueous phases of postprandial distal-duodenal content after boronic acid–inhibition of pancreatic lipase activity. After low-speed centrifugation, the total aspirates separated into an oily emulsion portion and a turbid triglyceride-free aqueous portion. Upon ultracentrifugation of the turbid portion a bile salt micellar phase, saturated with the products of lipolysis, and a liquid-crystalline phase, saturated with bile salts, were obtained (Figure 7).

Since liquid crystalline vesicles and micelles coexist during human fat digestion, the aqueous "phase" analyses in earlier studies probably represent a mixture of both particles. Laser light scattering reveals hydrodynamic radii of about 200Å for the micelles in the model micellar phase at the mixed lipid/bile salt phase boundary (91, 147). Similarly sized particles are found in separated aspirates of the human postprandial duodenum whose relative lipid composition plots on the micellar phase boundary (Figure 7). The structure of these large mixed micelles may be similar to, but larger than, that of the "mixed disc" model of bile salt–lecithin micelles (90). The aqueous lipids dispersed as liquid crystals—i.e. nonmicellar particles—have hydrodynamic radii of 400–600Å. These are probably unilamellar—i.e. single-shelled liposomes (R. J. Stafford, M. C. Carey, unpublished observations) (see Figure 7).

This discovery may have important pathophysiological consequences. It is well known that in many patients with low intraluminal bile salt concentrations, fat malabsorption may be minimal (148). Even in patients with biliary fistulae, triglycerides are apparently hydrolyzed completely, but the resulting free fatty acids are poorly solubilized in a "clear" phase ($<$ 0.05mM), yet fat absorption occurs (131). Phase analyses of the relative compositions of the *total* aqueous phase lipids from published data (136, 148) on such subjects suggest that free fatty acids and monoglycerides are present as a liquid crystalline phase whose relative lipid compositions fall on or close to the right-hand phase boundary in Figure 7. Previous investigators (136, 148) interpreted their qualitative findings to imply a "defective transfer of hydrolyzed dietary fat products to the micellar phase." In contrast to patients with pancreatic insufficiency (149), triglyceride absorption in bile salt–deficient patients occurs efficiently (148), suggesting the importance of a nonmicellar liposomal phase in fat assimilation.

Dynamic Scheme for Fat Digestion and Absorption in the Upper Small Intestine

As crudely emulsified lipids at low pH (Figure 3) are ejected from the stomach into the duodenum, the contents meet duodenal fluid arising from the pancreas, gallbladder, and small intestine. The pH is considerably higher in the duodenum (pH 5–7.5) than in the stomach. This abrupt change in pH causes an abrupt change in the physical behavior of the fatty acids in the crude emulsion. These become partly charged (ionized,) migrate to the interface of the emulsion particle, and commence limited "spontaneous emulsification." Simultaneously, biliary lipids ejected from the gallbladder in the form of biliary mixed micelles become rapidly diluted and also contact the emulsion coming from the stomach. When biliary mixed micelles are diluted they enlarge as a result of the altered micelle-monomer equilibrium (90). However, in the intestinal lumen where they are likely to come in contact with the emulsion particles it is likely that mixed biliary lipids collide and transfer (either by fusion or perhaps through a monomer phase) to the surface of emulsions. The cholesterol of the biliary micelle probably partitions between core and surface of the emulsion (38). The generation of new surface both from "spontaneous emulsification" of partly ionized fatty acids and from the addition of biliary lipids (Figure 4) markedly increases the surface and in concert with the mechanical emulsification creates smaller stabilized particles (150). As the high pH, enzyme rich fluid of the pancreas reaches such an emulsion system, pancreatic lipase-colipase, phospholipase A_2, and nonspecific esterases hydrolyze both core and surface components rapidly, creating a mass of products (Figure 6). The generating products create an increased surface pressure in the emulsion coat and bud off bilayered fragments, probably as unilamellar liposomes (Figure 7). Lipid exchange mediated via inter-particle monomeric exchange or by direct collision progressively enriches both micellar and liposomal particles with the hydrolytic products.

It is not known how the molecules of dispersed lipid products in the intestinal lumen gain entrance into the absorptive enterocytes (151). The dispersed lipids, which are bilayers themselves, are very soluble in membranes. Owing to the high intraluminal concentration, it is possible that such lipids can move passively and efficiently down their concentration gradients from lumen via apical membranes of enterocytes to cytosol. Patton (5) has suggested that this could occur via a hydrocarbon continuum; Dietschy and co-workers believe that absorption is mediated via the lipid monomers in the inter-particle aqueous phase (151). During absorption a series of diffusional barriers must be overcome in order for micellar or liposomal particles to make contact with membranes. These include bulk water, nonstirred water (Nernst diffusion layers), mucin gels, and glycocalyx (151). It is unlikely that the luminal micelles diffuse through these barriers intact since micellar integrity depends on the constancy of the intermicellar concentration of bile salts; if the latter were diluted (i.e. via faster diffusion in unstirred or gelled layers) the micelles would be transformed into unilamellar liposomes (90). However, if the monomeric concentration of bile salts in the diffusion layer becomes higher than that in the bulk aqueous phase the converse is possible.

FATE OF LIPIDS IN THE COLON

Volatile Fatty Acids (VFAs)

The products of large intestinal bacterial fermentation include the VFA—acetate, propionate, and buytrate. These are formed mainly from $C_6H_{10}O_5$, the major monomeric unit of cellulose. Though VFAs comprise the predominant solute fraction of stool water (152, 153), most VFAs are absorbed across the colonic wall and could provide appreciable metabolizable energy for humans whose diets regularly contain large amounts of plant fiber (154).

Dietary, Membrane, Bacterial, and Biliary Lipids

The upper gut of the average healthy person absorbs over 98% of the ≅ 150 g of lipid ingested, as well as the 15–40 g of endogenous lipid (biliary, sloughed cells, secretions) entering the intestinal lumen. The lipid that enters the colon consists primarily of nonabsorbed dietary nonpolar hydrocarbons, unhydrolyzed waxy lipids, undigested cellular lipids, and crystalline lipids. Most endogenous colonic and, ultimately, fecal lipids derive from membranes of sloughed cells and bacteria; remnants of unabsorbed biliary lipids are also present (155). Many of the lipids of bacterial origin are unique (156), and odd-numbered and branched-chain fatty acids have been identified in feces of conventional but not germ-free animals (157). About half of fecal lipid is endogenous, the remainder of dietary origin (158, 159). There is no evidence for absorption of long-chained lipids in the colon. During transit, several bacterial modifications occur. These include hydrolysis of glycerides, phospholipids, wax esters, and cholesterol esters by various bacterial lipases (160, 161), hydroxylation of double-bonds of fatty acids (160), and dehydrogenation, epimerization, and deconjugation of bile salts (162, 163).

Fecal Lipids

Some attempts have been made using conventional methods (acid, alkali, organic solvents, heat treatment) to measure separate classes of fecal lipids (164–170). In all of these methods, however, the physical-chemical state of the excreted lipid is altered during the extraction process. Thus while total lipids can be measured, these methods do not determine the physical state of lipids as they exist in feces at the time of excretion.

We have devised a method to separate fecal lipids according to their different physical states before chemical extraction and quantitation (161, 171, 172). Oil, water, and solid fractions were mechanically separated by a series of low and high speed centrifugations. Each fraction was then separately extracted using methods designed to alter the lipid as little as possible. The lipids were then quantified chromatographically (173). Figure 8 shows the chemical species, physical states, and relative amounts of the 4–6 g of fat that are normally excreted in the daily stool of healthy people. The major fractions are oil- or water-soluble fatty acids; soaps of divalent

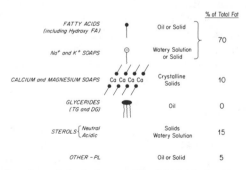

Figure 8 Chemical species and physical states of fecal fat in the healthy human (total output per day ~ 4–6 g). Note that fatty acids may be excreted in different phases depending on their chemical nature. Protonated fatty acids are solid or oil, while simple soaps may be in the water or solid phase. The phase separation depends in part on their melting points. On the other hand, divalent soaps form insoluble crystals. Glycerides are found only in patients with severe pancreatic insufficiency (161).

ions, sterols, and other lipids make up minor fractions. No triglyceride is found in normal feces. In pancreatic insufficiency, large amounts of triglycerides may be present (161) while in mucosal disease, divalent soaps may predominate (171).

ACKNOWLEDGMENTS

Dr. Carey is supported in part by NIH Research Grant AM 18559 and a grant from the Cystic Fibrosis Foundation. Dr. Bliss is supported in part by a grant from Boston University School of Medicine General Clinical Research Center RR-533. Dr. Small is supported in part by NIH Research Grant HL26335. We wish to thank Irene Miller and John Steiner of the Biophysics Institute for assistance in typing and for preparation of figures, and Rebecca Ankaner of Brigham and Women's Hospital for editorial assistance.

Literature Cited

1. Vaughan, J. G., ed. 1979. *Food Microscopy.* NY: Academic
2. Rizek, R. L., Friend, B., Page, L. 1974. Fat in today's food supply—level of use and source. *J. Am. Oil Chem. Soc.* 51: 244–50
3. Northfield, T. C., Hofmann, A. F. 1975. Biliary lipid output during three meals and an overnight fast. I. Relationship to bile acid pool size and cholesterol saturation of bile in gallstone and control subjects. *Gut* 16:1–17
4. Carey, M. C. 1982. The enterohepatic circulation. In *The Liver: Biology and Pathobiology,* ed. I. M. Arias, H. Popper, D. Schachter, D. Shafritz, pp. 429–65. NY: Raven Press
5. Patton, J. S. 1981. Gastrointestinal lipid digestion. In *Physiology of the Gastrointestinal Tract,* ed. L. R. Johnston, pp. 1123–46. NY: Raven Press
6. Shaffer, E. A., Small, D. M. 1977. Biliary lipid secretion in cholesterol gallstone disease. The effect of cholecystectomy and obesity. *J. Clin. Invest.* 59: 828–40
7. Small, D. M. 1983. *The Physical Chemistry of Lipids. Handbook of Lipid Research,* Vol. 3, Ch. 8, ed. D. Hanahan. NY: Plenum
8. Dorset, D. L., Pangborn, W. A., Hancock, A. J., Van Soest, T. C., Greenwald, S. M. 1978. Glycerol conformation and the crystal structure of lipids. *Z. Naturforsch. Teil C* 33:50–55
9. Wawra, H. 1978. Investigation of crystalline structures of fats of animals by x-ray scattering. *Z. Naturforsch. Teil C* 33:28–38
10. Larsson, K. 1972. Molecular arrangement in glycerides. *Fette Scifen. Anstrichen* 74:136–42
11. Callahan, P. T. 1979. The use of ^{13}C spin relaxation to investigate molecular motion in liquid tristearin. *Chem. Phys. Lipids* 19:56–73
12. Rossell, J. B. 1973. Interactions of triglycerides and of fats containing them. *Chem. Indust.* Sept. 1, pp. 832–35
13. Rossell, J. B. 1967. Phase diagrams of triglyceride systems. *Adv. Lipid Res.* 5:353–609
14. Schmidt-Nielsen, K. 1946. Melting points of human fats as related to their location in the body. *Acta Physiol. Scand.* 12(Suppl. 37):123–29
15. Small, D. M., Puppione, D. L., Phillips, M. L., Atkinson, D., Hamilton, J. A., Schumaker, V. N. 1980. Crystallization of a metastable lipoprotein. Massive change of lipoprotein properties during routine preparation. *Circulation* 62 (Suppl. III):III–118, Abstr. 444
16. Bennett-Clark, S., Atkinston, D., Hamilton, J. A., Forte, T., Russell, B., Feldman, E. B., Small, D. M. 1982. Physical studies of d < 1.006 g/ml lymph lipoproteins from rats fed palmitate-rich diets. *J. Lipid Res.* 23:28–41
17. Puppione, D. L., Kunitake, S. T., Hamilton, R. L., Phillips, M. L., Schumaker, V. N., Davis, L. D. 1982. Characterization of unusual intermediate density lipoproteins. *J. Lipid Res.* 23:283–90

18. Parks, J. S., Atkinson, D., Small, D. M., Rudel, L. R. 1981. Physical characterization of lymph chylomicra and very low density lipoproteins from nonhuman primates fed saturated dietary fat. *J. Biol. Chem.* 256:12992–99

19. Small, D. M. 1968. A classification of biologic lipids based upon their interaction in aqueous systems. *J. Am. Oil Chem. Soc.* 45:108–19

20. Dervichian, D. G. 1954. Surface properties of fatty acids and allied substances. In *Progress in Chemistry of Fats and Other Lipids,* ed. R. T. Holman, 2:193–243. NY: Pergamon

21. Funasaki, N., Hada, S., Suzuki, K. 1976. The dissolution state of a triglyceride molecule in water and its orientation state at the air-water interface. *Chem. Pharmacol. Bull. Jpn.* 24:731–35

22. Small, D. M. 1967. Observations on lecithin. Phase equilibria and structure of dry and hydrated egg lecithin. *J. Lipid Res.* 8:551–57

23. Tardieu, A., Luzzati, V., Reman, F. C. 1973. Structure and polymorphism of the hydrocarbon chains of lipids: A study of lecithin-water phases. *J. Mol. Biol.* 75:711–33

24. Janiak, M. J., Small, D. M., Shipley, G. G. 1976. The thermal pretransition of synthetic phospholipids: dimyristoyl and dipalmitoyl lecithin. *Biochemistry* 15:4575–80

25. Janiak, M. J., Small, D. M., Shipley, G. G. 1979. Temperate and compositional dependence of the structure of hydrated dimyristoyl lecithin. *J. Biol. Chem.* 254:6068–78

26. Chen, S. C., Sturtevant, J., Gaffney, B. J. 1980. Scanning calorimetric evidence of a third phase in phosphatidylcholine. *Proc. Natl. Acad. Sci. USA* 77:5060–62

27. Fuldner, H. H. 1981. Characterization of a third phase transition in multilamellar DPL liposomes. *Biochemistry* 20:5720–27

28. Ruocco, M., Shipley, G. G. 1982. Characterization of the subtransition of hydrated dipalmitoylphosphatidylcholine bilayers: x-ray diffraction study. *Biochim. Biophys. Acta* 684:59–66

29. Pearson, R. H., Pascher, I. 1979. Moleular structure of lecithin dihydrate. *Nature* 281:499–501

30. Sakurai, I., Iwayanagi, S., Sakurai, T., Seto, T. 1977. X-ray study of egg-yolk lecithin: Unit cell data and electron density profile. *J. Mol. Biol.* 117:285–91

31. Cadenhead, D. A., Demchak, R. J., Phillips, M. C. 1967. Monolayer characteristics of 1,3-dimyristin, 1–2 dimy-

ristoyl-3 cephalin and 1, 2-dimyristoyl-3 lecithin at the air-water interface. *Kolloid Z. Z. Polymer* 220:59–64

32. Bourgès, M., Small, D. M., Dervichian, D. G. 1967. Biophysics of lipidic associations. II. The ternary systems. Cholesterol-lecithin-water. *Biochim. Biophys. Acta* 137:157–67

33. Franks, N. P. 1976. Structural analysis of hydrated egg lecithin and cholesterol bilayers. I. X-ray diffraction. *J. Mol. Biol.* 100:359–75

34. Worcester, D. L., Franks, N. P. 1976. Structural analysis of hydrated egg lecithin and cholesterol bilayers. II. Neutron diffraction. *J. Mol. Biol.* 100:359–78

35. Brown, M. F., Seelig, J. 1978. Influence of cholesterol on the polar regions of phosphatidylcholine and phosphatidylethanolamine bilayers. *Biochemistry* 17:381–84

36. Phillips, M. C. 1972. The physical state of phospholipids and cholesterol in monolayers, bilayers and membranes. *Prog. Surface Membr. Sci.* 5:139–221

37. Borgström, B. 1980. Importance of phospholipids, pancreatic phospholipase A₂ and fatty acid for the digestion of dietary fat. *Gastroenterology* 78:954–62

38. Miller, K. W., Small, D. M. 1982. The phase behavior of triolein, cholesterol and lecithin emulsions. *J. Colloid Interface Sci.* 89:466–78

39. Hamilton, J. A., Small, D. M. 1981. Solubilization and localization of triolein in phosphatidylcholine bilayers: A carbon-13 NMR study. *Proc. Natl. Acad. Sci. USA* 78:6878–82

40. Burns, R. A. Jr., Roberts, M. F. 1981. Physical characterization and lipase susceptibility of short chain lecithin/triglyceride mixed micelles. *J. Biol. Chem.* 256:2716–22

41. Bläckberg, L., Hernell, O., Olivecrona, T. 1981. Hydrolysis of human milk fat globules by pancreatic lipase. *J. Clin. Invest.* 67:1748–52

42. Patton, J. S., Carey, M. C. 1981. The inhibition of human lipase-colipase activity by phospholipid-bile salt mixed micelles. *Am. J. Physiol.* 241:G328–36

43. Hamosh, M., Scow, R. O. 1973. Lingual lipase and its role in the digestion of dietary lipid. *J. Clin. Invest.* 52:88–95

44. Hamosh, M., Klaeneman, H. L., Wolf, R. O., Scow, R. O. 1975. Pharyngeal lipase and digestion of dietary triglyceride in man. *J. Clin. Invest.* 55:908 –13

45. Hamosh, M. 1979. A review. Fat digestion in the newborn: Role of lingual li-

pase and preduodenal digestion. *Pediatr. Res.* 13:615–22
46. Hamosh, M., Burns, W. A. 1977. Lipolytic activity of human lingual glands (Ebner). *Lab. Invest.* 37:603–8
47. Hamosh, M. 1978. Rat lingual lipase. Factors affecting enzyme activity and secretion. *Am. J. Physiol.* 235:E416–21
48. Kosikowski, F. V. 1977. *Cheese and Fermented Milk Foods,* ed. P. Edwards, pp. 213–27. Ann Arbor: Brookdale, NY: F. V. Kosikowski Assoc.
49. Nelson, J. H., Jensen, R. G., Pitas, R. E. 1976. Pregastric enterase and other oral lipases—a review. *J. Dairy Sci.* 60: 327–62
50. Roberts, I. M., Montgomery, R. K., Carey, M. C. 1982. Lingual lipase hydrolyses triglycerides in the presence of lecithin and bile salt micelles. *Gastroenterology* 82:1163 (Abstr.)
51. Edwards-Webb, J. D., Thompson, S. Y. 1977. Studies on lipid digestion in the preruminant calf. 2. A comparison of the products of lipolysis of milk fat by salivary and pancreatic lipases *in vitro. Br. J. Nutr.* 34:431–40
52. Fernando-Warnakulasuriya, G. J. P., Staggers, J. E., Frost, S. C., Wells, M. A. 1981. Studies on fat digestion, absorption and transport in the suckling rat. I. Fatty acid composition and concentrations of major lipid components. *J. Lipid Res.* 22:668–74
53. Staggers, J. E., Fernando-Warnakulasuriya, G. J. P., Wells, M. A. 1981. Studies on fat digestion, absorption, and transport in the suckling rat. II. Triacylglycerol molecular species, stereo-specific analysis and specificity of hydrolysis by lingual lipase. *J. Lipid Res.* 22:675–79
54. Paltauf, F., Esfandi, F., Holasek, A. 1974. Stereo-specificity of lipases. Enzymatic hydrolysis of enantiomeric aklyl diglycerides by lipoprotein lipase, lingual lipase and pancreatic lipase. *FEBS Lett.* 40:119–23
55. Hamosh, M., Ganot, D., Hamosh, P. 1979. Rat lingual lipase: Characteristics of enzyme activity. *J. Biol. Chem.* 24: 12121–25
56. Albert, A., Sergeant, E. P. 1971. *The Determination of Ionization Constants,* p. 84. London: Chapman & Hall 2nd ed.
57. Aw, T. Y., Grigor, M. R. 1980. Digestion and absorption of milk triacylglycerols in 14-day-old suckling rats. *J. Nutr.* 110:2133–40
58. Lucassen, J. 1966. Hydrolysis and precipitates in carboxylate soap solutions. *J. Phys. Chem.* 70:1824–30

59. McBain, J. W., Stewart, A. 1927. Acid soaps: A crystalline potassium hydrogen dioleate. *J. Chem. Soc.* 130:1392–95
60. Dervichian, D. G. 1955. Electrochimie des acides gras et des lipides ioniques. Biochemical Problems of Lipids, Proc. 2nd Int. Conf. held at the Univ. Ghent, 27–30 July. London: Butterworths
61. Ernst, J., Sheldrick, W. S., Fuhrhop, J. H. 1979. The structures of the essential unsaturated fatty acids. Crystal structures of linoleic acid and evidence for the crystal structures of α-linolenic acid and arachidonic acid. *Z. Naturforsch. Teil B* 34:706–11
62. Friberg, S., Gezelius, L-H., Wilton, I. 1971. Influence of acid-soap interactions on the solubility of soaps in triglycerides. *Chem. Phys. Lipids* 6:364–72
63. Davenport, H. W. 1982. *Physiology of the Digestive Tract.* Chicago: Year Book Medical Publishers. p. 147. 5th ed.
64. Linthorst, J. M., Bennett-Clark, S., Holt, P. R. 1977. Triglyceride emulsification by amphipaths present in the intestinal lumen during digestion of fat. *J. Colloid Interface Sci.* 60:1–10
65. Frazer, A. C., Schulman, J. H., Stewart, H. C. 1964. Emulsification of fat in the intestine of the rat and its relationship to absorption. *J. Physiol.* 103:306–16
66. Roy, C. C., Roulet, M., Lefebvre, D., Chartrand, L., Lepage, G., Fournier, L. A. 1979. The role of gastric lipolysis on fat absorption and bile acid metabolism in the rat. *Lipids* 14:811–15
67. Patton, J. S., Albertsson, P. A., Erlanson, C., Borgström, B. 1978. Binding of porcine pancreatic lipase and colipase in the absence of substrate studied by two-phase partition and affinity chromatography. *J. Biol. Chem.* 253:4195–202
68. Patton, J. S., Donnér, J., Borgström, B. 1978. Lipase-colipase interactions during gel filtration: High and low affinity binding situations. *Biochim. Biophys. Acta* 529:67–78
69. Rathelot, J., Julien, R., Bosc-Bierne, I., Gargouri, Y., Canioni, P., Sarda, L. 1981. Horse pancreatic lipase. Interaction with colipase from various species. *Biochimie* 63:227–34
70. Richardson, G. H., Nelson, J. H. 1967. Assay and characterization of pregastric esterase. *J. Dairy Sci.* 50:1061–65
71. Go, V. L. M. 1973. Coordination of the digestive sequence. *Mayo Clin. Proc.* 48:613–16

72. Go, V. L. M., Hofmann, A. F., Summerskill, W. H. J. 1970. Pancreozymin bioassay in man based on pancreatic enzyme secretion: Potency of specific amino acids and other digestive products. *J. Clin Invest* 49:1558–64

73. Dutta, S. K., Hamosh, M., Abrams, C. K., Hamosh, P., Hubbard, V. S. 1982. Quantitative estimation of lingual lipase activity in the upper small intestine in adult patients with pancreatic insufficiency. *Gastroenterology* 82:1047 (Abstr.)

74. Senior, J. R. 1964. Intestinal absorption of fats. *J. Lipid Res.* 5:495–521

75. Frazer, A. C. 1946. The absorption of triglyceride fat from the intestine. *Physiol. Rev.* 26:103–19

76. Elkes, J. J., Frazer, A. C., Schulman, J. H., Stewart, H. C. 1944. The mechanism of emulsification of triglyceride in the small intestine. *Proc. Physiol. Soc.* 103:318 (Abstr.)

77. Carlson, H. C., Code, C. F., Nelson, R. A. 1966. Motor action of the canine gastroduodenal junction: A cineradiographic, pressure and electrical study. *Am. J. Dig. Dis.* 11:155–72

78. Gopal, E. S. R. 1968. Principles of emulsion formation. In *Emulsion Science,* ed. P. Sherman, pp. 2–75. NY: Academic

79. Meyer, J. H., Stevenson, E. A., Watts, H. D. 1976. The potential role of protein in the absorption of fat. *Gastroenterology* 70:232–39

80. Saleeb, F. Z., Cante, C. J., Streckfus, T. K., Frost, J. R., Rosano, H. L. 1975. Surface pH and stability of oil-water emulsions derived from laurate solutions. *J. Am. Oil Chem. Soc.* 52:208–12

81. Eagland, D., Franks, F. 1965. Association equilibria in dilute aqueous solutions of carboxylic acid soaps. *Trans. Faraday Soc.* 61:2468–77

82. Peters, R. A. 1931. Interfacial tension and hydrogen ion concentration. *Proc. R. Soc. London, Ser. A* 133:140–154

83. Carey, M. C., Small, D. M. 1970. The characteristics of mixed micellar solutions with particular reference to bile. *Am. J. Med.* 49:590–608

84. Hofmann, A. F., Mekhjian, H. S. 1973. Bile acids and the intestinal absorption of fat and electrolytes in health and disease. In *The Bile Acids,* ed. P. P. Nair, D. Kritchevsky, 2:103–52. NY: Plenum

85. Shankland, W. 1970. The ionic behavior of fatty acids solubilized by bile salts. *J. Colloid Interface Sci.* 34:9–25

86. Small, D. M. 1971. The physical chem-

istry of cholanic acids. See Ref. 84, 1:249–356

87. Benzonana, G. 1968. Sur le role des ions calcium durant l'hydrolyze des triglycerides insolubles par le lipase pancréatique en presence de sels biliaires. *Biochim. Biophys. Acta* 151:137–46

88. Rochford, B. K. 1981. The influence of bile on the fat-splitting properties of pancreatic juice. *J. Physiol.* 12:72–92

89. Carey, M. C., Small, D. M. 1978. Physical chemistry of cholesterol solubility in bile: Relationship to gallstone formation and dissolution in man. *J. Clin. Invest.* 61:998–1026

90. Mazer, N. A., Benedek, G. B., Carey, M. C. 1980. Quasi-elastic light scattering studies of aqueous biliary lipid systems: Mixed micelle formation in bile salt-lecithin solutions. *Biochemistry* 19:601–15

91. Stafford, R. J., Carey, M. C. 1981. Physical-chemical nature of the aqueous lipoids in intestinal content after a fatty meal: Revision of the Hofmann-Borgström hypothesis. *Clin. Res.* 28:511A (Abstr.)

92. Lairon, D., Nalbone, G., Lafont, H., Leonardi, J., Domingo, N., Hauton, J. C., Verger, R. 1978. Possible roles of bile lipids and colipase in lipase adsorption. *Biochemistry* 17:5263–69

93. Nalbone, G., Lairon, D., Lafont, H., Domingo, N., Hauton, J. C. 1974. Behavior of biliary phospholipids in intestinal lumen during fat digestion in rat. *Lipids* 9:765–70

94. Borgström, B., Wielock, T., Erlanson-Albertsson, C. 1979. Evidence for a pancreatic pro-colipase and its activation by trypsin. *FEBS Lett.* 108:407–10

95. de Haas, G. H., Postema, N. M., Nieuwenhuizen, W., van Deenen, L. L. M. 1968. Purification and properties of anionic zymogen of phospholipase A from porcine pancreas. *Biochim. Biophys. Acta* 159:118–29

96. van Deenen, L. L. M., deHaas, G. H., Heemskerk, C. H. Th. 1963. Hydrolysis of synthetic mixed phosphatides by phospholipase A from human pancreas. *Biochim. Biophys. Acta* 67:295–306

97. van Deenen, L. L. M., deHaas, G. H. 1964. The synthesis of phosphoglycerides and some biochemical applications. *Adv. Lipid Res.* 2:167–234

98. Dijkska, B. W., Drenth, J., Kalk, K. H. 1981. Active site and catalytic mechanism of phospholipase A_2. *Nature* 289:604–6

99. Olive, J., Dervichian, D. G. 1968. Action d'une phospholipase sur la lecithine

a l'etat micellaire. *Bull. Soc. Chim. Biol.* 50:1409–18

100. Borgström, B., Erlanson, C. 1978. Interaction of serum albumin and other proteins with porcine pancreatic lipase. *Gastroenterology* 75:382–86

101. Klein, E., Lyman, R. B., Petersen, L., Berger, R. I. 1967. The effect of lecithin on the activity of pancreatic lipase. *Life Sci.* 6:1305–7

102. Sari, H., Dukes, J.-P., Tachoire, H., Entressangles, B., Desnuelle, P. 1981. Effet de l'addition de la colipase pancreatique de phase de liposome de phosphatidylcholine. *Biochimie* 63:389–95

103. Borgström, B., Erlanson-Albertsson, C., Wieloch, T. 1979. Pancreatic colipase: Chemistry and physiology. *J. Lipid Res.* 20:805–16

104. Cozzone, P. J., Canioni, P., Sarda, L., Kapstein, R. 1981. 360-MH$_z$ nuclear magnetic resonance and laser photochemically induced dynamic nuclear polarization studies of bile salt interaction with porcine colipase A. *Eur. J. Biochem.* 114:119–26

105. Borgström, B., Erlanson-Albertsson, C. 1982. Hydrolysis of milk fat globules by pancreatic lipase. Role of colipase, phospholipase A$_2$ and bile salts. *J. Clin. Invest.* 70:30–32

106. Bläckberg, L., Hernell, O., Bengtsson, G., Olivecrona, T. 1979. Colipase enhances hydrolysis in the absence of bile salts. *J. Clin. Invest.* 64:1303–8

107. Treadwell, C. R., Vahouny, G. V. 1968. Cholesterol absorption. In *Handbook of Physiology, Sect. 6, Alimentary Canal,* ed. C. Code, 3:1407–38. Washington DC: Am. Physiol. Soc.

108. Lombardo, D., Guy, O., Figarella, L. 1978. Purification and characterization of a carboxyl ester hydrolase from human pancreatic juice. *Biochim. Biophys. Acta* 527:142–49

109. Lombardo, D., Fauvel, J., Guy, O. 1980. Studies on the substrate specificity of a carboxyl ester hydrolase from human pancreatic juice. I. Action on carboxyl esters, glycerides and phospholipids. *Biochim. Biophys. Acta* 611:136–46

110. Lombardo, D., Guy, O. 1980. Studies on the substrate specificity of a carboxyl esters hydrolase from human pancreatic juice. II. Action on cholesterol esters and lipid-soluble vitamin esters. *Biochim. Biophys. Acta* 611:147–55

111. Lombardo, D., Guy, O. 1981. Binding of human pancreatic carboxylic ester hydrolase to lipid interfaces. *Biochim. Biophys. Acta* 659:401–10

112. Freudenberg, E. 1953. *Die Frauenmilch-Lipase.* Basel: S. Karger

113. Freudenberg, E. 1966. A lipase in the milk of the gorilla. *Experientia* 22:317–18

114. Wang, C.-S. 1980. Purification of human milk bile salt-activated lipase by cholic acid-coupled Sepharose 4B affinity chromatography. *Anal. Biochem.* 105:389–402

115. Wang, C.-S. 1981. Human milk bile salt-activated lipase: Further characterization and kinetic studies. *J. Biol. Chem.* 256:10918–11202

116. Hernell, O. 1975. Human milk lipases. III. Physiological implication of the bile salt-stimulated lipase. *Eur. J. Clin. Invest.* 5:267–72

117. Hernell, O., Olivecrona, T. 1974. Human milk lipases. II. Bile salt–stimulated lipase. *Biochim. Biophys. Acta* 369:234–44

118. Bläckberg, L., Hernell, O., Olivecrona, T., Domellöf, L., Malinov, M. R. 1980. The bile salt–stimulated lipase in human milk is an evolutionary newcomer derived from a non-milk protein. *FEBS Lett.* 112:51–54

119. Fredrikzon, B., Hernell, O., Bläckberg, L., Olivecrona, T. 1978. Bile salt–stimulated lipase in human milk: Evidence of activity in vivo and of a role in the digestion of milk retinol esters. *Pediatr. Res.* 12:1048–52

120. Olivecrona, T., Hernell, O. 1976. Human milk lipases and their possible role in fat digestion. *Paediatr. Pedagog.* 11:600–4

121. Williamson, S., Finucane, E., Ellis, H., Gamsu, H. R. 1978. Effect of heat treatment of human milk on absorption of nitrogen, fat, sodium, calcium and phosphorus by preterm infants. *Arch. Dis. Child.* 53:555–63

122. Alemi, B., Hamosh, M., Scanlon, J. W., Salzman-Mann, C., Hamosh, P. 1981. Fat digestion in very low-birth-weight infants: Effect of addition of human milk to low-birth-weight formula. *Pediatrics* 68:484–89

123. Malagelada, J.-R., Go, V. L. W., Summerskill, W. H. J. 1979. Different gastric, pancreatic and biliary responses to solid, liquid or homogenized meals. *Dig. Dis. Sci.* 24:101–10

124. Dutta, S. K., Russell, R. M., Iber, F. L. 1979. Influence of exocrine pancreatic insufficiency on the intraluminal pH of the proximal small intestine. *Dig. Dis. Sci.* 24:529–34

125. Sjövall, J. 1959. On the concentration of

676 CAREY, SMALL & BLISS

bile acids in the human intestine. *Acta Physiol. Scand.* 46:339–45

126. Patton, J. S., Carey, M. C. 1979. Watching fat digestion. *Science* 204:145–48

127. Arnesjö, B., Nilsson, A., Barrowman, J., Borgström, B. 1969. Intestinal digestion and absorption of cholesterol and lecithin in the human. *Scand. J. Gastroenterol.* 4:653–65

128. Porter, H. P., Saunders, D. R. 1971. Isolation of the aqueous phase of human intestinal contents during the digestion of a fatty meal. *Gastroenterology* 60:997–1007

129. Mansbach, C. M., Cohen, R. S., Leff, P. B. 1975. Isolation and properties of the mixed lipid micelles present in intestinal content during fat digestion in man. *J. Clin. Invest.* 56:781–91

130. Poley, J. R., Smith, J. D., Thompson, J. B., Seely, J. R. 1977. Improved micellar dispersal of dietary lipid by bile acids during replacement therapy in growth hormone-deficient children. *Pediatr. Res.* 12:1186–91

131. Porter, H. P., Saunders, D. R., Tytgat, G., Brunster, O., Rubin, C. E. 1971. Fat absorption in bile fistula man. A morphological and biochemical study. *Gastroenterology* 60:1008–19

132. Borgström, B., Hildebrand, H. 1975. Lipase and colipase activity of human small intestinal contents after a liquid test meal. *Scand. J. Gastroenterol.* 10:585–91

133. Hofmann, A. F., Borgström, B. 1962. Physical-chemical state of lipids in intestinal content during their digestion and absorption. *Fed. Proc.* 21:43–50

134. Hofmann, A. F., Borgström, B. 1964. The intraluminal phase of fat digestion in man: The lipid content of the micellar and oil phases of intestinal content obtained during fat digestion and absorption. *J. Clin. Invest.* 43:247–57

135. Rautureau, M., Bisalli, A., Rambaud, J.-C. 1981. Bile salts and lipids in aqueous intraluminal phase during the digestion of a standard meal in normal man. *Gastroenterol. Clin. Biol.* 5:417–25

136. Miettinen, T. A., Siurala, M. 1971. Micellar solubilization of intestinal lipids and sterols in gluten enteropathy and liver cirrhosis. *Scand. J. Gastroenterol.* 6:527–35

137. Ricour, C., Rey, J. 1972. Study on the hydrolysis and micellar solubilization of fats during intestinal perfusion. I. Results in the normal child. *Eur. J. Clin. Biol. Res.* 17:172–78

138. Ricour, C., Rey, J. 1970. Study of the oil and micellar phases during fat diges-

tion in the normal child. *Eur. J. Clin. Biol. Res.* 15:287–93

139. Miettinen, T. A., Siurala, M. 1971. Bile salts, sterols, sterol esters, glycerides and fatty acids in micellar and oil phases of intestinal contents during fat digestion in man. *Z. Klin. Chem. Klin. Biochem.* 9:47–52

140. Van Deest, B. W., Fortran, J. S., Morawski, S. G., Wilson, J. D. 1968. Bile salt and micellar fat concentration in proximal small bowel contents of ileectomy patients. *J. Clin. Invest.* 47:1314–24

141. Modai, M., Theodor, E. 1970. Intestinal contents in patients with viral hepatitis after a lipid meal. *Gastroenterology* 58:379–87

142. Schneider, R. E., Viteri, F. E. 1974. Liminal events of lipid absorption in protein-calorie malnourished children: Relationship with nutritional recovery and diarrhea. I. Capacity of the duodenal content to achieve micellar solubilization of lipids. *Am. J. Clin. Nutr.* 27:777–87

143. Schneider, R. E., Viteri, F. E. 1974. Luminal events of lipid absorption in protein-calorie malnourished children: Relationship with nutritional recovery and diarrhea. II. Alterations in bile acid content of duodenal aspirates. *Am. J. Clin. Nutr.* 27:788–96

144. Badley, B. W. D., Murphy, G. M., Bouchier, I. A. D., Sherlock, S. 1970. Diminished micellar phase lipid in patients with chronic non-alcoholic liver disease and steatorrhea. *Gastroenterology* 58:781–89

145. Krone, C. L., Theodor, E., Sleisenger, M. H., Jeffries, G. H. 1968. Studies on the pathogenesis of malabsorption: Lipid hydrolysis and micelle formation in the intestinal lumen. *Medicine* 47:89–106

146. Thompson, G. R., Barrowman, J., Gutierrez, L., Dowling, R. H. 1971. Action of neomycin on the intraluminal phase of lipid absorption. *J. Clin. Invest.* 50:319–23

147. Stafford, R. J., Donovan, J. M., Benedek, G. B., Carey, M. C. 1980. Physical-chemical characteristics of aqueous duodenal content after a fatty meal. *Gastroenterology* 80:1291 (Abstr.)

148. Mansbach, C. M., Newton, D., Stevens, R. D. 1980. Fat digestion in patients with bile acid malabsorption but minimal steatorrhea. *Dig. Dis. Sci.* 25:353–62

149. Shimoda, S. S., Saunders, D. R., Schuffler, M. D., Leinbach, G. L. 1974.

Electron microscopy of small intestinal mucosa in pancreatic insufficiency. *Gastroenterology* 67:19–24

150. Dasher, G. F. 1952. Surface activity of naturally occurring emulsifiers. *Science* 116:660–63

151. Thomson, A. B. R., Dietschy, J. M. 1981. Intestinal lipid absorption: Major extracellular and intracellular events. In *Physiology of the Gastrointestinal Tract*, ed. L. R. Johnson, pp. 1147–1220. NY: Raven Press

152. Wrong, O. M., Metcalfe-Gibson, A., Morrison, R. B. I., Ng, S. T., Howard, A. V. 1965. In vivo dialysis of feces as a method of stool analysis. I. Techniques and results on normal subjects. *Clin. Sci.* 28:357–75

153. Rubinstein, R., Howard, A. V., Wrong, O. M. 1969. In vivo dialysis of feces as a method of stool analysis. IV. The organic anion component. *Clin. Sci.* 37:549–64

154. McNeil, N. I., Cummings, J. H., James, W. P. T. 1978. Short chain fatty acid absorption by the human large intestine. *Gut* 19:819–22

155. Lewis, G. T., Partin, H. C. 1954. Fecal fat on an essentially fat-free diet. *J. Lab. Clin. Med.* 44:91–93

156. O'Leary, W. M. 1962. The fatty acids of bacteria. *Bacteriol. Rev.* 26:421–47

157. Demarne, Y., Sacquet, E., Lecourtier, M. J., Flanzy, J. 1979. Comparative study of endogenous fecal fatty acids in germ-free and conventional rats. *Am. J. Clin. Nutr.* 32:2027–32

158. Cotton, P. B. 1972. Non-dietary lipid in the intestinal lumen. *Gut* 13:675–81

159. Wiggins, H. S., Howell, K. E., Kellock, T. D., Stalder, J. 1969. The origin of faecal fat. *Gut* 10:400–3

160. Alford, J. A., Pierce, D. A., Suggs, F. G. 1964. Activity of microbial lipases on natural fats and synthetic triglycerides. *J. Lipid Res.* 5:390–94

161. Bliss, C. M., Small, D. M. 1970. A comparison of ileal and fecal lipid in pancreatic steatorrhea. *Gastroenterology* 58:928 (Abstr.)

162. Aries, V., Hill, M. J. 1970. Degradation of steroids by intestinal bacteria. I.

Deconjugation of bile salts. *Biochim. Biophys. Acta* 202:526–34

163. Aries, V., Hill, M. J. 1970. Degradation of steroids by intestinal bacteria. II. Enzymes catalyzing the oxidoreduction of the 3α-, 7α-, and 12α-hydroxyl groups in cholic acid, and the dehydroxylation of the 7-hydroxyl group. *Biochim. Biophys. Acta* 202:535–43

164. van de Kamer, J. H., ten Bokkel Huinink, H., Weyers, H. A. 1949. Rapid method for the determination of fat in feces. *J. Biol. Chem.* 177:347–55

165. Braddock, L. I., Fleisher, D. R., Barbero, G. J. 1968. A physical-chemical study of the van de Kamer method for fecal fat analysis. *Gastroenterology* 55:165–72

166. Jover, A., Gordon, R. S. 1962. Procedure for quantitative analysis of feces with special reference to fecal fatty acids. *J. Lab. Clin. Med.* 59:878–84

167. Folch, J., Lees, M., Stanley, G. H. 1957. A simple method for the isolation and purification of total lipids from animal tissues. *J. Biol. Chem.* 226:497–509

168. James, A. T., Webb, J., Kellock, T. D. 1961. The occurrence of unusual fatty acids in faecal lipids from human beings with normal and abnormal fab absorption. *Biochem. J.* 78:333–39

169. Aylword, F., Wood, P. D. S. 1962. Lipid excretion. 2. Fractionation of human fecal lipids. *Brit. J. Nutr.* 16:345–60

170. Thompson, J. B., Langley, R. L., Hess, D. R., Welsh, J. D. 1961. Fecal triglycerides. I. Methods. *J. Lab. Clin. Med.* 73:512–20

171. Bliss, C. M., Small, D. M., Donaldson, R. M. 1972. The excretion of calcium and magnesium fatty acid soaps in steatorrhea. *Gastroenterology* 62:724 (Abstr.)

172. Bliss, C. M., Small, D. M., Donaldson, R. M. 1973. Water phase fatty acid excretion in diarrhea. *Gastroenterology* 64:701 (Abstr.)

173. Robins, S. J., Small, D. M., Trier, J. S., Donaldson, R. M. Jr. 1971. Localization of fatty acid reesterification in the brush border region of intestinal absorptive cells. *Biochim. Biophys. Acta* 233:550–61

Ann. Rev. Physiol. 1983. 45:679–85
Copyright © 1983 by Annual Reviews Inc. All rights reserved.

BILE ACID SYNTHESIS

Gerald Salen

Department of Medicine, University of Medicine and Dentistry, New Jersey
Medical School, Newark, New Jersey and Veterans Administration Hospital,
East Orange, New Jersey

Sarah Shefer

Department of Medicine, University of Medicine and Dentistry, New Jersey
Medical School, Newark, New Jersey

BILE ACID SYNTHESIS

Biosynthetic Pathways of Bile Acid Synthesis

Cholesterol is the obligatory precursor of bile acids, and the liver is the sole
source and site of bile acid formation (1). In the transformation of cholesterol to bile acids, the cyclopentanophenanthrene nucleus is first believed
to undergo modifications followed by oxidation and cleavage of the cholesterol side-chain. The key reactions transforming the nucleus are illustrated
in Figure 1.

The first and perhaps most important step in bile acid synthesis is the 7
α-hydroxylation of cholesterol to form 7α-hydroxycholesterol (II). This
reaction is catalyzed by the microsomal enzyme system, cholesterol 7α-
hydroxylase (EC 1.14), which determines the rate of bile acid formation, but
the detailed mechanism of enzyme control is not known. The 7α-hydroxy-
cholesterol that is formed is totally committed to bile acid production (2,
3) with the next steps involving oxidation of the hydroxyl group at C-3 and
isomerization of the double bond from C-5,6 to C-4,5, which yields 7α-
hydroxy-4-cholesten-3-one (III). This compound is the last intermediate
common to both cholic acid and chenodeoxycholic acid. In cholic acid
synthesis, 12α-hydroxylation occurs to yield 7α,12α-dihydroxy-4-choles-
ten-3-one (IV), which then undergoes reduction of the double-bond at C 4–5
and the ketone at C-3 to give 5β-cholestane-3α,7α,12α-triol (V). Thus far,

679

0066-4278/83/0315-0679$02.00

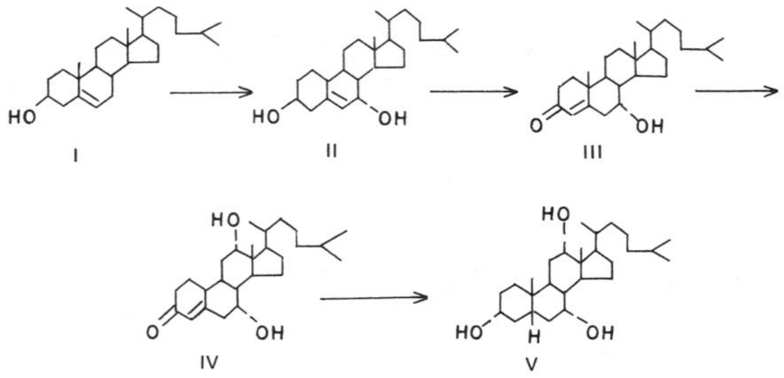

Figure 1   Key reactions transforming the cyclopentanophenanthrene nucleus

the ring has been modified without any changes to the hydrocarbon side-chain. In chenodeoxycholic acid formation, 7α-hydroxy-4-cholesten-3-one (III) undergoes reduction at C 4–5 and C–3 to yield 5β-cholestane-3α,7α-diol, which is now ready to undergo side-chain oxidation.

According to the classical theory, 26-hydroxylation of 5β-cholestane-3α,7α,12α-triol (1) is the first step in the side-chain oxidation (Figure 2). Although in rats the reaction is carried out by both microsomal and mitochondrial enzymes (4, 5) only the mitochondria have been shown to convert 5β-cholestane-3α,7α,12α-triol (V) to 5β-cholestane-3α,7α,12α,26-tetrol (VI) in humans (6). The next step involves the oxidation of this tetrol to 3α,7α,12α-trihydroxy-5β-cholestanoic acid (THCA, VII) by the cystosolic fraction (7). Preliminary experiments suggest that only the 25R isomer of 5β-cholestane-3α,7α,12α,26-tetrol is produced by the mitochondria. This in turn results in the formation of the 25R-isomer of THCA

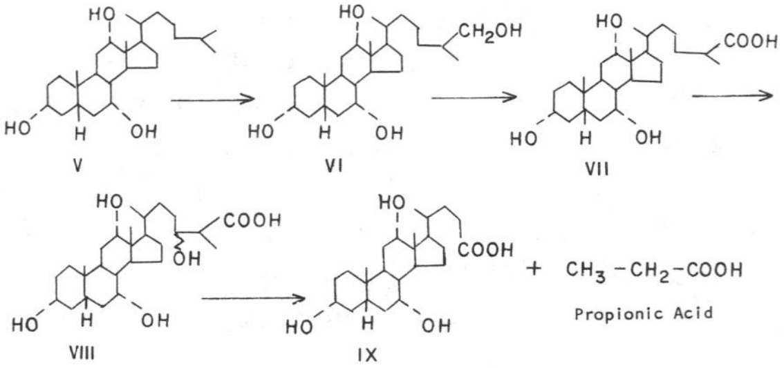

Figure 2   Side-chain oxidation

(8). THCA is then 24-hydroxylated to form varanic acid (VIII), which then undergoes cleavage of the C 24–25 bond with oxidation at C-24 to yield cholic acid (IX) and propionic acid. The 24-hydroxylation of THCA was shown to be catalyzed predominantly by microsomal enzymes fortified with the 100,000 Xg supernatant and ATP (9), whereas the cleavage is carried out by mitochondrial or cytosolic enzymes (10). The stereospecificity of these reactions has not been clarified yet. Recently, an alternative mechanism has been discovered for the oxidation of the hydrocarbon side-chain of 5β-cholestane-3α,7α,12α-triol that does not involve intermediates hydroxylated at C-26 [Figure 3; (11)].

The first step in the alternative pathway is the 25-hydroxylation of 5β-cholestane-3α,7α,12α-triol to give 5β-cholestane-3α,7α,12α,25-tetrol (X). This reaction is catalyzed by a microsomal enzyme system and is followed by the 24S-hydroxylation of the 5β-cholestanetetrol to yield 5β-cholestane-3α,7α,12α,24S,25-pentol (XI) (12). The pentol is then oxidized to give 3α,7α,12α,25-tetrahydroxy-5β-cholestan-24-one (XII) (13), which is cleaved by cytosolic enzymes to yield cholic acid and acetone. The 25-hydroxylation pathway in the conversion of cholesterol to cholic acid has been demonstrated in both rat and human liver (11).

Regulation of Bile Acid Synthesis

The enzymes, hydroxymethylglutaryl (HMG)-CoA reductase (E.C.1.1. 1.23) and cholesterol 7α-hydroxylase (E.C.1.14) are the major regulators of cholesterol and bile acid synthesis in the liver. Most factors, such as diurnal variations (14, 15), bile acid feeding (16, 17), bile fistula and cholestyramine treatment (17, 18), fasting (19, 20), and thyroid hormones (21) that produce a change in the activity of HMG-CoA reductase have

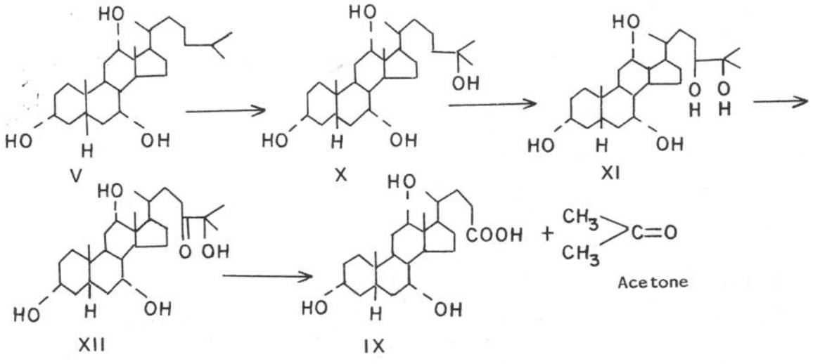

Figure 3 Alternative mechanism for oxidation of the hydrocarbon side-chain of 5β-cholestane-3α,7α,12α-triol

been shown to produce similar changes in the activity of cholesterol 7α-hydroxylase. Recent studies have shown (22, 23) that HMG-CoA reductase exists in two forms: phosphorylated (inactive) and dephosphorylated (active) and that cholesterol 7α-hydroxylase activity may also be modulated by a similar process. However, in contrast to HMG-CoA reductase, it is the phosphorylated form that results in increased cholesterol 7α-hydroxylase activity (24). Thus an activation/inactivation mechanism might exist in the short-term regulation of HMG-CoA reductase and cholesterol 7α-hydroxylase that does not require alterations in protein synthesis. The half-life of the cholesterol 7α-hydroxylase in vivo appears to be 3–4 hr (25). Newly synthesized cholesterol is believed to be the preferred substrate pool (26) for the cholesterol 7α-hydroxylase, which is localized in the smooth endoplasmic reticulum of the liver and requires NADPH and molecular oxygen (27). This enzyme is known to be a monooxygenase oxidase multicomponent system that includes cytochrome P-450, cytochrome P-450 reductase, and phospholipid (28, 29). However, the enzyme activity does not appear to be related to the total liver endoplasmic reticulum content of cytochrome P-450 (30), and has been shown to change without any difference in the total cytochrome P-450 content (25). Thus cytochrome P-450 associated with the cholesterol 7α-hydroxylase activity apparently constitutes only a small part of the total liver cytochrome P-450 content, and this explains the considerable difficulties encountered in the purification of the hemoprotein associated with this enzyme. Recently, it has been possible to achieve at least a partial separation of cholesterol 7α-hydroxylase activity from other hydroxylase activities in cytochrome P-450 fractions from rat, rabbit (31, 32), and human (28) liver microsomes. This revealed the existence of a specific cholesterol 7α-hydroxylating species of cytochrome P-450 with a shorter half-life than that of other species of cytochrome P-450 (33).

The key reaction in determing the relative amounts of cholic acid and chenodeoxycholic acid is 12α-hydroxylation. Two possible precursors may serve as substrates: 7α-hydroxy-4-cholesten-3-one (Figure 1, III) or 5β-cholestane-3α,7α-diol (1, 6). Both have been shown to undergo 12α-hydroxylation to yield the respective 12α-hydroxy derivatives (IV or V), which are then directed soley into the formation of cholic acid (XII). Little is known about the regulation of the 7α-hydroxy-4-cholesten-3-one-12α-hydroxylase. However, the enzyme is inhibited in cirrhosis as evidenced by the marked reduction in the amount of cholic acid in the bile of these individuals (34), whereas its activity was high in patients with cholelithiasis or cerebrotendinous xanthomatosis (CTX) (35) and was reflected by a high proportion of cholic acid relative to chenodeoxycholic acid in the bile of these patients.

THE REGULATION OF BILE ACID BIOSYNTHESIS IN DISEASE

Cerebrotendinous Xanthomatosis (CTX)

In 1971, Salen reported that the rare, inherited, lipid storage disease cerebrotendinous xanthomatosis (CTX) was associated with defective bile acid synthesis (36). Specifically, patients with this disorder excrete very little chenodeoxycholic acid in their bile but large amounts of bile alcohols (37). Characterization of the bile alcohol fraction showed compounds with 27 carbons and 4 or 5 hydroxyl groups. These bile alcohols contained hydroxyl groups at C-25 (37, 38) and were esterified at C-3 with glucuronic acid (39). Further studies demonstrated that the rate-controlling enzymes of cholesterol and bile acid synthesis, HMG CoA reductase and cholesterol 7α-hydroxylase, were elevated in subjects with CTX (40, 41), but the actual daily synthesis of bile acid was less than 50% of normal (42). Thus these patients apparently have sufficient cholesterol and 7α-hydroxycholesterol available for bile acid synthesis but are unable to complete bile acid synthesis, as evidenced by low fecal output of bile acids and the presence of bile alcohols. The block in the synthetic pathway has been suggested to result from the deficient conversion of 5β-cholestane-$3\alpha,7\alpha,12\alpha,25$-tetrol to the 5β-cholestane-$3\alpha,7\alpha,12\alpha,24S,25$-pentol (11, 43). This reaction, which is catalyzed by microsomal enzymes, is only 20% as active in CTX liver as in controls. It is of interest that patients with CTX apparently do not synthesize bile acids via the classical C-26 hydroxylation pathway (44, 45). Thus cerebrotendinous xanthomatosis, which is characterized clinically by large xanthomas in the tendons, brain, and lung, develops from a specific defect of bile acid synthesis. Patients with this condition are now being treated with chenodeoxycholic acid (46) in an effort to suppress the abnormal bile acid synthetic pathway and correct the clinical picture.

Biliary Artresia, Intrahepatic Cholestasis, and Abnormal Bile Acid Synthesis

In 1972 Eyssen and colleagues described two young children with intrahepatic cholestasis whose bile contained large amounts of $3\alpha,7\alpha,12\alpha$-trihydroxy-5β-coprostanoic acid (47). Since this compound is a part of the classical bile acid synthetic pathway of cholic acid, it was proposed that cholic acid biosynthesis was blocked. Further, Hanson et al (48) postulated that the impairment in bile acid synthesis played a role in the development of cholestasis in these subjects. A number of other children have also been found with neonatal cholestasis, incomplete bile duct formation, and the presence of either $3\alpha,7\alpha,12\alpha$-trihydroxy-5β-coprostanoic acid or $3\alpha,7\alpha,12\alpha,24$-tetrahydroxy-$5\beta$-coprostanoic acid (49, 50). These subjects have not lived long enough to allow metabolic studies. Therefore, the nature of the bile acid synthetic defect still requires elucidation.

Cholesterol Cholelithiasis

Cholesterol cholelithiasis is a common human disorder in which enhanced hepatic cholesterol secretion is associated with deficient bile acid pool (51). When the activities of the rate-controlling enzymes of cholesterol and bile acid synthesis were measured in the livers from patients with gallstones and compared to those of controls, hepatic cholesterol synthesis was found to be elevated while bile acid synthesis was reduced and liver cholesterol concentrations were increased (40, 41, 52). These results suggested that the reduction in hepatic bile acid synthesis as evidenced by decreased cholesterol 7α-hydroxylase activity might lead to a diminished enterohepatic bile acid pool that may signal the liver to produce more cholesterol for conversion to bile acids. The low level of cholesterol 7α-hydroxylase forces this newly synthesized cholesterol to accumulate within the liver and be secreted in the bile in amounts too great for the bile acid micelles to dissolve. As a result, cholesterol crystals precipitate and, under certain circumstances, aggregate to form gallstones. Recently, treatment with the bile acids chenodeoxycholic acid or ursodeoxycholic acid has been effective in dissolving these gallstones (53, 54). The mechanism of action has not been completely determined, but there is evidence that both chenodeoxycholic acid and ursodeoxycholic acid inhibit hepatic HMG CoA reductase and reduce the secretion of cholesterol in the bile (54). These bile acids hold promise as an alternative medical treatment of gallstones.

Acknowledgment

This work was supported by USPHS Grants AM-18707, HL-17818, and AM-26756.

Literature Cited

1. Danielsson, H. 1973. In *The Bile Acids,* ed. P. P. Nair, D. Kritchevsky, 2:1–32, 305–6. NY: Plenum
2. Shefer, S., Hauser, S., Bekersky, I., Mosbach, E. H. 1970. *J. Lipid Res.* 11: 404–11
3. Einarsson, K., Hellström, K., Kalner, M. 1973. *Metabolism* 22:1477–86
4. Cronholm, T., Johannsson, G. 1970. *Eur. J. Biochem.* 16:373–81
5. Björkhem, I., Gustafsson, J. 1974. *J. Biol. Chem.* 249:2528–35
6. Björkhem, I., Gustafsson, J., Johansson, G., Persson, B. 1975. *J. Clin. Invest.* 55:478–86

7. Danielsson, H. 1964. *J. Clin. Invest.* 43: 1443–48
8. Gustafsson, J., Sjöstedt, S. 1978. *J. Biol. Chem.* 253:199–201
9. Gustafsson, J. 1975. *J. Biol. Chem.* 250: 8243–47
10. Masui, T., Staple, E. 1965. *Biochim. Biophys. Acta* 104:305–7
11. Shefer, S., Cheng, F. W., Dayal, B., Hauser, S., Tint, G. S., Salen, G., Mosbach, E. H. 1975. *J. Clin. Invest.* 57: 897–903
12. Cheng, F. W., Shefer, S., Dayal, B., Tint, G. S., Setoguchi, T., Salen, G., Mosbach, E. H. 1977. *J. Lipid Res.* 18: 6–13

13. Shefer, S., Salen, G., Cheng, F. W., Batta, A. K., Dayal, B., Tint, G. S., Bose, A. K., Pramanik, B. N. 1982. *Anal. Biochem.* 121:23–30
14. Higgins, M., Kawachi, T., Rudney, H. 1971. *Biochem. Biophys. Res. Commun.* 45:138–44
15. Botham, K. M., Boyd, G. S. 1979. *Eur. J. Biochem.* 95:533–42
16. Shefer, S., Hauser, S., Lapar, V., Mosbach, E. H. 1973. *J. Lipid Res.* 14: 573–80
17. Shefer, S., Hauser, S., Mosbach, E. H. 1968. *J. Lipid Res.* 9:328–33
18. Boyd, G. S., Scholan, N. A., Mitton, J. R. 1969. *Adv. Exp. Med. Biol.* 4:443–56
19. Meyer, D. 1972. In *Bile Acids in Human Diseases.* Stuttgart: Schattaner. pp. 103–9
20. Bucher, N. L. R., Overath, P., Lynen, F. 1960. *Biochim. Biophys. Acta* 40: 491–501
21. Balasubramaniam, S., Mitropoulos, K. A., Myant, D. B. 1975 In *Advances in Bile Acid Research,* 3:61–67. Stuttgart: Schattaner
22. Mitropoulos, K. A., Knight, B. L., Reevers, B. E. A. 1980. *Biochem. J.* 985:435–41
23. Arebalo, R. E., Hardgrave, J. E., Scallen, T. J. 1981. *J. Biol. Chem.* 256: 571–74
24. Sanghvi, A., Grassi, E., Warty, V., Diven, W., Wight, C., Lester, R. 1981. *Biochem. Biophys. Res. Commun.* 103: 886–92
25. Brown, M. J. G., Boyd, G. S. 1974. *Eur. J. Biochem.* 44:37–47
26. Schwartz, C. C., Vlahcevic, Z. R., Halloran, L. G., Gregory, D. H., Meek, J. B., Swell, L. 1975. *Gastroenterology* 169:1379–85
27. Mitton, J. R., Scholan, N. A., Boyd, G. S., 1971. *Biochemistry* 20:569–79
28. Erickson, S. K., Bösterling, B. 1981. *J. Lipid Res.* 22:872–76
29. Björkhem, I., Danielsson, H., Wikvall, K. 1974. *Biochem. Biophys. Res. Commun.* 61:934–41
30. Botham, K. M., Boyd, G. 1979. *Eur. J. Biochem.* 95:533–42
31. Hansson, R., Wikvall, K. 1980. *J. Biol. Chem.* 255:1643–49
32. Boström, H., Hansson, R., Jöhsson, K. H., Wikvall, K. 1981. *Eur. J. Biochem.* 120:29–32
33. Danielsson, H., Wikvall, K. 1981. *Biochem. Biophys. Res. Commun.* 103: 46–51
34. Vlahcevic, Z. R., Juttijudata, P., Bell,

C. C. Jr., Swell, L. 1972. *Gastroenterology* 62:1174–81
35. Mosbach, E. H., Salen, G. 1974. In *Advances in Bile Acid Research,* ed. S. Matern, J. Hackenschmidt, P. Back, W. Gerok, 3:111. Stuttgart: Schattaner
36. Salen, G. 1971. *Ann. Intern. Med.* 75:843–51
37. Setoguchi, T., Salen, G., Tint, G. S., Mosbach, E. H. 1974. *J. Clin. Invest.* 53:1393–1401
38. Shefer, S., Dayal, B., Tint, G. S., Salen, G., Mosbach, E. H. 1975. *J. Lipid Res.* 16:280–86
39. Hoshita, T., Yasuhara, M., Une, M., Kibe, A., Itoga, E., Kito, S., Kuramoto, T. 1980. *J. Lipid Res.* 21:1015–21
40. Nicolau, G., Shefer, S., Salen, G., Mosbach, E. H. 1974. *J. Lipid Res.* 15:94–98
41. Nicolau, G., Shefer, S., Salen, G., Mosbach, E. H. 1974. *J. Lipid Res.* 15:146–51
42. Salen, G., Grundy, S. M. 1973. *J. Clin. Invest.* 52:2822–35
43. Salen, G., Shefer, S., Cheng, F. W., Dayal, B., Batta, A. K., Tint, G. S. 1979. *J. Clin. Invest.* 63:38–44
44. Oftebro, H., Björkhem, I., Skrede, S., Schriner, A., Pederson, J. 1980. *J. Clin. Invest.* 65:1418–30
45. Salen, G., Shefer, S., Setoguchi, T., Mosbach, E. H. 1975. *J. Clin. Invest.* 56:226–31
46. Salen, G., Merriwether, T. W., Nicolau, G. 1975. *Biochem. Med.* 14:57–74
47. Eyssen, H., Parmentier, G., Compernolle, F., Boon, J., Eggermont, E. 1972. *Biochim. Biophys. Acta* 273:212–21
48. Hanson, R. F., Isenberg, J. N., Williams, G. C., Hachey, D., Szczepanik, P., Klein, P. D., Sharp, H. L. 1975. *J. Clin. Invest.* 56:577–87
49. Hanson, R. F., Szczepanik, P., Grabowski, G., Williams, G., Sharp, H. L. 1978. *Clin. Res.* 26:320A (Abstr.)
50. Hanson, R. F., Szczepanik-Van Leeuwer, P., Williams, G. C., Grabowski, G., Sharp, H. L. 1978. *Science* 203:1107–8
51. Vlahcevic, Z. R., Bell, C. C., Buhac, I., Swell, L. 1970. *Gastroenterology* 59: 165–73
52. Salen, G., Nicolau, G., Shefer, S., Mosbach, E. H. 1975. *Gastroenterology* 69: 676–84
53. Danzinger, R. G., Hofmann, A. F., Thistle, J. L., et al. 1973. *J. Clin. Invest.* 52:2809–21
54. Danzinger, R. G., Hofmann, A. F., Schoenfield, L. J., Thistle, J. L. 1972. *N. Engl. J. Med.* 286:1–10

SUBJECT INDEX

A

Abetalipoproteinemia
apo A-IV levels and, 629
apo B synthesis and, 631–32
Acetate
in colon, 669
Acetylcholine
blood to brain transport of, 76
calcium channels in heart cells and, 353–54
enzymatic inactivation of, 76
hepatic synthetase I activity and, 97
Acetylcholine receptors
postsynaptic membrane and, 591
Acetylcholinesterase
extracellular matrix and, 584
muscle fiber basement membrane and, 592
at neuromuscular junctions, 591
Acetyl CoA carboxylase
fatty acid biosynthesis and, 45
Acetylsalicylic acid
sodium transport in frog skin and, 525
Acid phosphatase
invertebrate freezing injuries and, 294
ACTH
adrenal cortical secretion and, 21–22
cerebrospinal fluid bulk flow and, 78
hepatic steroid metabolism and, 53
21-hydroxylase activity in rat adrenal microsomes and, 20–21
microsomal cytochrome P-450 levels in adrenals and, 26
receptors in median eminence, 74
xenobiotic metabolism and, 58
Actin
calcium transport and, 380
Actinomycin D
apoVLDL-II synthesis and, 620
calcium uptake and, 377
Adenosine
coronary blood flow and, 221–22

Adenosine triphosphate
calcium pump and, 316–19, 384–85
calcium transport and, 313–14, 521
red cell calcium pump and, 303–9
Adipokinetic hormone
locust, 272–73
Adrenal glands
17α-hydroxylase activity in, 21–22
21-hydroxylase activity in, 20–21
C-17,20 lyase activity in, 26
Adrenal hyperplasia
congenital
21-hydroxylase deficiencies and, 20
Adrenoceptors
catecholamines and, 140
Airway obstruction
exercise-induced, 453–60
Albumin
in cerebrospinal fluid, 75
Aldehyde oxidase
hepatic, 45–46
Aldolase
invertebrate freezing injuries and, 294
Alkaline phosphatase
phosphate transport and, 379
Alkaline phosphatase-CaATPase complex
calcium absorption and, 378–79
Alpha-adrenergic vasoconstriction, 215–17
Alpha-tocopherol
freezing resistance of intertidal invertebrates and, 297
Altitude
barometric pressure and, 428
exercise at, 427–35
exercise capacity at, 428–29
metabolism and, 432–34
Alveolar gas tensions
altitude and, 429–30
Alveolar ventilation
exercise and, 475–76
Amiloride
sodium absorption in collecting ducts and, 543
sodium-hydrogen ion exchange in renal tubules and, 493

Amino acids
freezing-point depression in fish and, 246
Aminopyrine metabolism
growth hormone and, 58
Ammonium chloride
metabolic acid-base changes induced by ventilatory kinetics of, 402
Androgens
carbonic anhydrase induction and, 45
cytoplasmic androgen receptor in liver and, 40
ovarian
estrogen administration and, 26
sex difference in gene expression and, 38
steroid metabolism and, 51–53
Androstenedione
ovarian estrogen formation and, 28
Anesthesia
thermoregulation and, 207
Angiotensin II
calcium channels in heart cells and, 353
prolactin secretion and, 118
receptors in median eminence, 74
synthesis in brain, 75
Angiotensin-converting enzyme
captopril and, 76
Aniline
hepatic metabolism of, 51
Anorexia nervosa
estradiol hydroxylation in, 63
Anticholinergics
exercise-induced airway obstruction and, 459
Antioxidants
freezing resistance of intertidal invertebrates and, 297
Aplysia californica
gill withdrawal reflex suppression in, 280
Apolipoprotein B, 637–47
metabolism of, 645–47
structure of, 638–45
Apolipoprotein synthesis
hormonal regulation of, 618–21
mechanism of, 615–18
Arachidonic acid
rat ovarian 17α-hydroxylase specific activity and, 24

CUMULATIVE INDEXES

CONTRIBUTING AUTHORS, VOLUMES 41–45

702 CONTRIBUTING AUTHORS

CHAPTER TITLES, VOLUMES 41–45